OUTLINE COURSE OF PURE MATHEMATICS

OUTLINE COURSE OF PURE MATHEMATICS

A. F. HORADAM

Department of Mathematics,
University of New England,
Armidale, Australia

... a tract of beautiful country seen at first in the distance, but which will bear to be rambled through and studied in every detail of hillside and valley, stream, rock, wood and flower. But, as for everything else, so for a mathematical theory—beauty can be perceived but not explained.

CAYLEY, 1883

PERGAMON PRESS

OXFORD · LONDON · EDINBURGH · NEW YORK
TORONTO · SYDNEY · PARIS · BRAUNSCHWEIG

Pergamon Press Ltd., Headington Hill Hall, Oxford
4 & 5 Fitzroy Square, London W.1
Pergamon Press (Scotland) Ltd., 2 & 3 Teviot Place, Edinburgh 1
Pergamon Press Inc., 44–01 21st Street, Long Island City, New York 11101
Pergamon of Canada Ltd., 207 Queen's Quay West, Toronto 1
Pergamon Press (Aust.) Pty. Ltd., 19a Boundary Street, Rushcutters Bay, N.S.W. 2011, Australia
Pergamon Press S.A.R.L., 24 rue des Écoles, Paris 5e
Vieweg & Sohn GmbH, Burgplatz 1, Braunschweig

First edition 1968

Library of Congress Catalog Card No. 68-18523

PRINTED IN HUNGARY

08 012593 X

To my students: past, present and future

CONTENTS

CHAPTER 7. INDEFINITE INTEGRALS

CHAPTER 8. DEFINITE INTEGRALS

CHAPTER 9. INFINITE SERIES AND SEQUENCES

CHAPTER 10. COMPLEX NUMBERS

CHAPTER 11. MATRICES

PREFACE

Aim of the Course. The Pure Mathematics course outlined in this book seeks to present a unified treatment of the Algebra, Geometry, and Calculus considered basic for the foundation of undergraduate Mathematics. Principally, it is designed as a course for First Year University Pure Mathematics (Pass), though it possibly contains more material than can properly be coped with in the time available, namely three terms, or two semesters. It is intended to flow fairly smoothly from School Mathematics and to lead equally smoothly into Second Year University Pure Mathematics.

An attempt has been made to strike a balance between classical and modern Mathematics, though Calculus is considered to be the heart of the matter. With this in mind, Integration has been developed *ab initio.*

Essentially, the course is conceived as an intellectual discipline with its own aesthetic values, although the interests of the field and laboratory (and social) scientists have not been overlooked.

Aspects of theory which have been reluctantly, but deliberately, excluded are (i) the physical and mechanical applications of vectors, and (ii) the use of the definite integral in physical problems such as centres of gravity, moments of inertia, and fluid pressure.

Methods and order of presentation are dictated more by pedagogical considerations than by a desire for excessive rigour. Too much rigour inflicted too early can easily lead to *rigor mortis* of the imagination. However, the maximum rigour consistent with the size and comprehensiveness of this book will always be sought. New concepts are introduced as required. Most of the material has been experimented with and class-tested over a number of years.

Knowledge assumed. Though intentionally suitable for Australian undergraduates and advanced secondary school students, the book should be equally suitable for use by such students and undergraduates in other countries, and particularly in the U.S.A. and the U.K. Progressing through this outline, the reader will soon form an impression of the knowledge he is assumed to possess.

Roughly speaking, the background taken for granted includes fairly elementary treatments of the real number system; Calculus (differentiation and integration); applications of Calculus to the physical world (simple harmonic motion, Hooke's law, parabolic motion under gravity); Analytical Geometry of the plane (line, circle, parabola); Analytical Geometry in three dimensions; Trigonometry; sequences and series; logarithmic, exponential, trigonometric, and inverse trigonometric functions; polynomials; binomial theorem; theory of probability; and certain ideas (e.g. Simpson's rule for approximate integration, loci problems) which are logically related to these topics.

Attitudes featured. Emphasis is placed throughout on the unity in Mathematics. Wherever possible, apparently unrelated threads of the fabric are woven together. Because no subject loses more when divorced from its history than Mathematics, an endeavour has been made to present some degree of historical perspective and to display the creative human element. ("I didn't know they did Mathematics B.C.," a student once confessed.) A natural corollary to this is the emphasis on the fact that Mathematics is a continually evolving body of knowledge which is being added to daily at an astonishing rate. Moreover, the historical setting is important because Mathematics can be seen as a reliable guide of progress, "one of the large windows through which the philosophic eye looks into past ages and traces the line of intellectual development" (Cajori).

Furthermore, our presentation attempts to excite the reader's imagination and interest by the actual selection of material, by the beauty of certain theory and applications, and by the provision of useful information with which the educated student ought to be familiar. It is hoped that the reader will be sufficiently inspired to consult at least some of the references.

At every opportunity, an endeavour has been made to render the theory meaningful by applying it to problems of the real world. Coupled with the desire to heighten the student's aesthetic awareness and to make the study intellectually stimulating, this practical aspect should serve to give him the appreciation and sense of power so basic to success in Mathematics.

Exercises. Problems in Mathematics are as multitudinous as the sands of the ocean, but those chosen in this book (the Exercises) are intended to reflect the general philosophy enunciated above. Exercises form an integral part of the course, complementing the theory, which they may often illuminate. To some extent, the Exercises are graded, but individual difficulties could arise unexpectedly at any stage. In quality they range from the routine to the extremely challenging which require subtlety and insight. Each Exercise bears a reference number, e.g. Exercise 4.51 is exercise 51, Chapter 4 (≡ Exercises 4, number 51).

Normally, I am not concerned with mere arithmetical computation or with complicated algebraic manipulations, though these will occur.

A word of advice to the student. Understand the theory. Consult some of the references. Do plenty of Exercises. Genuine confidence only comes from much practice in problem solving.

It is suggested that the interested reader might provide for himself a detailed classification of problems, e.g. it may be handy to know just where to find problems on, say, Astronomy and Space, or Economics, or Relativity, or Psychology, or Electricity and Magnetism. A similar list of historical information and applications of theory might also be made, as well as a list of unfamiliar symbols (and where they first occur).

Acknowledgements. My thanks are due to the Council of the University of New England for granting me permission to use some examination questions set by that University; to the United States Information Service, Sydney, for satellite details; and to Professor W. N. Christiansen, School of Electrical Engineering, University of Sydney, for details of certain radio telescopes.

The selection of texts in the Bibliography and in the chapter references gives an idea of some of the influences at work in the preparation of this text.

Acknowledgement must be made of my indebtedness to those of my students who, all unwittingly, have contributed to improvements in the presentation of this material.

Thanks are also due to my typist, Mrs. M. Brown, who worked carefully and conscientiously through the jungle of my manuscript, avoiding the pitfalls unknowingly placed in her way; and to the Pergamon Press staff for their careful attention to my often exacting requests.

Nor must I overlook those of my colleagues who, though hard pressed with academic duties, nevertheless gave generously and willingly of their time and knowledge to read the manuscript and to offer suggestions for its improvement.

I should like to thank in advance those readers who will detect errors (for which I alone bear responsibility) and who, it is hoped, will let me know about them. One does not have to be clairvoyant to realise that mistakes will inevitably occur, and I can only plead those weaknesses to which the spirit and flesh are heir.

Finally, it is assumed that some people are born mathematicians, some people achieve Mathematics, and some people have Mathematics thrust upon them. But it is hoped that no one, into whichever category he fits, will be afraid of Mathematics.

University of New England
Armidale

A. F. HORADAM

December 1965

GREEK ALPHABET

A	α	Alpha
B	β	Beta
Γ	γ	Gamma
Δ	δ	Delta
E	ε	Epsilon
Z	ζ	Zeta
H	η	Eta
Θ	θ	Theta
I	ι	Iota
K	$\varkappa$	Kappa
Λ	λ	Lambda
M	μ	Mu
N	ν	Nu
Ξ	ξ	Xi
O	o	Omicron
Π	π	Pi
P	ϱ	Rho
Σ	σ	Sigma
T	τ	Tau
Υ	υ	Upsilon
Φ	ϕ	Phi
X	χ	Chi
Ψ	ψ	Psi
Ω	ω	Omega

SELECT BIBLIOGRAPHY

GENERAL AND HISTORICAL

1. ALEKSANDROV, A. D., KOLMOGOROV, A. N. and LAVRENT'EV, M. A., *Mathematics: Its Content, Methods and Meaning*, American Mathematical Society, Providence, 1963.
2. BELL, E. T., *The Development of Mathematics*, McGraw-Hill, New York, 1945.
3. BELL, E. T., *Men of Mathematics*, Simon & Schuster, New York, 1937.
4. CAJORI, F., *A History of Mathematics*, Macmillan, New York, 1919.
5. COURANT, R. and ROBBINS, H., *What is Mathematics?*, O.U.P., New York, 1946.
6. EVES, H. and NEWSOM, C. V., *An Introduction to the Foundations and Fundamental Concepts of Mathematics*, Holt, Rinehart & Winston, New York, 1958.
7. KASNER, E. and NEWMAN, J. R., *Mathematics and the Imagination*, Simon & Schuster, New York, 1940.
8. NEWMAN, J. R. (Ed.), *The World of Mathematics*, vols. 1–4, Simon & Schuster, New York, 1956.
9. SMITH, D. E., *A Source Book in Mathematics*, vols. 1–2, Dover, New York, 1959.
10. VAN DER WAERDEN, B. L., *Science Awakening*, Noordhoff, Groningen.

CALCULUS (SOME WITH ANALYTICAL GEOMETRY)

11. ABBOTT, P., *Teach Yourself Calculus*, E.U.P., London, 1957.
12. ALLENDOERFER, C. B., and OAKLEY, C. O., *Fundamentals of Freshman Mathematics*, McGraw-Hill, New York, 1959.
13. ANDREE, R. V., *Introduction to Calculus with Analytical Geometry*, McGraw-Hill, New York, 1962.
14. APOSTOL, T., *Calculus*, vol. 1, Blaisdell, New York, 1961.
15. AYRES, F., *Theory and Problems of Differential and Integral Calculus*, Schaum, New York, 1950.
16. BACON, H. M., *Differential and Integral Calculus*, McGraw-Hill, New York, 1955.
17. GERRISH, F., *Pure Mathematics*, vols. 1–2, C.U.P., Cambridge, 1960.
18. JOHNSON, R. E. and KIOKEMEISTER, F. L., *Calculus with Analytic Geometry*, Allyn & Bacon, Boston, 1964.
19. KELLS, L. M., *Analytic Geometry and Calculus*, Prentice-Hall, Englewood Cliffs, 1963.
20. MASANI, P. R., PATEL, R. C. and PATIL, D. J., *Elementary Calculus*, Academic Press, New York, 1965.
21. NARAYAN, S., *Differential Calculus. Integral Calculus*, 2 vols., S. Chand, New Delhi, 1959.
22. PLUMPTON, C. and CHIRGWIN, B. H., *A Course of Mathematics for Engineers and Scientists*, Pergamon, Oxford, 1961.
23. RANDOLPH, J. F., *Calculus and Analytic Geometry*, Wadsworth, San Francisco, 1961.
24. SMIRNOV, V. I., *A Course of Higher Mathematics*, vol. 1, Pergamon, Oxford, 1964.

25. Spiegel, M. R., *Theory and Problems of Advanced Calculus*, Schaum, New York, 1962.
26. Stephenson, G., *Mathematical Methods for Science Students*, Longmans, London, 1961.
27. Thomas, G. B., *Calculus and Analytic Geometry*, Addison–Wesley, Reading, 1956.
28. Tranter, C. J., *Techniques of Mathematical Analysis*, E.U.P., London, 1961.

ALGEBRA

29. Andree, R. V., *Selections from Modern Abstract Algebra*, Holt, Rinehart & Winston, New York, 1958.
30. Balfour, A., *An Introduction to Sets, Groups and Matrices*, Heinemann, London, 1965.
31. Benner, C. P., Newhouse, A., Rader, C. B. and Yates, R. L., *Topics in Modern Algebra*, Harper, New York, 1962.
32. Dubisch, R., *Introduction to Abstract Algebra*, Wiley, New York, 1965.
33. Kelly, J. L., *Introduction to Modern Algebra*, van Nostrand, Princeton, 1960.
34. Moore, J. T., *Elements of Abstract Algebra*, Macmillan, New York, 1962.
35. Robinson, G. de B., *Vector Geometry*, Allyn & Bacon, Boston, 1962.
36. Weiss, Marie and Dubisch, R., *Higher Algebra for Undergraduates*, Wiley, New York, 1961.
37. Whitesitt, J. E., *Principles of Modern Algebra*, Addison–Wesley, Reading, 1965.

GEOMETRY

38. Adler, C. F., *Modern Geometry*, McGraw-Hill, New York, 1958.
39. Coxeter, H. S. M., *Introduction to Geometry*, Wiley, New York, 1961.
40. Meserve, B. E., *Fundamental Concepts of Geometry*, Addison–Wesley, Reading, 1955.
41. Sommerville, D. M. Y., *Analytical Conics*, Bell, London, 1946.
42. Spain, B., *Analytical Conics*, Pergamon, Oxford, 1957.
43. Walker, R., *Analytical Conics*, Edward Arnold, London, 1950.
44. Walker, R., *Cartesian and Projective Geometry*, Edward Arnold, London, 1953.
45. Wexler, C., *Analytic Geometry: A Vector Approach*, Addison–Wesley, Reading, 1962.

Additionally, students ought to consult encyclopaedias such as the *Encyclopaedia Britannica* for particular topics, and to be generally familiar with journals such as *The Australian Mathematics Teacher*, *The Mathematical Gazette*, *Mathematics Magazine*, *The Fibonacci Quarterly*, *Scripta Mathematica*, *Mathematics Student*, and *The American Mathematical Monthly*.

CHAPTER 1

DIFFERENTIAL CALCULUS

"Begin at the beginning", the King said, gravely, "and go on till you come to the end: then stop."

(LEWIS CARROLL)

§ 1. DIFFERENTIATION (REVISION)

Fundamental concepts

Calculus, probably the single most valuable intellectual achievement of man for solving problems of the physical world, consists essentially of two complementary processes—differentiation and integration. Mathematics involving the former is called *differential calculus* while that depending upon the latter is known as *integral calculus*.

Behind the operation of differentiation lies the fundamental notion of limit, of which the reader is assumed to have at least an intuitive understanding to enable him to evaluate simple determinate limits as the variable approaches 0, a (finite) or ∞. Expressions such as $\frac{0}{0}, \frac{\infty}{\infty}$, known as indeterminate forms, can only be interpreted reasonably as limits (see § 10). A formal definition of the limit concept is given in § 7.

Suppose small *increments* (i.e. variations, positive or negative) δx, δy are made to the variables in the function $y = f(x)$. That is to say, the increment δx is made to the variable x and the other increment δy results from this action. Then the foundations of differential calculus rest on an examination of $\lim_{\delta x \to 0} \left(\frac{\delta y}{\delta x}\right)$, where $\delta y \to 0$ as $\delta x \to 0$, that is, on the limit of a set of ratios. Formally, the *first derivative (first differential coefficient)* is defined as

$$\boxed{\lim_{\delta x \to 0} \left(\frac{\delta y}{\delta x}\right) = \lim_{\delta x \to 0} \left\{\frac{f(x+\delta x)-f(x)}{\delta x}\right\} = \frac{dy}{dx}, \text{ say}} \tag{1}$$

if the limit exists. In this case, the function is said to be *differentiable*. The notation $\frac{dy}{dx}$ is used for brevity to express the rate of change of y with respect to x (w.r.t. x for short) and may, of course, be negative, as in the case of radioactive decay or electrical discharge caused by leakage. (Increment δx is usually restricted to small values, but otherwise unspecified.)

Geometrically, $\frac{dy}{dx}$ (= tan α, Fig. 1) measures the *gradient* (= *slope*) of the curve $y = f(x)$ at a variable point $P(x, y)$ on the curve, i.e. it measures the gradient of the tangent to the curve at P.

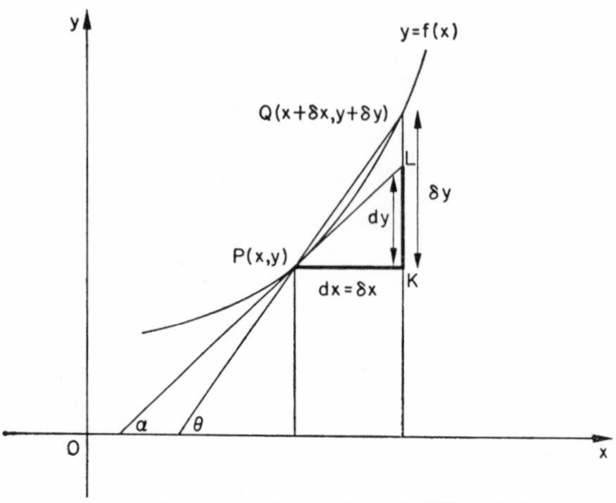

FIG. 1. Geometrical meaning of differentials

Fundamental first derivatives, whose knowledge is assumed, are summarised in the tables hereunder, where $f(x)$ and $g(x)$ are functions of x (abbreviated to f and g for simplicity when there is no ambiguity), k is a constant, and $f'(x) = \frac{dy}{dx}$ is an alternative notation for the first derivative of $y = f(x)$ w.r.t. x:

$f(x)$	k	x^n	kf	$f+g$	fg	$\frac{f}{g}$ $(g \neq 0)$
$f'(x)$	0	nx^{n-1}	kf'	$f'+g'$	$f'g+fg'$	$\frac{f'g-fg'}{g^2}$

(2)

$f(x)$	$\sin x$	$\cos x$	$\tan x$	$\operatorname{cosec} x$	$\sec x$	$\cot x$
$f'(x)$	$\cos x$	$-\sin x$	$\sec^2 x$	$-\frac{\cos x}{\sin^2 x}$	$\frac{\sin x}{\cos^2 x}$	$-\operatorname{cosec}^2 x$

(3)

Also, if $y = F(u)$ and $u = f(x)$, i.e. $y = F\{f(x)\}$ is a function F of the function f, we have the *chain rule* for the derivative of a function of a function:

$$\boxed{\frac{dy}{dx} = \frac{dy}{du}\frac{du}{dx}}\,. \tag{4}$$

Comments

(i) Initially, the derivative of x^n is proved to be valid for rational n, but the result is true also for real n.

(ii) Underlying limit theorems on which the derivatives are based are given in § 6.

(iii) Graphs of the trigonometrical functions are assumed known. Can you draw them? Note the periodicity of these functions, e.g. $\sin(x+2n\pi) = \sin x$ (n an integer), and the asymptotes, namely $x = (2n+1)\,\pi/2$ for $\tan x$ and $\sec x$, but $x = n\pi$ for $\operatorname{cosec} x$ and $\cot x$ (n an integer). [An *asymptote* (*a, syn, ptotos* (Greek) ≡ "not", "together", "falling") is defined to be a tangent to the curve at an infinitely distant point of the curve.] Angle measure is, of course, in radians.

(iv) A function $f(x)$ is an *even function* if $f(-x) = f(x)$ while $f(x)$ is an *odd function* if $f(-x) = -f(x)$. Only $\cos x$ and $\sec x$ of the trigonometrical functions are even; the others are odd.

(v) Derivatives of the sum, difference, and product of a finite number of functions of x follow by simple extension in (2). Likewise, the chain rule (4) is readily extended.

(vi)
$$\frac{dy}{dx} = \lim_{\delta x \to 0}\left[1\Big/\frac{\delta x}{\delta y}\right] = 1\Big/\lim_{\delta x \to 0}\left(\frac{\delta x}{\delta y}\right) = 1\Big/\frac{dx}{dy},$$

i.e.
$$\boxed{\frac{dy}{dx}\frac{dx}{dy} = 1}\,. \tag{5}$$

Pictorially, this means that the tangent to a curve makes complementary angles with the axes of x and y.

(vii) Besides the notation dy/dx, used by Leibniz (1646–1716, German), and $f'(x)$, used by Lagrange (1736–1813, French), another equivalent notation for the derivative of y w.r.t. x is Dy, due to Cauchy (1789–1857, French), where $D \equiv \dfrac{d}{dx}$ denotes the differentiation operator. Newton 1642–1727, English) employed the notation $\dot{y}$ for $\dfrac{dy}{dt}$.

(viii) Not all functions are expressible explicitly in the form $y = f(x)$, in which y is called an *explicit function* of x. Some, such as that given by $x^3+y^3-3axy = 0$, have to be written in the form $g(x, y) = 0$, in which y

is called an *implicit function* of x. An implicit equation $g(x, y) = 0$ will frequently define one or more functions y of x explicitly; for example, $x^2+y^2-1 = 0$ defines the two functions $y = \sqrt{1-x^2}$ and $y = -\sqrt{1-x^2}$. Differentiation of implicit functions is considered in § 21. See Thomas [27] for additional information concerning implicit functions.

(ix) Some people may prefer to differentiate $\dfrac{f}{g}$ in (2) as a product $f\left(\dfrac{1}{g}\right)$. This preference is, of course, perfectly acceptable.

Repeated differentiation

Repetition of the process of differentiation leads to the *second derivative* of y w.r.t. x, namely $\dfrac{d^2y}{dx^2} = \dfrac{d}{dx}\left(\dfrac{dy}{dx}\right)$, which therefore represents the rate of change of $\dfrac{dy}{dx}$ w.r.t. x. Geometrically, it measures the rate of change of the gradient. Continuing the process, we eventually reach the *nth derivative* $\dfrac{d^ny}{dx^n}$ $(\equiv f^{(n)}(x) \equiv D^ny)$ for which the differentiation operation has occurred n times, n a positive integer $\left(D^n \equiv \dfrac{d^n}{dx^n}\text{, i.e. } D \text{ applied } n \text{ times}\right)$. From (5) with (4), it follows that

$$\frac{d^2y}{dx^2} = -\frac{d^2x}{dy^2}\bigg/\left(\frac{dy}{dx}\right)^3 \neq 1\bigg/\frac{d^2x}{dy^2}.$$

Applications

If x represents the distance travelled in time t by a particle along a straight line (i.e. *rectilinear motion*), then $\dot{x} = \dfrac{dx}{dt} \equiv v$ and $\ddot{x} = \dfrac{d^2x}{dt^2} = \dfrac{dv}{dt} \equiv a$ measure the *velocity* v and *acceleration* a respectively of the particle. Graphically, a is the gradient of the curve of velocities.

Both first and second derivatives have wide applicability in a variety of problems relating to the physical Universe and (since they are associated with Newton's laws of motion) with rocketry and space satellites in particular. Equations involving derivatives are called *differential equations*, the *order* of such an equation being that of the highest derivative in it. Among the best-known second-order differential equations are those of (i) *simple harmonic motion* $\ddot{x}+kx = 0$ occurring when periodicity is present (e.g. electrical oscillations, planetary orbits, vibrating mechanisms, sound waves as produced by a musical instrument such as a flute), and (ii) *damped harmonic motion*, $\ddot{x}+l\dot{x}+kx = 0$, such as happens in the oscillations of a pendulum subject to friction. But for some resistance, a body with damped harmonic motion would have simple harmonic motion.

Time, however, is not necessarily one of the variables involved in measuring rates of change, though it is frequently the case in mechanics and physics problems. Chemists, for instance, might be concerned to study the variation of the length of a heated metal rod with temperature, or the rate at which gas pressure changes with volume (for a gas in a cylinder closed by a piston). Economists might be interested in the relation between production cost of, or revenue realised from, a certain commodity and the quantity manufactured (*marginal cost* or *marginal revenue*).

Higher derivatives also occur naturally in physical situations, e.g. $\frac{d^4y}{dx^4}=k$ (const.) relates to the deflection of a horizontal beam in the theory of structures.

Mathematical models

Everyone is familiar with the systematic attempt of Euclid (*ca.* 300 B.C., Greek) to describe mathematically (symbolically) our experience of physical space on the basis of certain assumptions and definitions and deductions therefrom. His geometry is an idealisation and abstraction of physical space, expressed in mathematical terms, and we therefore refer to it as a *mathematical model* (of space). Likewise, the equations of Newton's mechanics or of Einstein's relativity provide a mathematical model for the movement of material objects in space. The more closely the model approximates to the observed behaviour of those phenomena of nature it claims to represent, the more scientifically useful will it be. Ideally, we should like to be able to deduce mathematically, by pure reason, the existence of new, but previously unobserved, aspects of the Universe. Classical examples of such a happening are the discoveries of the planets Neptune and Pluto, and of non-Euclidean properties of space. Instances abound in which a differential equation is used as a model of a real situation in the social, biological, or physical sciences. Later, in Chapter 13, we will see how an algebraic system, Boolean algebra, has important practical interpretations.

Historical note

Historically, the quantity $\delta x \to 0$ (the spirit of a departed quantity, as someone called it) had a rough passage at birth. Much criticism, often valid, was levelled by philosophers, notably Berkeley in *The Analyst* (1734), against the foundations on which the process of differentiation was based. Voltaire, for instance, expressed something of the mystery felt about calculus when he described it as the "Art of numbering and measuring exactly a thing whose Existence cannot be conceived". Ultimately, criticism had the effect of removing some of the mysticism surrounding differentiation and of forcing mathematicians to examine more carefully the ideas to which they were giving symbolic expression. One serious consequence of the petty dispute between the followers of Newton and those of Leibniz over the rival claims for priority in discovering the calculus was the isolation of British mathematicians from the mainstream of mathematical research on the Continent. It is well to remember, however, that the germ of ideas about calculus (particularly integration) is traceable to Archimedes (287?–212 B.C., Greek).

EXAMPLE 1 (standard differentiation). Obtain the first derivative of

$$\text{(i)}\ \frac{x}{\sqrt{1-x^2}}\ ;\ \text{(ii)}\ \sin x - \frac{1}{3}\sin^3 x.$$

Solutions. (i) Write $y = \dfrac{u}{v}$ where $u = x$, $v = \sqrt{1-x^2} = w^{1/2}$, $w = 1-x^2$.

$$\therefore \frac{dv}{dx} = \frac{dv}{dw}\frac{dw}{dx} \qquad \text{by (4)}$$

$$= \tfrac{1}{2}w^{-1/2}.-2x \qquad (2)$$

$$= -\frac{x}{\sqrt{1-x^2}}. \qquad (\alpha)$$

$$\therefore \frac{dy}{dx} = \frac{v\dfrac{du}{dx} - u\dfrac{dv}{dx}}{v^2} \qquad \text{(2) [\textit{quotient rule}]}$$

$$= \frac{\sqrt{1-x^2}\cdot 1 - x(-x/\sqrt{1-x^2})}{1-x^2} \qquad \text{(2) and } (\alpha)$$

$$= \frac{1-x^2+x^2}{(1-x^2)^{3/2}} \qquad \text{on simplifying}$$

$$= (1-x^2)^{-3/2}.$$

(Confident students will, of course, avoid the detail of the fully worked solution (i). Always simplify, if possible.)

(ii) Put $y = \sin x - \frac{1}{3}\sin^3 x$.

$$\therefore \frac{dy}{dx} = \cos x - \tfrac{1}{3}\,3\sin^2 x\cos x \qquad \text{by (3), (4)}$$

$$= \cos x(1-\sin^2 x)$$

$$= \cos^3 x.$$

Sometimes, equations of curves are given parametrically, i.e. coordinates x, y of a point on the curve are expressed in terms of another variable *(parameter)*, say t, i.e. $x = f(t)$, $y = g(t)$. Hence

$$\boxed{\frac{dy}{dx} = \frac{dy}{dt}\bigg/\frac{dx}{dt} = \frac{f'(t)}{g'(t)}}. \tag{6}$$

Convention. For brevity, we may refer to the point P in the parameter t, written $P(t)$ for short, as "the point t". (Choice of the letter t as a parameter has no necessary connection with time.)

EXAMPLE 2 (parametric differentiation). What is the gradient of the tangent to the *nephroid* $x = \frac{3}{2}\cos t - \cos^3 t$, $y = \sin^3 t$ at the point for which $t = \pi/8$?

Solution. $\dfrac{dy}{dt} = 3\cos t \sin^2 t$, $\dfrac{dx}{dt} = \dfrac{3\sin t\cos 2t}{2}$ on simplifying

$$\begin{aligned}\therefore \frac{dy}{dx} &= \frac{3\cos t\sin^2 t}{(^3/_2)\sin t\cos 2t} \qquad \text{by (6)}\\ &= \tan 2t\\ &= 1 \quad \text{at} \quad t = \pi/8.\end{aligned}$$

Obviously, the geometrical meaning of t is that it is half the angle between the tangent and the positive direction of the x-axis.

Portion of the nephroid, a kidney-shaped curve (*nephros* (Greek) ≡ "kidney") may be observed as a bright curve on the surface of a liquid, such as tea, in a cylindrical cup illuminated by a distant light source, e.g. a beam of parallel rays of light from the Sun. Further properties of the nephroid (Fig. 103) are provided in the solutions to Exercises 23.36, 23.37.

§ 2. DIFFERENTIALS

Now, in Fig. 1,

$$\frac{dy}{dx} = \lim_{\delta x\to 0}\left(\frac{\delta y}{\delta x}\right) = f'(x) = \tan\alpha. \tag{i}$$

But

$$\frac{\delta y}{\delta x} = \tan\theta, \tag{ii}$$

i.e. $\tan\theta$ is a ratio (of increments). Comparison of (i) and (ii) suggests that $\dfrac{dy}{dx} = \tan\alpha$ could be considered as a ratio. When this happens, we say that dy, dx are *differentials*.

From Fig. 1

$$PK = \boxed{dx = \delta x} \tag{7}$$

i.e. *the differential of the independent variable = the actual increment in the variable.*

Next, define

$$KL = \boxed{dy = f'(x)\,dx = \frac{dy}{dx}\,dx} = \frac{KL}{PK}\,\delta x, \tag{8}$$

i.e. *the differential of a function = the derivative of the function multiplied by the differential of the independent variable.*

Consequently, the symbol $\dfrac{dy}{dx}$ represents:

(a) the operation of differentiation (when it is regarded as a single entity);
(b) the ratio of differentials.

No inconsistency arises, however, since $\dfrac{dy}{dx} = f'(x)$ is true in both interpretations.

Thus, for a pendulum of length l feet, the period t (time in seconds for a complete oscillation) is given by $t = 2\pi\sqrt{\dfrac{l}{g}}$, where g is the gravitational constant, and we have $dt = \dfrac{\pi}{\sqrt{lg}}\,dl$, $\dfrac{dt}{dl} = \dfrac{\pi}{\sqrt{lg}}$.

Observe, in Fig. 1, that for very small increments ($\theta \doteqdot \alpha$) we have $dy \doteqdot \delta y$, i.e. $\dfrac{dy}{dx} \doteqdot \dfrac{\delta y}{\delta x}$. Differentials may therefore be used in approximations, though our main concern with them is in integration.

§ 3. MAXIMA AND MINIMA (REVISION)

A *stationary value* of $y = f(x)$ occurs when $f'(x) = 0$. Let $x = a$ be one such value. Generally, there exist two alternative criteria for determining the maximum and minimum values of the function (which we may write for brevity as $y_{\max}$ and $y_{\min}$ respectively).

(a) Second derivative method

$$\boxed{\begin{array}{l} f''(a) < 0 \Rightarrow y_{\max}\ [= f(a)] \\ f''(a) > 0 \Rightarrow y_{\min}\ [= f(a)] \end{array}}\,. \tag{9.1}$$

Note. $f''(x) = 0, \infty \Rightarrow$ the test fails (and higher derivatives must then be used).

The symbol $\Rightarrow$ means "implies" or "imply". Hence the first part of (9.1) is to be read as "$f''(a) < 0$ implies y is a maximum", or, equivalently, "if $f''(a) < 0$, then y is a maximum".

(b) First derivative method

Given $\varepsilon > 0$ arbitrarily small,

$$\left| \begin{array}{l} f'(a-\varepsilon) > 0, f'(a+\varepsilon) < 0 \Rightarrow y_{\max} \ [= f(a)] \\ f'(a-\varepsilon) < 0, f'(a+\varepsilon) > 0 \Rightarrow y_{\min} \ [= f(a)] \end{array} \right| . \tag{9.2}$$

Note. $f'(a-\varepsilon), f'(a+\varepsilon)$ both the same sign $\Rightarrow$ y has neither a maximum nor a minimum. That is, a stationary value does not necessarily yield a maximum or a minimum.

Consider, for example, the cubical parabola $y = x^3$ (Fig. 89a) for which $\dfrac{dy}{dx} = 3x^2 = 0$ when $x = 0$, but for which $\dfrac{d^2y}{dx^2} = 6x = 0$ when $x = 0$ and $\dfrac{dy}{dx}$ remains +ve when $x = 0-\varepsilon, 0+\varepsilon$ ($\varepsilon > 0$). Neither a maximum nor a minimum therefore exists at $x = 0$.

Usually, the nature of the problem and the degree of complexity of the algebra will determine which method is the more appropriate. Always establish mathematically whether the stationary value produces a maximum or a minimum, even though in a physical situation the conclusion may be intuitively obvious.

Maxima and minima problems occur in a wide variety of mathematical, scientific, and technological contexts. For instance, they are of general importance in physical chemistry and theoretical physics where stationary values may indicate equilibrium (stationary potential energy).

Historically, it is interesting that from the time of Ptolemy (2nd cent., Greek) through to Kepler (1571–1630, German), scholars had observed that the variation of a quantity in the vicinity of a maximum or minimum became imperceptible, but none of them pursued the consequences. About 1629 it seems that Fermat (1601–65, French) first discovered a technique similar to the derivative methods.

EXAMPLE 3 (maxima and minima). Electric current flows in a circular coil of wire of radius r, and a small magnet, distant x from the plane of the circle, is placed so that its axis coincides with the axis of the circle. Assuming that the force exerted on the magnet by the current $\propto \dfrac{x}{(x^2+r^2)^{5/2}}$, determine the value of x which gives a maximum value to the force ($\propto \equiv$ "is proportional to").

Solution. Denote the force by F (in appropriate units), and let k be the factor of proportionality.

$$\therefore F = \frac{kx}{(x^2+r^2)^{5/2}}.$$

$$\therefore \frac{dF}{dx} = k\,\frac{\{(x^2+r^2)^{5/2}.1-x.5x(x^2+r^2)^{3/2}\}}{(x^2+r^2)^5}$$

$$= k\,\frac{(r-2x)(r+2x)}{(x^2+r^2)^{7/2}} \quad \text{after simplification}$$

$= 0$, when $x = \pm r/2$, i.e., when $x = r/2$, since the negative root is physically meaningless.

As x passes through values $< r/2$ to values $> r/2$, dF/dx changes from > 0 to < 0.

Therefore by (9.2) $x = r/2$ gives a maximum value $\left(F_{\max} = \dfrac{16k}{25\sqrt{5r^4}}\right)$.

[Check, using (9.1).]

Suggested topics for further study

(1) Numerical approximations using differentials.
(2) Related rates, i.e. problems in which two rates of change are involved, as in Exercise 1.34.

References

(Differential) calculus texts listed in the bibliography.

EXERCISES 1

Differentiate the functions $f(x)$ in 1–6:

1. $\dfrac{x}{x+\sqrt{x}}$. **2.** $\dfrac{\sin x}{1+\cos x}$. **3.** $\dfrac{1-\cos x}{\sin x}$.

4. $3\tan x+\tan^3 x$. **5.** $x\cos^2(x^n)$. **6.** $\sin^4 2x+\cos^4 2x$.

Elasticity as the term is used in economics of y w.r.t. x is defined to be $E(y) = \dfrac{x}{y}\dfrac{dy}{dx}$. (See Exercise 4.42.) Establish the results 7–9:

7. $E(uv) = E(u)+E(v)$. **8.** $E(u^n) = nE(u)$. **9.** $E(u/v) = E(u)-E(v)$.

[Observe that in 7–9 the formal laws of logarithms are obeyed.]

10. If $\dfrac{d}{dy}\left(\dfrac{x^2}{y}\right) = \dfrac{Ax}{y^2}$, determine A.

11. Acceleration a and velocity v of a particle of mass m in rectilinear motion are related by the formula $a = \dfrac{d}{dx}(\frac{1}{2}v^2)$. Prove this statement.

12. *Kinetic energy* of the particle in Exercise 1.11 is given by $E = \frac{1}{2}mv^2$, and the *force F* acting on it is $F = ma$. Supposing we graph the kinetic energy against the distance x, how should we represent the force?

Displacement x from a given point at time t of a particle moving along a straight line with velocity v and acceleration a is given by $x = c \sin(nt+k)$ where c, n, k are constants. Justify the equations (13–16) describing the (simple harmonic) motion:

13. $a = -n^2x$. **14.** $\dfrac{da}{dx} = \text{constant}$.

15. $v^2 - ax = \text{constant}$. **16.** $x\dfrac{da}{dt} = av$.

What are the gradients of the parametric curves 17–20?

17. $x = a \sec t$, $y = b \tan t$ (*hyperbola*—see Fig. 86).

18. $x = 3 \sin t - 2 \sin^3 t$, $y = 3 \cos t - 2 \cos^3 t$ (*astroid*—see Example 121).

19. $x = \dfrac{t}{1+t^3}$, $y = \dfrac{t^2}{1+t^3}$ (*folium of Descartes* (1596–1650, French)—see Fig. 102).

20. $x = a(\theta - \sin\theta)$, $y = a(1-\cos\theta)$ (*cycloid*—see Fig. 105).

21. Replace θ by ωt in the equations of the cycloid (Exercise 1.20), where t represents time and $\omega = \dfrac{d\theta}{dt}$ is the *angular velocity* of a particle moving (in *curvilinear motion*) on the cycloid. Components of acceleration in the directions of the x-, y-axes being $\ddot{x}$, $\ddot{y}$ respectively, prove that the acceleration $[(\ddot{x})^2+(\ddot{y})^2]^{1/2}$ is constant.

[Electrons subjected to constant electric and magnetic forces will, for instance, describe this cycloidal path.]

22. Obtain the gradient at $x = a/8$ of the curve (astroid) $x^{2/3}+y^{2/3} = a^{2/3}$. Can you discover parametric equations of this astroid? (See Fig. 104).

23. Check that $\dfrac{1}{y^2} = -x^4+kx^2$ is a solution of *Bernoulli's equation* $\dfrac{dy}{dx}+\dfrac{y}{x} = x^3y^3$. (James Bernoulli, 1654–1705, Swiss.)

24. Einstein's Theory of Special Relativity makes use of the equation $E^2 = c^2(m_0^2c^2+p^2)$, where E is the kinetic energy and $p = m_0v$ the *momentum* of a free particle of mass m_0, and c is the velocity of light (= 186,000 miles/sec). Given that $v = \dfrac{dE}{dp}$, prove that $p = m_0v\left(1-\dfrac{v^2}{c^2}\right)^{-1/2}$. (Einstein, 1879–1955, German, American.)

25. Masses m, m_0 of a particle as determined by two observers are related by Einstein's *velocity–mass relation* $m = m_0\left(1-\dfrac{v^2}{c^2}\right)^{-1/2}$. For the momentum $p = mv$ relative to one of the observers derive the result $\dfrac{dm}{dp} = \dfrac{v}{c^2}$.

26. The *Lorentz transformation* in relativity is

$$\begin{cases} x' = k(x-vt) \\ t' = k\left(t-\dfrac{vx}{c^2}\right), \end{cases}$$

where $k = \left(1-\dfrac{v^2}{c^2}\right)^{-1/2}$ (the *Lorentz factor* occurring in Exercises 1.24, 1.25), c is the velocity of light, v is a constant velocity, and x, x' and t, t' represent variable distances and times respectively. Express $\dfrac{dx'}{dt'}$ in terms of c, v, $\dfrac{dx}{dt}$. What is its value when $\dfrac{dx}{dt} = c$?

[Getting the reverse transformation, i.e. expressing x, t in terms of x', t', is manifestly an important problem, but it is more readily solved by matrices (Exercise 14.38).]

27. *Van der Waals' equation* $\left(p+\frac{a}{v^2}\right)(v-b) = c$ (a, b, c constants) relates pressure p and volume v in a gas. Express the rate of change of volume w.r.t. pressure in terms of a, b, p, v.

28. *Escape velocity* v of a rocket (i.e. the upward velocity so that the rocket can escape from the Earth's gravitational field and never return to Earth) is, neglecting all forces except the Earth's gravitational pull, given by $v^2 = \frac{2R^2g}{x}+c$ where, in appropriate units, R is the radius of the Earth, g is the gravitational constant at the Earth's surface, x is the height at time t of the rocket (of mass m) above the centre of the Earth, and c is a physical constant. Assuming v^2 satisfies the differential equation of motion $m\ddot{x} = \frac{k}{x^2}$, determine k.

29. Supposing the initial vertical velocity of the rocket in Exercise 1.28 to be V, i.e. $v = V$ when $x = R$, what is the minimum value of V for the rocket's escape? [Take $R = 4000$ miles, $g = 32$ ft/sec^2.]

30. Given $u = (w')^{-1/2}$, $v = w(w')^{-1/2}$, where $w = f(x)$ and primes represent differentiation w.r.t. x, prove, by the quickest method, that $\frac{v''}{v} = \frac{u''}{u}$ (a result due to Goursat, 1858–1936, French).

31. For the infinite *continued fraction* $y = \frac{x}{1+y}$:

(a) express $\frac{dy}{dx}$ as a continued fraction;

(b) putting $x = 1$, write out $\frac{\sqrt{5}-1}{2}$ as a continued fraction. (Just a few steps will be enough!)

[Discover what you can about the elementary properties of finite and infinite continued fractions. Both e (Chapter 4) and π have interesting expressions as continued fractions. The number $\frac{\sqrt{5}-1}{2}$ is known as the *golden section* and is associated with *Fibonacci numbers*—see Exercise 9.39).]

32. Imagine the length of the equator to be increased by one foot. By how much would the radius of the Earth necessarily have to expand to account for this geological phenomenon?

33. Distances x, y from a lens of a point and its image on the axis of the lens are connected by the formula $\frac{1}{x}+\frac{1}{y} = \frac{1}{f}$, where f is the focal length of the lens. Obtain the *longitudinal magnification* $\delta y/\delta x$ of a small object distant x from the lens.

34. Concentric ripples are formed on the surface of a placid lake when a stone is thrown in. Supposing that the outermost ripple increases steadily at the rate of 3 ft/sec, determine the rapidity with which the area of the disturbed water is increasing after 4 sec.

35. Attraction exerted by a uniform circular ring of radius a on a particle at a point on the axis of the ring distant x from the centre is known to be proportional to $x(x^2+a^2)^{-3/2}$. Maximise this expression.

36. Deflection angle y of the needle of a tangent galvanometer is related to the current i by $\tan y = ki$ (k constant). Derive the value of y which produces the least value of $\frac{\delta i}{i}$ (the *proportional error*) for a given error in reading y.

37. What is the maximum value of x^2y^3 when $x+y = 10$ ($x > 0$, $y > 0$)?

38. Deep-water waves of wavelength λ are known to have velocity proportional to $\left(\frac{\lambda}{a}+\frac{a}{\lambda}\right)^{1/2}$, where a is a constant. For what value of λ is this velocity a minimum?

39. Statisticians use the formula $s^2 = \sum_{i=1}^{n} (x-x_i)^2$, where x_i are constants obtained from an experiment. Minimise s^2.

40. Architects wish to design a Norman window, which has the shape of a rectangle of width $2r$ and height h surmounted by a semicircle of radius r, so that the quantity of light admitted should be a maximum for a given perimeter of the window. How are the dimensions of the rectangle and semicircle related for this to be so?

41. Intensity of light varies inversely as the square of the distance from its source. Searchlights A and B whose strengths are in the ratio 8:27 (A the weaker) are used to pick out an escaped convict. At what spot on the line AB should the convict (if he is a mathematician also) cross so as to be as inconspicuous as possible?

42. Efficiency E of a screw for angle of friction α and pitch p is $E = \frac{p(1-p\tan\alpha)}{p+\tan\alpha}$. What pitch of the screw produces maximum efficiency?

43. Campers use a bell-tent consisting of a circular cylindrical base surmounted by a conical portion of semi-vertical angle θ. For a fixed base and a given volume, determine θ in order that the amount of canvas used may be a minimum.

44. Manufacturers of a certain commodity net a profit of $16 for each of the first 200 articles made per day and thereafter each article produced reduces the profit by 2 cents. In order to maximise profits, what should be the daily production?

45. Cost C in dollars per hour of running a certain ship is proportional to $4+\frac{v^3}{1000}$, where v is the speed of the ship in knots (1 knot = 1 nautical mile per hour; 1 nautical mile = 6080 ft). Calculate the speed which gives the most economical trip from Tilbury (London) to Sydney.

CHAPTER 2

INVERSE TRIGONOMETRICAL FUNCTIONS

Beautiful maiden with beaming eyes, tell me, as thou understandest the right method of inversion ...

(ARYABHATA (5th cent., Indian))

THE concept of the inverse of a function is a natural complement of the function concept and, moreover, introduces a convenient notation.

§ 4. NATURE OF INVERSE FUNCTIONS

Assume as known:

(a) the general concept of inverse functions;
(b) in particular, the idea of inverse trigonometrical (circular) functions;
(c) the graphs of the inverse trigonometrical functions (refer to § 1, Comment (iii)); and
(d) the following summary of derivatives:

$f(x)$	$\sin^{-1} x$	$\cos^{-1} x$	$\tan^{-1} x$	$\operatorname{cosec}^{-1} x$	$\sec^{-1} x$	$\cot^{-1} x$
$f'(x)$	$\dfrac{1}{\sqrt{1-x^2}}$	$-\dfrac{1}{\sqrt{1-x^2}}$	$\dfrac{1}{1+x^2}$	$-\dfrac{1}{x\sqrt{x^2-1}}$	$\dfrac{1}{x\sqrt{x^2-1}}$	$-\dfrac{1}{1+x^2}$

(10)

($x > 1$ in the case of $\operatorname{cosec}^{-1} x$ and $\sec^{-1} x$).

Take care not to confuse the inverse notation, $\sin^{-1}x$, say, with the notation $(\sin x)^{-1} = \dfrac{1}{\sin x}$ for reciprocal. Thus, for instance, $[\sin^{-1}(x^{-1})]^{-1} = \dfrac{1}{\sin^{-1}(1/x)}$. Nor must one think of $\tan^{-1} x$ as being $\dfrac{\sin^{-1} x}{\cos^{-1} x}$. Inverse notation adopted here is due (1813) to the astronomer

Herschel, discoverer of the planet Uranus. Alternative notation used by some authors is arc sin $x \equiv \sin^{-1} x$, arc cos $x \equiv \cos^{-1} x$, etc.

By interchanging the roles played by x and y in a given function $y = f(x)$ we may readily derive the *inverse function* $x = f^{-1}(y) = g(y)$, say. Simple examples of this idea are $y = x^2$, $x^2 = y$, and $y = \sin x$, $x = \sin y$ (equivalent to the expression $y = \sin^{-1} x$). Graphs of these pairs should be drawn by the reader.

Geometrically, the process of establishing an inverse function is equivalent to a reflection in the line $y = x$. By the *reflection* of a point P in a line l we mean the point Q such that l is the perpendicular bisector of PQ. (What happens in the cases of the functions $y = x$, $y = -x$? What are their inverse functions?)

Notice that

$$f\{f^{-1}(y)\} = f(x) = y \tag{11.1}$$

$$f^{-1}\{f(x)\} = f^{-1}(y) = x. \tag{11.2}$$

Examples of (11.1), (11.2) are $\sin \sin^{-1} x = x$, $\sin^{-1} \sin x = x$ respectively. From the geometrical (reflection) point of view, eq. (5) is clearly true. (Nevertheless, check for $y = x^2$ and $y = \sin x$.)

Each inverse trigonometrical function is defined to be *single-valued*, i.e. to one value of x there corresponds just one value of the inverse function. Ranges of definition of the main inverse trigonometrical functions are:

$$-\frac{\pi}{2} \leqslant \sin^{-1}x \leqslant \frac{\pi}{2},\ 0 \leqslant \cos^{-1}x \leqslant \pi,\ -\frac{\pi}{2} < \tan^{-1} x < \frac{\pi}{2} \tag{12.1}$$

with corresponding domains

$$-1 \leqslant x \leqslant 1,\ -1 \leqslant x \leqslant 1,\ -\infty < x < \infty. \tag{12.2}$$

Intervals with equality signs at both ends are *closed* (e.g. the first two in (12.1) and (12.2)); if both equality signs are omitted, the interval is *open* (e.g. the third in (12.1) and (12.2)). Why is the interval for $\tan^{-1} x$ an open one?

Particular cases of (12.1) are, say, $\sin^{-1}(\frac{1}{2}) = \pi/6$, $\sin^{-1}(-1) = -\pi/2$, $\cos^{-1}(-1) = \pi$, $\cos^{-1} 0 = \pi/2$, $\tan^{-1} 1 = \pi/4$. Also, e.g., $\sin \tan^{-1} 1 = \frac{1}{\sqrt{2}}$, $\tan \sin^{-1} \frac{\sqrt{3}}{2} = \sqrt{3}$, $\sin^{-1} \tan \pi/4 = \pi/2$.

Overlooking the ranges of definitions (12.1) may involve the student in mystifying errors. Observe that the ranges of definition for $\sin^{-1} x$ and $\cos^{-1} x$ have length π. Could other ranges have been chosen? Why? Can you state the ranges of definition of $\text{cosec}^{-1} x$, $\sec^{-1} x$, and $\cot^{-1} x$?

§ 5. SPECIAL PROPERTIES OF INVERSE TRIGONOMETRICAL FUNCTIONS

(a) $x = \sin y = \cos [(\pi/2)-y] \Rightarrow y = \sin^{-1} x,\ (\pi/2)-y = \cos^{-1} x$.
Add these and similar results to obtain

$$\boxed{\sin^{-1} x+\cos^{-1} x = \tan^{-1} x+\cot^{-1} x = \sec^{-1} x+\operatorname{cosec}^{-1}x = \frac{\pi}{2}} \quad (13)$$

This explains why, for instance, $\frac{d}{dx}(\sin^{-1} x+\cos^{-1} x) = 0$. [Refer to (10).] Results like $\tan^{-1} x-\tan^{-1} y = \cot^{-1} y-\cot^{-1} x$ follow from (13).

(b) EXAMPLE 4 (inverse functions). Differentiate (i) $\tan^{-1}\left(\frac{x}{\sqrt{1-x^2}}\right)$ $(=y)$; (ii) $\sin^{-1}\left(2x\sqrt{1-x^2}\right)$; (iii) $\sin^{-1}(k \sin r)$ $(= i)$, k constant.

Solutions. (i) $\frac{dy}{dx} = \left(1\bigg/1+\left\{\frac{x}{\sqrt{1-x^2}}\right\}^2\right)(1-x^2)^{-3/2}$ by (10) and Example 1 (i)

$= (1-x^2)^{-1/2}$ on simplifying.

Alternative solution. Construct a right-angled triangle with sides x, $\sqrt{1-x^2}$, 1 (hypotenuse). Let $\sin t = x$.

$$\therefore \quad y = \tan^{-1}\left(\frac{x}{\sqrt{1-x^2}}\right) = t = \sin^{-1} x.$$

$$\therefore \quad \frac{dy}{dx} = \frac{d \sin^{-1} x}{dx} = (1-x^2)^{-1/2}.$$

(ii) Take the triangle used in (i) above.

$$\begin{aligned} \therefore \quad \sin^{-1}\left(2x\sqrt{1-x^2}\right) &= \sin^{-1}(2 \sin t \cos t) \\ &= \sin^{-1} \sin 2t \\ &= 2t \qquad \text{by (11.2)} \\ &= 2y. \end{aligned}$$

$$\begin{aligned} \therefore \quad \frac{d}{dx}\sin^{-1}\left(2x\sqrt{1-x^2}\right) &= 2\frac{dy}{dx} \\ &= \frac{2}{\sqrt{1-x^2}} \qquad \text{by (i) above.} \end{aligned}$$

[Or, differentiate directly as in the first part of (i).]

(iii) $\dfrac{di}{dr} = \dfrac{k\cos r}{\sqrt{1-k^2\sin^2 r}}$ by (10)

$= \dfrac{k\cos r}{\cos i}$ $\because$ $\sin i = k\sin r$. ($\because$ means "since".)

$= \tan i \cot r$ substituting for k.

[Part (iii) really relates to *Snell's law*, namely: the angles of incidence and refraction for light travelling from one homogeneous medium (say air) to another (say water) are connected by the equation $\dfrac{\sin i}{\sin r} = \dfrac{u}{v}$, where u, v are the velocities of light in the first and second media respectively. Can you derive Snell's law? Assume the Optics law *(Fermat's principle)* that light travels between two points along that path for which the time taken is minimum.]

Apart from illustrating the routine procedure in differentiating inverse trigonometrical functions, Example 4(i), (ii) demonstrate certain "tricks of the trade" which are intended to quicken the reader's insight into the nature of these functions. Not all differentiations admit of such elegant solutions, of course, but these subtleties should be cultivated.

References

As for Chapter 1.

EXERCISES 2

Write down the simplified numerical values of the expressions 1–3:

1. $\sec^{-1}\tan\dfrac{\pi}{4}$. **2.** $\cot\sin^{-1}\left(-\dfrac{1}{\sqrt{2}}\right)$. **3.** $\cos\operatorname{cosec}^{-1}2$.

Differentiate the functions $f(x)$ 4–19:

4. $\cos^{-1}\sin x$. **5.** $\cos\sin^{-1}x$.

6. $\sin^{-1}(1-x)$. **7.** $\sin^{-1}\sqrt{\sin x}$.

8. $\tan^{-1}(x^n)+(\tan^{-1}x)^n$. **9.** $\dfrac{x\tan^{-1}x}{1+x^2}$.

10. $\sin^{-1}x+\sin^{-1}\sqrt{1-x^2}$. **11.** $\tan^{-1}x+\tan^{-1}\left(\dfrac{1}{x}\right)$.

12. $\tan^{-1}\left(\dfrac{2x}{1-x^2}\right)$. **13.** $\cos^{-1}\left(\dfrac{1-x^2}{1+x^2}\right)$.

14. $\tan^{-1}\left(\dfrac{1+x}{1-x}\right)$.

15. $x\sin^{-1}3x+\dfrac{1}{3}\sqrt{1-9x^2}$.

16. $\cot^{-1}\left(\dfrac{2}{x}\right)+\tan^{-1}\left(\dfrac{x}{2}\right)$.

17. $x\sqrt{1-x^2}+\sin^{-1}x$.

18. $\cot^{-1}\left(\dfrac{1+\sqrt{1+x^2}}{x}\right)$.

19. $x(\cos^{-1}x)^2-2\sqrt{1-x^2}\cos^{-1}x-2x$.

20. Establish the identity: $\sin^{-1}x+\sin^{-1}y = \sin^{-1}(x\sqrt{1-y^2}+y\sqrt{1-x^2})$.

21. Express $\sec^{-1}\tan x$ in terms of x.

22. Simplify $\cos(2\tan^{-1}x)$.

23. Differentiate $\tan^{-1}(\sec x+\tan x)$. Does the answer suggest anything to you?

24. Simplify $\tan^{-1}\frac{1}{5}+\tan^{-1}\frac{1}{8}+\tan^{-1}\frac{1}{10}+\tan^{-1}\frac{8}{21}$.

Differentiate the functions $f(x)$ in 25–28:

25. $2\cos^{-1}\sqrt{\dfrac{a-x}{a-b}}$ $(a > x > b)$.

26. $2\tan^{-1}\sqrt{\dfrac{x-b}{a-x}}$ $(a > x > b)$.

27. $\dfrac{2}{\sqrt{a^2-b^2}}\tan^{-1}\left\{\sqrt{\dfrac{a-b}{a+b}}\tan\dfrac{x}{2}\right\}$.

28. $\tan^{-1}\sqrt{\dfrac{1-\cos x}{1+\cos x}}$.

29. Verify that $y = \cos(k\cos^{-1}x)$ satisfies the differential equation

$$(1-x^2)\frac{d^2y}{dx^2}-x\frac{dy}{dx}+k^2y = 0 \quad (k \text{ constant}).$$

30. Differentiate $\tan^{-1}\left(\dfrac{2x}{1-x^2}\right)$ w.r.t. $\sin^{-1}\left(\dfrac{2x}{1+x^2}\right)$.

CHAPTER 3

ELEMENTARY ANALYSIS

JULIET: My bounty is as boundless as the sea,
My love as deep; the more I give to thee
The more I have, for both are infinite.
(SHAKESPEARE)

WE NOW ask: What exactly is meant by the limit of a function? And how shall a continuous curve be described in precise mathematical language? Discussion of these concepts takes us into the realm of analysis. One of our prime objectives is to "evaluate" indeterminate forms such as $\frac{0}{0}$ and $\infty - \infty$, which literally are meaningless (division by 0 is not possible; ∞ is not a number). Recall the definition of a derivative $\lim_{\delta x \to 0} \frac{\delta y}{\delta x}$; it is tempting, though incorrect, to put $\delta x = \delta y = 0$.

§ 6. LIMITS (REVISION). THE SYMBOL ∞

Limit theorems

Some of the derivatives in (2) and (3) depend on the following limit theorems, which we assume.

If $\lim_{x \to a} f(x) = \alpha$, $\lim_{x \to a} g(x) = \beta$ (α, β both finite, a unrestricted), then:

$$\lim_{x \to a} (kf) = k\alpha \quad (k \text{ constant}) \tag{14.1}$$

$$\lim_{x \to a} (f+g) = \alpha+\beta \tag{14.2}$$

$$\lim_{x \to a} (fg) = \alpha\beta \tag{14.3}$$

$$\lim_{x \to a} \left(\frac{f}{g}\right) = \frac{\alpha}{\beta} \quad (\beta \neq 0). \tag{14.4}$$

It is important to notice that $x \to a$ in both the given limits.

3*

Limit of a variable

By the behaviour of a function as x approaches a $(x \to a)$ we mean its behaviour, for $0 < |x-a| < \delta$, where $\delta > 0$ is arbitrarily small, i.e. when the absolute difference in value between x and a can be made as small as we please. [See Fig. 2, where $\delta <$ smaller of b, c, i.e. $\delta < \min(b, c)$.]

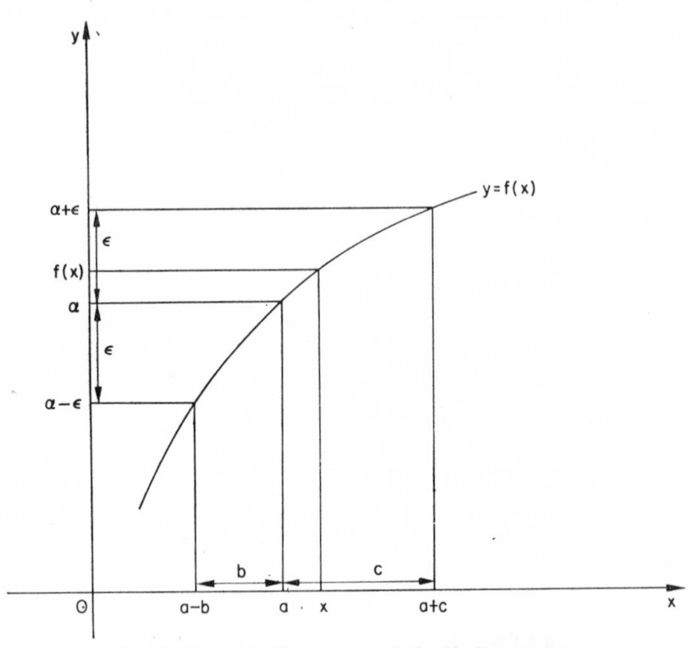

FIG. 2. Formal illustration of the limit concept

Infinity

To describe behaviour for arbitrarily large x (i.e., for x as large as we please), i.e., for $x > N$, N arbitrary, it is convenient to introduce the symbol ∞ (infinity) and to use the phrase "as x approaches infinity $(x \to \infty)$".

Remember (and it is very important!) that

∞ is not a number

but it is a conventional symbol, first used by Wallis (1616–1703, English).

Beware of imagining that ∞ obeys the rules of ordinary arithmetic. Expressions like $\infty - \infty$ and $\dfrac{\infty}{\infty}$ may be finite or infinite, depending on their context, i.e. initially they are indeterminate. However, $\infty + \infty$ is infinite. Do not confuse ∞ with very large finite numbers. For instance, *Skewes' number S*, connected with the distribution of primes and discovered in 1937 by Skewes (English), may be written as $\log_{10}\log_{10} S = 10^{34}$; though it is a large number, perhaps the largest one of any use to mathematicians, it is not infinite. Try writing it out! [Consult J. E. Littlewood, *The Mathematical Gazette*, **32** (300), 163–71 (1948).]

EXAMPLE 5 (limits). Calculate (i) $\lim_{x\to 0}\left(\frac{x}{\sqrt{1+x^2}}\right)$, (ii) $\lim_{x\to\infty}\left(\frac{x}{\sqrt{1+x^2}}\right)$.

Solutions.

$$\text{(i)}\ \lim_{x\to 0}\left(\frac{x}{\sqrt{1+x^2}}\right) = \frac{\lim_{x\to 0} x}{\lim_{x\to 0}\sqrt{1+x^2}} \quad \text{by (14.4)}$$
$$= \tfrac{0}{1}$$
$$= 0.$$

$$\text{(ii)}\ \lim_{x\to\infty}\left(\frac{x}{\sqrt{1+x^2}}\right) = \lim_{x\to\infty}\left(\frac{1}{\sqrt{x^{-2}+1}}\right)$$
$$= 1\Big/\lim_{x\to\infty}\sqrt{x^{-2}+1} \quad \text{by (14.4)}$$
$$= \tfrac{1}{1}$$
$$= 1.$$

§ 7. CONCEPT OF THE LIMIT OF A FUNCTION

Limits will not be examined in a rigorous analytical way, but it seems desirable to give a precise, formal statement of the concept of a limit. It is customary to adopt *Cauchy's definition* (1820):

$$\lim_{x\to a} f(x) = \alpha(\text{finite}) \text{ if for each } \varepsilon > 0,\ \exists \text{ a } \delta : |f(x)-\alpha| < \varepsilon \text{ for all } x,\ |x-a| < \delta.$$

[The symbol $\exists$ means "there is (are)", "there exist(s)". In Cauchy's definition, and elsewhere, a colon (:) is to be interpreted to mean "such that". On other occasions, a colon merely represents a pause. The context should make it clear which meaning is intended.]

An alternative notation for $\lim_{x\to a} f(x) = \alpha$ is "$f(x) \to \alpha$ as $x \to a$".

For purposes of clarification, δ and ε are magnified in Fig. 2, which illustrates Cauchy's definition. Exercise 3.30 (in which the actual value of the limit is quite obvious) merely demonstrates that a number δ *can* be found. Normally, we are not required to discover a value of δ in a particular problem.

Generally, we may have (i) $\lim_{x \to a} f(x) = f(a)$; (ii) $\lim_{x \to a} f(x) \neq f(a)$; or (iii) neither (i) nor (ii) is true, e.g. if $f(x)$ is not defined at $x = a$; $\sin \frac{1}{x}$, for instance, is not defined at $x = 0$.

Representing the fact that x may approach a from the right or from the left by $x \to a_+$, $x \to a_-$ respectively, we say (if both limits exist) that the unique limit α exists only if $\lim_{x \to a_+} f(x) = \alpha = \lim_{x \to a_-} f(x) (= \lim_{x \to a} f(x))$. (Note Exercise 8.14.)

Query. Can you modify Cauchy's definition, and hence Fig. 2, to cover the cases (1) $f(x) \to \infty$ as $x \to a$; (2) $f(x) \to \alpha$ as $x \to \infty$; (3) $f(x) \to \infty$ as $x \to \infty$? No number ε exists for $f(x) \to \infty$, and no number δ exists when $x \to \infty$.

§ 8. CONCEPT OF CONTINUITY

Associated with the concept of limit is that of a *continuous function* which we may regard intuitively as one without any gaps, i.e. one which can be graphed without taking pencil off paper. More precisely,

$f(x)$ is continuous at $x = a$ if $f(x) \to f(a)$ as $x \to a$.

Three things are required by this definition: (i) $f(x)$ is defined at $x = a$, (ii) $\lim_{x \to a} f(x)$ exists, and (iii) this limit equals $f(a)$. Thus, $\sin x$ is continuous for all values of x, but $\tan x$ has discontinuities at $x = (2n+1)\frac{\pi}{2}$.

Extending this concept of local continuity (i.e. at $x = a$), we say that

$f(x)$ is continuous in an interval if it is continuous at all points of the interval.

Continuity theorems, which follow as corollaries to the four limit theorems (14) may be assumed, e.g. the sum (difference) of two continuous functions is a continuous function.

While every function which is differentiable is necessarily continuous, *it does not follow that every continuous function is differentiable.**

Illustrations of the concepts of continuity and discontinuity at the origin are shown in Fig. 3a, b, c. Curve (a), $y = \sin \frac{1}{x}$, has a finite discontinuity at the origin O since $\sin \left(\frac{1}{x}\right)$ is not defined at $x = 0$, finite because values of the sine function are restricted to be between 1 and -1. Curve (b),

* See Exercise 3.15.

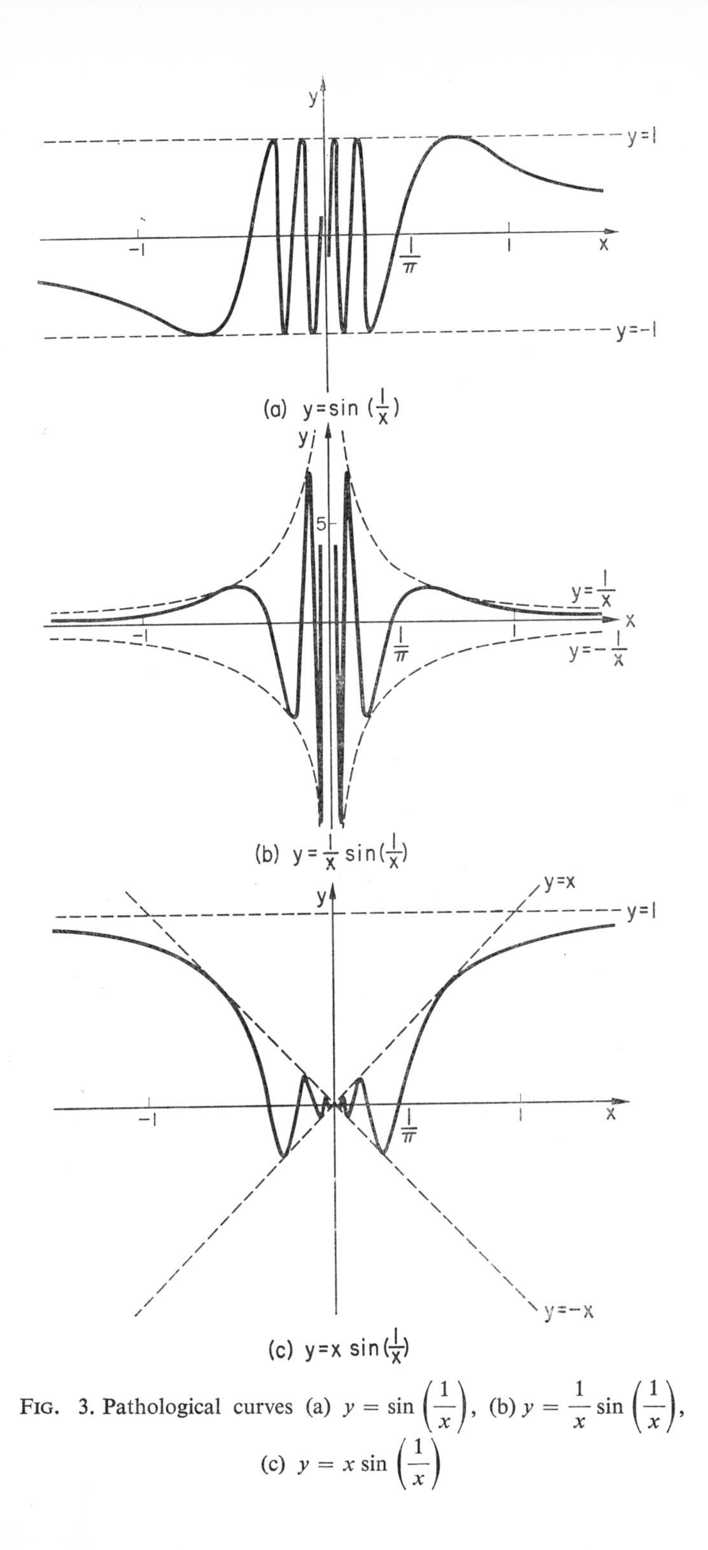

FIG. 3. Pathological curves (a) $y = \sin\left(\frac{1}{x}\right)$, (b) $y = \frac{1}{x}\sin\left(\frac{1}{x}\right)$, (c) $y = x\sin\left(\frac{1}{x}\right)$

$y = \frac{1}{x} \sin\left(\frac{1}{x}\right)$, has an infinite discontinuity at O because $\frac{1}{x} \to \infty$ as $x \to 0$.

Curve (*c*), $y = x \sin\left(\frac{1}{x}\right)$, is continuous at O since $\lim_{x \to 0}\left(x \sin \frac{1}{x}\right) = 0$.

However, $\frac{dy}{dx} = -\frac{1}{x}\cos\frac{1}{x} + \sin\frac{1}{x}$ and $\lim_{x\to 0} \sin\frac{1}{x}$ does not exist.

$\therefore\ y = x \sin \frac{1}{x}$ is directionless at O.

Thus, we have found a curve which is continuous at O but not differentiable there.

Comments

(i) Sin $\frac{1}{x}$ is an odd function whereas both $\frac{1}{x} \sin \frac{1}{x}$ and $x \sin \frac{1}{x}$ are even functions.

(ii) In (c) for $x > \frac{2}{\pi}$ we have $\frac{1}{x} < \frac{\pi}{2}$ so that $\sin \frac{1}{x} > 0$ for $x > \frac{2}{\pi}$.

What about $x < -\frac{2}{\pi}$?

(iii) For (c), $y = \frac{\sin 1/x}{1/x}$ $\therefore \lim_{x\to\infty}\left\{\frac{\sin 1/x}{1/x}\right\} = \lim_{t\to 0}\left(\frac{\sin t}{t}\right) = 1\left(t = \frac{1}{x}\right)$.

$\therefore\ y = 1$ is an asymptote.

(iv) Enveloping curves for (a), (b), (c) are, respectively,
$y = \pm 1$ (lines), $y = \pm 1/x$ (rectangular hyperbolas) and
$y = \pm x$ (lines).

Pathological curves

Curves, as in Fig. 3a, b, c, are (with justification!) called *pathological*, like people with similar aberrations. Weierstrass (1815–97, German) discovered curves which behave at every point as $y = x \sin 1/x$ does at O. One such curve which is easy to construct is the "*snowflake*" *curve* (1906) of von Koch (1870–1924, Swedish) which has infinite length but finite area (Exercise 9.26), and at no point possesses a tangent. Another well-known pathological curve is Peano's *space-filling curve* (Peano, 1858–1932, Italian). Continuous but tangentless curves were used by Boltzmann as a visual aid for theorems in the kinetic theory of gases.

Problem. How different from Fig. 3a, c will the curves $y = \cos 1/x$, $y = x \cos 1/x$ be?

From the definition of continuity, *if* $f'(x)$ *is continuous at* $x = a$ *then* $\lim_{x\to a} f'(x) = f'(a)$. [Write this in the "$\varepsilon$, δ" form of the Cauchy definition of a limit.] Thus, if $f(x) = 3x^2+5x+1$, $\lim_{x\to 0} f'(x) = 5 = f'(0)$ since $6x+5$ is continuous. But note Exercises 3.23–3.25.

§ 9. THE MEAN VALUE THEOREM. ROLLE'S THEOREM

Assume:

> *The Mean Value Theorem* (abbreviated as M.V.T.): If $f(x)$ is
> (i) single-valued and continuous in the closed interval $a \leqslant x \leqslant b$;
> (ii) differentiable in the open interval $a < x < b$,
> then $\exists$ a point ξ (in the interval $a < \xi < b$):
>
> $$f'(\xi) = \frac{f(b)-f(a)}{b-a}.$$

(The M.V.T. may be used in estimating answers to practical problems, e.g. the increase in volume of a spherical ball when the radius increases, but this is only incidental to our purpose. The M.V.T. tells us about the behaviour of a function in the vicinity of a point; see Exercise 3.26.)

Geometrical interpretation of the M.V.T.

In Fig. 4, $\tan \alpha = \dfrac{f(b)-f(a)}{b-a} = f'(\xi)$.

Therefore at some point $\xi (a < \xi < b)$, the tangent is parallel to the chord AB. (There may be several points such as ξ.)

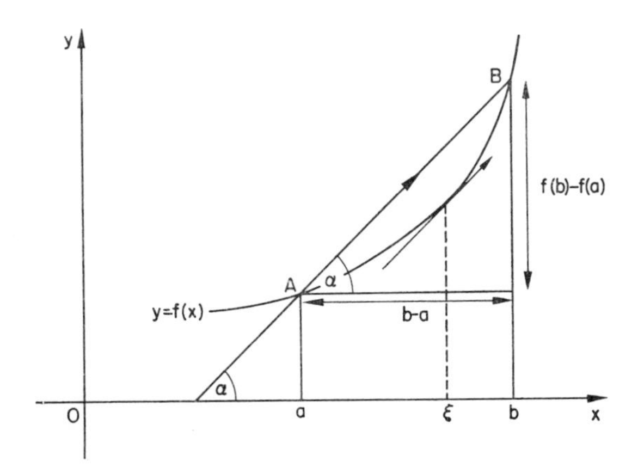

FIG. 4. Geometrical meaning of the mean value theorem

EXAMPLE 6 (M.V.T.). Determine a point (or points) $\xi(-2 < \xi < 2)$ on the *cubical parabola* $y = x^3$ satisfying the M.V.T.—see Fig. 89b.

Solution. It is readily seen that $y = f(x) = x^3$ is single-valued and continuous in $-2 \leqslant x \leqslant 2$, and differentiable in $-2 < x < 2$. Hence the criteria for the M.V.T. are valid.

$$\begin{aligned} \text{Now } f'(\xi) &= 3\xi^2 \\ &= \frac{8-(-8)}{2-(-2)} \quad \text{by the M.V.T.} \\ &= 4 \\ \therefore\ \xi &= \pm\frac{2}{\sqrt{3}}, \end{aligned}$$

i.e. on the cubical parabola there are two points $\left(\pm\frac{2}{\sqrt{3}}, \pm\frac{8}{3\sqrt{3}}\right)$ at which the tangent is parallel to the chord AB joining $A(-2, -8)$ to $B(2, 8)$.

Assume:

> *Rolle's theorem* (1691) (Rolle, 1652–1719, French): If $f(x)$ is:
> (a) conditions (i), (ii) of the M.V.T. hold;
> (b) $f(b) = f(a)$,
> then $\exists$ a point ξ (in $a < \xi < b$): $f'(\xi) = 0$.

Geometrical interpretation of Rolle's theorem

Rolle's theorem indicates the existence of a point or points on the curve $y = f(x)$ at which the tangent is parallel to the x-axis.

Theory of equations interpretation of Rolle's theorem

When $f(x)$ is a polynomial, Rolle's theorem indicates that between any 2 roots of the equation $f(x) = 0$ there is at least one root of the equation $f'(x) = 0$; e.g. if $f(x) = x^2-1 = 0$ so that $x = \pm 1$, we have $f'(x) = 2x = 0$, i.e. $x = 0$ and $-1 < 0 < 1$.

Remarks on the M.V.T. and Rolle's theorem

(i) Why are the various restrictions in (12) and (13) necessary?

(ii) Rolle's theorem is a weaker theorem than the M.V.T. by virtue of condition (b). In fact, Rolle's theorem is a special case of the M.V.T. when $f(b) = f(a)$. Draw your own diagram to illustrate Rolle's theorem.

(iii) Generalising the M.V.T. we arrive at Taylor's theorem and Taylor's series. (See Chapter 9.)

(iv) Extending the M.V.T. to two functions $f(x)$, $g(x)$, we obtain the result (subject to certain provisos) known as *Cauchy's mean value theorem:*

$$\frac{f(b)-f(a)}{g(b)-g(a)} = \frac{f'(\xi)}{g'(\xi)}$$

from which we may deduce l'Hospital's rule which is applied to limits involving the indeterminate expression $\frac{0}{0}$.

§ 10. L'HOSPITAL'S RULE (1694) (L'Hospital, 1661–1704, French)

(Actually discovered by John Bernoulli, 1667–1748, Swiss)

Let $f(x)$ and $g(x)$ be two functions of x.

l'Hospital's rule

If $f(a) = g(a) = 0$ (a finite or infinite)

$$\text{then } \lim_{x\to a}\left\{\frac{f(x)}{g(x)}\right\} = \lim_{x\to a}\left\{\frac{f'(x)}{g'(x)}\right\}. \tag{15}$$

E.g. $\lim_{x\to 0}\left(\frac{\sin x}{x}\right) = \lim_{x\to 0}\left(\frac{\cos x}{1}\right) = \frac{1}{1} = 1.$

If $\lim_{x\to a}\frac{f'(x)}{g'(x)}$ is still of the form $\frac{0}{0}$ we apply the rule again,

i.e. $$\lim_{x\to a}\frac{f'(x)}{g'(x)} = \lim_{x\to a}\frac{f''(x)}{g''(x)}$$

and so on until the indeterminateness disappears.

Other indeterminate forms are reducible to the form 0/0 (so that l'Hospital's rule applies to them also), because $\frac{\infty}{\infty}$ may be written as $\frac{1/0}{1/0} = \frac{0}{0}$, $0.\infty$ may be written as $\frac{\infty}{\infty}$ or $\frac{0}{0}$, $\infty - \infty$ may be written as $0.\infty$ and hence as $\frac{0}{0}$ $\left[\text{since } f-g = fg\left(\frac{1}{g}-\frac{1}{f}\right)\right]$. Forms 0^0, ∞^0, 1^∞ reduce to the form $0.\infty$ $\left(\text{and so to } \frac{0}{0}\right)$ on taking logarithms. The calculations below are designed to show the great power and simplicity of l'Hospital's rule.

EXAMPLE 7 (l'Hospital's rule). Calculate the limits (*a*)–(*e*).

Solutions.

(a) $$\lim_{x\to 3/2}\left(\frac{4x^2-9}{2x-3}\right) = \lim_{x\to 3/2}\left(\frac{8x}{2}\right) \quad \text{by (15)}$$
$$= 6.$$

Or: Simplify first to avoid the form $\frac{0}{0}$.

$$\therefore \lim_{x\to 3/2}\left(\frac{4x^2-9}{2x-3}\right) = \lim_{x\to 3/2}\left\{\frac{(2x-3)(2x+3)}{2x-3}\right\}$$
$$= \lim_{x\to 3/2}(2x+3)$$
$$= 6.$$

(b) $$\lim_{x\to 0}\left(\frac{\sqrt{1+x}-\sqrt{1-x}}{x}\right) = \lim_{x\to 0}\left\{\frac{\dfrac{1}{2\sqrt{1+x}}-\dfrac{-1}{2\sqrt{1-x}}}{1}\right\} \quad \text{by (15)}$$
$$= 1.$$

Or: Rationalise first to avoid the form $\frac{0}{0}$.

$$\therefore \lim_{x\to 0}\left(\frac{\sqrt{1+x}-\sqrt{1-x}}{x}\right)$$
$$= \lim_{x\to 0}\left\{\frac{(\sqrt{1+x}-\sqrt{1-x})}{x}\frac{(\sqrt{1+x}+\sqrt{1-x})}{(\sqrt{1+x}+\sqrt{1-x})}\right\}$$
$$= \lim_{x\to 0}\left\{\frac{1+x-(1-x)}{x(\sqrt{1+x}+\sqrt{1-x})}\right\}$$
$$= \lim_{x\to 0}\left\{\frac{2}{\sqrt{1+x}+\sqrt{1-x}}\right\}$$
$$= 1.$$

(c) Reduce the form $\infty - \infty$ to the form $\frac{0}{0}$.

$$\therefore \lim_{x\to \pi/2}(\sec x - \tan x) = \lim_{x\to \pi/2}\left(\frac{1-\sin x}{\cos x}\right)$$
$$= \lim_{x\to \pi/2}\left\{\frac{-\cos x}{-\sin x}\right\} \quad \text{by (15)}$$
$$= 0.$$

Or: Obtain an alternative expression to avoid the form $\frac{0}{0}$.

$$\therefore \lim_{x\to \pi/2}(\sec x - \tan x) = \lim_{x\to \pi/2}\left\{\frac{(1-\sin x)}{\cos x}\frac{(1+\sin x)}{(1+\sin x)}\right\}$$
$$= \lim_{x\to \pi/2}\left\{\frac{\cos^2 x}{\cos x\,(1+\sin x)}\right\}$$
$$= \lim_{x\to \pi/2}\left(\frac{\cos x}{1+\sin x}\right)$$
$$= 0.$$

(d) $$\lim_{x\to\pi/2}\left(\frac{\cos x}{\pi-2x}\right) = \lim_{x\to\pi/2}\left(\frac{-\sin x}{-2}\right) \quad \text{by (15)}$$
$$= \tfrac{1}{2}.$$

Or: Substitute $y = \dfrac{\pi}{2}-x$ to avoid the form $\dfrac{0}{0}$.

$$\therefore \lim_{x\to\pi/2}\left\{\frac{\cos x}{\pi-2x}\right\} = \tfrac{1}{2}\lim_{y\to 0}\left(\frac{\sin y}{y}\right)$$
$$= \tfrac{1}{2}.$$

(e) Reduce the form $0.\infty$ to the form $\dfrac{0}{0}$.

$$\therefore \lim_{x\to 0}\left(x\cot\frac{\pi}{2}x\right) = \lim_{x\to 0}\left\{\frac{x}{\tan \pi x/2}\right\}$$
$$= \lim_{x\to 0}\left\{1\Big/\frac{\pi}{2}\sec^2\left(\frac{\pi x}{2}\right)\right\} \quad \text{by (15)}$$
$$= \frac{2}{\pi}.$$

Or: By suitable trigonometrical manipulation,

$$\lim_{x\to 0}\left(x\cot\frac{\pi x}{2}\right) = \lim_{x\to 0}\left(\cos\frac{\pi x}{2}\cdot\frac{\pi x/2}{\sin \pi x/2}\cdot\frac{2}{\pi}\right)$$
$$= \frac{2}{\pi} \quad \text{by (14.1) and (14.3).}$$

(The curve $y = x\cot\dfrac{\pi x}{2}$ is called the *quadratrix of Hippias* (4th cent. B.C., Greek) or *quadratrix of Dinostratus* (*ca.* 4 B.C., Greek) and was used by the Greeks in the problems of squaring a circle and trisecting an angle.)

Not all problems in which (15) may be used will admit of a simple alternative solution. Look for alternative solutions in Exercises 3, nevertheless.

Suggested topics for further study:

(1) Approximations using the M.V.T.
(2) More rigorous and detailed study of elementary analysis, e.g. proofs of the limit and continuity theorems, of the M.V.T., and of the theorems of Rolle, Cauchy, l'Hospital, and Taylor.
(3) Large numbers.

References

As for Chapter 1, together with

(a) *A First Course in Mathematical Analysis*, J. C. Burkill (C.U.P., 1962).
(b) *Limits and Continuity*, W. K. Smith (Collier–Macmillan, 1964).

EXERCISES 3

1. How many times does $y = \sin \dfrac{1}{x}$ attain the value $+1$ between $x = \dfrac{1}{8\pi}$ and $x = \dfrac{1}{\pi}$? What is the gradient of this curve at $x = \dfrac{3}{\pi}$?

Evaluate the limits 2–17 by any lawful means:

2. $\lim\limits_{x\to\infty} \left(\dfrac{x}{\sqrt{9x^2+1}}\right)$. **3.** $\lim\limits_{x\to 0} \left(\dfrac{\sin 7x}{3x}\right)$. **4.** $\lim\limits_{x\to 0} \left(\dfrac{\sin ax}{\sin bx}\right)$.

5. $\lim\limits_{x\to 0} \left\{\dfrac{(3+x)^2-9}{x}\right\}$. **6.** $\lim\limits_{x\to\infty} \cos x$. **7.** $\lim\limits_{x\to a} \left(\dfrac{x^p-a^p}{x^q-a^q}\right)$.

8. $\lim\limits_{x\to\infty} (\sqrt{x}\{\sqrt{x+a}-\sqrt{x}\})$. **9.** $\lim\limits_{x\to 2} \left(\dfrac{\sin \pi x}{x-2}\right)$. **10.** $\lim\limits_{x\to \pi} \left(\dfrac{\sin x}{\sqrt{x-\pi}}\right)$.

11. $\lim\limits_{x\to 0} \left(\dfrac{x^3}{1-\cos x}\right)$. **12.** $\lim\limits_{x\to 0} \left(\dfrac{x+\sin 2x}{x-\sin 2x}\right)$. **13.** $\lim\limits_{x\to 0} \left(\dfrac{\tan x-x}{x-\sin x}\right)$.

14. $\lim\limits_{x\to 0} \left(\dfrac{\sin x-x}{x\cos x-x}\right)$. **15.** $\lim\limits_{x\to 0} \left(\dfrac{\sin^{-1} x}{x}\right)$. **16.** $\lim\limits_{x\to \pi/2} \left(\left\{x-\dfrac{\pi}{2}\right\}\tan x\right)$.

17. $\lim\limits_{x\to\infty} \left\{\dfrac{\pi/2-\tan^{-1} x}{1/x}\right\}$.

18. Two straight lines with gradients m, m' intersect at the point P. Do they form a continuous curve? Does a derivative exist at P?

19. Show that $\dfrac{\cos a-\cos b}{\sin b-\sin a} = \tan \xi \quad (a < \xi > b)$.

20. If $f'(x) = 0$ at all points of the open interval $a < x < b$, prove that $f(x)$ must be a constant in that interval.

21. State a corresponding result if $f'(x) > 0$ at all points in the open interval $a < x < b$.

22. Explain why Rolle's theorem is inapplicable to the function $y = 1-(x-1)^{2/3}$ in $0 \leqslant x \leqslant 2$. (What sort of a curve does this function represent?)

Answer 23–25 for the function $f(x) = x^2 \sin \dfrac{1}{x}$ for $x \neq 0$.

23. Can $f(0)$ be defined to make $f(x)$ a continuous function at $x = 0$?

24. Is it differentiable at $x = 0$?

25. Is $f'(x)$ continuous there?

26. Derive the expansion $f(a+h) = f(a)+hf'(a+\theta h) \quad (0 < \theta < 1)$.

27. Obtain $\dfrac{b-a}{1+b^2} < \tan^{-1} b-\tan^{-1} a < \dfrac{b-a}{1+a^2} \quad (a < b)$.

Deduce $\dfrac{2}{13} < \tan^{-1}\left(\dfrac{3}{2}\right)-\dfrac{\pi}{4} < \dfrac{1}{4}$.

28. Apply Rolle's theorem to the cubic function x^3-12x in $0 \leqslant x \leqslant 2\sqrt{3}$.

29. Which point on the parabola $y = x^2+x+1$ satisfies the M.V.T. in the range $-1 \leqslant x \leqslant 3$?

30. Using Cauchy's definition, show how to find a number δ (>0) for which $\lim\limits_{x\to 3} x^2 = 9$. Check the value of δ when (i) $\varepsilon = 0{\cdot}01$, (ii) $\varepsilon = 0{\cdot}000001$.

CHAPTER 4

EXPONENTIAL AND LOGARITHMIC FUNCTIONS

The Form remains, the Function never dies.

(WORDSWORTH)

NOWHERE in mathematics is there a more important pair of inverse functions than the logarithm and exponential functions which, moreover, are basic for so many problems in scientific and technological contexts.

§11. EXPONENTIAL FUNCTION. EXPONENTIAL NUMBER

Throughout our work we use the symbol $n!$ (n integer ≥ 0) to mean "factorial n", i.e. $n! = n(n-1)(n-2) \ldots 3.2.1$. *Convention:* $0! = 1$.

Definitions

Exponential function	$e^x = 1+\frac{x}{1!}+\frac{x^2}{2!}+\frac{x^3}{3!}+\ldots+\frac{x^n}{n!}+\ldots$	(16.1)
Exponential number ($x = 1$)	$e = 1+\frac{1}{1!}+\frac{1}{2!}+\frac{1}{3!}+\ldots+\frac{1}{n!}+\ldots$ $= 2{\cdot}718\ldots$	(16.2)

i.e. e^x and e are given by infinite series, with which the reader is assumed to be familiar. Infinite series and the related problem of convergence are treated in detail in Chapter 9.

Euler (1707–83, Swiss) denoted the number (16.2) by e in about 1727 so it is sometimes called *Euler's number*. When first used it was denoted by M by Cotes (1682–1716, English). Hermite (1822–1905, French) proved in 1881 that e is transcendental; it is, of course, also irrational. (See Chapter 10.) Its value has been computed to many hundreds of decimal places.

Numerical values and e

Using 4-figure tables for (16.2), we find

$$\log_{10} e = 0{\cdot}4343\ldots \tag{17.1}$$

$$\therefore \qquad \log_e 10 = 2{\cdot}303\ldots \tag{17.2}$$

$$\text{and} \qquad \boxed{\log_e a = 2{\cdot}303 \log_{10} a}. \tag{17.3}$$

Merely for reference, the following values are appended:

$e^{-1} = 0{\cdot}3679\ldots, e^{1/2} = 1{\cdot}6487\ldots, e^{-1/2} = 0{\cdot}6066\ldots, e^2 = 7{\cdot}3891\ldots,$
$e^{-2} = 0{\cdot}1353\ldots, e^3 \doteqdot 20, e^4 \doteqdot 55, e^5 \doteqdot 148, e^{10} \doteqdot 22{,}026.$
$(e^e = ?;\ e^{e^e} = e^{(e^e)} = ?)$

A function like e^x which never decreases as x increases ($x \geqslant 0$) is said to be *monotonically increasing*. On the other hand, a function like e^{-x} ($x \geqslant 0$) is *monotonically decreasing*.

Functions and e

Any function $f(x)$ may be written in the form

$$\boxed{f(x) = e^{\log_e f(x)}} \tag{18.1}$$

as may be readily verified from the ordinary definition of a logarithm. In particular,

$$\boxed{e^{\log_e x} = x}. \tag{18.2}$$

Thus, $e^{4 \log_e 3} = 3^4 = 81$, $e^{3 \log_e 4} = 4^3 = 64$, $e^{x \log_e x} = x^x$.

Furthermore, any function $f(x)$ may also be expressed as

$$\boxed{f(x) = \log_e e^{f(x)}}. \tag{19}$$

EXAMPLE 8 (exponential number e).

(a) Sum the infinite series

$$S = \log 3 - \frac{1}{2!}(\log 3)^2 + \frac{1}{3!}(\log 3)^3 - \ldots + \frac{(-1)^{n-1}}{n!}(\log 3)^n + \ldots$$

Solution. From (16.1),

$$e^{-x} = 1 - \frac{x}{1!} + \frac{x^2}{2!} - \frac{x^3}{3!} + \ldots + \frac{(-x)^n}{n!} + \ldots \qquad (\alpha)$$

Substitute $x = \log 3$ in (α).

$$\therefore \quad e^{-\log 3} = 1 - S$$

$$\begin{aligned} \therefore \qquad S &= 1 - e^{-\log 3} \\ &= 1 - e^{\log 1/3} \\ &= 1 - \tfrac{1}{3} \qquad \text{by (18.1)} \\ &= \tfrac{2}{3}. \end{aligned}$$

(b) Evaluate $\lim\limits_{n \to \infty} \sqrt[n]{n}$.

Solution. By (18.1), $\sqrt[n]{n} = n^{1/n} = e^{(\log n)/n}$ and $\dfrac{\log n}{n} \to 0$ since $n \to \infty$ more rapidly than $\log n$ does.

$$\therefore \quad \lim_{n \to \infty} \sqrt[n]{n} = e^0 = 1.$$

Limits and e

Readers are assumed to be familiar with the finite binomial expansion $(1+x)^n$ for n a positive integer. Extension to real n is covered in the infinite series (96). Had we wished, this infinite series, which is in no way dependent on the exponential function, could have been derived without (90). Anticipating (96), we have

$$\begin{aligned} \left(1 + \frac{1}{n}\right)^n &= 1 + n\,\frac{1}{n} + \frac{n(n-1)}{2!}\,\frac{1}{n^2} + \frac{n(n-1)(n-2)}{3!}\,\frac{1}{n^3} + \ldots \\ &= 1 + 1 + \frac{(1-1/n)}{2!} + \frac{(1-1/n)(1-2/n)}{3!} + \ldots \end{aligned}$$

$$\therefore \quad \lim_{n \to \infty} \left(1 + \frac{1}{n}\right)^n = 1 + 1 + \frac{1}{2!} + \frac{1}{3!} + \frac{1}{4!} + \ldots \quad \text{(assuming that the limit of a sum = the sum of the limits)}$$

$$= e \qquad \text{by (16.2),}$$

i.e.

$$\boxed{\lim_{n\to\infty}\left(1+\frac{1}{n}\right)^n = e = \lim_{m\to 0}(1+m)^{1/m}} \tag{20}$$

on substituting $m = \dfrac{1}{n}$.

Furthermore, by (96),

$$\left(1+\frac{1}{n}\right)^{nx} = 1+nx\frac{1}{n}+\frac{nx(nx-1)}{2!}\frac{1}{n^2}+\frac{nx(nx-1)(nx-2)}{3!}\frac{1}{n^3}+\ldots$$

$$= 1+x+\frac{x(x-1/n)}{2!}+\frac{x(x-1/n)(x-2/n)}{3!}+\ldots$$

Therefore $\displaystyle\lim_{n\to\infty}\left[\left(1+\frac{1}{n}\right)^{nx}\right] = e^x$ by the above method and (16.1),

i.e.

$$\boxed{\lim_{n\to\infty}\left(1+\frac{1}{n}\right)^{nx} = e^x = \lim_{p\to\infty}\left(1+\frac{x}{p}\right)^p} \tag{21}$$

on putting $p = nx$.

Taking logs to base 10 in (20) and assuming the result that the *logarithm of a limit = the limit of a logarithm*, we have

$$\boxed{\lim_{n\to\infty}\left\{\log_{10}\left(1+\frac{1}{n}\right)^n\right\} = \log_{10} e = 0{\cdot}4343\ldots} \tag{22}$$

Continuous growth, e.g. cell-splitting in a bacterial culture, or insect growth in a colony, is a natural law of organic change, and is represented mathematically by the exponential function, i.e. the exponential function serves as a mathematical model for organic growth. Decay occurs if this growth is negative as in the case of the dissipation of atoms in a radioactive substance such as radium.

Bank interest, if compounded continuously instead of discretely, would involve the exponential function. Because of this, Lord Kelvin (1824–1907, English) called the law of growth the *compound interest law*. Correspondingly, for simple interest accruing continuously, the function would be linear. No bank could, of course, stand the financial strain of compounding its depositors' interest continuously! Notwithstanding this, we examine this hypothetical process as it illuminates the biological aspect.

EXAMPLE 9 (continuous compounding of bank interest).

Solution. For principal P dollars initially deposited, let the amount at the end of t years be A dollars, assuming interest at $r/m\%$ is added m times annually. Rate is said to be $r\%$.

$$\therefore \quad A = P\left(1+\frac{r}{100m}\right)^{mt}$$

$$= P\left(1+\frac{1}{n}\right)^{nrt/100} \qquad \left(\frac{r}{100m} = \frac{1}{n}\right)$$

$$= P\left\{\left(1+\frac{1}{n}\right)^{n}\right\}^{rt/100}$$

$$= P\left\{\lim_{n\to\infty}\left(1+\frac{1}{n}\right)^{n}\right\}^{rt/100}$$

{ if $n \to \infty$, i.e. interest is added on at indefinitely small intervals, i.e. growth of P is continuous.

$$= Pe^{rt/100} \qquad \text{by (20)}$$

$$= Pe^{x} \qquad \left(\frac{rt}{100} = x\right).$$

§ 12. GRAPHS OF THE EXPONENTIAL AND LOGARITHMIC FUNCTIONS

Concerning the graphs of e^x and $\log x$ (Fig. 5a, b) we make the following observations:

(i) Obviously the exponential function $y = e^x$ and the logarithm function $y = \log_e x$, i.e. $x = e^y$, are inverse functions.

(ii) Only one algebraic point (§ 43) of the plane, namely (0, 1), lies on $y = e^x$.

(iii) In the function $\log x$, $x > 0$. If $\log(-x)$ exists, then $x < 0$.

(iv) The relationship between corresponding ordinates of $y = \log_{10} x$ and $y = \log_e x$ is $\log_{10} x \doteqdot 0{\cdot}4343 \log_e x$ by (17.1). Logarithm curves were discovered about 1640 by Torricelli (1608–47, Italian).

(v) The general exponential curve $y = a^x$ is related to $y = e^x$ according to the relation between a and e, i.e. $y = 3^x$ will resemble $y = e^x$ more than will $y = 100^x$.

(vi) Logarithms to base 10 are called *Briggsian (common) logarithms*, while logarithms to base e are called *Napierian (natural) logarithms* after Briggs (1561–1631, English) and Napier (1550–1617, Scots). Earliest tables of logarithms were prepared in 1614 by Napier, in 1620 by Gunter (1581–1626, English) and Bürgi (1552–1632 Swiss) and in 1624 by Briggs and Kepler. Originally, Napier defined a logarithm in terms of velocities of points moving rectilinearly. Essentially, logarithms denote a correspond-

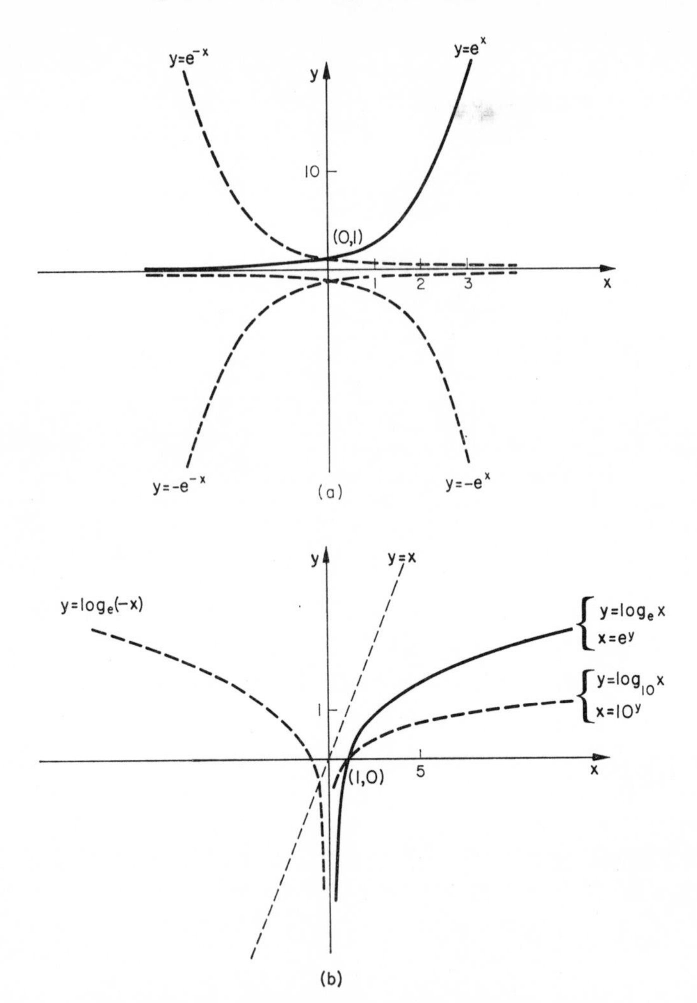

FIG. 5. (a) Exponential curves. (b) Logarithmic curves

ence between two sets of numbers. Astronomers particularly found them a great help in computation.

(vii) Many mathematical models used by social scientists involve the exponential and logarithmic functions. For example, Fechner, the psychologist, enunciated the law $R = k \log S$ for the relation between a stimulus S (say brightness of light) and the response R (k a factor of proportionality).

Convention. Unless otherwise specified, $\log x$, *with no base stipulated, will mean* $\log_e x$. Alternative notation, not used here, is $\ln x$ instead of $\log x$.

[Skewes' number S (§ 6) may be expressed as $\log \log \log S \doteqdot 79$.]

§ 13. DIFFERENTIATION OF THE EXPONENTIAL AND LOGARITHMIC FUNCTIONS

Differentiation of e^x

Given $y = e^x$, take small increments δx, δy in the variables.

$$\therefore \quad y+\delta y = e^{x+\delta x}.$$

$$\therefore \quad \delta y = e^{x+\delta x}-e^x = e^x(e^{\delta x}-1)$$

$$= e^x\left(\delta x+\frac{(\delta x)^2}{2!}+\frac{(\delta x)^3}{3!}+\ldots+\frac{(\delta x)^n}{n!}+\ldots\right) \qquad \text{by (16.1)}$$

$$\therefore \quad \frac{\delta y}{\delta x} = e^x\left(1+\frac{\delta x}{2!}+\frac{(\delta x)^2}{3!}+\ldots+\frac{(\delta x)^{n-1}}{n!}+\ldots\right).$$

Therefore in the limit,

$$\boxed{\frac{de^x}{dx} = e^x}. \tag{23}$$

Alternative proof. Given $y = e^x = 1+\frac{x}{1!}+\frac{x^2}{2!}+\frac{x^3}{3!}+\ldots$,

then $$\frac{dy}{dx} = 1+\frac{x}{1!}+\frac{x^2}{2!}+\frac{x^3}{3!}+\ldots = e^x$$

on differentiating term-by-term. Thus e^x is such that its derivative leaves it unaltered (in fact, its *nth* derivative leaves it unaltered) and it is the only function in mathematics with this fascinating and important property. Many problems occurring in the physical, biological, and social sciences and in engineering are involved in the simple first-order differential equation $\frac{dy}{dx} = y$ whose solution is the exponential function.

EXAMPLE 10 (exponential function). Differentiate (i) $e^{f(x)}$, (ii) $\sin(e^{x^2})$.

Solutions. (i) Writing $y = e^{f(x)} = e^u$, where $u = f(x)$, we have, by (4),

$$\frac{dy}{dx} = f'(x)\, e^{f(x)}.$$

(E.g. $f(x) = a-bx^n$, $1/\sqrt{x}$, $\tan x \Rightarrow \frac{dy}{dx} = -bnx^{n-1}e^{a-bx^n}$, $\frac{-e^{1/\sqrt{x}}}{2x^{3/2}}$, $\sec^2 x e^{\tan x}$ respectively.)

(ii) Setting $y = \sin t$, $t = e^u$, $u = x^2$, we have, by extended (4),

$$\frac{dy}{dx} = 2x\, e^{x^2} \cos(e^{x^2}).$$

Differentiation of $\log x$

Given $y = \log_e x$, i.e. $x = e^y$, then

$$\frac{dx}{dy} = e^y = x \qquad \text{by (23)},$$

i.e. $$\frac{dy}{dx} = \frac{1}{x} \qquad \text{by (5)},$$

i.e. $$\boxed{\frac{d \log_e x}{dx} = \frac{1}{x}}. \tag{24}$$

If $y = \log_a x = \log_e x \cdot \log_a e$, then $\dfrac{dy}{dx} = \dfrac{1}{x} \log_a e$ by (24),

i.e. $$\boxed{\frac{d \log_a x}{dx} = \frac{\log_a e}{x}}. \tag{25.1}$$

In particular, with $a = 10$,

$$\boxed{\frac{d \log_{10} x}{dx} = \frac{\log_{10} e}{x}}. \tag{25.2}$$

Results (24), (25.1), and (25.2) may be obtained from first principles without recourse to the exponential function, i.e. by starting with $y = \log_{10} x$ and taking increments so that $y+\delta y = \log_{10}(x+\delta x)$. If this approach is made, and it is an instructive one, it will eventually be necessary to use (22).

Example 11 (logarithm function). Differentiate (i) $\log \sin x$, (ii) $\sin \log x$, (iii) $\log \sqrt{\dfrac{1+x}{1-x}}$, (iv) $\sqrt{\dfrac{1+x^4}{1-x^4}}$.

Solutions. (i) $\dfrac{dy}{dx} = \dfrac{\cos x}{\sin x} = \cot x$ by (4). (ii) $\dfrac{dy}{dx} = \dfrac{\cos \log x}{x}$ by (4).

(iii) $y = \log \sqrt{\dfrac{1+x}{1-x}} = \dfrac{1}{2}\{\log(1+x) - \log(1-x)\}$

$$\therefore \frac{dy}{dx} = \frac{1}{2}\left\{\frac{1}{1+x} - \frac{-1}{1-x}\right\}$$

$$= \frac{1}{1-x^2}.$$

(iv) $y = \sqrt{\dfrac{1+x^4}{1-x^4}} \Rightarrow \log y = \dfrac{1}{2}\{\log(1+x^4) - \log(1-x^4)\}$

$$\therefore \frac{1}{y}\frac{dy}{dx} = \frac{1}{2}\left\{\frac{4x^3}{1+x^4} - \frac{-4x^3}{1-x^4}\right\} \text{ using (4)}$$

$$\therefore \frac{dy}{dx} = \frac{4x^3}{(1+x^4)^{1/2}(1-x^4)^{3/2}}.$$

Comments

(a) Example 11(iv) is an example of *logarithmic differentiation* which may be used whenever y is of the form $uv \ldots w$, u/v, u^n, a^u, i.e. whenever taking logarithms of both sides is advantageous ($u, v, w, \ldots$ being functions of x).

(b) In Example 11(ii), $\frac{d^2y}{dx^2} = \left(x\,\frac{-\sin\log x}{x} - \cos\log x \cdot 1\right)\Big/ x^2$, whence $x^2\frac{d^2y}{dx^2} + x\frac{dy}{dx} + y = 0$, i.e. $y = \sin\log x$ $(x > 0)$ is a solution of this second-order differential equation.

(c) Note: $\frac{d\log y}{dx} = \frac{d\log y}{dy}\frac{dy}{dx} = \frac{1}{y}\frac{dy}{dx}$ by (4) and (24).

Differentiation of a^x

Given $y = a^x$, $\log_a y = x$ (taking logs to base a of both sides) *or* $\log y = x\log a$ (using the method for logarithmic differentiation).

$$\therefore \frac{\log_a e}{y}\frac{dy}{dx} = 1 \quad \text{by (25.1) or} \quad \frac{1}{y}\frac{dy}{dx} = \log a.$$

Hence, in either case,

$$\boxed{\frac{da^x}{dx} = a^x \log a}. \tag{26}$$

[Also by (18.1), $a^x = e^{x\log a}$, $\therefore \frac{da^x}{dx} = \log a . e^{x\log a} = a^x\log a.$]

Differentiation of x^x

Given $y = x^x$, proceed logarithmically (there is no other choice here).

$$\therefore \log y = x\log x$$

$$\therefore \frac{1}{y}\frac{dy}{dx} = \log x + x\cdot\frac{1}{x} = 1+\log x$$

$$\boxed{\frac{dx^x}{dx} = x^x(1+\log x)}. \tag{27}$$

Summary of derivatives of exponential and logarithmic functions

$f(x)$	e^x	a^x	x^x	$\log x$	$\log_a x$
$f'(x)$	e^x	$a^x \log a$	$x^x(1+\log x)$	$\dfrac{1}{x}$	$\dfrac{1}{x \log a}$

EXAMPLE 12 (applications to geometry: subtangent and subnormal). Which curves have constant subtangent and constant subnormal?

Solution. In $\triangle PTM$ (Fig. 6), the *subtangent* $TM = y\Big/\dfrac{dy}{dx} = 1\Big/\dfrac{d}{dx}\log y$.

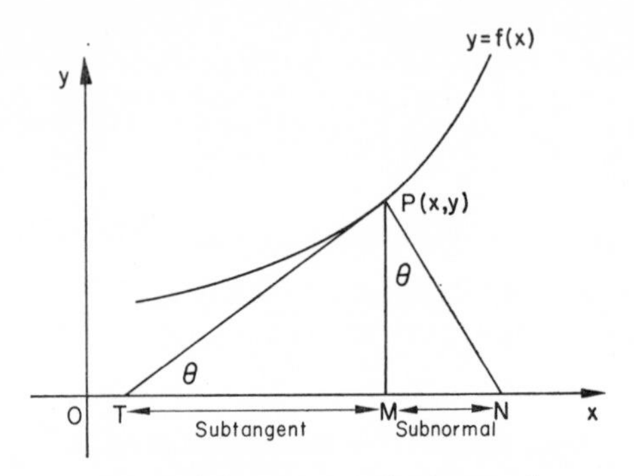

FIG. 6. Subtangent and subnormal

Suppose this subtangent is constant $\left(=\dfrac{1}{k}\right)$, $\therefore \dfrac{d}{dx}(\log y) = k$.

$\therefore \log y = kx,$ i.e. $y = e^{kx}$. (α)

Therefore *the only curve with constant subtangent is the exponential curve.*

In $\triangle PMN$, the *subnormal* $MN = y\dfrac{dy}{dx} = \dfrac{1}{2}\dfrac{dy^2}{dx}\left(= \dfrac{1}{2}\dfrac{dy^2}{dy}\dfrac{dy}{dx}\right)$.

Suppose the subnormal is constant $(= 2a)$. $\therefore \dfrac{dy^2}{dx} = 4a$,

i.e. $y^2 = 4ax$. (β)

Therefore *the only curve with constant subnormal is the parabola.*

(Strictly speaking, solutions (α) and (β) are incomplete. See § 23 for a clarification of this assertion.)

EXAMPLE 13 (L'Hospital's rule). Evaluate $\lim\limits_{x \to 0} (\cos x)^{x^{-2}}$.

[Previously, in § 10, it was observed that the indeterminate forms 0^0, ∞^0, 1^∞ in limit problems are reducible to the form $0 . \infty$ by taking logarithms.

If, on taking logarithms, the answer is w, then the answer to the original problem is e^w.]

Query. Is 0^∞ indeterminate? [Remember that $\log 0 = -\infty$.]

Solution. Given $y = \lim_{x\to 0} (\cos x)^{1/x^2}$ (which is of the form 1^∞)

$$\therefore \log y = \lim_{x\to 0}\left\{\frac{\log \cos x}{x^2}\right\} \quad \text{of the form } \frac{0}{0}$$

$$= \lim_{x\to 0}\left(\frac{-\tan x}{2x}\right) \quad \text{by (15)} \left(\text{still of the form } \frac{0}{0}\right)$$

$$= \lim_{x\to 0}\left(\frac{-\sec^2 x}{2}\right) \quad \text{by (15)}$$

$$= -\tfrac{1}{2}$$

$$\therefore \lim_{x\to 0} (\cos x)^{1/x^2} = e^{-1/2} = \frac{1}{\sqrt{e}}.$$

References

As for Chapter 1.

EXERCISES 4

1. Simplify $\log x^{\log x}$.

Differentiate the functions $f(x)$ in 2–25:

2. $e^{\log \cos x}$.

3. $e^{\sin^2 x}$.

4. e^{x^x}.

5. $\cos e^x$.

6. $x^2 e^{1/x}$.

7. $e^{-x^2} \cos 2x$.

8. $e^{-\log x}$.

9. $\cos^{-1} (e^{x^3})$.

10. $\log \log x$.

11. $\log (x+\sqrt{x^2-a^2})$.

12. $\log (\sqrt{x+1}+\sqrt{x-1})$.

13. $\dfrac{x}{(\log x)^2}$.

14. $\log \left(\dfrac{x}{\sqrt{1+x^2}}\right)$.

15. $\log \cos (1+x^2)$.

16. $\sqrt{x}-\log (1+\sqrt{x})$.

17. $\log_x 10$.

18. $\log (1+e^x)$.

19. $\tan \log x$.

20. $\log \tan \left(\dfrac{x}{2}+\dfrac{\pi}{4}\right)$.

21. $(\sin x)^{\cos x}$.

22. $x \tan^{-1}x-\log \sqrt{1+x^2}$.

23. $x^a a^x$.

24. $\log \left(\dfrac{1+x}{1-x}\right)$.

25. $e^{-e^{-x}}$ (a biological growth function, due to Gompertz).

26. Bacterial growth (increase per second) in a culture where an unrestricted food supply is present is represented by the first-order differential equation $\dfrac{dN}{dt} = aN$, where N is the number alive at time t. Given the solution $N = ce^{kt}$, find a (c, k are constants).

27. If $y = \left(\frac{1}{2}e\right)^x$ prove that $\frac{1}{y}\frac{dy}{dx}$ is constant. Compute its value to two decimal places.

28. You are given that $y = ae^x + be^{-x}$ is a solution of the differential equation $\frac{d^2y}{dx^2} + k\frac{dy}{dx} + my = 0$. Determine k, m.

29. Damped harmonic oscillation, given by $\ddot{x} + k\dot{x} + n^2x = 0$, has a solution $x = ae^{-kt/2}\cos(qt+\varepsilon)$, where a, k, n, q, ε are constants. Find n.

30. Current j (amperes) in a coil containing a resistance R (ohms), an inductance L (henries), and a constant electromotive force E (volts) at time t is given by $j = \frac{E}{R}(1 - e^{-Rt/L})$. When R is *very* small (i.e. $R \to 0$), calculate a suitable approximaion to j.

Evaluate the limits 31–36:

31. $\lim_{x\to 0}\left(\frac{2^x - 3^x}{x}\right)$. **32.** $\lim_{x\to\infty}\left(\frac{x^n}{e^x}\right)$. **33.** $\lim_{x\to\infty}\left(\frac{x+\log x}{x\log x}\right)$.

34. $\lim_{x\to\infty}(1+x)^{1/x}$. **35.** $\lim_{x\to 1} x^{1/(x-1)}$. **36.** $\lim_{x\to 2}\left\{\frac{x^2\log x - 4\log 2}{x^2-4}\right\}$.

37. *Adiabatic pressure p* of a gas, volume v, expanding or compressing without loss of heat in a vessel, is given by the law $pv^\gamma = c$ (c, γ constants). At what rate is the pressure changing w.r.t. volume?

38. Maximise $x^{1/x}$.

39. When is the ratio of a logarithm of a number to the number itself greatest?

40. Which is greater: e^π or π^e? (No computation required.)

41. Simplify $x^{1/\log x}$.

42. Prove that the elasticity function $E(y) = \frac{d\log y}{d\log x}$ (Exercise 1.7). If $E(y) = k$ (constant), obtain y as a function of x.

43. Capital invested in a building trust fund accrues interest, compounded continuously, at 5%. How long will it take for the principal to double?

With reference to Fig. 6, establish the two results:

44. $PN = y\sqrt{1+\left(\frac{dy}{dx}\right)^2}$. **45.** $PT = y\sqrt{1+\left(\frac{dy}{dx}\right)^2}\Big/\frac{dy}{dx}$.

46. Imagine a curve constructed so that the velocity v of a particle is taken as ordinate and the distance s travelled is taken as abscissa. Acceleration is then represented by the subnormal. Prove.

47. Signalling speed in a submarine telegraph cable is proportional to $x^2\log\left(\frac{1}{x}\right)$, where x = (radius of core of copper wire)/(thickness of the covering). Quickest signals are sent when $x = e^{-1/2}$. Prove.

48. Solve for real x : $\log(1+x) = \log(1-x)+1$.

49. Raindrops (i.e. falling bodies in a resisting medium, air) drop a distance x in time t given by $x = \frac{1}{k}\left\{gt + \frac{g-ku}{k}(e^{-kt}-1)\right\}$, where g is the gravitational constant and k, u are other constants. Verify that the motion is given by $\ddot{x} = g - k\dot{x}$. (This is motion with resistance proportional to the velocity.)

50. Einstein's model of a crystal involves the partition function $f = e^{-x/2}+e^{-3x/2}+$ $+e^{-5x/2}+\ldots$, where $x = \dfrac{h\nu}{KT}$. Sum this infinite series (see Example 44), and calculate the internal energy $E = NKT^2\dfrac{d}{dT}\log f$, where N is the number of atoms and h, ν, k are other physical constants.

51. Fuel in a rocket (e.g. liquid oxygen–petrol fuel) is ejected in a series of n impulsive bursts. If the mass of the rocket is m_0 when fuel tanks are full, and m_n when fuel tanks are empty, the *mass ratio* R is defined as $R = \dfrac{m_0}{m_n}$. Mechanical considerations allow us to assume $\dfrac{m_{i-1}}{m_i} = 1+\dfrac{v}{nc}$ $(i = 1, \ldots, n)$, where c is the backward velocity of the exhaust gases relative to the rocket, v is the final velocity attainable by the rocket from rest in the absence of any external forces, and m_i is the combined mass of rocket and remaining fuel after the *ith* impulse. Assuming the rocket to be continuously accelerated, i.e. $n \to \infty$, calculate R.

52. For what values of R can the rocket (Exercise 4.51) attain a velocity equal to twice its own exhaust velocity?

53. Evaluate $\lim\limits_{x\to 0} (\cos \sqrt{x})^{1/x}$.

54. Samuelson (1948) conceived the differential equation $\ddot{k}+n\dot{k}+\dfrac{n^2}{4}k = 0$ as an investment model. Verify that a solution is $k = \left\{k_0+t\left(I_0+\dfrac{n}{2}k_0\right)\right\} e^{-nt/2}$, where I_0 is the investment at time $t = 0$, and k_0 is the excess of capital over equilibrium amount at time $t = 0$ (n a constant).

55. Oscillations of an electric charge q at time t in a simple series electronic oscillator circuit are determined by the *vibration equation* $5\ddot{q}+2\dot{q}+q = 0$. Verify that $q = ke^{-t/5}\sin\left(\dfrac{2t}{5}\right)$ is a solution of this differential equation, where $k\left(= \dfrac{e^{1/5}}{\sin 2/5}\right)$ is a constant.

56. Between any two real roots of $e^x \sin x = 1$ there lies at least one real root of $e^x \cos x = -1$. Prove by using Rolle's theorem.

57. Deduce, from the M.V.T., that $1-\dfrac{a}{b} < \log\dfrac{b}{a} < \dfrac{b}{a}-1$. Hence, obtain

$$\frac{1}{2} < \log 2 < 1.$$

58. Derive $\left(\dfrac{101}{100}\right)^{100} < e < \left(\dfrac{100}{99}\right)^{100}$.

59. Given $f(x) = \log_a (\frac{1}{2}x)$, calculate (i) $f^{-1}(x)$, (ii) $\cos^{-1} f(2)$.

60. Define $\phi(x) = \frac{1}{2}(a^x+a^{-x})$, $\psi(x) = \frac{1}{2}(a^x-a^{-x})$. Obtain the expressions

$$\phi(x+y) = \phi(x)\,\phi(y)+\psi(x)\,\psi(y)$$
$$\psi(x+y) = \phi(x)\,\psi(y)+\phi(y)\,\psi(x).$$

Write down expressions for $\phi(2x)$, $\psi(2x)$.

CHAPTER 5

HYPERBOLIC FUNCTIONS

"When *I* use a word", Humpty Dumpty said, in rather a scornful tone, "it means just what I choose it to mean—neither more nor less!"

"The question is," said Alice, "whether you *can* make words mean so many different things."

"The question is," said Humpty Dumpty, "which is to be master—that's all."

(LEWIS CARROLL)

SUM and difference of e^x, e^{-x} occur as natural combinations, so it is convenient to have an abbreviated notation to express these relations. Functions thus defined are found to possess properties closely paralleling those of the trigonometrical functions.

§ 14. THE HYPERBOLIC FUNCTIONS

Definitions

Hyperbolic sine

$$\sinh x = \frac{e^x - e^{-x}}{2} = \frac{x}{1!} + \frac{x^3}{3!} + \frac{x^5}{5!} + \ldots \tag{28.1}$$

Hyperbolic cosine

$$\cosh x = \frac{e^x + e^{-x}}{2} = 1 + \frac{x^2}{2!} + \frac{x^4}{4!} + \ldots \tag{28.2}$$

Other hyperbolic functions are defined in terms of sinh x and cosh x, namely:

$$\tanh x = \frac{\sinh x}{\cosh x}, \quad \coth x = \frac{\cosh x}{\sinh x}, \quad \text{sech}\, x = \frac{1}{\cosh x},$$

$$\text{cosech}\, x = \frac{1}{\sinh x}. \tag{28.3}$$

Because the hyperbolic functions are defined exponentially, we can expect them also to have wide applicability in science.

Remarks

(i) $\left.\begin{array}{l}\cosh 0 = 1, \ \cosh 1 = 1{\cdot}543\ldots \\ \sinh 0 = 0, \ \sinh 1 = 1{\cdot}176\ldots\end{array}\right\}$ on calculation, or from hyperbolic tables.

(ii) $\cosh x$ is an even function, $\sinh x$ is an odd function.

(iii) The variable x does not represent an angle in hyperbolic functions (as it would in circular function theory). Hyperbolic functions are exponential, not periodic.

(iv) The equation of the *catenary* (see Fig. 7a) is

$$y = a \cosh \frac{x}{a} = a \frac{e^{x/a} + e^{-x/a}}{2}.$$

The catenary is the curve in which a uniform flexible chain (Latin *catena* ≡ "chain") will hang if no forces, other than gravity, are acting on it. Thus, electricity transmission cables suspended between two pylons will also assume the form of a catenary. Galileo (1564–1642, Italian) thought the chain curve was a parabola. James Bernoulli (1690) proposed and solved the problem of finding the true curve. Leibniz (1691) and Huygens (1629–95, Dutch) also solved it. Further, the catenary occurs as the solution of the soap-film problem.

(v) Hyperbolic functions bear the same relation to the rectangular hyperbola as the circular functions bear to the circle. More precisely, a point on the circle $x^2+y^2 = a^2$ may be expressed parametrically as $x = a\cos\theta$, $y = a \sin\theta$, whereas a point on one branch of the rectangular hyperbola $x^2-y^2 = a^2$ may be represented by $x = a\cosh\phi$, $y = a \sinh\phi$. What are the geometrical meanings of θ, ϕ? (Refer to §§ 95, 97.) G. Mercator (the cartographer) made the first and most important application of hyperbolic functions when he issued his map on Mercator's projection in the sixteenth century. However, the claim to have actually discovered the principles of the hyperbolic functions seems to belong (1757) to Riccati (1707–75, Italian). Our notation is due to Lambert (1728–77, German) who systematised the subject.

Basic formulae for the hyperbolic functions

From (28.1) and (28.2), $\cosh x+\sinh x = e^x$, $\cosh x-\sinh x = e^{-x}$.

$$\therefore \quad \boxed{\cosh^2 x-\sinh^2 x = 1} \tag{29.1}$$

(on multiplying the two equations), whence we derive

$$\operatorname{sech}^2 x = 1-\tanh^2 x, \quad \operatorname{cosech}^2 x = \coth^2 x-1. \tag{29.2}$$

Memorise (29.1); it is important. Recall (Remark (i) above) that $\cosh^2 0-\sinh^2 0 = 1$, $\cosh^2 1-\sinh^2 1 = 1$.

$$\text{Now } \cosh(x+y) = \tfrac{1}{2}(e^{x+y}+e^{-(x+y)})$$
$$= \tfrac{1}{2}(e^{x}e^{y}+e^{-x}e^{-y})$$
$$= \tfrac{1}{2}\{(\cosh x+\sinh x)(\cosh y+\sinh y)$$
$$+(\cosh x-\sinh x)(\cosh y-\sinh y)\}.$$

Simplify. $\therefore$ $$\boxed{\cosh(x+y) = \cosh x\cosh y+\sinh x\sinh y}. \quad (30)$$

Put $y = x$. $\therefore$ $$\boxed{\cosh 2x = \cosh^2 x+\sinh^2 x}. \quad (31)$$

Similarly $$\boxed{\sinh(x+y) = \sinh x\cosh y+\cosh x\sinh y} \quad (32)$$

$$\boxed{\sinh 2x = 2\sinh x\cosh x}. \quad (33)$$

Comments

(i) Results (29)–(33) should be carefully compared with the corresponding results involving circular functions.

(ii) Equation (29.1) implies the existence of a right-angled triangle whose sides are 1, $\sinh x$, $\cosh x$ (hypotenuse) leading to an angle $\phi : \sin\phi = \tanh x$. (See § 18.)

(iii) $\cosh(x+y)+\sinh(x+y) = e^{x+y} = e^{x}e^{y} = (\cosh x+\sinh x)\times(\cosh y+\sinh y)$.

(iv) Replacing y by $-y$ in (30) and (32) yields expressions for $\cosh(x-y)$ and $\sinh(x-y)$. Suitable combinations of these with (30) and (32) produce interesting simplifications, for which see Reference (a) at the end of this chapter.

§ 15. DIFFERENTIATION OF THE HYPERBOLIC FUNCTIONS

Clearly, from (28.1) and (28.2),

$$\frac{d\sinh x}{dx} = \frac{e^{x}+e^{-x}}{2} = \cosh x \quad \text{and} \quad \frac{d\cosh x}{dx} = \frac{e^{x}-e^{-x}}{2} = \sinh x.$$

Summary of derivatives of hyperbolic functions

(Verify where necessary.)

Function	$\sinh x$	$\cosh x$	$\tanh x$	$\coth x$	$\operatorname{sech} x$	$\operatorname{cosech} x$
Derivative	$\cosh x$	$\sinh x$	$\operatorname{sech}^2 x$	$-\operatorname{cosech}^2 x$	$-\dfrac{\sinh x}{\cosh^2 x}$	$-\dfrac{\cosh x}{\sinh^2 x}$

(34)

§ 16. GRAPHS OF THE HYPERBOLIC FUNCTIONS

Figure 7a, b gives the basic pictorial facts about the hyperbolic functions. Observe in Fig. 7a, b, that

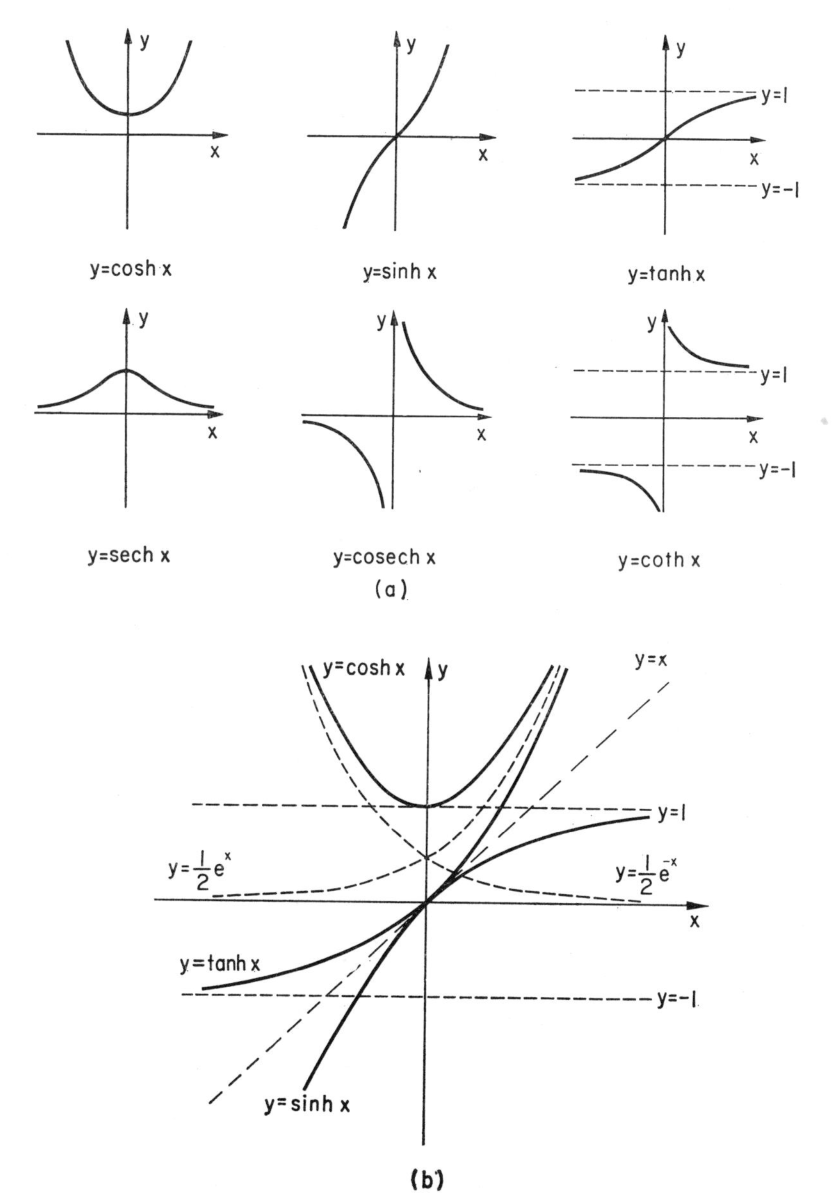

FIG. 7. (a) Hyperbolic functions. (b) Relationships among sinh x, cosh x, and tanh x curves

(i) $y = \sinh x$ is always less than $y = \cosh x$

$$= \frac{e^x - e^{-x}}{2} \qquad\qquad = \frac{e^x + e^{-x}}{2}$$

$$\begin{cases} \to \dfrac{e^x}{2} \text{ as } x \to \infty \\ \to -\dfrac{e^{-x}}{2} \text{ as } x \to -\infty \end{cases} \qquad \begin{cases} \to \dfrac{e^x}{2} \text{ as } x \to \infty \\ \to \dfrac{e^{-x}}{2} \text{ as } x \to -\infty \end{cases}$$

(ii) $$\tanh x = \frac{e^x - e^{-x}}{e^x + e^{-x}} = \frac{1 - e^{1/2x}}{1 + e^{1/2x}} \to 1 \text{ as } x \to \infty$$

$$= \frac{e^{2x} - 1}{e^{2x} + 1} \to -1 \text{ as } x \to -\infty$$

i.e. $y = \pm 1$ are asymptotes to $y = \tanh x$.

(iii) $$\underbrace{\frac{d \tanh x}{dx} = \frac{1}{\cosh^2 x} \qquad \frac{d \sinh x}{dx} = \cosh x}_{= 1, \text{ when } x = 0.}$$

Therefore $y = \sinh x$ and $y = \tanh x$ have the common tangent $y = x$ at the origin.

Properties of the general catenary, $y = c \cosh (x/c)$

EXAMPLE 14 (catenary and tractrix). Investigation of the geometrical properties of the general catenary $y = c \cosh (x/c)$.

Solution. Refer to Fig. 8 for the tangent to the catenary at $x = k$ (k, c constants).

$$\therefore \frac{dy}{dx} = \tan \phi = \sinh \frac{k}{c}. \tag{i}$$

Combining (i) with (29.1), we deduce

$$\sec \phi = \cosh \frac{k}{c}. \tag{ii}$$

Since

$$\phi = \frac{\pi}{2} - \theta, \tag{iii}$$

$$\cos \phi = \sin \theta. \tag{iv}$$

Now the equation of the tangent at P is, by (i), (ii),

$$y - c \sec \phi = \tan \phi \, (x - k) \tag{v}$$

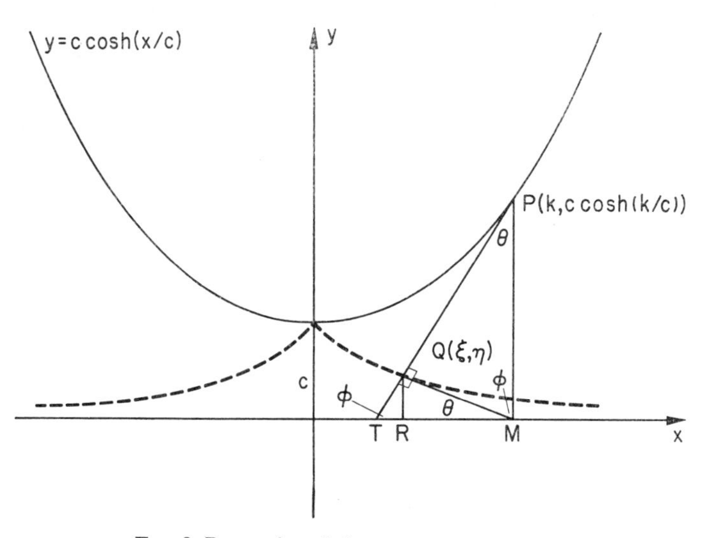

FIG. 8. Properties of the catenary and tractrix

and therefore the perpendicular line QM has equation

$$y = -\cot\phi\,(x-k). \tag{vi}$$

Solve (v), (vi) to obtain the coordinates of Q:

$$\xi = k - c\sin\phi, \quad \eta = c\cos\phi\ (= c\sin\theta). \tag{vii}$$

But, writing $s = e^{k/c}$, $t = \tan\left(\dfrac{\phi}{2}\right)$ in (i) for simplicity, we have by (28.1) $\dfrac{s-s^{-1}}{2} = \dfrac{2t}{1-t^2}$, i.e. a quadratic in s, namely,

$$(1-t^2)s^2 - 4ts - (1-t^2) = 0$$

with roots
$$s = \frac{1+t}{1-t},\quad \frac{-(1-t)}{1+t}$$
$$= \tan\left(\frac{\pi}{4}+\frac{\phi}{2}\right),\quad -\tan\left(\frac{\pi}{4}-\frac{\phi}{2}\right).$$

Ignore the second root which for k involves the logarithm of a negative number since $0 \leqslant \phi < \dfrac{\pi}{2}$ (in the first quadrant).

$$\therefore\ k = c\log\tan\left(\frac{\pi}{4}+\frac{\phi}{2}\right) = c\log(\tan\phi + \sec\phi). \tag{viii}$$

Trigonometrical calculations yield

$$\tan\left(\frac{\pi}{4}+\frac{\phi}{2}\right) = \cot(\theta/2) \tag{ix}$$

on substituting from (iii).

Results (vii)–(ix) together give

$$\left.\begin{aligned} \xi &= c \log \cot\left(\frac{\theta}{2}\right) - c \cos\theta, \\ \eta &= c \sin\theta. \end{aligned}\right\} \tag{35}$$

Tractrix

Equations (35), as Q varies, are the parametric equations of a curve, the *tractrix* (Fig. 8), generated physically as the path of a heavy object Q (a stone, say) dragged by a taut string QM whose other end M moves along the x-axis. (Similarly, it is the path of a barge towed by a tugboat.) From $\eta = c \sin\theta$ in (vii), applied to $\triangle QRM$, it follows at once that $QM = c$ (constant) as we expect, because the string is taut, i.e. of fixed length. Intuitively, from physical considerations, we feel that QM ought to be a tangent to the tractrix, a fact which may be mathematically proved (see Exercise 5.25). Geometrically, the parameter θ is the supplement of the gradient of the tractrix. Exercises 5.25–5.29 provide for a further study of the catenary and tractrix, which also occur in Chapters 20, 21, and 23.

Non-Euclidean geometry

Imagine the tractrix rotated about its asymptote (x-axis) so as to form a double-trumpet shaped surface (called a *pseudosphere*). On the pseudosphere we have a partial model in Euclidean space of the plane non-Euclidean geometry discovered jointly by Bólyai (1802–60, Hungarian) and Lobatschewsky (1793–1856, Russian), one of the towering achievements of the human intellect. This Lobatschewsky–Bólyai non-Euclidean geometry is sometimes called *hyperbolic geometry* to distinguish it from the other non-Euclidean geometry, *elliptic geometry*, discovered by Riemann (1826–66, German). A model of plane elliptic geometry is the surface of a sphere with antipodal points identified.

Having properties in common with both non-Euclidean geometries, Euclidean geometry may be regarded as a limiting form of each, and is accordingly sometimes called *parabolic geometry*.

Basically, a study of non-Euclidean geometry and its history reveals to us the enormous creative potential of the human brain and the far horizons to which the searching mind is impelled.

§17. INVERSE HYPERBOLIC FUNCTIONS

If $y = \sinh^{-1} x$ then $x = \sinh y = \frac{1}{2}(e^y - e^{-y})$.

$$\therefore\ e^{2y} - 2xe^y - 1 = 0 \qquad \text{(a quadratic in } e^y\text{)}.$$

$$\therefore\ e^y = x \pm \sqrt{x^2+1}$$

i.e.

$$e^y = x + \sqrt{x^2+1} \qquad \text{for real } y$$

$$\therefore\ \boxed{\sinh^{-1} x = \log(x+\sqrt{x^2+1})} \tag{36}$$

$\therefore\ \sinh^{-1} 1 = \log(1+\sqrt{2}) = \cosh^{-1}\sqrt{2}$ by (29.1) and (36).

Similarly
$$\begin{cases} \cosh^{-1} x = \log(x \pm \sqrt{x^2-1}) = \pm \log(x+\sqrt{x^2-1}) \\ \left(\because\ x+\sqrt{x^2-1} = \dfrac{1}{x-\sqrt{x^2-1}}\right); \\ \tanh^{-1} x = \dfrac{1}{2}\log\left(\dfrac{1+x}{1-x}\right),\ |x| < 1. \end{cases}$$

Thus, the inverse hyperbolic functions may be replaced by logarithm functions.

Given $y = \sinh^{-1} x$, i.e. $\sinh y = x$, we have

$$\frac{dx}{dy} = \cosh y = \sqrt{x^2+1} \quad \text{by (29.1)}$$

$$\therefore\ \boxed{\frac{d\sinh^{-1} x}{dx} = \frac{1}{\sqrt{1+x^2}}}. \tag{37}$$

Similarly, $\dfrac{d\cosh^{-1} x}{dx} = \pm\dfrac{1}{\sqrt{x^2-1}}$, $\dfrac{d\tanh^{-1} x}{dx} = \dfrac{1}{1-x^2}$.

[You should differentiate the remaining inverse hyperbolic functions as an exercise.]

§18. THE GUDERMANNIAN AND INVERSE GUDERMANNIAN

Definition

Gudermannian $\boxed{\phi = \tan^{-1}\sinh x = gd\, x}$ $\left(-\dfrac{\pi}{2} < \phi < \dfrac{\pi}{2}\right)$. (38)

Hence, we deduce (noting that gd is an entire symbol)

(i) $gd(-x) = -gd\, x$, i.e. the Gudermannian is an odd function.

(ii) $gd\, 0 = 0$.

(iii) $\boxed{\dfrac{d\,gd\,x}{dx} = \text{sech}\,x}$. (39)

(iv) If $x = \log\tan\left(\dfrac{\pi}{4}+\dfrac{\phi}{2}\right)$, then $e^x = \dfrac{1+\tan\phi/2}{1-\tan\phi/2}$ whence $\tan\dfrac{\phi}{2} =$

$\dfrac{e^x-1}{e^x+1}$ and $\tan\phi = \dfrac{2\tan\phi/2}{1-\tan^2(\phi/2)} = \sinh x$ on simplification (refer to

Example 14).

$\therefore\ \phi = \tan^{-1}\sinh x = 2\tan^{-1}e^x - \dfrac{\pi}{2} = gd\,x$, giving the

Inverse Gudermannian $\boxed{x = \log\tan\left(\dfrac{\pi}{4}+\dfrac{\phi}{2}\right) = gd^{-1}\phi = \sinh^{-1}\tan\phi}$.

(40)

(v) $gd^{-1}(-\phi) = -gd^{-1}\phi$, i.e. the inverse Gudermannian is an odd function.

(vi) $gd^{-1}0 = 0$.

(vii) $\boxed{\dfrac{d\,gd^{-1}\phi}{d\phi} = \sec\phi}$. (41)

(viii) From (38), $\sec\phi = \cosh x$, $\cos\phi = \text{sech}\,x$, $\sin\phi = \tanh x$, $\text{cosec}\,\phi = \coth x$, $\cot\phi = \text{cosech}\,x$. Therefore, by means of the Gudermannian function, work involving hyperbolic functions can be handled by circular functions, and vice-versa.

The graph of the Gudermannian is complicated and requires constant reference to tables (e.g. $x = 1$, $\phi = 49°35'$; $x = 2$, $\phi = 74°35'$), but its general form resembles that of the inverse tan curve. Horizontal asymptotes are $\phi = \pm\dfrac{\pi}{2}$, of course.

Lambert introduced the transcendental angle ϕ. Gudermann (1798–1851, German) published an important memoir on cyclic-hyperbolic functions in 1830, and in recognition of his contribution to the subject Cayley (1821–95, English) in 1862 proposed the name "Gudermannian" for ϕ. Equation (40) is, in essence, the solution of Mercator's deep-sea navigational problem, namely to discover a projection for which the *loxodrome* (i.e. the line cutting all meridians of longitude at a constant angle) would be a straight line.

Our preliminary study of the properties of the elementary functions is now complete.

Suggested topic for further study

Non-Euclidean geometry: (i) Euclid's fifth postulate; (ii) pioneering work of Saccheri (1667–1733, Italian) and Gauss (1777–1855, German); (iii) effect of non-Euclidean geometry on the Kantian philosophy of space; (iv) unifying role of projective geometry; (v) models of Klein (1849–1925, German) and Poincaré (1854–1912, French), in addition to the sphere and pseudosphere; (vi) Gauss' inconclusive experiment with optical instruments from three mountain peaks, designed to establish the "truth" of Euclidean or non-Euclidean geometries; (vii) applications of Riemann's geometry to relativity; (viii) essential differences (parallelism, angle-sum of a triangle) between Euclidean and non-Euclidean geometries; (ix) something of the life of Lobatschewsky, "the Copernicus of Geometry", as Einstein called him.

References

As for Chapter 1, together with

(a) *Hyperbolic Functions* (Smithsonian Institute Mathematical Tables),
(b) *Non-Euclidean Geometry*, R. Bonola (Dover), which contains the original researches of N. Lobatschewsky, *Geometrical Researches on the Theory of Parallels*, and J. Bólyai, *The Science of Absolute Space*.

EXERCISES 5

If $\sinh x = \frac{4}{3}$ and $\sinh y = \frac{3}{4}$, evaluate:

1. $\sinh(x+y)$. **2.** $\tanh(x+y)$.

3. Establish the formula $\sinh A + \sinh B = 2\sinh\left(\frac{A+B}{2}\right)\cosh\left(\frac{A-B}{2}\right)$.

4. Prove that $\tanh\frac{x}{2} = \frac{\sinh x}{\cosh x+1} = \frac{\cosh x-1}{\sinh x} = \sqrt{\frac{\cosh x-1}{\cosh x+1}}$.

5. Solve $\tanh x = \frac{4}{5}$.

6. Given $a = 5\cosh x - 4\sinh x$, $b = 4\cosh x - 5\sinh x$, compute $\sqrt{a^2-b^2}$.

For the catenary, determine the lengths of

7. The subtangent. **8.** The subnormal.

In Fig. 8:

9. Establish that $QM = y\left\{1+\left(\frac{dy}{dx}\right)^2\right\}^{-1/2}$.

10. Derive, by differentiation, that $QM = c$.

Differentiate the functions $f(x)$ in 11–13:

11. $\log\tanh x$. **12.** $\tanh^{-1}\left(\frac{x+a}{1+ax}\right)$ (a constant). **13.** $\frac{\cosh x+\sinh x}{\cosh x-\sinh x}$.

14. If $\frac{d}{dx}\{\sinh \log(x+\sqrt{1+x^2})\} = c$, find c.

15. Confirm that $x = a \cosh nt + b \sinh nt$ is a solution of $\ddot{x} = n^2 x$ whereas $x = a \cos nt + b \sin nt$ is a solution of the simple harmonic motion $\ddot{x} = -n^2 x$ (a, b, n constants).

[It follows that $y = a \cos nt + b \sin nt + c \cosh nt + d \sinh nt$ is a solution of the structure theory equation $\frac{d^4 y}{dx^4} = n^4 y$.]

16. Lobatschewsky's non-Euclidean geometry makes use of the formula $\tanh (a/2) = e^{-b}$ in dealing with segments. Express a in terms of b.

17. Referring to Exercise 5.16, prove that $\sinh a \sinh b = 1$.

18. Bólyai and Lobatschewsky are both credited with the discovery of the famous result in non-Euclidean trigonometry $\tan \alpha/2 = e^{-k/k}$ in connection with the theory of parallels, where α is the *angle of parallelism*. Express $\sin \alpha$ in terms of h/k.

19. Express $\cosh (\tanh^{-1} x)$ in terms of x ($|x| < 1$).

20. Establish the result $2 \tan^{-1} \tanh \frac{x}{2} = \sin^{-1} \tanh x$ ($= gd\ x$).

Evaluate 21–23:

21. $\lim_{x \to 1} \left(\frac{\sinh x - \sinh 1}{\cosh x - \cosh 1} \right)$.   **22.** $\lim_{x \to 0} \left(\frac{\log \cosh 2x}{\log \cosh 3x} \right)$.   **23.** $\lim_{x \to \infty} (\cosh x)^{1/x}$.

24. Simplify $\frac{\sinh 3x}{\sinh x} - \frac{\cosh 3x}{\cosh x}$.

25. Without referring to Example 14, obtain the gradient of the tangent at Q to the tractrix $x = c \log \cot \theta/2 - c \cos \theta$, $y = c \sin \theta$.

26. If the tangent to the tractrix at Q cuts the x-axis at M, verify that $QM = c$.

27. The Cartesian equation of the tractrix, given parametrically by (35), is

$$x = c \log \left\{ \frac{c + \sqrt{c^2 - y^2}}{y} \right\} - \sqrt{c^2 - y^2}.$$ Prove.

28. Using Exercise 5.27, determine the gradient of the tractrix.

29. Interpret the Gudermannian ϕ geometrically in terms of the catenary.

30. Show that $\tanh^{-1} \left(\frac{x^2 - 1}{x^2 + 1} \right) = \log x$.

31. Taking air resistance as proportional to v^2 for an object of mass m falling from rest under gravity with velocity v and acceleration a, we form the differential equation of motion $ma = mg - kv^2$, where k is a factor of proportionality and g is the gravitational constant. Writing $k = \frac{mg}{c^2}$, prove that $v = c \tanh \frac{gt}{c}$. (Ionisation of a gas involves a similar equation.)

32. Determine the limiting value of v if the object is falling for a very long time.

33. Making small increments in both x and y, where $y = \sinh x$, deduce from first principles that $\frac{dy}{dx} = \cosh x$.

Establish the formulae 34–38:

34. $\sinh^{-1} x = \operatorname{cosech}^{-1} \frac{1}{x}$.

35. $\cosh \sinh^{-1} x = \sqrt{1+x^2}$.

36. $\cosh^{-1} \frac{1}{2}\left(x+\frac{1}{x}\right) = \log x$.

37. $\tanh^{-1} \tan\left(\frac{\phi}{2}\right) = \frac{1}{2} gd^{-1}\phi$.

38. $\coth^{-1} x = \frac{1}{2}\log\left(\frac{x+1}{x-1}\right)$ $(|x| > 1)$.

Evaluate 39–41:

39. $\tan(\pi \sinh \log 2)$. **40.** $\cosh^{-1}(\coth \log 3)$ $(= \pm\log 2)$.

41. $e^{-\coth^{-1}(13/5)}$.

42. Prove that $1+2\cosh x+2\cosh 2x+\ldots+2\cosh nx = \dfrac{\sinh(n+\frac{1}{2})x}{\sinh \frac{1}{2}x}$.

(Refer to Example 44.)

Express 43–46 in terms of $gd\, x$ and $gd\, y$:

43. $\sec gd(x+y)$. **44.** $\tan gd(x+y)$.

45. $\sin gd(x+y)$. **46.** $\cos gd(x+y)$.

47. Solve simultaneously: $4\sinh x+3\sinh y = 7$
$4\cosh x-3\cosh y = 0$.

Formulae of great importance in hyperbolic geometry are:

48. $\sinh\frac{a}{k} : \sinh\frac{b}{k} : \sinh\frac{c}{k} = \sin\lambda : \sin\mu : \sin\nu$.

49. $\cosh\frac{c}{k} = \cosh\frac{a}{k}\cosh\frac{b}{k} - \sinh\frac{a}{k}\sinh\frac{b}{k}\cos\nu$.

50. $\cosh\frac{c}{k} = \cosh\frac{a}{k}\cosh\frac{b}{k}$,

where a, b, c are sides of a triangle opposite the angles λ, μ, ν respectively, and k, constant, is a "natural unit of length". Allowing a, b, c to be small in relation to k, i.e. ignoring powers of k greater than the second, prove that these formulae are the hyperbolic analogues of the sine law (48), cosine law (49), and Pythagoras' theorem (50) (Pythagoras, 6th cent. B.C., Greek) in Euclidean Geometry.

Small regions of the hyperbolic plane therefore approximate to the Euclidean plane.

CHAPTER 6

PARTIAL DIFFERENTIATION

. . . to be
Constant, in Nature were inconstancy.

(ABRAHAM COWLEY)

SCIENTIFIC problems often deal with situations in which several variables occur, and frequently some of these variables are temporarily held fixed. Here, we aim to deal briefly with functions of more than one variable—quite a natural extension of the function of one variable—and to introduce the very important concept of partial differentiation. In the process it will be necessary to extend our coordinate system and to present the theory against the setting of a generalised Euclidean space of n-dimensions.

§ 19. n-DIMENSIONAL GEOMETRY

Though this course is mostly concerned with plane (= two-dimensional) geometry, it is sometimes convenient to refer to higher dimensional space.

Mention has already been made of Lobatschewsky's invention of a non-Euclidean geometry, an advance which sprang essentially from deficiencies in Euclid's fifth postulate. Other weaknesses of a logical nature had long been apparent to scholars. What meaning, for instance, can possibly be given to his definition of a point as "that which has no part"? Eventually it was realised that Euclid, in attempting in his *Elements* to present an idealised interpretation of the physical world of space perception, was trying to define the undefinable.

Nowadays, the concepts of "point" and "line" are, along with other notions, taken as undefined, the raw materials from which the structure of axiomatic geometry is moulded. No longer is an axiom a "self-evident truth" as Euclid supposed—it is merely a suitable assumption, the "truth" of which is irrelevant. The test of the validity of the axioms is that meaningful consequences should flow logically from them.

Hilbert (1862–1943, German), in *Foundations of Geometry*, 1899, first gave a satisfactory set of axioms which removed the blemishes from Euclid's thinking. Since this breakthrough, many other sound axiomatic treatments have been developed. The nature of these axiomatic systems made it relatively easy to extend the theory to n (finite) dimensions. More recently, the restriction of finiteness has been removed to allow for an important mathematical space of infinitely many dimensions, *Hilbert space*, which is very useful in quantum mechanics.

So far we have been speaking only of the synthetic (= purely geometrical) approach to geometry. Analytically, the problem is rather simpler. Essentially, analytical (= co-ordinate) geometry deals with the application of numbers (often disguised as symbols), to diagrams, a union which, had it occurred to the Greeks, would have had considerable significance for civilisation. As it was, this fruitful union was not consummated until the time of Descartes. By virtue of this amalgamation of ideas we may view symbolic relations pictorially, and we may consider geometrical problems divorced from their spatial and visual content. Abstractions then have concrete representations, e.g. in the plane we may represent graphically the relation of the growth of penicillin to humidity, the economic dependence of supply and demand of commodities, or the distribution of intelligence in a sample population.

Ordinary Cartesian coordinates in the plane associate with every point of the plane (finite) an ordered pair of real numbers, the ordering being related to a fixed frame of reference consisting of two oriented axes (usually perpendicular, though possibly oblique) and their point of intersection. Ordered sets of 3, 4, . . ., n real numbers, by simple extension, may then be associated with a point in 3, 4, . . . *n-dimensional Euclidean space* which, for $n > 3$, is a mathematical, rather than a physical, concept. Although it has no material counterpart ($n > 3$), its structure may be mathematically described by pure reason. (Can you visualise four-space?) Naturally, other geometries (non-Euclidean, finite, projective) extend to n-dimensions besides Euclidean geometry.

n-dimensional thinking is a valuable technique, quite apart from its applications in pure mathematics. Any problem dealing with n variables (which may be taken as coordinates) may be expressed in an n-dimensional setting, e.g. problems relating to dynamical systems or to statistical experiments. Thus, in Newtonian physics, a force acting on a rigid body may be considered as having six components—three translational and three rotational. Relativity's four-dimensional space-time is a form of non-Euclidean space, so it must be given a different coordinate description.

§ 20. POLAR COORDINATES

Besides the (rectangular) Cartesian system, the other main coordinate system in the plane is that of *polar coordinates*. (Still other systems are introduced in Chapter 21.) In *two* dimensions, the position of a point is uniquely fixed, relative to a frame of reference, by *two* independent numbers (coordinates). Geographical coordinates of latitude and longitude, for example, uniquely locate a position on the two-dimensional surface of the Earth.

Suppose we select a fixed point O (*pole*) and an oriented line OX (*initial line*). A point P has polar coordinates (r, θ) if $OP = r$ (*radius vector*) and $X\hat{O}P = \theta$ (*vectorial angle*, measured anti-clockwise in radians). Usually, the initial line is chosen to coincide with the x-axis.

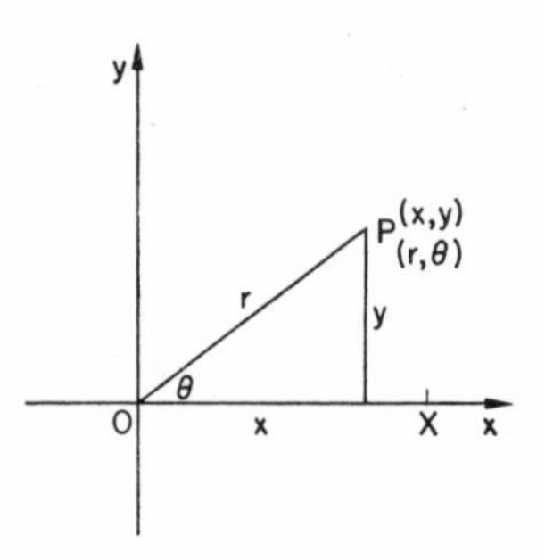

FIG. 9. Polar and Cartesian coordinates

Assuming P to be described by the ordered number-pairs (x, y) and (r, θ) in the two systems (Fig. 9), we clearly have the following transformations from one system to the other:

$$\begin{array}{|c|c|} x = r\cos\theta & r = \sqrt{x^2+y^2} \\ y = r\sin\theta & \theta = \tan^{-1}\left(\dfrac{y}{x}\right) \end{array} . \tag{42}$$

Just one point corresponds to a given pair of polar coordinates, but the converse is not true since $(r, \theta) = (r, \theta \pm 2n\pi) \equiv (-r, \theta \pm (2n+1)\pi)$ (n integer, $\geqslant 0$) all describe the same point. Interpret $(-r, \alpha)$ as $(r, \pi+\alpha)$. The point $(r, -\theta)$ is the optical image (reflection) of (r, θ) in the initial line (see Fig. 20). Coordinates of O in particular are $(0, \theta)$, where θ is quite arbitrary. Normally, we think of O as $(0, 0)$. Equations of curves in polar coordinates are, generally, $r = f(\theta)$ or $\theta = g(r)$. (See Chapter 22.)

Scientific applications of polar coordinates

Astronomical and geodetic surveys use polar coordinates. Meteorological charts often relate wind direction to barometric height, say, by means of them. Three-dimensional spherical polar coordinates (as in Exercise 6.20) are valuable in describing physical systems where spherical symmetry is present, e.g. the solar system or Bohr's theory of the atom.

§ 21. PARTIAL DIFFERENTIATION

Functions of two real variables

If u is a function of two or more variables $x, y, \ldots$, we write $u = f(x, y, \ldots)$. It is not too difficult to think of instances of functions of several variables, e. g. we know that the volume of a gas depends on the pressure and temperature so $v = f(p, t)$. Less familiar, perhaps, is the expression, from medical physiology, $z = \dfrac{100x}{y}$, where z refers to cardiac output and x, y are variables relating to carbon dioxide in the blood stream. Or, again, an insurance premium is a function of the capital insured and the length of the policy.

Limits and continuity are defined similarly as for a function of one variable. In the case of $\lim\limits_{x\to a,\, y\to b} f(x, y)$, say, we have, corresponding to the restriction $|x-a| < \delta$ in the case of a function of one variable (see § 6), the restriction that the point (x, y) lies within a circle of radius δ and centre (a, b), or within a square of side 2δ and centre (a, b). Extensions to functions of n variables and to *hyper-spheres* (generalisation of circles) and *hyper-cubes* (generalisation of squares) in n dimensions readily follow.

Partial differentiation

If $u = f(x, y)$, i.e. u is a function of two variables x, y, then the rate at which u changes w.r.t.

$$\begin{cases} x \\ y \end{cases} \text{when} \quad \begin{cases} y \\ x \end{cases} \text{is kept constant}$$

is in the notation of Jacobi (1804–51, German) defined to be, respectively,

$$\left.\boxed{\begin{aligned} \frac{\partial u}{\partial x} &= \lim_{\delta x\to 0}\left\{\frac{f(x+\delta x, y)-f(x, y)}{\delta x}\right\} \\ \frac{\partial u}{\partial y} &= \lim_{\delta y\to 0}\left\{\frac{f(x, y+\delta y)-f(x, y)}{\delta y}\right\} \end{aligned}}\right\}. \tag{43}$$

$\dfrac{\partial u}{\partial x}, \dfrac{\partial u}{\partial y}$ are the *partial differential coefficients (partial derivatives)* of u w.r.t. x, y respectively.

Partial derivatives are used widely in the sciences, e.g. in thermodynamics and physical chemistry, and in economics as well as in pure and applied mathematics. Many of the fundamental equations of mathematical physics are expressed in terms of partial derivatives. Besides those incorporated in the examples and exercises of this Chapter, there are, for instance, those associated with the names of Clerk Maxwell and Schrödinger. It is an instructive exercise to apply (43) to the volume–pressure–temperature relation of a gas $v = t/p$ allowing small increments δt, δp, δv and obtaining $\frac{\partial v}{\partial p}, \frac{\partial v}{\partial t}$ from first principles.

Note. (i) $\frac{\partial u}{\partial x} \neq 1 \Big/ \frac{\partial x}{\partial u}$ (Why?)

(ii) $\frac{\partial u}{\partial x}, \frac{\partial u}{\partial y}$ stand for operations and ∂u, ∂y, ∂x are not to be considered separately.

(iii) $\frac{\partial u}{\partial x}, \quad \frac{\partial u}{\partial y}, \quad \frac{\partial^2 u}{\partial x^2} = \frac{\partial}{\partial x}\left(\frac{\partial u}{\partial x}\right), \quad \frac{\partial^2 u}{\partial x \partial y} = \frac{\partial}{\partial x}\left(\frac{\partial u}{\partial y}\right), \quad \frac{\partial^2 u}{\partial y \partial x} = \frac{\partial}{\partial y}\left(\frac{\partial u}{\partial x}\right)$

may be written

$$\begin{cases} u_x \quad u_y \quad u_{xx} \quad u_{xy} \quad u_{yx} & \text{or} \\ f_x \quad f_y \quad f_{xx} \quad f_{xy} \quad f_{yx}. \end{cases}$$

(iv) *Bernoulli's theorem* (1742)

$$\boxed{\frac{\partial^2 u}{\partial x\, \partial y} = \frac{\partial^2 u}{\partial y\, \partial x}} \tag{44}$$

[Nicolaus Bernoulli (1687–1759, Swiss)]

i.e. $u_{xy} = u_{yx}$, where u, u_x, u_y are continuous functions.

Of course, $\frac{\partial^2 u}{\partial x\, \partial y} \neq \frac{\partial u}{\partial x} \frac{\partial u}{\partial y}$, i.e. $u_{xy} \neq u_x u_y$.

EXAMPLE 15 (partial differentiation).

(i) Given $u = e^{-x} \sin y$, we derive

$$\frac{\partial u}{\partial x} = -e^{-x} \sin y, \quad \frac{\partial u}{\partial y} = e^{-x} \cos y$$

$\frac{\partial^2 u}{\partial x^2} = e^{-x} \sin y, \quad \frac{\partial^2 u}{\partial y^2} = -e^{-x} \sin y \quad (\therefore \frac{\partial^2 u}{\partial x^2} + \frac{\partial^2 u}{\partial y^2} = 0$ — see Part (iii) below)

$$\frac{\partial^2 u}{\partial x\, \partial y} = -e^{-x} \cos y = \frac{\partial^2 u}{\partial y\, \partial x}.$$

(ii) From (42),

$$\frac{\partial x}{\partial r} = \cos\theta = \frac{x}{r} \qquad \frac{\partial y}{\partial r} = \sin\theta = \frac{y}{r}$$

$$\frac{\partial x}{\partial \theta} = -r\sin\theta = -y \qquad \frac{\partial y}{\partial \theta} = r\cos\theta = x$$

$$\frac{\partial r}{\partial x} = \frac{x}{\sqrt{x^2+y^2}} = \frac{x}{r} \qquad \frac{\partial r}{\partial y} = \frac{y}{\sqrt{x^2+y^2}} = \frac{y}{r}$$

$$\frac{\partial \theta}{\partial x} = \frac{-y}{x^2+y^2}, \qquad \frac{\partial \theta}{\partial y} = \frac{x}{x^2+y^2}.$$

(iii) Components of force on a particle of unit mass in a plane *conservative field* of force (i.e. energy conserved) with potential V are $-\frac{\partial V}{\partial x}$, $-\frac{\partial V}{\partial y}$. Compute these components when $V = \log\sqrt{x^2+y^2}$ and evaluate $\frac{\partial^2 V}{\partial x^2}+\frac{\partial^2 V}{\partial y^2}$.

Solution. $-\frac{\partial V}{\partial x} = -\frac{x}{x^2+y^2}, \quad -\frac{\partial V}{\partial y} = -\frac{y}{x^2+y^2}.$

$$\therefore \frac{\partial^2 V}{\partial x^2} = \frac{-x^2+y^2}{(x^2+y^2)^2}, \quad \frac{\partial^2 V}{\partial y^2} = \frac{x^2-y^2}{(x^2+y^2)^2} \quad \text{on calculation.}$$

$$\therefore \frac{\partial^2 V}{\partial x^2} + \frac{\partial^2 V}{\partial y^2} = 0. \qquad \text{[Refer to Part (i) and to Example 17.]}$$

[Graphical illustrations of some of the partial derivatives in (ii) are given in, for instance, *An Analytical Calculus*, Vol. 3, E. A. Maxwell (O.U.P., 1954).]

Geometrical significance of partial derivatives

Now $z = f(x, y)$ is the equation of a surface in three dimensions, e.g. the sphere of radius a, $x^2+y^2+z^2 = a^2$ (centre at origin), for which $z = \pm\sqrt{a^2-x^2-y^2}$. Take a section of this surface by a plane $x = c$ parallel to the yz-plane i.e. the equations of the curve of section (a circle in the case of the sphere) are $z = f(x, y)$, $x = c$ (Fig. 10b).

$\therefore \frac{\partial z}{\partial y}$ = gradient of the tangent to this curve.

Similarly for $\frac{\partial z}{\partial x}$. Hence:

The partial derivatives $\frac{\partial z}{\partial x}, \frac{\partial z}{\partial y}$ *represent the gradients of the surface* $z = f(x, y)$ *in the x- and y-directions respectively.*

Following Maxwell (vol. 3) we may visualise this meaning better if we regard the surface as a hill and the point P as the position of a climber so that the x- and y-axes could be regarded as giving (say) the directions east and north respectively. Of course, each path from P will have a separate gradient, but we are only interested in a certain selection of these paths, viz. those in the directions of x and y.

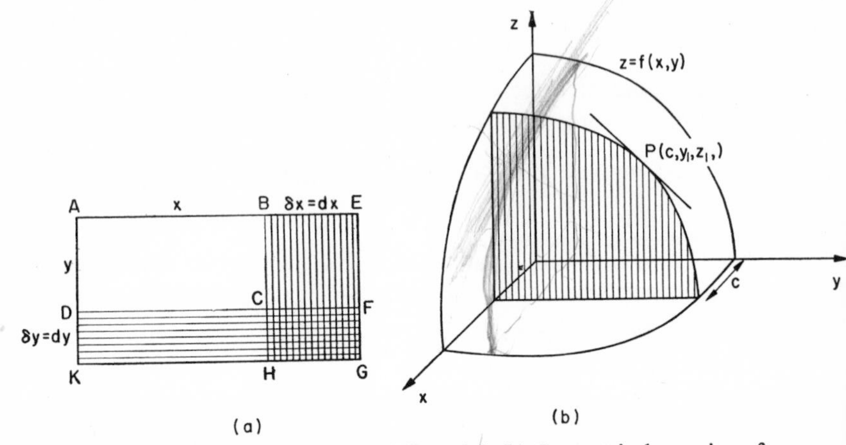

FIG. 10. (a) Illustration of the total differential. (b) Geometrical meaning of partial differentiation

The chain rule for partial differentiation of a function of functions

If $u = f(x, y, z)$, where $x = g_1(\xi, \eta, \zeta)$, $y = g_2(\xi, \eta, \zeta)$, $z = g_3(\xi, \eta, \zeta)$, i.e. $u = g(\xi, \eta, \zeta)$, then we have (assume) the *chain rule* for partial differentiation [compare with (4)]:

$$\begin{aligned} \frac{\partial u}{\partial \xi} &= \frac{\partial u}{\partial x}\frac{\partial x}{\partial \xi} + \frac{\partial u}{\partial y}\frac{\partial y}{\partial \xi} + \frac{\partial u}{\partial z}\frac{\partial z}{\partial \xi} \\ \frac{\partial u}{\partial \eta} &= \frac{\partial u}{\partial x}\frac{\partial x}{\partial \eta} + \frac{\partial u}{\partial y}\frac{\partial y}{\partial \eta} + \frac{\partial u}{\partial z}\frac{\partial z}{\partial \eta} \\ \frac{\partial u}{\partial \zeta} &= \frac{\partial u}{\partial x}\frac{\partial x}{\partial \zeta} + \frac{\partial u}{\partial y}\frac{\partial y}{\partial \zeta} + \frac{\partial u}{\partial z}\frac{\partial z}{\partial \zeta} \end{aligned} \tag{45}$$

subject to obvious modifications for the case of only two variables x, y, and to equally obvious extensions to a function of m variables each of which is a function of n variables.

EXAMPLE 16 (application of the chain rule). Given $u = xyz$, where $x = \cos\theta\sin\phi$, $y = \sin\theta\sin\phi$, $z = \cos\phi$, evaluate $\dfrac{\partial u}{\partial\theta}, \dfrac{\partial u}{\partial\phi}$.

Solution.
$$\frac{\partial u}{\partial\theta} = \frac{\partial u}{\partial x}\frac{\partial x}{\partial\theta}+\frac{\partial u}{\partial y}\frac{\partial y}{\partial\theta}+\frac{\partial u}{\partial z}\frac{\partial z}{\partial\theta}$$
$$= yz\,(-\sin\theta\sin\phi) + xz\cos\theta\sin\phi + xy\cdot 0$$
$$= \sin\theta\sin\phi\cos\phi\,(-\sin\theta\sin\phi) + \cos\theta\sin\phi\cos\phi\cos\theta\sin\phi$$
$$= \sin^2\phi\cos\phi\cos 2\theta$$

and
$$\frac{\partial u}{\partial\phi} = \frac{\partial u}{\partial x}\frac{\partial x}{\partial\phi}+\frac{\partial u}{\partial y}\frac{\partial y}{\partial\phi}+\frac{\partial u}{\partial z}\frac{\partial z}{\partial\phi}$$
$$= yz\cos\theta\cos\phi+xz\sin\theta\cos\phi+xy(-\sin\phi)$$
$$= \sin\theta\cos\theta\sin\phi\,(2\cos^2\phi - \sin^2\phi) \text{ on substituting and simplifying.}$$

EXAMPLE 17 (*Laplace's equation;* Laplace, 1749–1827, French). Show that $V = 1/r$, where $r^2 = x^2+y^2+z^2$ satisfies Laplace's equation (1787) in three dimensions,
$$\nabla^2 V \equiv \frac{\partial^2 V}{\partial x^2}+\frac{\partial^2 V}{\partial y^2}+\frac{\partial^2 V}{\partial z^2} = 0.$$

[$\nabla^2 \equiv \dfrac{\partial^2}{\partial x^2}+\dfrac{\partial^2}{\partial y^2}+\dfrac{\partial^2}{\partial z^2} \equiv \sum\dfrac{\partial^2}{\partial x^2}$ (read ∇^2 as "del-squared") is *Laplace's operator.*]

Solution.
$$\frac{\partial V}{\partial x} = \frac{\partial V}{\partial r}\frac{\partial r}{\partial x} = -\frac{1}{r^2}\frac{x}{r} = -\frac{x}{r^3} \quad \because \frac{\partial r}{\partial x} = \frac{x}{r}.$$
$$\therefore \frac{\partial^2 V}{\partial x^2} = -\frac{1}{r^3} - x\frac{\partial}{\partial x}\left(\frac{1}{r^3}\right) = -\frac{1}{r^3} - x\left(-\frac{3}{r^4}\right)\frac{x}{r} = -\frac{1}{r^3}+\frac{3x^2}{r^5}.$$
$$\therefore \nabla^2 V = -\frac{3}{r^3}+3\left\{\frac{x^2+y^2+z^2}{r^5}\right\} = 0.$$

Comments

(i) Laplace's (second-order partial differential) equation is one of the most important equations in physics. Interpreting V in different contexts, we find the equation occurring in hydrodynamics, gravitation theory, electrostatics and magnetism, among others. Originally, Laplace used it in his study of the rings of Saturn.

(ii) $\nabla^2 r = \dfrac{2}{r}$.

(iii) $\nabla^2 \log r = \dfrac{1}{2r}$.

(iv) $\nabla^2(r^m V) = m(m+2n+1)r^{m-2}V$ where V is a homogeneous polynomial of degree n in x, y, z.

(v) Various solutions of Laplace's equation in the plane ($z = 0$) are $\log(x^2+y^2)^n$, $e^x \cos y$, $ax+by$, $\tan^{-1}\left(\frac{y}{x}\right)$, $\cosh mx \cos my$ and, of course, $(x^2+y^2)^{-1/2}\left(=\frac{1}{r}\right)$. [Refer to Example 15.]

You should check all the statements (ii)–(v). Have a look also at Exercises 12.67–12.70.

Physical meaning of $\nabla^2 V$

More advanced mathematical methods allow us to prove that $\nabla^2 V$ measures the difference between the value of V at a point and the average value of V in some very small neighbourhood of that point.

Thus, Laplace's equation shows that the value of V is constant in the neighbourhood of a point, e.g. a gravitational field in a region where attracting matter is absent. When this is not so, we have $\nabla^2 V \neq 0$.

Under a rotation of axes (and under a translation also), the operator ∇^2 is invariant—see § 53. For this reason (and others), ∇^2 occurs naturally in scientific equations.

Differentiation of implicit functions

As explained in § 1, the equation $g(x, y) = 0$ defines y as an *implicit function* of x [in contradistinction to the *explicit function* $y = f(x)$], e.g. $x^3+y^3-3axy = 0$ (the folium of Descartes, Fig. 102)—*folium* (Latin) $\equiv$ "leaf". Thinking of y as a differentiable function of x, we may differentiate the given equation w.r.t. x and then solve the resulting relation for dy/dx. This process is called *implicit differentiation.* Differentiating $g(x, y) = 0$ implicitly in this way, we have

$$\frac{\partial g}{\partial x}+\frac{\partial g}{\partial y}\frac{dy}{dx} = 0$$

$$\therefore \boxed{\frac{dy}{dx} = -\frac{\partial g/\partial x}{\partial g/\partial y}}. \tag{46}$$

For the folium, $\dfrac{dy}{dx} = \dfrac{ay-x^2}{y^2-ax}$ (= -1 at the point $\left(\frac{3a}{2}, \frac{3a}{2}\right)$ in which it cuts the line $y = x$).

§ 22. TOTAL DIFFERENTIALS

Definition

Total differential of u

$$du = \frac{\partial u}{\partial x}\,dx + \frac{\partial u}{\partial y}\,dy. \tag{47}$$

Dividing throughout by dt, we immediately derive the corresponding formula for *total differentiation*. [Refer to Exercise 6.11. Compare (47) and (8).]

As a standard and simple illustration of the total differential, take Fig. 10a (attributed to Simson, 1687–1768, English) where the area $ABCD$ is $u = xy$. Increment δu in u is $BCFE + DKHC + CHGF$, i.e. $\delta u = y\,\delta x + x\,\delta y + \delta x\,\delta y$ [$\delta x = dx$, $\delta y = dy$]. Because we are dealing with increments $\to 0$, we can ignore the product $\delta x\,\delta y$, whence (47) follows, since, for small increments, $du \doteqdot \delta u$. Hence, as in the case for a single variable, the differential (which here involves partial differentiation) may be used in making approximations. Notice that in Fig. 10a, du differs from δu by the rectangle $\delta x\,\delta y = dx\,dy$. Of course, $\dfrac{\partial u}{\partial x} = y$, $\dfrac{\partial u}{\partial y} = x$, when $u = xy$. $\therefore$ $du = d(xy) = y\,dx + x\,dy = \dfrac{\partial u}{\partial x}\,dx + \dfrac{\partial u}{\partial y}\,dy$.

Formula (47) can obviously be extended to a function of 3 or more variables.

Next, let us apply the idea of the total differential to Cartesian and polar coordinates.

$$\text{Since } \left.\begin{aligned} x &= r\cos\theta \\ y &= r\sin\theta \end{aligned}\right\} \text{ we have } \left\{\begin{aligned} dx &= -r\sin\theta\,d\theta + \cos\theta\,dr \\ dy &= r\cos\theta\,d\theta + \sin\theta\,dr. \end{aligned}\right.$$

Squaring and adding, we have

$$dx^2 + dy^2 = r^2\,d\theta^2 + dr^2 \tag{48}$$

a result which we use later in § 120.

Suggested topics for further study

(1) Numerical applications of the total differential to approximations.
(2) Use of partial derivatives in obtaining maximum, minimum, and saddle points of a surface.
(3) Role of partial differentiation in mathematical physics.
(4) Something of the lives and achievements of the remarkable Bernoulli family (Reference, Bell [3]).

References

As for Chapter 1, together with:
(a) *Partial Differentiation*, R. P. Gillespie (Oliver & Boyd, 1951).
(b) *Differential Equations for Engineers and Scientists*, C. G. Lambe and C. J. Tranter (E.U.P., 1961).
(c) *Differential Equations*, H. T. H. Piaggio (Bell, 1946).

EXERCISES 6

1. Given $u = \frac{y}{z}+\frac{z}{x}+\frac{x}{y}$, compute $x\frac{\partial u}{\partial x}+y\frac{\partial u}{\partial y}+z\frac{\partial u}{\partial z}$ $\left(\text{written } \sum x\frac{\partial u}{\partial x} \text{ for brevity}\right)$.

2. Illustrate Bernoulli's theorem in the case of the function $z = \frac{e^{yx}}{x}$. Deduce the value of $\frac{\partial^2}{\partial x\,\partial y}\left(\frac{e^{xy}}{y}\right)$, giving a reason. [U.N.E.]

3. If $f(x, y) = \frac{\sqrt{1-yx^2}}{y}$, find $\frac{\partial^2 f}{\partial x^2}$. [U.N.E.]

4. Calculate $\sum \frac{\partial^2 u}{\partial x^2}$ when $u = z\tan^{-1}\left(\frac{x}{y}\right)$.

5. For the homogeneous polynomial $u = \sum a_{\alpha\beta}x^\alpha y^\beta$ of degree n in x and y, i.e. $\alpha+\beta = n$, in which α, β are constants, show that $\sum x\frac{\partial u}{\partial x} = nu$ (*Euler's theorem for a homogeneous polynomial* of degree n in x and y).

6. Check Euler's theorem for the function $u = x^3-3x^2y+5xy^2-y^3$.

7. When $z = x^2\tan^{-1}\left(\frac{y}{x}\right)-y^2\tan^{-1}\left(\frac{x}{y}\right)$, prove that $\frac{\partial^2 z}{\partial y\,\partial x} = \frac{x^2-y^2}{x^2+y^2}$.

8. Express both $\frac{\partial V}{\partial x}$ and $\frac{\partial V}{\partial y}$ in terms of $\frac{\partial V}{\partial r}$ and $\frac{\partial V}{\partial \theta}$, where $x = r\cos\theta$, $y = r\sin\theta$ and V is a function of x and y (and therefore of r and θ also).

9. Motion of a *one-dimensional progressive wave* is given by the partial differential equation *(wave equation)* $\frac{\partial^2 z}{\partial t^2} = c^2\frac{\partial^2 z}{\partial x^2}$ (c a physical constant). Verify that a solution is $z = f(u)+g(v)$, where $u = x-ct$, $v = x+ct$.

10. Evaluate $\frac{\partial z}{\partial x}, \frac{\partial z}{\partial y}$ given that $z = e^u\cos v$, where $u = x+y$, $v = x-y$.

11. Supposing $z = (x-3)^2+y^2$ and $x = 5\sin t$, $y = 4\cos t$, obtain the maximum and minimum values of z by using the formula for total differentiation

$$\frac{dz}{dt} = \frac{\partial z}{\partial x}\frac{dx}{dt}+\frac{\partial z}{\partial y}\frac{dy}{dt}.$$

[This is the analytical statement of the problem of determining the greatest and least distances of a point (x, y) on the ellipse $\frac{x^2}{5^2}+\frac{y^2}{4^2} = 1$ from the focus $(3, 0)$ (see Chapter 18). Of course, a more direct method is to substitute for x, y to get $z = f(t)$ and then proceed in the usual way.]

12. Transform $\frac{\partial V}{\partial t} = \frac{\partial^2 V}{\partial x^2} - hV$ into $\frac{\partial W}{\partial t} = \frac{\partial^2 W}{\partial x^2}$ *(equation of one-dimensional heat conduction)* by putting $V = e^{-ht}W$.

[Before transformation, the equation represents the temperature of a conducting rod whose surface is allowed to radiate heat into air at zero temperature. The given transformation reduces the problem to one without radiation.]

13. Assuming that $W = Ae^{-kx} \sin (nt - kx)$ is a solution of the transformed equation in Exercise 6.12, express n in terms of k (A, k, n positive constants).

14. Show that $V = (r^n + r^{-n}) \sin n\theta$ satisfies *Laplace's equation for polar coordinates*

$$\frac{\partial^2 V}{\partial r^2} + \frac{1}{r}\frac{\partial V}{\partial r} + \frac{1}{r^2}\frac{\partial^2 V}{\partial \theta^2} = 0.$$

15. Obtain $\sum x \frac{\partial u}{\partial x}$ for $u = f\left(\frac{x}{y}\right)$. $\left(\text{Think of } u = \sin\left(\frac{x}{y}\right), \text{ say.}\right)$

16. Obtain the gradient of the section of the *ellipsoid* $\frac{x^2}{a^2} + \frac{y^2}{b^2} + \frac{z^2}{c^2} = 1$ by the plane $z = 0$. [What does an ellipsoid look like?]

17. *Clapeyron's equation* for a gas is $pv = RT$, where p, v, T refer to the pressure, volume, and absolute temperature, and R is a gas constant (constant for one gram-molecule of any gas). Establish the relationship

$$\frac{\partial v}{\partial T}\frac{\partial T}{\partial p}\frac{\partial p}{\partial v} = -1.$$

18. More generally, given $F(x, y, z) = 0$, prove that

$$\frac{\partial x}{\partial y}\frac{\partial y}{\partial z}\frac{\partial z}{\partial x} = -1.$$

19. Wave equation describing a disturbance is given by

$$\frac{1}{x^2}\frac{\partial}{\partial x}\left(x^2 \frac{\partial z}{\partial x}\right) = c^2\left(\frac{\partial^2 z}{\partial t^2}\right).$$

Verify that a solution is $z = \frac{f(x-ct)+g(x+ct)}{x}$.

20. Equations transforming three-dimensional rectangular Cartesian coordinates x, y, z (for which $ds^2 = dx^2 + dy^2 + dz^2$) into *spherical polar coordinates* r, θ, ϕ are $x = r \sin\theta \cos\phi$, $y = r \sin\theta \sin\phi$, $z = r\cos\theta$. Derive $ds^2 = dr^2 + r^2 d\theta^2 + r^2 \sin^2\theta \, d\phi^2$.

Can you visualise how spherical polar coordinates are constructed to describe a point on a sphere?

21. If $x = e^u \cosh v$, $y = e^u \sinh v$, verify that $\frac{\partial^2 V}{\partial u^2} - \frac{\partial^2 V}{\partial v^2} = e^{2u}\left(\frac{\partial^2 V}{\partial x^2} - \frac{\partial^2 V}{\partial y^2}\right)$.

22. Given $u = \tan^{-1}\left(\frac{\cos x}{\sinh y}\right)$, $v = \tanh^{-1}\left(\frac{\sin x}{\cosh y}\right)$, verify the *Cauchy–Riemann equations* (Exercise 10.72) $\frac{\partial u}{\partial x} = \frac{\partial v}{\partial y}$, $\frac{\partial u}{\partial y} = -\frac{\partial v}{\partial x}$.

These equations are very useful in potential theory, e.g., in electrostatics, aerodynamics, and gravitation theory.

23. Calculate $\sum x \frac{\partial z}{\partial x}$, given $\sin z = \frac{\sqrt{x}-\sqrt{y}}{\sqrt{x}+\sqrt{y}}$.

24. Laplace's equation for three-dimensions is satisfied by $V = xyz(x^2+y^2+z^2)^{-1/2}$. Justify this assertion.

25. You are given the transformation $x = \cosh \xi \cos \eta$, $y = \sinh \xi \sin \eta$. Establish the equation for the function u (function of x, y and also of ξ, η)

$$\frac{\partial^2 u}{\partial \xi^2}+\frac{\partial^2 u}{\partial \eta^2} = (\sinh^2 \xi+\sinh^2 \eta)\left(\frac{\partial^2 u}{\partial x^2}+\frac{\partial^2 u}{\partial y^2}\right).$$

CHAPTER 7

INDEFINITE INTEGRALS

Nature and Nature's laws lay hid in night: God said, Let Newton be! and all was light.

(ALEXANDER POPE)

TEMPORARILY leaving the differential calculus, to which we will return in Chapters 20–23 where it is used to deepen our understanding of the properties of curves, we now turn to the integral calculus.

§ 23. THE INDEFINITE INTEGRAL

The problem

In the *differential calculus* we are given $y = f(x)$ and the problem is to find $\frac{dy}{dx}$; the process is called *differentiation*.

In the *integral calculus*, we are given $\frac{dy}{dx} = f(x)$, and the problem is to find $y = F(x)$; the process is called *integration*, sometimes *anti-differentiation*, i.e. the process of integration is the inverse of the process of differentiation. Corresponding to the symbol $\frac{d}{dx}$ for the operation of differentiation w.r.t. x, we have the symbol $\int dx$ for the operation of integration w.r.t. x. [If the symbol for the operation of differentiation is D, then that for integration is D^{-1}.]

The solution

Now $$\frac{dy}{dx} = f(x) \qquad \text{(i)}$$

may be written

$$dy = f(x)\,dx \qquad \text{using differentials,}$$

i.e. $$\int dy = \int f(x)\,dx \qquad \begin{cases}\text{performing the operation inverse to differentiation on both sides of the equation}\end{cases}$$

i.e. $$y = \int f(x)\,dx. \qquad \text{(ii)}$$

Let $F(x)$ be a function: $$\frac{dF(x)}{dx} = f(x),$$

i.e. $$\frac{dy}{dx} = \frac{dF(x)}{dx} \quad \text{by (i)},$$

$$\therefore \ y = F(x)+C,$$

where C is an arbitrary *constant of integration*, without which the solution is incomplete. Any constant symbol other than C may be used.

$\therefore$ by (ii), $$\boxed{\int f(x)\,dx = F(x)+C}. \tag{49}$$

The left-hand side of (49) is called the *indefinite integral* of $f(x)$ w.r.t. x and $f(x)$ is called the *integrand*. The arbitrariness of C makes the solution indefinite (see Example 12.) [In the alternative notation, if $Dy = f(x)$, then $y = D^{-1}f(x) = F(x)+C$.] Notice that $\frac{d}{dx}\left\{\int f(x)\,dx\right\} = f(x)$, i.e. $DD^{-1}f(x) = f(x)$ as we expect. Observe that, whereas not all continuous functions are differentiable (§ 8), all continuous functions are *integrable* (assume).

Once you know how to tackle a given integral, there is no excuse for getting the wrong answer. All you have to do, by virtue of (49), is to differentiate the answer; if it is correct, the integrand will result. Always check indefinite integral answers in this way.

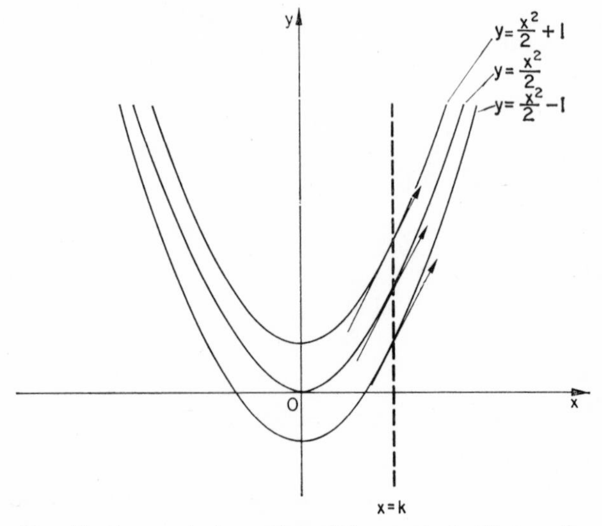

FIG. 11. Geometrical meaning of the constant of integration

Geometrical interpretation of the constant of integration

For different constant values of C, $y = F(x)+C$ represents a family of "parallel" curves which have the same slope for a particular value of x. E.g. if $y = \dfrac{x^2}{2}+C$ (solution of $\int x\,dx$), then $\dfrac{dy}{dx} = x = k$ when $x = k$ (Fig. 11).

Full solutions of the problem of curves with constant subtangent and subnormal are thus (equations (α), (β) of Example 12) the family of exponential curves $y = e^{kx}+c$ and the family of parabolas $y^2 = 4ax+c$ respectively.

§ 24. STANDARD INTEGRALS (50)

$\int 0\,dx = C$	$\int a^x\,dx = \dfrac{a^x}{\log a}+C$
$\int x^n\,dx = \dfrac{x^{n+1}}{n+1}+C \quad (n \neq -1)$	$\int \cos x\,dx = \sin x+C$
$\int \dfrac{dx}{x} = \log x+C$	$\int \sin x\,dx = -\cos x+C$
$\int e^x\,dx = e^x+C$	$\int \sec^2 x\,dx = \tan x+C$
	$\int \dfrac{dx}{\sqrt{x^2+a^2}} = \log\{x+\sqrt{x^2+a^2}\}+C$
$\int \tan x\,dx = \log\sec x+C$	$= \sinh^{-1}\dfrac{x}{a}+C$
	$\int \dfrac{dx}{\sqrt{x^2-a^2}} = \log\{x+\sqrt{x^2-a^2}\}+C$
$\int \cot x\,dx = \log\sin x+C$	$= \cosh^{-1}\dfrac{x}{a}+C$
$\int \dfrac{dx}{\sqrt{a^2-x^2}} = \sin^{-1}\left(\dfrac{x}{a}\right)+C$	$\int \dfrac{dx}{x^2-a^2} = \dfrac{1}{2a}\log\left(\dfrac{x-a}{x+a}\right)+C \quad (x^2 > a^2)$
or $-\cos^{-1}\left(\dfrac{x}{a}\right)+C$	$= -\dfrac{1}{a}\coth^{-1}\dfrac{x}{a}+C$
$\begin{cases} a > 0 \\ a^2 > x^2 \end{cases}$	
	$\int \dfrac{dx}{a^2-x^2} = \dfrac{1}{2a}\log\left(\dfrac{a+x}{a-x}\right)+C \quad (x^2 < a^2)$
$\int \dfrac{dx}{a^2+x^2} = \dfrac{1}{a}\tan^{-1}\left(\dfrac{x}{a}\right)+C$	$= \dfrac{1}{a}\tanh^{-1}\dfrac{x}{a}+C$

Using § 17, we may express the answers to some of these integrals by means of inverse hyperbolic functions as indicated. Classification of an integral as standard is largely a matter of personal choice—there is nothing absolute about the table (50). Generally, an integral is standard if the integrand is the derivative of some important elementary function.

Assume the two general theorems (where u, v, ... are functions of x):

$$\begin{array}{l} \int ku\,dx = k\int u\,dx \quad (k \text{ constant}) \\ \int (u \pm v \pm w \pm \ldots)\,dx = \int u\,dx \pm \int v\,dx \pm \int w\,dx \pm \ldots \end{array} \tag{51}$$

Comments

(i) It is a convention to use the same symbol C in each integration.

(ii) $\log\left\{\dfrac{x+\sqrt{x^2\pm a^2}}{a}\right\}(=\log\{x+\sqrt{x^2\pm a^2}\}-\log a)$ and $\log\{x+\sqrt{x^2\pm a^2}\}$ are equivalent solutions since $-\log a$ may be absorbed into C.

(iii) Every integration is a challenge to our mathematical resources since there is no single rule to follow; § 24 is fundamental and §§ 25–29 classify the main elementary techniques.

Preliminaries of fact and theory completed, we now attempt a systematic organisation of the methods of integration.

§25. TECHNIQUES OF INTEGRATION: CHANGE OF VARIABLE (SUBSTITUTION, TRANSFORMATION)

Essentially the purpose of the various techniques is to provide us with methods by which awkward integrals can be simplified, preferably to the standard formulae.

In $y = \int f(x)\,dx$, substitute $x = \phi(t)$. (This means our integration is taken over a (probably) different range of values for the new variable.)

$$\therefore \frac{dy}{dt} = \frac{dy}{dx}\frac{dx}{dt} = f(x)\frac{dx}{dt}$$

$$\therefore dy = f(x)\frac{dx}{dt}\,dt,$$

i.e.

$$\int f(x)\,dx = \int f(x)\frac{dx}{dt}\,dt$$

$$\therefore y = \int dy = \int f(x)\frac{dx}{dt}\,dt,$$

i.e.

$$\boxed{\int f(x)\,dx = \int f\{\phi(t)\}\frac{d\phi(t)}{dt}\,dt}. \tag{52}$$

Note that there is nothing special about the symbol used in the substitution. Any letter, other than x, would do equally well. However, *the answer must always be given in terms of the original variable, x*. Practice in doing exercises develops insight into spotting the appropriate transformation which needs to be made to a variable.

As the first step in this direction, let us consider (Example 18) some integrals in which the integrands resemble very closely those in the standard table and where, consequently, the substitutions suggest themselves. In Example 19, the guide ropes are removed and we have to find our own way, but in Examples 20, 21, 22 and 24 some definite techniques are emphasised. Example 23 casts us back on our own intellectual resources again. (Students experiencing difficulty with the appropriate choice of substitution might gain confidence by understanding §§ 27, 28 first.)

EXAMPLE 18 (simple extensions of standard integrals).

(a) $$\int (ax+b)^m\,dx = \int \frac{t^m\,dt}{a} \qquad \left\{\begin{array}{l}\text{putting } t = ax+b \\ \therefore\ dt = adx, \text{ i.e. } dx = \dfrac{1}{a}\,dt = \dfrac{dt}{a}\end{array}\right.$$

$$= \frac{t^{m+1}}{a(m+1)} + C$$

$$= \frac{(ax+b)^{m+1}}{a(m+1)} + C \quad (m \neq -1).$$

(b) $$\int \frac{dx}{ax+b} = \int \frac{dw}{aw} \qquad \left\{\begin{array}{l}\text{putting } w = ax+b \\ \therefore\ dw = a\,dx, \text{ i.e. } dx = \dfrac{1}{a}\,dw\end{array}\right.$$

$$= \frac{\log w}{a} + C$$

$$= \frac{\log (ax+b)}{a} + C.$$

(c) $$\int e^{ax+b}\,dx = \frac{1}{a}\int e^j\,dj \qquad \left\{\begin{array}{l}\text{putting } j = ax+b \\ \therefore\ dj = a\,dx, \text{ i.e. } dx = \dfrac{1}{a}\,dj\end{array}\right.$$

$$= \frac{e^j}{a} + C$$

$$= \frac{e^{ax+b}}{a} + C.$$

(d) $$\int \sin(ax+b)\,dx = \int \sin p\,\frac{dp}{a} \quad \left\{ \begin{array}{l} \text{putting } p = ax+b \\ \therefore\ dp = a\,dx, \text{ i.e. } dx = \dfrac{1}{a}\,dp. \end{array} \right.$$

$$= -\frac{\cos(ax+b)}{a} + C.$$

(e) $$\int x(x^2+a)^n\,dx = \frac{1}{2}\int q^n dq \qquad \left\{ \begin{array}{l} \text{putting } q = x^2+a \\ \therefore\ dq = 2x\,dx \end{array} \right.$$

$$= \frac{q^{n+1}}{2(n+1)} + C$$

$$= \frac{(x^2+a)^{n+1}}{2(n+1)} + C \quad (n \neq -1).$$

(f) $$\int \frac{dx}{\sqrt{2ax-x^2}} = \int \frac{dx}{\sqrt{a^2-(x-a)^2}} \qquad \left\{ \begin{array}{l} \text{putting } r = x-a \\ \therefore\ dr = dx \end{array} \right.$$

$$= \int \frac{dr}{\sqrt{a^2-r^2}}$$

$$= \sin^{-1}\left(\frac{r}{a}\right) + C$$

$$= \sin^{-1}\left(\frac{x-a}{a}\right) + C.$$

[Integrals like (b) often occur in problems of first-order chemical reaction, e.g. Wilhelmy's law (1850) in physical chemistry.]

EXAMPLE 19 (miscellaneous elementary problems based on standard formulae).

(a) $$\int \tan^2 x\,dx = \int (\sec^2 x - 1)\,dx$$

$$= \tan x - x + C.$$

(b) $$\int \frac{x^2}{x-1}\,dx = \int \left(x+1+\frac{1}{x-1}\right) dx$$

$$= \frac{x^2}{2} + x + \log(x-1) + C.$$

(c) $$\int \cos^2 x\,dx = \int \frac{1+\cos 2x}{2}\,dx$$

$$= \frac{x}{2} + \frac{\sin 2x}{4} + C.$$

(d) $$\int \sin^2 x\,dx = \int \frac{(1-\cos 2x)\,dx}{2}$$
$$= \frac{x}{2}-\frac{\sin 2x}{4}+C$$

or $$\int \sin^2 x\,dx = \int (1-\cos^2 x)\,dx$$
$$= x-\left\{\frac{x}{2}+\frac{\sin 2x}{4}+C\right\}+C' \qquad \text{by Example 19(c)}$$
$$= \frac{x}{2}-\frac{\sin 2x}{4}+c, \qquad \text{where } c = C'-C.$$

(e) $$\int \frac{dx}{\sqrt{1+x}+\sqrt{x}} = \int (\sqrt{1+x}-\sqrt{x})\,dx \qquad \text{(rationalising denominator)}$$
$$= \frac{2}{3}\{(1+x)^{3/2}-x^{3/2}\}+C.$$

EXAMPLE 20 *(numerator of integrand = differential coefficient of denominator of integrand).*

$$\int \frac{f'(x)}{f(x)}\,dx = \int \frac{du}{u} \qquad \text{putting } u = f(x) \;\therefore\; du = f'(x)\,dx$$
$$= \log u+C$$
$$= \log f(x)+C$$

e.g.
$$\int \frac{\cos 2x}{1+\sin 2x}\,dx = \frac{1}{2}\log(1+\sin 2x)+C$$
$$\int \frac{x^2}{2-x^3}\,dx = -\frac{1}{3}\log(2-x^3)+C.$$

EXAMPLE 21.

$$\int \sin x \cos^3 x\,dx = -\int y^3\,dy \qquad \left\{\begin{array}{l}\text{putting } y = \cos x\\ \therefore\; dy = -\sin x\,dx\end{array}\right.$$
$$= -\frac{y^4}{4}+C$$
$$= -\frac{\cos^4 x}{4}+C$$

or $$\int \sin x \cos^3 x\,dx = -\int \cos^3 x\,d\cos x$$
$$= -\frac{\cos^4 x}{4}+C.$$

This problem emphasises the fact that when making a substitution, we do not have to set out all the steps in the transformation but can proceed immediately to the new variable. Use of this quicker method requires some mathematical maturity, though the student who is uncertain of himself should stick to the longer, routine method of writing out all the steps involved in the substitution. The alternative method is merely a sophisticated way of saving energy as we are really only avoiding using y for $\cos x$. You are encouraged to use this more mature method.

Similarly, $\int \sec^2 x e^{\tan x}\, dx = e^{\tan x} + C$

$$\int x \sin(x^2)\, dx = -\tfrac{1}{2}\cos(x^2) + C$$

$$\int \frac{(\log x)^n}{x}\, dx = \frac{(\log x)^{n+1}}{n+1} + C \qquad (n \neq -1).$$

[Cases $n = 1, -2$ are common. What happens when $n = -1$?]

EXAMPLE 22 (trigonometrical substitutions).

(i) $\int \sqrt{a^2-x^2}\, dx = a^2 \int \cos^2\theta\, d\theta \qquad \left\{\begin{array}{l}\text{putting } x = a\sin\theta \\ \therefore\ dx = a\cos\theta\, d\theta\end{array}\right.$

$$= \frac{a^2}{2}\left\{\theta + \frac{\sin 2\theta}{2}\right\} + C \qquad \text{[by Example 19(c)]}$$

$$= \frac{a^2}{2}\left\{\sin^{-1}\left(\frac{x}{a}\right) + \frac{x}{a}\sqrt{1-\frac{x^2}{a^2}}\right\} + C$$

$$= \frac{a^2}{2}\sin^{-1}\left(\frac{x}{a}\right) + \frac{x}{2}\sqrt{a^2-x^2} + C,$$

or

$$\left\{\begin{array}{l}\text{put } x = a\cos\theta \text{ and use } \sin^{-1}\left(\dfrac{x}{a}\right) + \cos^{-1}\left(\dfrac{x}{a}\right) = \dfrac{\pi}{2}; \\ \text{put } x = a\tanh t \text{ and use integration by parts (§ 27).}\end{array}\right.$$

See also Example 25(c).

(ii) $\int \sqrt{\frac{a-x}{a+x}}\, dx = \int \frac{a-x}{\sqrt{a^2-x^2}}\, dx \qquad$ (rationalising numerator)

$$= a\int \frac{dx}{\sqrt{a^2-x^2}} - \int \frac{x\, dx}{\sqrt{a^2-x^2}}$$

$$= a\sin^{-1}\left(\frac{x}{a}\right) + \sqrt{a^2-x^2} + C,$$

or

$$\int \sqrt{\frac{a-x}{a+x}}\,dx = a\int (1-\sin\theta)\,d\theta \qquad \text{putting } x = a\sin\theta \text{ and simplifying}$$

$$= a\{\theta+\cos\theta\}+C$$

$$= a\sin^{-1}\left(\frac{x}{a}\right)+\sqrt{a^2-x^2}+C.$$

Other useful substitutions:

$$\left.\begin{array}{l}\text{When the integrand involves } \sqrt{x^2+a^2}, \text{ use } x = a\tan\theta \text{ or } x = a\sinh t.\\ \text{When the integrand involves } \sqrt{x^2-a^2}, \text{ use } x = a\sec\theta,\ x = a\operatorname{cosec}\theta\\ \text{or } x = a\cosh t.\end{array}\right\} \tag{53}$$

EXAMPLE 23 (miscellaneous problems).

(a) $$\int \frac{dx}{x\sqrt{1+x}} = 2\int \frac{dy}{y^2-1} \qquad \text{putting } 1+x = y^2 \quad \therefore\ dx = 2y\,dy$$

$$= 2\frac{1}{2\cdot 1}\log\left(\frac{y-1}{y+1}\right)+C$$

$$= \log\left(\frac{\sqrt{1+x}-1}{\sqrt{1+x}+1}\right)+C$$

or

$$\int \frac{dx}{x\sqrt{1+x}} = -2\int \frac{dt}{\sqrt{t^2+1}} \qquad \text{putting } x = \frac{1}{t^2} \quad \therefore\ dx = -\frac{2}{t^3}\,dt$$

$$= -2\log\{t+\sqrt{t^2+1}\}+C$$

$$= \log\left(\frac{\sqrt{1+x}-1}{\sqrt{1+x}+1}\right)+C \qquad \text{on simplifying.}$$

(When the answer has several log forms it is often convenient to write C as $\log C$, which allows us to tidy up the final form.)

(b) $$\int \frac{dx}{\sqrt{1-3x-x^2}} = \int \frac{d(x+(3/2))}{\sqrt{\frac{13}{4}-(x+(3/2))^2}} \qquad \left\{\begin{array}{l}\text{changing the variable}\\ \text{from } x \text{ to } x+3/2\end{array}\right.$$

$$= \sin^{-1}\left(\frac{2x+3}{\sqrt{13}}\right)+C.$$

§26. TECHNIQUES OF INTEGRATION: TRIGONOMETRIC DENOMINATOR

EXAMPLE 24 (miscellaneous trigonometrical denominators).

(a) $$\int \frac{dx}{\sin x} = \frac{1}{2}\int \frac{dx}{\sin(x/2)\cos(x/2)}$$

$$= \frac{1}{2}\int \frac{\sec^2(x/2)\,dx}{\tan(x/2)} \qquad \text{dividing numerator and denominator by } \cos^2(x/2)$$

$$= \int \frac{d\tan(x/2)}{\tan(x/2)} = \log\tan(x/2)+C.$$

[Here, the process of integration is equivalent to making the important substitution $t = \tan\frac{x}{2}$ whence $\sin x = \frac{2t}{1+t^2}$, $\cos x = \frac{1-t^2}{1+t^2}$, $dx = \frac{2\,dt}{1+t^2}$,

i.e. $$\int \frac{dx}{\sin x} = \int \frac{1+t^2}{2t}\cdot\frac{2\,dt}{1+t^2} = \int \frac{dt}{t} = \log t+C = \log\tan\frac{x}{2}+C.]$$

(b) $$\int \frac{dx}{\cos x} = \int \frac{d(x+(\pi/2))}{\sin(\pi/2+x)}$$

$$= \log\tan\left(\frac{x}{2}+\frac{\pi}{4}\right)+C \qquad \text{by (a)}$$

$$= gd^{-1}x \qquad \text{by (40).}$$

$\left[\text{Try } \cos x = \sin\left(\frac{\pi}{2}-x\right).\right]$

(c) $$\int \frac{dx}{a+b\cos x} = \int \frac{dx}{a(\cos^2(x/2)+\sin^2(x/2))+b(\cos^2(x/2)-\sin^2(x/2))}$$

$$= \frac{2}{a-b}\int \frac{d\tan(x/2)}{[(a+b)/(a-b)]+\tan^2(x/2)} \qquad \text{as in (a)}$$

$$= \frac{2}{\sqrt{a^2-b^2}}\tan^{-1}\left(\sqrt{\frac{a-b}{a+b}}\tan(x/2)\right)+C.$$

(d) $$\int \frac{dx}{a+b\sin x} = \int \frac{dx}{a\cos^2(x/2)+2b\sin(x/2)\cos(x/2)+a\sin^2(x/2)}$$

$$= \frac{2}{a}\int \frac{d\,(\tan(x/2)+(b/a))}{[(a^2-b^2)/a^2]+(\tan(x/2)+(b/a))^2}$$

$$= \frac{2}{\sqrt{a^2-b^2}}\tan^{-1}\left(\frac{a}{\sqrt{a^2-b^2}}\left(\tan(x/2)+\frac{b}{a}\right)\right)+C.$$

(e) $$\int \frac{dx}{a^2 \cos^2 x + b^2 \sin^2 x} = \frac{1}{b^2} \int \frac{d \tan x}{a^2/b^2 + \tan^2 x}$$
$$= \frac{1}{ab} \tan^{-1}\left(\frac{b}{a} \tan x\right) + C.$$

(f) $$\int \frac{dx}{\sin x + \cos x} = \frac{1}{\sqrt{2}} \int \frac{d(x+\pi/4)}{\sin (x+\pi/4)}$$
$$= \frac{1}{\sqrt{2}} \log \tan \left(\frac{x}{2} + \frac{\pi}{8}\right) + C \qquad \text{by (a).}$$

Exercise. Do (c) and (d) by substituting $t = \tan x/2$.

§ 27. TECHNIQUES OF INTEGRATION: INTEGRATION BY PARTS

Now $\dfrac{duv}{dx} = u\dfrac{dv}{dx} + v\dfrac{du}{dx}$; $\therefore\ uv = \displaystyle\int u \frac{dv}{dx}\, dx + \int v \frac{du}{dx}\, dx.$

$$\therefore \quad \boxed{\int u \frac{dv}{dx}\, dx = uv - \int v \frac{du}{dx}\, dx.} \tag{54}$$

The process indicated in (54) is known as the method of *integration by parts*. Essentially, it transforms the integration of the product of two factors into the integration of another product which is easier to manipulate.

EXAMPLE 25 (integration by parts).

(a) $$\int x^2 \cos x\, dx = \int x^2 \frac{d \sin x}{dx}\, dx \qquad \text{writing } \cos x = \frac{d \sin x}{dx}$$
$$= x^2 \sin x - 2 \int x \sin x\, dx \qquad \text{by (54)}$$
$$= x^2 \sin x + 2 \int x \frac{d \cos x}{dx}\, dx$$
$$= x^2 \sin x + 2x \cos x - 2 \sin x + C \qquad \text{by (54) again.}$$

(b) $$\int \log x\, dx = \int \log x \frac{dx}{dx}\, dx \qquad \text{writing } 1 = \frac{dx}{dx} \qquad \textit{(note well!)}$$
$$= x \log x - \int x \frac{1}{x}\, dx$$
$$= x (\log x - 1) + C.$$

(c) $I = \int \sqrt{a^2-x^2}\, dx$

$$= x\sqrt{a^2-x^2} - \int \frac{(a^2-x^2-a^2)\, dx}{\sqrt{a^2-x^2}}$$

$$= x\sqrt{a^2-x^2} - I + a^2 \sin^{-1}\left(\frac{x}{a}\right) + C'$$

$$\therefore \int \sqrt{a^2-x^2}\, dx = \tfrac{1}{2}x\sqrt{a^2-x^2} + \frac{a^2}{2}\sin^{-1}\left(\frac{x}{a}\right) + C. \qquad (C = \tfrac{1}{2}C')$$

[Part (c) is Example 22(i) done by another method.]

(d) $I = \int e^{ax} \cos bx\, dx$

$$= \frac{1}{a}\int \cos bx \frac{de^{ax}}{dx}\, dx$$

$$= \frac{e^{ax}\cos bx}{a} + \frac{b}{a}\int e^{ax}\sin bx\, dx$$

$$= \frac{e^{ax}\cos bx}{a} + \frac{b}{a}\left\{\frac{e^{ax}\sin bx - bI}{a}\right\}$$

$$\therefore I = \frac{e^{ax}}{a^2+b^2}(a\cos bx + b\sin bx) + C \qquad \text{on simplifying;}$$

or

$$I = \frac{1}{b}\int e^{ax}\frac{d\sin bx}{dx}\, dx$$

$$= \frac{e^{ax}\sin bx}{b} - \frac{a}{b}\left\{\frac{-e^{ax}\cos bx + aI}{b}\right\} \qquad \text{as in (d) above}$$

$$\therefore I = \frac{e^{ax}}{a^2+b^2}(a\cos bx + b\sin bx) + C.$$

(d′) $I = \int e^{ax}\cos bx\, dx$, $J = \int e^{ax}\sin bx\, dx$

$$\therefore I = \frac{e^{ax}\cos bx}{a} + \frac{b}{a}J; \quad J = \frac{e^{ax}\sin bx}{a} - \frac{b}{a}I$$

$$\therefore \begin{cases} aI - bJ = e^{ax}\cos bx \\ bI + aJ = e^{ax}\sin bx. \end{cases}$$

Solve these two simultaneous linear equations:

$$\therefore \begin{cases} I = \dfrac{e^{ax}}{a^2+b^2}(a\cos bx + b\sin bx) + C \\[2ex] J = \dfrac{e^{ax}}{a^2+b^2}(a\sin bx - b\cos bx) + C. \end{cases}$$

§ 28. TECHNIQUES OF INTEGRATION: PARTIAL FRACTIONS

Next, let us consider the rational function $\frac{P(x)}{Q(x)}$, where $P(x)$, $Q(x)$ are polynomial in x such that the degree of $P(x)$ is less than the degree of $Q(x)$ and $Q(x)$ factorises. Four cases only may usefully arise depending on whether the factors of $Q(x)$ are linear or quadratic, distinct, or repeated.

I. Unequal linear factors

Assume

$$\frac{P(x)}{(x-\alpha_1)(x-\alpha_2)\dots(x-\alpha_n)} = \frac{A_1}{x-\alpha_1}+\frac{A_2}{x-\alpha_2}+\dots+\frac{A_n}{x-\alpha_n} \tag{55}$$

($A_1 \dots A_n$ are constants to be found)

where $P(x)$ is a polynomial in x of degree less than that of the denominator. Each fraction on the right-hand side of (55) is called a *partial fraction*. Simple problems of this type often occur in chemistry, e.g. in the work of Arrhenius on the hydrolysis of ethyl acetate. If $n = 2$, we have a second-order chemical reaction, where α, α_2 are initial masses of two substances (measured in gram molecules).

EXAMPLE 26 (unequal linear factors).

$$\frac{x}{(x-1)(x+1)(x+2)} = \frac{A}{x-1}+\frac{B}{x+1}+\frac{C}{x+2}$$ on resolving into partial fractions. Clear the equation of denominators.

$$\therefore\quad x = A(x+1)(x+2)+B(x-1)(x+2)+C(x-1)(x+1) \quad \text{(i)}$$

$$\therefore\quad x = (A+B+C)x^2+(3A+B)x+2A-2B-C.$$

Equate coefficients:

$$A+B+C = 0,$$

$$3A+B = 1,$$

$$2A-2B-C = 0,$$

whence $A = \frac{1}{6}$, $B = \frac{1}{2}$, $C = -\frac{2}{3}$;

or in (i) put $x = 1, \quad \therefore A = \frac{1}{6}$
$x = -1, \therefore B = \frac{1}{2}$
$x = -2, \therefore C = -\frac{2}{3}$

(This is equivalent to using the *Heaviside formula* $A = \left\{\frac{x}{(x+1)(x+2)}\right\}_{x=1}$ etc.)

$$\therefore \int \frac{x\,dx}{(x-1)(x+1)(x+2)} = \frac{1}{6}\int\frac{dx}{x-1}+\frac{1}{2}\int\frac{dx}{x+1}-\frac{2}{3}\int\frac{dx}{x+2}$$

$$= \log\left\{\frac{C(x-1)^{1/6}(x+1)^{1/2}}{(x+2)^{2/3}}\right\}$$

on writing the constant of integration as log C to tidy up the answer.

II. Repeated linear factors

Assume:

For each linear factor $x-\alpha$ which occurs r times, we have a series of r partial fractions of the form

$$\frac{A_1}{x-\alpha}+\frac{A_2}{(x-\alpha)^2}+\ldots+\frac{A_r}{(x-\alpha)^r} \quad (A_i (i=1,\ldots,r) \text{ are constants to be found}).$$

(56)

EXAMPLE 27 (repeated linear factors).

$$\frac{1}{(x-1)^2(x+1)} = \frac{A}{x-1}+\frac{B}{(x-1)^2}+\frac{C}{x+1},$$

$$\therefore 1 = A(x^2-1)+B(x+1)+C(x-1)^2, \qquad \text{(i)}$$

whence $A+C = 0$, $B-2C = 0$, $-A+B+C = 1$, $\therefore A = -\frac{1}{4}$, $B = \frac{1}{2}$, $C = \frac{1}{4}$,

or in (i) put $x = 1$, $\quad \therefore B = \frac{1}{2}$
$x = -1$, $\quad \therefore C = \frac{1}{4}$
$x = 0$ (say), $\quad \therefore -A+B+C = 1$
$\therefore A = -\frac{1}{4}$

$$\therefore \int\frac{dx}{(x-1)^2(x+1)} = -\frac{1}{4}\int\frac{dx}{x-1}+\frac{1}{2}\int\frac{dx}{(x-1)^2}+\frac{1}{4}\int\frac{dx}{x+1}$$

$$= \log\left\{C\left(\frac{x+1}{x-1}\right)^{1/4}\right\}-\frac{1}{2(x-1)}.$$

[Integrals like this occur in chemistry, e.g. in the work of Meyerhofer in 1888.]

III. Unequal quadratic factors

Assume:

For each quadratic factor (ax^2+bx+c) which occurs only once, we have a fraction of the form $\dfrac{Ax+B}{ax^2+bx+c}$ (A, B are constants to be found).	(57)

EXAMPLE 28 (unequal quadratic factors).

$$\frac{x}{(x^2+a^2)(x^2+b^2)} = \frac{Ax+B}{x^2+a^2}+\frac{Cx+D}{x^2+b^2}$$

$$\therefore\ x = (Ax+B)(x^2+b^2)+(Cx+D)(x^2+a^2) \tag{i}$$

$$\therefore\ A+C = 0,\quad B+D = 0,\quad Ab^2+Ca^2 = 1,\quad Bb^2+Da^2 = 0$$

$$\therefore\ B = D = 0,\quad A = \frac{1}{b^2-a^2},\quad C = -\frac{1}{b^2-a^2}$$

or in (i) put $x = \pm\sqrt{-1}a$, $\pm\sqrt{-1}b$ successively.

$$\therefore \int \frac{x}{(x^2+a^2)(x^2+b^2)}\,dx = \frac{1}{b^2-a^2}\left\{\int \frac{x}{x^2+a^2}\,dx - \int \frac{x}{x^2+b^2}\,dx\right\}$$

$$= \frac{1}{2(b^2-a^2)}\log\left\{C\left\{\frac{x^2+a^2}{x^2+b^2}\right\}\right\}.$$

Use here, and in Example 29, of the important number $\sqrt{-1}$, which has not previously been mentioned in this book, is not really necessary. Justification for its brief presence now is that it arises in a natural way following the alternative methods in Examples 26 and 27, and consequently it may satisfy the inquiring student. Formal treatment of $\sqrt{-1}$ and its implications is deferred until Chapter 10. Anyone who is uneasy about its occurrence just now could ignore it temporarily.

IV. Repeated quadratic factors

Assume:

For each quadratic factor which occurs r times, we have a series of r partial fractions of the form $\dfrac{A_1x+B_1}{ax^2+bx+c}+\dfrac{A_2x+B_2}{(ax^2+bx+c)^2}+\ldots+\dfrac{A_rx+B_r}{(ax^2+bx+x)^r}$ (A_i, B_i ($i = 1,\ldots, r$) are constants to be found).	(58)

EXAMPLE 29 (general example involving mixed factors).

$$\frac{x^2}{(x-1)^2(x^2+1)} = \frac{A}{x-1}+\frac{B}{(x-1)^2}+\frac{Cx+D}{x^2+1}$$

$$\therefore\ x^2 = A(x-1)(x^2+1)+B(x^2+1)+(Cx+D)(x-1)^2 \tag{i}$$

whence $A+C = 0,\ -A+B-2C+D = 1,\ A+C-2D = 0,$
$-A+B+D = 0,$

$$\therefore A = B = -C = \tfrac{1}{2},\ D = 0,$$

or in (i) put

$$\left.\begin{array}{ll} x = 1, & \therefore B = \tfrac{1}{2} \\ x = \pm\sqrt{-1}, & \therefore C = -\tfrac{1}{2},\ D = 0 \\ x = 0, & \therefore A = \tfrac{1}{2} \end{array}\right\}$$

$$\therefore \int \frac{x^2}{(x-1)^2(x^2+1)}\,dx = \frac{1}{2}\int\frac{dx}{x-1} - \frac{1}{2}\int\frac{x\,dx}{x^2+1} + \frac{1}{2}\int\frac{dx}{(x-1)^2}$$

$$= \log\left\{\frac{C(x-1)^{1/2}}{(x^2+1)^{1/4}}\right\} - \frac{1}{2(x-1)}.$$

§ 29. TECHNIQUES OF INTEGRATION: QUADRATIC DENOMINATOR

A $\displaystyle\int \frac{k}{ax^2+bx+x}\,dx$: If denominator factorises, use partial fractions. Otherwise, complete the square. (59)

B $\displaystyle\int \frac{px+q}{ax^2+bx+c}\,dx$: If denominator factorises, use partial fractions. Otherwise, get numerator as differential coefficient of denominator and use case A. (60)

Lastly in our systematic organisation of techniques of integration, we attack the problem of the quadratic denominator. This may, or may not, have a square root associated with it, and in the latter case it may, or may not, factorise. Four possibilities therefore arise.

EXAMPLE 30 (quadratic denominator).

$$\int \frac{5x+4}{3x^2-5x+6}\,dx = \frac{5}{6}\int\frac{6x+\frac{24}{5}}{3x^2-5x+6}\,dx = \frac{5}{6}\int\frac{6x-5+\frac{49}{5}}{3x^2-5x+6}\,dx$$

$$= \frac{5}{6}\log(3x^2-5x+6) + \frac{49}{18}\int\frac{dx}{(x-\frac{5}{6})^2+\frac{47}{36}}$$

$$= \frac{5}{6}\log(3x^2-5x+6) + \frac{49}{3\sqrt{47}}\tan^{-1}\left(\frac{6x-5}{\sqrt{47}}\right) + C.$$

C $\displaystyle\frac{k}{\sqrt{ax^2+bx+c}}\,dx$: Complete the square. (61)

D	$\displaystyle\frac{px+q}{\sqrt{ax^2+bx+c}}\,dx$: Get integrand as differential coefficient of denominator and use case C.	(62)

EXAMPLE 31 (quadratic surd denominator).

$$\int \frac{3x-7}{\sqrt{5x^2-4x+3}}\,dx = \frac{3}{5}\int \frac{5x-\frac{35}{3}}{\sqrt{5x^2-4x+3}}\,dx = \frac{3}{5}\int \frac{5x-2-\frac{29}{3}}{\sqrt{5x^2-4x+3}}\,dx$$

$$= \frac{3}{5}\sqrt{5x^2-4x+3}-\frac{29}{5\sqrt{5}}\int \frac{dx}{\sqrt{(x-\frac{2}{5})^2+\frac{11}{25}}} \qquad \textit{(note well!)}$$

$$= \frac{3}{5}\sqrt{5x^2-4x+3}-\frac{29}{5\sqrt{5}}\log\left\{x-\frac{2}{5}+\sqrt{x^2-\tfrac{4}{5}x+\tfrac{3}{5}}\right\}+C$$

$$= \frac{3}{5}\sqrt{5x^2-4x+3}-\frac{29}{5\sqrt{5}}\log\{5x-2$$

$$+\sqrt{5}\sqrt{5x^2-4x+3}\}+C'.$$

Note the rule:

$\displaystyle\int\frac{P(x)}{Q(x)}\,dx$:	If degree of $P(x) \geqslant$ degree of $Q(x)$, first divide to obtain $\dfrac{P(x)}{Q(x)} = R(x)+\dfrac{P_1(x)}{Q(x)}$, where degree of $P_1(x) <$ degree of $Q(x)$.

See, for example, Example 19(b).

Suggested topic for further study

Practice, more practice, and still more practice, in methods of integration, especially the change of variable technique.

References

(Integral) calculus texts listed in the bibliography.

EXERCISES 7

Integrate the functions $f(x)$ in 1–27:

1. $\dfrac{1}{\sqrt{x(1-x)}}$. **2.** $\dfrac{x}{(x^2+9)^{5/2}}$. **3.** $\dfrac{1}{\sin^2 x\cos^2 x}$.

4. $\dfrac{1}{x\log x}$. **5.** $\dfrac{1}{x(\log x)^2}$. **6.** $\dfrac{(\tan^{-1}x)^3}{1+x^2}$.

7. $\sin x\cos x$. **8.** $\dfrac{\sin x}{\cos^2 x}$. **9.** $\operatorname{cosec}^2 x$.

10. $\dfrac{1}{(1-x)\sqrt{1-x^2}}$. **11.** $\dfrac{\sqrt{1-x^2}}{x^4}$. **12.** $\dfrac{1}{\sqrt{x}-2}$.

13. $\dfrac{\sqrt{1+\log x}}{x}$. **14.** $\cos 2x \cos 4x$. **15.** $x \sec^2 x$.

16. $\dfrac{1}{x^2+2x+2}$. **17.** $\dfrac{1}{\sqrt{x^2+2x+2}}$. **18.** $\dfrac{x}{x^2+2x+2}$.

19. $\dfrac{2x-3}{x^2-x-42}$. **20.** $\sqrt{a^2+x^2}$. **21.** $\dfrac{\sin \log x}{x}$.

22. $\dfrac{1}{1+\cos^2 x}$. **23.** $\dfrac{1}{1+\sin x}$. **24.** $\dfrac{x \sin^{-1} x}{\sqrt{1-x^2}}$.

25. $x^2 \cos x$. **26.** $x^2 e^{3x}$. **27.** $\dfrac{1}{(e^x-1)^2}$.

28. In a psychological investigation of "war fever", Richardson used the model (formula)

$$-t = \int \frac{dy}{y(y-1)(2y-1)},$$

where y is the proportion of articulate population openly favouring war at time t. Express t in terms of y.

29. Helmholtz, 1902, used the integral $\int x^2 \sqrt{a^2-x^2}\, dx$ in the study of molecular dynamics. Integrate.

30. Integrate $\displaystyle\int \frac{dx}{(a-x)\sqrt{b-x}}$ (used by Bodenstein, 1899, for the rate of formation of hydrogen sulphide from its elements).

CHAPTER 8

DEFINITE INTEGRALS

I have finished a monument more lasting than bronze and loftier than the pyramids reared by Kings, that neither corroding rain nor the uncontrolled north wind can dash apart, nor the countless succession of years and the flight of ages. I shall not wholly die; that greater part of me shall escape Death and ever shall I grow, still fresh in the praise of posterity.

(HORACE)

ALREADY we are aware of the intimate connection between calculus and geometry, e.g. the problem of drawing a tangent to a curve is connected with the discovery of the derivative, and the geometrical significance of partial differentiation relates to curved surfaces in space. So, too, with the integral which, we shall find, is linked with area.

§ 30. ELEMENTARY FIRST-ORDER DIFFERENTIAL EQUATIONS (METHOD OF SEPARATION OF VARIABLES)

EXAMPLE 32 (first-order differential equations).

(a) Given $x \dfrac{dy}{dx} = y$, solve for y.

Solution. Separate the variable and integrate to obtain

$$\int \frac{dy}{y} = \int \frac{dx}{x}$$

$$\therefore \log y = \log x + \log k = \log kx$$

$$\therefore \quad y = kx.$$

Therefore the solution of the differential equation is $y = kx$ which, geometrically, represents a family of lines through the origin.

A differential equation $M\,dx+N\,dy = 0$ (M, N functions of x, y) is *exact* if $\dfrac{\partial M}{\partial y} = \dfrac{\partial N}{\partial x}$. (Why is this so?) Thus, $y\,dx - x\,dy = 0$ is not exact

$\left(\because \dfrac{\partial M}{\partial y} = 1, \dfrac{\partial N}{\partial x} = -1\right)$, whereas $y\,dx + x\,dy = 0$ is exact, with solution $xy = c$ (family of rectangular hyperbolas).

(b) If $(1+x^2)\dfrac{dy}{dx} = 1$, find y in terms of x, given that $y = \pi/4$ when x is infinite.

Solution. Separating variables we have

$$\int dy = \int \frac{dx}{1+x^2}.$$

$$\therefore\ y = \tan^{-1}x + c$$

$$\therefore\ \frac{\pi}{4} = \frac{\pi}{2} + c \qquad \text{using the given condition}$$

$$\therefore\ c = -\frac{\pi}{4}.$$

Therefore the solution is

$$y = \tan^{-1} x - \frac{\pi}{4},$$

i.e. $x = \tan(y + \pi/4)$.

Notice that whereas the solution of (a) was general, i.e. an infinite number of solutions existed, that of (b) is specific. This, of course, is due to the presence of the *initial condition* which enables us to fix the constant of integration specifically. However, y is still a function of x, so y is not completely definite yet.

Problem. Deflection y of a cantilever, length l, loaded at one end, is given by the second-order differential equation $\dfrac{d^2y}{dx^2} = l - x$. Integrating twice by separating variables, and using the *two* given initial conditions $x = 0$, $y = 0$ and $x = 0$, $\dfrac{dy}{dx} = 0$, solve for y at $x = l$. [*Answer:* $y = l^3/3$.]

EXAMPLE 33 (law of organic growth). Assume that the rate of change of the amount of a substance at time t is proportional to the amount present at that time t. Construct a differential equation to describe this growth, and solve it.

Solution. Let $f(t)$ be the amount of the substance present at time t.

$\therefore\ f'(t) = k\,f(t)$ (k a factor of proportionality called the *growth constant*) (i)

$$\therefore\ \frac{f'(t)}{f(t)} = k$$

$$\therefore\ \int \frac{f'(t)}{f(t)}\,dt = \int k\,dt \quad \text{integrating both sides w.r.t. } t$$

$$\therefore\ \log f(t) = kt+c$$

$$\therefore\ \log f(0) = 0+c \quad \text{if } f(0) \text{ is the amount at time } t = 0.$$

$$\therefore\ c = \log f(0)$$

$$\therefore\ \log \frac{f(t)}{f(0)} = kt$$

$$\therefore\ f(t) = f(0)e^{kt}. \qquad \text{(ii)}$$

[Illustrations of this type of behaviour are, for instance, the growth under ideal conditions of a bacteria culture ($k > 0$) and radioactive decay ($k < 0$). (Refer to § 11 and Example 9.) Many other instances of the occurrence of the organic growth law, e.g. in chemical reactions (such as sugar or salt in solution) and sociological models, will be seen in Exercises 8.]

Corollary. Replace k by $-k$ *(decay constant)* in (i) so that we are now dealing with decay, not growth. Then (ii) gives

$$f(t) = f(0)e^{-kt}. \qquad \text{(iii)}$$

An interesting problem is to determine the *half-life* of a radioactive substance, i.e. the time taken for a given quantity $f(0)$ to be reduced to $f(0)/2$. (Radium has half-life of about 1600 years.)

Let T be the half-life of a given radioactive material.

$$\therefore\ \frac{f(T)}{f(0)} = \tfrac{1}{2} = e^{-kT} \qquad \text{from (iii),}$$

i.e.

$$-kT = \log\left(\tfrac{1}{2}\right)$$

$$\therefore\ T = \frac{1}{k}\log 2.$$

Draw a rough sketch of the curve of radioactive decomposition of a substance. Indicate on this exponential curve how the half-life of the substance is derived. Mark on it also the points corresponding to $T/2$ and $\frac{1}{8}f(0)$. [*Answers:* $2^{-1/2}f(0)$, $3T$.]

§ 31. THE DEFINITE INTEGRAL

In (49), suppose $y = c$ when $x = a$.

$$\therefore\ c = F(a)+C \qquad \text{whence } C = c-F(a),$$

i.e. $\quad y-c = F(x)-F(a).$

Further, suppose $y = d$ when $x = b$.

$$\begin{aligned}\therefore\ d-c &= F(b)-F(a) = \Big[F(x)\Big]_a^b, \quad \text{say}\\ &= \{F(b)+C\}-\{F(a)+C\}\\ &= \{\textstyle\int f(x)\,dx\}_{x=b} - \{\textstyle\int f(x)\,dx\}_{x=a}\\ &= \int_a^b f(x)\,dx \qquad \text{using the conventional notation.}\end{aligned}$$

We call

$$\boxed{\int_a^b f(x)\,dx = \Big[F(x)\Big]_a^b} \tag{64}$$

the *definite integral* of $f(x)$ w.r.t. x between the limits b *(upper limit)* and a *(lower limit)*. Notice how the constant of integration C has been absorbed into other quantities. Also, note that $\int_a^a f(x)\,dx = 0$. Result (64) is known as the *fundamental theorem of calculus*. Observe that

$$\boxed{\frac{d}{dx}\int_a^x f(t)\,dt = f(x)} \tag{65}$$

a result attributed to Isaac Barrow (1630–77, English) and James Gregory (1638–75, Scots) in the 1660's. (Note a similar result in § 23.)

Evidently, in (64), $I = \int_a^b f(x)\,dx$ is a function of the limits a, b, and so will vary whenever either of these limits varies. With a fixed and b variable, we obtain $\dfrac{dI}{db} = f(b)$ (65), the differential coefficient of the definite integral w.r.t. the upper limit. Details of the proof of (65), which involves showing that I is a continuous function of b, may be found on pp. 211–12 of Lamb [Chapter 20, reference (a)]. State a similar result for dI/da.

As immediate consequences of (64), we deduce that

$$\begin{aligned} &\text{(i)} \int_a^b f(x)\,dx = -\int_b^a f(x)\,dx \\ &\text{(ii)} \int_a^b f(x)\,dx = \int_\xi^b f(x)\,dx + \int_a^\xi f(x)\,dx \quad (a < \xi < b). \end{aligned} \tag{66}$$

EXAMPLE 34 (use of the definite integral).

(a) $$\int_0^a \sqrt{a^2-x^2}\,dx = \left[\frac{a^2}{2}\sin^{-1}\frac{x}{a}+\frac{x}{2}\sqrt{a^2-x^2}\right]_0^a \quad \text{by Example 22 (i)}$$

$$= \frac{a^2}{2}\sin^{-1} 1$$

$$= \frac{\pi a^2}{4}.$$

(b) $$\int_1^2 \log x\,dx = [x\log x - x]_1^2 \quad \text{by Example 25(b)}$$

$$= 2\log 2 - 2 + 1$$

$$= \log 4 - 1$$

$$= \log\left(\frac{4}{e}\right).$$

(c) $$I = \int_0^{\pi/2} \cos x \cosh x\,dx = \Big[\cos x \sinh x\Big]_0^{\pi/2} - \int_0^{\pi/2} \sinh x \frac{d}{dx}\cos x\,dx$$

$$(\because\ d\sinh x = \cosh x\,dx)$$

$$= 0 + \int_0^{\pi/2} \sin x \sinh x\,dx$$

$$= \Big[\sin x \cosh x\Big]_0^{\pi/2} - \int_0^{\pi/2} \cosh x \frac{d\sin x}{dx}\,dx$$

$$= \cosh\frac{\pi}{2} - I$$

$$\therefore\ I = \tfrac{1}{2}\cosh\frac{\pi}{2}.$$

(d) $$\int_0^1 \frac{x}{\sqrt{1+x^2}}\,dx = \Big[\sqrt{1+x^2}\Big]_0^1$$

$$= \sqrt{2} - 1;$$

or $$\int_0^1 \frac{x}{\sqrt{1+x^2}}\,dx = \int_0^{\pi/4} \frac{\tan\theta \sec^2\theta\, d\theta}{\sec\theta}$$ (putting $x = \tan\theta$ so that when $x = 1$, $\theta = \pi/4$ and when $x = 0$, $\theta = 0$)

$$= \int_0^{\pi/4} \tan\theta \sec\theta\, d\theta$$

$$= \Big[\sec\theta\Big]_0^{\pi/4}$$

$$= \sqrt{2}-1.$$

Note particularly: If, as in (d), we make a transformation of variable, *we must necessarily change the limits of integration* of the original variable into the limits of the new variable.

§ 3 2. IMPROPER INTEGRALS

When either (I) one, or both, of the limits of integration is ∞, or (II) the integrand becomes infinite at or between the limits of integration, then the integral is an *improper integral.*

Case I. Infinite limit(s) of integration

Define:

$$\text{(i)} \int_a^\infty f(x)\,dx = \lim_{b\to\infty} \int_a^b f(x)\,dx$$

$$\text{(ii)} \int_{-\infty}^b f(x)\,dx = \lim_{a\to-\infty} \int_a^b f(x)\,dx \qquad (67)$$

$$\text{(iii)} \int_{-\infty}^\infty f(x)\,dx = \lim_{\substack{b\to\infty \\ a\to-\infty}} \int_a^b f(x)\,dx$$

When one, or both, of the limits of integration is infinite, the definite integral is said to *converge* or *diverge* according as its value is finite or infinite.

EXAMPLE 35 (upper limit infinite).

$$\int_1^\infty \frac{dx}{x} = \lim_{b\to\infty} \int_1^b \frac{dx}{x} \quad \text{by (67)(i)}$$

$$= \lim_{b\to\infty} \Big[\log x\Big]_1^b = \lim_{b\to\infty} \log b \quad = \infty$$

or

$$\int_1^\infty \frac{dx}{x} = \Big[\log x\Big]_1^\infty$$

$$= \log \infty \quad = \infty,$$

i.e.

$$\int_1^\infty \frac{dx}{x} \text{ diverges.}$$

[On the other hand, $\int_0^\infty e^{-5x}\,dx = \frac{1}{5}$ converges. Further, $\int_0^\infty \cos x\,dx = \lim_{b\to\infty} \sin b$, which does not exist, since $\sin x$ oscillates between $+1$ and -1.]

In practice, do not use the full setting out of the limiting process but use the alternative abbreviated procedure. You are assumed to know that the symbol ∞ represents a limiting process, and the shorter method is merely a conventional acceptance of this fact.

Case II. Integrand discontinuous

The principle used here is to isolate the discontinuity (or discontinuities) and then to proceed with a limiting process. When confronted with the evaluation of a definite integral, always *look first to see if the integrand is discontinuous within the limits of integration.* Discontinuities may occur at one, or both, of the limits, or at a point between them, or at combinations of these. As a typical illustration, suppose $f(x)$ is discontinuous at c where $a < c < b$.

Define:
$$\boxed{\int_a^b f(x)\,dx = \lim_{\varepsilon_2\to 0} \int_{c+\varepsilon_2}^b f(x)\,dx + \lim_{\varepsilon_1\to 0} \int_a^{c-\varepsilon_1} f(x)\,dx} \qquad (68)$$

where ε_1, ε_2 are arbitrarily small positive numbers (Fig. 12).

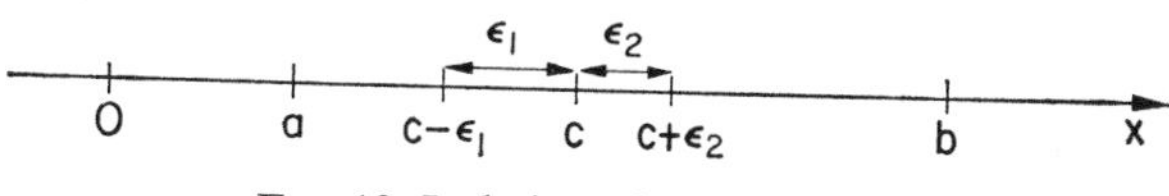

FIG. 12. Isolation of a discontinuity

You should construct similar definitions and diagrams for discontinuities at a or b, or a and b, and for combinations of (67) and (68).

EXAMPLE 36 (discontinuous integrand).

$$\int_{-1}^{1} \frac{dx}{x^{2/3}} = \lim_{\varepsilon_2 \to 0} \int_{0+\varepsilon_2}^{1} \frac{dx}{x^{2/3}} + \lim_{\varepsilon_1 \to 0} \int_{-1}^{0-\varepsilon_1} \frac{dx}{x^{2/3}}$$

$$= \lim_{\varepsilon_2 \to 0} \left[3x^{1/3} \right]_{\varepsilon_2}^{1} + \lim_{\varepsilon_1 \to 0} \left[3x^{1/3} \right]_{-1}^{-\varepsilon_1}$$

$$= \lim_{\varepsilon_2 \to 0} 3(1 - \varepsilon_2^{1/3}) + \lim_{\varepsilon_1 \to 0} 3\,\{(-\varepsilon_1)^{1/3} - (-1)^{1/3}\}$$

$$= 3 + 3$$

$$= 6.$$

$\left[\text{Now try proving } \int_{1}^{\infty} \frac{dx}{x\sqrt{x^2 - 1}} = \frac{\pi}{2}.\right]$

§ 33. THE DEFINITE INTEGRAL AS AN AREA AND AS THE LIMIT OF A SUM

Consider (Fig. 13) the curve $y = f(x)$ continuous between $x = a$ and $x = b$.

Subdivide the interval $b - a$ into n portions each of length δx so that $n\,\delta x = b - a$ (i.e. $b = a + n\,\delta x$). Construct rectangles as in Fig. 13 (obtaining an organ-pipe-like effect).

Now the difference between the sum of the outer rectangles and the sum of the inner rectangles of Fig. 13 can be made as small as we please by letting $\delta x \to 0$, i.e. $n \to \infty$.

The sum of the inner rectangles is

$$f(a)\,\delta x + f(a + \delta x)\,\delta x + f(a + 2\,\delta x)\,\delta x + \ldots + f(a + \overline{n-1}\,\delta x)\,\delta x$$

$$= \sum_{r=0}^{n-1} f(a + r\,\delta x)\,\delta x. \qquad (\alpha)$$

The sum of the outer rectangles is

$$f(a + \delta x)\,\delta x + f(a + 2\,\delta x)\,\delta x + \ldots f(a + n\,\delta x)\,\delta x$$

$$= \sum_{r=1}^{n} f(a + r\,\delta x)\,\delta x. \qquad (\beta)$$

Suppose that P and Q are neighbouring points on the curve $y = f(x)$ (Fig. 14). Let Δ = area $AMPR$ under the curve

$\therefore\ \Delta + \delta\Delta = \ldots ANQR \ldots$

$\therefore\ y\,\delta x < \delta\Delta < (y + \delta y)\,\delta x$ from the rectangles on MN.

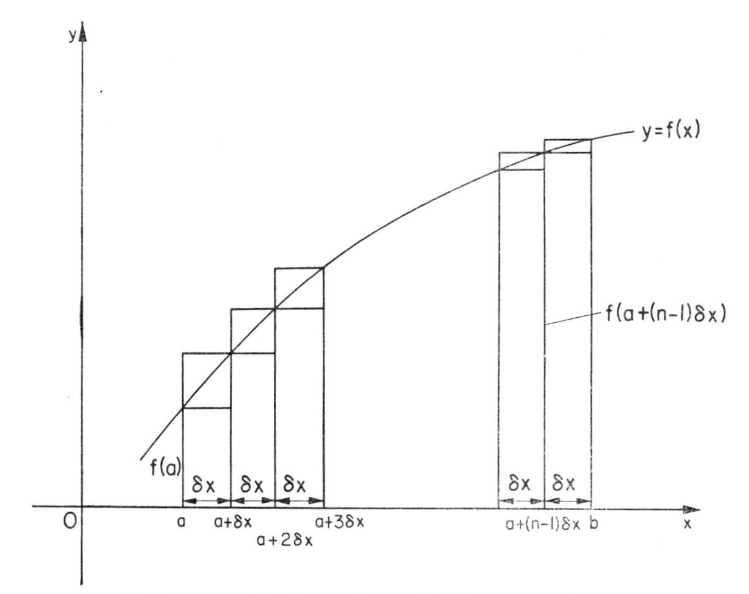

FIG. 13. Definite integral as a limiting summation

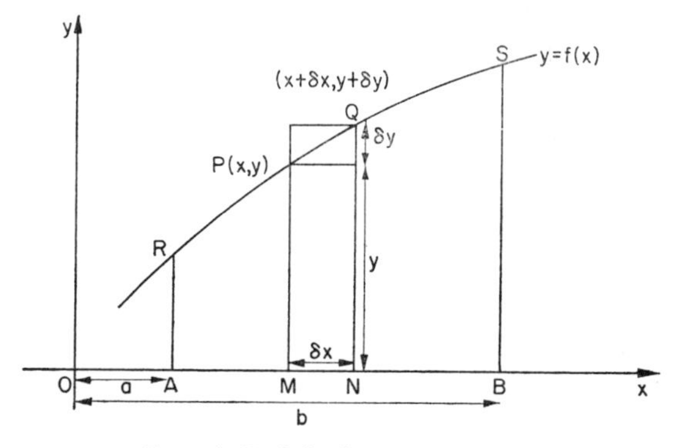

FIG. 14. Definite integral as an area

$$\therefore \; y < \frac{\delta \Delta}{\delta x} < y+\delta y$$ (with reversed inequality signs if the gradient of the curve is negative)

$$\therefore \text{ as } \delta x \to 0, \; \frac{d\Delta}{dx} = y = f(x)$$

$$\therefore \; \Delta = \int f(x)\,dx = F(x)+C \quad \text{where} \quad \frac{dF(x)}{dx} = f(x).$$

$$\therefore \; 0 = F(a)+C \qquad \text{since } \Delta = 0 \quad \text{when} \quad x = a$$

$$\therefore \; C = -F(a) \qquad \text{so that } \Delta = F(x)-F(a).$$

Move M to B and we have that *the area of the curve $y = f(x)$ included between the ordinates at $x = a$ and $x = b$, the x-axis and the curve is*

$$\Delta = F(b)-F(a) = [F(x)]_a^b, \quad \text{i.e.} \quad \int_a^b f(x)\,dx.$$

Similarly, $\int_c^d f(y)\,dy$ is the area of the curve $x = f(y)$ included between the abscissae at $y = c$ and $y = d$, the y-axis, and the curve.

Thus, we have shown that the notion of area under a curve affords a simple concrete illustration of the abstract definition of the definite integral (64).

Reverting to (α) and (β), we see obviously that the area under the curve lies between the sum of the inner rectangles and the sum of the outer rectangles. Consequently, this area is the limit of either sum as $\delta x \to 0$.

Using (α), say, and (62), we may write (and never forget!)

$$\boxed{\int_a^b f(x)\,dx = \lim_{\delta x \to 0} \sum_a^b f(x)\,\delta x}\,. \qquad (69)$$

Thus we have developed the concept of integration as a limiting summation. This was the approach of Leibniz and, in essence, Archimedes, whereas Newton conceived integration as the operation inverse to differentiation. From this notion of summation we derive our symbol $\int$ for integration; it is an elongated S, an abbreviation of the Latin word *summa* meaning "sum".

Just as the definite integral as an area is a concrete representation of the abstract definition (64), so the definite integral as a limiting sum [equated to an area in (69)] can be abstracted from physical interpretations. This is the basis for the *Riemann theory of integration* which forms a pretty excursion into higher mathematics. Other theories of integration, such as those of Lebesgue (1875–1941, French) and Stieltjes (1856–94, Dutch), also exist. Lebesgue's concept generalised integrals to allow for discontinuities to be applied, i.e. the limitation of continuity was removed. Modern physics, in which discontinuity plays an important role, utilises *Lebesgue integration* as a most valuable technique.

[Incidentally, mechanical devices have been invented for approximating to plane areas. Of these precision machines, the most famous is probably *Amsler's planimeter* (Amsler, 1823–1912, Swiss). (See Lamb, Reference (a), Chapter 20, for a description of its workings.)]

EXAMPLE 37 (evaluation of a definite integral as the limit of a sum—illustration of theory).

Evaluate $\int_1^3 x^2\,dx$.

Solution. First of all, note that

$$\begin{cases} \sum_{r=1}^{n} r = \frac{1}{2}n(n+1) & \text{(i)} \\ \sum_{r=1}^{n} r^2 = \frac{1}{6}n(n+1)(2n+1). & \text{(ii)} \end{cases}$$

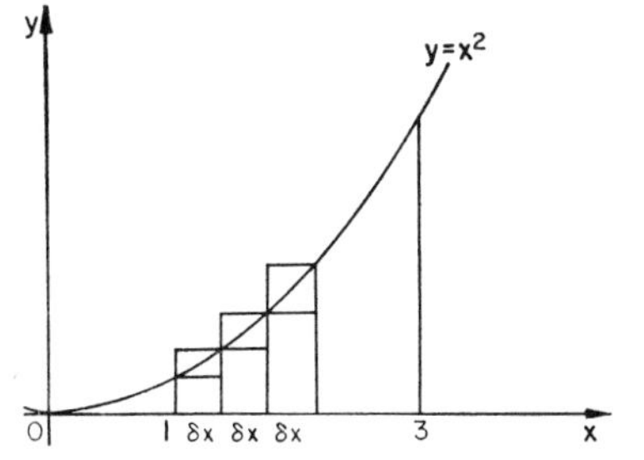

FIG. 15. Limiting summation for a parabola

The area under the parabola $y = x^2$ included between the x-axis and the ordinates at $x = 1$, $x = 3$ (so that $n\,\delta x = 2$, i.e. $\delta x = 2/n$) is (Fig. 15)

$$\int_1^3 f(x)\,dx = \lim_{\delta x \to 0} \{f(1)\,\delta x + f(1+\delta x)\,\delta x + f(1+2\,\delta x)\,\delta x + \ldots$$

$$\ldots + f(1+\overline{n-1}\,\delta x)\,\delta x\}$$

$$= \lim_{n\to\infty} \left\{\frac{2}{n}\left[f(1) + f\left(1+\frac{2}{n}\right) + f\left(1+2\,\frac{2}{n}\right) + \ldots + f(1+\overline{n-1}\,\frac{2}{n}\right]\right\}$$

$$= \lim_{n\to\infty} \left\{\frac{2}{n}\left[1^2 + \left(1+\frac{2}{n}\right)^2 + \left(1+2\,\frac{2}{n}\right)^2 + \left(1+3\,\frac{2}{n}\right)^2 + \ldots\right.\right.$$

$$\left.\left.\ldots + \left(1+\overline{n-1}\,\frac{2}{n}\right)^2\right]\right\} \qquad \because f(x) = x^2$$

$$= \lim_{n\to\infty} \left\{\frac{2}{n}\left[1^2\,n + \frac{2}{n}\,2(1+2+\ldots+\overline{n-1}) + \ldots\right.\right.$$

$$\left.\left.\ldots + \left(\frac{2}{n}\right)^2 (1^2+2^2+\ldots+\overline{n-1^2})\right]\right\}$$

$$= \lim_{n\leftarrow\infty} \left\{\frac{2}{n}\left[n + \frac{2}{n}\,2\,\frac{1}{2}\,(n-1)n + \frac{4}{n^2}\,\frac{1}{6}\,(n-1)n(2n-1)\right]\right\} \qquad \text{using (i), (ii)}$$

$$= 2\lim_{n\to\infty} \left\{1 + 2\left(1-\frac{1}{n}\right) + \frac{4}{6}\left(1-\frac{1}{n}\right)\left(2-\frac{1}{n}\right)\right\}$$

$$= 2\{1+2+1\tfrac{1}{3}\} = 8\tfrac{2}{3}.$$

Note. Clearly, the *use of the limiting summation method is a time-wasting procedure and is very cumbersome*, even in simple cases. Therefore, we would never use this approach in practice (except as an illustration of the summation technique). Proceed thus:

$$\int_1^3 x^2\,dx = \left[\frac{x^3}{3}\right]_1^3 = \tfrac{1}{3}(27-1) = 8\tfrac{2}{3}.$$

Next, suppose the curve $y = f(x)$ cuts the x-axis; we then have several areas to consider and so we must adopt some convention about the sign to be attributed to them.

Convention. The *sign of an area* is + or − according as the area lies above or below the x-axis (the curve being supposed described in the +ve direction of x).

Knowing that an area is fundamentally signless, how do we interpret a negative area, e.g., A_2 in Example 38? Because A_2 represents an area below the x-axis it follows from the limiting summation (69), where each value of $y = f(x)$ is now negative while each δx is positive (representing an increase), that the sum is negative. The actual area is thus $-A_2$. Altogether the situation may be summarised as follows:

$\int_a^b f(x)\,dx$ *measures the amount by which the area above the x-axis is* $>(<)$ *the area below the x-axis.*

In Fig. 16 the total area of three portions is $A = A_1 - A_2 + A_3$ whereas

$$\int_a^b f(x)\,dx = A_1 + A_2 + A_3 \quad (A_2 < 0).$$

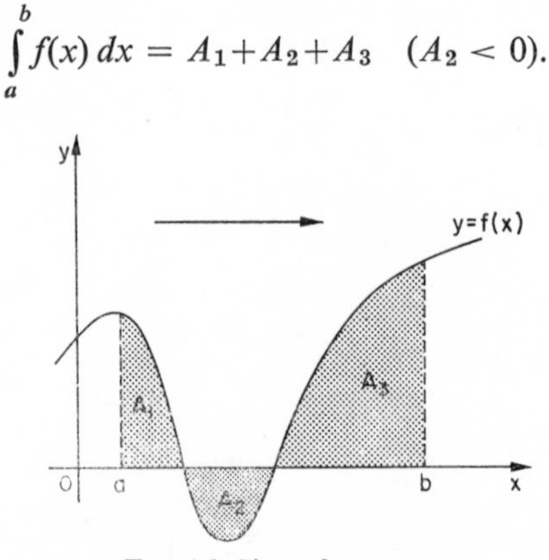

FIG. 16. Sign of an area

EXAMPLE 38 (sign of an area; area common to two curves). Determine the area between the parabolas $y = x^2 - 1$, $y = -x^2 + 9$ (Fig. 17).

Solution. Now

$$\int_{-\sqrt{5}}^{\sqrt{5}} (x^2-1)\,dx = \left[\frac{x^3}{3}-x\right]_{-\sqrt{5}}^{\sqrt{5}} = \lim_{\delta x \to 0} \sum_{-\sqrt{5}}^{\sqrt{5}} (x^2-1)\,\delta x$$

$$= \left(\frac{5\sqrt{5}}{3}-\sqrt{5}\right)-\left(-\frac{5\sqrt{5}}{3}+\sqrt{5}\right)$$

$$= \tfrac{2}{3}\sqrt{5}+\tfrac{2}{3}\sqrt{5}$$

$$= \tfrac{4}{3}\sqrt{5}$$

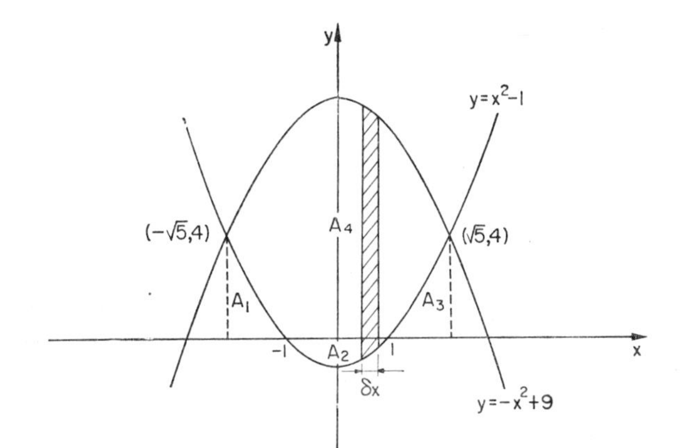

FIG. 17. Common area of two parabolas

whereas

$$A_1 = \int_{-\sqrt{5}}^{-1} (x^2-1)\,dx = \left[\frac{x^3}{3}-x\right]_{-\sqrt{5}}^{-1} = (-\tfrac{1}{3}+1)-(-\tfrac{2}{3}\sqrt{5}) = \tfrac{2}{3}+\tfrac{2}{3}\sqrt{5} = \tfrac{2}{3}(\sqrt{5}+1)$$

$$A_2 = \int_{-1}^{1} (x^2-1)\,dx = \left[\frac{x^3}{3}-x\right]_{-1}^{1} = (\tfrac{1}{3}-1)-(-\tfrac{1}{3}+1) = -\tfrac{2}{3}-\tfrac{2}{3} = -\tfrac{4}{3}$$

$$A_3 = \int_{1}^{\sqrt{5}} (x^2-1)\,dx = \left[\frac{x^3}{3}-x\right]_{1}^{\sqrt{5}} = \tfrac{2}{3}\sqrt{5}-(\tfrac{1}{3}-1) = \tfrac{2}{3}\sqrt{5}+\tfrac{2}{3} = \tfrac{2}{3}(\sqrt{5}+1)$$

$$\therefore\ A_1+A_2+A_3 = \tfrac{2}{3}(\sqrt{5}+1)-\tfrac{4}{3}+\tfrac{2}{3}(\sqrt{5}+1) = \tfrac{4}{3}\sqrt{5} = \int_{-\sqrt{5}}^{\sqrt{5}} (x^2-1)\,dx,$$

i.e. $\int_{-\sqrt{5}}^{\sqrt{5}} (x^2-1)\,dx$ shows that the area (under this parabola) which lies above the x-axis exceeds that lying below by $\frac{4}{3}\sqrt{5}$ sq. units.

The total area bounded by the parabola, the x-axis, and the ordinates at $x = \sqrt{5}$, $x = -\sqrt{5}$, is

$$A_1 - A_2 + A_3 = \tfrac{4}{3}(\sqrt{5}+2).$$

Put $$B = \int_{-\sqrt{5}}^{\sqrt{5}} (-x^2+9)\,dx \quad \text{and} \quad A = \int_{-\sqrt{5}}^{\sqrt{5}} (x^2-1)\,dx.$$

Therefore the area common to the two parabolas is

$$\begin{aligned} B - A &= A_1 + A_4 + A_3 - (A_1 - A_2 + A_3) = A_4 + A_2 \\ &= 2\int_{-\sqrt{5}}^{\sqrt{5}} (-x^2+5)\,dx \\ &= 2\left[-\frac{x^3}{3} + 5x\right]_{-\sqrt{5}}^{\sqrt{5}} \\ &= 2\{(-\tfrac{5}{3}\sqrt{5} + 5\sqrt{5}) - (\tfrac{5}{3}\sqrt{5} - 5\sqrt{5})\} \\ &= \frac{40\sqrt{5}}{3}. \end{aligned}$$

Query. If the area between the parabolas $y = kx^2$ and $y = \frac{1}{2}x^2$ is "bisected" by the parabola $y = x^2$, what is the value of k? (Apostol [14], p. 148.) [*Answer:* $k = \frac{16}{9}$ (k^2 gives Ahmes' approximation to π (§ 42)).]

§ 34. PROPERTIES OF $\int_a^b f(x)\,dx$

Some useful properties, additional to (66) are

I. $$\boxed{\int_0^{\pi/2} f(\sin x)\,dx = \int_0^{\pi/2} f(\cos x)\,dx} \tag{70}$$

since $$\begin{aligned} \int_0^{\pi/2} f(\sin\theta)\,d\theta &= \int_{\pi/2}^{0} f(\cos\phi)(-d\phi) && \text{putting } \theta = \pi/2 - \phi \\ &= \int_0^{\pi/2} f(\cos\phi)\,d\phi && \text{using (66) (i)} \\ &= \int_0^{\pi/2} f(\cos\theta)\,d\theta && \text{since the choice of symbol for the variable of integration is immaterial.} \end{aligned}$$

More generally $$\int_0^a f(x)\,dx = \int_0^a f(a-x)\,dx \tag{70.1}$$

on putting $x = a - y$ and using (66) (i).

EXAMPLE 39.

$$\text{(i)} \quad \int_0^{\pi/2} \sin^2\theta\, d\theta = \int_0^{\pi/2} \cos^2\theta\, d\theta \qquad \text{by (70)}$$

$$= \frac{1}{2}\int_0^{\pi/2} (\sin^2\theta+\cos^2\theta)\, d\theta$$

$$= \frac{1}{2}\int_0^{\pi/2} d\theta$$

$$= \frac{\pi}{4}$$

or, from Example 19,

$$\left\{\begin{aligned} \int_0^{\pi/2} \sin^2\theta\, d\theta &= \left[\frac{\theta}{2}-\frac{\sin 2\theta}{4}\right]_0^{\pi/2} = \frac{\pi}{4} \\ \int_0^{\pi/2} \cos^2\theta\, d\theta &= \left[\frac{\theta}{2}+\frac{\sin 2\theta}{4}\right]_0^{\pi/2} = \frac{\pi}{4}. \end{aligned}\right.$$

$$\text{(ii)} \int_0^{\pi/2} \frac{dx}{a^2\cos^2 x+b^2\sin^2 x} = \left[\frac{1}{ab}\tan^{-1}\left(\frac{b}{a}\tan x\right)\right]_0^{\pi/2} \qquad \text{by Example 24(e)}$$

$$= \frac{1}{ab}\,\frac{\pi}{2}$$

$$= \frac{\pi}{2ab}$$

$$= \int_0^{\pi/2} \frac{dx}{a^2(1-\sin^2 x)+b^2\sin^2 x} \qquad \text{reverting to the original integral}$$

$$= \int_0^{\pi/2} f(\sin x)\, dx$$

$$= \int_0^{\pi/2} f(\cos x)\, dx \qquad \text{by (70)}$$

$$= \int_0^{\pi/2} \frac{dx}{a^2(1-\cos^2 x)+b^2\cos^2 x}$$

$$= \int_0^{\pi/2} \frac{dx}{a^2\sin^2 x+b^2\cos^2 x}.$$

II.

$f(x)$ even	$\int_{-a}^{a} f(x)\,dx = 2\int_{0}^{a} f(x)\,dx$

(71)

e.g.
$$\int_{-1}^{1} x^2dx = 2\int_{0}^{1} x^2dx = 2\left[\frac{x^3}{3}\right]_0^1 = \frac{2}{3} \quad \text{[Fig. 18(a)].}$$

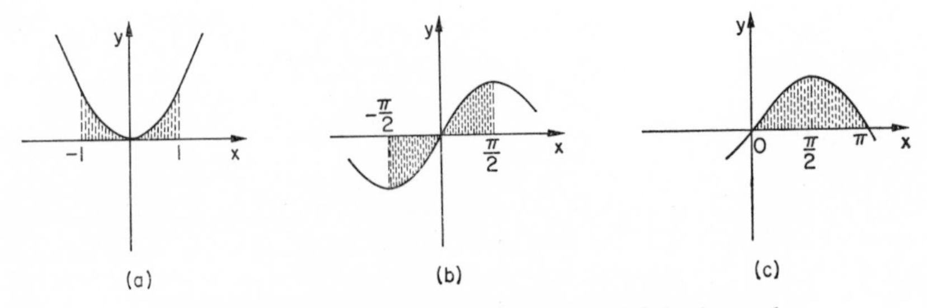

FIG. 18. Illustrations of properties of the definite integral

III.

$f(x)$ odd	$\int_{-a}^{a} f(x)\,dx = 0$

(72)

e.g.
$$\int_{-\pi/2}^{\pi/2} \sin x\,dx = \Big[-\cos x\Big]_{-\pi/2}^{\pi/2} = 0 \quad \text{[Fig. 18(b)].}$$

IV.

$$\boxed{\int_0^{\pi} f(\sin x)\,dx = 2\int_0^{\pi/2} f(\sin x)\,dx} \tag{73}$$

since $\sin x = \sin(\pi - x)$

e.g.
$$\int_0^{\pi} \sin x\,dx = 2\int_0^{\pi/2} \sin x\,dx = 2\Big[-\cos x\Big]_0^{\pi/2} = 2 \quad \text{[Fig 18(c)].}$$

Whereas distinct indefinite integrals can never lead to the same answer, many unrelated definite integrals yield the same answer, e.g.

$$\int_0^{\pi/2} \sin x\,dx = 1 = \int_0^1 dx = \int_{-1}^{1} \frac{3x^2}{2}\,dx = \int_{-\infty}^{0} e^x\,dx.$$

Also, refer to (72).

§ 35. REDUCTION FORMULAE

EXAMPLE 40.

(a) Let $u_n = \int_0^{\pi/2} \cos^n \theta \, d\theta$

$$= \int_0^{\pi/2} \cos^{n-1} \theta \frac{d \sin \theta}{d\theta} \, d\theta \qquad \text{integrating by parts}$$

$$= \Big[\cos^{n-1} \theta \sin \theta\Big]_0^{\pi/2} - \int_0^{\pi/2} \sin \theta\{(n-1) \cos^{n-2} \theta(-\sin \theta)\} \, d\theta$$

$$= (n-1) \int_0^{\pi/2} \cos^{n-2} \theta(1-\cos^2 \theta) \, d\theta$$

$$= (n-1) \left\{\int_0^{\pi/2} \cos^{n-2} \theta \, d\theta - \int_0^{\pi/2} \cos^n \theta \, d\theta\right\}$$

$$= (n-1) \{u_{n-2}-u_n\}$$

$\therefore \; (n-1+1)u_n = (n-1)u_{n-2}$

$$\therefore \quad \boxed{u_n = \frac{n-1}{n} u_{n-2}}$$

i.e. the power of $\cos \theta$ has been reduced from n to $n-2$. Ultimately, u_n depends on $u_1 = \int_0^{\pi/2} \cos \theta \, d\theta = 1$, or $u_0 = \int_0^{\pi/2} d\theta = \frac{\pi}{2}$, according as n is odd or even.

[Reduction formulae are not restricted to definite integrals. Allowing $U_n = \int x^n e^x \, dx$, for instance, we easily deduce the formula $U_n = x^n e^x - nU_{n-1}$.]

(b) Similarly, if $v_n = \int_0^{\pi/2} \sin^n \theta \, d\theta$, we deduce $\boxed{v_n = \frac{n-1}{n} v_{n-2}}$.

Ultimately, v_n depends on $v_1 = \int_0^{\pi/2} \sin \theta \, d\theta = 1$, or $v_0 = \int_0^{\pi/2} d\theta = \frac{\pi}{2}$, according as n is odd or even.

Hence,

n odd:

$$\int_0^{\pi/2} \cos^n \theta \, d\theta = \int_0^{\pi/2} \sin^n \theta \, d\theta = \frac{(n-1)(n-3)\dots 2}{n(n-2)\dots 3} \tag{74}$$

n even:

$$\int_0^{\pi/2} \cos^n \theta \, d\theta = \int_0^{\pi/2} \sin^n \theta \, d\theta = \frac{(n-1)(n-3)\dots 1}{n(n-2)\dots 2} \frac{\pi}{2}$$

e.g.

$$\int_0^{\pi/2} \sin^8 x \, dx = \frac{7}{8}\,\frac{5}{6}\,\frac{3}{4}\,\frac{1}{2}\,\frac{\pi}{2} = \frac{35}{256}\pi$$

$$\int_0^{\pi/2} \cos^9 x \, dx = \frac{8}{9}\,\frac{6}{7}\,\frac{4}{5}\,\frac{2}{3} = \frac{128}{315}.$$

(c) Let $u_{m,n} = \int_0^{\pi/2} \sin^m\theta \cos^n \theta \, d\theta$

$= \int_0^{\pi/2} \sin^m \theta \cos^{n-1} \theta \frac{d \sin \theta}{d\theta} \, d\theta$ integrating by parts on $\cos^n \theta$

$= \Big[\sin^{m+1} \theta \cos^{n-1} \theta\Big]_0^{\pi/2} - \int_0^{\pi/2} \sin \theta\{(m \sin^{m-1} \theta \cos \theta)$

$\cos^{n-1} \theta + [(n-1) \cos^{n-2} \theta(-\sin \theta)] \sin^m \theta\} \, d\theta$

$= \int_0^{\pi/2} \{-m \sin^m \theta \cos^n \theta + (n-1) \sin^m \theta \cos^{n-2} \theta$

$(1-\cos^2 \theta)\} \, d\theta$

$= \int_0^{\pi/2} \{-m \sin^m \theta \cos^n \theta + (n-1)$

$(\sin^m \theta \cos^{n-2} \theta - \sin^m \theta \cos^n)\} \, d\theta$

$= \int_0^{\pi/2} \{(-m-n+1) \sin^m \theta \cos^n \theta + (n-1) \sin^m \theta \cos^{n-2} \theta\} \, d\theta$

$= (-m-n+1)u_{m,n} + (n-1)u_{m,n-2}$

$\therefore\ (m+n-1+1)u_{m,n} = (n-1)u_{m,n-2}$

$$\therefore \quad \boxed{u_{m,n} = \frac{n-1}{m+n}\, u_{m,n-2}} \tag{75}$$

(with a similar formula if we had operated on $\sin^m \theta$).

[Formula (75) may be obtained more quickly by noticing that

$$u_{m,n} = \frac{1}{m+1}\int_0^{\pi/2} \cos^{n-1}\theta\, \frac{d \sin^{m+1}\theta}{d\theta}\, d\theta.]$$

Formulae (74) and (75) are due to Wallis.

Ultimately, $u_{m,n}$ depends on $u_{1,1} = \int_0^{\pi/2} \sin\theta \cos\theta\, d\theta = \frac{1}{2}$,

$$u_{0,0} = \int_0^{\pi/2} d\theta = \frac{\pi}{2},\ u_{1,0} = \int_0^{\pi/2} \sin\theta\, d\theta = 1, \text{ or } u_{0,1} = \int_0^{\pi/2} \cos\theta\, d\theta = 1.$$

[If m and n are both odd, $2u_{m,n}$ is called the *beta function*.]

E.g. $$\int_0^{\pi/2} \sin^6\theta \cos^5\theta\, d\theta = \frac{4}{11}\,\frac{2}{9}\int_0^{\pi/2} \sin^6\theta \cos\theta\, d\theta \qquad \text{using (72) twice}$$

$$= \frac{8}{99}\int_0^1 \sin^6\theta\, d\sin\theta \qquad \text{(changing the variable to } \sin\theta)$$

$$= \frac{8}{99}\left[\frac{\sin^7\theta}{7}\right]_0^{\theta=\pi/2}$$

$$= \frac{8}{693}.$$

Note: In (a), (b), (c) the limits are $\pi/2$, 0. Care must be taken if the limits are otherwise, in particular, π, 0;

e.g. $$\int_0^{\pi} \sin^6\theta\, d\theta = 2\int_0^{\pi/2} \sin^6\theta\, d\theta \qquad \text{by (73)}$$

$$= 2\,\frac{5}{6}\,\frac{3}{4}\,\frac{1}{2}\,\frac{\pi}{2} \qquad \text{by (74)}$$

$$= \frac{5\pi}{16}.$$

$$\int_0^{\pi} \sin^3\theta \cos^6\theta \, d\theta = 2\int_0^{\pi/2} \sin^3\theta \cos^6\theta \, d\theta \quad \text{by (73)} \because \cos^6\theta = (\cos^2\theta)^3$$

$$= (1-\sin^2\theta)^3$$

$$= 2\frac{5}{9}\,\frac{3}{7}\,\frac{1}{5}\int_0^{\pi/2} \sin^3\theta \, d\theta \quad \text{by (75)}$$

$$= \frac{2}{21}\,\frac{2}{3} \quad \text{by (74)}$$

$$= \frac{4}{63}.$$

Another reduction formula along the lines of Example 40(a), (b), (c) is now obtained. Limits of integration in Example 40(d) should be carefully noted.

EXAMPLE 40d.

(d) Write $w_n = \int_0^{\pi/4} \tan^n\theta \, d\theta = \int_0^{\pi/4} \tan^{n-2}\theta(-1+\sec^2\theta)\, d\theta$

$$= -w_{n-2} + \int_{\theta=0}^{\theta=\pi/4} \tan^{n-2}\theta \, d\tan\theta \quad \because \sec^2\theta\, d\theta = d\tan\theta$$

$$= -w_{n-2} + \left[\frac{\tan^{n-1}\theta}{n-1}\right]_0^{\pi/4}$$

$$= -w_{n-2} + \frac{1}{n-1}$$

$$\therefore w_n + w_{n-2} = \frac{1}{n-1} \qquad \text{(i)}$$

with $w_0 = \int_0^{\pi/4} d\theta = \frac{\pi}{4}$ and by (50),

$$w_1 = \int_0^{\pi/4} \tan\theta \, d\theta = -\Big[\log\cos\theta\Big]_0^{\pi/4} = \tfrac{1}{2}\log 2. \qquad \text{(ii)}$$

Thus, for instance, from (i) and (ii),

$$w_6 = \frac{1}{5} - \frac{1}{3} + 1 - \frac{\pi}{4}, \quad w_5 = \frac{1}{4} - \frac{1}{2} + \frac{1}{2}\log 2.$$

Extending these results and letting $n \to \infty$, we deduce the infinite series

$$\begin{cases} \dfrac{\pi}{4} = 1 - \dfrac{1}{3} + \dfrac{1}{5} - \dfrac{1}{7} + \dots \\[2ex] \log 2 = 1 - \dfrac{1}{2} + \dfrac{1}{3} - \dfrac{1}{4} + \dots \end{cases}$$

which are equations (101) and (93) of Chapter 9.

EXAMPLE 41 (area of an astroid).

Solution (see Fig. 104). Area of the astroid = $4 \times$ area in first quadrant

$$= 4 \int_0^a (a^{2/3} - x^{2/3})^{3/2}\, dx$$

$$= 4 \int_0^{\pi/2} a \cos^3 \theta \; 3a \sin^2 \theta \cos \theta \, d\theta \qquad \text{putting } x = a \sin^3 \theta$$

$$= 12a^2 \int_0^{\pi/2} \sin^2 \theta \cos^4 \theta \, d\theta$$

$$= 12a^2 \, \frac{3}{6} \, \frac{1}{4} \int_0^{\pi/2} \sin^2 \theta \, d\theta \qquad \text{by (75)}$$

$$= \frac{3a^2}{2} \, \frac{\pi}{4} \qquad \text{by (74)} \qquad \text{or Example 39 (i)}$$

$$= \frac{3\pi a^2}{8}.$$

EXAMPLE 42 (the *gamma function*).

Definition. Gamma function (due to Euler, 1729)

$$\Gamma(n+1) = \int_0^\infty x^n e^{-x}\, dx \quad (n > 0 \text{ but not necessarily an integer})$$

$$= -\int_0^\infty x^n \frac{de^{-x}}{dx}\, dx$$

$$= \Big[-x^n e^{-x} \Big]_0^\infty + \int_0^\infty e^{-x} n x^{n-1}\, dx$$

$$= n \int_0^\infty x^{n-1} e^{-x}\, dx \qquad \text{using Exercise 4.32}$$

$$\therefore \Gamma(n+1) = n\Gamma(n)$$

$$= n(n-1)\Gamma(n-1) \qquad \text{applying the reduction formula again,}$$

i.e. $\boxed{\Gamma(n+1) = n!}$ eventually.

Comments

(i) Thus, e.g. $\Gamma(3) = 2$, $\Gamma(2) = 1$, $\Gamma(1) = \Gamma(0+1) = 0\Gamma(0) = 1$.

$\therefore \Gamma(0) = \frac{1}{0} = \infty$. Of course, $n = 0$ in the definition gives $\Gamma(1) = \int_0^\infty e^{-x}\,dx = 1$.

(ii) A very useful approximation to $\Gamma(n+1)$ when n is large, is *Stirling's formula* (Stirling (1696–1770, Scots)):

$$n! = \left(\frac{n}{e}\right)^n \sqrt{2\pi n}.$$

(iii) A useful gamma-function formula (the *duplication formula*) is

$$\Gamma(n)\Gamma(1-n) = \frac{\pi}{\sin n\pi} \quad (0 < n < 1, \text{ i.e. } n \text{ fractional})$$

whence, e.g. $\{\Gamma(\tfrac{1}{2})\}^2 = \pi$, i.e. $\Gamma(\tfrac{1}{2}) = \sqrt{\pi}$, and $\Gamma(\tfrac{3}{4})\Gamma(\tfrac{1}{4}) = \pi\sqrt{2}$.

(iv) One may use this (in conjunction with the beta-function–gamma-function relation preceding Exercise 8.71) to obtain, for instance,

$$\int_0^{\pi/2} \sqrt{\cot\theta}\,d\theta = \frac{\pi}{\sqrt{2}} = \int_0^{\pi/2} \sqrt{\tan\theta}\,d\theta$$

$$\int_0^{\pi/2} \sqrt{\sin\theta}\,d\theta = \frac{(2\pi)^{3/2}}{\{\Gamma(\frac{1}{4})\}^2} = \int_0^{\pi/2} \sqrt{\cos\theta}\,d\theta \ (\doteqdot 1{\cdot}198).$$

§ 36. AN INTEGRAL APPROACH TO THE THEORY OF LOGARITHMIC FUNCTIONS

Approaching the theory of logarithms from an elementary point of view we should proceed somewhat along these lines:

(i) commence with the element a^n, where n is an integer ($a > 0$);

(ii) define $a^{1/m} = \sqrt[m]{a}$ to obtain a^r for rational $r = n/m$;

(iii) define a^x for irrational x, so that a^x is continuous for real x.

Then if $y = a^x$, we write $x = \log_a y$.

Integration affords a more advanced treatment of the logarithm function so we address our attention to gaining some insight into this method.

Definition:
$$\boxed{\log x = \int_1^x \frac{dt}{t} \quad (x \text{ real and } > 0)}\,. \tag{76}$$

The lower limit 1 is chosen for convenience. Absence of a base does not imply that it is e, since, in this approach, e is yet to be defined—see (80).

Immediately, we deduce
$$\boxed{\log 1 = \int_1^1 \frac{dt}{t} = 0}\,. \tag{76.1}$$

From (76), $\log ab = \displaystyle\int_1^{ab} \frac{dt}{t}$

$$= \int_{1/b}^{a} \frac{b\,du}{b\,u} \qquad \text{putting } t = bu, \quad \therefore\ dt = b\,du$$

$$= \int_{1/b}^{a} \frac{du}{u}$$

$$= \int_1^a \frac{du}{u} + \int_{1/b}^{1} \frac{du}{u} \qquad \text{by (66) (ii)}$$

$$= \log a - \int_b^1 \frac{w\,dw}{w^2} \qquad \text{putting } u = 1/w \text{ in the second integral, } \therefore\ du = -dw/w^2$$

$$= \log a + \int_1^b \frac{dw}{w} \qquad \text{by (66) (i)}$$

$$= \log a + \log b$$

$$\therefore \boxed{\log (ab) = \log a + \log b}\,. \tag{77}$$

Substituting $t = \dfrac{u}{b}$ in $\log \dfrac{a}{b} = \displaystyle\int_1^{a/b} \frac{dt}{t}$ we obtain, similarly,

$$\boxed{\log \left(\frac{a}{b}\right) = \log a - \log b}\,. \tag{78}$$

In particular, if $a = 1$, $\log\left(\frac{1}{b}\right) = -\log b$.

$$\text{Furthermore, } \log(a^n) = \int_1^{a^n} \frac{dt}{t}$$

$$= \int_1^{a} \frac{nu^{n-1}\,du}{u^n} \qquad \text{putting } t = u^n \quad \therefore\ dt = nu^{n-1}\,du$$

$$= n\int_1^{a} \frac{du}{u}$$

$$= n \log a.$$

$$\therefore \quad \boxed{\log(a^n) = n \log a}\,. \tag{79}$$

Thus we have preserved all the main properties of logarithms which we are familiar with from elementary theory. Many different treatments diverge at this point: notice that we have said nothing about the base of the logarithm. One method is to define e as the number whose logarithm is 1, i.e. $\log e = 1$. That is

Definition:

$$\boxed{1 = \int_1^{e} \frac{dt}{t} = \log e}\,. \tag{80}$$

From (79) we obtain $\log e^x = x \log e = x$ for all real x. Therefore the equations $x = \log y$, $y = e^x$ have the same meaning.

Then the exponential function e^x is defined to be the inverse of the logarithmic function. (Fuller details of this sophisticated approach may be found in many standard works, e.g. G. H. Hardy, *A Course of Pure Mathematics* (C.U.P., 1946).)

Suggested topics for further study

(1) Multiple integrals, particularly double integrals, in relation to area and to beta and gamma functions.
(2) Deeper analysis of the consequences of the integral definition of the logarithm function.
(3) Linear first-order differential equations using the *integrating factor*.
(4) Scientific applications of differential equations (Piaggio and Lambe & Tranter references, Chapter 6).

(5) (For the adventurous) Riemann's theory of integration, treated rigorously (consult Apostol [14]).

(6) Calculus applications to the behavioural sciences. *Introduction to Finite Mathematics*, Kemeny, J. G., Snell, J. L. and Thompson, G. L. (Prentice-Hall, 1959); *Modern Mathematical Methods and Models* (Vol. 1), Dartmouth College Writing Group (Mathematical Association of America, 1958), p. II. 31 of which gives further references for mathematical biology, psychology and economics.

References

As for Chapter 7.
For historical purposes, try to consult:

(a) *Principia*, I. Newton (in modern English, translated by F. Cajori) (Univ. of California Press, 1946);

(b) *The Method of Fluxions and Infinite Series, with its Application to the Geometry of Curve Lines*, I. Newton (translated by J. Colson, 1736), a rare book.

EXERCISES 8

Solve the following differential equations 1–3 by separating variables. Explain the geometrical meanings of the solutions of 1 and 2.

1. $x\,dx+y\,dy = 0$. **2.** $\sqrt{1-x^2}\,dy = x\,dx$. **3.** $\tan y\,dx+\tan x\,dy = 0$.

4. In the economist Domar's model (1946) of National Income, the differential equation $\frac{du}{dt}-\frac{a}{b}u = 0$ is used, where u represents the income at time t and a, b are constants. Obtain u as a function of t, given that $u = k$ at time $t = 0$.

5. Bacterial growth is proportional to the amount present. If the population of a strain of bacteria doubles in one hour, by how much will it have increased from noon till midnight? [The rate of growth is the increase per unit time in unit volume.]

Experimenting with animal learning, the psychologist Thurstone devised (1930) the learning model $\frac{ds}{dt} = kp$, $\frac{dr}{dt} = -k(1-p)$, where r, s (measures of certain animal behaviour) are functions of time t, $p = \frac{s}{r+s}$ is the probability of success (i.e. $0 < p < 1$), and k, c (Exercise 8.6) are constants. Derive the results:

6. $rs = c$. **7.** $s^2 = cp(1-p)^{-1}$.

8. Radio engineering theory involves the equation $L\frac{dI}{dt}+RI = E$, where L (inductance), R (resistance), and E (electromotive force) are constant, in the appropriate units. Only t (time) and I (current) are variable. Solve for I in terms of t and the constants, given that $I = 0$ when $t = 0$. (Refer to Example 4.30.)

Evaluate the integrals 9–21:

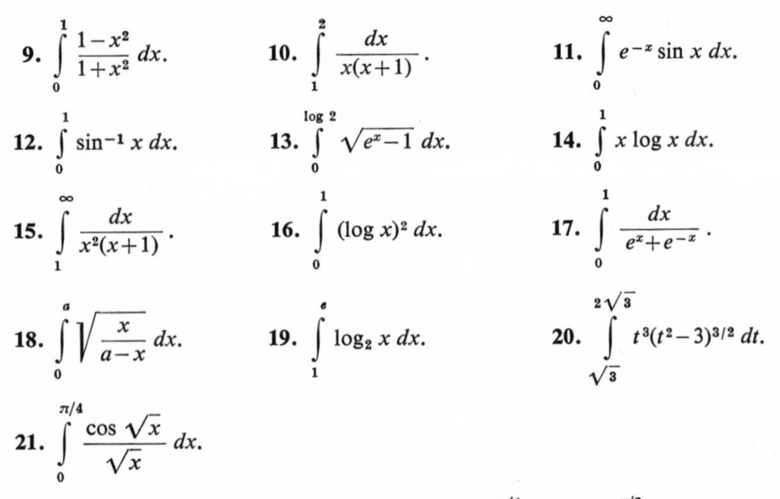

9. $\int_0^1 \frac{1-x^2}{1+x^2}\,dx.$ **10.** $\int_1^2 \frac{dx}{x(x+1)}.$ **11.** $\int_0^\infty e^{-x}\sin x\,dx.$

12. $\int_0^1 \sin^{-1} x\,dx.$ **13.** $\int_0^{\log 2} \sqrt{e^x-1}\,dx.$ **14.** $\int_0^1 x\log x\,dx.$

15. $\int_1^\infty \frac{dx}{x^2(x+1)}.$ **16.** $\int_0^1 (\log x)^2\,dx.$ **17.** $\int_0^1 \frac{dx}{e^x+e^{-x}}.$

18. $\int_0^a \sqrt{\frac{x}{a-x}}\,dx.$ **19.** $\int_1^e \log_2 x\,dx.$ **20.** $\int_{\sqrt{3}}^{2\sqrt{3}} t^3(t^2-3)^{3/2}\,dt.$

21. $\int_0^{\pi/4} \frac{\cos\sqrt{x}}{\sqrt{x}}\,dx.$

22. By means of a suitable substitution, show that $\int_0^{\pi/4} \frac{dx}{\cos x} = \int_{\pi/4}^{\pi/2} \frac{dx}{\sin x}$, and prove that their common value is $\log(\sqrt{2}+1)$.

23. Two long coaxal cylinders of radii a, b are charged to form a condenser. If the potential of the outer is zero, then the potential of the inner one is given by

$$P = K\int_0^\infty \left(\frac{1}{\sqrt{a^2+x^2}} - \frac{1}{\sqrt{b^2+x^2}}\right) dx. \quad \text{Find } P.$$

24. The radius of the Earth is R inches and the height above the Earth's surface of a point at which the atmospheric pressure is p lb/in² is h miles. It can be shown that

$$\frac{dp}{dh} = -K\left(\frac{R}{R+h}\right)^2 p, \text{ where } K \text{ is a +ve constant.}$$

Supposing that $p = p_0$ at $h = 0$, obtain p as a function of h.

25. Investigate $\lim_{h\to\infty} p$.

26. Find the area above the x-axis which lies inside the circle $y^2 = 2ax - x^2$ and outside the parabola $y^2 = ax$.

27. What is the area of the *cissoid of Diocles* (Diocles, *ca.* 2 B.C., Greek) $y^2 = \frac{x^3}{1-x}$ between the limits $x = 0$ and $x = 1$? (See Fig. 99.)

28. Obtain the area (between $x = 0$ and $x = 1$) of the *witch of Agnesi* (Maria Agnesi, 1718–99, Italian) $y^2 = \frac{1-x}{x}$. (See Fig. 100.)

29. What is the area of the loop of the *strophoid* $y^2 = x^2\left(\frac{1+x}{1-x}\right)$? Limits are $x = 0$, $x = -1$. (See Fig. 98.)

30. Find the area in the first quadrant bounded by the curves $y = e^x$, $y = e^{-x}$ and $x = 2$. (See Fig. 5a.)

31. The *root mean square* (r.m.s.) of $f(x)$ for $a \leq x \leq b$ is defined to be $\left\{\frac{1}{b-a}\int_a^b \{f(x)\}^2\,dx\right\}^{1/2}$. An important r.m.s. is that of an alternating electric current $i = I\sin(wx+\varepsilon)$, where I, w, ε are constants (w an integer). Determine the r.m.s. of i in the range $0 \leq x \leq 2\pi$.

32. Statistical problems (e.g. collisions of gas molecules) often require the calculation of the *statistical mean value* of the function $f(x)$ defined by $\int_a^b xf(x)\,dx \div \int_a^b f(x)\,dx$. Calculate the statistical mean value of $\log x$ in the range $1 \leq x \leq 2$.

33. If $f(x) = \int_x^5 3^{-x^2}\,dx$, find $f'(2)$.

Define the (ordinary) *mean value* of $f(x)$ in $a \leq x \leq b$ to be $\frac{1}{b-a}\int_a^b f(x)\,dx$. A particle of mass m is moving rectilinearly with velocity v in simple harmonic motion $x = a\cos nt$ (a, n constants) and its kinetic energy $E = \frac{1}{2}mv^2$.

34. Calculate the mean value of E w.r.t. t for one complete vibration.

35. Establish that $E_{max} = 2E_{mean}$.

36. How different would the relationship between E_{max} and E_{mean} be in Exercise 8.35 if we had computed the mean w.r.t. x?

37. *Hooke's law* applies to an elastic string, viz. $T = k\left(\frac{x-l_0}{l_0}\right)$, where T is the tension in the string when stretched from initial (natural) length l_0 to l, and k is a constant. Defining the work done in stretching the string to be $W = \int_{l_0}^{l} T\,dx$, calculate W.

38. Natural length of a given helical spring is 8 in. and a force of 4 lb stretches it to a total length of 10 in. Applying Hooke's law, viz. that the force required to stretch the spring is proportional to the distance stretched, calculate the work done in extending the natural length to 13 in.

39. Price adjustment for the marketing of a certain commodity was described in 1930 by Evans by the model $\frac{dp}{dt} = ap+b$, where p represents the price at time t and a, b are constants. Initially, $p = P$ at time $t = 0$. Solve for p.

40. Velocity of a chemical reaction between two substances A, B is proportional to the amount of A remaining. Build up a differential equation to describe the reaction. Offer a solution.

41. *Newton's law of cooling* states that the rate at which a body changes temperature is proportional to the difference between its temperature and that of its surrounding medium. Construct a differential equation to describe this chemical change for a heated bar in a centrally-heated room thermostatically controlled to remain at 40°C. Solve the equation.

The *Laplace transform* of $f(x)$ is defined to be $\int_0^\infty e^{-px}f(x)\,dx$. Obtain Laplace transforms of

42. e^{qx} $(p > q)$. **43.** $\sin wx$.

44. Bacteria number 1000 at a given time and half an hour later number 2178. Determine the law of growth relating to this bacterial culture.

45. Once upon a time, the "ghost" township of Newchum's Folly was a thriving gold-rush metropolis of 5000 goldminers. Ten years later its population had dwindled to 1840 due to the opening up of the black opal diggings at Thunder Bluff. Estimate the population of the Folly in a further 10 years' time if this rate of drift continues.

46. Deceleration of a ship, unimpeded by strong wind waves, when the engine is cut off is proportional to the velocity (in ft/sec). How far will it travel in 5 sec?

47. Insects (ants) in a certain colony, in a rare burst of fratricidal strife, are decimated in 4 h by the onslaught of 300 predatory ants. If these predators increase in number at the same rate as their victims decrease, how many of them will there be at the end of 2 h?

Evaluate the integrals 48–52:

48. $\displaystyle\int_0^\infty \frac{1}{1+x^a}\cdot\frac{1}{1+x^2}\,dx.$ **49.** $\displaystyle\int_0^{\pi/2} \frac{\cos x}{1-\sin^2\alpha\cos^2 x}\,dx.$

50. $\displaystyle\int_0^\infty \frac{dx}{(x+\sqrt{x^2+1})^n}$ $(n > 1)$. **51.** $\displaystyle\int_0^{\pi/2} \frac{\tan x}{1+3\tan^2 x}\,dx.$

52. $\displaystyle\int_0^\infty x^{2n+1}e^{-x^2}\,dx.$

53. If $I_n = \displaystyle\int_0^\pi \sin n\phi \cot\left(\frac{\phi}{2}\right) d\phi$, show that $I_1 = \pi$ and that $I_{n+1}-I_n = 0$. Deduce a general expression of I_n for all n.

54. Aeroplane wing design theory uses the *conjugate* $\psi(\theta)$ of a function $f(\theta)$ defined as

$$\psi(\theta) = \frac{1}{2\pi}\int_0^\pi [f(\theta+\phi)-f(\theta-\phi)]\cot\left(\frac{\phi}{2}\right) d\phi.$$

Find the conjugate of $f(\theta) = \cos n\theta$ using the reduction formula found in Exercise 8.53.

55. *Operational calculus* (developed by Heaviside (1850–1925, English) with applications to engineering and electricity) involves the notion of a *convolution* $c(t)$ of two functions $a(t)$, $b(t)$ defined by

$$c(t) = \int_0^t a(t-u)\,b(u)\,du.$$

Determine the convolution for $a(t) = t^2$, $b(t) = e^t$.

56. What is the convolution of $a(t) = b(t) = \sin t$?

57. Is convolution commutative? [Associativity is also valid, but its proof depends on the technique of double integration.]

58. Planetary orbits involve a solution of $\displaystyle\int_0^\pi \frac{d\theta}{(1+e\cos\theta)^2}$. Evaluate this in the case of the ellipse for which $e > 1$.

59. What curve has PN constant ($= 1$) [Fig. 6]?

60. Making use of Exercises 1.24, 1.25 derive *Einstein's mass energy relation* $E = mc^2$ (i.e. mass is a manifestation of energy, and vice versa). [Assume the constant of integration is zero, from relativity theory.]

61. *Lambert's quadrilateral* in the hyperbolic plane consists of three right angles and an acute angle α. Assuming that the area A of this quadrilateral is given by

$$A = k\int_0^a \frac{\cosh x/k\, dx}{\sqrt{(\sinh a/k \sec \alpha)^2 - \sinh^2 x/k}} \quad (a, k \text{ constants}), \text{ evaluate } A.$$

62. Demographers Pearl and Reed, assuming the growth of organisms in an environment is a function of the number y alive at any time t, used (in 1920) the model $dy/dt = ky(N-y)$ to estimate the population of the United States of America in future years, N being the maximum population possible. Given $y = N/2$, when $t = T$, solve this differential equation.

[This model gave quite accurate estimates for the decennial population of the U.S.A. from 1790 to 1910; it also predicted the U.S. population from 1910 to 1950 almost as accurately.]

[Insect colonies often develop according to a similar growth model. Inhibiting factors restricting growth might be the supply of food, the presence of creatures preying on them, and the prevalence of insecticides.]

One of the famous conjectures in number theory relates to the number of primes less than a given number x. A satisfactory approximation to this number is the integral

$$l(x) = \int_2^x \frac{dt}{\log t} \quad (x \geq 2).$$

63. Given $\displaystyle\int_a^{\log x} \frac{e^t}{t}\, dt = l(x)$, determine the value of a.

64. Express $\displaystyle\int_{\log(2/e)}^{x} \frac{e^t}{t+1}\, dt$ in terms of $l(x)$.

65. Two liquids (quantities x, y) are boiling in a beaker. The experiment shows that the ratio of the quantities converted into vapour is proportional to the ratio of the quantities still in the liquid state. Form a differential equation describing this phenomenon. Work out a solution of it.

66. Bending of a uniform heavy beam of length a at two horizontal points is given by $B\left(\dfrac{dy}{dx} - k\right) = \dfrac{wx^2}{12}(2x - 3a)$, where w is the weight of the beam per unit length and B is the flexural rigidity of the beam; x is measured horizontally from one support and y is measured vertically downward from that support. Determine the sag at the mid point of the beam.

67. A meteorite is assumed to fall vertically in to the Earth. Newton's law of gravitational attraction describes the motion by $\dfrac{d^2x}{dt^2} = \dfrac{-gR^2}{x^2}$, where R is the radius of the Earth, x measures the distance from the centre of the Earth to the meteorite which is *very high*, h miles, above the surface of the Earth at time $t = 0$, and g is the gravitational constant. (Air resistance is neglected.) With what velocity does the meteorite strike the Earth?

68. Differential equation for the work W done in an electrical circuit by a voltaic battery is $\frac{dW}{dR} = \frac{k(r-R)}{(R+r)^3}$, where R, r relate to the resistance (in ohms) of the circuit and the battery respectively, and k is a constant. Evaluate W, given $W = 0$ when $R = 0$. [Notice that W is maximised when $r = R$.]

69. *Hydrostatic (fluid) pressure* in a vertical masonry dam on a circular floodgate of radius 1 ft whose centre is at a depth of 5 ft is given by

$$F = 2\omega \int_{-4}^{-6} y\sqrt{1-(y+5)^2}\, dy,$$

where ω is the weight of the fluid (water) per unit volume, and y measures the depth of submersion. Determine the pressure on the floodgate.

70. *Moment of inertia* I of a uniform solid sphere of mass M and radius a about a diameter is defined to be $I = \frac{\pi}{2}\varrho \int_{-a}^{a} (a^2-x^2)^2\, dx = Mk^2$, where ϱ is the density of the sphere and k is the *radius of gyration*. Determine I, k. [Note: $M = \varrho V$, where V is the volume of the sphere. Radius of gyration is a r.m.s. value.]

Defining the *beta function* $B(m, n)$ as $B(m, n) = \int_0^1 x^{m-1}(1-x)^{n-1}\, dx$ $(m > 0, n > 0)$ and assuming the fundamental property, provable by double integrals, $B(m, n) = \frac{\Gamma(m)\Gamma(n)}{\Gamma(m+n)}$ (i.e. $B(2, 1) = \frac{1}{2}$, $B(2, 2) = \frac{1}{6}$), prove 71–74:

71. $B(m, n) = B(n, m)$. **72.** $B(m+1, n) = \frac{m}{m+n}B(m, n)$.

73. $\int_0^\infty \frac{e^{-x}}{\sqrt{x}}\, dx = \sqrt{\pi}$. **74.** $\int_0^\infty e^{-y^2}\, dy = \frac{\sqrt{\pi}}{2}$.

[Probability and statistics questions often involve Exercise 8.74, which cannot be computed by elementary methods.]

75. Using the integrals $\int_0^1 \frac{t^4(1-t)^4}{1+t^2}\, dt$ and $\int_0^1 t^4(1-t)^4\, dt$, establish the inequalities

$$\frac{1}{1260} < \frac{22}{7} - \pi < \frac{1}{630}.$$

76. Filtering through water in a deep well, sunlight loses its intensity at the rate of k% per foot. At what depth will the intensity be 25% of that at the surface?

77. Coefficients of linear and cubical expansion for a metal rod of length l and a solid metal box of volume V are a, b respectively. Knowing that $\frac{a}{b} = \frac{d \log l}{d \log V}$, determine the relationship between V, l when $b = 3a$.

78. *Euler's crippling (critical) load* for a long strut (length l, flexural rigidity f) is given by $P = fn^2$, where $\frac{d^2y}{dx^2}+n^2y = 0$ is the deflection equation. End conditions of the strut are $y = 0, x = 0$ and $y = 0, x = l$. Obtain P.

79. Parametric equations of a point on an *elastic catenary* (i.e. an elastic string which is uniform when unstretched between two fixed points) are

$x = \int \left(\frac{c}{\sqrt{c^2+s^2}}+kc\right) ds, \quad y = \int \left(\frac{s}{\sqrt{c^2+s^2}}+ks\right) ds,$ where c, k are physical constants. Assuming that $s = 0$ when $x = 0$, $y = 0$ (i.e. lowest point of the string), obtain the parametric coordinates of the elastic catenary.

80. "And the Sun stood still [upon Gibeon], and the Moon stayed [in the valley of Ajalon]"(Joshua x. 13). Arrested thus in its orbit, how long should the Moon have taken to plunge into the surface of the Earth?

CHAPTER 9

INFINITE SERIES AND SEQUENCES

One, two, many—some primitive tribes.

a Flea
Hath smaller Fleas that on him prey;
And these have smaller still to bite 'em,
And so proceed *ad infinitum*.

(SWIFT)

SCIENTIFIC problems may often be expressed in the form of differential equations whose solutions are given in terms of infinite series. Philosophical problems, such as Zeno's paradox (Exercise 9.23), require a solution in series. In the exponential function we have already seen the importance of a particular infinite series. Precise statements will now be given to sharpen our intuitive understanding of the nature of infinite series. Principally, though certainly not exclusively, we are concerned with series of positive terms.

§ 37. SEQUENCES

Definition. A *sequence* is an ordered set of numbers $S_1, S_2, \ldots, S_n, \ldots$ It is often denoted by $\{S_n\}$.

For instance, if the nth term of a sequence is $S_n = \dfrac{1}{n(n+1)}$ we have

$$\{S_n\} = \frac{1}{2}, \frac{1}{6}, \frac{1}{12}, \frac{1}{20} \cdots$$

A sequence is said to *converge* to the limit S, i.e. $\lim_{n\to\infty} S_n = S$ or merely $S_n \to S$ as $n \to \infty$, if for each $\varepsilon > 0$, $\exists N(\varepsilon)$

$$\boxed{|S - S_n| < \varepsilon \quad \text{for} \quad n > N(\varepsilon)} \tag{81}$$

$$\text{e.g. } \frac{1}{10}, \frac{11}{100}, \frac{111}{1000}, \ldots \to \frac{1}{9}, \text{ and,}$$

$$\text{by (21), } \left(1\frac{1}{2}\right)^2, \left(1\frac{1}{3}\right)^3, \left(1\frac{1}{4}\right)^4, \ldots \to e.$$

Compare (81) with Cauchy's definition (§ 7). As a sequence is a special case of a function (integral values of n instead of continuous values of x), the limit theorems (14.1)–(14.4) are valid. If a monotonic increasing sequence does not converge, then it *diverges* to ∞, i.e. $\lim S_n = \infty$, or just $S_n \to \infty$. It is not necessary to write "$\lim\limits_{n\to\infty}$", merely "lim" will do, since it is inherent in the idea of the limit of a sequence that $n \to \infty$. In the instance quoted above, $\lim S_n = 0$ so the sequence converges.

EXAMPLE 43 (some simple sequence limits). Calculate the limits (i)–(iv).

Solutions.

(i) $\lim \left(\dfrac{3n+5}{7n-1}\right) = \lim \left(\dfrac{3+5/n}{7-1/n}\right) = \dfrac{3}{7}.$

(ii) $\lim \left(\dfrac{3n+5}{2n^2-3n+1}\right) = \lim \left(\dfrac{3/n+5/n^2}{2-3/n+1/n^2}\right) = \dfrac{0}{2} = 0.$

(iii) $\lim \left(\sqrt{n}-\sqrt[3]{n}\right) = \lim \sqrt{n}\left(1-\dfrac{1}{\sqrt[6]{n}}\right) = \infty\cdot 1 = \infty.$

(iv) $\lim \left(\dfrac{\log (3n^5)}{\log n}\right) = \lim \left(\dfrac{\log 3+5 \log n}{\log n}\right) = \lim \left(5+\dfrac{3}{\log n}\right) = 5.$

§ 38. CONVERGENCE AND DIVERGENCE OF INFINITE SERIES

Definition. A *series* is the sum of the terms of a sequence.
Given the series of positive terms

$$\sum_{n=1}^{\infty} u_n = u_1+u_2+u_3+\ldots+u_n+\ldots,$$

form the sequence of partial sums

$$\begin{aligned} S_1 &= u_1 \\ S_2 &= u_1+u_2 \\ S_3 &= u_1+u_2+u_3 \\ S_n &= u_1+u_2+u_3+\ldots+u_n. \end{aligned}$$

Then $\{S_n\}$, being a monotonic increasing sequence, either converges or diverges to ∞.

If $\begin{cases} S_n \to S, \text{ we say that } \sum_{n=1}^{\infty} u_n \textit{ converges} \text{ to the sum } S. \\ S_n \to \infty, \text{ we say that } \sum_{n=1}^{\infty} u_n \textit{ diverges} \text{ (to } \infty). \end{cases}$

Convention: Unless otherwise stated, $\sum u_n \equiv \sum_{n=1}^{\infty} u_n$.

Remarks

(i)
$$\begin{aligned} u_n &= (u_1+u_2+\ldots+u_{n-1}+u_n)-(u_1+u_2+\ldots+u_{n-1}) \\ &= S_n - S_{n-1} \\ &= (S-S_{n-1})-(S-S_n) \quad \text{for convergent } \sum u_n. \end{aligned}$$

But $S_{n-1} \to S$, $S_n \to S$.

$\therefore u_n \to 0$ as $n \to \infty$.

$\therefore$ $u_n \to 0$ is a *necessary* condition for a series to converge, but it is not a *sufficient* one, for we may have a divergent series in which $u_n \to 0$ as $n \to \infty$ [e.g. $\sum 1/n$ (cf. Example 45)]. (82)

In other words, for every convergent series, $u_n \to 0$ by necessity, but $u_n \to 0$ does not imply that the series must be convergent.

(ii) Consider
$$\sum_{r=1}^{n} u_r = \frac{1}{1\cdot 2}+\frac{1}{2\cdot 3}+\frac{1}{3\cdot 4}+\ldots+\frac{1}{(n-1)n}+\frac{1}{n(n+1)}$$
$$= \sum_{r=1}^{n} \frac{1}{r(r+1)} = \sum_{r=1}^{n}\left(\frac{1}{r}-\frac{1}{r+1}\right)$$
$$= \underbrace{1-\frac{1}{2}}_{u_1}+\underbrace{\frac{1}{2}-\frac{1}{3}}_{u_2}+\underbrace{\frac{1}{3}-\frac{1}{4}}_{u_3}+\ldots$$
$$+\underbrace{\frac{1}{n-1}-\frac{1}{n}}_{u_{n-1}}+\underbrace{\frac{1}{n}-\frac{1}{n+1}}_{u_n} = 1-\frac{1}{n+1} = S_n.$$

$$\therefore \sum_{r=1}^{\infty} u_r = \lim\left(1-\frac{1}{n+1}\right) = 1 = S, \text{ i.e. } \sum u_n \text{ converges to the sum 1.}$$

$$\therefore S-S_n = \frac{1}{n+1} < \varepsilon \quad \text{if} \quad n > \frac{1}{\varepsilon}-1 \qquad \text{by (81)}$$

e.g. if $\varepsilon = 10^{-6}$ then $n > 10^6 - 1$.

Therefore the least possible value of n would be a million.

EXAMPLE 44 (examination of the *geometric series* $a+ax+ax^2+ax^3+\ldots$)

$$= a(1+x+x^2+x^3+\ldots).$$

Solution. Now $S_n = a\left(\dfrac{1-x^n}{1-x}\right)$ (assumed known)

$$= \frac{a}{1-x} - \frac{ax^n}{1-x}.$$

If $x = 1$, $S_n = na$ which $\to \infty$.

If $0 < x < 1$, $x^n \to 0$, so that $S_n \to \dfrac{a}{1-x}$.

If $x > 1$, $x^n \to \infty$ $\therefore$ $S_n \to \infty$.

$\therefore$ the geometric series $\begin{cases} \text{converges for } 0 < x < 1 \\ \text{diverges for } x \geqslant 1. \end{cases}$ (83)

§ 39. TESTS FOR CONVERGENCE

(A) *Comparison tests for series of positive terms* (assume)

(i) If $u_n \leqslant v_n$ and $\sum v_n$ converges, then $\sum u_n$ converges.

(ii) If $u_n \geqslant v_n$ and $\sum v_n$ diverges, then $\sum u_n$ diverges.

(iii) If $\dfrac{u_n}{v_n} \to$ (positive) limit, then $\sum u_n$ and $\sum v_n$ converge or diverge together.

(iv) If $\dfrac{u_n}{v_n} \to 0$ and $\sum v_n$ converges, then clearly $u_n < v_n$ for $n \to \infty$, so that $\sum u_n$ converges.

(v) If $\dfrac{u_n}{v_n} \to \infty$ and $\sum v_n$ diverges, then clearly $u_n > v_n$ for $n \to \infty$, so that $\sum u_n$ diverges.

(84)

[When he uses comparison tests, the onus is always on the student to choose a suitable $\sum v_n$. Usually, a selected value of p in (87) will suffice.]

(B) *D'Alembert's ratio test* (assume) [D'Alembert, 1717–83, French]

If $\lim \left(\dfrac{u_{n+1}}{u_n}\right) = k$, then $\sum u_n$ converges if $k < 1$
diverges if $k > 1$.
If $k = 1$, the test fails. (85)

For example, D'Alembert's test fails for the harmonic series $\sum \frac{1}{n}$ which we know to be divergent (Example 45 below).

(C) *Cauchy's integral test* (actually discovered by Maclaurin (1698–1746, Scots) but rediscovered by Cauchy).

If $f(x)$ is a $\left\{\begin{array}{l}\text{monotonically} \\ \text{steadily}\end{array}\right.$ decreasing function of x for all $x \geqslant 1$, then the series $\sum u_n$ (where $u_n = f(n)$)

$$\begin{cases} \text{converges if } \int_1^\infty f(x)\,dx \text{ converges} \\ \text{diverges if } \int_1^\infty f(x)\,dx \text{ diverges.} \end{cases} \tag{86}$$

Proof. Let the partial sum $S_N = u_1 + u_2 + \ldots + u_N$.

Considering the N inner rectangles and the N outer rectangles, we see their sum is $< S_N$ and $= S_N$, respectively.

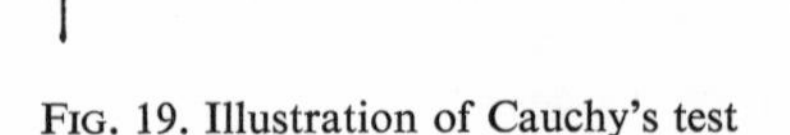

FIG. 19. Illustration of Cauchy's test

Therefore from Fig. 19, we have

$$\begin{aligned} \int_1^{N+1} f(x)\,dx &= \text{area under the curve between } x = 1 \text{ and } x = N+1 \\ &< \text{sum of the outer rectangles} \\ &= u_1 + u_2 + u_3 + \ldots + u_N \, (= S_N) \end{aligned}$$

$$\begin{aligned} \int_1^{N} f(x)\,dx &= \text{area under the curve between } x = 1 \text{ and } x = N \\ &> \text{sum of the inner rectangles} \\ &= u_2 + u_3 + \ldots + u_N \, (= S_N - u_1) \end{aligned}$$

whence $$\int_1^{N+1} f(x)dx < S_N < u_1 + \int_1^N f(x)\,dx.$$

If $\int_1^{\infty} f(x)\,dx = I$, and $\lim S_N = S$, then $I < S < u_1 + I (=$ a fixed number)

i.e. $\sum u_n$ converges with the integral.

Clearly, if the integral $\to \infty$, then $S_N \to \infty$ also.

EXAMPLE 45 (examination of the p-series $\sum \frac{1}{n^p}$ $(p > 0)$).

Solution.

Write $f(x) = \frac{1}{x^p}$, which is a $\begin{cases}\text{monotonically} \\ \text{steadily decreasing function of } x \text{ for } x \geqslant 1.\end{cases}$

$$\text{Put } I = \int_1^{\infty} \frac{dx}{x^p}$$

$$= \frac{1}{1-p}[x^{1-p}]_1^{\infty} \quad (p \neq 1)$$

$$= [\log x]_1^{\infty} \quad (p = 1).$$

If $p = 1$, $I = \infty$ since $\log x \to \infty$ as $x \to \infty$.

If $0 < p < 1$, $I = \infty$ since $x^{1-p} \to \infty$ as $x \to \infty$

If $p > 1$, $I = \frac{1}{p-1}$ since $\frac{1}{x^{p-1}} \to 0$ as $x \to \infty$.

$$\therefore \boxed{\sum \frac{1}{n^p} \begin{array}{l}\text{diverges for } p \leqslant 1 \\ \text{converges for } p > 1\end{array}\Bigg\}.} \tag{87}$$

By the theory of the proof, the sum (for $p > 1$) lies between I and $1 + I$, i.e. between $\frac{1}{p-1}$ and $\frac{p}{p-1}$. [There are other methods of investigating the important series $\sum \frac{1}{n^p}$, but Cauchy's test is perhaps the most elegant. As an exercise, you should treat in detail (as for the proof) the special cases $p = \frac{1}{2}$, $p = 2$.]

It is an instructive exercise to parallel the theory of Cauchy's test for the *harmonic series* $\sum \frac{1}{n}$ (i.e. $p = 1$), obtaining $\log (n+1) < S_n < 1 + \log n$. Thus, if $n = 10^{12}$ (i.e. one billion) so that $\log 10^{12} = 12 \log 10 = 12 \times 2{\cdot}3\ldots$, then the sum of the harmonic series to one billion terms lies between 27·6 and 28·6 (approximately), and the sum to 10^{120} terms lies between 276 and 277.

EXAMPLE 46 (general illustrations of convergence).

(i) Given the series $\sum\left(\frac{2^n}{n!}\right) = \frac{2}{1!}+\frac{2^2}{2!}+\frac{2^3}{3!}+\frac{2^4}{4!}+\ldots+\frac{2^n}{n!}+\ldots$

$$\therefore \quad \frac{u_{n+1}}{u_n} = \frac{2^{n+1}}{(n+1)!}\frac{n!}{2^n} = \frac{2}{n+1} \to 0 \quad \text{as} \quad n \to \infty.$$

$\therefore$ by D'Alembert's test the series converges. [Observe that, from (16.1), the sum of the series is e^2-1.]

(ii) Given the series $\sum \frac{1}{2n-1} = 1+\frac{1}{3}+\frac{1}{5}+\ldots+\frac{1}{2n-1}+\ldots.$

clearly, $\frac{u_{n+1}}{u_n} = \frac{2n-1}{2n+1} \to 1$ as $n \to \infty$, so D'Alembert's test fails.

Let $u_n = \frac{1}{2n-1}$, $v_n = \frac{1}{n}$.

$$\therefore \quad \frac{u_n}{v_n} = \frac{n}{2n-1} \to \frac{1}{2}.$$

But $\sum v_n$ diverges; $\therefore$ $\sum u_n$ diverges by the comparison test.

[Try using Cauchy's test on (i) and (ii).]

§ 40. ALTERNATING SERIES. ABSOLUTE AND CONDITIONAL CONVERGENCE

Up till now we have considered only the convergence or divergence of positive terms. If the terms are not all positive, the sequence of partial sums will not be monotonic but, as before, the series is said to converge to S if $S_n \to S$. If $\lim S_n$ does not exist, the series is said to diverge.

Definition. An *alternating series*, $\sum a_n$, is one whose terms are alternately positive and negative.

Form the corresponding series of absolute (positive) terms $\sum |a_n|$.

Alternating series test (= Leibniz's test)

$$\boxed{\sum a_n \text{ converges if (i) } a_n \to 0, \quad \text{and} \quad \text{(ii) } \frac{|a_{n+1}|}{|a_n|} < 1.} \tag{88}$$

Definitions. (a) $\sum a_n$ is *absolutely convergent* if $\sum |a_n|$ is convergent, i.e. an absolutely convergent series *is* convergent, as may be proved.

(b) $\sum a_n$ is *conditionally convergent* if $\sum |a_n|$ is divergent but $\sum a_n$ is convergent.

E.g. $\sum \frac{(-1)^{n+1}}{\log(n+1)}$ is conditionally convergent since $\sum \frac{1}{\log(n+1)}$ is divergent, by comparison with the harmonic series, while $\frac{1}{\log 2} - \frac{1}{\log 3} + \frac{1}{\log 4} - \ldots$ is convergent by (88).

Series of the form $\sum k_n x^n$ (k_n constants), of which the geometric series is a particular instance, are called *power series*. Other examples, all of them special cases of the binomial series (96), are ($|x| < 1$):

$$\frac{1}{1-x} = 1+x+x^2+x^3+\ldots \qquad \text{(refer to Exercise 9.36)}$$

$$\frac{1}{1+x} = 1-x+x^2-x^3+\ldots$$

$$\frac{1}{(1-x)^2} = 1+2x+3x^2+4x^3+\ldots$$

$$\frac{1}{(1+x)^2} = 1-2x+3x^2-4x^3+\ldots$$

Substituting $x = -1$ in the first of these power series, we have $\frac{1}{2} = 1-1+1-1+1-1+\ldots$. which is clearly incorrect. Why is it wrong?

What comments can you make from this result? Mathematicians, often very eminent, have in bygone times imputed theological qualities to it.

§ 41. MACLAURIN'S SERIES

Generalizing the M.V.T. (§ 9), we may derive *Taylor's theorem* for the expansion of $f(a+x)$ [$=f(b)$] in ascending powers of x:

$$f(a+x) = f(a)+xf'(a)+\frac{x^2}{2!}f''(a)+\frac{x^3f'''}{3!}(a)+\ldots+\frac{x^nf^{(n)}}{n!}(\xi) \quad (a<\xi<b). \tag{89}$$

Write $R_n \equiv \frac{x^n}{n!}f^{(n)}(\xi)$—this is *Lagrange's form of the remainder*. Then it may be shown for certain functions, e.g. E. A. Maxwell, *An Analytical Calculus* Vol. 2 (C.U.P., 1954), that $R_n \to 0$ as $n \to \infty$ and Taylor's series results, i.e. the right-hand side of (89) converges to $f(a+x)$.

Taylor's series (discovered in 1712 by Taylor (1685–1731, English)) is:

$$f(a+x) = f(a) + \frac{x}{1!}f'(a) + \frac{x^2}{2!}f''(a) + \dots + \frac{x^{(n)}}{n!}f^{(n)}(a) + \dots \qquad (89.1)$$

which may be alternatively expressed by writing $b = a+x$, i.e. $x = b-a$. Of course, it is assumed that all the derivatives actually exist and are finite at the point a.

Put $x = 0$ in (89.1) to obtain *Maclaurin's series* (actually discovered in 1717 by Stirling and known earlier to Taylor, but rediscovered in 1742 by Maclaurin):

$$f(x) = f(0) + \frac{x}{1!}f'(0) + \frac{x^2}{2!}f''(0) + \dots + \frac{x^n}{n!}f^{(n)}(0) + \dots \qquad (90)$$

This provides us with a powerful method of representing a function as a power series. All functions in this text whose Maclaurin expansions are required may be assumed to have the property that $R_n = \frac{x^n}{n!}f^{(n)}(\xi)\ [0<\xi<x] \to 0$ as $n \to \infty$, i.e. whenever the resulting infinite series is convergent, i.e. the (infinite) Taylor's series converges to $f(x)$.

Applications of Maclaurin's series to circular functions

It is simple to deduce from (90) that

$$\sin x = x - \frac{x^3}{3!} + \frac{x^5}{5!} - \frac{x^7}{7!} + \dots \qquad (91.1)$$

$$\cos x = 1 - \frac{x^2}{2!} + \frac{x^4}{4!} - \frac{x^6}{6!} + \dots \qquad (91.2)$$

both of which were known to Newton.

For instance, with $f(x) = \sin x$, we have

$$\begin{aligned} f'(x) &= \cos x & \therefore f'(0) &= 1 \\ f''(x) &= -\sin x & \therefore f''(0) &= 0 \\ f'''(x) &= -\cos x & \therefore f'''(0) &= -1 \end{aligned}$$

whence (91.1) follows immediately. (Notice that $f^{(n)}(\xi)$, being a sine or a cosine, implies $|f^{(n)}(\xi)| \leqslant 1$, whence $|R_n| \leqslant \frac{|x^n|}{n!} = \frac{|x|^n}{n!} \to 0$ as $n \to \infty$, i.e. the infinite series (91.1) converges to $\sin x$ for all values of x). Other circular functions may be expressed as power series by means of (91.1) and/or (91.2). Maclaurin's series may be also used for direct computing, e.g.

$$\sin 10^\circ = \sin\frac{\pi}{18} = \frac{\pi}{18} - \frac{1}{3!}\left(\frac{\pi}{18}\right)^3 + \frac{1}{5!}\left(\frac{\pi}{18}\right)^5 - \dots$$
$$= 0{\cdot}174532 - 0{\cdot}000886 + 0{\cdot}000001 - \dots$$
$$= 0{\cdot}17365 \text{ (to 5 decimal places).}$$

Applications of Maclaurin's series to logarithms

One may easily verify that

$$\boxed{\log(1+x) = x - \frac{x^2}{2} + \frac{x^3}{3} - \frac{x^4}{4} + \dots} \qquad (92)$$

a result known to N. Mercator (1640–87, German, English) in 1668. [Log $(1+x)$ converges if $-1 < x \leqslant 1$.]

Put $x = 1$ in (90) to obtain

$$\boxed{\log 2 = 1 - \frac{1}{2} + \frac{1}{3} - \frac{1}{4} + \frac{1}{5} - \frac{1}{6} + \frac{1}{7} - \dots} \qquad (93)$$

In (90), put $x = -1$, $\quad\therefore \log 0 = -\infty$

put $x = 0$, $\quad\therefore \log 1 = 0$

replace x by $-x$,

$$\therefore \quad \boxed{\log(1-x) = -x - \frac{x^2}{2} - \frac{x^3}{3} - \frac{x^4}{4} - \dots} \qquad (94)$$

[Log $(1-x)$ converges if $-1 \leqslant x < 1$.] From (92) and (94),

$$\boxed{\log\left(\frac{1+x}{1-x}\right) = 2\left(x + \frac{x^3}{3} + \frac{x^5}{5} + \frac{x^7}{7} + \dots\right)} \qquad (95)$$

which converges if $-1 < x < 1$.

Put $x = \dfrac{1}{3}$ in (95).

$$\therefore \log 2 = \frac{2}{3}\left\{1 + \frac{1}{3}\left(\frac{1}{3}\right)^2 + \frac{1}{5}\left(\frac{1}{3}\right)^4 + \frac{1}{7}\left(\frac{1}{3}\right)^6 + \dots\right\}$$
$$= 0{\cdot}6931 \text{ on calculation.}$$

[Check using $\log 2 = 2{\cdot}303 \log_{10} 2$.]

Since $\log x$ and its derivatives have infinite discontinuities at $x = 0$, it follows that $\log x$ cannot be expanded into a series of powers of x.

However,

$$(\log (1+x-1)=)\ \log x = (x-1)-\frac{(x-1)^2}{2}+\frac{(x-1)^3}{3}-\dots \qquad (92.1)$$

which is convergent for $-1 < x-1 \leqslant 1$, i.e. $0 < x \leqslant 2$.

Use of infinite series in evaluating limits

EXAMPLE 47.

(i) $$\lim_{x\to 0}\left(\frac{x-\sin x}{x^3}\right) = \lim_{x\to 0}\left(\left\{x-\left(x-\frac{x^3}{3!}+\frac{x^5}{5!}-\dots\right)\right\}\Big/ x^3\right)$$

$$= \lim_{x\to 0}\left(\left\{\frac{x^3}{3!}-\frac{x^5}{5!}+\dots\right\}\Big/ x^3\right)$$

$$= \lim_{x\to 0}\left\{\frac{1}{3!}-\frac{x^2}{5!}+\frac{x^4}{7!}-\dots\right\}$$

$$= \frac{1}{6};$$

or $$\lim_{x\to 0}\left(\frac{x-\sin x}{x^3}\right) = \lim_{x\to 0}\left\{\frac{1-\cos x}{3x^2}\right\} \qquad \text{using (15)}$$

$$= \lim_{x\to 0}\left(\frac{\sin x}{6x}\right) \qquad \text{using (15)}$$

$$= \frac{1}{6}\lim_{x\to 0}\left(\frac{\sin x}{x}\right)$$

$$= \frac{1}{6}.$$

(ii) $$\lim_{x\to 0}\left(\frac{e^{kx}-1}{x}\right) = \lim_{x\to 0}\left\{\frac{\left(1+kx+\frac{(kx)^2}{2!}+\frac{(kx)^3}{3!}+\dots\right)-1}{x}\right\}$$

$$= \lim_{x\to 0}\left(k+\frac{k^2x}{2!}+\frac{k^3x^2}{3!}+\dots\right)$$

$$= k;$$

or $$\lim_{x\to 0}\left(\frac{e^{kx}-1}{x}\right) = \lim_{x\to 0}\left(\frac{ke^{kx}}{1}\right) \qquad \text{by (15)}$$

$$= ke^0$$

$$= k.$$

(iii) In (ii) put $k = \log a$, $\therefore\ e^{kx} = e^{x \log a} = e^{\log a^x} = a^x$ by (18.1)

$$\therefore\ \lim_{x\to 0}\left(\frac{a^x-1}{x}\right) = \log a.$$

Reviewing our methods for evaluating limits, we see that we have the following techniques: l'Hospital's rule (where applicable); infinite series (where applicable); and (when these fail) any other legitimate stratagem available to us.

Application of Maclaurin's series to the binomial theorem

Writing $f(x) = (1+x)^n$, where n is real, so that $f'(x) = n(1+x)^{n-1}$, $f''(x) = n(n-1)(1+x)^{n-2}$, ..., we have the *binomial series*

$$\boxed{(1+x)^n = 1+\frac{nx}{1!}+\frac{n(n-1)}{2!}x^2+\frac{n(n-1)(n-2)}{3!}x^3+\dots} \tag{96}$$

known to Newton in 1676. [It converges for $|x| < 1$.]

If n is an integer > 0, the expansion is finite:

$$\boxed{(1+x)^n = 1+\binom{n}{1}x+\binom{n}{2}x^2+\dots+\binom{n}{r}x^r+\dots+x^n} \tag{97}$$

where $\binom{n}{r} = \dfrac{n!}{r!(n-r)!}$ are the binomial coefficients and

$$\binom{n}{r} = \binom{n}{n-r}.$$

Coefficients of the powers of x in the various expansions of $(1+x)^n$, where n is a positive integer, can be represented by means of *Pascal's triangle (= Chinese triangle)* [Blaise Pascal, 1623–62, French]:

$$\left.\begin{array}{lccccccccccc}
n=0 & & & & & & 1 & & & & & \\
n=1 & & & & & 1 & & 1 & & & & \\
n=2 & & & & 1 & & 2 & & 1 & & & \\
n=3 & & & 1 & & 3 & & 3 & & 1 & & \\
n=4 & & 1 & & 4 & & 6 & & 4 & & 1 & \\
n=5 & 1 & & 5 & & 10 & & 10 & & 5 & & 1 \\
\dots & & & & & & \dots & & & & &
\end{array}\right\} \tag{98}$$

What is the nth row in Pascal's triangle?

Suitably imagined "lines" drawn upwards from left to right contain, with addition, the numbers 1, 1, 1+1, 1+2, 1+3+1, 1+4+3, 1+5+6+1, ..., i.e. the Fibonacci numbers 1, 1, 2, 3, 5, 8, 13. ... [See the end of this chapter and Exercise 9.44.]

Note: (i) the special power series which we studied in Example 44; (ii) the more general binomial expansion $(a+b)^n$ relates to two elements

a, b; by extension, there are trinomial expansions $(a+b+c)^n$ [see Exercise 9.44] and, generally, multinomial expansions.

Esoteric series, for functions like $\log \cos x$ and $e^{\sin x}$, may be obtained from (90) by patient computation.

§42. LEIBNIZ'S FORMULA

This is used in getting the nth derivative of the product of 2 or more functions of x. Its expression involves binomial coefficients. Herewith is *Leibniz's formula* for two functions u, v of x:

$$\begin{aligned} D^n(uv) &= (D^n u)v + \binom{n}{1} D^{n-1}u\, Dv + \binom{n}{2} D^{n-2}u\, D^2v + \dots \\ &+ \binom{n}{2} D^2u\, D^{n-2}v + \binom{n}{1} Du\, D^{n-1}v + u\, D^n v. \end{aligned} \tag{66}$$

EXAMPLE 48 (use of Leibniz's formula). Find $D^n(x \log x)$.

Solution. Write $x \log x = uv$ choosing $x = v$, $\log x = u$.

$$\begin{aligned} \therefore D^n(x\log x) &= xD^n \log x + nDx\, D^{n-1}\log x + \frac{n(n-1)}{2} D^2x\, D^{n-2}\log x + \dots \\ &= x(-1)^{n-1}\frac{(n-1)!}{x^n} + n\, 1(-1)^{n-2}\frac{(n-2)!}{x^{n-1}} + 0 \\ &= \frac{(-1)^n}{x^{n-1}}\{-(n-1)! + n(n-2)!\} \\ &= \frac{(-1)^n(n-2)!}{x^{n-1}}. \end{aligned}$$

Expressions involving π

We know that

$$\begin{aligned} \frac{d}{dx}\tan^{-1} x &= \frac{1}{1+x^2} = (1+x^2)^{-1} \qquad \text{from (10)} \\ &= 1 - x^2 + x^4 - x^6 + \dots \qquad \text{by (96).} \end{aligned}$$

Integrate both sides to obtain the *Gregory (1671)–Leibniz (1673) series*

$$\tan^{-1}x = x - \frac{x^3}{3} + \frac{x^5}{5} - \frac{x^7}{7} + \dots \tag{100}$$

or, if $x = \tan\theta$, in alternative form, the *tangent series*

$$\theta = \tan\theta - \frac{1}{3}\tan^3\theta + \frac{1}{5}\tan^5\theta - \dots$$

The constant of integration is zero since $\tan^{-1} 0 = 0$. At a more sophisticated level, we could define $\tan^{-1} x = \int_0^x \frac{dt}{1+t^2}$.

In (100), put $x = 1$ to obtain *Gregory's series:*

$$\boxed{\frac{\pi}{4} = 1 - \frac{1}{3} + \frac{1}{5} - \frac{1}{7} + \frac{1}{9} - \frac{1}{11} + \dots} \tag{101}$$

As a means of evaluating π, this series is tedious. Indeed, it requires $n =$ 500 to yield π correct to only three decimal places. Consequently, we need a more rapidly converging series.

Let $\alpha = \tan^{-1}\frac{1}{5}$.

$$\therefore \tan 2\alpha = \frac{2\tan\alpha}{1-\tan^2\alpha} = \frac{5}{12} \quad \text{and} \quad \tan 4\alpha = \frac{2\tan 2\alpha}{1-\tan^2 2\alpha} = \frac{120}{119}.$$

$$\therefore \tan\left(4\alpha - \frac{\pi}{4}\right) = \frac{\tan 4\alpha - 1}{1+\tan 4\alpha} = \frac{1}{239}.$$

$$\therefore \frac{\pi}{4} = 4\alpha - \tan^{-1}\frac{1}{239},$$

i.e.

$$\frac{\pi}{4} = 4\tan^{-1}\frac{1}{5} - \tan^{-1}\frac{1}{239}. \tag{102}$$

Machin (1680–1751, English), to whom this neat result was due, in 1706, calculated π to 100 places by it .Without much effort, one may compute π correct to five places with it. Shanks, in 1873, used this formula to calculate π to 707 places.

Other useful formulae are:

(i) $\frac{\pi}{4} = \tan^{-1}\frac{1}{2} + \tan^{-1}\frac{1}{3}$ (due to Euler);

(ii) $\tan^{-1}\frac{1}{2} = \tan^{-1}\frac{1}{3} + \tan^{-1}\frac{1}{7}$.

Add $\tan^{-1}\frac{1}{3}$ to both sides of (ii) and use Euler's result (i) to obtain

(iii) $\frac{\pi}{4} = 2\tan^{-1}\frac{1}{3} + \tan^{-1}\frac{1}{7}$ (due to Clausen, 1801–85, German).

Both these formulae (i) and (ii), also (iv) are special cases of the identity (due to C. L. Dodgson, alias Lewis Carroll, 1832–98, English):

$$\tan^{-1}\frac{1}{p} = \tan^{-1}\left(\frac{1}{p+q}\right) + \tan^{-1}\left(\frac{1}{p+r}\right), \quad \text{where } qr = 1+p^2.$$

(iv) *Note. Ferguson–Morris formulae* (1944–46): $\frac{\pi}{4} = 3\tan^{-1}\frac{1}{4} + \tan^{-1}\frac{1}{20} + \tan^{-1}\frac{1}{1985} = 3\tan^{-1}\frac{1}{4} + \tan^{-1}\frac{5}{99}$.

Query. In how many different ways (e.g. as a series, as a sequence, as a product, as a continued fraction) can π be expressed? Answer the same question in the case of e.

History of π

Earliest approximation $\pi = 3$ was made by the Babylonians, Chinese, and Hebrews (1 Kings, VII. 23). Ahmes (17th cent. B.C., Egyptian), the scribe of the Rhind Papyrus and the first *known* writer on mathematics, took $\pi = \left(\frac{16}{9}\right)^2$. Approximations $\frac{22}{7}$ and $\frac{355}{113}$ are due to Heron (2nd cent. B.C., Greek) and Tsu Ch'ung-Chih (5th cent., Chinese).

Four distinct stages are evident in the evolution of the history of π: (i) the stage indicated above when scholars tried all resources available; (ii) the use of the method of inscribed and circumscribed polygons ["the method of exhaustion" (!)], exploited effectively by Archimedes $\left(\text{who discovered the inequalities } 3\frac{10}{71} < \pi < 3\frac{10}{70}\right)$, but discarded in the seventeenth century; (iii) the use of infinite series, beginning with Machin (1706) and culminating with Shanks and, later, Ferguson, who (1946) calculated π correctly to 810 decimal places, using (iv) above to remove some errors from Shanks' evaluation; and (iv) the use of electronic digital computers which have pinpointed π to over 100,000 decimal places.

Actually, for practical purposes, 4 decimal places are sufficiently accurate for dealing with problems of stress in aeroplane engines, while about 30 places give the boundary of the visible Universe to a quantity imperceptible with the most powerful telescope.

A landmark was reached in 1882 when Lindemann (1852–1939, German) established the transcendental nature of π (§ 43), thus demonstrating the impossibility of squaring the circle.

Read D. F. Ferguson, *The Mathematical Gazette*, **30** (289), 89–90 (1946).

Classical Greek construction problems

Three geometrical problems puzzled the Greeks in antiquity. Using only *Euclidean instruments,* namely a straightedge for drawing a line (not for measuring length) and a pair of compasses, they sought to (a) *square the circle,* i.e. construct the side of a square whose area equals that of a given circle; (b) *trisect any angle;* and (c) *duplicate the cube* (the *Delian problem,* posed by the Oracle at Delos), i.e. construct the side of a cube (= cubical altar) whose volume is twice that of a given cube. Modern algebraic techniques have shown these problems to be unsolvable by Euclidean means (restrictions probably due to Plato's influence). Algebraic statements of these ancient problems are: (a) $x^2 = \pi$, (b) $4x^3 - 3x = a$ (Why? See Exercise 14.78), (c) $x^3 = 2$. Ingenuity being a hallmark of the Greek mind, curves were invented by them (Chapter 20) for performing operations (a), (b), (c), thus overcoming the necessity of being limited to the Euclidean instruments method. Several mechanical devices were invented to construct these curves, but such instruments were condemned by Plato because they reduced geometry from pure thought to the world of sense.

Fibonacci numbers (Fibonacci ≡ Pisano ≡ Leonardo of Pisa, 1175–1250, Italian)

The *Fibonacci sequence,*

$$\begin{matrix} \dots F_{-1} & F_0 & F_1 & F_2 & F_3 & F_4 & F_5 & F_6 & F_7 & F_8 & F_9 & F_{10} \dots \\ \dots & 0 & 1 & 1 & 2 & 3 & 5 & 8 & 13 & 21 & 34 & 55 & 89 \dots \end{matrix}$$

is such that $F_{n+2} = F_{n+1} + F_n$ (a *recurrence relation*). Exercise 9.39 shows that F_n is expressible in terms of a and b, the roots of $x^2 - x - 1 = 0$. [Recall that $-b$ was expanded as an infinite continued fraction in Exercise 1.31(b).] Moreover, F_n converges rapidly to its limiting value

$$\frac{a^n}{\sqrt{5}} (\because\ b \to 0 \text{ as } n \to \infty), \text{ e.g. } F_{10} = 89, \frac{a^{10}}{\sqrt{5}} = 88{\cdot}998.\dots.$$

Fibonacci numbers occur widely in art (e.g. Greek pottery and Egyptian design) and in nature. Botanists studying *phyllotaxis* (leaf distribution) come across them, and they appear in electrical networks also and, genetically, in the genealogy of the male bee (which hatches from unfertilised eggs). With them is associated the number $\dfrac{\sqrt{5}-1}{2} = \dfrac{1}{a} = 0{\cdot}618$ ... called the *golden section* because a unit segment divided at this point is aesthetically pleasing. Temples were reputedly built by the Greeks on this principle. Linguists have recently found evidence of a knowledge of Fibonacci numbers among Vergil and other poets of classical antiquity who, it seems, used them in the structural patterns of their poems.

Incidentally, it is to Fibonacci that Europe owes the introduction of the mathematical learning of the Arabs.

Suggested topics for further study

(1) Other tests for convergence (e.g. Gauss' test).
(2) Uniform convergence.
(3) Solution in series of ordinary second-order differential equations.
(4) Detailed history of π. (B. W. Thompson, *The Australian Mathematics Teacher*, **14** (1) 5–12 (1958).
(5) Detailed history of the three Greek problems (The author, *The Australian Mathematics Teacher*, **15** (2) 30–39 (1959).
(6) Fibonacci numbers. (Consult: The author, *The Australian Mathematics Teacher*, **19** (3) 1963, 54–60 (1963); any issue of the *Fibonacci Quarterly; Fibonacci Numbers*, N. Vorob'ev (Pergamon, 1961)).
(7) Fourier Series (Fourier 1758–1830, French).

References

As for Chapter 1, together with

Sequences and Series, J. A. Green (Routledge and Kegan Paul, 1958).

EXERCISES 9

1. Gulliksen, the psychologist, in a test on learning in 1950, used a formula equivalent to

$$R = \frac{a\sqrt{n}}{\sqrt{1+b(n-1)}},$$

where a, b are constants and R, n vary. Evaluate Gulliksen's limit, $\lim_{n\to\infty} R$.

Test for convergence the series 2–9 whose nth terms are:

2. $\frac{1}{n!}$. **3.** $\frac{1}{2n+3}$. **4.** $\frac{1+n}{2+n^2}$. **5.** $n^{\log x}$.

6. nx^{n-1}. **7.** $\frac{n^3}{e^n}$. **8.** $\frac{1}{n(\log n)^2}$ $(n > 1)$.

9. $\frac{1}{n \log n \log \log n}$ $(n > 1)$.

What is the limit of the sequences whose nth terms are:

10. $\frac{1}{n^2}(1+2+3+4+\ldots+n)$?

11. $\frac{1}{n^3}(1^2+2^2+3^2+4^2+\ldots+n^2)$?

12. What is the least value of n for which the sum of the first n terms of the geometric series

$$1+\tfrac{1}{2}+(\tfrac{1}{2})^2+(\tfrac{1}{2})^3+\ldots$$

differs by less than 10^{-10} from the sum to infinity?

13. Given the series $\sum \frac{1}{(10+n)^2}$, write down the first five terms, and use a suitable comparison test to show that it converges. By means of Cauchy's test, determine the values between which its sum lies.

Obtain infinite series for:

14. $\sinh x$. **15.** $\cosh x$. **16.** $\tan x$ [as far as x^5 $(x < 1)$].

17. Establish the identity $\frac{\pi}{4} = 4\tan^{-1}\frac{1}{5} - \tan^{-1}\frac{1}{70} + \tan^{-1}\frac{1}{99}$.

18. Assuming the identity $\frac{1}{2}(\pi - x) = \sin x + \frac{1}{2}\sin 2x + \frac{1}{3}\sin 3x + \frac{1}{4}\sin 4x + \ldots$ and integrating between 0 and π, find an expression for $\pi^2/8$.

19. Expand $\sin^{-1} x$. Hence obtain a series for $\pi/6$.

20. Given $\int_1^0 \frac{\log x}{1-x}\,dx = \frac{\pi^2}{6}$, obtain an infinite series for $\frac{\pi^2}{6}$. [*Hint:* substitute $x = 1-y$.] (Probability theory tells us that the chance that two numbers chosen at random will be mutually prime is $\frac{6}{\pi^2}$. Experiment with this problem.)

21. Using the binomial theorem, expand $\left(1-\frac{2}{3}\right)^{-3/2}$.

Hence, sum to infinity $2+\frac{5}{2!3}+\frac{5\cdot 7}{3!3^2}+\frac{5\cdot 7\cdot 9}{4!3^3}+\ldots$.

22. If $y = x\sin ax$, find $\frac{d^ny}{dx^n}$ by using Leibniz's theorem.

23. *Zeno's paradox* (Zeno, 5th cent. B.C., Greek) relates to a race between *Achilles and the tortoise.* Assume that Achilles can run 100 times as fast as the tortoise and let the tortoise be given a start of, say, 1 min. According to the paradox, when Achilles reaches the point T_1 where the tortoise started, the tortoise has moved on to a new position T_2 which is 1/100 of the distance travelled by Achilles; when Achilles reaches this position the tortoise has moved on 1/100 of this distance travelled by Achilles; and so on. Therefore, argued Zeno, Achilles will never catch the tortoise. Common sense tells us that Achilles *will* overtake the tortoise.

(i) Where will Achilles actually catch the tortoise?

(ii) What is wrong with Zeno's argument?

(Take, as the unit of length, the distance covered by the tortoise in 1 min in going from the initial position T_0 (coinciding with the position A_1 of Achilles) to its "starting" position T_1.)

24. Prove that, for $n > 2$, $\int_2^n \frac{dx}{x\log x} = \log_e(\log_2 n)$.

Hence, show graphically that the sum

$$S_n = \frac{1}{2\log 2}+\frac{1}{3\log 3}+\frac{1}{4\log 4}+\ldots+\frac{1}{n\log n}$$

is greater than $\log(\log_2 n)$ and describe the behaviour of S_n as n increases indefinitely. If $n = 512$, show that $S_n > 2$. (You may assume that $e < 3$.) [U.N.E.]

25. Write $S_n = 1+\frac{1}{2}+\frac{1}{3}+\ldots+\frac{1}{n}$ and assume $\lim_{n\to\infty}(S_n-\log n) \doteqdot \gamma = 0{\cdot}577$ *(Euler's constant)*. Calculate $\lim_{n\to\infty}\left(\frac{1}{n+1}+\ldots+\frac{1}{2n}\right)$, a series occurring in the theory of transfinite numbers (Chapter 10). Generalise this result to compute $\lim_{n\to\infty}\left(\frac{1}{jn}+\frac{1}{jn+1}+\ldots+\frac{1}{kn}\right)$ $(j<k)$.

26. Von Koch's "snowflake" curve (§ 7) has area $A = \lim_{n\to\infty} A_n$,

where
$$A_n = 4\frac{\Delta}{3}+\frac{4}{3}\frac{\Delta}{3^2}+\ldots+\left(\frac{4}{3}\right)^{n-1}\frac{\Delta}{3^n}$$

in which Δ is the area of a triangle occurring initially in the construction of the curve. Calculate A.

27. Elliptic (non-Euclidean) plane geometry contains the formula

$$\cos\frac{c}{k} = \cos\frac{a}{k}\cos\frac{b}{k},$$

where a, b, c are the sides of a triangle and k a constant. If a, b, c are small compared with k, prove that this formula approximates to Pythagoras' theorem (i.e. for small regions of space, elliptic and Euclidean geometries are approximately the same).

28. Studying the *parallax* of the star Sirius, Lobatschewsky used the non-Euclidean formula $\tan\left(\frac{\alpha}{2}\right) = e^{-x/k}$ with $\frac{\pi}{2}-p < \alpha$, where α is the Lobatschewskian angle of parallelism, x is the radius of the Earth's orbit (approximately circular) around the Sun, and k is a constant. Show that $\tan p > \frac{x}{k}$, where p is the parallax [Lobatschewsky took $p = 1{\cdot}24''$ for Sirius (now known to be $0{\cdot}38''$), giving $\frac{x}{k} < 0{\cdot}000006012$, i.e. k is very great compared with the Earth's orbit.

Query: What precisely is the meaning of the parallax of a star?]

Examine the absolute and conditional convergence of the series 29–33 whose nth terms are:

29. $\frac{(-1)^{n+1}}{n}$. **30.** $\frac{(-1)^{n+1}}{n!}$. **31.** $\frac{(-1)^{n+1}}{2n-1}$.

32. $\frac{(-1)^{n+1}}{n^2}$. **33.** $\frac{(-1)^{n+1}|\sin nx|}{n^2}$.

34. *Bernoulli numbers* (James Bernoulli) B_n $(n = 0, 1, 2, \ldots)$, of importance in a nalysis, are defined by the relation $\frac{x}{e^x-1} = \sum_{n=0}^{\infty} B_n\frac{x^n}{n!}$. Calculate $B_0, B_1, \ldots, B_5$.

35. Test for convergence ($|x| \neq 1$) the *hypergeometric series*

$$F(a, b, c; x) = 1+\frac{ab}{1!c}x+\frac{a(a+1)b(b+1)}{2!\,c(c+1)}x^2+\ldots+$$
$$+\frac{a(a+1)\ldots(a+n-1)b(b+1)\ldots(b+n-1)}{n!\,c(c+1)\ldots(c+n-1)}x^n+\ldots.$$

How do we derive from the hypergeometric series the series

36. $(1-x)^{-1}$? **37.** $(1+x)^n$? **38.** $\log(1+x)$?

39. Assuming a solution of the form $F_n = Aa^{n+1}+Bb^{n+1}$ ($A \neq 0$, $B \neq 0$, $a \neq 0$, $b \neq 0$) for the nth Fibonacci number F_n, establish *Binet's formula* (Binet 1786–1856, French)

$$F_n = \frac{a^{n+1}-b^{n+1}}{\sqrt{5}},$$

where $a = \frac{1+\sqrt{5}}{2}$, $b = \frac{1-\sqrt{5}}{2}$ are the roots of $x^2-x-1 = 0$. (Check with $n = 2, 3, 4$ to verify that Binet's formula *does* produce integral values of F_2, F_3, F_4.)

Writing $\sinh\alpha = \frac{1}{2}$, establish that, for the Fibonacci sequence,

40. $F_n = \begin{cases} \dfrac{\sinh(n+1)\alpha}{\cosh\alpha} & \text{if } n \text{ is odd} \\ \dfrac{\cosh(n+1)\alpha}{\cosh\alpha} & \text{if } n \text{ is even.} \end{cases}$

41. $\lim\limits_{n\to\infty}\left(\dfrac{F_n}{F_{n-1}}\right) = a = e^{\alpha}.$

Develop the formulae 42–44:

42. $F_{n-1}F_{n+1}-F_n^2 = (-1)^{n+1}$ (a result due to Simson, and the basis of an interesting geometrical paradox).

43. $\sum\limits_{i=0}^{n} F_i = F_{n+2}-1.$

44. $\sum\limits_{n=0}^{\infty} F_n x^n = (1-x-x^2)^{-1}$ (i.e. the Fibonacci numbers are generated by this function).

A certain *generalised sequence* $\{\omega_n(a, b; p, q)\}$ is defined by $\omega_0 = a$, $\omega_1 = b$, $\omega_{n+2} = p\omega_{n+1}-q\omega_n$ (so that $\omega_{-1} = \frac{pa-b}{q}$). What values of a, b, p, q lead to the following sequences 45–55?

45 Integers. **46.** Even integers. **47.** Odd integers.

48. Arithmetic progressions (first term a, common difference d).

49. Geometric progressions (first term a, ratio q).

50. Fibonacci sequence.

51. 2 1 3 4 7 11 18 ... (Lucas, 1842–91, French).

52. 2 3 5 9 17 33 65 ... $= \{2^n+1\}$ (Fermat).

53. 1 2 5 12 29 70 169 . . . (Pell, 1610–85, English).

54. $\{2 \cos n\theta\}$ (Tschebyscheff, 1821–94, Russian).

55. $\left\{\dfrac{\sin (n+1)\theta}{\sin \theta}\right\}$ (Tschebyscheff).

[*Tschebyscheff's sequences* are useful in some aerodynamical problems and in numerical analysis. Examine $\{\omega_n\}$ further to discover other interesting sequences. Notice the occurrence of the trivial sequence . . ., 2, 2, 2, 2 . . . .]

Replacing F_n by U_{n+1} in the Fibonacci sequence (Exercise 9.50) and letting V_n be the nth term of the *Lucas sequence* (Exercise 9.51), show that

56. $V_n = a^n + b^n$. **57.** $U_{2n} = U_n V_n$.

58. Given that $u_{n+1} = \sqrt{1+u_n}$, $u_1 = 1$, prove that $\lim u_n = a$. [*Hint:* First obtain $u_{n+1} < 1 + \dfrac{1}{u_{n+1}}$.]

59. Calculate the value of the least positive integer N for which $\left|\dfrac{3n+5}{7n-1} - \dfrac{3}{7}\right| < \varepsilon$ for all $n > N$, given $\varepsilon = 0{\cdot}001$. (Refer to Example 43.)

60. By differentiating the terms indicated in the series

$$J_0(x) = 1 - \frac{x^2}{2^2} + \frac{x^4}{2^2.4^2.6^2} - \frac{x^6}{2^2.4^2.6^2} + \ldots,$$

verify that $J_0(x)$ *(Bessel's function of order zero)* is a solution of *Bessel's equation of order zero* $x\dfrac{d^2y}{dx^2} + \dfrac{dy}{dx} + xy = 0$. (Bessel, 1784–1846, German.)

CHAPTER 10

COMPLEX NUMBERS

God made the integers, all the rest is the work of man.
(KRONECKER (1823–91, German))

"I doubt it", said the Carpenter,
And shed a bitter tear.
(LEWIS CARROLL)

EXPERIENCE with numbers, the raw material of much of mathematics, convinces us that the system of real numbers is an inadequate apparatus for describing all facets of mathematical thinking, or even the features of the physical world. These limitations are removed by an extension to a more general system called complex numbers.

The existence of several different number systems prompts us to investigate properties which the systems share in common. This introduces the concept of important algebraic structures called fields and rings.

§43. THE REAL NUMBER SYSTEM

Rationals and irrationals

Number theory has a long interesting history, since counting, on which it is based, was one of the most ancient intellectual exercises of man. By the time of Pythagoras (6th cent. B.C., Greek), the study of the properties of the *natural numbers* (= positive integers) and fractions had been well investigated under stimulation from the commercial world. Surprisingly, knowledge about negative numbers and the concept of zero (usually attributed to the Hindus, *ca*. 9th cent. but, according to the most recent archaeology, possibly known to the Babylonians a good deal earlier) came much later. To Pythagoras, or one of his followers, is due the discovery that there exist numbers other than the *rationals* (= positive and negative fractions and integers, including zero). These are the *irrationals* which occupy the "gaps" in the rational number axis. Together, the rationals and irrationals constitute the *real number system*, represented pictorially by the real number axis.

Rational numbers can be represented either as terminating decimals $\left(\text{e.g. } \frac{3}{4} = 0{\cdot}75\right)$ or as repeating decimals, e.g. if $R = 0{\cdot}272727\ldots = 0{\cdot}\dot{2}\dot{7}$, then $99R (= 100R - R) = 27$ giving $R = \frac{27}{99} = \frac{3}{11}$. Irrational numbers cannot be so represented. By inserting digits at random in, say, $0{\cdot}2727\ldots$, we can create an infinite variety of irrationals.

Simplest of the irrationals is $\sqrt{2}$, the positive solution of $x^2 = 2$, which may be geometrically constructed as the diagonal of a unit square.

Proof that $\sqrt{2}$ is irrational

Suppose p, q (both not even integers) exist:

$\frac{p}{q} = \sqrt{2}$, i.e. suppose $\sqrt{2}$ is rational.

$\therefore \left(\frac{p}{q}\right)^2 = 2$

$\therefore p^2 = 2q^2$ (i)

$\therefore$ right-hand side of (i) is even.

$\therefore$ left-hand side of (i) is even.

$\therefore p$ is even ($= 2r$, say) (ii)

$\therefore q^2$ is even [$= 2r^2$ from (i)]

$\therefore q$ is even,

i.e. p, q are both even, which is contrary to our hypothesis.

$\therefore \sqrt{2}$ is not a rational number, i.e. $\sqrt{2}$ is irrational.

Algebraic and transcendental numbers

Another classification of real numbers is that into algebraic and transcendental numbers. *Algebraic numbers* are real numbers which are the roots of equations with integer coefficients. *Transcendental numbers* are real numbers which are not algebraic. Quite clearly, algebraic numbers may be rational or irrational (e.g. solutions of $x^2 = 1$, $x^2 = 2$, respectively), whereas transcendental numbers are necessarily irrational.

Lindemann proved in 1882 that π is transcendental. Consequently, $x^2 = \pi$ (which is the algebraic expression of the famous ancient Greek problem of squaring the circle) has no algebraic number for a solution. This means that the circle cannot be "squared" by straightedge and compasses (the Euclidean instruments). Other examples of transcendental numbers are the exponential number e and the *Hilbert number* $2^{\sqrt{2}}$.

Cantor-Dedekind Axiom

The *Cantor–Dedekind Axiom* (Cantor, 1845–1918, German; Dedekind, 1831–1916, German) states that the real numbers can be put in 1–1 correspondence with the points of an infinite straight line (the *real number axis* = one-dimensional Euclidean space). Real numbers are thus:

(a) *closed* (i.e. no new numbers are produced under addition, subtraction, multiplication and division);
(b) *ordered* (i.e. of any two distinct real numbers, one is always the lesser);
(c) *dense* (i.e. between any 2 distinct real numbers, another one may be found);
(d) *complete* (i.e. to each point of the number axis corresponds a number, and conversely).

Residue classes

If a, b are integers: $a-b$ is divisible by p, then a is *congruent to b modulo p*, written $a \equiv b \pmod p$, i.e. $a = b+rp$ for some integer r. E.g. $25 \equiv 4 \bmod 7$, $-17 \equiv 3 \bmod 5$, $1 \equiv 16 \bmod 5$. Usually, p is a prime, though the nature of p is always explicitly stated. A *prime* is, of course, a positive integer having no factors except itself and 1, e.g. 2, 3, 5, 7, 11,...

Consequently, the integers are arranged into p residue sets written $\{0\}$, $\{1\}$, $\{2\}$, ..., $\{p-1\}$ containing no integer divisible by p except in the case of $\{0\}$. For instance, with $p = 3$, we have

$$\{0\} = \{\ldots, -3, 0, 3, 6, 9, \ldots\}$$
$$\{1\} = \{\ldots, -2, 1, 4, 7, 10, \ldots\}$$
$$\{2\} = \{\ldots, -1, 2, 5, 8, 11, \ldots\}.$$

Residue sets are called *residue classes mod p*. It is convenient to think of q representing the residue class $\{q\}$ $(0 \leqslant q \leqslant p-1)$. Residues (= remainders on division by p) belong to the same class if they are congruent.

Notation. Assuming the language of set theory (Chapter 13) with which the reader is familiar, we use the following notation to refer to the various number systems:

$\mathcal{N} \equiv \{x\colon\ x \text{ a natural number}\}$
$\mathcal{I} \equiv \{x\colon\ x \text{ an integer}\}$
$\mathcal{R} \equiv \{x\colon\ x \text{ rational}\}$
$\mathcal{R}^* \equiv \{x\colon\ x \text{ real}\}$
$\mathcal{I}_p \equiv \{0, 1, \ldots, p-1\}$ (*integers mod p*, one from each residue class)
$\mathcal{C} \equiv \{x\colon\ x \text{ a complex number}\}$
$\mathcal{Q} \equiv \{x\colon\ x \text{ a quaternion}\}$.

For a rigorous treatment of real number theory, consult Dubisch [32].

§ 44. NUMBER RINGS AND FIELDS

Field axioms

Suppose a, b, c are *any* three real numbers. Then they are known to satisfy the following arithmetical (algebraic) laws, where the symbols A, M, D denote axioms for arithmetic addition, multiplication, and distribution.

Law	Addition	Multiplication
Closure law	A_1. $a+b$	M_1. ab
Associative law	A_2. $a+(b+c) = (a+b)+c$	M_2. $a(bc) = (ab)c$
Existence of identity law	A_3. $a+0 = a$	M_3. $a1 = a$
Existence of inverse law	A_4. $a+(-a) = 0$	M_4. $aa^{-1} = 1$ $(a \neq 0)$
Commutative law	A_5. $a+b = b+a$	M_5. $ab = ba$
Distributive laws	D_1. $a(b+c) = ab+ac$	D_2. $(a+b)c = ac+bc$

(103)

D_1, D_2 are right and left distribution respectively for multiplication w.r.t. addition. Under addition, the identity is zero whereas under multiplication the identity is unity.

A mathematical number system possessing the structure (103) is called a *(number) field F*, i.e. the real numbers form a field. Mathematical systems do exist in which some of these laws, notably M_5, do not hold. Quaternions (§ 52) and matrices (Chapter 11) are instances of this breakdown. Vectors under vector multiplication (§§ 55, 64) also violate M_5. Observe particularly that the *set of integers does not form a field* since the inverse (reciprocal) of an integer a is generally not an integer but a fraction, i.e. M_4 is invalidated. Neither, of course, do the natural integers form a field. (Fields, as defined above, naturally have nothing at all to do with the notion of physical fields (of force), e.g. a magnetic field.)

Do the sets of integers mod p form a field? *Answer* (assumed): Yes, if p is prime. No, if p is non-prime. Fields mod p, p prime, are known as *Galois fields*, e.g. the field of integers mod 3 is the Galois field mod 3, written $GF(3)$. Galois fields (Galois, 1812–31, French) are very important in mathematics, e.g. they give rise to coordinates in finite projective geometries.

A *subfield* is a subset of the elements of F possessing the properties (103) of a field, e.g. the rationals form a subfield of the field of real numbers. (Verify that $\mathcal{R}$, $\mathcal{R}^*$ do satis fy (103).)

Number rings

Removal of certain of the laws in (103) leads to other important mathematical structures.

A *(number) ring* R satisfies the 9 axioms A_1–A_5, D_1, D_2, M_1, M_2, where a, b, c are elements of the ring, expressed symbolically as $a, b, c \in R$ ($\in \Rightarrow$ "is a member of"). These are the minimum requirements for a ring. A *subring* is a subset of the elements of R having the ring properties, e.g. the rationals form a subring of the ring of reals. (Verify.)

A *ring with divisors of zero* is a ring for which $ab = 0$ (or $ba = 0$)$\Rightarrow$ $a \neq 0$ and $b \neq 0$ (a, b being *left* and *right divisors of zero*, respectively if $ab = 0$). Zero division does not exist if $ab = 0 \Rightarrow a = 0$, or $b = 0$ ($a, b \in R$). Ordinary number rings do not possess divisors of zero, though integers mod p do, if p is non-prime, e.g. $2 \times 3 \equiv 0 \bmod 6$ so 2 and 3 are divisors of zero mod 6.

Under multiplication it is possible that R may not be commutative, that it may not possess a unity, and that its elements may not all have inverses (even if R has a unit element).

Special rings may thus be:

(i) a *ring with unity* is a ring which also satisfies M_3;
(ii) a *commutative ring* is a ring which also satisfies M_5;
(iii) an *integral domain* D is a commutative ring with unity (i.e. M_3, M_5 are both valid) and without divisors of zero, e.g. the integers form an integral domain. (Verify). A *sub-domain* is a subset of the elements of D having the structure of an integral domain, e.g. the integers constitute a subdomain of the rationals.

Therefore, a field is an integral domain in which M_4 holds. A *skew-field* ($\equiv$ *division ring*) obeys (103) except for M_5.

§ 45. INTUITIVE APPROACH TO COMPLEX NUMBERS

So much for real numbers. But what about an equation like $x^2 = -1$ with solutions $x = \pm\sqrt{-1}$? What meaning can be attached to these solutions? And how can we represent such numbers pictorially if they exist? Previously, in Examples 28, 29, we recognised how naturally these numbers occur in the solution of a problem as an adjunct to real numbers. Presumably, then, they have some hidden mathematical significance quite apart from the challenge they offer to our curiosity. In fact, they turn out to be the basis for a good deal of modern science and technology.

Problems involving the square root of a negative number mystified people throughout the centuries. Leibniz, for instance, saw in entities like $\sqrt{-1}$ "a fine and wonderful refuge of the Divine Spirit, almost an amphibian between being and non-being," and Euler was astonished that $\sqrt{-1}$ was neither smaller nor greater than 1, was neither positive nor negative, and in fact could not be compared with ordinary numbers. Cardan (1501–76, Italian) wished to discover two numbers whose sum is 10 and whose product is 40. Finding his solutions to be $5\pm\sqrt{-15}$, he called them "impossible". Nevertheless, he did not destroy his calculations, but left them for posterity to see.

Solutions like Cardan's and $x = \pm\sqrt{-1}$ require an extension of the real number system, i.e. the introduction of a more comprehensive system called *complex numbers*. A complex number consisting of no real part at all, e.g. $\sqrt{-15}$, is called a (pure) *imaginary*.

Scientifically, complex numbers have considerable utility in a variety of situations, e.g. electrically in the calculation of alternating currents in electrical circuits and chemically in the study of the variation of temperature in solids. Surprising as this may seem, it is striking evidence of (i) the achievement and possibilities of the human mind when freed from the tyranny of the senses (cf. Lobatschewsky's non-Euclidean geometry), and (ii) the oft-demonstrated historical fact that the pure research of mathematicians is applicable to the problems of the scientists. On the other hand, much mathematical discovery has been stimulated by problems of the physical world. Further comments on applications of complex numbers are made at the end of § 51.

How do two complex numbers $p = a+b\sqrt{-1}, q = c+d\sqrt{-1}$ behave under arithmetical operations? Very clearly, we have

$$p\pm q = (a+c)+(b\pm d)\sqrt{-1}$$

$$pq = (ac-bd)+(ad+bc)\sqrt{-1}$$

$$\frac{p}{q} = \frac{a+b\sqrt{-1}}{c+d\sqrt{-1}}\,\frac{c-d\sqrt{-1}}{c-d\sqrt{-1}} = \frac{(ac+bd)+(bc-ad)\sqrt{-1}}{c^2+d^2},$$

where, for the quotient, we have simplified the fraction by removing the imaginary from the denominator. A formal treatment of complex numbers from an axiomatic point of view will require us to take these facts into consideration.

Experience with coordinates makes us familiar with ordered sets of numbers as single entities, e.g. an ordered set (x, y, z) may represent a point in ordinary three-dimensional Euclidean space. Consequently, it would seem a natural challenge to construct a system of numbers, each considered as an ordered set so that as many as possible of the laws of algebra for real numbers (103) will hold. For ordered pairs of real numbers it proves unnecessary to sacrifice any of these laws, while for ordered sets of 4 real numbers (quaternions) only the commutative law of multiplication needs to be abandoned. Other systems require further modifications of the laws, e.g. the elimination of a multiplicative inverse. Non-associative algebras, with important physical applications, e.g. to quantum theory, have been constructed (see Exercises 14.65–14.72).

§ 46. FORMAL DEVELOPMENT OF COMPLEX NUMBERS

Our treatment of complex numbers is largely that of Hamilton (1805–65, Irish).

Definitions

A *complex number* z is an ordered pair (= number couple) of real numbers x, y written $z = (x, y)$, where $x \equiv$ *real part of* z, written $x = R(z)$, and $y \equiv$ *imaginary part of* z, written $y = I(z)$.

Despite the description of x, y as "real" and "imaginary" parts, do not forget that *x, y are real numbers.*

The *modulus* of z is $|z| = +\sqrt{x^2+y^2}$.

$\therefore \ |z| = 0 \Rightarrow x = 0, y = 0.$

Equality. If $z' = (x', y')$, then $z' = z \Rightarrow x' = x, y' = y$.

No ordering exists among complex numbers, i.e. a statement like $z' \gtrless z$ is meaningless. *Inequalities apply only to the moduli of two complex numbers.*

Addition and subtraction

Define

(i) $z+z' = (x+x', y+y')$.

(ii) $-z' = (-x', -y')$.

(iii) $z-z' = (x-x', y-y')$.

Thus, if $z = (4, 3)$, $z' = (-1, 5)$, it follows that $z+z' = (3, 8)$, $z-z' = (5, -2)$.

Under addition, the identity is $(0, 0)$ and the inverse of z is $-z = (-x, -y)$.

Multiplication and division

Define

(iv) $$zz' = (xx'-yy', xy'+x'y).$$

While the definitions for addition and subtraction look sensible enough, that for multiplication appears awkward. However, subsequent theory will completely validate this as a definition which explains the mathematics of $\sqrt{-1}$.

Under multiplication, the identity is (1, 0) since, by (iv),

$$\begin{aligned}(x, y)(1, 0) &= (x \cdot 1 - y \cdot 0,\ x \cdot 0 + y \cdot 1)\\ &= (x, y).\end{aligned}$$

What of the inverse element z^{-1} for which $zz^{-1} = (1, 0)$? Suppose $z^{-1} = (u, v)$ so that our problem is to express u, v in terms of x, y. We have

$$(x, y)(u, v) = (1, 0),$$

i.e. $$(xu - yv,\ xv + yu) = (1, 0) \qquad \text{by (iv)}.$$

Equate real and imaginary parts.

$$\therefore \begin{cases} xu - yv = 1, \\ xv + yu = 0. \end{cases}$$

Solve these two simultaneous linear equations for u, v and we obtain the unique solution

$$z^{-1} = \left(\frac{x}{x^2+y^2},\ \frac{-y}{x^2+y^2}\right) \qquad \text{provided } |z| \neq 0.$$

From the definitions it is fairly easy to verify that complex numbers obey the laws (103). Consequently, the algebras of real and complex numbers are identical in form, though the meanings are different.

Obviously, there is a 1–1 correspondence (= *isomorphism*) between the complex numbers $(x, 0)$ and real numbers x, so that we may adopt the convention that $(x, 0) \equiv x$, though it must be remembered that any real number occurring in an equation involving complex numbers should be regarded as a complex number. We may call the multiplication identity element (1, 0) the *unit of reals*. Similarly, complex numbers $(0, y)$ correspond to purely imaginary numbers $y\sqrt{-1}$.

The imaginary number i

(Electrical engineers sometimes use the symbol j instead of i since i is used to denote electric current.)

Let $i = (0, 1)$ be the *unit of imaginaries* (due to Gauss, Euler).

$$\begin{aligned}\therefore\ i^2 &= (0, 1)\,(0, 1)\\ &= (0 \cdot 0 - 1 \cdot 1,\quad 0 \cdot 1 + 1 \cdot 0) \qquad \text{using § 46 (iv)}\\ &= (-1, 0)\end{aligned}$$

$$\therefore\ i^2 = -1 \quad \text{or} \quad i = \sqrt{-1}.$$

Also
$$\begin{aligned} x+iy &= (x,0)+(0,1)(y,0) \\ &= (x,0)+(0\cdot y-1\cdot 0,\quad 0\cdot 0+1\cdot y) \qquad \text{by § 46 (iv)} \\ &= (x,0)+(0,y) \\ &= (x+0,\ 0+y) \qquad \text{by § 46 (i)} \\ &= (x,y) \\ &= z \end{aligned}$$

i.e.
$$\boxed{z=(x,y)=x+iy}\,. \tag{104}$$

EXAMPLE 49 (verification of certain theorems on moduli).

If $\left\{\begin{array}{l} z_1 = 4-3i \\ z_2 = 5+2i \end{array}\right\}$ verify the theorems (*a*) $|z_1z_2| = |z_1|\,|z_2|$, (*b*) $\left|\dfrac{z_1}{z_2}\right| = \dfrac{|z_1|}{|z_2|}$.

Solution. Clearly

$$|z_1| = \sqrt{4^2+(-3)^2} = 5 \quad\text{and}\quad |z_2| = \sqrt{5^2+2^2} = \sqrt{29}.$$

$$\therefore\ |z_1|\,|z_2| = 5\sqrt{29} \quad\text{and}\quad \frac{|z_1|}{|z_2|} = \frac{5}{\sqrt{29}}.$$

(a) Now
$$\begin{aligned} z_1z_2 &= (4-3i)(5+2i) \\ &= 20+8i-6i^2-15i \\ &= 26-7i \end{aligned}$$
$$\begin{aligned} \therefore\ |z_1z_2| &= \sqrt{26^2+(-7)^2} \\ &= \sqrt{725} \\ &= 5\sqrt{29} \qquad \therefore \text{ theorem } (a) \text{ is verified.} \end{aligned}$$

(b) Further,

$$\begin{aligned} \frac{z_1}{z_2} &= \frac{4-3i}{5+2i}\times\frac{5-2i}{5-2i} \\ &= \frac{14-23i}{29} \end{aligned}$$
$$\begin{aligned} \therefore\ \left|\frac{z_1}{z_2}\right| &= \frac{1}{29}\sqrt{14^2+(-23)^2} \\ &= \frac{1}{29}\sqrt{725} \\ &= \frac{5}{\sqrt{29}} \qquad \therefore \text{ theorem } (b) \text{ is verified.} \end{aligned}$$

Conjugate complex number

Define

$$\boxed{\bar{z} = x - iy \text{ is the } \textit{conjugate} \text{ of } z = x+iy} \tag{105}$$

e.g., 5–2*i* is the conjugate of $5+2i$ in Example 49(b). Thus $I(\bar{z}) = -I(z)$.

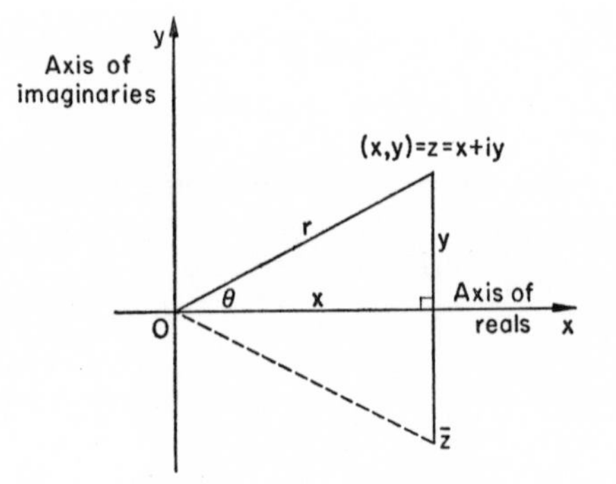

FIG. 20. Argand diagram

Geometrically, $\bar{z}$ is the reflection of z in the x-axis (Fig. 20).

Verify the following: $\overline{z_1 z_2} = \bar{z}_1 \bar{z}_2$; $\overline{z_1+z_2} = \bar{z}_1+\bar{z}_2$; $z\bar{z} = |z|^2$;
$z+\bar{z} = 2R(z)$; $z-\bar{z} = 2iI(z)$; $\bar{\bar{z}} = z$.

§47. GEOMETRICAL REPRESENTATION OF COMPLEX NUMBERS. THE ARGAND DIAGRAM

From Fig. 20 (see also Fig. 9), we have, by Pythagoras' theorem,

$$\boxed{r = \sqrt{x^2+y^2} = |z|}\,. \tag{106}$$

Now $x = r\cos\theta$, $y = r\sin\theta$

$\therefore\ z = r(\cos\theta + i\sin\theta)$

$$\therefore\ \boxed{z = (x, y) = x+iy = r(\cos\theta+i\sin\theta)}\,. \tag{107}$$

Also

$$\boxed{\begin{aligned}\theta &= \tan^{-1}\left(\frac{y}{x}\right)\\ &= \textit{argument} \text{ of } z = \arg z\end{aligned}}\,. \tag{108}$$

Compare (106), (108) with (42).

The argument is not unique, for if θ is a value of the argument, so also is $\theta+2n\pi$ (n integer). The *principal value* of arg z is:

$$\boxed{-\pi < \arg z \leqslant \pi}\,. \tag{109}$$

(Why *this* range? Notice it is partly open, partly closed.)

Such a representation of complex numbers as that given above is called the *Argand diagram* (1806) (Argand, 1768–1822, French), though this geometrical interpretation was known to both Gauss and Wessel (1745–1818, Norwegian) earlier in 1797.

Point at infinity

To every ordinary (i.e. non-infinite) point in the plane corresponds a complex number and, conversely. In order to complete the complex plane, we postulate the existence of a single *point at infinity* defined to be the point corresponding to the origin in the transformation $z' = 1/z$. The complex plane is thus a perfect continuum. We can now say that *complex numbers are closed* (under arithmetical operations), *continuous, and dense, but not ordered.* (Compare with real numbers, § 43.)

Geometrical significance of multiplication by i, $-i$

In Fig. 21, $iz = ix+i^2y = -y+ix, \quad -iz = -ix-i^2y = y-ix.$

$\therefore$ *multiplication by $i(-i)$ is geometrically equivalent to rotation through $\pi/2$ in an anti-clockwise (clockwise) direction.*

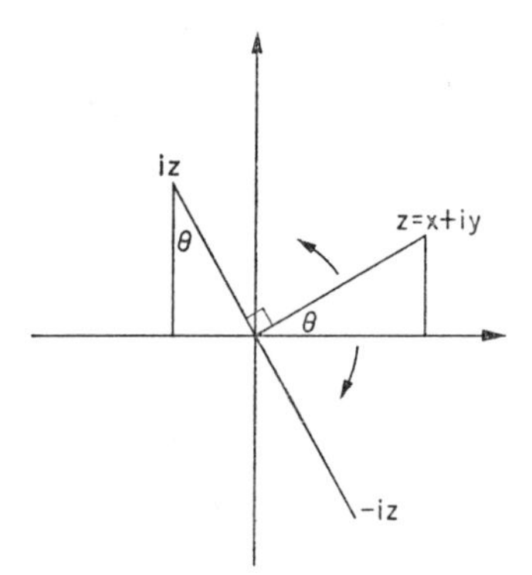

FIG. 21. Multiplication by i

Electric current is generated in coils of wire rotating in a magnetic field—hence the significance of multiplication by i or $-i$.

Geometrical meanings of z_1+z_2, z_1-z_2

Stippled triangles in Fig. 22a, b are congruent in pairs. Diagrams illustrating sum and difference may be combined as in Fig. 23.*

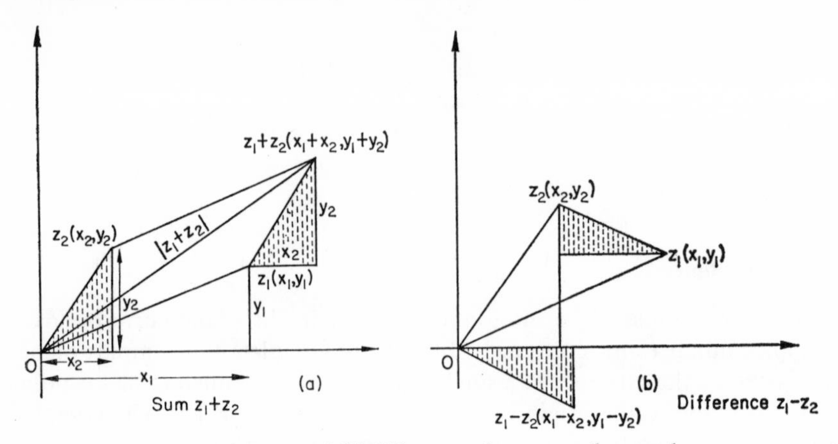

FIG. 22. (a) Sum and (b) difference of two complex numbers

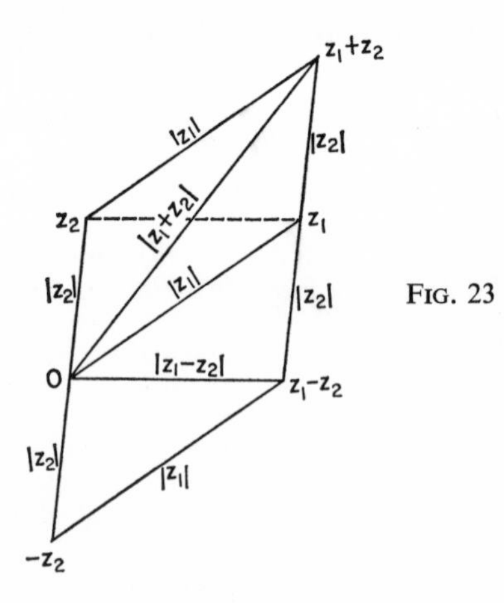

FIG. 23

EXAMPLE 50 (sum and difference for $z_1 = 4+3i$, $z_2 = 3-6i$).

Solution.

$$z_1+z_2 = 7-3i \qquad\qquad z_1-z_2 = 1+9i$$

$$\therefore \begin{cases} |z_1+z_2| = \sqrt{58} \\ \arg(z_1+z_2) = \tan^{-1}\left(\dfrac{-3}{7}\right) \end{cases} \qquad \therefore \begin{cases} |z_1-z_2| = \sqrt{82} \\ \arg(z_1-z_2) = \tan^{-1} 9. \end{cases}$$

See Fig. 24a, b.

* i.e z_1+z_2 is one diagonal, and z_1-z_2 is parallel to the other diagonal, of the parallelogram formed from z_1, z_2.

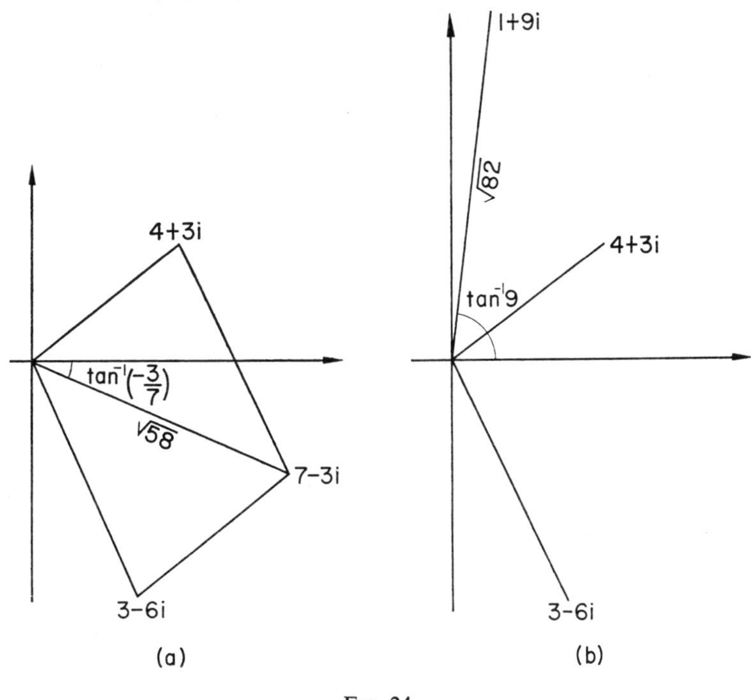

FIG. 24

Clearly, by Euclid's theorem (the sum of any two sides of a triangle is ⩾ the third side) we have the *triangle inequality:*

$$|z_1 \pm z_2| \leqslant |z_1|+|z_2| \qquad (\alpha)$$

which, for a finite number of complex numbers $z_1, \ldots, z_n$ may be generalised thus:

$$|z_1 \pm z_2 \pm \ldots \pm z_n| \leqslant |z_1|+|z_2|+\ldots+|z_n|,$$

i.e. the modulus of the algebraic sum of the numbers is ⩽ the sum of the moduli.

Also note that $|z_1| \leqslant |z_1 - z_2|+|z_2|$

i.e. $$|z_1-z_2| \geqslant |z_1|-|z_2|. \qquad (\beta)$$

Can you verify (α) and (β) taking the values for z_1, z_2 as in Example 50?

Geometrical meanings of z_1z_2, z_1/z_2

In Fig. 25a, given P_1, P_2 construct Q by making $\triangle$s OP_1Q, OIP_2 similar.

$$\therefore \frac{OQ}{OP_1} = \frac{OP_2}{OI}, \quad \text{i.e. } OQ = OP_1.OP_2.$$

Construct R by making $\triangle$s ORP_1, OIP_2 similar. (Fig. 25(b).)

$$\therefore \frac{OP_1}{OP_2} = \frac{OR}{OI}, \quad \text{i.e.} \quad OR = \frac{OP_1}{OP_2}.$$

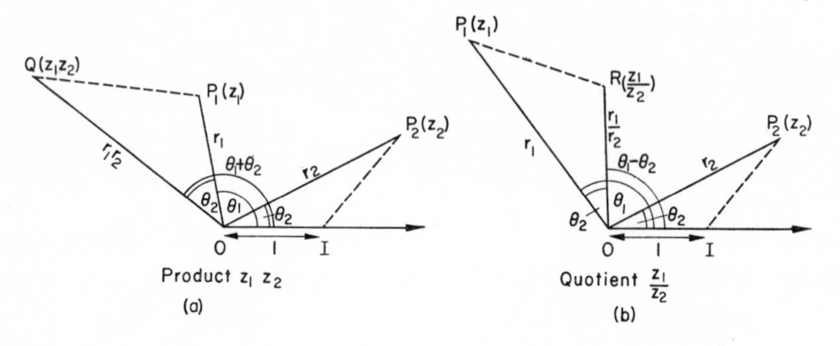

FIG. 25. (a) Product and (b) quotient of two complex numbers

EXAMPLE 51 (product and quotient for $z_1 = 4+3i$, $z_2 = 3-6i$).

Solution.

$$z_1z_2 = 15(2-i) \qquad z_1/z_2 = \frac{-2+11i}{15}$$

$$\therefore \begin{cases} |z_1z_2| = 15\sqrt{5} = |z_1|\,|z_2| \\ \arg(z_1z_2) = \tan^{-1}\left(\frac{1}{2}\right) \end{cases} \qquad \therefore \begin{cases} \left|\frac{z_1}{z_2}\right| = \frac{\sqrt{5}}{3} = \frac{|z_1|}{|z_2|} \\ \arg\left(\frac{z_1}{z_2}\right) = \tan^{-1}\left(-\frac{11}{2}\right) \end{cases}$$

$$= \tan^{-1}\left(\frac{3}{4}\right) + \tan^{-1}(-2) \qquad = \tan^{-1}\left(\frac{3}{4}\right) - \tan^{-1}(-2)$$

$$= \arg z_1 + \arg z_2 \qquad = \arg z_1 - \arg z_2.$$

See Fig. 26a, b.

Complex exponents. Hitherto, we have been concerned only with real exponents, e.g. e^x where x is real. How do we expand this notion to account for complex exponents? Adopting previous experience as a guide, we define, for the complex number z, the complex power series

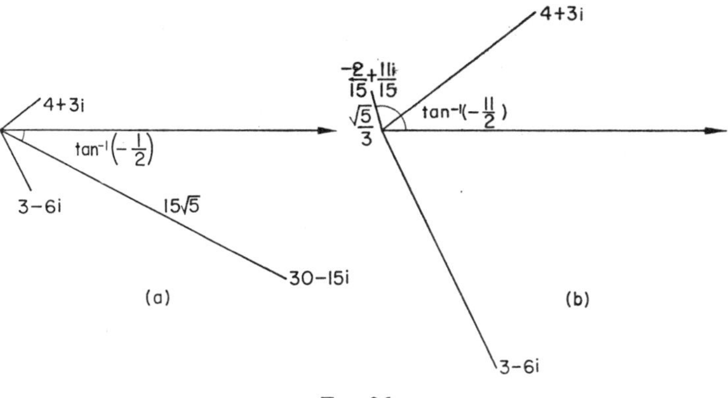

FIG. 26

$$e^z = 1+z+\frac{z^2}{2!}+\frac{z^3}{3!}+\ldots+\frac{z^n}{n!}+\ldots \qquad (16.1)'$$

$$\cos z = 1-\frac{z^2}{2!}+\frac{z^4}{4!}-\ldots+(-1)^n\frac{z^{2n}}{(2n)!}+\ldots \qquad (91.1)'$$

$$\sin z = z-\frac{z^3}{3!}+\frac{z^5}{5!}-\ldots+(-1)^n\frac{z^{2n+1}}{(2n+1)!}\ldots \qquad (91.2)'$$

Behaviour of complex exponents is generally similar to that for real exponents.

§ 48. EULER'S THEOREM (1742)

Euler's theorem $\boxed{e^{i\theta} = \cos\theta+i\sin\theta \quad (\theta \text{ real})}$. (110)

Proof.

$$e^{i\theta} = 1+i\theta+\frac{(i\theta)^2}{2!}+\frac{(i\theta)^3}{3!}+\ldots \qquad \text{replacing } x \text{ by } i\theta \text{ in (16.1)}$$

$$= 1+i\theta-\frac{\theta^2}{2!}-\frac{i\theta^3}{3!}+\frac{\theta^4}{4!}+\frac{i\theta^5}{5!}-\ldots$$

$$= \left(1-\frac{\theta^2}{2!}+\frac{\theta^4}{4!}-\frac{\theta^6}{6!}+\ldots\right)+i\left(\theta-\frac{\theta^3}{3!}+\frac{\theta^5}{5!}-\ldots\right)$$

$$= \cos\theta+i\sin\theta \qquad \text{by (91.1) and (91.2)}$$

$$\therefore \quad \boxed{z = (x, y) = x+iy = r(\cos\theta+i\sin\theta) = re^{i\theta}}. \qquad (111)$$

Observe that $e^{i\theta} = \sqrt{\cos^2\theta+\sin^2\theta} = 1$.

Results deducible from Euler's theorem

Result I. $e^{in\theta} = \cos n\theta + i \sin n\theta$ replacing θ by $n\theta$ in (110).
But $e^{in\theta} = (e^{i\theta})^n = (\cos\theta + i\sin\theta)^n$ by (110).
Therefore we deduce *De Moivre's theorem* (De Moivre, 1667–1754, English) for n real, namely,

$$\boxed{(\cos\theta + i\sin\theta)^n = \cos n\theta + i\sin n\theta}. \tag{112}$$

Thus, swiftly, De Moivre's theorem is seen in its proper perspective against the background of Euler's theorem.

Result II. $e^{i\theta} = \cos\theta + i\sin\theta$
$\therefore\ e^{-i\theta} = \cos\theta - i\sin\theta$

$$\therefore\quad \boxed{\cos\theta = \frac{e^{i\theta}+e^{-i\theta}}{2}} \quad \boxed{\sin\theta = \frac{e^{i\theta}-e^{-i\theta}}{2i}}. \tag{113}$$

Result III. From (28.1), (28.2) we have (with de Foncenex, 1734–99, French):

$$\boxed{\begin{aligned} \sinh ix &= i\sin x \\ \cosh ix &= \cos x \end{aligned}}. \tag{114}$$

From these, de Foncenex deduced analogues of Euler's and De Moivre's theorems, namely:

$$e^{\pm ix} = \cosh ix \pm \sinh ix, \ (\cosh ix \pm \sinh ix)^n = \cosh inx \pm \sinh inx.$$

Immediately it follows from (32) and (114) that $\sinh(x \pm iy) = \sinh x \cos y \pm i \cosh x \sin y$ and similarly for $\cosh(x \pm iy)$. Also, $\sinh n\pi i = 0$ (n integer), $\cosh(n\pi i) = (-1)^n$, $\sinh(x + n\pi i) = (-1)^n \sinh x$, etc. Additional details are given in Reference (a), Chapter 5.

Result IV. The formal process of taking arguments is similar to that of taking logarithms, for, if $z = re^{i\theta}$, $z' = r'e^{i\theta'}$, then $zz' = rr'e^{i(\theta+\theta')}$,

$$\frac{z}{z'} = \frac{r}{r'} e^{i(\theta-\theta')},\ z^n = r^n e^{in\theta}:$$

$$\therefore \left\{ \begin{aligned} \arg(zz') &= \theta + \theta' = \arg z + \arg z' \quad \text{(see Examples 50, 51)} \\ \arg\left(\frac{z}{z'}\right) &= \theta - \theta' = \arg z - \arg z' \\ \arg(z^n) &= n\theta \qquad = n \arg z. \end{aligned} \right.$$

Result V: From Euler's theorem we find (n integer)

$$e^{(4n+1)\pi i/2} = i;\ e^{(4n+3)\pi i/2} = -i$$

$$e^{\pm in\pi} = -1\ (n \text{ odd});\ e^{\pm in\pi} = 1\ (n \text{ even, including } 0).$$

In particular,

$$\boxed{\begin{aligned} e^{\pi i/2} &= i, \quad e^{-\pi i/2} = -i \\ e^{i\pi} &= e^{-i\pi} = -1 \\ e^{2\pi i} &= e^{-2\pi i} = e^0 = 1 \end{aligned}} \quad (115)$$

Euler's identity

$$\boxed{e^{i\pi}+1 = 0} \quad (116)$$

contains the five most important numbers in mathematics, as well as two of the basic operations, + and =. Reflect, for a moment, on the actual nature and values of e, π, i and you will realise just what a beautiful and impressive result this is.

§ 49. COMPLEX NUMBERS AND POLYNOMIAL EQUATIONS

Assume the *fundamental theorem of algebra* (due to Euler and Gauss) w.r.t. the polynominal $f(x) \equiv a_0x^n+a_1x^{n-1}+\ldots+a_{n-1}x+a_n = 0$ (degree n):

$$\boxed{f(x) = 0 \text{ has a root}} \quad (117)$$

(which may be real or complex).

By repeated application of the fundamental theorem, we deduce with Harriot (1560–1621, English):

$$\boxed{f(x) = 0 \text{ has exactly } n \text{ roots}} \quad (118)$$

(not all necessarily distinct—they may be real or complex).

Complex roots (if they occur) *must* occur in conjugate pairs if the coefficients $a_0, \ldots, a_n$ in $f(x) = 0$ are all real. For example, $x^3-3x^2+4x-2 = 0 = (x-1)(x-1+i)(x-1-i)$ has roots $x = 1,\ 1+i,\ 1-i$.

EXAMPLE 52 (n (complex) roots of unity: $z^n = 1$).

Solution. Now $z^n = e^{2\pi qi} \quad (q = 0, 1, \ldots, n-1)$

$$= \cos 2\pi q + i \sin 2\pi q$$

$$\therefore z = e^{2\pi qi/n} = \boxed{\cos\frac{2\pi q}{n} + i \sin\frac{2\pi q}{n}} \quad (q = 0, 1, \ldots, n-1). \quad (119)$$

Principal root: $q = 0$, i.e. $z = 1$.

The n roots of unity form the vertices of a regular n-gon inscribed in the unit circle $|z| = 1$, one vertex being at the point $z = 1$ (Fig. 27).

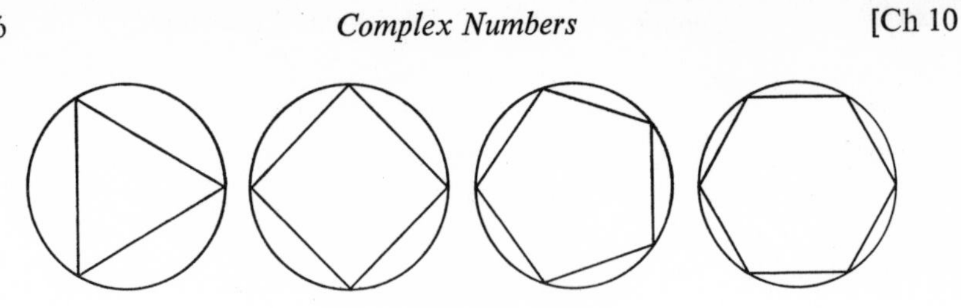

FIG. 27. n roots of unity

In particular, the *cube roots of unity* are

$$1, \quad \cos\frac{2\pi}{3}+i\sin\frac{2\pi}{3}, \cos\frac{4\pi}{3}+i\sin\frac{4\pi}{3}$$

i.e.

$$\boxed{1, \quad \underset{=\varepsilon}{\frac{-1+\sqrt{3}i}{2}}, \quad \underset{=\varepsilon^2}{\frac{-1-\sqrt{3}i}{2}}}. \tag{120}$$

[Note that $1+\varepsilon+\varepsilon^2 = 0, \quad \varepsilon^3 = 1, \quad \varepsilon^{-1} = \varepsilon^2, \varepsilon^{-2} = \varepsilon$.]

§ 50. ELEMENTARY SYMMETRIC FUNCTIONS

(due to Vieta (1540–1603, French), Girard (1590?–1633?, Dutch), Harriot)

Suppose $\alpha, \beta, \gamma, \ldots, \nu$ are the n roots of $f(x) = 0$.

$$\therefore f(x) \equiv a_0(x-\alpha)(x-\beta)(x-\gamma)\ldots(x-\nu) \quad (a_0 \neq 0).$$

Equate coefficients of corresponding powers of x and we obtain the elementary symmetric functions of the roots:

$$\boxed{\begin{aligned} \sum\alpha &= -\frac{a_1}{a_0} \\ \sum\alpha\beta &= \frac{a_2}{a_0} \\ \sum\alpha\beta\gamma &= -\frac{a_3}{a_0} \\ &\ldots\ldots\ldots\ldots \end{aligned}}. \tag{121}$$

Here, in (121), $\sum$ means summation over the roots or products of roots.

EXAMPLE 53 (elementary symmetric functions). If a, b, c are the roots of $x^3+px^2+qx+r = 0$, find the equation whose roots are bc, ca, ab.

Solution 1. The elementary symmetric functions are

$$\begin{cases} \sum a = -p \\ \sum ab = q \\ abc = -r. \end{cases}$$

Let the new equation be

$$x^3+Px^2+Qx+R = 0,$$

where
$$-P = bc+ca+ab = q$$
$$Q = \sum ab\ bc$$
$$= abc \sum a$$
$$= rp$$

and
$$-R = ab\ bc\ ca$$
$$= a^2b^2c^2$$
$$= r^2.$$

Therefore the required equation is $x^3-qx^2+rpx-r^2 = 0$.

Solution 2. Now $bc = \dfrac{abc}{a} = -\dfrac{r}{a}$.

Put
$$y = -\frac{r}{x}.$$

Therefore the three values of y corresponding to values a, b, c of x are bc, ca, ab.
Therefore put $x = -r/y$ in the original.

Therefore the required equation is $\left(-\dfrac{r}{y}\right)^3+p\left(-\dfrac{r}{y}\right)^2+q\left(-\dfrac{r}{y}\right)+r = 0$

i.e.
$$y^3-qy^2+pry-r^2 = 0.$$

[Solution 1 is quite routine and should always give the correct answer. On the other hand, solution 2 demands greater mathematical insight and finesse and is therefore to be preferred.]

Suppose we are given a particular polynomial with real coefficients to solve. Various steps may be used (if the solution is not immediate):

(a) *Descartes' rule of signs* enables us to determine the numbers of positive and negative roots;

(b) *Sturm's theorem* (Sturm, 1803–55, Swiss) enables us to locate each of these roots between two consecutive integers;

(c) Certain numerical methods then allow us to approximate to the root quite accurately. Of these, the best known are those of Newton and Horner (1773–1827, English), though it is instructive to realise that *Horner's method* was known in 1247 to Ch'in Chiu-shao (13th cent., Chinese). Essentially, Horner's method consists of a number of steps (the number depending on the required degree of accuracy) each of which involves transforming according to a fixed procedure an equation into another equation with roots related to those of the former. A clear statement of the principles and practical processes of Horner's method may be found in C. V. Durell (and A. Robson), *Advanced Algebra*, Vol. I (Bell, 1946). Nowadays, electronic computers are used to help solve awkward equations.

Interested students wishing to learn more about the theory of equations could consult any standard work for further details.

§ 51. SOME TYPICAL PROBLEMS INVOLVING COMPLEX NUMBERS

EXAMPLE 54 (formulae for $\cos 3\theta$, $\sin 3\theta$ (attributed to Ulug Beg, 1393–1449, Arab)—these can, of course, be obtained by ordinary trigonometrical methods).

Solution. Now $\cos 3\theta + i \sin 3\theta = (\cos\theta + i\sin\theta)^3$ by (112)

$$= \cos^3\theta + 3\cos\theta(i\sin\theta)^2 + 3\cos^2\theta(i\sin\theta) + (i\sin\theta)^3$$
$$= \cos^3\theta - 3\cos\theta\sin^2\theta + i(3\cos^2\theta\sin\theta - \sin^3\theta)$$
$$= \cos^3\theta - 3\cos\theta(1-\cos^2\theta) + i(3\sin\theta(1-\sin^2\theta) - \sin^3\theta)$$
$$= 4\cos^3\theta - 3\cos\theta + i(3\sin\theta - 4\sin^3\theta).$$

Equate real and imaginary parts

$$\therefore \boxed{\cos 3\theta = 4\cos^3\theta - 3\cos\theta \quad \sin 3\theta = 3\sin\theta - 4\sin^3\theta}. \tag{122}$$

Similarly, but more easily, we obtain

$$\boxed{\sin 2\theta = 2\sin\theta\cos\theta}, \quad \boxed{\cos 2\theta = \cos^2\theta - \sin^2\theta}$$
$$\boxed{\tan 2\theta = 2\tan\theta/(1-\tan^2\theta)}. \tag{122.1}$$

Obviously, this gives us a convenient technique for obtaining expressions for $\cos n\theta$ and $\sin n\theta$.

EXAMPLE 55. Solve $\cos z = 4$. (Do not be alarmed that $\cos z > 1$! We are dealing with complex, not real, numbers. But you ask, how is the definition of $\cos\theta$ (θ real) widened to allow of $\cos z$ (z complex)?) Paralleling Euler's theorem (110) for θ real, using (16.1)′, (91.1)′, (91.2)′, we obtain:

$$\boxed{\begin{array}{l} e^{iz} = \cos z + i\sin z \\ \cos z = \dfrac{e^{iz}+e^{-iz}}{2}, \quad \sin z = \dfrac{e^{iz}-e^{-iz}}{2i} \end{array}}. \qquad \begin{array}{r}(110)' \\ (113)'\end{array}$$

Solution. $\dfrac{e^{iz}+e^{-iz}}{2} = 4$ using (113)

i.e. $e^{2iz}-8e^{iz}+1=0$ (quadratic in e^{iz})

$$\therefore\ e^{iz}=\frac{8\pm\sqrt{60}}{2}=4\pm\sqrt{15}$$

$$\therefore\ iz=\log(4\pm\sqrt{15})$$

$$\therefore\ z=-i\log(4\pm\sqrt{15}).$$

[Note: $\cos^2 z+\sin^2 z=1$ so if $\cos z=4$ then $\sin z=i\sqrt{15}$.]

EXAMPLE 56. Express (i) $\sqrt{5+12i}$, (ii) $\sqrt{i}$ in the form $a+ib$ (a, b real).

Solutions. $\sqrt{5+12i}=\sqrt{(a+ib)^2}=\sqrt{a^2-b^2+2iab}$

whence
$$\begin{cases} a^2-b^2=5 \\ ab=6 \end{cases}$$

whence
$$a=3,\ b=2$$

$$\therefore\ \sqrt{5+12i}=3+2i;$$

or
$$\sqrt{5+12i}=\sqrt{13}\left(\frac{5}{13}+\frac{12}{13}i\right)^{1/2}=\sqrt{13}(e^{i\theta})^{1/2}$$

by (110) where
$$\begin{cases} \cos\theta=\dfrac{5}{13}\ \therefore\ \cos\dfrac{\theta}{2}=\sqrt{\dfrac{\cos\theta+1}{2}}=\dfrac{3}{\sqrt{13}} \\ \sin\theta=\dfrac{12}{13}\ \therefore\ \sin\dfrac{\theta}{2}=\sqrt{\dfrac{1-\cos\theta}{2}}=\dfrac{2}{\sqrt{13}} \end{cases}$$

$$\therefore\ \sqrt{5+12i}=\sqrt{13}\left(\cos\frac{\theta}{2}+i\sin\frac{\theta}{2}\right)\quad(=\sqrt{13}\,e^{i\theta/2})$$

$$=\sqrt{13}\left(\frac{3}{\sqrt{13}}+\frac{2i}{\sqrt{13}}\right)$$

$$=3+2i.$$

(ii) $\sqrt{i}=\sqrt{a^2-b^2+2iab}$ $\quad\therefore\ \begin{cases} a^2-b^2=0 \\ ab=\frac{1}{2} \end{cases}$ whence $a=b=\dfrac{1}{\sqrt{2}}$

$$\therefore\ \sqrt{i}=\frac{1}{\sqrt{2}}(1+i);$$

or
$$\sqrt{i}=(e^{\pi i/2})^{1/2}\quad\text{by (115)}$$
$$=e^{\pi i/4}$$
$$=\frac{1}{\sqrt{2}}(1+i)\quad\text{by (110).}$$

[It is a good idea to mark the points representing these complex numbers, together with moduli and arguments, in the Argand diagram.]

EXAMPLE 57. Find a meaning for each of the following:

(i) i^{i^i} (ii) π^{-i} (iii) $(1-i)^i$ (iv) $i^{\sqrt{i}}$.

Solution.

(i) $i^i = (e^{i\pi/2})^i = e^{-\pi/2}$ (real) by (115).

$$\therefore\ i^{(i^i)} = i^{e^{-\pi/2}}$$

$$= (e^{i\pi/2})^{e^{-\pi/2}} \quad \text{by (115)}$$

$$= e^{i(\pi/2)e^{-\pi/2}}$$

$$= \cos\left(\frac{\pi}{2}\, e^{-\pi/2}\right) + i \sin\left(\frac{\pi}{2}\, e^{-\pi/2}\right) \quad \text{by (110).}$$

(ii) $\pi^{-i} = e^{-i \log \pi}$ using (18.1)

$$= \cos \log \pi - i \sin \log \pi \quad \text{by (110).}$$

(iii) $(1-i)^i = (\sqrt{2}e^{-i\pi/4})^i \quad \because\ e^{-i\pi/4} = \dfrac{1-i}{\sqrt{2}}$

$$= e^{\pi/4}(\sqrt{2})^i$$

$$= e^{\pi/4}\, e^{i \log \sqrt{2}} \quad \text{by (18.1)}$$

$$= e^{\pi/4}\{\cos \log \sqrt{2} + i \sin \log \sqrt{2}\} \quad \text{by (110).}$$

(iv) $i^{\sqrt{i}} = i^{e^{i\pi/4}}$ by Example 56 (ii)

$$= e^{(i\pi/2)e^{i\pi/4}} \quad \text{by (115)}$$

$$= e^{i(\pi/2)(1+i)/\sqrt{2}}$$

$$= e^{\pi(i-1)/(2\sqrt{2})}$$

$$= e^{-\pi/(2\sqrt{2})}\left\{\cos\left(\frac{\pi}{2\sqrt{2}}\right) + i \sin\left(\frac{\pi}{2\sqrt{2}}\right)\right\} \quad \text{by (110).}$$

Note. In the work above, we have restricted ourselves to the simplest expression for the answer, whereas more general expressions exist on account of the many-valuedness of the argument, e.g.

$$i^i = e^{[(2n+1/2)\pi i]i}$$

$$= e^{-[(4n+1)/2]\pi}$$

and $(1-i)^i = e^{2n\pi+\pi/4}(\cos \log \sqrt{2} + i \sin \log \sqrt{2}) \because \dfrac{1-i}{\sqrt{2}} = e^{-i(\pi/4+2n\pi)}$.

To illustrate the variety of mathematical usages of complex numbers, consider the following [Example 25(d′)]:

$$\int e^{(\alpha+i\beta)x}\, dx = \frac{e^{(\alpha+i\beta)x}}{\alpha+i\beta} + C + iD$$

$$= \int e^{\alpha x} e^{i\beta x}\, dx \qquad = \frac{(\alpha - i\beta)e^{(\alpha+i\beta)x}}{\alpha^2+\beta^2} + C + iD$$

$$= \int e^{\alpha x} (\cos \beta x + i \sin \beta x)\, dx \qquad = \frac{(\alpha - i\beta)}{\alpha^2+\beta^2} e^{\alpha x} (\cos \beta x + i \sin \beta x) + C + iD$$

$$= \int e^{\alpha x} \cos \beta x\, dx + i \int e^{\alpha x} \sin \beta x\, dx \qquad = \frac{e^{\alpha x}}{\alpha^2+\beta^2} \{(\alpha \cos \beta x + \beta \sin \beta x) + i(\alpha \sin \beta x - \beta \cos \beta x)\} + C + iD.$$

Equating real and imaginary parts, we have

$$\begin{cases} \displaystyle\int e^{\alpha x} \cos \beta x\, dx = \frac{e^{\alpha x}(\alpha \cos \beta x + \beta \sin \beta x)}{\alpha^2+\beta^2} + C \\ \displaystyle\int e^{\alpha x} \sin \beta x\, dx = \frac{e^{\alpha x}(\alpha \sin \beta x - \beta \cos \beta x)}{\alpha^2+\beta^2} + D. \end{cases}$$

Loci problems

Before proceeding with problems concerning loci in the complex plane, we deduce as for real points that:

(i) if P_1, P_2 represent the points $z_1 = x_1 + iy_1$, $z_2 = x_2 + iy_2$ respectively, and

$$\boxed{\text{if } Q \text{ divides } P_1P_2 \text{ in the ratio } \lambda : \mu, \text{ then } Q \text{ represents the point } \frac{\mu z_1 + \lambda z_2}{\lambda + \mu}} \tag{123}$$

i.e. the mid-point is the complex number $\dfrac{z_1+z_2}{2} = \dfrac{x_1+x_2}{2} + i\dfrac{y_1+y_2}{2}$;

(ii) the *complex equation of a line* is

$$\boxed{\bar{a}z + a\bar{z} + b = 0} \tag{124}$$

on substituting $x = \dfrac{z+\bar{z}}{2}$, $y = \dfrac{z-\bar{z}}{2i}$ in the equation $lx + my + n = 0$ (l, m, n real) and writing $l + im = a$, $2n = b$;

(iii) the *complex equation of a circle* with centre α (complex) and radius r is

$$\boxed{|z - \alpha| = r}\,. \tag{125}$$

EXAMPLE 58 (general locus problem). The points B, P, Q in the Argand diagram represent the complex numbers 2, z, $1/z$ respectively. If P describes the circle on OB as diameter, what is the locus of Q?

Solution. If $z = re^{i\theta}$, then $\dfrac{1}{z} = \dfrac{1}{r} e^{-i\theta}$.

Clearly (Fig. 28) $\triangle$s QOA, AOP are similar $\left[\because \frac{r}{1} = \frac{1}{1/r}\right] \therefore QO = QA$. Therefore the locus of Q is the $\perp$ bisector of OA whose equation is $R(z) = \frac{1}{2}$, i.e. $z+\bar{z} = 1$. [Note the substitution $z = re^{i\theta}$ rather than $z = x+iy$ when the nature of the question seems to suggest it.]

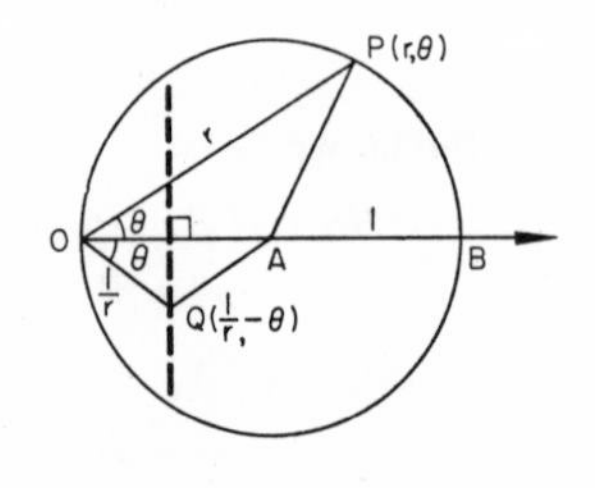

FIG. 28

EXAMPLE 59 (regions of the complex plane). Identify the points in the complex plane which satisfy the inequalities

(i) $R(z) \geqslant 1$. (ii) $|z+3i| < 2$. (iii) $0 \leqslant \arg z < \frac{\pi}{2}$, $|z| > 2$.

(iv) $I(z^2) \geqslant 1$.

Solution. (i) All points in the *half-plane* to the right of and on the line $x = 1$ (Fig. 29).

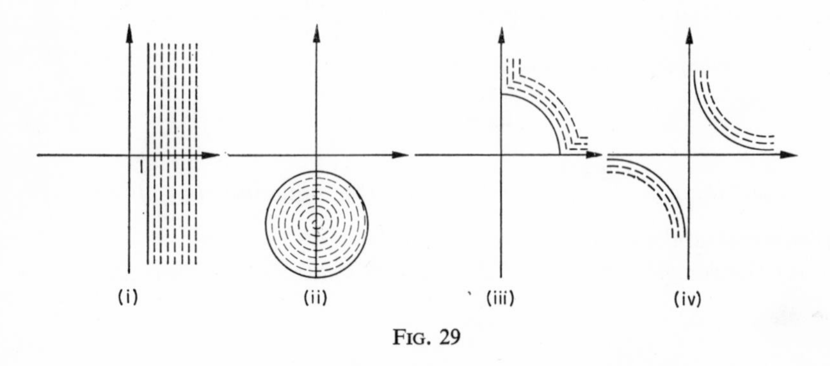

FIG. 29

(ii) All points inside the circle centre $(0, -3)$ and radius 2.

(iii) All points in the first quadrant outside the circle $z = 2$, and on the x-axis but not on the y-axis.

(iv) All points on and outside the rectangular hyperbola $2xy = 1$. In (iv), $I(z^2) = I[(x+iy)^2] = 2xy$.

EXAMPLE 60 (*circle of Apollonius*, 3rd cent. B.C., Greek). Determine the locus

$$\frac{z-\alpha}{z-\beta} = k \quad (\alpha, \beta \text{ complex}, k \text{ constant}).$$

Solution. Write $z = x+iy$, $\alpha = a+ib$, $\beta = c+id$.

$$\therefore\ |x-a+i(y-b)| = k|x-c+i(y-d)| \quad \because\ |z-\alpha| = k|z-\beta|$$

$$\therefore\ (x-a)^2+(y-b)^2 = k^2\{(x-c)^2+(y-d)^2\}. \tag{I}$$

Simplify to get $$\left(x-\frac{a-k^2c}{1-k^2}\right)^2+\left(y-\frac{b-k^2d}{1-k^2}\right)^2$$

$$= \frac{k^2}{(1-k^2)^2}\{(a-c)^2+(b-d)^2\},$$

i.e. a circle centre $\left(\frac{a-k^2c}{1-k^2}, \frac{b-k^2d}{1-k^2}\right)$, radius $\frac{k}{1-k^2}\sqrt{(a-c)^2+(b-d)^2}$ (circle of Apollonius), i.e. a circle centre $\frac{\alpha-k^2\beta}{1-k^2}$, radius $\frac{k|\alpha-\beta|}{|1-k^2|}$.

Putting $k^2 = 1$ in (I) we have $2(a-c)x+2(b-d)y = a^2-c^2+b^2-d^2$,

i.e. $y-\frac{b+d}{2} = -\frac{a-c}{b-d}\left(x-\frac{a+c}{2}\right)$,

i.e. line through $\left(\frac{a+c}{2}, \frac{b+d}{2}\right)$ with gradient $1\Big/\left(\frac{b-d}{a-c}\right) = -\frac{1}{\text{gradient } PQ}$,

i.e. locus is the $\perp$ bisector of PQ (see Fig. 30a, b).

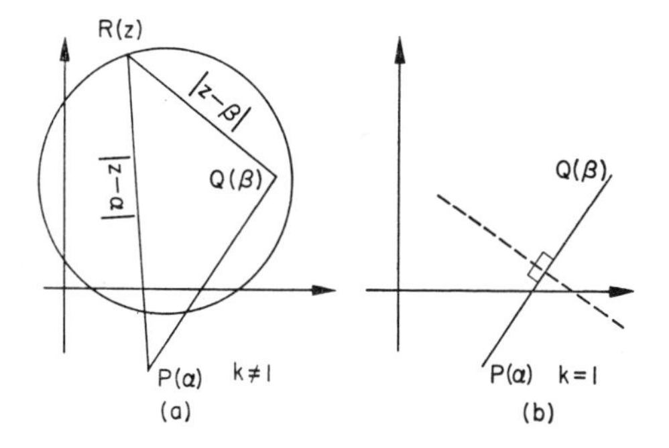

FIG. 30. (a) Circle of Apollonius.

EXAMPLE 61. Determine the locus $\arg\left(\frac{z-\alpha}{z-\beta}\right)$ = constant (α, β complex).

Solution. $\arg\left(\frac{z-\alpha}{z-\beta}\right) = \arg(z-\alpha)-\arg(z-\beta)$ by § 48, Result IV.

$$= \theta-\phi = \psi \text{ (const.)}$$

Therefore locus is a circle through α, β. [Actually it is a circular arc. See Fig. 31.]

Corollary. Let $P_1(z_1)$, $P_2(z_2)$, $P_3(z_3)$, $P_4(z_4)$ be four concyclic points (Fig. 32).

$\therefore\ P_1\hat{P}_3P_2 = P_1\hat{P}_4P_2 = \text{const.}$ (on the same arc P_1P_2)

$$\therefore\ \arg\left(\frac{z_3-z_1}{z_3-z_2}\right) = \arg\left(\frac{z_4-z_1}{z_4-z_2}\right)$$

$$= z$$

$$\therefore\ \arg\left(\overbrace{\frac{z_3-z_1}{z_3-z_2}\,\frac{z_4-z_2}{z_4-z_1}}\right) = 0 \qquad \text{by § 48, Result IV.}$$

This is so if $z = re^{i(\theta+2n\pi)} = r$, i.e. z is a real number.

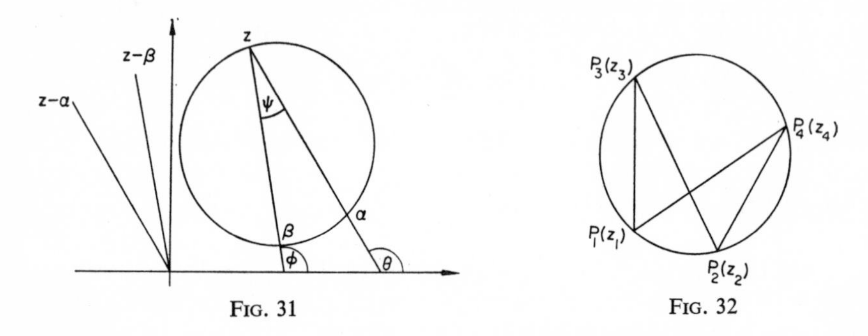

FIG. 31 FIG. 32

Therefore four points $P_i(z_i)$ are concyclic only if their *cross-ratio*

$$\frac{z_3-z_1}{z_3-z_2}\,\frac{z_4-z_2}{z_4-z_1} \quad \text{is real.}$$

Later, in Chapter 15, we deal with the elementary theory of cross-ratio in the ordinary Euclidean plane.

Applications of complex numbers

Among the many ways in which complex numbers may be applied scientifically we may mention problems involving elasticity, analysis of *X*-ray diffraction, wave propagation, quantum theory, electrical and hydroelectric engineering, circuit analysis for a.c. circuits, hydrodynamics (fluid flow), and aerodynamics (e.g. the flow of an airstream past an aerofoil), many of which have a strong practical value. In aerofoil theory (Joukovsky, 1847–1921, Russian), the problem is to calculate the strength of the circulation of the airstream about a shaped body (say, the shape of an aeroplane wing) and so to know the lift exerted on it. These things are known for a circular cylinder. What is then desired is to use this information to deduce the flow around a wing of more complicated shape. Complex numbers allow us to do this by a suitable transformation. Air-flow is studied in a variety of different circumstances, e.g. in domestic ventilation, air conditioning, blast furnaces, naval architecture.

Another interesting application of complex numbers occurs when we map a surface on to a plane by means of a transformation which preserves angles, i.e. an explorer reading the plane map can then be sure of his directions on the surface of the Earth. An angle-preserving transformation like this is known as a *conformal transformation (mapping)*. One of the most famous conformal maps, of great use to geographers, is *Mercator's projection* which we find in school atlases. Allied to this theory is the work on *stereographic projection* by which the points of the surface of the unit sphere are projected from the "North Pole" on to the equatorial plane. Corresponding to the North Pole itself is a single point at infinity in the plane. When the unit sphere is used in this way to represent complex variables it is called a *Riemann sphere*.

With these thoughts in mind, it is worth meditating on the tremendous power of the purely imaginary number $\sqrt{-1}$.

§ 52. HYPERCOMPLEX NUMBERS (QUATERNIONS)

Having constructed a system of real number-pairs which obeys the laws of arithmetic for ordinary real numbers, we naturally ask: Can we extend this idea to sets of more than two real numbers? The answer is: Yes, but not all the laws are satisfied.

Beyond complex numbers, then, there lie *hypercomplex numbers* of which the simplest are *quaternions* (discovered by Hamilton) in which each number has four real ordered components. A quaternion is defined, for a, b, c, d real, as

$$\boxed{q = a+ib+jc+kd = (a, b, c, d)} \tag{126}$$

where

$$\boxed{\begin{array}{lll} i^2 = j^2 = k^2 = -1 & & \\ ij = -ji, & jk = -kj, & ki = -ik \\ \quad = k & \quad = i & \quad = j \end{array}} \tag{127}$$

and $a = (a, 0, 0, 0)$, $i = (0, 1, 0, 0)$, $j = (0, 0, 1, 0)$, $k = (0, 0, 0, 1)$.

Quaternions are non-commutative under multiplication, i.e. quaternions form a skew-field. Verify that the other ring properties hold. Addition (subtraction) is defined as for complex numbers which occur as special cases of quaternions when $c = d = 0$. Zero quaternion for addition is $0 = (0, 0, 0, 0)$ and the multiplicative unit is $1 = (1, 0, 0, 0)$. Thus, we may speak of a *quaternion ring* (but not a quaternion field). Quaternions are useful in physics and relativity, e.g. in Minkowski's four-dimensional space-time world.

Results (127) may be expressed by the *multiplication table:*

$\times$	1	i	j	k
1	1	i	j	k
i	i	-1	k	$-j$
j	j	$-k$	-1	i
k	k	j	$-i$	-1

EXAMPLE 62 (quaternions). Given the quaternions $A = (1, 1, 1, 1)$, $B = (1, -2, 0, 1)$ calculate (i) $A+B$, (ii) AB, (iii) $1/A$.

Solution. (i) $A+B = (1+1, 1-2, 1+0, 1+1) = (2, -1, 1, 2)$.

(ii) $AB = (1+2+0-1, -2+1+1+0, 0-1+1-2, 1+0+2+1) = (2, 0, -2, 4)$.

(iii)
$$\frac{1}{A} = \frac{1}{(1,1,1,1)}\,\frac{(1,-1,-1,-1)}{(1,-1,-1,-1)}$$
$$= \frac{(1,-1,-1,-1)}{(1+1+1+1, -1+1-1+1, -1+1+1-1, -1-1+1+1)}$$
$$= \frac{(1,-1,-1,-1)}{4}.$$

(See Exercises 10.64–10.66.)

Structural hierarchy of the number system

Starting from the natural numbers, we have seen how the number system is hierarchically constructed. Anticipating transfinite numbers in Chapter 13, we may describe the various interrelationships of numbers schematically thus:

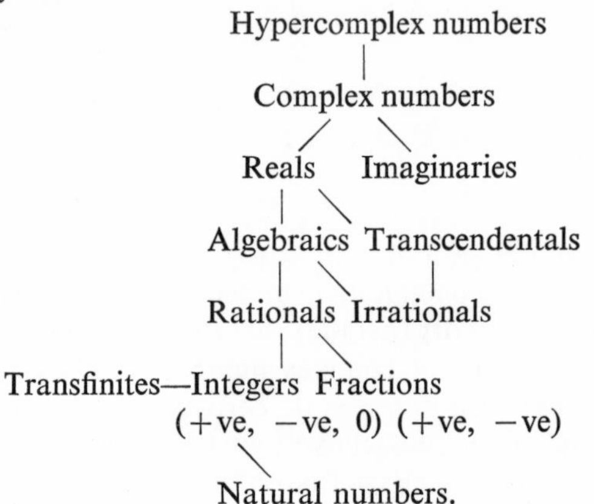

Suggested topics for further study

(1) Conformal mapping (including Joukovsky and Möbius transformations (Exercise 14.75), Möbius, 1790–1868, German).
(2) Numerical solutions of equations.
(3) Achievements and tragic life of Galois (Reference, Bell [3]).
(4) Solutions of Cardan and Ferrari (1522–65, Italian) for the cubic and quartic equations, respectively. [See *Theory of Equations*, H. W. Turnbull (Oliver & Boyd, 1947).]

References

(a) *Complex Numbers*, W. Ledermann (Routledge and Kegan Paul, 1960).
(b) *Higher Mathematics*, F. G. W. Brown (Macmillan, 1946).
(c) *Advanced Trigonometry*, C. V. Durell and A. Robson (Bell, 1930).
(d) Dubisch [32]; Smirnov [24]; Tranter [28].

EXERCISES 10

Say whether the following numbers 1–7 are irrational, giving a reason:

1. $\sqrt[3]{2}\,\sqrt[3]{4}$. **2.** $\sqrt{2}+\sqrt{3}$. **3.** $\sqrt{27}/\sqrt{3}$.

4. $\sqrt{2}-1$. **5.** $\sqrt{625}+\sqrt{841}$. **6.** $0{\cdot}\dot{9}$.

7. $\sin 7°30'$.

8. Under what circumstances is $\log_{10} k$ rational? (Generally, it is irrational.)

9. Does the set $\{2m : m \in \mathcal{J}\}$ form an integral domain? Why? (Think up other examples of integral domains.)

Determine whether or not the following sets 10–17 form a ring. Mention any special features—commutativity, unity ring, divisors of zero—of the ring.

10. $\mathcal{N}$. **11.** $\mathcal{J}$. **12.** $\mathcal{R}$. **13.** $\mathcal{R}^*$.

14. $\mathcal{J}_3$. **15.** $\mathcal{J}_4$. **16.** $\{x : x \in \mathcal{R}, x > 0\}$.

17. Real-valued continuous functions in $-1 \leqslant x \leqslant 1$ where addition and multiplication of functions $f(x), g(x)$ are defined by $(f+g)(x) = f(x)+g(x)$, $(fg)(x) = f(x)\,g(x)$. [Invent some other examples of rings.]

State whether the following sets 18–24 form (a) a ring, (b) a field:

18. $\{a+b\sqrt{2} : a, b \in \mathcal{R}\}$.

19. $\left\{a+b\left(\dfrac{1+\sqrt{5}}{2}\right) : \quad a, b \in \mathcal{R}\right\}$.

20. $\{a+b\sqrt{2}+c\sqrt{3} : \quad a, b, c \in \mathcal{R}\}$.

21. $\{a+b\sqrt{2}+c\sqrt{3}+d\sqrt{6} : \quad a, b, c, d \in \mathcal{R}\}$.

22. $\{a+b\sqrt{2}: \quad a, b \in \mathcal{J}\}$.

23. $\mathcal{C}$.

24. $\mathcal{Q}$.

25. A famous theorem of elementary number theory, due to Euclid, states: *the number of primes is infinite.* Can you prove it? If not, can you find Euclid's proof (one of the simplest and most beautiful in all Mathematics)?

With $z_1 = 5-3i$, $z_2 = 4+2i$, compute 26–28:

26. z_1-z_2. **27.** z_1z_2. **28.** $\dfrac{z_1}{z_2}$.

29. Is $|z|^{1/2} = |z^{1/2}|$? Illustrate by taking $z = -15+8i$.

Simplify 30–32:

30. $\left(\dfrac{1-i\sqrt{3}}{2}\right)^3$. **31.** $(1+i)^{-2}+(1-i)^{-2}$. **32.** $\dfrac{1+\cos\theta+i\sin\theta}{\cos\theta/2+i\sin\theta/2}$.

Find the modulus and argument of 33–36:

33. $\dfrac{2+3i}{3-2i}$. **34.** e^z, where $z = x+iy$. **35.** $(1+i)^{1/2}$.

36. $(3-3i)^{2/3}$.

Express each of the following 37–46 in the form $a+ib$ (a, b real):

37. 2^i. **38.** $i^{-\pi}$. **39.** $(-i)^{-i}$. **40.** $i^{\log(1+i)}$.

41. $(1+i)^{-1}$. **42.** e^{1+i}. **43.** $i^{1/\pi}$. **44.** $e^{1+\pi i}$.

45. $e^{3-4\pi i}$. **46.** $\sinh(1-i)$.

47. Establish *Fagnano's formula* (Fagnano, 1682–1755, Italian): $\log\dfrac{1-i}{1+i} = \dfrac{\pi}{2i}$.

48. Given
$$\begin{cases} C = 1+\cos\dfrac{2\pi}{n}+\cos\dfrac{4\pi}{n}+\ldots+\cos\dfrac{2(n-1)\pi}{n} \\ S = \sin\dfrac{2\pi}{n}+\sin\dfrac{4\pi}{n}+\ldots+\sin\dfrac{2(n-1)\pi}{n}, \end{cases}$$
prove $C = S = 0$.

49. Show that $\sqrt{-1}^{\sqrt{-1}}$ is a real number and calculate it to two decimal places. *(Frankel's problem.)*

50. Suppose that z_1, z_2, z_3 are three complex numbers whose corresponding points in the Argand diagram are Z_1, Z_2, Z_3. If $z_1z_2 = z_3^2$, show that OZ_3 bisects the angle Z_1OZ_2.

51. What is the locus in the complex plane of the point representing the complex number z subject to the relation $|z+2| = |z-5i|$?

52. Obtain the complex numbers z which simultaneously satisfy $|z| = 15$, $|z-4| = 13$. Show also how a geometrical solution may be obtained.

53. Given that x, y, r, θ are all real, find them if
$$\frac{2i-3}{(1+i)^2} = x+iy = re^{i\theta}.$$

54. Obtain a solution of $\dfrac{\sqrt{2}\,e^{-ix}}{2+i} = \dfrac{1-3i}{5}$.

55. If $a+ib = \sinh^{-1}(1+i)$, prove that $b = \tan^{-1}(\tanh a)$.

56. Show that $\sinh(x+iy)$ has modulus $\sqrt{\cosh^2 x - \cos^2 y}$ and argument $\tan^{-1}(\coth x \tan y)$.

57. The roots of $x^4 - hx^3 - kx + 1 = 0$ are a, b, c, d. Write down the values of the following functions of the roots: $\sum a$, $\sum \dfrac{1}{a}$, $\sum a^2$, $\sum \left(\dfrac{1}{a^2}\right)$.

58. If a, b, c are the roots of $x^3+px^2+qx+r = 0$, what is the equation whose roots are $b+c$, $c+a$, $a+b$? (A general cubic like the one given may always be reduced to the simpler form $x^3+Hx+G = 0$.)

59. If $\log \sin(x+iy) = \alpha+i\beta$, prove that $2e^{2\alpha} = \cosh 2y - \cos 2x$ (α, β real).

60. In the complex plane, a curve passes through the points representing the numbers $1+i$, $4+2i$, $9+3i$, $16+4i$, $25+5i$. What is the nature of the curve? Name some other points on the curve.

61. Allowing that $\displaystyle\int_0^1 \frac{dx}{x+i} = A+iB$, determine A, B (both real).

62. Beginning with $f(\theta) = \cos\theta + i\sin\theta$, deduce Euler's theorem by differentiating first and then integrating.

63. Express $\cos(3\cos^{-1} x)$ in terms of x (an expression associated with the problem of trisecting an angle).

Perform the following operations 64–66 for the quaternions A and B of Example 62:

64. $A-B$. **65.** BA. **66.** A/B.

67. Obtain the *inverse quaternion* q^{-1} of the quaternion $q = (a, b, c, d)$. [*Hint.* Use the *conjugate quaternion* $\bar{q} = (a, -b, -c, -d)$, i.e. $\bar{\bar{q}} = q$, $q+\bar{q} = 2a$. Assume $a^2+b^2+c^2+d^2 \neq 0$.]

Using complex exponential powers, prove the formulae 68–70:

68. $\sin(A \pm B) = \sin A \cos B \pm \cos A \sin B$.

69. $\cos(A \pm B) = \cos A \cos B \mp \sin A \sin B$.

70. $\tan(A \pm B) = (\tan A \pm \tan B)/(1 \mp \tan A \tan B)$.

71. Telephone line current is given by the real part of $e^{iwt}\,\mathrm{sech}\,(1+i)a$. Given the current in the form $A\sin(wt+\varepsilon)$, determine A, ε.

72. Fluid dynamics problems (e.g. stream lines in aerofoil theory) often deal with equations like $w = u+iv = f(z)$ where $f(z) = x+iy$ (u, v, x, y all real). Obtain the Cauchy–Riemann equations (Exercise 6.22) from first principles, and deduce Laplace's equation in two dimensions (Example 17).

73. Check Exercise 10.72 in the cases e^z, $1/z$.

74. *Velocity potential* ϕ and *stream function* ψ are given by $f(z) = \phi + i\psi$ (Exercise 10.72). Given $\phi = x^2 - y^2 + 3x$, find ψ and $f(z)$.

75. Given $w = z^z$, $z = x+iy$, express $R(w)$, $I(w)$ in terms of x, y. [Proposed by A. A. Mullin, *The American Mathematical Monthly*, **66**, 513 (1959).]

76. Determine the real part of $e^{pix}\,\{D(D+2pi)\}^{-1}\cdot 1$ $\left(D \equiv \dfrac{d}{dx}\right)$. [The solution represents an oscillation with an indefinitely increasing amplitude (the phenomenon of *resonance*) and is associated with the military practice of breaking step in crossing a bridge so that the soldiers' steps are out of time with the natural oscillation of the structure of the bridge.]

Cayley (*Collected Mathematical Papers*, **5**, 86–88) defined the *complex Gudermannian*

$$\phi = G(x) = \frac{1}{i} \log \tan \left(\frac{\pi}{4}+\frac{ix}{2}\right), \text{ where } x = \log \tan \left(\frac{\pi}{4}+\frac{\phi}{2}\right).$$

Confirm his results 77–80:

77. $ix = G\{iG(x)\}$.

78. $i\,G^{-1}(x) = G(ix)$.

79. $\sec G(x) = \cos ix$.

80. $\tan G(x) = -i \sin ix$.

CHAPTER 11

MATRICES

"I must do something to arouse the spiritual side: something desperate; study something, something dry and tough. What shall it be? Theology? Algebra? What's Algebra?"

"It's dry and tough enough," said I, "$a^2+2ab+b^2$."

"It's stimulating, though?" he enquired.

The next day . . . he got word of a young lady . . . who was willing and able to conduct him in these bloomless meadows [of Algebra].

(R. L. Stevenson and Lloyd Osbourne, *The Wrecker*)

Essentially, Calculus involves a limiting process, i.e. the concept of infinity plays a dominant role. Within the past century or so, other types of thinking have come to enjoy a more significant influence. Especially is this so in the case of matrix theory where we are usually concerned with a *finite* arrangement of elements. So widespread are matrices now that they must be regarded as fundamental in any study of higher mathematics. Our development of matrix theory leads naturally to a discussion of the ideas of vectors and linear independence.

Objects of this chapter are to discuss briefly:

(i) elementary properties of matrices;

(ii) some applications of matrices; and

(iii) the relation of matrices to determinants.

Matrices were first developed in 1858 by Cayley (1821–95, English) who thought of a matrix as a "convenient mode of expression of the equations $x' = ax+by$, $y' = cx+dy$". Since Cayley's time, matrices have become an indispensable tool not only in mathematics but in the physical and social sciences as well. Their ramifications extend far beyond the original purpose for which they were invented.

One may introduce matrices in a variety of ways but it seems natural to think of them geometrically in terms of linear transformations. This presents us with a concrete approach from which we can develop the theory abstractly. Our main mathematical application will relate to the solving of simultaneous linear equations.

§ 53. LINEAR TRANSFORMATIONS AND MATRICES

Restricting ourselves initially to the plane, we conceive a *linear transformation* to be an operation by which points are transformed into other points and lines are transformed into other lines. Such a transformation may be regarded as a physical movement of points and lines in the plane. A point (or line) which transforms into itself under a linear transformation (i.e. which is left unchanged in position) is said to be an *invariant point* (or *invariant line*) of the transformation. These ideas extend quite naturally to higher dimensions so that generally we speak about *invariant spaces*.

Strictly, the linear transformation in two dimensions is conceived as carrying the points and lines of one plane π into the points and lines of another plane ω. Usually, however, we take $\pi = \omega$ for simplicity. That is, points and lines of a given plane are permuted amongst themselves by a linear transformation.

Of the many physical linear transformations, e.g. strains, stresses, reflections, rotations, we choose the last-mentioned to describe the value of matrix notation.

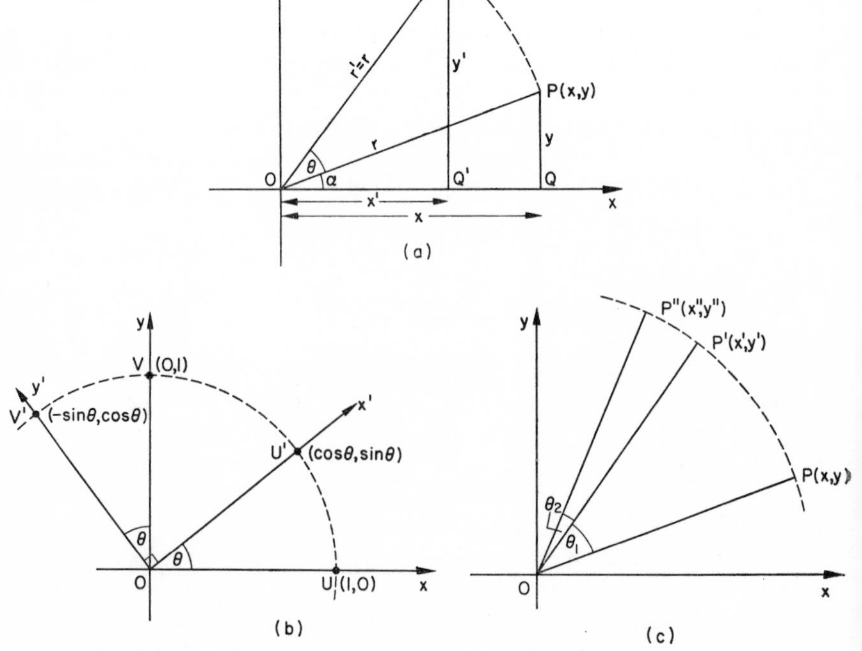

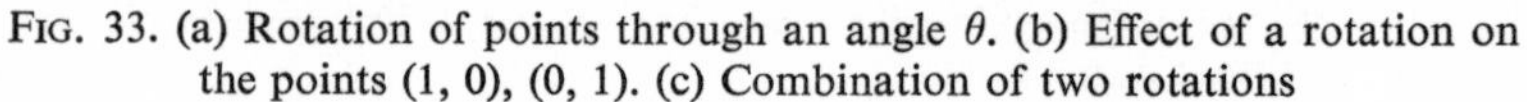
FIG. 33. (a) Rotation of points through an angle θ. (b) Effect of a rotation on the points (1, 0), (0, 1). (c) Combination of two rotations

Consider Fig. 33 in which a physical anti-clockwise rotation through θ of the plane w.r.t. fixed axes takes the point $P(x, y)$ into the point $P'(x', y')$. Then, from $\triangle$s OQP, $OQ'P'$,

$$\begin{aligned} x' &= r\cos(\theta+\alpha) \\ &= r(\cos\alpha\cos\theta-\sin\alpha\sin\theta) \\ &= r\left(\frac{x}{r}\cos\theta-\frac{y}{r}\sin\theta\right) \\ &= x\cos\theta-y\sin\theta \qquad \text{(i)} \end{aligned}$$

and

$$\begin{aligned} y' &= r\sin(\theta+\alpha) \\ &= x\sin\theta+y\cos\theta, \qquad \text{(ii)} \end{aligned}$$

i.e.

$$\boxed{\begin{aligned} x' &= x\cos\theta-y\sin\theta \\ y' &= x\sin\theta+y\cos\theta \end{aligned}}\,. \qquad (128)$$

Multiplying (i) by $\cos\theta$ and (ii) by $\sin\theta$ and adding, we have

$$x = x'\cos\theta+y'\sin\theta. \qquad \text{(iii)}$$

Multiplying (i) by $\sin\theta$ and (ii) by $\cos\theta$ and subtracting, we have

$$y = -x'\sin\theta+y'\cos\theta, \qquad \text{(iv)}$$

i.e.

$$\boxed{\begin{aligned} x &= x'\cos\theta+y'\sin\theta \\ y &= -x'\sin\theta+y'\cos\theta \end{aligned}}\,. \qquad (129)$$

Notice that (a) the transformation (128) carries the points $U = (1, 0)$ and $V = (0, 1)$ into the points $U' = (\cos\theta, \sin\theta)$ and $V' = (-\sin\theta, \cos\theta)$ respectively, and (b) $OU = OU'$, $OV = OV'$, i.e. lengths of segments are invariant under the rotation. (See Fig. 33b.)

Equations (128) and (129) together may be represented in tabular form thus:

	x	y
x'	$\cos\theta$	$-\sin\theta$
y'	$\sin\theta$	$\cos\theta$

. (130)

Write, for convenience, (128) in the symbolic form

$$X' = AX, \qquad (128.1)$$

where $A = \begin{bmatrix} \cos\theta & -\sin\theta \\ \sin\theta & \cos\theta \end{bmatrix}$ is a 2×2 *matrix* (i.e. with two rows and two columns),

$X' = \begin{bmatrix} x' \\ y' \end{bmatrix}$, $X = \begin{bmatrix} x \\ y \end{bmatrix}$ are *column* (2×1) *matrices.*

Read 2×2 as "two by two". Column and row matrices are also called *vectors*. (The mould into which a printer casts his type is called a matrix (Latin *matrix* ≡ "womb"). Mathematically, a matrix suggests that we have a space into which numbers expressing a transformation can be put.) Note particularly that a matrix is just an arrangement of objects, usually numbers—it has no value.

How would we multiply two 2×2 matrices? To illustrate this process, make two successive anti-clockwise rotational transformations through angles θ_1, θ_2 (Fig. 33c). Describe these in matrix notation by

$$X' = A_1X, \quad X'' = A_2X'.$$

$$\therefore\ X'' = A_2X' = A_2A_1X$$

$$= \begin{bmatrix} \cos\theta_2 & -\sin\theta_2 \\ \sin\theta_2 & \cos\theta_2 \end{bmatrix} \begin{bmatrix} \cos\theta_1 & -\sin\theta_1 \\ \sin\theta_1 & \cos\theta_1 \end{bmatrix} X \tag{I}$$

$$= \begin{bmatrix} \cos(\theta_1+\theta_2) & -\sin(\theta_1+\theta_2) \\ \sin(\theta_1+\theta_2) & \cos(\theta_1+\theta_2) \end{bmatrix} X$$

$\because$ the two rotations through θ_1, θ_2 are equivalent to a single rotation through $(\theta_1+\theta_2)$.

$$= \begin{bmatrix} \cos\theta_1\cos\theta_2 - \sin\theta_1\sin\theta_2 & -\sin\theta_1\cos\theta_2 - \cos\theta_1\sin\theta_2 \\ \cos\theta_1\sin\theta_2 + \sin\theta_1\cos\theta_2 & \cos\theta_1\cos\theta_2 - \sin\theta_1\sin\theta_2 \end{bmatrix} X. \tag{II}$$

With Exercises 10.68, 10.69, steps (I), (II) tell us how to multiply two matrices A_1, A_2 to obtain the product A_2A_1—more about this in (132), if you are not clear about the multiplication rule just yet.

Remarks. (a) Putting $\theta_2 = \theta_1\ (= \theta)$ we have $A_2 = A_1\ (= A)$. Hence, we may write down the matrix $A^2 = AA$ in its simplest form.

(b) The *reverse* (clockwise) transformation through θ (i.e. anti-clockwise through $-\theta$), given by (129), may be written in matrix form as

$$X = A^{-1}X', \tag{129.1}$$

where $A^{-1} = \begin{bmatrix} \cos\theta & \sin\theta \\ -\sin\theta & \cos\theta \end{bmatrix}$ (the *inverse* (*matrix*) of A).

(c) Taken together, (128.1) and (129.1) give (substituting for X')

$$X = A^{-1}AX$$

suggesting that $A^{-1}A = I$ (the *unit matrix*) where I represents no physical rotation, i.e. it leaves everything exactly as it is. This is only as we expect when an operation and its inverse act together. [Refer to (11.1), (11.2).] Likewise, $AA^{-1} = I$.

Imagine now an anti-clockwise rotation of axes through an angle ϕ from the original x-, y-axes to new x'-, y'-axes, the origin being kept fixed (Fig.

34a). Then

$$\left.\begin{aligned} x &= OR - MR, \text{ i.e. } x = x'\cos\phi - y'\sin\phi, \\ y &= RN + QP, \text{ i.e. } y = x'\sin\phi + y'\cos\phi, \end{aligned}\right\} \quad (128)'$$

whence, by appropriate multiplication followed by addition and subtraction,

$$\left.\begin{aligned} x' &= x\cos\phi + y\sin\phi, \\ y' &= -x\sin\phi + y\cos\phi. \end{aligned}\right\} \quad (129)'$$

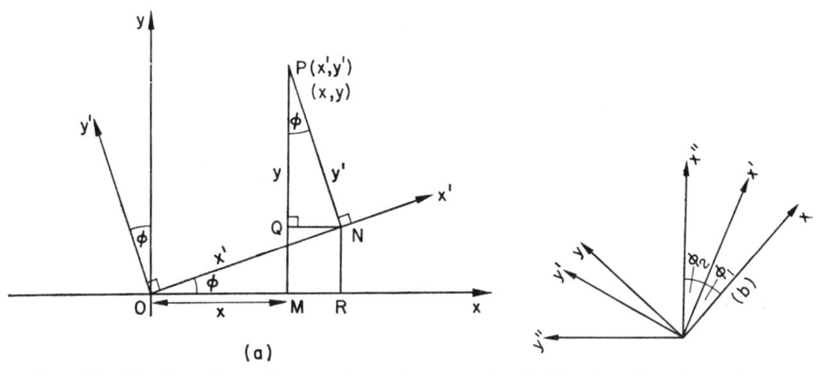

FIG. 34. (a) Rotation of axes through an angle θ. (b) Combination of two rotations of axes

These equations express points in one coordinate system (i.e. w.r.t. one set of axes) in terms of another coordinate system. One consequence of this is that the equation $f(x, y) = 0$ of a curve w.r.t. the x-, y-axes becomes $f(x'\cos\phi - y'\sin\phi,\ x'\sin\phi + y'\cos\phi) = 0$ referred to the x'-, y'-axes.

Schematically, the situation is represented by means of a table similar to (130). Matrix expressions for (128)′ and (129)′ are, respectively,

$$X = P^{-1}X', \quad (128.1)'$$

$$X' = PX, \quad (129.1)'$$

where $P = \begin{bmatrix} \cos\phi & \sin\phi \\ -\sin\phi & \cos\phi \end{bmatrix}$, $P^{-1} = \begin{bmatrix} \cos\phi & -\sin\phi \\ \sin\phi & \cos\phi \end{bmatrix}$.

Observe that A has the same form as P^{-1}. The reason for this is as follows: A represents an anti-clockwise rotation of the plane through an angle θ; P represents an anti-clockwise rotation of the coordinate axes through ϕ, i.e. the motion of the plane relative to the new coordinate axes is clockwise through ϕ.

There are thus two interpretations for a linear transformation represented by (128) and (129) or by (128)′ and (129)′: (a) a rotation of points and lines (O fixed); and (b) a rotation of axes (change of coordinates).

Generally, a non-singular linear transformation [given by (131) below] will represent (a) a transformation of points and lines in the plane (axes fixed), and (b) a change of coordinates (i.e. points fixed but a change of axes). As an example, other than a rotation, consider the transforming equations $x' = x+3$, $y' = y-1$. Interpretations of these are: (a) every point in the plane is translated (displaced) through a distance 3 units east and 1 unit south, e.g. $(-1, 6)$ is carried into $(2, 5)$, and (b) there is a change of (parallel) axes with new origin $O'(-3, 1)$ w.r.t. O, e.g. $(-1, 6)$ w.r.t. axes through O is written $(2, 5)$ w.r.t. parallel axes through O'.

From the point of view of (a), the transformation may be called an *alibi* (since a point is taken somewhere else), whereas from the point of view of (b) the transformation may be called an *alias* (since the point is merely relabelled, i.e. given a different name).

Observe that, from (129)′, using (45), for $V(x, y)$ we derive

$$\frac{\partial^2 V}{\partial x^2} = \cos^2\phi\,\frac{\partial^2 V}{\partial x'^2} - \sin 2\phi\,\frac{\partial^2 V}{\partial x'\partial y'} + \sin^2\phi\,\frac{\partial^2 V}{\partial y'^2},$$

$$\frac{\partial^2 V}{\partial y^2} = \sin^2\phi\,\frac{\partial^2 V}{\partial x'^2} + \sin 2\phi\,\frac{\partial^2 V}{\partial x'\partial y'} + \cos^2\phi\,\frac{\partial^2 V}{\partial y'^2},$$

whence
$$\frac{\partial^2 V}{\partial x^2} + \frac{\partial^2 V}{\partial y^2} = \frac{\partial^2 V}{\partial x'^2} + \frac{\partial^2 V}{\partial y'^2},$$

i.e., $\nabla^2 V$ is invariant under a rotation through θ.

If the rotational transformation (128) is replaced by the *general linear transformation*,

$$\left.\begin{aligned} x' &= a_{11}x + a_{12}y, \\ y' &= a_{21}x + a_{22}y, \end{aligned}\right\} \tag{131}$$

i.e., say, $X' = AX$ (131.1)

and repeated,

$$\left.\begin{aligned} x'' &= b_{11}x' + b_{12}y', \\ y'' &= b_{21}x' + b_{22}y', \end{aligned}\right\} \tag{131a}$$

i.e. say, $X'' = BX'$, (131.1a)

then $X'' = BAX$

where
$$BA = \begin{bmatrix} b_{11} & b_{12} \\ b_{21} & b_{22} \end{bmatrix}\begin{bmatrix} a_{11} & a_{12} \\ a_{21} & a_{22} \end{bmatrix} = \begin{bmatrix} b_{11}a_{11}+b_{12}a_{21} & b_{11}a_{12}+b_{12}a_{22} \\ b_{21}a_{11}+b_{22}a_{21} & b_{21}a_{12}+b_{22}a_{22} \end{bmatrix}.$$

Query: Would AB produce the same matrix as BA does?

For simplicity, write the matrix of the general linear transformation as $\begin{bmatrix} a & c \\ b & d \end{bmatrix}$ rather than as $\begin{bmatrix} a_{11} & a_{12} \\ a_{21} & a_{22} \end{bmatrix}$.

If $ad-bc \neq 0$, the matrix is *non-singular*, but if $ad-bc = 0$ the matrix is *singular*. In both (128) and (129), $ad-bc = \cos^2\theta+\sin^2\theta = 1$, i.e. the rotational transformation is non-singular. Later (Chapter 12) we see that a singular matrix has no inverse. The form of the general linear transformation (131) shows that the work in the plane can be extended to higher dimensions.

EXAMPLE 63 (some geometry of the general linear transformation in two dimensions).

Case 1: Non-singular matrix

Solution.

By (131) $$\begin{bmatrix} a & c \\ b & d \end{bmatrix}\begin{bmatrix} 0 \\ 0 \end{bmatrix} = \begin{bmatrix} 0 \\ 0 \end{bmatrix}$$

$$\begin{bmatrix} a & c \\ b & d \end{bmatrix}\begin{bmatrix} 1 \\ 0 \end{bmatrix} = \begin{bmatrix} a \\ b \end{bmatrix}$$

$$\begin{bmatrix} a & c \\ b & d \end{bmatrix}\begin{bmatrix} 1 \\ 1 \end{bmatrix} = \begin{bmatrix} a+c \\ b+d \end{bmatrix}$$

$$\begin{bmatrix} a & c \\ b & d \end{bmatrix}\begin{bmatrix} 0 \\ 1 \end{bmatrix} = \begin{bmatrix} c \\ d \end{bmatrix},$$

i.e. the general linear transformation carries the vertices of a square into the vertices of a parallelogram, and, of course, the sides of the square into the sides of the parallelogram (Fig. 35).

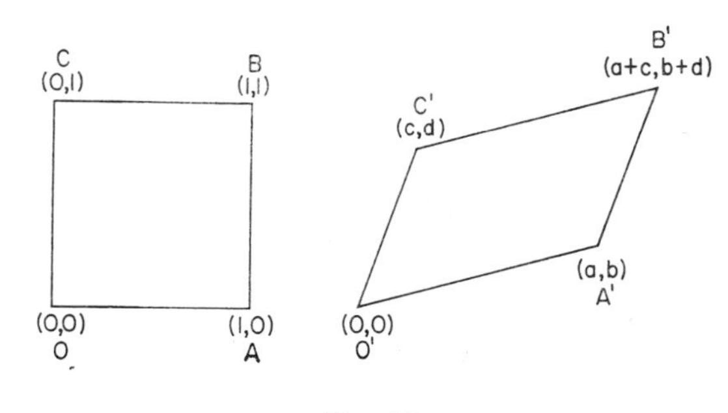

FIG. 35

Case 2: Singular matrix

We have $ad = bc \quad \therefore \quad \dfrac{b}{a} = \dfrac{d}{c} = \lambda,$

i.e. $\left.\begin{aligned} b &= \lambda a \\ d &= \lambda c \end{aligned}\right\}$, i.e. row 2 of the matrix depends on row 1.

Then, by (131),

$$\begin{bmatrix} a & c \\ \lambda a & \lambda c \end{bmatrix}\begin{bmatrix} 0 \\ 0 \end{bmatrix} = \begin{bmatrix} 0 \\ 0 \end{bmatrix}$$

$$\begin{bmatrix} a & c \\ \lambda a & \lambda c \end{bmatrix}\begin{bmatrix} 1 \\ 0 \end{bmatrix} = \begin{bmatrix} a \\ \lambda a \end{bmatrix}$$

$$\begin{bmatrix} a & c \\ \lambda a & \lambda c \end{bmatrix}\begin{bmatrix} 1 \\ 1 \end{bmatrix} = \begin{bmatrix} a+c \\ \lambda(a+c) \end{bmatrix}$$

$$\begin{bmatrix} a & c \\ \lambda a & \lambda c \end{bmatrix}\begin{bmatrix} 0 \\ 1 \end{bmatrix} = \begin{bmatrix} c \\ \lambda c \end{bmatrix},$$

i.e. the square $OABC$ is transformed into the line $y = \lambda x$ through the origin.

Therefore the area of the square is reduced to zero.

In fact, any plane area is reduced to zero, for, given any point (ξ, η),

$$\begin{bmatrix} a & c \\ \lambda a & \lambda c \end{bmatrix}\begin{bmatrix} \xi \\ \eta \end{bmatrix} = \begin{bmatrix} a\xi + c\eta \\ \lambda(a\xi + c\eta) \end{bmatrix} = \begin{bmatrix} x \\ y \end{bmatrix} \quad \text{or} \quad y = \lambda x,$$

i.e. the singular matrix transforms any point of the plane to a point on $y = \lambda x$, i.e. the singular matrix compresses the whole plane into a line.

Therefore any line in the plane through the origin can be regarded as the compression of the plane under the transformation of a singular matrix.

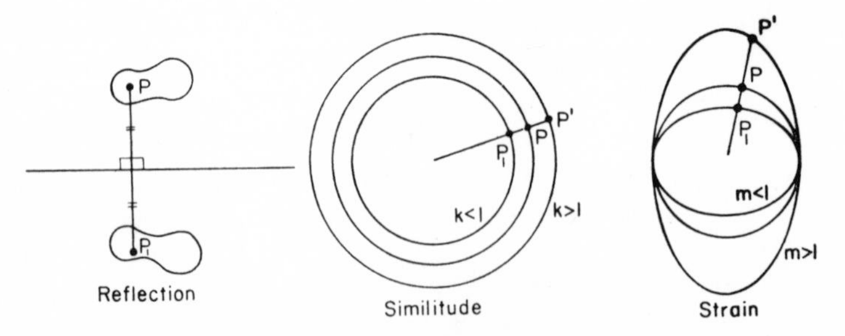

FIG. 36. Linear transformations

EXAMPLE 64 (some special linear transformations) (Fig. 36).

(1) *Reflection* (in the x-axis): $\begin{cases} x' = x \\ y' = -y \end{cases}$ with matrix $\begin{bmatrix} 1 & 0 \\ 0 & -1 \end{bmatrix}$.

(2) *Similitude transformations:* $\begin{cases} x' = kx \\ y' = ky \end{cases}$ with matrix $\begin{bmatrix} k & 0 \\ 0 & k \end{bmatrix}$.

$k > 1 \Rightarrow$ *stretching*; $k < 1 \Rightarrow$ *shrinking*.

(3) *Strain* (along y-axis) $\begin{cases} x' = x \\ y' = \quad my \end{cases}$ with matrix $\begin{bmatrix} 1 & 0 \\ 0 & m \end{bmatrix}$

(along x-axis) $\begin{cases} x' = mx \\ y' = \quad y \end{cases}$ with matrix $\begin{bmatrix} m & 0 \\ 0 & 1 \end{bmatrix}$

$\begin{cases} m > 1 \Rightarrow \textit{elongation}, \\ m < 1 \Rightarrow \textit{compression}. \end{cases}$

Query. How would you express a translation (Exercise 14.25) in matrix form? (See § 79.)

From the above concrete illustrations of matrices we may abstract and generalise to give a formal treatment of elementary matrix theory.

§ 54. FORMAL DEFINITIONS

An $m \times n$ *matrix* is an array of mn elements (usually real or complex numbers) having m rows $R_i (i = 1, \ldots, m)$ and n columns $C_j (j = 1, \ldots, n)$, written $[a_{ij}]$ where a_{ij} is the element in R_i and C_j:

$$\begin{array}{c} \\ R_i \end{array} \begin{bmatrix} a_{11} & a_{12} & \vdots & a_{1j} & \vdots & a_{1n} \\ a_{21} & a_{22} & \vdots & a_{2j} & \vdots & a_{2n} \\ \cdots & \cdots & \vdots & \cdots & \vdots & \cdots \\ a_{i1} & a_{i2} & \vdots & a_{ij} & \vdots & a_{in} \\ \cdots & \cdots & \vdots & \cdots & \vdots & \cdots \\ a_{m1} & a_{m2} & \vdots & a_{mj} & \vdots & a_{mn} \end{bmatrix} \equiv [a_{ij}]. \tag{132}$$

(column C_j marked above the a_{ij} column; row R_i marked at left.)

We say the matrix is of *order* $m \times n$. Generally, $m \neq n$.

Special cases: $\begin{cases} m = 1 & \text{row matrix (vector)} \\ n = 1 & \text{column matrix (vector)} \\ m = n & \textit{square matrix} \text{ (of } \textit{order } n \times n \text{ or just } n). \end{cases}$

For simplicity and convenience, we may take $m, n \leqslant 3$. Actually, matrices may be infinite, but our concern is only with finite matrices, i.e. m, n both finite.

Aaron's breastplate, we are told (Exodus XXVIII. 15–20), shone with twelve precious stones arranged in the pattern of a 4×3 matrix.

Addition (subtraction) of two matrices

Define
$$[a_{ij}] \pm [b_{ij}] = [a_{ij} + b_{ij}]. \tag{133}$$

Clearly, addition (subtraction) can only take place if the matrices have the same shape ($\equiv$ size $\equiv$ order), i.e. are both $m \times n$; e.g.:

$$\begin{bmatrix} 2 & 0 \\ 1 & 4 \\ 3 & -1 \end{bmatrix} + \begin{bmatrix} 4 & 2 \\ -1 & 0 \\ -5 & 9 \end{bmatrix} = \begin{bmatrix} 6 & 2 \\ 0 & 4 \\ -2 & 8 \end{bmatrix} = 2 \begin{bmatrix} 3 & 1 \\ 0 & 2 \\ -1 & 4 \end{bmatrix}.$$

Here it must be emphasised that the symbol + represents a certain operation between matrices, and should not be confused with the same symbol used to represent a similar operation between numbers in arithmetic. In this context it is only necessary to remind the reader that throughout the centuries many different symbols have been used to represent the fundamental arithmetical operations, such as addition.

Multiplication by a scalar

By simple extension of (133),

$$\lambda[a_{ij}] = [\lambda a_{ij}] = \underbrace{[a_{ij}]+\ldots+[a_{ij}]}_{\lambda \text{ terms}}$$

e.g. $$3\begin{bmatrix} 2 & -1 \\ 4 & 0 \end{bmatrix} = \begin{bmatrix} 6 & -3 \\ 12 & 0 \end{bmatrix}.$$

Multiplication of two matrices

The (Cayley) *product* $AB = C$ is the matrix whose element c_{ij} in R_i and C_j is the sum of the product of corresponding elements of R_i of A by C_j of B,

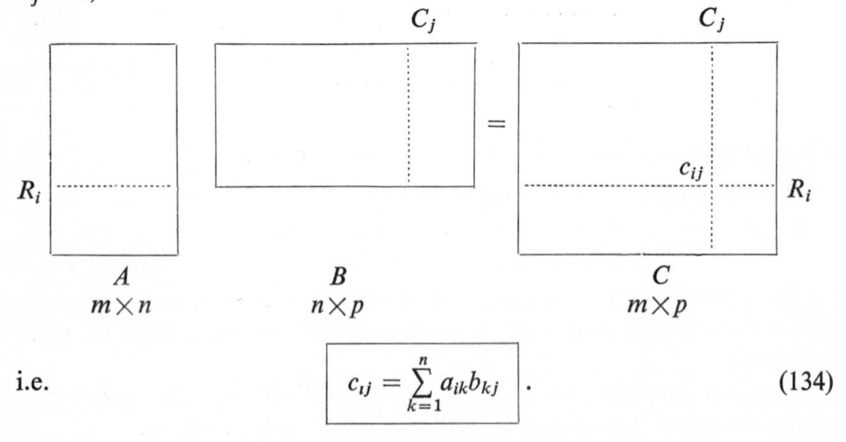

i.e. $$\boxed{c_{ij} = \sum_{k=1}^{n} a_{ik}b_{kj}} \,. \tag{134}$$

Clearly, the *product matrix AB is only defined when the number of columns of A is equal to the number of rows of B.*

Notes

(1) A rectangular matrix cannot be multiplied by itself.

(2) A square matrix A multiplied by itself n times is written A^n.

(3) $AB \neq BA$ generally, i.e. matrices are generally non-commutative under multiplication. Examples:

(a) Rectangular matrices: If A is $m\times n$ and B is $n\times m$,

then $\begin{cases} AB \text{ is } m\times m, \\ BA \text{ is } n\times n \end{cases}$ i.e. both square but different $\because$ $m \neq n$.

(b) Square matrices:

e.g. if $A = \begin{bmatrix} 1 & 2 \\ 3 & 5 \end{bmatrix}$ and $B = \begin{bmatrix} 3 & 1 \\ 2 & 0 \end{bmatrix}$ then by (134) $AB = \begin{bmatrix} 3+4 & 1+0 \\ 9+10 & 3+0 \end{bmatrix}$

$$= \begin{bmatrix} 7 & 1 \\ 19 & 3 \end{bmatrix}, \quad BA = \begin{bmatrix} 3+3 & 6+5 \\ 2+0 & 4+0 \end{bmatrix} = \begin{bmatrix} 6 & 11 \\ 2 & 4 \end{bmatrix}.$$

Hence $\begin{cases} (A+B)(A-B) = A^2-AB+BA-B^2. \\ (A-B)(A+B) = A^2+AB-BA-B^2. \end{cases}$

It is instructive to draw "shapes" of matrices under multiplication, as above (134), to appreciate the effect; for instance, three matrices of orders $1\times n$, $n\times n$, $n\times 1$ when multiplied in that order give a matrix of order 1×1, i.e. a single element. For n large, the diagram is quite striking.

Special matrices

Null ($\equiv$ *Zero*) *matrix* $O \equiv$ a matrix generally $m\times n$ having all its elements zero.

Unit matrix $I \equiv$ a square matrix with zeros everywhere except in the diagonal where the elements are all unity.

(Orders of O, I are obvious from the context.)

Inverse of a matrix A is A^{-1}: $AA^{-1} = A^{-1}A = I$.

Therefore a rectangular matrix cannot have an inverse.

Transpose of a matrix A: A^T whose rows (columns) are the columns (rows) of A

e.g. if $A = \begin{bmatrix} a_{11} & a_{12} \\ a_{21} & a_{22} \end{bmatrix}$ then $A^T = \begin{bmatrix} a_{11} & a_{21} \\ a_{12} & a_{22} \end{bmatrix}$.

Note: $\begin{cases} A-A = O, \\ IA = AI = A, \\ OA = AO = O, \end{cases}$

i.e. *I, O play the roles in matrix theory that 1, 0 play in number theory.*

Symmetric and skew-symmetric matrices. A symmetric $\Rightarrow a_{ij} = a_{ji}$; *A skew-symmetric* $\Rightarrow a_{ij} = -a_{ji}$. Observe that for a skew-symmetric matrix, $a_{ii} = -a_{ii}$, i.e. $a_{ii} = 0$, i.e. all the diagonal elements are zero. E.g.,

$\begin{bmatrix} a & h & g \\ h & b & f \\ g & f & c \end{bmatrix}$ is symmetric [it is the matrix for a conic (Chapter 16)], while $\begin{bmatrix} 0 & b & c \\ -b & 0 & d \\ -c & -d & 0 \end{bmatrix}$ is skew-symmetric. For a symmetric matrix, $A^T = A$, whereas for a skew-symmetric matrix $A^T = -A$.

General Comments

(1) A *diagonal* matrix of order $n \times n$, written diag $(a_{11}, a_{22}, \ldots, a_{nn})$, is one whose only non-zero elements $a_{11}, a_{22}, \ldots, a_{nn}$ occur in the diagonal positions. Only square matrices may be diagonal. Rectangular matrices cannot be diagonal.

(2) Matrices may be *divisors of zero*, i.e., $AB = 0$ $(A \neq 0,\ B \neq 0)$ e.g., $\begin{bmatrix} 1 & \cdot \\ \cdot & \cdot \end{bmatrix}\begin{bmatrix} \cdot & \cdot \\ 1 & \cdot \end{bmatrix} = \begin{bmatrix} \cdot & \cdot \\ \cdot & \cdot \end{bmatrix}$ or, say, Exercise 11.19. *Convention:* zero matrix elements may be indicated by dots for convenience, as in this illustration, and when there is no likelihood of ambiguity.

(3) The *trace* of a square matrix A, written tr A, is defined to be the sum of the diagonal elements, i.e. $\operatorname{tr} A = \sum_{i=1}^{n} a_{ii}$. Of course, $\operatorname{tr} A^T = \operatorname{tr} A$. Furthermore, $\operatorname{tr} AB = \operatorname{tr} BA$. Convince yourself of the truth of this latter result—use (134).

(4) Experience shows the truth of the index law for multiplication $A^p A^q = A^{p+q}$ (p, q integers).

It is easy to verify that matrices obey the fundamental laws of algebra (103), except for commutativity of multiplication.

In Examples 65, 66 take

$$\begin{cases} I = \begin{bmatrix} 1 & \cdot \\ \cdot & 1 \end{bmatrix} & \text{(unit } 2\times 2 \text{ matrix)} \\ i = \begin{bmatrix} \cdot & 1 \\ -1 & \cdot \end{bmatrix} \therefore\ i^2 = -I = \begin{bmatrix} -1 & \cdot \\ \cdot & -1 \end{bmatrix}. \end{cases}$$

EXAMPLE 65 (matrices as an alternative interpretation of complex numbers).

Solution. The matrix $z = xI + yi = \begin{bmatrix} x & y \\ -y & x \end{bmatrix}$ (where x and y are real numbers) behaves w.r.t. addition and multiplication exactly like the complex number z, e.g.

$$\begin{aligned} zz' &= (xI+yi)(x'I+y'i) \\ &= (xx'-yy')\,I + (xy'+x'y)i \qquad \because\ i^2 = -I \\ &= \begin{bmatrix} x & y \\ -y & x \end{bmatrix}\begin{bmatrix} x' & y' \\ -y' & x' \end{bmatrix} = \begin{bmatrix} xx'-yy' & xy'+x'y \\ -(xy'+x'y) & xx'-yy' \end{bmatrix}. \end{aligned}$$

Also $zz^T = (x^2+y^2)I$, where z^T is the transpose of z, i.e. the transpose behaves like the conjugate complex number $\bar{z}$.

Further, $A = I\cos\theta + i\sin\theta$ using § 53.
$\therefore$ if $\theta = \pi/2$, $A = i$.
$\therefore$ i is the matrix operation of rotation through $\pi/2$.
$\therefore$ i plays the role of $\sqrt{-1}$ in complex numbers.

EXAMPLE 66 (quaternions in matrix form).

Solution. Take $j = \begin{bmatrix} \cdot & \sqrt{-1} \\ \sqrt{-1} & \cdot \end{bmatrix}$, $k = \begin{bmatrix} \sqrt{-1} & \cdot \\ \cdot & -\sqrt{-1} \end{bmatrix}$

$$\therefore \left.\begin{aligned} ij &= k = -ji \\ jk &= i = -kj \\ ki &= j = -ik \end{aligned}\right\} \text{(non-commutative) and } i^2 = j^2 = k^2 = -I.$$

Therefore matrices I, i, j, k correspond to the quaternion elements $1, i, j, k$.

Applications of matrices

Matrices have very wide applicability. Whenever a state of stress of strain exists, e.g. in engineering construction, matrices may be used to specify the process. In aerodynamics (the study of air flowing past aeroplane wings) imagine a small square of smoke pulled into the air-stream: as it moves along, this square will change shape and this shape will reveal what is happening in the air-stream. So matrices may be employed. The special virtues of matrices as a notation are their compactness and their facility for extension to n dimensions. Atomic physics uses matrix notation for many purposes, so we have spin matrices, scattering matrices, creation matrices, and annihilation matrices—in fact, we have matrix mechanics. [Consult, for instance, J. Heading, *Matrix Theory for Physicists* (Longmans, 1958) and A. Mary Tropper, *Matrix Theory of Electrical Engineering Students* (Harrap, 1962).]

Statistics uses probability and transition matrices (in Markov chain processes) with applications to, say, genetics or gas diffusion. Electronic digital computers express many problems in terms of matrices and, in this respect, the inverses and eigenvalues of matrices (§§ 61, 63) are significant.

Quite apart from their implications for engineering and science generally, matrices occupy a central position in modern mathematics where they are a valuable tool in, say, projective geometry, group theory, mechanics, relativity, and quantum mechanics. Naturally enough, there exists a very extensive literature on the theory of matrices considered as a study in its own right.

As the social and behavioural sciences have become more scientific in their approach to problems, matrices have been found to be more and more useful, e.g. in psychology (especially in factor analysis), in sociology and anthropology, in industrial management, in economics and in education (learning models). Consult the Kemeny, Snell, and Thompson reference, Chapter 8, for details. Incidentally, the word "finite" in that text suggests the fundamental difference between the sort of mathematics discussed in this chapter and the type of thinking involved in the calculus which depends on infinite limiting processes.

Special mention of the usefulness of the matrix notation must be made in connection with the *theory of games*, a recent mathematical development due largely to the economist, Morgenstern, and the mathematician, von Neumann (1903–57, German, American), who made the breakthrough in 1944 in their book, *The Theory of Games and Economic Behaviour*. The principles of this theory, though of particular value to economists, may be applied to any situation (e.g. business organization, warfare, games of skill) in which strategy rather than luck is the main factor. (Consult Kemeny, Snell, and Thompson.)

Emphasis on the recentness of this new branch of mathematics serves to illustrate the important fact that mathematics is a continuous creation. From Iceland to India, creative mathematical research is being produced at a prodigious rate.

Infinite series and matrices

Infinite series whose elements are matrices occur in aeronautical engineering, physics, statistics, and other modern scientific contexts. (Refer to Exercises 11.83–11.89.)

Functions and matrices

Given a square matrix A, functions like $\sin A$, e^A which arise in a variety of practical problems, behave analogously to $\sin z$, e^z (z complex). Thus, for example, it may be shown that, $e^{iA} = \cos A + i \sin A$ (A a square matrix), $\sin(A+B) = \sin A \cos B + \cos A \sin B$ (A, B commuting) and $e^{\begin{bmatrix} 1 & 2 \\ 0 & 1 \end{bmatrix}} = \begin{bmatrix} e & 2e \\ 0 & e \end{bmatrix}$. See reference (c) of this chapter.

§ 55. MATRICES AND VECTORS

Fundamental concepts

Rename the coordinates x, y in § 53, a_1, a_2 respectively. Then we know that a column vector $a = \begin{bmatrix} a_1 \\ a_2 \end{bmatrix}$ and its transpose row vector $a^T = [a_1, a_2]$ are suitable notations for an ordered pair of elements (a_1, a_2). We say that a_1, a_2 are the *components* of the vector $\mathbf{a}$ in the directions of the x- and

y-axes respectively. Evidently, these ideas readily extend to higher dimensional space. Arrows may also be inserted, as below, to indicate vectors.

Diagrammatically (Fig. 37), the vector $\mathbf{a} = (a_1, a_2)$ is represented by the directed line-segment $\overrightarrow{OA}$ joining the origin O, representing the *zero* (≡ *null*) *vector* $\mathbf{0} = (0, 0)$, to the point $A(a_1, a_2)$, i.e. vectors issue from O. Originally, the mathematical study of vectors, as pioneered by Gibbs (1839–1903, American), was motivated by the requirements of physics where force, velocity, and acceleration are well-known examples (of vectors), i.e. they possess both magnitude (= length) and direction, the two essential attributes of a physical vector. (Temperature and volume are thus not representable by a vector.) Being an abstraction and generalisation of these physical concepts, the mathematical theory must necessarily reflect the known laws of nature obeyed by vectors.

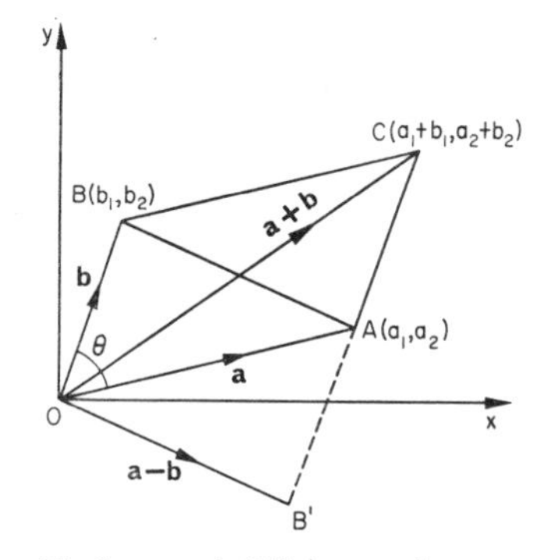

FIG. 37. Sum and difference of two vectors

Still in two dimensions, let $\mathbf{a} = (a_1, a_2)$, $\mathbf{b} = (b_1, b_2)$ be any two vectors. Define

$$\text{(i)} \quad \boxed{k\mathbf{a} = (ka_1, ka_2)}, \tag{135.1}$$

i.e. $k\,\mathbf{a}$ is a vector in the same direction as $\mathbf{a}$ but with magnitude k times that of $\mathbf{a}$, where k is an ordinary real number, called a *scalar* to distinguish it from a vector;

$$\text{(ii)} \quad \boxed{\mathbf{a}+\mathbf{b} = (a_1, a_2)+(b_1, b_2) = (a_1+b_1, a_2+b_2) = \mathbf{c}, \text{ say}}\,. \tag{135.2}$$

Definition (ii), which shows that vectors are closed under addition, is in accord with the parallelogram (triangle) law of forces occurring in physical (e.g. mechanical or air navigational) situations if we allow the extension that any vector $\mathbf{u} = (u_1, u_2)$, equal and parallel to $\mathbf{a}$ in the same direction, is equal to $\mathbf{a}$, i.e. $\mathbf{u} = \mathbf{a}$. Thus, our vector concept is a generalisation of the idea of a vector with one end "tied" to O (i.e. a particular directed line-segment). That is, we may think of a vector as an equivalence class (§ 66) of directed line-segments, i.e. equality of vectors *is* a true equivalence relation. Obviously, two vectors are equal if and only if their components are equal, i.e. $\mathbf{u} = \mathbf{a} \Rightarrow u_1 = a_1,\ u_2 = a_2$ (and conversely). To every vector, then, there is an equal vector issuing from O. Note that the symbol $+$, as in $\mathbf{a}+\mathbf{b}$, is a vector operation. There must be no confusion with the use of the same symbol in ordinary addition.

Referring to Fig. 37 (and Fig. 22a also), we have, clearly, from congruent triangles

$$\overrightarrow{OA}+\overrightarrow{AC} = \overrightarrow{BC}+\overrightarrow{OB}\,(=\overrightarrow{OC})$$

i.e. $\mathbf{a}+\mathbf{v} = \mathbf{u}+\mathbf{b}\ (= \mathbf{a}+\mathbf{b} = \mathbf{c})$,

where $\mathbf{u} = \mathbf{a},\ \mathbf{v} = \mathbf{b}$.

Vector addition is both commutative and associative, as may be readily verified. Additive inverse of $\mathbf{a}$ is, from (135.2), $-\mathbf{a} = (-a_1, -a_2)$, i.e. a vector having the same magnitude as $\mathbf{a}$ but the opposite direction.

Ascending to three dimensions, we introduce three mutually perpendicular (= orthogonal) *unit vectors* (each of magnitude unity) $\mathbf{i} = (1, 0, 0)$, $\mathbf{j} = (0, 1, 0)$, $\mathbf{k} = (0, 0, 1)$, or, in matrix notation,

$$\begin{bmatrix}1\\0\\0\end{bmatrix},\ \begin{bmatrix}0\\1\\0\end{bmatrix},\ \begin{bmatrix}0\\0\\1\end{bmatrix}.$$

Any vector $\mathbf{a} = (a_1, a_2, a_3)$ may then (Fig. 38) be expressed as

$$\boxed{\mathbf{a} = (a_1, a_2, a_3) = a_1\,\mathbf{i}+a_2\,\mathbf{j}+a_3\,\mathbf{k}} \tag{136}$$

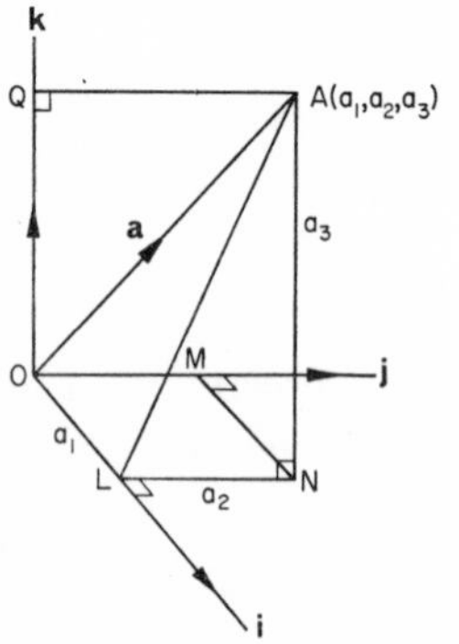

FIG. 38. Unit vectors **i, j, k**

since $\mathbf{a} = \overrightarrow{ON}+\overrightarrow{NA} = \overrightarrow{OL}+\overrightarrow{LN}+\overrightarrow{NA}$ and $\overrightarrow{OL} = a_1\mathbf{i}$, etc. Expressed otherwise, a general vector in three-dimensional space is linearly dependent (§ 56) on the three vectors **i, j, k**. Had the vector been restricted to two dimensions, say the plane determined by **i, j**, then it would have depended on just these two vectors.

Note. Vectorial representation of addition of complex numbers (§ 46) by two-dimensional vectors (135.2) does not, of course, extend to three dimensions.

Inner product

Next, define the *inner* ($\equiv$ *dot* $\equiv$ *scalar*) *product* of **a**, **b** as

$$\boxed{\mathbf{a}\cdot\mathbf{b} = (a_1, a_2, a_3)\cdot(b_1, b_2, b_3) = a_1b_1 + a_2b_2 + a_3b_3 = a^Tb = b^Ta = \mathbf{b}\cdot\mathbf{a}} \tag{137}$$

i.e. the *inner (scalar) product of two vectors is a scalar*, i.e. scalar multiplication denies closure to vectors. Obviously, from (137), the inner product is commutative. One may also demonstrate that the distributive laws for vector addition over inner product are valid, i.e. for any three vectors **a**, **b**, **c**, $(\mathbf{a}+\mathbf{b})\cdot\mathbf{c} = \mathbf{a}\cdot\mathbf{c}+\mathbf{b}\cdot\mathbf{c}$.

Length (magnitude) of **a** is defined to be

$$\boxed{|\mathbf{a}| = OA = +\sqrt{a_1^2+a_2^2+a_3^2} = \sqrt{\mathbf{a}\cdot\mathbf{a}} = \sqrt{a^Ta}}\,. \tag{138}$$

(Particularly note that $a^Ta \neq aa^T$. Why?) Unit vectors have length 1. Zero vectors have length 0. From any vector **a**, a unit vector $\hat{\mathbf{a}} = \mathbf{a}/|\mathbf{a}|$ may be formed ($|\mathbf{a}| \neq 0$). Always distinguish between the zero vector, **0**, and the scalar zero 0.

Notice that

$$\mathbf{i}\cdot\mathbf{i} = \mathbf{j}\cdot\mathbf{j} = \mathbf{k}\cdot\mathbf{k} = 1 \tag{139.1}$$

$$\mathbf{i}\cdot\mathbf{j} = \mathbf{j}\cdot\mathbf{k} = \mathbf{k}\cdot\mathbf{j} = 0 \tag{139.2}$$

Relabelling **i**, **j**, **k** as $\mathbf{e}_r$ ($r = 1, 2, 3$), we have $\mathbf{e}_r\cdot\mathbf{e}_s = \delta_s^r = 1 (r = s), = 0$ $(r \neq s)$ where the symbol δ_s^r is the *Kronecker delta*.

Reverting to Fig. 37, let $\widehat{AOB} = \theta$. By the cosine law for $\triangle OAB$,

$$\begin{aligned} 2|\mathbf{a}|\mathbf{b}|\cos\theta &= |\mathbf{a}|^2+|\mathbf{b}|^2-(BA)^2 \\ &= |\mathbf{a}|^2+|\mathbf{b}|^2-|\mathbf{a}-\mathbf{b}|^2 \quad \because \overrightarrow{OB}(=\mathbf{b})+\overrightarrow{OB'} = \overrightarrow{OA}(=\mathbf{a}) \\ &\quad \text{by (135.2) and } \overrightarrow{BA} = \overrightarrow{OB'} \\ &= |\mathbf{a}|^2+|\mathbf{b}|^2-(\mathbf{a}-\mathbf{b})\cdot(\mathbf{a}-\mathbf{b}) \qquad \text{by (138)} \\ &= |\mathbf{a}|^2+|\mathbf{b}|^2-(\mathbf{a}^2+\mathbf{b}^2-2\mathbf{a}\cdot\mathbf{b}) \quad \because \mathbf{b}\cdot\mathbf{a} = \mathbf{a}\cdot\mathbf{b} \qquad \text{by (137)} \\ &= 2\mathbf{a}\cdot\mathbf{b} \end{aligned}$$

$$\therefore \quad \boxed{\mathbf{a}\cdot\mathbf{b} = |\mathbf{a}||\mathbf{b}|\cos\theta} \tag{140}$$

a result which, of course, is true in higher dimensions as well as in the plane. Identity (140) is equivalent to asserting that $\mathbf{a}\cdot\mathbf{b}$ is the product of the length of one vector and its orthogonal projection on the other. It follows from (140) that

$$\boxed{\mathbf{a}\cdot\mathbf{b} = 0 \Rightarrow \mathbf{a} \perp \mathbf{b} \text{ (and conversely)}}\,. \tag{140.1}$$

Many physical concepts, such as work, are expressible as terms of the inner product.

One of the chief mathematical applications of vectors is in the study of the geometry of planes, lines, and points in space, but we wish merely to introduce the concept of a vector and the basic vector algebra mainly as it relates to matrices and determinants. In the branches of mathematics known as *differential geometry* and *vector differential operators* we have the fusion of the concepts of vectors and calculus. Generally, vectors are of great significance for the scientist in any context with a geometrical setting. Quite recently, vectors have been applied to problems in mathematical economics and geology (crystallography).

Query: What meaning, if any, can be extracted from the expression $(\mathbf{a}\cdot\mathbf{b})\cdot\mathbf{c}$? *Answer:* Absolutely none whatever! Hence, the associative law is violated by the inner product.

Simple extension. Generalise the theory of § 55 to the vector $(a_1, a_2, \ldots, a_n)$ in n dimensions. What is its length? Its inner product?

EXAMPLE 67 (inner product). For the vectors $\mathbf{a} = (1, 3, -7)$, $\mathbf{b} = (5, -2, 4)$ determine (i) $\mathbf{a}+\mathbf{b}$, (ii) $\mathbf{a}-\mathbf{b}$, (iii) $\mathbf{a}\cdot\mathbf{b}$, (iv) $|\mathbf{a}|$, $|\mathbf{b}|$, (v) the angle θ between $\mathbf{a}$, $\mathbf{b}$ (Fig. 39).

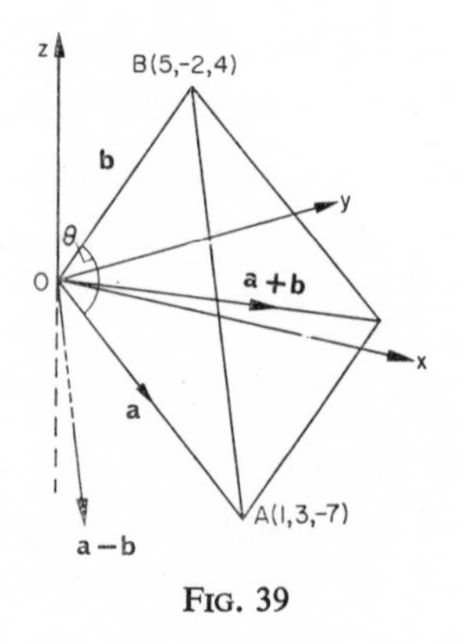

FIG. 39

Solution

(i) $\mathbf{a}+\mathbf{b} = (1+5,\ 3-2,\ -7+4) = (6,\ 1,\ -3)$.

(ii) $\mathbf{a}-\mathbf{b} = (1-5,\ 3+2,\ -7-4) = (-4,\ 5,\ -11)$.

(iii) $\mathbf{a}\cdot\mathbf{b} = 1.5+3.-2+\ -7.4 = -29$.

(iv) $|\mathbf{a}| = \sqrt{1^2+3^2+(-7)^2} = \sqrt{59}, |\mathbf{b}| = \sqrt{5^2+(-2)^2+4^2} = \sqrt{45}.$

(v) $\cos\theta = \dfrac{\mathbf{a}\cdot\mathbf{b}}{|\mathbf{a}||\mathbf{b}|} = \dfrac{-29}{\sqrt{59}\sqrt{45}} = \dfrac{-29}{3\sqrt{295}} \doteqdot -0{\cdot}5628$

$\therefore\ \theta = 124°15'$

(obtuse). The supplementary acute angle 55°45′ is the angle between **a**, −**b** or −**a**, **b**.

Further details concerning the algebra of the inner product (with applications to geometry and mechanics) may be found in, say, *Elementary Vector Analysis*, C. E. Weatherburn (Bell, 1946).

Vector space

Vectors, as we shall appreciate even more vividly in the next chapter, violate so many of the rules to which we are accustomed that they rightly belong to a special type of mathematical structure called a *vector space*. Besides vectors, other examples of objects forming a vector space are polynomials, functions, and solutions of equations. Simplest example of a vector space is Euclidean n-space, in particular, the Euclidean plane. How would you think of the polynomial $ax+b$ as a vector?

Matrix theory is properly developed against a background of linear transformations in vector spaces. This viewpoint we have endeavoured to present in a very elementary way.

§ 56. MATRICES AND LINEAR EQUATIONS

Historically, matrices arose in efforts to solve linear equations. Consider the set of linear equations

$$\begin{cases} a_1x+b_1y+c_1z = h_1 \\ a_2x+b_2y+c_2z = h_2 \\ a_3x+b_3y+c_3z = h_3 \end{cases}$$

i.e.

$$\begin{bmatrix} a_1b_1c_1 \\ a_2b_2c_2 \\ a_3b_3c_3 \end{bmatrix} \begin{bmatrix} x \\ y \\ z \end{bmatrix} = \begin{bmatrix} h_1 \\ h_2 \\ h_3 \end{bmatrix}$$

i.e.

$$A \quad X = H.$$

If this were an ordinary algebraic equation, then would $X = H/A$. But we cannot divide like this in matrix theory as a matrix is not a number but an array. There is, however, an operation in matrix theory corresponding to division in ordinary number theory. Such an operation produces the inverse matrix of a given matrix.

Pre-multiply by A^{-1} $\quad \therefore A^{-1}AX = A^{-1}H$

i.e. $IX = A^{-1}H$

i.e. $X = A^{-1}H$

i.e. $$\begin{bmatrix} x \\ y \\ z \end{bmatrix} = \begin{bmatrix} a_1 & b_1 & c_1 \\ a_2 & b_2 & c_2 \\ a_3 & b_3 & c_3 \end{bmatrix}^{-1} \begin{bmatrix} h_1 \\ h_2 \\ h_3 \end{bmatrix}$$

$$= \begin{bmatrix} a'_1 & b'_1 & c'_1 \\ a'_2 & b'_2 & c'_2 \\ a'_3 & b'_3 & c'_3 \end{bmatrix} \begin{bmatrix} h_1 \\ h_2 \\ h_3 \end{bmatrix}$$ on writing down a general matrix for $A^{-1}(a'_1, \ldots, c'_3$ to be determined)

$$= \begin{bmatrix} a'_1h_1+b'_1h_2+c'_1h_3 \\ a'_2h_1+b'_2h_2+c'_2h_3 \\ a'_3h_1+b'_3h_2+c'_3h_3 \end{bmatrix}$$ by (134)

whence $$\begin{cases} x = a'_1h_1+b'_1h_2+c'_1h_3 \\ y = a'_2h_1+b'_2h_2+c'_2h_3 \\ z = a'_3h_1+b'_3h_2+c'_3h_3. \end{cases}$$

EXAMPLE 68 (simple illustration of the matrix method).

Solve $$\begin{cases} 2x-y = 1 \\ x+2y = 8. \end{cases}$$

Solution. $$\therefore \begin{bmatrix} 2 & -1 \\ 1 & 2 \end{bmatrix} \begin{bmatrix} x \\ y \end{bmatrix} = \begin{bmatrix} 1 \\ 8 \end{bmatrix}$$

$$\therefore \quad \begin{bmatrix} x \\ y \end{bmatrix} = \begin{bmatrix} 2 & -1 \\ 1 & 2 \end{bmatrix}^{-1} \begin{bmatrix} 1 \\ 8 \end{bmatrix}$$

$$= \frac{1}{5}\begin{bmatrix} 2 & 1 \\ -1 & 2 \end{bmatrix} \begin{bmatrix} 1 \\ 8 \end{bmatrix}$$ on calculating the inverse by inspection (or otherwise)

$$= \frac{1}{5}\begin{bmatrix} 10 \\ 15 \end{bmatrix}$$

$$= \begin{bmatrix} 2 \\ 3 \end{bmatrix}$$

$$\therefore \begin{cases} x = 2 \\ y = 3. \end{cases}$$

Geometrically, lines $2x-y = 1$, $x+2y = 8$ meet at (2, 3).

[The inverse above may have been calculated by trial and error, but in the next chapter a standard procedure for obtaining an inverse is developed.]

Linear (in)dependence

A finite set of objects $\{A_1, A_2, \ldots, A_n\}$ (e.g. vectors, numbers) is said to be *linearly dependent* if $\exists$ a set of constants $a_1, a_2, \ldots, a_n$ (not all zero):

$$\sum_{i=1}^{n} a_i A_i = 0. *$$

If no such constants exist, then the set is *linearly independent*. E.g.:

(i) the polynomials $\{1, x, x^2, a+bx+cx^2\}$ are linearly dependent since

$a \cdot 1 + b \cdot x + c \cdot x^2 - 1 \cdot (a+bx+cx^2) = 0$;

(ii) the rows and columns of the matrix $M = \begin{bmatrix} 1 & 2 & 3 \\ 2 & 3 & 4 \\ 0 & 1 & 2 \end{bmatrix}$ are linearly dependent (i.e. $R_3 = 2R_1 - R_2$, $C_3 = 2C_2 - C_1$);

(iii) unit vectors $\mathbf{i}, \mathbf{j}, \mathbf{k}$ are linearly independent;

(iv) vectors $\mathbf{a} = (1, 3, 5)$, $\mathbf{b} = (2, -1, 4)$, $\mathbf{c} = (4, -9, 2)$ are linearly dependent since $2\mathbf{a} - 3\mathbf{b} + \mathbf{c} = \mathbf{0}$.

In the case of (ii), it would follow that the inverse of M does not exist, i.e. M is singular.

Take a simpler matrix. Suppose we wished to solve $2x - y = 1$, $6x - 3y = 3$ the matrix of which is $N = \begin{bmatrix} 2 & -1 \\ 6 & -3 \end{bmatrix}$. Since $R_2 = 3R_1$, N^{-1} does not exist (i.e. N is singular) and it is impossible to solve the equations to obtain just one solution. If a square matrix of order $n \times n$ is non-singular, we say its *rank* is n. However, when it is singular, the rank is $< n$. In fact, the ranks of M, N above are 2, 1 respectively.

Having indicated the significance of linear independence and rank in the context of matrices, we now relate them to the new concept of a determinant.

§ 57. MATRICES AND DETERMINANTS

We saw in Example 63 that if the rows (and columns) of the 2×2 matrix $\begin{bmatrix} a & c \\ b & d \end{bmatrix}$ were not independent, i.e. $\frac{a}{b} = \frac{c}{d} = \lambda$ or $\frac{a}{c} = \frac{b}{d} = k$, the matrix was singular, i.e. $ad - bc = 0$.

The expression $ad - bc$ is called a *determinant*, written

$$\begin{vmatrix} a & c \\ b & d \end{vmatrix} = ad - bc.$$

If $ad - bc \neq 0$ the determinant is non-singular. Otherwise it is singular (and the rank of the corresponding matrix is $\leqslant 1$).

* Here, 0 is the zero of the set of objects. It follows that a linearly independent set does not contain 0.

Singularity occurs in a 3×3 matrix if rows (and columns) are dependent, i.e. (say) $\lambda C_1+\mu C_2+\nu C_3 = 0$,

i.e.
$$\begin{bmatrix} a_1 & b_1 & c_1 \\ a_2 & b_2 & c_2 \\ a_3 & b_3 & c_3 \end{bmatrix}\begin{bmatrix} \lambda \\ \mu \\ \nu \end{bmatrix} = \begin{bmatrix} 0 \\ 0 \\ 0 \end{bmatrix}$$

i.e.
$$\begin{cases} \lambda a_1+\mu b_1+\nu c_1 = 0 \\ \lambda a_2+\mu b_2+\nu c_2 = 0 \\ \lambda a_3+\mu b_3+\nu c_3 = 0. \end{cases}$$

Eliminate λ, μ, ν by ordinary algebraic methods and we obtain the vanishing of the 3×3 determinant

$$\begin{vmatrix} a_1 & b_1 & c_1 \\ a_2 & b_2 & c_2 \\ a_3 & b_3 & c_3 \end{vmatrix} = \begin{matrix} a_1b_2c_3+a_2b_3c_1+a_3b_1c_2 \\ -a_1b_3c_2-a_2b_1c_3-a_3b_2c_1 \end{matrix} = a_1\begin{vmatrix} b_2c_2 \\ b_3c_3 \end{vmatrix} - b_1\begin{vmatrix} a_2c_2 \\ a_3c_3 \end{vmatrix} + c_1\begin{vmatrix} a_2b_2 \\ a_3b_3 \end{vmatrix}.$$

And so on for square matrices and determinants of any finite size.

Note that (i) if two rows of a 3×3 determinant are dependent, space compresses to a plane (and the rank of the matrix is 2), while (ii) if three rows of a 3×3 determinant are dependent, space compresses to a line (and the rank of the matrix is 1). (What happens if the rank is 0?)

Instances of (i) and (ii) are, respectively,

$$\begin{vmatrix} 2 & 1 & 3 \\ 3 & -2 & 0 \\ 1 & 4 & 6 \end{vmatrix} \quad \text{and} \quad \begin{vmatrix} 1 & 2 & 5 \\ 2 & 4 & 10 \\ 3 & 6 & 15 \end{vmatrix}$$

for which $2R_1-R_2-R_3 = 0$, $6C_1+9C_2-7C_3 = 0$ and $5R_1-R_2-R_3 = 0$, $3C_1+C_2-C_3 = 0$.

Plainly, $\begin{bmatrix} 1 & 0 & 0 \\ 0 & 1 & 0 \end{bmatrix}\begin{bmatrix} x \\ y \\ z \end{bmatrix} = \begin{bmatrix} x \\ y \end{bmatrix}$, i.e., the 3×2 rectangular matrix $\begin{bmatrix} 1 & 0 & 0 \\ 0 & 1 & 0 \end{bmatrix}$ projects a point (x, y, z) in three-dimensional space into a point (x, y) in the xy-plane. Is there any linear transformation which will take this point back? (No. Why?)

Interpret the projections $\begin{bmatrix} 2 & 0 & 0 \\ 0 & 0 & 2 \end{bmatrix}$, $\dfrac{1}{5}\begin{bmatrix} 0 & 3 & 4 \\ 0 & -4 & 3 \end{bmatrix}$.

EXAMPLE 69 (geometrical significance of a non-singular determinant).

Solution. From Example 63, we derive Fig. 40, for which the area of the original square is 1.

$$\begin{aligned}\text{Area of the parallelogram} &= (a+c)(b+d)-2(\tfrac{1}{2}ab)-2(\tfrac{1}{2}cd)-2bc \\ &= ab+ad+bc+cd-ab-cd-2bc \\ &= ad-bc \\ &= \begin{vmatrix} a & c \\ b & d \end{vmatrix},\end{aligned}$$

i.e. the non-singular 2×2 determinant represents the ratio in which the corresponding matrix changes areas. (If the matrix is singular, the area is 0.)

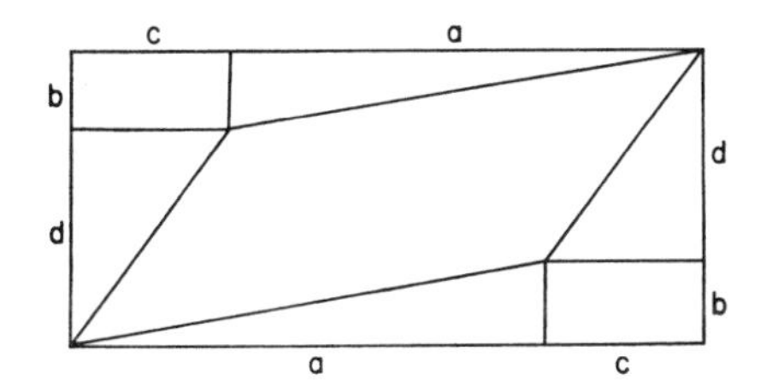

FIG. 40. Geometrical meaning of a determinant

Similarly in three dimensions the general matrix transforms the cube into a parallelepiped. Then the 3×3 determinant represents the ratio in which the corresponding matrix changes volumes.

Though we cannot visualise the geometric extension of $n \times n$ non-singular determinants to n dimensions ($n \geqslant 4$), logically there is no difficulty. Quantities which in higher dimensions correspond to volume are called *hyper-volumes* and the geometrical bodies to which they are related are called *hyper-cubes* and *hyper-parallelepipeds*.

Suggested topics for further study

(1) Linear independence.
(2) Rank of a matrix.
(3) Theory of games.
(4) Differentiation and integration of matrices.
(5) Vector spaces and linear transformations.
(6) Applications of matrices to any area of study in which you are interested.

References

(a) *An Introduction to Determinants and Matrices*, F. Bowman (E.U.P., 1962).
(b) *An Introduction to Matrices*, A. E. Coulson (Longmans, 1965).

(c) *An Introduction to Matrices, Sets and Groups*, G. Stephenson (Longmans, 1965).
(d) *The Core of Mathematics*, A. J. Moakes (Macmillan, 1964).
(e) Andree [29], Balfour [30], Kelly [33], Robinson [35], Weiss and Dubisch [36].

EXERCISES 11

If the orders of matrices A, B, C, D are 2×3, 4×3, 3×3, 3×2 respectively, what are the orders of matrices 1–7?

1. AC. **2.** DA. **3.** AD.
4. BC. **5.** CB. **6.** DAC.
7. $BCDA$.

With the same A, B, C, D, can

8. A, D commute? **9.** B, C commute?

10. Is it possible to define $A+B$ when A has 3 rows, B has 3 columns?

When $A = \begin{bmatrix} 1 & 3 & 2 \\ 2 & 0 & 5 \\ 6 & 1 & 7 \end{bmatrix}$, $B = \begin{bmatrix} 2 & 0 & -1 \\ 3 & -5 & 2 \\ -8 & -2 & 1 \end{bmatrix}$ calculate 11–14:

11. $A+B$. **12.** $A-B$. **13.** AB. **14.** BA.

[Observe that $\text{tr}(AB) = \text{tr}(BA)$ $[= -12]$, a result always valid for the product of two square matrices.]

15. Given $A = \begin{bmatrix} 2 & -5 \\ 3 & 1 \end{bmatrix}$, find scalars α, β, γ not all zero satisfying the quadratic matrix equation $\alpha I+\beta A+\gamma A^2 = O$.

16. If $A = \begin{bmatrix} 1 & 3 & 2 \\ 2 & 0 & -1 \\ 1 & 2 & 3 \end{bmatrix}$, determine $A^3-4A^2-3A+11I$.

Show that matrices $A = \begin{bmatrix} 1 & -1 & 1 \\ 1 & -1 & 1 \\ 1 & -1 & 1 \end{bmatrix}$, $B = \begin{bmatrix} 1 & -2 & 1 \\ -1 & 2 & -1 \\ -2 & 4 & -2 \end{bmatrix}$ satisfy 17–22:

17. $A^2 = A$. **18.** $B^2 = B$. **19.** $AB = O = BA$.
20. $(A+B)^2 = A+B$. **21.** $(A+B)^3 = A+B$ **22.** $(AB)^T = B^TA^T$.

[Matrices $X : X^p = X$ are said to be *idempotent of degree p*.]

Given $U = \begin{bmatrix} 2 & -2 & -4 \\ -1 & 3 & 4 \\ 1 & -2 & -3 \end{bmatrix}$, $V = I-U$, $W = \begin{bmatrix} . & 1 & . & . \\ . & . & 1 & . \\ . & . & . & 1 \\ . & . & . & . \end{bmatrix}$, calculate 23–30:

23. $U+V$. **24.** U^2. **25.** V^2. **26.** UV. **27.** VU. **28.** W^2.
29. W^3. **30.** W^4.

With $A = \begin{bmatrix} 0 & 1 & -1 \\ 3 & -2 & 3 \\ 2 & -2 & 3 \end{bmatrix}$, $B = \begin{bmatrix} 4 & -3 & 3 \\ 2 & -1 & 2 \\ -3 & 3 & -2 \end{bmatrix}$, compute 31–34:

31. A^2. **32.** B^2. **33.** $\left(\dfrac{A+B}{2}\right)^2$. **34.** $(A-B)^2$.

For an *involutory matrix* A, i.e. $A^2 = I$, show that:

35. $\frac{1}{2}(I \pm A)$ are idempotent. **36.** $\frac{1}{2}(I+A)\cdot\frac{1}{2}(I-A) = O$.

37. Show that matrices A, B are: $(A+B)^2 = A^2+B^2$ if and only if A, B are anti-commuting. Illustrate in the case of $A = \begin{bmatrix} 1 & -1 \\ 2 & -1 \end{bmatrix}$, $B = \begin{bmatrix} 1 & 1 \\ 4 & -1 \end{bmatrix}$. (An "if and only if" statement requires the proof of the converse as well.)

38. *Nilpotent matrices of degree p* are matrices $A : A^p = O$. Determine all nilpotent 2×2 matrices of degree 2.

39. Establish the theorem: A, B commute if and only if $A-kI$, $B-kI$ commute for every scalar k, and A, B are square matrices.

40. Rotations leave lengths of segments invariant. Prove.

41. Quantum mechanics uses a type of result like $AB-BA = I$. Demonstrate that $A^kB-BA^k = kA^{k-1}$ $(k = 1, 2, \ldots)$.

Electron spin theory in atomic physics utilises the *Pauli spin matrices* $a = \begin{bmatrix} \cdot & 1 \\ 1 & \cdot \end{bmatrix}$ $b = \begin{bmatrix} \cdot & -i \\ i & \cdot \end{bmatrix}$, $c = \begin{bmatrix} 1 & \cdot \\ \cdot & -1 \end{bmatrix}$ in relation to the x-, y-, z-axes respectively ($i = \sqrt{-1}$).

42. Do the Pauli spin matrices commute? **43.** Are they involutory?
44. Are they unitary? **45.** Are they Hermitian?

[Denote by $\bar{A} = [\bar{a}_{ij}]$ the matrix obtained from A by replacing every element by its complex conjugate. Define $A^* = \bar{A}^T = \overline{A^T}$. A *unitary matrix* U is: $U^* = U^{-1}$. *A Hermitian matrix* H is: $H^* = H$ (after Hermite).]

46. If all the elements of a Hermitian matrix are real, is the matrix then symmetric?

47. Why must the diagonal elements of a Hermitian matrix always be real numbers?

The *commutator* of A, B is $AB-BA$ (refer to Exercise 11.41). What are the commutators of the Pauli spin matrices 48–50?

48. a, b. **49.** b, c. **50.** c, a.

An *orthogonal matrix* L (necessarily square) is: $L^T = L^{-1}$ (i.e. $L^TL = LL^T = I$). [Orthogonal matrices form the *orthogonal group* (Chapter 14). Orthogonal transformations (matrices) preserve the invariance of: distance, inner product, orthogonality, angle magnitude.]

51. Prove that the product of two orthogonal matrices is orthogonal.

52. Show that the inverse of an orthogonal matrix is orthogonal.

53. What restrictions must be placed on a, b, c, d in order that $\begin{bmatrix} a & b \\ c & d \end{bmatrix}$ be orthogonal?

54. If P, Q, R, S are $p\times p$ matrices such that the matrix $A = \begin{bmatrix} P & Q \\ R & S \end{bmatrix}$ is orthogonal and if also $B = [X \; Y]$ is orthogonal, prove that $C = [XP+YR, XQ+YS]$ is orthogonal if it exists, and state the orders of X, Y. [U.N.E.]

Consider the matrix $Q = \begin{bmatrix} w & x & y & z \\ -x & w & -z & y \\ -y & z & w & -x \\ -z & -y & x & w \end{bmatrix}$.

55. What connection is there between quaternions and the rows (and columns) of Q?

56. Determine the relationship connecting w, x, y, z if Q is orthogonal.

Let y, Y be two solutions of a differential equation and suppose they are dependent, i.e. $Y = ky$.

57. Prove that the *Wronskian* $W \equiv \begin{vmatrix} y & Y \\ \dfrac{dy}{dx} & \dfrac{dY}{dx} \end{vmatrix} = 0$ (Wronski, 1778–1853, Polish).

58. Check for the solutions $y = a \cosh nt$, $Y = b \sinh nt$ of $\ddot{y} = n^2 y$.

Let $F(\theta)$ be the matrix function defined by $F(\theta) = \begin{bmatrix} \cos\theta & -\sin\theta \\ \sin\theta & \cos\theta \end{bmatrix}$.

59. Prove that, for any two scalars α, β the matrix product $F(\alpha)\,F(\beta) = F(\alpha+\beta)$. Deduce that $\{F(\alpha)\}^2 = F(2\alpha)$, $\{F(\alpha)\}^3 = F(3\alpha)$ and, more generally, that $\{F(\alpha)\}^n = F(n\alpha)$, for every positive integer n.

60. If $A = \begin{bmatrix} \sqrt{3} & -1 \\ 1 & \sqrt{3} \end{bmatrix}$, choose scalars k, α such that $A = kF(\alpha)$.

61. Hence, or otherwise, find A^{13}. [U.N.E.]

Given that the matrices $A = \begin{bmatrix} a & b & c \\ b & c & a \\ c & a & b \end{bmatrix}$, $B = \begin{bmatrix} b & c & a \\ c & a & b \\ a & b & c \end{bmatrix}$ commute:

62. Show that $\sum bc = \sum a^2$.

63. Find A^2.

64. Evaluate A^2 when a, b, c are replaced by $1, \varepsilon, \varepsilon^2$ respectively (ε a complex cube root of unity).

65. Calculate AB under the same conditions.

66. Verify that $(I-A)^{-1} = I+A$.

67. If a, b, c, are the roots of $x^3+x^2+k = 0$ (k constant), prove that the matrix A of Exercises 11.62–11.66 is orthogonal.

Let P be a skew-symmetric matrix and Q a symmetric matrix. Determine the symmetry or skew-symmetry of 68–71:

68. $A^T PA$ (any A). **69.** P^2. **70.** $PQ-QP$. **71.** PQ if P, Q commute.

72. *Upper triangular matrices* of order 3×3 are of the form $\begin{bmatrix} a_1 & a_2 & a_3 \\ 0 & b_2 & b_3 \\ 0 & 0 & c_3 \end{bmatrix}$, i.e. all elements in the bottom left-hand corner are zero.

Given $A = \begin{bmatrix} 1 & 2 & 4 \\ 0 & 2 & 3 \\ 0 & 0 & 3 \end{bmatrix}$, find A^{-1} by considering the equation $AX = I$.

73. Let $Y = AX$ be a linear transformation of points w.r.t. given axes. Make a non-singular transformation of coordinates $X' = PX$ to new axes. Express, in matrix form, the transformation w.r.t. these new axes. What does the matrix A of the transformation now become?

A two-dimensional *shear* parallel to the y-axis is a linear transformation whose matrix is $\begin{bmatrix} c & 0 \\ kc & c \end{bmatrix}$ (c, k constants) having the effect of moving each point along a line parallel to the y-axis a distance proportional to its abscissa. What effect on the line $y = 3x+1$ have 74–77?

74. Shear $S = \begin{bmatrix} 1 & 0 \\ 2 & 1 \end{bmatrix}$. **75.** Elongation $E = \begin{bmatrix} 1 & 0 \\ 0 & 4 \end{bmatrix}$. **76.** SE. **77.** ES.

78. What is the actual equation of the line into which the line $lx+my+n = 0$ is transformed by the general linear transformation (131) of matrix A? Specialising A as diag. $(-1, -1)$, show that the transformation (an *inversion*) leaves every line through the origin invariant.

Given the *quaternion matrices* $I = \begin{bmatrix} 1 & . & . & . \\ . & 1 & . & . \\ . & . & 1 & . \\ . & . & . & 1 \end{bmatrix}$, $J = \begin{bmatrix} . & 1 & . & . \\ -1 & . & . & . \\ . & . & . & -1 \\ . & . & 1 & . \end{bmatrix}$,

$K = \begin{bmatrix} . & . & 1 & . \\ . & . & . & 1 \\ -1 & . & . & . \\ . & -1 & . & . \end{bmatrix}$, $L = \begin{bmatrix} . & . & . & 1 \\ . & . & -1 & . \\ . & 1 & . & . \\ -1 & . & . & . \end{bmatrix}$, verify 79–82.

79. $JK = -KJ = L$.

80. $KL = -LK = J$.

81. $LJ = -JL = K$.

82. $J^2 = K^2 = L^2 = -I$.

[Under matrix multiplication, I, J, K, L behave exactly as do quaternion elements $1, i, j, k$ under arithmetical multiplication.]

Matthews [*The Mathematical Gazette* **47** (359), 2–8, 1963.] introduced the matrix $5P = \begin{bmatrix} 1 & 4 \\ 2 & 3 \end{bmatrix}$.

Derive 83–86.

83. $5P^2 = I+4P$.

84. $25P^3 = 4I+21P$.

85. $125P^4 = 21I+104P$.

86. $625P^5 = 104I+521P$.

87. Write down the corresponding expression involving P^6.

88. If $\lim P^n = \dfrac{I+kP}{m}$, determine k, m.

89. Coefficients of I, P in 83–86 are successive terms in a certain recurrence sequence which is a special case of $\{\omega_n(a, b; p, q)\}$. (See Exercises 9.45–9.55.) Determine this sequence.

90. Suppose that, in Fig. 38, OA makes angles α, β, γ with the x-, y-, z-axes respectively, e.g. $\alpha = \widehat{LOA}$. Calculate $\cos^2\alpha+\cos^2\beta+\cos^2\gamma$. [We call $\cos\alpha$, $\cos\beta$, $\cos\gamma$ the *direction cosines* of OA.] Find α if OA is equally inclined to the three axes.

91. Determine the direction cosines of the vector $\overrightarrow{AB}$ in Example 67.

Given the vectors $\mathbf{a} = (2, -1, 1)$, $\mathbf{b} = (1, 1, -4)$:

92. Simplify $2\mathbf{a}-\mathbf{b}(= \mathbf{c}$ say) and find a unit vector parallel to $\mathbf{c}$.

93. Solve the vector equation $2\mathbf{a}-\mathbf{b}+3\mathbf{x} = \mathbf{0}$.

94. Illustrate the *Cauchy–Schwarz inequality* $|\mathbf{a}.\mathbf{b}| \leqslant |\mathbf{a}||\mathbf{b}|$ [see (140)] for the vectors $\mathbf{a} = (1, 1, 0)$, $\mathbf{b} = (1, 0, 1)$ (Schwarz, 1843–1921, German).

95. Determine the angle between the vectors $\mathbf{a}$, $\mathbf{b}$ in Exercise 11.94.

96. Are the vectors $\mathbf{u} = (6, 4, -7)$, $\mathbf{v} = (5, -4, 2)$ perpendicular?

Check on the linear independence of the following sets, 97–100:

97. Vectors (1, 1, 0), (1, 0, 1), (0, 1, 1), (1, 1, 1).

98. Functions $1, x, x^2, \ldots, x^n$ (n integer).

99. Solutions e^x, e^{3x} of the differential equation $\dfrac{d^2y}{dx^2}-4\dfrac{dy}{dx}+3 = 0$. [Also test by the Wronskian, Exercise 11.57.]

100. $\sin x, \sin 2x, \sin 3x, \ldots, \sin nx$ in $0 \leqslant x \leqslant \pi$.

CHAPTER 12

DETERMINANTS

> As the sun eclipses the stars by his brilliancy, so the man of knowledge will eclipse the fame of others in assemblies of the people if he proposes algebraic problems, and still more if he solves them.
>
> (BRAHMAGUPTA (7th cent., Indian))

MATRICES, as we saw, are closely associated with determinants. These latter are now investigated formally along with a deeper study of their connection with matrices in which the important concept of eigenvalue is introduced.

Objects of this chapter are:

(i) to obtain quick and sophisticated methods for evaluating determinants; and
(ii) to apply the theory and techniques of determinants.

§58. FORMAL DEFINITIONS AND BASIC PROPERTIES

Historical

Determinants, which are closely related to matrices, arose from the study of simultaneous linear equations and, indeed, are most helpful in solving such equations. As early as 1100 B.C. the Chinese had used simple determinants for this purpose. In modern times, the discoverer of determinants was Leibniz who stated their law of formation in 1693 though Seki Kowa (1642–1708, Japanese) had come close to discovering their nature 10 years earlier. However, Leibniz's work was overlooked and it was left to Cramer (1704–52, Swiss) to rediscover determinants and state their law of formation in 1750. Vandermonde (1735–96, French) may be regarded as the founder (1771) of a notation and algebra of determinants. We use the notation devised in 1841 by Cayley. Other important early contributors to the theory of determinants were Cauchy, Laplace, Lagrange, Jacobi (1804–51, German), and Wronski. The term "determinant" is due to Cauchy (1812), though it had been used in 1801 by Gauss in a different context.

Determinants are used extensively as a notation in mathematics, particularly in geometry, in transformation theory, and in the theory of equations. In this latter case, they are especially valuable in connection with electrical networks, e.g. the Wheatstone bridge network, and for natural modes of free vibrations of certain mechanical systems, e.g. a triatomic molecule. Economics also finds use for them in a similar context.

Inversions

Natural order is defined to be, for numbers, 1 2 3 4 . . . , and for letters, *a b c d* . . . .

When two elements in a permutation are out of natural order, the greater one preceding the lesser, such a derangement is called an *inversion*. E.g. (1 2 4 3 5) is a permutation (1 2 3 4 5) with 4 3 as an inversion.

A permutation is *even* or *odd* according as the number of inversions is even or odd.

EXAMPLE 70 (inversions). Is (4 3 5 2 1) an even or odd permutation?

Solution 1. 4 precedes 3 smaller numbers
3 precedes 2 smaller numbers
5 precedes 2 smaller numbers
2 precedes 1 smaller numbers

$\therefore \exists$ 8 inversions
$\therefore$ (4 3 5 2 1) is an even permutation.

Solution 2. (Diagrammatic—Fig. 41): Intersections correspond to inversions.

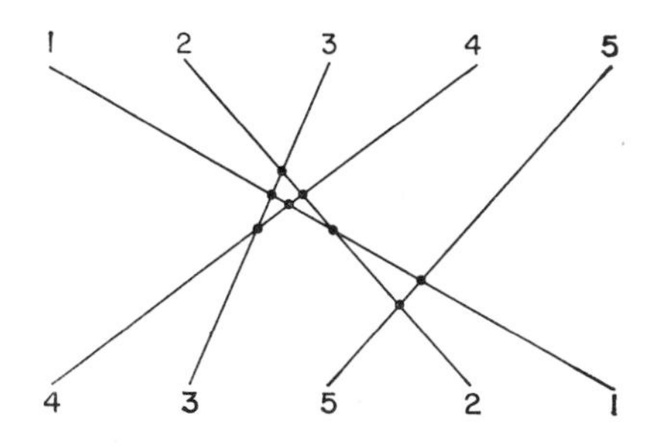

FIG. 41. Geometrical representation of inversions

Formal definitions

A determinant is a number derived from a square matrix by the rule stated below and is usually denoted by arranging its elements in a square array with an upright line on each side.

Ultimately, a determinant always equals some number.

Definition. A *determinant* of *order n*, containing n^2 elements, is defined to be

$$D \equiv \begin{vmatrix} a_{11} & a_{12} & a_{13} & \dots & a_{1j} & \dots & a_{1n} \\ a_{21} & a_{22} & a_{23} & \dots & a_{2j} & \dots & a_{2n} \\ a_{31} & a_{32} & a_{33} & \dots & a_{3j} & \dots & a_{3n} \\ \dots & & & & & & \\ a_{i1} & a_{i2} & a_{i3} & \dots & a_{ij} & \dots & a_{in} \\ \dots & & & & & & \\ a_{n1} & a_{n2} & a_{n3} & \dots & a_{nj} & \dots & a_{nn} \end{vmatrix} = \sum (-1)^t a_{i_1 1} a_{i_2 2} \dots a_{i_n n} \equiv |a_{ij}| \qquad (141)$$

(column C_j, row R_i)

where $i_1, i_2, \dots, i_n$ is an arrangement of $1\ 2\ 3\ \dots\ n$ derived from it by t inversions. Uprights about a_{ij} in (141) must not be confused with similar symbolism relating to moduli and absolute values. Instead of $|a_{ij}|$, the notation det A is commonly used for D, where $A = [a_{ij}]$. From (141),

$$\begin{vmatrix} a_{11} & a_{12} \\ a_{21} & a_{22} \end{vmatrix} = a_{11}a_{22} - a_{12}a_{21} \qquad (n=2)$$

$$\begin{vmatrix} a_{11} & a_{12} & a_{13} \\ a_{21} & a_{22} & a_{23} \\ a_{31} & a_{32} & a_{33} \end{vmatrix} \left.\begin{matrix} = a_{11}\,a_{22}\,a_{33} - a_{11}\,a_{32}\,a_{23} - a_{21}\,a_{12}\,a_{33} \\ + a_{21}\,a_{32}\,a_{13} + a_{31}\,a_{12}\,a_{22} - a_{31}\,a_{22}\,a_{13} \end{matrix}\right\} (n=3).$$

Then, if we put numerical values for the a_{ij}, the value of a determinant may be obtained. Verify, e.g., that

$$\begin{vmatrix} 8 & 1 & 6 \\ 3 & 5 & 7 \\ 4 & 9 & 2 \end{vmatrix} = -360. \text{ (Refer to Example 75.)}$$

Remarks

(1) Term $a_{11}\,a_{22}\,a_{33}\,\dots\,a_{nn}$ consisting entirely of diagonal elements is the *leading* or *principal term.* Elements $a_{11}, a_{22}, \dots, a_{nn}$ are said to lie in the *principal diagonal.*

(2) As there are $n!$ different ways of arranging n things, e.g. the natural order $1\ 2\ 3\ \dots\ n$, there are $n!$ terms in the expression for D, of which $\frac{1}{2}(n!)$ are positively signed and $\frac{1}{2}(n!)$ are negatively signed.

(3) Each of these $n!$ terms contains just one element from each row and just one element from each column.

(4) Any theorem true for $\begin{cases}\text{rows}\\ \text{columns}\end{cases}$ is equally true for $\begin{cases}\text{columns.}\\ \text{rows.}\end{cases}$

(5) (i) Two corresponding rows (columns) of two determinants can be added (subtracted) provided that the remaining corresponding rows

(columns) are the same, e.g.

$$\begin{vmatrix} a & c \\ b & d \end{vmatrix} + \begin{vmatrix} \alpha & \gamma \\ b & d \end{vmatrix} = \begin{vmatrix} a+\alpha & c+\gamma \\ b & d \end{vmatrix}.$$

Explore this notion a little further yourself, e.g. express

$$\begin{vmatrix} 2+1 & 3-4 \\ 0+1 & 2-1 \end{vmatrix} \quad \text{as the sum of 4 determinants.}$$

(ii) The rule for multiplication of two matrices (§ 54) holds for determinants but, since determinants are merely numbers (or numbers in disguise) they obey the commutative law of multiplication. E.g.

$$\left.\begin{array}{l} \begin{vmatrix} 1 & 2 \\ 3 & 5 \end{vmatrix} \begin{vmatrix} 3 & 1 \\ 2 & 0 \end{vmatrix} = \begin{vmatrix} 7 & 1 \\ 19 & 3 \end{vmatrix} \\ \begin{vmatrix} 3 & 1 \\ 2 & 0 \end{vmatrix} \begin{vmatrix} 1 & 2 \\ 3 & 5 \end{vmatrix} = \begin{vmatrix} 6 & 11 \\ 2 & 4 \end{vmatrix} \end{array}\right\} = 2$$

(iii) While division is clearly impossible with matrices, it is evidently valid in the case of determinants (unless $D=0$).

(iv) The *transpose* D^T of a determinant D is defined as for the matrix.

(v) If a determinant has value $+1$, its corresponding matrix is said to be *unimodular*. E.g.

$$\begin{vmatrix} \cos\theta & \sin\theta \\ -\sin\theta & \cos\theta \end{vmatrix} \quad \text{is unimodular.}$$

(vi) Symmetric and skew-symmetric determinants are defined as for symmetric and skew-symmetric matrices (§ 54).

Basic properties

The following fundamental properties follow from (141) and are assumed without proof (though an effort should be made to prove them):

(I) A determinant and its transpose have the same value, i.e. $D^T = D$.

(II) A determinant is unaltered in value but changed in sign by the interchange of two rows or columns. E.g.:

$$\begin{aligned} \begin{vmatrix} 4 & 1 & 2 \\ -1 & 3 & 0 \\ 5 & 2 & 6 \end{vmatrix} &= -\begin{vmatrix} 5 & 2 & 6 \\ -1 & 3 & 0 \\ 4 & 1 & 2 \end{vmatrix} && \text{interchanging } R_1, R_3 \\ &= +\begin{vmatrix} 5 & 6 & 2 \\ -1 & 0 & 3 \\ 4 & 2 & 1 \end{vmatrix} && \text{interchanging } C_2, C_3 \\ &= -\begin{vmatrix} -1 & 0 & 3 \\ 5 & 6 & 2 \\ 4 & 1 & 2 \end{vmatrix} && \text{interchanging } R_1, R_2. \end{aligned}$$

(III) The value of a determinant in which two rows (or columns) are identical is zero.

(IV) If all the elements of one row (or column) are multiplied (or divided) by the same non-zero quantity, then the whole determinant is multiplied (or divided) by that number. E.g.

$$\begin{vmatrix} 1 & 0 & 4 \\ 6 & 3 & 24 \\ -1 & 2 & -4 \end{vmatrix} = 3 \begin{vmatrix} 1 & 0 & 4 \\ 2 & 1 & 8 \\ -1 & 2 & -4 \end{vmatrix} \quad \text{taking out 3 from } R_2$$

$$= 12 \begin{vmatrix} 1 & 0 & 1 \\ 2 & 1 & 2 \\ -1 & 2 & -1 \end{vmatrix} \quad \text{taking out 4 from } C_3$$

$$= 0 \qquad \because C_1 \equiv C_3.$$

Note how different (IV) is from the corresponding matrix theory; e.g.:

$$\begin{bmatrix} 2 & 4 & -4 \\ 6 & 2 & 0 \\ 8 & 0 & 2 \end{bmatrix} = 2 \begin{bmatrix} 1 & 2 & -2 \\ 3 & 1 & 0 \\ 4 & 0 & 1 \end{bmatrix}$$

but
$$\begin{vmatrix} 2 & 4 & -4 \\ 6 & 2 & 0 \\ 8 & 0 & 2 \end{vmatrix} = 2^3 \begin{vmatrix} 1 & 2 & -2 \\ 3 & 1 & 0 \\ 4 & 0 & 1 \end{vmatrix}.$$

(V) A determinant is unaltered in value by adding (or subtracting) a nonzero multiple of the elements of one row (or column) to corresponding elements of another row (or column). E.g.

$$\begin{vmatrix} 2 & 1 & 5 \\ 7 & -1 & 3 \\ -1 & 2 & 4 \end{vmatrix} = \begin{vmatrix} 0 & 1 & 0 \\ 9 & -1 & 8 \\ -5 & 2 & -6 \end{vmatrix} \quad \begin{cases} C_1 - 2C_2 \\ C_3 - 5C_2 \end{cases}$$

or
$$\begin{vmatrix} 2 & 1 & 5 \\ 7 & -1 & 3 \\ -1 & 2 & 4 \end{vmatrix} = \begin{vmatrix} 2 & 1 & 5 \\ 9 & 0 & 8 \\ -5 & 0 & -6 \end{vmatrix} \quad \begin{cases} R_2 + R_1 \\ R_3 - 2R_1 . \end{cases}$$

Also
$$\begin{vmatrix} 1 & 1 & 1 \\ \alpha & \beta & \gamma \\ \alpha^2 & \beta^2 & \gamma^2 \end{vmatrix} = \begin{vmatrix} 1 & 0 & 0 \\ \alpha & \beta-\alpha & \gamma-\alpha \\ \alpha^2 & (\beta-\alpha)(\beta+\alpha) & (\gamma-\alpha)(\gamma+\alpha) \end{vmatrix} \quad \begin{cases} C_3 - C_1 \\ C_2 - C_1 \end{cases}$$

$$= (\beta-\alpha)(\gamma-\alpha) \begin{vmatrix} 1 & 0 & 0 \\ \alpha & 1 & 1 \\ \alpha^2 & \beta+\alpha & \gamma+\alpha \end{vmatrix} \quad \begin{cases} \text{taking out } \beta-\alpha \\ \text{from } C_2,\ \gamma-\alpha \text{ from } C_3 \end{cases}$$

$$= (\beta-\alpha)(\gamma-\alpha) \begin{vmatrix} 1 & 0 & 0 \\ \alpha & 1 & 0 \\ \alpha^2 & \beta+\alpha & \gamma-\beta \end{vmatrix} \quad (C_3 - C_2)$$

$$= (\beta-\alpha)(\gamma-\alpha)(\gamma-\beta)\begin{vmatrix} 1 & 0 & 0 \\ \alpha & 1 & 0 \\ \alpha^2 & \beta+\alpha & 1 \end{vmatrix} \quad \left\{\begin{array}{l}\text{taking out} \\ \gamma-\beta \text{ from } C_3\end{array}\right.$$

$$= (\alpha-\beta)(\beta-\gamma)(\gamma-\alpha)\begin{vmatrix} 1 & 0 & 0 \\ \alpha & 1 & 0 \\ \alpha^2 & \beta+\alpha & 1 \end{vmatrix} \quad \begin{array}{l}\text{making the factors} \\ \text{cyclic for aesthetic} \\ \text{purposes.}\end{array}$$

[See § 59 for the complete evaluation of this determinant.]

(VI) det (AB) = det A det B.

For example, see (5)(ii) above.

Important general observations for any determinant

(i) The operation $R_1+R_2 \neq$ the operation R_2+R_1, i.e. (row 2 added to row 1) $\neq$ (row 1 added to row 2).

(ii) Danger! kR_1+R_2 is only permissible if the factor $1/k$ is inserted outside the determinant.

(iii) The operation R_1-R_2 followed by R_2-R_3 is permissible but we cannot at the same time perform R_3-R_1 $\because$ R_1 is altered by the operation R_1-R_2.

§ 59. MINORS AND COFACTORS. EXPANSION OF A DETERMINANT

Definition. The *minor* of a_{ij}, written α_{ij}, is the determinant of order $n-1$ obtained by suppressing R_i and C_j.

E.g. in $\begin{vmatrix} 2 & 1 & 5 \\ 7 & 0 & 3 \\ -1 & 2 & 4 \end{vmatrix}$ the minor of 3 is $\begin{vmatrix} 2 & 1 \\ -1 & 2 \end{vmatrix}$ (= 5).

Definition. The *cofactor* of a_{ij}, written A_{ij}, is merely the minor with a + or − attached.

Define
$$\boxed{A_{ij} = (-1)^{i+j}\,\alpha_{ij}}\,. \tag{142}$$

By means of cofactors we can evaluate any determinant. E.g. from definition,

$$\begin{vmatrix} a_{11} & a_{12} & a_{13} \\ a_{21} & a_{22} & a_{23} \\ a_{31} & a_{32} & a_{33} \end{vmatrix} = a_{11}(a_{22}\,a_{33}-a_{32}a_{23})-a_{12}(a_{21}\,a_{33}-a_{31}\,a_{23}) + a_{13}(a_{21}\,a_{32}-a_{31}\,a_{22})$$

$$= a_{11}\begin{vmatrix} a_{22} & a_{23} \\ a_{32} & a_{33} \end{vmatrix} + a_{12}\cdot - \begin{vmatrix} a_{21} & a_{23} \\ a_{31} & a_{33} \end{vmatrix} + a_{13}\begin{vmatrix} a_{21} & a_{22} \\ a_{31} & a_{32} \end{vmatrix}$$

$$= a_{11}A_{11} + a_{12}A_{12} + a_{13}A_{13}.$$

This is called *expanding along* R_1.

Equally well, we may expand along R_2 or R_3, or *down* any of the columns. Clearly, the value of the determinant is the same in each case. In general,

$$\boxed{\begin{aligned} D &= a_{i1}A_{i1}+a_{i2}A_{i2}+a_{i3}A_{i3}+\ldots+a_{in}A_{in} \\ &= a_{1j}A_{1j}+a_{2j}A_{2j}+a_{3j}A_{3j}+\ldots+a_{nj}A_{nj} \end{aligned} \left.\begin{matrix}\text{exp. along } R_i \\ \text{exp. down } C_j\end{matrix}\right.} \quad (143)$$

$$\text{i.e. } \left.\begin{aligned} D &= \sum_{k=1}^{n} a_{ik}A_{ik} \\ &= \sum_{h=1}^{n} a_{hj}A_{hj} \end{aligned}\right\}.$$

E.g.
$$\begin{vmatrix} 1 & 1 & 1 \\ \alpha & \beta & \gamma \\ \alpha^2 & \beta^2 & \gamma^2 \end{vmatrix} = (\alpha-\beta)(\beta-\gamma)(\gamma-\alpha) \begin{vmatrix} 1 & 0 & 0 \\ \alpha & 1 & 0 \\ \alpha^2 & \beta+\alpha & 1 \end{vmatrix} \text{ from § 58}$$

$$= (\alpha-\beta)(\beta-\gamma)(\gamma-\alpha) \begin{vmatrix} 1 & 0 \\ \beta+\alpha & 1 \end{vmatrix} \text{ expanding along } R_1$$

or
$$= (\alpha-\beta)(\beta-\gamma)(\gamma-\alpha) \begin{vmatrix} 1 & 0 \\ \alpha & 1 \end{vmatrix} \text{ expanding down } C_3$$

$= (\alpha-\beta)(\beta-\gamma)(\gamma-\alpha)$ in both cases, of course. (The determinant is a simple form of *Vandermonde's determinant*.)

EXAMPLE 71.

$$\begin{vmatrix} 2 & -1 & 3 & -2 \\ 1 & 7 & 1 & -1 \\ 3 & 5 & -5 & 3 \\ 4 & -3 & 2 & -1 \end{vmatrix} = \begin{vmatrix} 0 & -15 & 1 & -2 \\ 0 & 0 & 0 & -1 \\ 6 & 26 & -2 & 3 \\ 3 & -10 & 1 & -1 \end{vmatrix} \begin{cases} C_1+C_4 \\ C_2+7C_4 \\ C_3+C_4 \end{cases}$$

$$= -1 \begin{vmatrix} 0 & -15 & 1 \\ 6 & 26 & -2 \\ 3 & -10 & 1 \end{vmatrix} \text{ exp. along } R_2$$

$$= - \begin{vmatrix} 0 & -15 & 1 \\ 0 & 46 & -4 \\ 3 & -10 & 1 \end{vmatrix} \quad \{R_2-2R_3$$

$$= -3 \begin{vmatrix} -15 & 1 \\ 46 & -4 \end{vmatrix} \text{ exp. down } C_1$$

$$= -3(60-46)$$

$$= -42.$$

EXAMPLE 72.

$$\begin{vmatrix} 1+a & 1 & 1 & 1 \\ 1 & 1+a & 1 & 1 \\ 1 & 1 & 1+a & 1 \\ 1 & 1 & 1 & 1+a \end{vmatrix} = (4+a)\begin{vmatrix} 1 & 1 & 1 & 1 \\ 1 & 1+a & 1 & 1 \\ 1 & 1 & 1+a & 1 \\ 1 & 1 & 1 & 1+a \end{vmatrix} \quad \left\{\begin{array}{l} C_1+\overline{C_2+C_3+C_4}, \\ \text{and take out } 4+a \\ \text{from new } C_1 \end{array}\right.$$

$$= (4+a)\begin{vmatrix} 1 & 0 & 0 & 0 \\ 1 & a & 0 & 0 \\ 1 & 0 & a & 0 \\ 1 & 0 & 0 & a \end{vmatrix} \quad \left\{\begin{array}{l} C_2-C_1 \\ C_3-C_1 \\ C_4-C_1 \end{array}\right.$$

$$= (4+a)\,a^3.$$

EXAMPLE 73.

$$\begin{vmatrix} x & a & a & \dots & a \\ a & x & a & \dots & a \\ a & a & x & \dots & a \\ \dots & \dots & \dots & \dots & \dots \\ a & a & a & \dots & x \end{vmatrix} = (x+\overline{n-1}a)\begin{vmatrix} 1 & a & a & \dots & a \\ 1 & x & a & \dots & a \\ 1 & a & x & \dots & a \\ \dots & \dots & \dots & \dots & \dots \\ 1 & a & a & \dots & x \end{vmatrix} \quad \left\{\begin{array}{l} C_1+\overline{C_2+\dots+C_n}, \\ \text{and take out } (x+\overline{n-1}a) \\ \text{from the new } C_1 \end{array}\right.$$

$$= (x+\overline{n-1}a)\begin{vmatrix} 1 & a & a & \dots & a \\ 0 & x-a & 0 & \dots & 0 \\ 0 & 0 & x-a & \dots & 0 \\ \dots & \dots & \dots & \dots & \dots \\ 0 & 0 & 0 & \dots & x-a \end{vmatrix} \quad \left\{\begin{array}{l} \text{subtracting } R_1 \text{ from} \\ \text{each of the re-} \\ \text{maining rows.} \end{array}\right.$$

$$= (x+\overline{n-1}a)\,(x-a)^{n-1}.$$

(Example 72 is a special case of Example 73 when $n = 4$, $x = 1+a$, $a = 1$ (different a's).)

EXAMPLE 74. Solve the determinantal equation $\begin{vmatrix} 2x-1 & x+7 & x+4 \\ x & 6 & 2 \\ x-1 & x+1 & 3 \end{vmatrix} = 0.$

Solution. We have $\begin{vmatrix} 0 & 0 & x-1 \\ x & 6 & 2 \\ x-1 & x+1 & 3 \end{vmatrix} = 0 \qquad \{R_1-(R_2+R_3)$

$$(x-1)\begin{vmatrix} x & 6 \\ x-1 & x+1 \end{vmatrix} = 0 \text{ exp. along } R_1$$

$$(x-1)\{x^2-5x+6\} = 0$$

$$(x-1)(x-2)(x-3) = 0.$$

Therefore the roots of determinantal equation are 1, 2, 3.

[A check should be made to verify that these values of x do satisfy the determinantal equation.]

EXAMPLE 75 (simple magic square). A *magic square* is a square array of numbers such that the sum along any row, down any column and through both diagonals is always the same. [The magic square or *lo-shu* was reputedly discovered by Emperor Yu (*ca.* 2200 B.C.) on the back of a sacred tortoise near the Yellow River! Dürer's famous engraving, "Melancholy", contains a magic square of order 4.]

$$\begin{vmatrix} 8 & 1 & 6 \\ 3 & 5 & 7 \\ 4 & 9 & 2 \end{vmatrix} = 15 \begin{vmatrix} 1 & 1 & 6 \\ 1 & 5 & 7 \\ 1 & 9 & 2 \end{vmatrix} \quad C_1+\overline{C_2+C_3}, \text{ then take out 15 from the new } C_1$$

$$= 15 \begin{vmatrix} 1 & 1 & 6 \\ 0 & 4 & 1 \\ 0 & 8 & -4 \end{vmatrix} \quad \begin{cases} R_2-R_1 \\ R_3-R_1 \end{cases}$$

$$= -360.$$

[It may be shown that the value of a magic square of order n is divisible by $\frac{n^2(n^2+1)}{4}$ (n even), or by $\frac{n^2(n^2+1)}{2}$ (n odd). Try it!]

Expansion by alien cofactors

Consider the determinant Δ obtained from D in (141) by replacing R_1 by R_2.

$$\therefore\ \Delta = \begin{vmatrix} a_{21} & a_{22} & \dots & a_{2n} \\ a_{21} & a_{22} & \dots & a_{2n} \\ a_{31} & a_{32} & \dots & a_{3n} \\ \dots & \dots & \dots & \dots \\ a_{n1} & a_{n2} & \dots & a_{nn} \end{vmatrix} = 0 \quad \because \quad R_1 \equiv R_2 .$$

Expand Δ along R_1.

$$\therefore a_{21} A_{11} + a_{22} A_{12} + \dots + a_{2n} A_{1n} = 0,$$

i.e. expanding by "alien" cofactors (i.e. using cofactors of another row, or column) yields zero value for the determinant.

$$\therefore \quad \boxed{\sum_{j=1}^{n} a_{ij} A_{kj} \begin{cases} = 0 \text{ if } i \neq k \\ = D \text{ if } i = k \end{cases}} \qquad (144)$$

§ 60. ADJOINT DETERMINANT

Definition. The *adjoint* D^* of D is the determinant of the same order formed by replacing the elements of D by their corresponding cofactors.

E.g. if $D = \begin{vmatrix} a_{11} & a_{12} & a_{13} \\ a_{21} & a_{22} & a_{23} \\ a_{31} & a_{32} & a_{33} \end{vmatrix}$ then $D^* = \begin{vmatrix} A_{11} & A_{12} & A_{13} \\ A_{21} & A_{22} & A_{23} \\ A_{31} & A_{32} & A_{33} \end{vmatrix}$.

[The adjoint is used widely in, for example, algebra and projective geometry.]

$$\text{Consider } DD^* = \begin{vmatrix} a_{11} & a_{12} & a_{13} \\ a_{21} & a_{22} & a_{23} \\ a_{31} & a_{32} & a_{33} \end{vmatrix} \begin{vmatrix} A_{11} & A_{12} & A_{13} \\ A_{21} & A_{22} & A_{23} \\ A_{31} & A_{32} & A_{33} \end{vmatrix}$$

$$= \begin{vmatrix} a_{11} & a_{12} & a_{13} \\ a_{21} & a_{22} & a_{23} \\ a_{31} & a_{32} & a_{33} \end{vmatrix} \begin{vmatrix} A_{11} & A_{21} & A_{31} \\ A_{12} & A_{22} & A_{32} \\ A_{13} & A_{23} & A_{33} \end{vmatrix} \quad \because (D^*)^T = D^* \text{ by § 58(I)}$$

$$= \begin{vmatrix} D & . & . \\ . & D & . \\ . & . & D \end{vmatrix} \quad \text{using (144) and representing zero by a dot}$$

$$= D^3$$

$$\therefore \qquad D^* = D^2 \qquad \text{if } D \neq 0.$$

Therefore in general, for non-singular D of order n, we have *Cauchy's result:*

$$\boxed{D^* = D^{n-1}}. \tag{145}$$

Therefore for $n = 3$, the adjoint of the adjoint is

$$\begin{aligned}(D^*)^* &= (D^2)^* \\ &= (D^2)^2 \\ &= D^4\end{aligned}$$

and, in general, $\qquad (D^*)^* = D^{(n-1)^2}$.

Result (145) is also true for D singular.

Jacobi's theorem

$$\text{Let } D = \begin{vmatrix} a & h & g \\ h & b & f \\ g & f & c \end{vmatrix}$$

$$= abc - af^2 - bg^2 - ch^2 + 2fgh$$

$$\therefore \begin{cases} A = bc - f^2, & B = ac - g^2, \quad C = ab - h^2, \\ F = gh - af, & G = hf - bg, \quad H = gf - ch. \end{cases}$$

Let A', B', C', F', G', H' be the cofactors of A, B, C, F, G, H respectively in $D^* = \begin{vmatrix} A & H & G \\ H & B & F \\ G & F & C \end{vmatrix}$

$$\therefore \; A' = BC - F^2$$
$$= (ac-g^2)(ab-h^2)-(gh-af)^2$$
$$= aD \qquad \text{on calculation}$$
$$\therefore \; \frac{A'}{a} = D. \qquad \text{Similarly, for the others.}$$

$$\therefore \; \boxed{\frac{A'}{a} = \frac{B'}{b} = \frac{C'}{c} = \frac{F'}{f} = \frac{G'}{g} = \frac{H'}{h} = D} \qquad \textit{Jacobi's theorem} \qquad (146)$$

$$\therefore \begin{vmatrix} A' & H' & G' \\ H' & B' & F' \\ G' & F' & C' \end{vmatrix} = \begin{vmatrix} aD & hD & gD \\ hD & bD & fD \\ gD & fD & cD \end{vmatrix}$$
$$= D^3 \begin{vmatrix} a & h & g \\ h & b & f \\ g & f & c \end{vmatrix}$$
$$= D^4 \text{ thus verifying our previous result}$$
$$(D^*)^* = D^4 \quad (n = 3).$$

[Jacobi's theorem is quite valuable, e.g. in projective geometry if we wish to replace the line equation of a conic by the point equation.]

§ 61. INVERSE OF A MATRIX

For $n = 3$, define

$$\boxed{\begin{bmatrix} a_{11} & a_{12} & a_{13} \\ a_{21} & a_{22} & a_{23} \\ a_{31} & a_{32} & a_{33} \end{bmatrix}^{-1} = \frac{\begin{bmatrix} A_{11} & A_{21} & A_{31} \\ A_{12} & A_{22} & A_{32} \\ A_{13} & A_{23} & A_{33} \end{bmatrix}}{\begin{vmatrix} a_{11} & a_{12} & a_{13} \\ a_{21} & a_{22} & a_{23} \\ a_{31} & a_{32} & a_{33} \end{vmatrix}}} . \qquad (147)$$

Definition (147) may be symbolically expressed as

$$\mathbf{A}^{-1} = \frac{\mathbf{A}^{*T}}{A}$$

where $A = |\mathbf{A}|$ ($= D$ in our previous notation) is the determinant of the matrix **A**. To remove any possible ambiguity in this section, we have indicated a matrix by bold-face type e.g. **A** is the matrix corresponding to the determinant A. We call $\mathbf{A}^{*T}$ the *adjoint matrix* of **A**. Recall the corresponding definition (§ 60) for the adjoint determinant D^* but note $D^* = D^{*T}$ by § 58 (I).

Verification of (147):

$$\mathbf{AA}^{-1} = \mathbf{A}\,\frac{\mathbf{A}^{*T}}{A}$$

$$= \frac{1}{A}\begin{bmatrix} A & \cdot & \cdot \\ \cdot & A & \cdot \\ \cdot & \cdot & A \end{bmatrix} \qquad \text{using (144)}$$

$$= \begin{bmatrix} 1 & \cdot & \cdot \\ \cdot & 1 & \cdot \\ \cdot & \cdot & 1 \end{bmatrix}$$

$$= \mathbf{I} \text{ thus verifying that } \mathbf{A}^{-1} = \frac{\mathbf{A}^{*T}}{A} \text{ is the inverse of } \mathbf{A}.$$

Obviously our definition is quite general and applies to square matrices of any finite order. Implicit in the definition is the assumption that $|\mathbf{A}| \neq 0$. That is, *a singular matrix has no inverse.*

This statement may also be deduced by the following argument: Suppose **A** has an inverse $\mathbf{A}^{-1}$, i.e. $\mathbf{AA}^{-1} = \mathbf{I}$. Taking determinants and using property (VI) § 58, we have $|\mathbf{A}||\mathbf{A}^{-1}| = |\mathbf{I}| = 1$. If $|\mathbf{A}| = 0$, i.e. A is singular, this is impossible.

In the above definition and verification, the det A notation may be employed alternatively to avoid the use of bold type.

§ 62. SOLUTION OF SIMULTANEOUS LINEAR EQUATIONS

Consider the n simultaneous linear equations in the variables $x_1, \ldots, x_n$:

$$\begin{cases} a_{11}x_1 + a_{12}x_2 + \ldots + a_{1n}x_n = h_1 \\ a_{21}x_1 + a_{22}x_2 + \ldots + a_{2n}x_n = h_2 \\ a_{31}x_1 + a_{32}x_2 + \ldots + a_{3n}x_n = h_3 \\ \cdots\cdots\cdots\cdots\cdots\cdots\cdots\cdots \\ a_{n1}x_1 + a_{n2}x_2 + \ldots + a_{nn}x_n = h_n \end{cases}$$

where the a_{ij} and h_i are constants.

Take D as in (141).

$$\text{Then}\quad x_1D = \begin{vmatrix} a_{11}x_1 & a_{12} & \dots & a_{1n} \\ a_{21}x_1 & a_{22} & \dots & a_{2n} \\ \dots & \dots & \dots & \dots \\ a_{n1}x_1 & a_{n2} & \dots & a_{nn} \end{vmatrix} \quad \text{on multiplying } C_1 \text{ by } x_1$$

$$\therefore \quad x_1D = \begin{vmatrix} a_{11}x_1+a_{12}x_2+\dots+a_{1n}x_n & a_{12} & \dots & a_{1n} \\ a_{21}x_1+a_{22}x_2+\dots+a_{2n}x_n & a_{22} & \dots & a_{2n} \\ \dots & \dots & \dots & \dots \\ a_{n1}x_1+a_{n2}x_2+\dots+a_{nn}x_n & a_{n2} & \dots & a_{nn} \end{vmatrix}$$

$$\overline{(C_1+x_2C_2+x_3C_3+\dots+x_nC_n)}$$

$$= \begin{vmatrix} h_1 & a_{12} & \dots & a_{1n} \\ h_2 & a_{22} & \dots & a_{2n} \\ h_3 & a_{32} & \dots & a_{3n} \\ \dots & \dots & \dots & \dots \\ h_n & a_{n2} & \dots & a_{nn} \end{vmatrix} \quad \text{replacing the elements of } C_1 \text{ by means of the original equations}$$

$$= H_1$$

$$\therefore \; x_1 = \frac{H_1}{D}.$$

Hence, we obtain *Cramer's rule:*

$$\boxed{x_k = \frac{H_k}{D}} \tag{148}$$

where H_k is the determinant formed by substituting $h_1, h_2, \dots, h_n$ for the elements of C_k in D. [One of the useful applications of determinants for solving equations occurs in electrical circuit theory, e.g. in Wheatstone bridge problems.]

EXAMPLE 76. Solve

$$\begin{cases} x-y+z = 7 \\ x+2y-z = -5 \\ 2x-3y+2z = 16. \end{cases}$$

Determinantal solution:

$$H_1 = \begin{vmatrix} 7 & -1 & 1 \\ -5 & 2 & -1 \\ 16 & -3 & 2 \end{vmatrix}, \quad H_2 = \begin{vmatrix} 1 & 7 & 1 \\ 1 & -5 & -1 \\ 2 & 16 & 2 \end{vmatrix} \quad H_3 = \begin{vmatrix} 1 & -1 & 7 \\ 1 & 2 & -5 \\ 2 & -3 & 16 \end{vmatrix}$$

$$= \begin{vmatrix} 7 & -1 & 1 \\ 2 & 1 & 0 \\ 2 & -1 & 0 \end{vmatrix} \quad = \begin{vmatrix} 1 & 7 & 1 \\ 0 & -12 & -2 \\ 0 & 2 & 0 \end{vmatrix} \quad = \begin{vmatrix} 1 & -1 & 7 \\ 0 & 3 & -12 \\ 0 & -1 & 2 \end{vmatrix}$$

$$= -4 \qquad\qquad = 4 \qquad\qquad = -6$$

$$D = \begin{vmatrix} 1 & -1 & 1 \\ 1 & 2 & -1 \\ 2 & -3 & 2 \end{vmatrix}$$

$$= \begin{vmatrix} 1 & 0 & 0 \\ 1 & 3 & -2 \\ 2 & -1 & 0 \end{vmatrix}$$

$$= -2$$

$$\therefore \quad x = \frac{H_1}{D} = 2, \quad y = \frac{H_2}{D} = -2, \quad z = \frac{H_3}{D} = 3.$$

Therefore solution is $\begin{cases} x = 2 \\ y = -2 \\ z = 3. \end{cases}$

Matrix solution:

$$\begin{bmatrix} 1 & -1 & 1 \\ 1 & 2 & -1 \\ 2 & -3 & 2 \end{bmatrix} \begin{bmatrix} x \\ y \\ z \end{bmatrix} = \begin{bmatrix} 7 \\ -5 \\ 16 \end{bmatrix}$$

$$\therefore \quad \begin{bmatrix} x \\ y \\ z \end{bmatrix} = \begin{bmatrix} 1 & -1 & 1 \\ 1 & 2 & -1 \\ 2 & -3 & 2 \end{bmatrix}^{-1} \begin{bmatrix} 7 \\ -5 \\ 16 \end{bmatrix}$$

$$= \frac{\begin{bmatrix} 1 & -1 & -1 \\ -4 & 0 & 2 \\ -7 & 1 & 3 \end{bmatrix} \begin{bmatrix} 7 \\ -5 \\ 16 \end{bmatrix}}{-2}$$

$$= -\tfrac{1}{2} \begin{bmatrix} -4 \\ 4 \\ -6 \end{bmatrix}$$

$$= \begin{bmatrix} 2 \\ -2 \\ 3 \end{bmatrix}.$$

Therefore solution is $\begin{cases} x = 2 \\ y = -2 \\ z = 3. \end{cases}$

Of course, you should verify that this solution is correct by substituting these values in the original equation. Which method (the determinantal or matrix) do you prefer? The matrix technique is the more elegant.

15*

§ 63. ELIMINATION AND EIGENVALUES

Problem. What is the condition that the three linear equations

$$\left.\begin{aligned} a_1x+b_1y+c_1 &= 0 \ldots \text{(i)} \\ a_2x+b_2y+c_2 &= 0 \ldots \text{(ii)} \\ a_3x+b_3y+c_3 &= 0 \ldots \text{(iii)} \end{aligned}\right\} \text{should be simultaneously true?}$$

Solution. Multiply (i), (ii), (iii) by C_1, C_2, C_3 (respectively), the cofactors of

$$c_1, c_2, c_3 \quad \text{in} \quad \begin{vmatrix} a_1 & b_1 & c_1 \\ a_2 & b_2 & c_2 \\ a_3 & b_3 & c_3 \end{vmatrix} = \delta.$$

Therefore, by addition

$$(a_1C_1+a_2C_2+a_3C_3)x+(b_1C_1+b_2C_2+b_3C_3)y+(c_1C_1+c_2C_2+c_3C_3) = 0$$

$$0\cdot x+0\cdot y+c_1C_1+c_2C_2+c_3C_3 = 0 \qquad \text{by (144)}$$

$$\sum_{i=1}^{3} c_iC_i(=\delta) = 0.$$

Therefore required condition is

$$\boxed{\begin{vmatrix} a_1 & b_1 & c_1 \\ a_2 & b_2 & c_2 \\ a_3 & b_3 & c_3 \end{vmatrix} = 0}\,. \qquad (149)$$

Geometric significance of (149): Condition that three lines (i), (ii), (iii) be concurrent.

Corollary. If x, y, z are not all zero, the condition that the three homogeneous linear equations

$$\left.\begin{aligned} a_1x+b_1y+c_1z &= 0 \\ a_2x+b_2y+c_2z &= 0 \\ a_3x+b_3y+c_3z &= 0 \end{aligned}\right\}$$

should be valid is (149). What does this mean geometrically? (See § 78.)

[Another useful method of elimination is *Sylvester's method* (Sylvester, 1814–97, English) but we do not pursue it here.]

EXAMPLE 77 (eigenvalues). Find the value of λ for which the three equations

$$\begin{aligned} x-\ y+\ z &= \lambda x \\ 2x-3y-2z &= \lambda y \\ 2x-5y\qquad &= \lambda z \end{aligned} \quad \text{i.e.} \quad \begin{bmatrix} 1 & -1 & 1 \\ 2 & -3 & -2 \\ 2 & -5 & 0 \end{bmatrix}\begin{bmatrix} x \\ y \\ z \end{bmatrix} = \lambda \begin{bmatrix} x \\ y \\ z \end{bmatrix} \quad \text{or} \quad AX = \lambda X$$

may be satisfied by values of x, y, z which are not all zero.

Solution. The condition for the equations to be true is, by (149),

$$\begin{vmatrix} 1-\lambda & -1 & 1 \\ 2 & -3-\lambda & -2 \\ 2 & -5 & -\lambda \end{vmatrix} = 0$$

$$\begin{vmatrix} 1-\lambda & -1 & 1 \\ 2 & -3-\lambda & -2 \\ 0 & -2+\lambda & -\lambda+2 \end{vmatrix} = 0 \quad (R_3-R_2)$$

$$(\lambda-2)\begin{vmatrix} 1-\lambda & -1 & 1 \\ 2 & -3-\lambda & -2 \\ 0 & 1 & -1 \end{vmatrix} = 0$$

$$(\lambda-2)\begin{vmatrix} 1-\lambda & 0 & 0 \\ 2 & -3-\lambda & -2 \\ 0 & 1 & -1 \end{vmatrix} = 0 \quad (R_1+R_3)$$

$$(\lambda-2)(1-\lambda)(\lambda+5) = 0 \qquad \text{(i)}$$

$$\therefore \lambda = 1, 2, -5.$$

These solutions are called *eigenvalues* (or *characteristic roots*) and (i) is the *characteristic equation* of A. Notice that the sum ($= -2$) of the eigenvalues is equal to the sum of the diagonal elements of the matrix A, while the product ($= -10$) of the eigenvalues is equal to the value of the determinant of A. This is a general result. Eigenvalues occur frequently in matrix theory and application; e.g. in quantum mechanics, in electric circuit theory (filter analysis), and in the rotation of axes of certain loci (conics, quadrics). Incidentally, the word *eigen* is a German word which is translatable as "peculiar to". (It may be thought of as equivalent to French *propre*, as in *amour-propre*.) The famous *Cayley–Hamilton theorem* states: *A matrix satisfies its characteristic equation* (see Exercise 12.39). High-speed electronic computers often use eigenvalues in certain types of numerical problems.

§ 64. DETERMINANTS AND VECTORS

Outer product

Experience in dealing with problems relating to vectors leads to the definition of the *outer* (≡ *cross* ≡ *vector*) *product* of two vectors $\mathbf{a} = (a_1, a_2, a_3)$, $\mathbf{b} = (b_1, b_2, b_3)$ as the vector

$$\boxed{\mathbf{a}\times\mathbf{b} = (a_2b_3-a_3b_2,\ a_3b_1-a_1b_3,\ a_1b_2-a_2b_1)} \qquad (150)$$

i.e. under the operation of the outer product vectors are closed.

From (138) and (150), the magnitude is given by

$$\left.\begin{aligned} |\mathbf{a}\times\mathbf{b}|^2 &= (a_2b_3-a_3b_2)^2+(a_3b_1-a_1b_3)^2+(a_1b_2-a_2b_1)^2 \\ &= (a_1^2+a_2^2+a_3^2)(b_1^2+b_2^2+b_3^2)-(a_1b_1+a_2b_2+a_3b_3)^2 \end{aligned}\right\} \textit{Lagrange's identity}$$

$$= |\mathbf{a}|^2|\mathbf{b}|^2-|\mathbf{a}|^2\,|\mathbf{b}|^2\cos^2\theta \qquad \text{by (138), (140)}$$

$$= |\mathbf{a}|^2\,|\mathbf{b}|^2\sin^2\theta$$

$$\therefore \qquad \boxed{|\mathbf{a}\times\mathbf{b}| = |\mathbf{a}|\,|\mathbf{b}|\sin\theta} \tag{151}$$

i.e. the magnitude of $\mathbf{a}\times\mathbf{b}$ is equal to the area, $|\mathbf{a}||\mathbf{b}|\sin\theta$, of the parallelogram formed from **a**, **b**. Consideration of physical situations require the direction of $\mathbf{a}\times\mathbf{b}$ to be perpendicular to the plane of **a**, **b** such that **a**, **b**, $\mathbf{a}\times\mathbf{b}$ form a *right-hand screw* (not a left-hand screw)—see Fig. 42. Accordingly,

$$\boxed{\mathbf{a}\times\mathbf{b} = |\mathbf{a}|\,|\mathbf{b}|\sin\theta\;\;\hat{\mathbf{n}} = -\mathbf{b}\times\mathbf{a}} \tag{152}$$

where $\hat{\mathbf{n}}$ is the unit normal to the plane of **a**, **b** forming a right-hand screw with **a**, **b**. Thus, the vector product is essentially a feature of three dimensions and not of the plane.

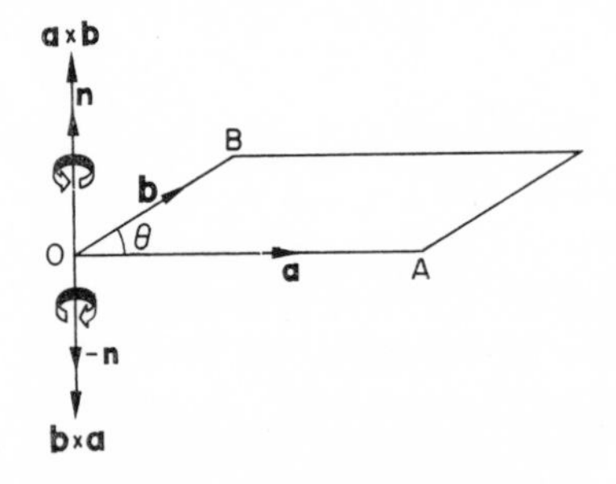

FIG. 42. Vector product

Very clearly, from (152), vectors are non-commutative under the outer product. Addition is distributive over the outer product, as may be verified.

A physical interpretation of the outer product occurs in Ampère's law $\mathbf{T}\times\mathbf{M} = \mathbf{Q}$ relating to electric current **T** in a wire subjected to a mechanical force **Q** and a magnetic force **M** from a magnetic pole.

Obviously, by (§ 55),

$$\mathbf{i}\times\mathbf{i} = \mathbf{j}\times\mathbf{j} = \mathbf{k}\times\mathbf{k} = \mathbf{0} \tag{153.1}$$

$$\mathbf{k} = \mathbf{i}\times\mathbf{j},\quad \mathbf{i} = \mathbf{j}\times\mathbf{k},\quad \mathbf{j} = \mathbf{k}\times\mathbf{i}$$

$$= -\mathbf{j}\times\mathbf{i} \quad = -\mathbf{k}\times\mathbf{j} \quad = -\mathbf{i}\times\mathbf{k}\,. \tag{153.2}$$

Again,

$$\boxed{\mathbf{a}\times\mathbf{a} = \mathbf{0}} \ . \tag{154}$$

From (152), it follows that, for $\mathbf{a} \neq \mathbf{0}, \mathbf{b} \neq \mathbf{0}$,

$$\boxed{\mathbf{a}\times\mathbf{b} = \mathbf{0} \Rightarrow \mathbf{a}//\mathbf{b} \quad \text{(and conversely)}} \ . \tag{152.1}$$

Together, (136) and (150) give the determinantal form

$$\boxed{\mathbf{a}\times\mathbf{b} = \begin{vmatrix} \mathbf{i} & \mathbf{j} & \mathbf{k} \\ a_1 & a_2 & a_3 \\ b_1 & b_2 & b_3 \end{vmatrix}} \ . \tag{155}$$

Scalar triple product

It follows from (137), (150), and (155) that the *scalar triple product* $\mathbf{a}\cdot(\mathbf{b}\times\mathbf{c})$ (written $[\mathbf{a}, \mathbf{b}, \mathbf{c}]$) of three vectors $\mathbf{a}, \mathbf{b}, \mathbf{c}$ is the scalar

$$\mathbf{a}\cdot(\mathbf{b}\times\mathbf{c}) = \begin{vmatrix} a_1 & a_2 & a_3 \\ b_1 & b_2 & b_3 \\ c_1 & c_2 & c_3 \end{vmatrix} \ . \tag{156}$$

Comments

(i) It may be proved that $[\mathbf{a}, \mathbf{b}, \mathbf{c}] = V$, the volume of the parallelepiped built up from the coterminous vectors $\mathbf{a}, \mathbf{b}, \mathbf{c}$, a result which was anticipated in § 57.

(ii) Geometrically, $[\mathbf{a}, \mathbf{b}, \mathbf{c}] = 0 \Rightarrow \mathbf{a}\perp\mathbf{b}\times\mathbf{c}$ (140.1) $\Rightarrow \mathbf{a}, \mathbf{b}, \mathbf{c}$ are coplanar ($\because\ \mathbf{b}\times\mathbf{c}\perp\mathbf{b}, \mathbf{c}$). With $\mathbf{a}, \mathbf{b}, \mathbf{c}$ emanating from O (i.e. coterminous), $[\mathbf{a}, \mathbf{b}, \mathbf{c}] = 0$ is the condition that three lines be concurrent (149). Clearly, $V = 0$ under these circumstances.

(iii) If $\mathbf{a}, \mathbf{b}, \mathbf{c}$ are mutually perpendicular and in the directions of the x-, y-, z-axes respectively, then $V = |\mathbf{a}|\,|\mathbf{b}|\,|\mathbf{c}|$.

(iv) $[\mathbf{i}, \mathbf{j}, \mathbf{k}] = 1$ (particular case of (iii)—a unit cube).

(v) $[\mathbf{a}, \mathbf{b}, \mathbf{c}] = [\mathbf{b}, \mathbf{c}, \mathbf{a}] = [\mathbf{c}, \mathbf{a}, \mathbf{b}]$ which is deducible either from consideration of the volume of the parallelepiped or from (156) by suitable interchange of rows.

(vi) $[\mathbf{a}, \mathbf{b}, \mathbf{c}] = -[\mathbf{a}, \mathbf{c}, \mathbf{b}]$ by (152).

(vii) $[\mathbf{a}, \mathbf{b}, \mathbf{a}] = 0$. Why?

EXAMPLE 78 (outer product). Verify the value for θ in Example 67.

Solution. $\mathbf{a}\times\mathbf{b} = (-2, -39, -17)(= -\mathbf{b}\times\mathbf{a})$ by (150)

$\therefore$ by (138), $|\mathbf{a}\times\mathbf{b}| = \sqrt{(-2)^2+(-39)^2+(-17)^2} = \sqrt{1814}.$

$\therefore$ by (151) and Example 67, $\sin\theta = \dfrac{\sqrt{1814}}{\sqrt{59}\sqrt{45}} = \dfrac{\sqrt{1814}}{3\sqrt{295}}$.

$\therefore \quad \theta = \sin^{-1}\left(\dfrac{1}{3}\sqrt{\dfrac{1814}{295}}\right) = \cos^{-1}\left(-\dfrac{1}{3}\dfrac{29}{\sqrt{295}}\right)$. [Remember that $\sin\theta = \sin(\pi-\theta)$.]

Note that $\dfrac{\mathbf{a}\times\mathbf{b}}{|\mathbf{a}\times\mathbf{b}|} = \dfrac{1}{\sqrt{1814}}(-2, -39, -17)$ is a unit vector.

Products of vectors

Other useful vector products are:

Vector triple product: $\mathbf{a}\times(\mathbf{b}\times\mathbf{c}) = \mathbf{a}\cdot\mathbf{c}\mathbf{b}-\mathbf{a}\cdot\mathbf{b}\mathbf{c}$ (157.1)

Scalar quadruple product: $(\mathbf{a}\times\mathbf{b})\cdot(\mathbf{c}\times\mathbf{d}) = \begin{vmatrix} \mathbf{a}\cdot\mathbf{c} & \mathbf{b}\cdot\mathbf{c} \\ \mathbf{a}\cdot\mathbf{d} & \mathbf{b}\cdot\mathbf{d} \end{vmatrix}$ (Lagrange) (157.2)

Vector quadruple product:
$$(\mathbf{a}\times\mathbf{b})\times(\mathbf{c}\times\mathbf{d}) = \left.\begin{aligned}&[\mathbf{a}, \mathbf{c}, \mathbf{d}]\mathbf{b}-[\mathbf{b}, \mathbf{c}, \mathbf{d}]\mathbf{a} \\ &= [\mathbf{a}, \mathbf{b}, \mathbf{d}]\mathbf{c}-[\mathbf{a}, \mathbf{b}, \mathbf{c}]\mathbf{d}\end{aligned}\right\}. \quad (157.3)$$

Consult the Weatherburn text quoted in § 55 for additional details and applications of the outer product and the triple and quadruple products.

Area of a triangle

Convention. The area of a triangle described in an anti-clockwise sense is positive; otherwise, it is negative.

In Fig. 43(a) area $\triangle\, OPQ = \tfrac{1}{2}r_1\cdot r_2 \sin(\theta_2-\theta_1)$ [i.e. $= \tfrac{1}{2}OP\cdot RQ$]
$$= \tfrac{1}{2}r_1r_2(\sin\theta_2\cos\theta_1-\cos\theta_2\sin\theta_1)$$
$$= \tfrac{1}{2}(x_1y_2-x_2y_1). \quad (158)$$

In Fig. 43b, area $\triangle\, ABC$ = area $\triangle\, OAB$ − area $\triangle\, OAC$ − area $\triangle\, OCB$
$$= \tfrac{1}{2}\{(x_1y_2-x_2y_1)+(x_2y_3-x_3y_2)+(x_3y_1-x_1y_3)\}$$
$$= \frac{1}{2}\begin{vmatrix} x_1 & y_1 & 1 \\ x_2 & y_2 & 1 \\ x_3 & y_3 & 1 \end{vmatrix} \quad (159)$$
$= 0$ if A, B, C are collinear.

If the sides of the triangle ABC have equations $a_ix+b_iy+c_i = 0$ $(i = 1, 2, 3)$, we solve to find the vertices and then calculate the area to be $\dfrac{1}{2}\dfrac{\delta^2}{C_1C_2C_3}$ wherein the symbols are defined in § 63. Given that these three lines are concurrent, then $\delta = 0$ as we found in (149).

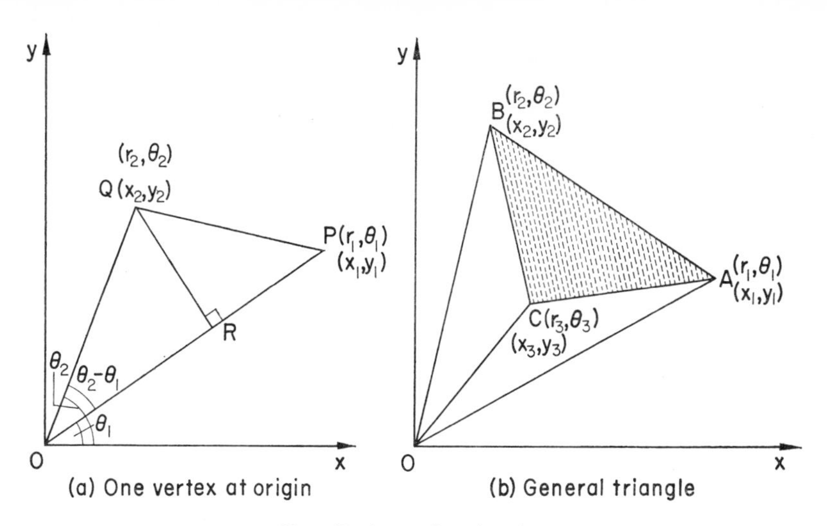

FIG. 43. Area of a triangle

Vector treatment of area of triangle

Revert to Figs. 37 and 42. Let us find expressions for the area S of $\triangle OAB$ whose sides are $OA = a = |\mathbf{a}|$, $OB = b = |\mathbf{b}|$, $AB = c = |\mathbf{c}|$. Write $s = \dfrac{a+b+c}{2}$.

Now $|\mathbf{a}\times\mathbf{b}| = ab \sin\theta$ is the area $2S$ of the parallelogram in Fig. 42.

$$\begin{aligned}
\therefore\quad 4S^2 &= a^2b^2\sin^2\theta \\
&= a^2b^2-(\mathbf{a}\cdot\mathbf{b})^2 \qquad \text{by (140)} \\
&= a^2b^2-a^2b^2\cos^2\theta = (ab+\mathbf{a}\cdot\mathbf{b})(ab-\mathbf{a}\cdot\mathbf{b}) \\
&= a^2b^2-\left(\frac{c^2-a^2-b^2}{2}\right)^2 \qquad \text{by the cosine law} \\
&= \frac{2(a^2b^2+b^2c^2+c^2a^2)-(a^4+b^4+c^4)}{4} \\
&= 4s(s-a)(s-b)(s-c) \qquad \text{on calculation.}
\end{aligned}$$

$$\therefore\quad S = \sqrt{s(s-a)(s-b)(s-c)}, \tag{160}$$

the well-known formula of Heron (2nd cent. B.C., Greek).

Heron's formula (160) is equivalent to (158) if, for instance, a, b, c are replaced by $\sqrt{x_1^2+y_1^2}$, $\sqrt{x_2^2+y_2^2}$, $\sqrt{(x_1-x_2)^2+(y_1-y_2)^2}$ respectively.

Comparison between determinants and matrices

Matrix	*Determinant*
An array	A number
Rectangular or square	Square
Addition is direct	Addition is not direct
Has inverse, if square	Has reciprocal
Division impossible whether singular or not	Division possible if non-singular
Non-commutative (generally) under multiplication	Always commutative under multiplication
Transforms points	Does not transform points
A factor must come from the whole matrix	A factor may come from a row or column.

Suggested topics for further study

(1) Differentiation of determinants.

(2) Applications of vector to the geometry of lines and planes.

(3) Differentiation and integration of vectors
(4) Vector differential operators.
} *Advanced Vector Analysis*, Weatherburn (Bell, 1947).

(5) Electronic computers in relation to determinants and matrices.

References

Andree [29], Bowman (Chapter 11, Reference (a)), Brown (Chapter 10 Reference (b)), Tranter [28].

EXERCISES 12

1. Is $(\beta\ \delta\ \gamma\ \varepsilon\ \alpha)$ an even or odd permutation of $(\alpha\ \beta\ \gamma\ \delta\ \varepsilon)$?

2. What are the signs attached to the terms (i) $a_{31}\, a_{42}\, a_{14}\, a_{23}$ and (ii) $a_{14}\, a_{21}\, a_{33}\, a_{42}$ in the expansion of the determinant $|a_{ij}|$ of order 4?

3. Which of the terms a^4, a^3b, a^2b^2, a^2c^2 occur in the expansion of

$$\begin{vmatrix} a & b & c & d \\ d & a & b & c \\ c & d & a & b \\ b & c & d & a \end{vmatrix}$$

? Find the coefficient and sign in each case.

Evaluate the determinants 4–13 by the neatest methods.

4. $\begin{vmatrix} 1 & 2 & 3 & 4 \\ 5 & 6 & 7 & 8 \\ 9 & 10 & 11 & 12 \\ 13 & 14 & 15 & 16 \end{vmatrix}$ **5.** $\begin{vmatrix} 1 & a & b+c \\ 1 & b & c+a \\ 1 & c & a+b \end{vmatrix}$ **6.** $\begin{vmatrix} 1+a & 1 & 1 \\ 1 & 1+b & 1 \\ 1 & 1 & 1+c \end{vmatrix}$

7. $\begin{vmatrix} 3 & 2 & 2 & 2 \\ 2 & 3 & 2 & 2 \\ 2 & 2 & 3 & 2 \\ 2 & 2 & 2 & 3 \end{vmatrix}$ **8.** $\begin{vmatrix} 1+x & 2 & 3 & 4 \\ 1 & 2+x & 3 & 4 \\ 1 & 2 & 3+x & 4 \\ 1 & 2 & 3 & 4+x \end{vmatrix}$ **9.** $\begin{vmatrix} 4 & 1 & 3 & 2 \\ 6 & 5 & -2 & 1 \\ 3 & 0 & 2 & 5 \\ 7 & -2 & 0 & 5 \end{vmatrix}$

10. $\begin{vmatrix} 1+i & 1-i & i \\ 1-i & i & 1+i \\ i & 1+i & 1-i \end{vmatrix}$ **11.** $\begin{vmatrix} 1 & \sin\theta & 2 \\ \sin\theta & 1 & \cos\theta \\ 0 & \cos\theta & 1 \end{vmatrix}$ **12.** $\begin{vmatrix} 1 & 2 & 4 & 8 \\ 8 & 1 & 2 & 4 \\ x & 8 & 1 & 2 \\ y & z & 8 & 1 \end{vmatrix}$

13. $\begin{vmatrix} \cos\theta & -\sin\theta & \cdot & \cdot \\ \sin\theta & \cos\theta & \cdot & \cdot \\ \cdot & \cdot & \cosh\phi & \sinh\phi \\ \cdot & \cdot & \sinh\phi & \cosh\phi \end{vmatrix}$ **14.** If $\begin{vmatrix} x & -3i & 1 \\ y & 1 & i \\ 0 & 2i & -i \end{vmatrix} = 6+11i$, find x, y.

15. Find the value of $\begin{vmatrix} 1 & 1 & 1 \\ 1 & e^{i\theta} & 1 \\ 1 & -1 & e^{-i\theta} \end{vmatrix}$ when $\theta = \dfrac{\pi}{3}$.

16. If $x = r\sin\theta\cos\phi$, $y = r\sin\theta\sin\phi$, $z = r\cos\theta$

(transformation from rectangular Cartesian coordinates to spherical polar coordinates in three dimensions), evaluate the *Jacobian*

$$\begin{vmatrix} \dfrac{\partial x}{\partial r} & \dfrac{\partial x}{\partial \theta} & \dfrac{\partial x}{\partial \phi} \\ \dfrac{\partial y}{\partial r} & \dfrac{\partial y}{\partial \theta} & \dfrac{\partial y}{\partial \phi} \\ \dfrac{\partial z}{\partial r} & \dfrac{\partial z}{\partial \theta} & \dfrac{\partial z}{\partial \phi} \end{vmatrix}.$$

Solve the determinantal equations 17–20:

17. $\begin{vmatrix} 1 & x & 0 & x \\ x & 1 & x & 0 \\ 0 & x & 1 & x \\ x & 0 & x & 1 \end{vmatrix} = 0$ **18.** $\begin{vmatrix} 2x-1 & x+2 & 4 \\ x & 3 & 1 \\ x-1 & x+1 & 3 \end{vmatrix} = 0$ **19.** $\begin{vmatrix} 1 & 1 & 1 \\ x & a & b \\ x^3 & a^3 & b^3 \end{vmatrix} = 0$

20. $\begin{vmatrix} x & -\sin\theta & -\cos\theta\sin\phi \\ \sin\theta & x & -\cos\theta\cos\phi \\ \cos\theta\sin\phi & \cos\theta\cos\phi & x \end{vmatrix} = 0$

21. Using (a) the determinantal method, (b) the matrix method, solve

$$3x-2y = 7$$
$$3y-2z = 6$$
$$3z-2x = -1.$$

22. Chemists Roscoe and Schorlemmer (1878) used the following set of equations in the analysis of a mixture of gases containing C_2H_4, C_3H_6, and C_6H_6 gases:

$$x+y+z = a,$$
$$2x+3y+6z = b,$$
$$2x+\tfrac{5}{2}y+\tfrac{5}{2}z = c,$$

where a, b, c are numbers obtained from the gas burette. Solve for x, y, z.

Using matrices A and B of Exercises 11.11–11.14, verify:

23. $(A^T)^{-1} = (A^{-1})^T$.
24. $(A^2)^{-1} = (A^{-1})^2$ [from which we can generalise to $(A^n)^{-1} = (A^{-1})^n = A^{-n}$].
25. $(AB)^{-1} = B^{-1}A^{-1}$.
26. Using the matrix A of Exercises 11.62–11.66, find the values of λ for which $|A-\lambda I| = 0$.

27. For what values of k can the equations

$$x+y+z = 0,$$
$$x+2y+3z = 0,$$
$$x+3y+kz = 0,$$

be satisfied by values of x, y, z other than zero?

28. For what values of λ are the three straight lines

$$3\lambda x+5y-7 = 0,$$
$$2x-6\lambda y-3 = 0,$$
$$5x-y-10\lambda = 0,$$

concurrent?

29. The "magic matrix" $M = \begin{vmatrix} 2 & 7 & 6 \\ 9 & 5 & 1 \\ 4 & 3 & 8 \end{vmatrix}$ is such that each row, column, and diagonal has sum $s = 15$. Verify the result of Fox (1956) that the inverse matrix M^{-1} is also magic with corresponding sum $\dfrac{1}{s} = \dfrac{1}{15}$. (Refer to Example 75.)

30. Bickley and McNamee (*Philosophical Transactions of the Royal Society of London*, January 1960, p. 106) produced results which lead to the equation $AX = B$, where

$$A = \begin{bmatrix} 16 & -8 & 1 \\ -8 & 17 & -8 \\ 1 & -8 & 16 \end{bmatrix}, \qquad B = \begin{bmatrix} 4 & 10 \\ 6 & 16 \\ 4 & 10 \end{bmatrix}.$$

What is X?

Given the two *Clifford matrices* (Clifford, 1845–79, English)

$$V = \begin{bmatrix} \cdot & \cdot & 1 \\ \varepsilon & \cdot & \cdot \\ \cdot & \varepsilon^2 & \cdot \end{bmatrix}, \qquad W = \begin{bmatrix} \cdot & \cdot & 1 \\ \varepsilon^2 & \cdot & \cdot \\ \cdot & \varepsilon & \cdot \end{bmatrix}$$

where ε is a complex cube root of unity and dots indicate zeros, find:

31. V^2W. **32.** WV^2. **33.** V^{-1}.

(These matrices were not actually invented by Clifford, but are named to honour similar work he did. They seem to have been first used by Sylvester.)

34. Evaluate $\displaystyle\int_0^{\pi/6} \begin{vmatrix} \cos\theta & 1 & 0 \\ 0 & 2\cos\theta & 1 \\ 0 & 1 & 2\cos\theta \end{vmatrix} d\theta.$ [U.N.E.]

35. Determine the eigenvalues of $A = \begin{bmatrix} 1 & 0 & -1 \\ 1 & 2 & 1 \\ 2 & 2 & 3 \end{bmatrix}$. If $P = \begin{bmatrix} 1 & 2 & 1 \\ -1 & -1 & -1 \\ 0 & -2 & -2 \end{bmatrix}$, calculate $P^{-1}AP$.

36. A triangle has angles α, β, γ opposite the sides a, b, c respectively. Using the (obvious) results $c\cos\beta + b\cos\gamma = a$, $a\cos\gamma + c\cos\alpha = b$, $b\cos\alpha + a\cos\beta = c$, solve for $\cos\alpha$ by Cramer's rule. (The solution will be the cosine law.)

37. Evaluate Sylvester's *circulant* of order n (1853)

$$\begin{vmatrix} a & -1 & -1 & \cdots & -1 \\ -1 & a & -1 & \cdots & -1 \\ -1 & -1 & a & \cdots & -1 \\ \cdot & \cdot & \cdot & \cdots & \cdot \\ -1 & -1 & -1 & \cdots & a \end{vmatrix}.$$

If λ is a scalar and I is the unit 3×3 matrix and $B = \begin{bmatrix} 0 & 1 & 1 \\ 1 & 0 & 1 \\ 1 & 1 & 0 \end{bmatrix}$,

38. Write down the matrix $B - \lambda I$ and show that its determinant is equal to $2+3\lambda-\lambda^3$.

39. Determine the matrix $2I+3B-B^3$.

40. Using matrices, solve the equations $y+z = 3$, $x+z = 4$, $x+y = 5$. [U.N.E.]

Are the following sets 41, 42 of vectors linearly independent? (Use a determinantal method.)

41. $(1, 1, 1)$, $(2, 0, 1)$, $(1, 2, -1)$.

42. $(1, 4, 3)$, $(-1, 7, 4)$, $(5, -13, -6)$.

43. Matrices A, $A' = P^{-1}AP$ are *similar* (cf. Exercise 11.73). Prove that similar matrices have the same characteristic equation (and therefore the same eigenvalues).

44. In Exercise 12.43, if A is symmetric and P is orthogonal, then A' is symmetric. Prove.

45. Show that, if λ is an eigenvalue of A, λ^{-1} is an eigenvalue of A^{-1}.

46. Express as hyperbolic functions the eigenvalues of $\begin{bmatrix} a & a^{-1} \\ a^{-1} & a \end{bmatrix}$, where $\log a = \theta$ (a calculation associated with the analysis of crystal lattice structure).

47. Determine, in exponential form, the eigenvalues of $\begin{bmatrix} a & c(1+a) \\ b & a \end{bmatrix}$ where $a = 1+bc = \cosh x$ (a, b, c complex), a problem occurring in electric circuit analysis.

48. Rearrange Pascal's triangle (98) determinantally thus: $P = \begin{vmatrix} 1 & 1 & 1 & 1 \\ 1 & 2 & 3 & 4 \\ 1 & 3 & 6 & 10 \\ 1 & 4 & 10 & 20 \end{vmatrix}$ Prove $P = 1$ (a particular case of a result proved by Rupp in 1951 for the $m \times m$ determinant similarly formed).

49. *Sarrus' rule* (Sarrus, 1798–1861, French) for expanding a 3×3 determinant is to write down R_1, R_2 again under R_3. Then the products formed diagonally (with a + (−) sign attached if the diagonal is downwards (upwards) towards the right-hand corner) are the terms of the expansion of the determinant. Why does not Sarrus' rule extend naturally to a 4×4 determinant?

50. Prove: $[\mathbf{a}\times\mathbf{b}, \mathbf{b}\times\mathbf{c}, \mathbf{c}\times\mathbf{a}] = [\mathbf{a}, \mathbf{b}, \mathbf{c}]^2$.

51. Express the result of Exercise 12.50 determinantally.

52. Orthogonal matrices have determinantal values ± 1. Prove.

[Orthogonal matrices thus cannot be singular. Those with value $+1(-1)$ are called *proper (improper)* orthogonal matrices. Rotations (combinations of rotations and reflections) correspond to proper (improper) orthogonal matrices.]

53. Skew-symmetric determinants of odd order vanish. Establish the truth or falsity of this statement.

Given $x = f(u, v)$ and $y = g(u, v)$, where $u = \phi(r, s)$ and $v = \psi(r, s)$, prove:

54. The Jacobian $\dfrac{\partial(x, y)}{\partial(r, s)} \left(= \begin{vmatrix} \dfrac{\partial x}{\partial r} & \dfrac{\partial x}{\partial s} \\ \dfrac{\partial y}{\partial r} & \dfrac{\partial y}{\partial s} \end{vmatrix} \right) = \dfrac{\partial(x, y)}{\partial(u, v)} \dfrac{\partial(u, v)}{\partial(r, s)}$.

55. $\dfrac{\partial(x, y)}{\partial(u, v)} \dfrac{\partial(u, v)}{\partial(x, y)} = 1$. Interpret this geometrically.

56. If $H = \begin{vmatrix} \cosh x & \sinh x \\ \sinh x & \cosh x \end{vmatrix}$, prove that $H^n = \begin{vmatrix} \cosh nx & \sinh nx \\ \sinh nx & \cosh nx \end{vmatrix}$.

57. A square $n\times n$ determinant Δ_n is such that every element in the principal diagonal is 2, every element next to an element in the principal diagonal is 1, while every other element is 0. Establish the recurrence $\Delta_n = 2\Delta_{n-1} - \Delta_{n-2}$. Hence, evaluate Δ_n. (Refer to Exercise 9.45.)

Find a unit vector perpendicular to both $(1, 1, -1)$ and $(1, -1, 1)$, using:

58. The scalar (dot) product method. **59.** The vector (cross) product method.

60. Calculate $\mathbf{a}\times(\mathbf{b}\times\mathbf{c})+\mathbf{b}\times(\mathbf{c}\times\mathbf{a})+\mathbf{c}\times(\mathbf{a}\times\mathbf{b})$ *(Jacobi's identity)*.

From the Pauli spin matrix b (Exercises 11.42–11.45), the astronomer–mathematician Eddington (1882–1944, English) formed a 4×4 matrix $B = \begin{bmatrix} \cdot & -b \\ b & \cdot \end{bmatrix}$.

61. Write down the matrix $\overline{B}$ (cf. Exercise 11.44).

62. Find B^2.

63. Simplify $\overline{B}^T B$ (B is unitary; see Exercise 11.44).

64. Verify, in the case of B, the theorem: Eigenvalues of a unitary matrix lie on the unit circle in the complex plane.

On the surface of a unit sphere, centre O, a *spherical triangle ABC* has its components defined thus: sides a, b, c of the spherical triangle are the angles BOC, COA, AOB respectively; the angle A of the spherical triangle is the angle between the planes AOB, AOC, with angles B, C similarly described. Placing $\overrightarrow{OA} = \hat{\mathbf{l}}$, $\overrightarrow{OB} = \hat{\mathbf{m}}$, $\overrightarrow{OC} = \hat{\mathbf{n}}$, and using the quadruple scalar product and the quadruple vector product for $\hat{\mathbf{l}} \times \hat{\mathbf{m}}$, $\hat{\mathbf{l}} \times \hat{\mathbf{n}}$, derive the fundamental formulae 65, 66:

65. $\cos a = \cos b \cos c + \sin b \sin c \cos A$ (Ptolemy; Al-Battani, 9th cent., Arab).

66. $\dfrac{\sin A}{\sin a} = \dfrac{\sin B}{\sin b} = \dfrac{\sin C}{\sin c}$.

Let f, g, h, u, v, w be functions of x, y, z and let $\mathbf{F} = f\mathbf{i}+g\mathbf{j}+h\mathbf{k}$, $\mathbf{V} = u\mathbf{i}+v\mathbf{j}+w\mathbf{k}$ ($\mathbf{F}$, $\mathbf{V}$ are vector functions of x, y, z). Define the "curl" of $\mathbf{F}$, the "divergence" of $\mathbf{V}$, and the "gradient" of the scalar function $U(x, y, z)$ thus:

$$\operatorname{curl} \mathbf{F} = \begin{vmatrix} \mathbf{i} & \mathbf{j} & \mathbf{k} \\ \dfrac{\partial}{\partial x} & \dfrac{\partial}{\partial y} & \dfrac{\partial}{\partial z} \\ f & g & h \end{vmatrix}, \quad \operatorname{div} \mathbf{V} = \frac{\partial u}{\partial x}+\frac{\partial v}{\partial y}+\frac{\partial w}{\partial z} = \mathbf{i}\cdot\frac{\partial \mathbf{V}}{\partial x}+\mathbf{j}\cdot\frac{\partial \mathbf{V}}{\partial y}+\mathbf{k}\cdot\frac{\partial \mathbf{V}}{\partial z}$$

$\operatorname{grad} U = \mathbf{i}\dfrac{\partial U}{\partial x}+\mathbf{j}\dfrac{\partial U}{\partial y}+\mathbf{k}\dfrac{\partial U}{\partial z}$. Establish the results 67–70 in which $\mathbf{r} = x\mathbf{i}+y\mathbf{j}+z\mathbf{k}$:

67. $\operatorname{div} \mathbf{r} = 3$. **68.** $\operatorname{grad} \mathbf{r}^2 = 2\mathbf{r}$. **69.** $\operatorname{curl} \operatorname{grad} U = \mathbf{0}$. **70.** $\operatorname{div} \operatorname{curl} \mathbf{F} = 0$.

[Curl, div, and grad are called *vector differential operators* and are of very great mathematical and scientific significance. Zero curl with simultaneous zero divergence, for instance, refers to irrotational motion in an incompressible fluid. Observe that (i) curl and grad are vectors, whereas div is a scalar, (ii) div grad $U = \nabla^2 U$ (Laplace's operator).]

CHAPTER 13

SETS AND THEIR APPLICATIONS. BOOLEAN ALGEBRA

Let us be glad that we can enter into the theory of sets, into that paradise from which no one can drive us out.

(HILBERT)

... an independent world
Created out of pure intelligence.

(WORDSWORTH)

MOTIVATION for a study of sets comes from many sources. Firstly, the symbolic language of sets is a natural one (e.g. in probability theory) which gives precision to mathematical considerations in a variety of circumstances. Certain problems are best handled in terms of sets, e.g. are there more irrational numbers than rational numbers? Are there more points inside a cube than on a side of the cube? Furthermore, the laws of operation among sets give us a concrete illustration of an important modern abstract system, Boolean algebra. Moreover, the algebra of sets furnishes us with an interesting comparison and contrast with the algebra of real numbers. Briefly, then, the concept of set, though simple, is powerful and unifying. Since in mathematics we search for ideas which allow us to unify and generalise other ideas, the importance of sets is obvious.

§65. THE LANGUAGE OF SET THEORY

Up till now we have taken the fundamental notion of a set of objects to be intuitively clear. Within the last hundred years or so the previously unanalysed ideas about sets have crystallised into precise mathematical form. Much of the research in set theory originated with Cantor (in his study of the convergence of trigonometric series), to whom our definition is due (1895):

Definition. A *set* is a collection of definite distinct objects of our perception or of our thought, called elements of the set.

Such objects may be:

perceptual: e.g. stars in the Milky Way, electrons in an atom, cells in a living organism, books in a library;

conceptual: e.g. prime numbers.

Membership. If the elements of the set S are $a, b, c, \ldots$, we may write $S = \{a, b, c, \ldots\}$.

Membership of S is represented by $\in$, i.e. $a \in S \Rightarrow a$ is an element (member) of S, e.g. Earth $\in S$ (set of planets). Symbol $\notin$ represents denial of $\in$, i.e $a \notin S \Rightarrow a$ is not an element of S. (Do not confuse the symbols $\in$ and ε (Greek epsilon).)

If x is a typical member of S, $S = \{x : x \text{ has property } p\} \Rightarrow S$ consists of all elements x possessing the given property p. For example, all real points in the closed interval $-1 \leqslant x \leqslant 1$ may be expressed as

$$S = \{x \text{ real} : -1 \leqslant x \leqslant 1\}.$$

Finiteness. A set may be finite or infinite depending on the number of elements in it. Would the set of all ideas that human minds have ever conceived be finite? Is the set of points on a straight line finite?

Subsets. A proper *subset* T of the set S is such that every element of T is contained in S (Fig. 44a where $T = A$ and $S = B$). Symbolically,

$$T \subset S \quad \text{or} \quad S \supset T,$$

e.g. girl members of the pure mathematics I class form a subset of all members of this class. Good examples of subsets occur in the number system, e.g. $\mathcal{J} \subset \mathcal{R} \subset \mathcal{R}^* \subset \mathcal{C}$.

[$\subset$ is the *inclusion sign* and means "is contained in"; $\supset$ means "contains".]

Special *(improper)* subsets of S are

(i) S itself,

(ii) the *empty (= null = zero) set O*.

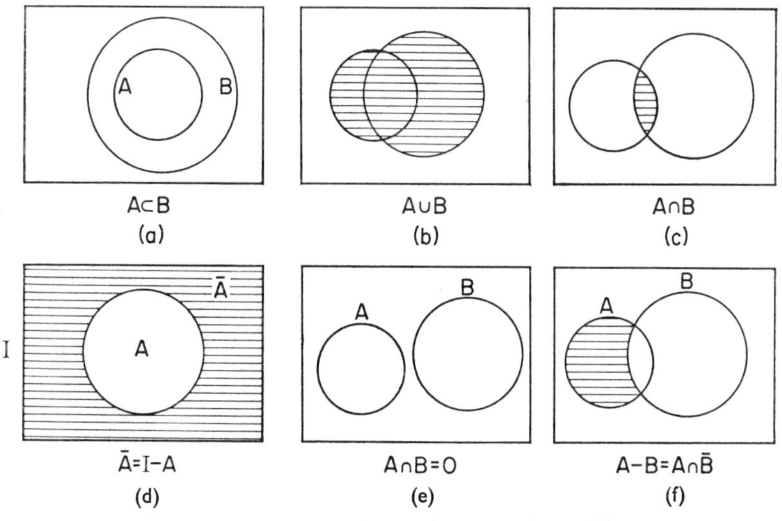

FIG. 44. Venn diagrams illustrating operations with sets

The statement $T \subset S$ includes the possibility that $T = S$.

Distinguish carefully between the empty set and the set $\{0\}$ containing only the number zero. Sometimes the Scandinavian letter Ø or the symbol $\{\}$ is used to denote the empty set. The empty set O is a proper subset of every set except itself (of which it is an improper subset).

Query: Can $T \subset S$ and $S \supset T$ be simultaneously true? If so, what can we say about T?

The total number of subsets of S (having n finite elements) is, by (97),

$$1+\binom{n}{1}+\binom{n}{2}+\binom{n}{3}+\ldots+\binom{n}{n-1}+\binom{n}{n} = (1+1)^n = 2^n.$$

Universal set. If $A, B, C, \ldots$ are subsets of a fixed set of objects, this fixed set is called the *universal set*, usually denoted by I. For example, in plane geometry the universal set (of points) comprises all the points of the plane.

Operations between sets. The *union* (= *sum*) of sets A and B, written $A \cup B$ (read $\cup$ as "cup"), or, alternatively, $A+B$, is defined (Fig. 44b) as

$$\boxed{A \cup B = \{x : x \in A \text{ or } x \in B\}}. \tag{161.1}$$

The *intersection* (= *product*) of sets A and B, written $A \cap B$ (read $\cap$ as "cap") or, alternatively, $A \cdot B$ or just AB, is defined (Fig. 44c) as

$$\boxed{A \cap B = \{x : x \in A \text{ and } x \in B\}}. \tag{161.2}$$

For instance, the intersection P of two lines a, b may be written $a \cap b = P$ provided by a, b we mean the sets of points on the lines as well as the names of the lines and by P the unit set consisting of just one point, as well as the name of that point.

Symbols $\cup$, $\cap$ (or $+$, $.$) merely represent operations, as specified, between sets in the same way that certain operations (addition, multiplication) involving vectors or matrices are different from operations we are familiar with in arithmetic.

The *complement* of A, written $\bar{A}$, is defined (Fig. 44d) as

$$\boxed{\bar{A} = \{x : x \notin A\} = I - A}. \tag{162}$$

Plainly, $A \subset B \Rightarrow \bar{B} \subset \bar{A}$. See also (167).

The *difference* of A and B, written $A-B$, is defined (Fig. 44f) as

$$\boxed{A-B = \{x : x \in A,\ x \notin B\} = A \cap \bar{B}} \tag{163}$$

so that $\bar{A}$ is the difference of I and A.

Two sets A, B are said to be *disjoint* if (Fig. 44e)

$$\boxed{A \cap B = O}. \tag{164}$$

As an illustration of set-theoretic language, we prove a fundamental property of two sets, called *De Morgan's law* (De Morgan, 1806–71, English). (Another law of De Morgan's, namely $\overline{A \cap B} = \overline{A} \cup \overline{B}$ follows similarly. Try it as an exercise.)

EXAMPLE 79 (De Morgan's law). $\overline{A \cup B} = \overline{A} \cap \overline{B}$.

Solution. Let $x \in \overline{A \cup B}$ $\therefore$ $x \notin A$, $x \notin B$ $\therefore$ $x \in \overline{A} \cap \overline{B}$.

$$\therefore \text{ every } x \in \overline{A \cup B} \text{ must also } \in \overline{A} \cap \overline{B}.$$

$$\therefore \overline{A \cup B} \subset \overline{A} \cap \overline{B}. \tag{i}$$

Let $y \in \overline{A} \cap \overline{B}$ $\therefore$ $y \notin A$, $y \notin B$ $\therefore$ $y \in \overline{A \cup B}$

$$\therefore \text{ every } y \in \overline{A} \cap \overline{B} \text{ must also } \in \overline{A \cup B}$$

$$\therefore \overline{A} \cap \overline{B} \subset \overline{A \cup B} \tag{ii}$$

$\therefore$ (i), (ii) $\Rightarrow$ $\overline{A \cup B} = \overline{A} \cap \overline{B}$.

Cartesian product

The Cartesian product, written $A \times B$ (nothing to do with vectors) of two sets A, B is defined:

$$A \times B = \{(a, b) : a \in A, b \in B\} \tag{165}$$

where (a, b) represents the ordered pair of elements a, b.

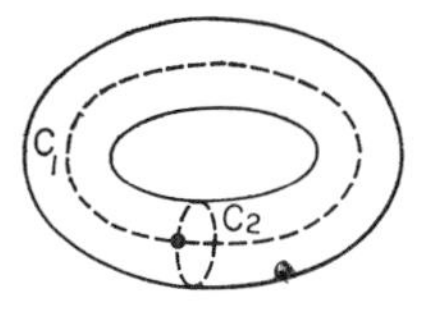

FIG. 45. Torus

Thus, if A $\{x : x = \text{real}\}$, then $A \times A$ gives the Cartesian coordinates of points in the Euclidean plane. By extension, the coordinates of points in Euclidean n-space are given by $A \times A \times A \times \ldots \times A$ (n terms). A more sophisticated example is that of the inflated bicycle tube (*torus*, Fig. 45) whose points are determined uniquely by $C_1 \times C_2 = \{(c_1, c_2) : c_1 \in C_1, c_2 \in C_2\}$, where c_1, c_2 are typical circles of the two sets C_1, C_2 existing on the torus.

Normally, $A \times B \neq B \times A$, but if equality does exist, then $A = B$.

Geometrically, a torus may be generated by revolving a circle about a non-intersecting line, say, the x-axis (see Exercise 23.24). Toral surfaces and their invariants are among the major objects of investigation in elementary topology.

§ 66. TRANSFINITE NUMBERS

Next, we come to transfinite numbers, one of the "purest" parts of pure mathematics, which, if studied in depth, leads on to logic and philosophy. Interestingly, the theory of transfinite numbers is an abstract construction devoid of any motivation from the natural sciences or technology. (No doubt Plato would have enjoyed it!) Endeavour to get hold of a copy of Cantor's *Contributions to the Founding of the Theory of Transfinite Numbers* (Dover) to appreciate something of the flavour of a rigorous treatment of the subject. Our treatment is informal and non-rigorous.

Definitions. Two sets A and B are *equivalent* if their elements are uniquely related in a $1-1$ correspondence (= mapping).* The sets then have the same *cardinal number* $|A| = |B|$, e.g. the lines $y = 2x+c$ (as c varies) map off two equivalent sets of points on the x- and y-axes.

If there is no proper subset of A equivalent to A, the set is finite. If there is a proper subset of A equivalent to A, then the set is infinite. E.g.:

$$\left.\begin{aligned} \mathcal{N} &= \{1, 2, 3, 4, \ldots, n, \ \ldots\} \\ \mathcal{E} &= \{2, 4, 6, 8, \ldots, 2n, \ldots\} \end{aligned}\right\}$$

i.e. *the natural numbers are in* $1-1$ *correspondence with the even integers*, i.e. with a subset of itself. This is an amazing fact! Hence, Euclid's axiom: "The whole is greater than any of its parts" is not valid for infinite sets (an observation first made by Galileo (1564–1642, Italian)).

The cardinal number defined by the equivalent infinite sets above is a *transfinite number*. Distinguish here between the transfinite number (the actual infinity of the set $\mathcal{N}$) and the potential infinity of the symbol ∞ as a limiting process.

Countable sets. A *countable (= denumerable) set* is one in $1-1$ correspondence with $\mathcal{N}$.

Countable sets have transfinite cardinal number $\aleph_0$ *(aleph-null* or *aleph-zero)*. [$\aleph$ = "aleph", is the first letter of the Hebrew alphabet.] Sets with cardinality $\aleph_0$ are: integers, even numbers, odd numbers, primes, rationals, and algebraic numbers. (See Cantor's diagram for the countability of the rationals.)

* A *mapping* (which need not be $1-1$) associates with every element of one set A a unique element of another set B—see p. 231. (A and B may coincide.) If the correspondence is $1-1$, the mapping is also called an isomorphism (p. 146).

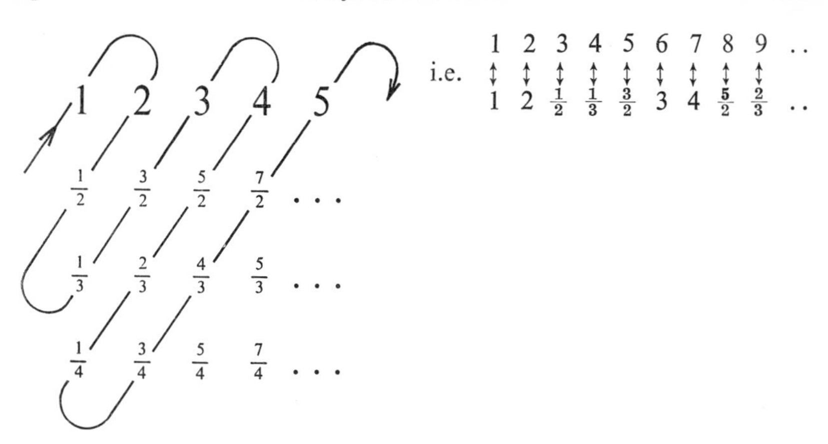

Cantor's diagram for the countability of positive rational numbers.

(In Cantor's diagram we have omitted fractions like $\frac{2}{2}$, $\frac{3}{3}$, $\frac{2}{4}$ which have been included in simplified form in an earlier row. It would not matter if we included them in the diagram in their appropriate positions so long as we do not count them. Incidentally, the $\leftrightarrow$ notation means that the pairs of numbers correspond to each other in the mapping.)

Non-countable sets. A *non-countable (= non-denumerable) set* is one not in $1-1$ correspondence with $\mathcal{N}$.

Such a set is the set of real numbers (> set of algebraic numbers) and its cardinal number is $\aleph_1$ or $C =$ the *cardinal number of the continuum* (the *continuum number*). It has the property

$$C > \aleph_0.$$

The *problem of the continuum* asks: Is there a number $\aleph : \aleph_0 < \aleph < C$?

The *hypothesis of the continuum* asserts (Cantor): No!

Beyond this again is the transfinite number $\aleph_2$ (= the number of all geometrical curves, i.e. the number of all single-valued functions) which is: $\aleph_2 > C > \aleph_0$. There is no last transfinite number.

The arithmetic of transfinite numbers is quite different from ordinary arithmetic, e.g. $\aleph_0+\aleph_0 = \aleph_0$, $\aleph_0+C = C$, $\aleph_0 C = C$, $\aleph_0{}^{\aleph_0} = C$, $CC = C$.

In Fig. 46a we illustrate the fact that there are as many points on a line 1 in. long as there are in a line 2 in. long. (On the 2 in. segment, the points are *not* "twice as big", as a student once declared!) Extending this idea, we say that there are as many points in a line 1 in. as there are from here to the star Betelgeuse or in the diameter of the galactic system (i.e. 100,000 light-years). In other words, the lengths of the two line-segments are immaterial. In fact, a unit segment and a straight line have the same transfinite number of points.

Figure 46b reveals how the points in a unit segment are uniquely mapped into the points in the interior of a square, by pairing the digits of the decimal alternately (a result due in 1890 to Peano, 1858–1932, Italian). Similarly, the points of the unit segment could be mapped uniquely into the points of a cube in three dimensions by selecting (as coordinates of the point in the cube) sets of digits placed positionally 3 from each other. Generally, then,

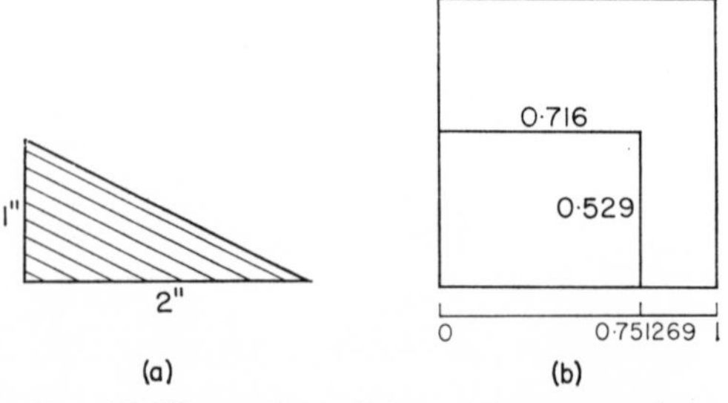

FIG. 46. Illustrations of the continuum number

no. of points in a line-segment (or line) = no. of points in a square (or plane)
= no. of points in a cube (or space)
= no. of points in a hypercube (or n-dimensional space).

Thus we have answered the following worrying problems:

Are there more integers than there are even numbers?
Does an infinite straight line contain more points than a line segment?
Does a plane contain less points than space?

Paradoxes of the infinite

Finally, it is worth commenting that thinking of the above type led to *paradoxes of the infinite*, not the paradoxes of the ancients like Zeno's problem of Achilles and the tortoise, but paradoxes like those propounded by Cantor and Bertrand Russell (1872– , English).

A (logical) paradox of a different kind, also due to Russell (in 1903), is worth mentioning here. In a certain village a barber shaves all those (and only those) who do not shave themselves. Does the barber shave himself? See Eves and Newsom [6] and Kasner and Newman [7].

Foundations of mathematics

Set theory has provided much stimulus for the study of the *Foundations of Mathematics*, and within the last century serious differences of opinion of a philosophical nature have arisen between the *Formalists* (such as Cantor and Hilbert) and the *Intuitionists* (such as Kronecker, Brouwer (1882– , Dutch), and Weyl (1885–1955, German, American). Other important philosophers of mathematics have been, for instance, Bertrand Russell, Gödel, and Wittgenstein.

Equivalence relation

An *equivalence relation* r connecting pairs of the objects $a, b, c, \ldots$ of the same kind, written $a\,r\,b$, possesses three basic properties: (i) $a\,r\,a$ *(reflexive)*, (ii) $a\,r\,b \Rightarrow b\,r\,a$ *(symmetric)*, (iii) $a\,r\,b,\; b\,r\,c \Rightarrow a\,r\,c$ *(transitive)*. Examples of equivalence relations are: similarity, parallelism, equality of vectors, arithmetic equality, and congruence (both geometric and arithmetic). On the other hand, arithmetic inequality is not an equivalence relation since property (ii) is violated. Set equivalence is clearly an equivalence relation.

Mappings into and onto

Denote by f a mapping between sets A and B, written $f: A \rightarrow B$. Suppose $a \in A$, $b \in B$ are typical elements of the sets. Then $f(a) = b$ is the *image* of a under f. Let $f(A)$ = the set of all image elements of the elements of A. Then, we say that f is a mapping of A *onto* B if $f(A) = B$, whereas f is a mapping of A *into* B if $f(A) \subset B$. For example, $f(x) = x^2$ $(x \in \mathcal{R}^*)$ is not a mapping of the real numbers onto itself since no negative number is the square of a real number. On the other hand, a geometric rotation or translation is a 1–1 mapping of the set of points of the plane onto itself.

§ 67. VENN DIAGRAMS

In set-theoretic problems it is often helpful to think pictorially and for this reason *Venn diagrams* are used (Venn, 1834–1923, English). But, let it be emphasised, these pictorial illustrations do not constitute mathematical proofs of operations with sets. Conventionally, I is drawn here as a rectangle and subsets as circles.

Certain laws of algebra relating to sets, and analogous to laws for real numbers, may be seen intuitively from Venn diagrams (Fig. 47). The second distributive law should be noted well. Commutative laws for $\cup$ and $\cap$ are evidently valid from Figs. 44b, c.

Note that in a Venn diagram two circles are never shown as touching, as no meaning would be attributed to this situation—it is understood that a certain set is represented by points *inside* a circle.

Comments on abstract symbolism

Experience in handling the $\cup$, $\cap$ notation, particularly with more than two sets, convinces us that it is indeed cumbersome and confusing. Greater visual comfort and simplicity are attained by discarding this notation in favour of $+$, $\cdot$ respectively with the convention that $A \cdot B\,(= A \cap B)$ will

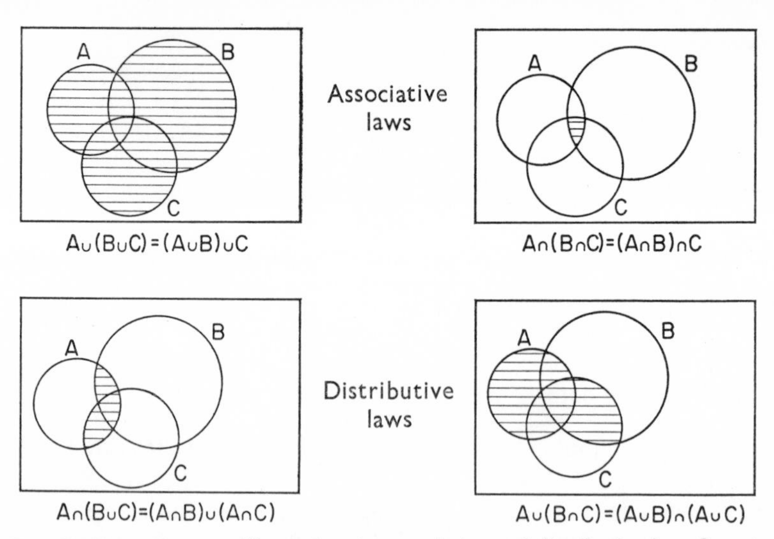

FIG. 47. Venn diagrams illustrating the associative and distributive laws for sets

be expressed merely as AB. It is assumed that the reader will no more confuse the $+$, $\cdot$ notation for set-theoretic operations with ordinary arithmetical addition and multiplication than he would the similar notation used for operations with matrices and vectors. Any other pair of symbols would do equally well but $+$, $\cdot$ suggest the nature of the operation.

Suppose we wished to construct a system of algebraic rules obeyed by sets, how should we go about it? One method is outlined below.

§ 68. BOOLEAN ALGEBRA AND SETS

Let $\mathcal{B} = \{A, B, C, \ldots\}$ be a set of sets $A, B, C, \ldots$ with two operations of combination, $+$ and $\cdot$, obeying the following axioms:

Axiom	$+$	$\cdot$
B_1. Commutative laws	$A+B = B+A$	$AB = BA$
B_2. Identity laws	$O+A = A$	$IA = A$
B_3. Distributive laws	$A(B+C) = AB+AC$	$A+BC=(A+B)(A+C)$
B_4. Inverse (complement) laws	$A+\bar{A} = I$ and	$A\bar{A} = O$

where in B_4 the two rules must be simultaneously true.

Notice that if in a particular result we replace O by I and I by O and, at the same time, replace $+$ by $\cdot$ and $\cdot$ by $+$, we arrive at another (dual) result. This balance is called the *principle of duality* and it signifies that to every result proved there corresponds a dual result which we do not have to prove but which is automatically valid.

Proceeding, let us next explore the logical possibilities of $B_1 - B_4$ by developing a few fundamental properties of the algebra of sets.

EXAMPLE 80 (idempotent laws). $A+A = A$ (duals) $AA = A$.

Solution.
$$\begin{aligned} A+A &= (A+A)I && \text{by } B_1, B_2 \\ &= (A+A)(A+\bar{A}) && B_4 \\ &= A+A\bar{A} && B_3 \\ &= A+O && B_4 \\ &= A && B_1, B_2. \end{aligned}$$

EXAMPLE 81. $A+I = I$ (duals) $AO = O$.

Solution.
$$\begin{aligned} A+I &= I(A+I) && \text{by } B_2 \\ &= (A+\bar{A})(A+I) && B_4 \\ &= A+\bar{A}I && B_3 \\ &= A+\bar{A} && B_2 \\ &= I && B_4. \end{aligned}$$

EXAMPLE 82 (absorption laws). $A+AB = A$ (duals) $A(A+B) = A$.

Solution.
$$\begin{aligned} A+AB &= A+BA && \text{by } B_1 \\ &= IA+BA && B_2 \\ &= (I+B)A && B_3 \\ &= IA && B_1, \text{ Example 81} \\ &= A && B_2. \end{aligned}$$

EXAMPLE 83 (De Morgan's laws). $\overline{AB} = \bar{A}+\bar{B}$ (duals) $\overline{A+B} = \bar{A}\bar{B}$

Solution.
$$\begin{aligned} AB+\bar{A}+\bar{B} &= \bar{A}+\bar{B}+AB && \text{by } B_1 \\ &= (\bar{A}+\bar{B}+A)(\bar{A}+\bar{B}+B) && B_3 \\ &= (I+\bar{B})(I+\bar{A}) && B_1, B_4 \\ &= I\ \ I && \text{Example 81} \\ &= I && B_2 \qquad \text{(i)} \\ AB(\bar{A}+\bar{B}) &= AB\bar{A}+AB\bar{B} && B_3 \\ &= BA\bar{A}+AB\bar{B} && B_1 \\ &= BO+AO && B_4 \\ &= O+O && \text{Example 81} \\ &= O && B_2 \qquad \text{(ii)} \end{aligned}$$

$\therefore$ (i), (ii) $\Rightarrow \bar{A}+\bar{B} = \overline{AB}$.

(Compare the point-set proof of Example 79 with this proof involving formal algebra.)

EXAMPLE 84 (uniqueness of $\bar{A}$). In B_4, $\bar{A}$ is unique.

Solution. Assume that both $A+X = I, AX = O$ and $A+Y = I, AY = O$ are true.

$$
\begin{aligned}
\therefore Y &= IY && \text{by } B_2\\
&= (X+A)Y && \text{hypothesis, } B_1\\
&= XY+AY && B_3\\
&= XY+O && \text{hypothesis}\\
&= XY && B_1, B_2\\
&= YX && B_1\\
&= O+YX && B_2\\
&= AX+YX && \text{hypothesis}\\
&= (A+Y)X && B_3\\
&= IX && \text{hypothesis}\\
&= X && B_2
\end{aligned}
$$

$\therefore$ $\bar{A}$ is unique ($= X = Y$).

Looking back over axioms $B_1 - B_4$ and Examples 80–84, we see that the basic structure of an algebra of sets has been erected except that the following important results have not yet been established: (a) $\bar{\bar{A}} = A$, (b) $\bar{I} = O$, $\bar{O} = I$, (c) the associative laws. Whereas (a) and (b) are easy to prove and are left as exercises, (c) is quite tedious, so its truth will be assumed.

Summing up, then, we assert that set algebra obeys the following rules:

Law	$+$ ($\cup$)	$\cdot$ ($\cap$)
Closure	$A+B \in \mathcal{B}$	$AB \in \mathcal{B}$
Associative	$A+(B+C) = (A+B)+C$	$A(BC) = (AB)C$
Identity	$O+A = A$	$IA = A$
Complement	$A+\bar{A} = I$	$A\bar{A} = O$
Commutative	$A+B = B+A$	$AB = BA$
Distributive	$(A+B)(A+C) = A+BC$	$AB+AC = A(B+C)$
Idempotent	$A+A = A$	$AA = A$
Absorption	$A+AB = A$	$A(A+B) = A$
De Morgan's	$\overline{A+B} = \bar{A}\,\bar{B}$	$\overline{AB} = \bar{A}+\bar{B}$
Operations with O, I	$I+A = I$, $\bar{I} = O$	$OA = O$, $\bar{O} = I$
Double complementation	$\bar{\bar{A}} = A$	

(166)

Such a structure, starting from axioms B_1–B_4, is called a *Boolean algebra* after Boole (1815–64, English), who was the first to make a fundamental systematic investigation into the laws of thought and the mathematical analysis of logic. Have a look at Boole's *An Investigation of the Laws of Thought* (Dover) written in 1854. Axioms B_1–B_4 are due (1904) to Huntington (1874–1952, American) though other systems of axioms may be used. Symbolically, we may express by $(\mathcal{B}, +, \cdot)$ the fact that the set $\mathcal{B}$ forms a Boolean algebra B under the operations $+$, $\cdot$.

Compare (166) with (103). Clearly, O, I in set-theory play the roles of 0, 1 in real number theory. Some of the structure of the real number system is applicable to the algebra of sets. Contrasts, however, are more striking than similarities. Idempotent and absorption laws, and all operations relating to the complement, have no analogue in number theory. Neither has $A+I = I$.

What about the set-theoretic operation of inclusion $\subset$, i.e. $A \subset B$? Expressed as an equation, this becomes

$$\boxed{A \subset B \Rightarrow A+B = B \Rightarrow A\bar{B} = O}\,. \tag{167}$$

Numbers a, b must be such that $a \leqslant b$ or $a \geqslant b$. Sets A, B, on the other hand, may be such that neither $A \subset B$ nor $B \subset A$, e.g. if $A = \{1, 2\}$, $B = \{2, 3\}$. Two very simple results relating to set inclusion are: $A \subset B \Leftrightarrow \bar{B} \subset \bar{A}$, $O \subset A \subset I$ where the symbol $\Leftrightarrow$ signifies implication both ways. Can you prove them, using (167)? Their set-theoretic interpretations are simple. [Implication both ways is valid for many statements in this outline.] Observe, in (166), further evidence of the principle of duality.

EXAMPLE 85. Simplify $AB+A\bar{B}+\bar{A}B$.

Solution.

$$\begin{aligned} AB+A\bar{B}+\bar{A}B &= \{A\,(B+\bar{B})\} + \bar{A}B && \text{by } B_3 \\ &= AI \qquad\quad + \bar{A}B && B_4 \\ &= A \qquad\quad\;\, + \bar{A}B && B_1, B_2 \\ &= (A+\bar{A})(A+B) && B_3 \\ &= I\,(A+B) && B_4 \\ &= A+B && B_2. \end{aligned}$$

(You should illustrate this by means of a Venn diagram.)

Imagine now that the union $(+)$ and intersection $(\cdot)$ operations are abstracted from any necessary set-theoretic considerations. Allow the symbols A, B, ... also to be abstracted from any set-theoretic connotation. An abstract set of elements A, B, ... which combine with two abstract operations $+$ and $\cdot$ according to (166) defines an *(abstract) Boolean algebra.* Evidently, the actual symbols used to represent the elements and operations are immaterial—Phoenician, musical, or financial symbols (say)—would have done equally well (if less aesthetically). In some interpretations of Boolean algebra, + and · are defined to be the ordinary arithmetic operations of lowest common multiple and highest common factor. (See Exercise 13.27.)

The simplest Boolean algebra is the set $\mathcal{B} = \{0, 1\}$ consisting of just two elements 0, 1 combining under multiplication and addition as follows:

+	0	1
0	0	1
1	1	1

·	0	1
0	0	0
1	0	1

(Justify this assertion.)

Concrete illustrations of Boolean algebra are:

(I) sets with set operations ∪, ∩ — a famous theorem due 1936 to Stone (1903– , American) establishes this in detail;
(II) switching circuits (= networks)—see below;
(III) sentence logic (the algebra of propositions).

Although we do not study it in this course, a structure closely related to Boolean algebra is a *lattice*. When endowed with a complement and distributivity, a lattice becomes a Boolean algebra.

Cases (II) and (III) are examples of the two-valued (0 and 1) Boolean algebra whose tables are given above. Thus, the algebra of switches and the algebra of propositions have the same formal structure. Allied to (II) is the use of Boolean algebra in the design of logic circuits in electronic computers.

Electrical (switching) circuits

Herewith is a brief description of (II). For our purposes, a switch is a two-state device electrically operated by means of an electromagnet. (Other devices for which the Boolean algebra applies include, for example, transistors and electron tubes.) Designate a switch by a letter of the

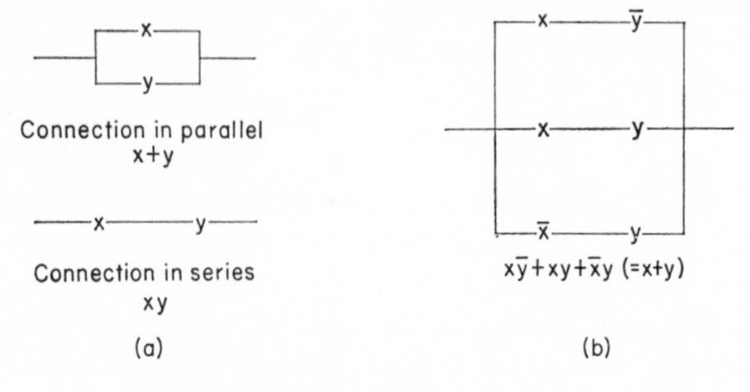

FIG. 48. Boolean algebra circuits

alphabet $x, y, \ldots$. The two states with which we are concerned are the states of being open or closed, i.e. we are not interested in electrical properties of the circuit such as voltage. If two switches open and close simultaneously, denote them by the same letter. Given x, there exists an x' such that x open (closed) $\Rightarrow$ x closed (open). To a closed switch, where current can flow, we give the value 1; to an open switch where current cannot flow, we give the value 0. (Correspondingly, in propositional algebra, values 1 and 0 are given to true and false propositions respectively.)

A circuit consisting of two switches x, y *connected in parallel* is denoted by $x+y$, while a circuit with x, y *connected in series* is represented by xy (Fig. 48a). Tables for these circuits are:

x	y	$x+y$
0	0	0
0	1	1
1	0	1
1	1	1

x	y	xy
0	0	0
0	1	0
1	0	0
1	1	1

.

Rewriting these suitably, we see that they are precisely the tables of the two-valued Boolean algebra given earlier.

More complicated circuits involving combinations of series—and parallel—connection are clearly expressible algebraically in terms of Boolean algebra elements. Often these simplify according to the rules (166), e.g. Example 85 (Fig. 48b) simplifies to a single parallel circuit. As switching circuits are used in telephone systems and electronic systems (e.g. computers), simplification in design of switching circuits is financially valuable from an industrial point of view because of the economy effected by the manufacturer.

Thus, to every parallel- and series-circuit corresponds an expression in Boolean algebra, and vice versa. Historically, we note that the application of Boolean algebra to switches was discovered in 1938 by Shannon, an American electrical engineer.

Earlier, we have become accustomed to having a differential equation as a mathematical model. Now we appreciate that an algebraic system may also be a mathematical model. Biologists, we note further, have found Boolean algebra a suitable model for giving a mathematical and theoretical description of neural networks. (Consult *Mathematical Biophysics*, N. Rashevsky (Dover, 1960.))

Sometimes, we are required to determine whether or not a set of objects has the Boolean algebra structure. Checking of the laws is tedious for more than three elements. Hence, it is easier to prove a set does not form a Boolean algebra by pin-pointing an invalid result. (See Exercise 13.27.)

§69. NUMBER OF ELEMENTS IN A SET

Turning now to set theory, denote by $n(A)$ the number of elements in the set A.

EXAMPLE 86. $n(A+B) = n(A)+n(B)-n(AB).$ (168)

Solution. (Carefully note the difference between the two uses of the symbol $+$. When connecting sets it is, of course, set union; when connecting numbers like $n(A)$, $n(B)$, it is ordinary arithmetic addition.)

Now $\quad A = AB+A\bar{B} \qquad \because (AB)(A\bar{B}) = O, \quad$ or by B_3

$$\therefore n(A) = n(AB)+n(A\bar{B}).$$

Similarly, $\quad n(B) = n(BA)+n(\bar{A}B).$

Add $\quad \therefore n(A)+n(B) = n(A\bar{B})+n(\bar{A}B)+2n(AB) \qquad \because AB = BA.$

$$\therefore n(A)+n(B)-n(AB) = n(A\bar{B})+n(\bar{A}B)+n(AB)$$

$$= n\,(A+B) \qquad \text{by Example 85}$$

i.e. (168) is proved.

[A Venn diagram shows immediately the intuitive truth of (168).]

EXAMPLE 87. $n(A+B+C) = n(A)+n(B)+n(C)-n(AB)-n(BC)-n(CA)$ $+n(ABC).$ (169)

Solution. Put $B+C = D.$

$$\therefore n(A+B+C) = n(A)+n(D)-n(AD) \qquad \text{by (168)}$$

$$= n(A)+\{n(B)+n(C)-n(BC)\}-\{n(AB)+n(AC)-$$
$$-n(ABC)\} \qquad \text{by (168)}$$

i.e. (169) is proved.

EXAMPLE 88. A university official made a statistical report concerning 100 first-year science students studying mathematics, physics, and chemistry as follows: mathematics 45, physics 41, chemistry 38; mathematics and physics 16; mathematics and chemistry 12; physics and chemistry 11; all three subjects 14. Naturally, the official was reprimanded by his superiors. Why?

Solution. Represent by M, P, C the sets of students doing mathematics, physics and chemistry, respectively.

$$\therefore n(M+P+C) = n(M)+n(P)+n(C)-n(MP)-n(PC)-n(CM)+n(MPC) \qquad \text{by (169)}$$

$$= 45+41+38-16-11-12+14$$

$$= 99.$$

But $n(M+P+C) = 100$. Hence, the report was inconsistent.

Many branches of mathematics are illuminated by the language and ideas of set theory. Applications of sets, besides those already mentioned, include, for instance, probability, topology, real function theory, linear programming (ultimately linked with games theory), and algebraic systems such as (abstract) rings, fields, and groups which we now approach.

Suggested topics for further study

(1) Linear programming (Kemeny, Snell, and Thompson reference, Chapter 8).
(2) Lattices [*Lattices to Logic*, R. Dubisch (Blaisdell, 1964)].
(3) Mathematical logic and switching circuits [*Boolean Algebra and its Applications*, J. E. Whitesitt (Addison–Wesley, 1960)].
(4) Electronic computers and Boolean algebra [*Thinking Machines*, I. Adler (Dobson, 1961); *An Introduction to Number Scales and Computers*, F. J. Budden (Longmans, 1965); Reference (d), Chapter 1.]
(5) Topology (*Elementary Concepts of Topology*, P. Alexandroff (Dover, 1961); *Introduction to Topology*, B. Mendelson (Blackie, 1963); *Experiments in Topology*, S. Barr (John Murray, 1965).
(6) Transfinite numbers [*Introduction to the Theory of Sets*, J. Breuer (translated by H. Fehr) (Prentice-Hall, 1958)].
[*Query:* What are *Eudoxus numbers?* (Eudoxus, 408–335 B.C., Greek). See the Budden reference in (4) above.]

References

Text on algebra in the bibliography, plus:

(a) *Theory and Problems of Set Theory and Related Topics*, S. Lipschutz (Schaum, 1964).

EXERCISES 13

1. Construct all the subsets of $S = \{1, 3, 5, 7\}$.

2. Defining a *lattice point* to be one whose coordinates are integers, is the set of lattice points in the region bounded by the circles $x^2+y^2 = 4$, $x^2+y^2 = 6$ an empty set?

3. Let K be the set of lattice points interior to the circle $x^2+y^2 = 7$. Let P be the set of two-digit prime numbers. Which of the following statements is correct? (a) $|K| < |P|$; (b) $|K| = |P|$; (c) $|K| > |P|$.

When $A = \{1, 2, 3\}$, $B = \{3, 4\}$, determine the Cartesian products:

4. $A \times B$. **5.** $B \times A$.

6. Is $\subset$ an equivalence relation?

7. Give a formula which maps $\mathcal{N} = \{1, 2, 3, 4, \ldots\}$ one-to-one onto the set $\mathcal{M} = \{1, 3, 9, 27, \ldots\}$.

8. How many mappings of $S = \{a, b, c, d\}$ onto itself are there? Write out at least five of these mappings.

In Cantor's diagram for the countability of rational numbers:

9. What integer is mapped on to $\frac{4}{3}$?

10. What rational number corresponds to 19?

Use Venn diagrams to illustrate:

11. $\overline{A \cup B} = \overline{A} \cap \overline{B}$. **12.** $A \cap (B-C) = (A \cap B)-(A \cap C)$.

13. Simplify $(A \cap B) \cup (A \cap \overline{B})$.

In a statistically correct survey of 100 students, the numbers playing various sports were: cricket 28, football 30, tennis 42, cricket and football 8; cricket and tennis 10; football and tennis 5; all three sports 3.

14. How many students were playing no sport at all?

15. How many students had tennis as their only game?

16. How many students played football if they played tennis?

17. Blood-testing involves three types of antigens: A, B, Rh. Every person is classified doubly. He (she) is Rh+ if he has the Rh antigen and Rh− otherwise. He is type AB, A, or B depending on which of the other antigens he has, with type O having neither A nor B. Identify each of the 8 possibilities in a Venn diagram.

[Here, O does not mean that a man has "no blood", i.e. is "dead as a doornail!" as a student once declared.]

18. How may the transfinite division C/C be interpreted?

19. Without appealing to duality (i.e. using Huntington's axioms) prove that in a Boolean algebra $a0 = 0$. (Model your proof on that in Example 81.)

20. Show that $a+x = b+x$, $a+\bar{x} = b+\bar{x} \Rightarrow a = b$, where a, b, x are elements of a Boolean algebra.

21. Justify the equivalence of $a+b = b$, $a\bar{b} = 0$.

22. Give a proof, using (167), of the symbolic form of the Aristotelian syllogism: $a \subset b$, $b \subset c \Rightarrow a \subset c$ ("All men are mortal, Socrates is a man, therefore Socrates is mortal").

23. Zero and unity in Boolean algebra are both unique. Prove.

24. Simplify $(\overline{\bar{A}B})(\overline{AC})BC$.

25. Simplify $\overline{\{\bar{A}(A+B)+\bar{B}(A+B)\}}$.

[This symbolic expression represents an electronic process in the IBM 1620 computer.] [U.N.E.]

26. For any elements a, b, c of a Boolean algebra, prove that $ab+bc+ca = (a+b)(b+c)(c+a)$. What is the dual of this result?

27. Given the set 1, 2, 3, 6, 9, 18, define the operations $+$, $\cdot$ to be the L.C.M and H.C.F. respectively of two elements of the set. Is the set a Boolean algebra? Justify your answer.

28. Express $x(\bar{x}+y)+y(y+z)+y$ as an electrical (switching) circuit. Use Boolean algebra to simplify this circuit.

29. Do these two-valued tables represent a Boolean algebra?

$\cup$	0	1
0	0	1
1	1	1

$\cap$	0	1
0	1	0
1	0	1

30. Express all the laws (166) of a Boolean algebra in terms of switches.

[Exercise 13.3 is taken from Breuer's book, reference Chapter 13; Exercise 13.17 is an adaptation from the Kemeny, Snell, and Thompson text, reference § 54. These exercises are here used by kind permission of the publishers of both books, Prentice-Hall Inc., U.S.A.]

CHAPTER 14

GROUPS

The science of Pure Mathematics, in its modern developments, may claim to be the most original creation of the human spirit.

(A. N. WHITEHEAD)

IN THIS chapter we continue the study of algebraic structures begun with number systems and Boolean algebra. Whereas in the case of rings, fields, and Boolean algebras two operations exist for combining elements, in the case of groups only one operation exists between pairs of elements. Principally we are interested in groups and abstract rings and fields, but associated structures will be mentioned. Like sets, in terms of which they are defined, groups have a considerable unifying character.

§ 70. INTUITIVE APPROACH TO GROUPS

Quite apart from its purely abstract algebraic development and its usefulness in other branches of pure mathematics, such as number theory, geometry, and topology, the theory of groups provides an important technique in the study of many physical problems, as, for example, those dealing with crystal structure, quantum theory, molecular orbits and spectra, and the theory of relativity. Regarding the value of groups in pure mathematics, we emphasise that in his comprehensive *Erlanger Programm* (1872), Klein showed how different types of geometry can be regarded as the study of those properties of suitable spaces which are left invariant by appropriate groups of linear transformations, e.g. Euclidean geometry consists of those properties of space invariant under the Euclidean group of transformations. (See § 79.)

Though the concept of group is traceable to the elementary geometry of the ancient Greeks, the theory of groups is of relatively modern development. Much of the early work on groups centred around permutations and roots of equations and was achieved in the nineteenth century by mathematicians of the calibre of Gauss, Galois, Abel (1802–29, Norwegian), Hamilton, Cayley, Cauchy and Jordan (1838–1922, French).

Immediate objects of this brief treatment are:

(i) to clarify the nature of the group concept; and
(ii) to develop a few basic properties of groups.

Mostly, we are concerned with finite groups.

Consider the integers..., -2, -1, 0, 1, 2,... Clearly, the following four rules hold (for addition):

(i) $a+b = k$,
(ii) $a+(b+c) = (a+b)+c$,
(iii) $0+a = a = a+0$,
(iv) $-a+a = 0 = a+(-a)$,

where a, b, c, k are any four integers.

Next consider the fractions $p/q\,(q \neq 0)$ under the operation of multiplication. Obviously, we have the rules:

(i) $a\times b = k$,
(ii) $a\times(b\times c) = (a\times b)\times c$,
(iii) $1\times a = a = a\times 1$,
(iv) $a^{-1}\times a = 1 = a\times a^{-1}$,

where a, b, c, k are any four fractions. Notice that the two sets of rules are identical in form, bearing in mind that under addition the inverse of a is $-a$ and the identity is 0, while under multiplication they are a^{-1} and 1 respectively.

Finally, consider the rotations of a bar hinged at a fixed point and initially at rest. Let the star symbol $*$ represent the law of combination of two rotations, that is, let $A*B$ mean the result after first rotating through an angle β (this movement is labelled B), followed by rotating through an angle α (this is the movement A). Then, for any rotations A, B, C, K (through angles $\alpha, \beta, \gamma, \varkappa$) we have the rules

(i) $A*B = K$,
(ii) $A*(B*C) = (A*B)*C$,
(iii) $I*A = A = A*I$,
(iv) $A^{-1}*A = I = A*A^{-1}$,

where A^{-1} means rotation through the angle $-\alpha$ and I signifies rotation through the angle 0, i.e. no movement at all.

In the above illustrations, we have been dealing in each case with a set of objects (integers, fractions, rotations) and an associated law of combination (addition, multiplication, one rotation followed by another) connecting elements of the set. A clear pattern common to all these procedures is thus apparent which suggests the existence of a new mathematical concept based on two things: the elements of a set and a law relating to these elements. This structure is called a group. From these specific instances, we can abstract the rules which give us the generalised notion of a a group. *As a convention, we take the law of combination of an abstract group to be multiplication.*

§ 71. FORMAL DEFINITIONS AND BASIC PROPERTIES

Definition [due to E. H. Moore (1862–1932, American).]

A *group* G is a mathematical system composed of a set of elements $A, B, C, \ldots$ with a law of combination:

(i) $AB \in G$ *(law of closure)*.

(ii) $A(BC) = (AB)C$ *(associative law)*. (170)

(iii) $\exists$ an *identity (unit) element* $I: AI = IA = A$ for all A.

(iv) $\exists$ an *inverse element* $A^{-1}: AA^{-1} = A^{-1}A = I$ for all A.

Thus, for the existence of a group, four things are necessary: closure, association, identity, inverses. Of course, inverses belong to the group.

Note. AB means B followed by A. However, some writers adopt the opposite convention.

We may write $G = \{A, B, C, \ldots\}$ to specify the elements of G. Removal of some of the restrictions in (170) leads to simpler algebraic systems, e.g. a *semi-group* for which only (i), (ii) are valid. Rather surprisingly as it may seem, much research work is being done into the properties of semi-groups which by definition, have a very loose structure. Axioms (170) are not the minimal set of axioms necessary to define a group, e.g. if the left identity $IA = A$ and left inverse $A^{-1}A = I$ are assumed, we may derive the existence of the right-hand identity and right-hand inverse.

If, instead of the multiplicative notation, we employ the additive notation [consult *Introduction to the Theory of Groups*, P. Alexandroff (Blackie, 1959)], we then write:

$A+B$ in place of AB
O in place of I
$-A$ in place of A^{-1}
$A-B$ in place of AB^{-1}.

Explanation of some terms

(a) *Order* of the group $G =$ the number of elements in G.
$\therefore$ G may be *finite* or *infinite*.

(b) *Period* of an element A = the least positive power of A which equals I, i.e. if $A^m = I$, then the period of A is m.

(c) *Abelian group*. If $AB = BA$, the group is *Abelian* (or *commutative*). [See Example 89 (iv) for an instance of a non-Abelian group.]

EXAMPLE 89 (simple examples of finite groups).

(i) The set 1, ε, ε^2 of the cube roots of unity (under the operation of multiplication) is an Abelian group of order 3.

(ii) The set 0, 1, 2, 3 of all integers mod 4 (under the operation of addition) is an Abelian group of order 4.

(iii) The set of rotations of a regular hexagon (under the operation of one rotation followed by another) is an Abelian group of order 6.

(iv) The set of quaternion elements ± 1, $\pm i$, $\pm j$, $\pm k$ (see § 52) is a *non-Abelian* group of order 8 since $ij \neq ji$, etc. (operation of multiplication).

(d) *Cyclic group*. A *cyclic group* is one whose elements may all be expressed as powers of one element, called the *generator*, i.e.

$$I, A, A^2, A^3, \ldots, A^{g-1}$$

is a cyclic group C_g of order g generated by A where g is the least positive integer: $A^g = I$, e.g. the set 1, ε, ε^2 of cube roots of unity form a cyclic group C_3 of order 3. (Observe that $\varepsilon = e^{2\pi i/3}$.)

Obviously, all cyclic groups are Abelian. Numerous examples of cyclic groups could be given from art and architecture where, because cyclic symmetry has an immediate aesthetic appeal, it is used to great advantage [e.g. the Doge's Palace in Venice, the Baptistry of St. John (Pisa)].

Symmetry in one form or another occurs widely in nature and in art where balance and harmony have functional as well as aesthetic value. Neolithic men had a strong feeling for simple symmetric patterns involving parallelism, congruence, and similarity, which were used ornamentally for decorating pottery as archaeological excavations in Babylonia, Predynastic Egypt and some Etruscan caves (for instance) reveal. Inorganic nature affords us a fantastically beautiful example of hexagonal symmetry in the form of snow crystals. Here we remark that, while pentagonal symmetry does not occur in crystal structure, it does occur in the plant world, e.g. in the case of the geranium, and in the Pentagon Building, Washington, D.C. Organically, symmetry is so obvious at a physiological level that it hardly needs exemplifying, though the bilateral symmetry of, say, the centipede (or scolopendrid, to give it its technical zoological name) and the translational symmetry (metamerism) of a maple shoot could be mentioned. For a fascinating description of the mathematics of symmetry, consult *Symmetry* by H. Weyl (Princeton, 1952) wherein there also occurs an account of the asymmetries of the internal organs of the human body.

EXAMPLE 90 (simple examples of infinite groups). The set of:

(i) Even integers including 0 (under the operation of addition).
(ii) Powers of 2 (under the operation of multiplication).
(iii) Movement of a rigid body (under the operation of one movement followed by another).
(iv) Matrices $R(\theta) = \begin{bmatrix} \cos\theta & \sin\theta \\ -\sin\theta & \cos\theta \end{bmatrix}$ (under the operation of matrix multiplication.) Identity and inverse are $R(\theta)$, $R(-\theta)$, while $R(\theta)\cdot R(\phi) = R(\theta+\phi)$. [Matrices like this, of course, represent rotations through an angle θ. (See § 53.)] Matrices $R(\theta)$ and $\begin{bmatrix} 1 & \cdot \\ \cdot & -1 \end{bmatrix} R(\theta) = \begin{bmatrix} \cos\theta & \sin\theta \\ \sin\theta & -\cos\theta \end{bmatrix}$ are the only two 2×2 orthogonal matrices. [See Reference (c) (p. 256) of this Chapter, and Exercises 12.51 − 12.53.] Geometrically, they represent a rotation and a rotation followed by a reflection [in the x-axis (Example 64)], respectively. Refer to Exercises 15.17, 15.18.
(v) Complex numbers (under addition and multiplication).

Groups (i)–(v) are Abelian, but note that matrices are generally non-commutative under matrix multiplication and so, in general, do not form an Abelian group.

EXAMPLE 91 (simple examples of sets which are not groups).

(i) The infinite set of integers (under the operation of multiplication) does not form a group since the inverse of an integer is not an integer.
(ii) The finite set 1, 2, 3 mod 4 (under the operation of addition) does not form a group since there is no identity element, e.g. $3+1 \equiv 0 \pmod 4$ i.e. closure is lacking.

Associated with every group is a *multiplication table* in which the products of the elements of the group are arranged. This notion is due to Cayley, 1854. Each element of the group appears just once in each row and just once in each column.

§ 72. SURVEY OF GROUPS OF ORDER 2, 3, 4, 5, 6

Group of order 2

	I	A
I	I	A
A	A	I

Multiplication table for C_2

There is clearly only one group of order 2 the *cyclic group* C_2. Simple concrete examples of this abstract group are: (i) the numbers 1, −1 (under multiplication), (ii) 2 points equidistant from a line and on opposite sides of it (under the operation of reflection in the line).

Group of order 3

Let the elements be I, A, B. Then the multiplication table must commence as indicated in (a). Now $x = A^2$ must also equal either I or B. But $A^2 = I \Rightarrow y = AB$ must also equal B. This $\Rightarrow A = I$ which is impossible since I, A, B are distinct by hypothesis. $\therefore A^2 = B$ so we obtain table (b). Since the elements of the group are thus I, A, A^2, it must be the *cyclic group* C_3 whose multiplication table is given in (c).

(a)

	I	A	B
I	I	A	B
A	A	x	y
B	B		

(b)

	I	A	B
I	I	A	B
A	A	B	I
B	B	I	A

(c)

	I	A	A^2
I	I	A	A^2
A	A	A^2	I
A^2	A^2	I	A

Multiplication table for C_3

Simple examples of C_3 are (i) the set $1, \varepsilon, \varepsilon^2$ of cube roots of unity, (ii) the set of rotations of an equilateral triangle about its centre.

Groups of order 4

EXAMPLE 92. Every group of order 4 is either cyclic or the Klein group.

Solution. Let the elements be I, A, B, C.

Then G may be either (i) cyclic or (ii) non-cyclic. Case (i) gives us C_4. Suppose G is non-cyclic.

Multiply the elements by A to obtain A, A^2, AB, AC. These elements, in some order, must be the same as I, A, B, C.

Three cases arise (since $A^2 \neq A$):

(1) $A^2 = B$. (2) $A^2 = C$. (3) $A^2 = I$.

If $A^2 = B$, then (a) $AB = I$, $AC = C$

or (b) $AB = C$, $AC = I$.

Case (a) is impossible since $AC = C \Rightarrow A = I$.

Case (b) is impossible since $A^2 = B$, $AB = C \Rightarrow A^3 = C$ which would make the group cyclic.

$$\therefore A^2 \neq B.$$

Similarly $$A^2 \neq C.$$

$$\therefore A^2 = I.$$

$$\therefore \text{either (c) } AB = B,\ AC = C$$

$$\text{or (d) } AB = C,\ AC = B.$$

Case (c) is impossible since it $\Rightarrow A = I$.

Hence $$A^2 = I,\quad AB = C,\quad AC = B.$$

Similarly,
$$\begin{cases} BA = C, & B^2 = I, \quad BC = A, \\ CA = B, & CB = A, \quad C^2 = I. \end{cases}$$

This non-cyclic group K of order 4 is called the *Klein group*, sometimes called the *four group* (Klein's *Vierergruppe*).

Concrete representations of these abstract groups are:

C_4: the set $1, i, -1, -i$ of fourth roots of unity (identify $1, i, -1, -i$ with I, A, A^2, A^3 respectively);

K: the set of reflectional symmetries of the rectangle (Fig. 49).

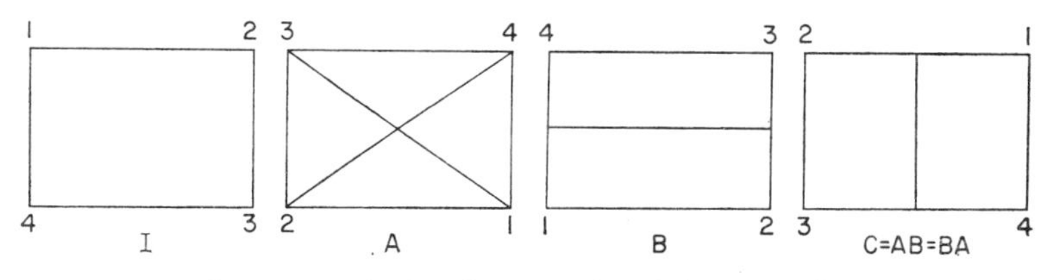

FIG. 49. Reflectional symmetries of the rectangle

These reflectional symmetries have the effect of permuting the vertices of the rectangle amongst themselves and thus leaving it invariant as a whole. (The position represented by the movement A, for instance, is obtained from the given position I by the operation of interchanging vertices 1 and 3, and vertices 2 and 4 simultaneously—it is equivalent to reflection about the centre of the rectangle.) Clearly, these positions could be represented in matrix form thus (see Example 93):

$$\underset{I}{\begin{bmatrix} 1 & \cdot & \cdot & \cdot \\ \cdot & 1 & \cdot & \cdot \\ \cdot & \cdot & 1 & \cdot \\ \cdot & \cdot & \cdot & 1 \end{bmatrix}}, \quad \underset{a}{\begin{bmatrix} \cdot & \cdot & 1 & \cdot \\ \cdot & \cdot & \cdot & 1 \\ 1 & \cdot & \cdot & \cdot \\ \cdot & 1 & \cdot & \cdot \end{bmatrix}}, \quad \underset{b}{\begin{bmatrix} \cdot & \cdot & \cdot & 1 \\ \cdot & \cdot & 1 & \cdot \\ \cdot & 1 & \cdot & \cdot \\ 1 & \cdot & \cdot & \cdot \end{bmatrix}}, \quad \underset{c}{\begin{bmatrix} \cdot & 1 & \cdot & \cdot \\ 1 & \cdot & \cdot & \cdot \\ \cdot & \cdot & \cdot & 1 \\ \cdot & \cdot & 1 & \cdot \end{bmatrix}}. \quad [\text{Does } c = ab = ba?]$$

By comparison with K, C_4 is the group of cyclical rotations of the square.

	I	A	A^2	A^3
I	I	A	A^2	A^3
A	A	A^2	A^3	I
A^2	A^2	A^3	I	A
A^3	A^3	I	A	A^2

Multiplication table for C_4

	I	A	B	C
I	I	A	B	C
A	A	I	C	B
B	B	C	I	A
C	C	B	A	I

Multiplication table for K

Unusual cases of K are to be found in Reference (d), Chapter 11. Included are electrical and mechanical models, and the example of a peal of bells as sounded by change-ringers.

Group of order 5

An important theorem (Exercise 14.53) states: *Groups of prime order are cyclic.* This means that the only group of order 5 is C_3 (e.g. the group of rotations of a regular pentagon). It also explains why there is only one group of order 2, and only one group of order 3. [See Exercise 14.26.] Periwinkle flowers have C_5 as their symmetry group.

Groups of order 6

Analysing groups of order 6, we find there are just two of them: C_6 and S (cross-ratio group; see Chapter 15) of which S is non-Abelian. Thus, S is the smallest non-Abelian group, a fact which explains why we could not give any simpler illustrations of non-Abelian groups.

Summary of groups of order $\leqslant 6$

So far we have investigated *all* the groups of order $\leqslant 6$:

C_2:	cyclic group of order	2
C_3:	cyclic group of order	3
C_4:	cyclic group of order	4
K :	Klein group of order	4
C_5:	cyclic group of order	5
C_6:	cyclic group of order	6
S :	cross-ratio group of order	6.

EXAMPLE 93 (rotational symmetries of the equilateral triangle).

There are six movements which self-transform the equilateral triangle, i.e. which interchange the vertices so as to leave the triangle as a whole invariant. They are (Fig. 50):

(i) (cyclical) rotations about the centre of the triangle through

$$0, \quad \frac{2\pi}{3}, \quad \frac{4\pi}{3};$$

(ii) (axial) rotations through π of the plane about an altitude of the triangle.

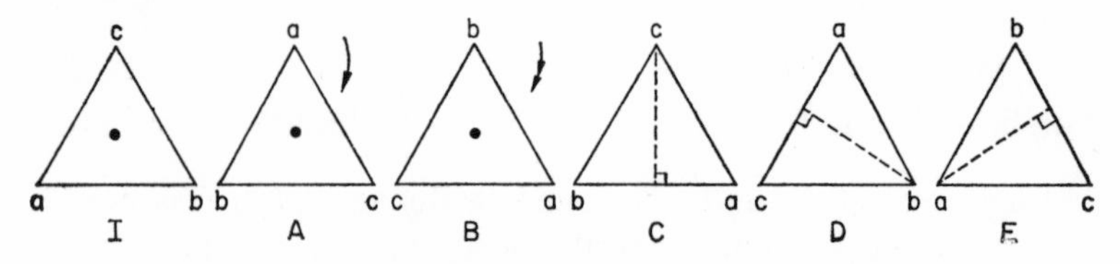

FIG. 50. Rotational symmetries of the equilateral triangle

Let I, A and $B = A^2$ represent the rotations (i), and C, D, E the rotations (ii). Geometrically, we see that

$$A^3 = C^2 = D^2 = E^2 = I$$

and that, for instance, $AC = E = CA^2$, $CA = D = A^2C$.

To simplify the multiplication of movements (rotations), introduce the *permutation matrices* **I, A, B, C, D, E** corresponding to the movements I, A, B, C, D, E respectively:

$$\mathbf{I} = \begin{bmatrix} 1 & . & . \\ . & 1 & . \\ . & . & 1 \end{bmatrix}, \quad \mathbf{A} = \begin{bmatrix} . & 1 & . \\ . & . & 1 \\ 1 & . & . \end{bmatrix}, \quad \mathbf{B} = \begin{bmatrix} . & . & 1 \\ 1 & . & . \\ . & 1 & . \end{bmatrix},$$

$$\mathbf{C} = \begin{bmatrix} . & 1 & . \\ 1 & . & . \\ . & . & 1 \end{bmatrix}, \quad \mathbf{D} = \begin{bmatrix} . & . & 1 \\ . & 1 & . \\ 1 & . & . \end{bmatrix}, \quad \mathbf{E} = \begin{bmatrix} 1 & . & . \\ . & . & 1 \\ . & 1 & . \end{bmatrix}.$$

A permutation matrix, corresponding to a permutation, contains only one non-zero element (= 1) in each row and column. The matrix **B**, for example, operating on the initial order of vertices *abc* produces the permuted order *cab*, i.e.

$$\begin{bmatrix} . & . & 1 \\ 1 & . & . \\ . & 1 & . \end{bmatrix} \begin{bmatrix} a \\ b \\ c \end{bmatrix} = \begin{bmatrix} c \\ a \\ b \end{bmatrix}.$$

Permutations evidently form a group, the *permutation group* of the objects under consideration.

Using the permutation matrices we easily see that $A^3 = C^2 = D^2 = E^2 = I$ and that $AC = E$, $CA = D$, i.e. the group of rotational symmetries of the equilateral triangle is non-Abelian and non-cyclic. Consequently, it must have the same structure as S, i.e. it is isomorphic to S (§ 74).

	I	A	A^2	C	D	E
I	I	A	A^2	C	D	E
A	A	A^2	I	E	C	D
A^2	A^2	I	A	D	E	C
C	C	D	E	I	A	A^2
D	D	E	C	A^2	I	A
E	E	C	D	A	A^2	I

Multiplication table for S

Vertices of the equilateral triangle may represent atoms of a triatomic molecule, or three protons in a physical system.

How many symmetries exist for the isosceles triangle?

§73. CONCEPTS OF SUBGROUP AND GENERATORS

Definition. A subset H of G is a *subgroup* of G if and only if it obeys the four postulates for a group: closure, association, identity, inverse.

Note that *the identity for G is also the identity for H*, i.e. $I \in$ every subgroup of G. Both I and G itself satisfy the conditions for the existence of a subgroup, so we call them *improper subgroups.*

The most important theorem about subgroups is *Lagrange's theorem*, which we assume: If H is a subgroup (of order h) of a finite group G (of order g) then $g/h = n$, an integer (g, h, n finite; n is the *index* of H in G).

Examples of subgroups

(i) C_4 has one subgroup of order 2, viz., $\{I, A^2\}$

(ii) K has three subgroup of order 2, viz., $\{I, A\}$, $\{I, B\}$, $\{I, C\}$.

Definition. A *set of independent generators* of a non-cyclic group G is a set of elements generating the group such that none of them is expressible in terms of the others. Each element of G is a function of the generators.

Every finite group has *at least* one set of independent generators. Among the generators there usually exist *defining relations* enabling us to construct the multiplication table completely.

Example of generators

$$\text{For } K,\ A^2 = B^2 = (AB)^2 = I,$$

i.e. K is generated by two operations A, B each of period 2 with a defining relation $(AB)^2 = I$.

§74. ISOMORPHISM

Two groups $G = \{A, B, C, \ldots\}$ and $G' = \{A', B', C', \ldots\}$ are *isomorphic* (and we then write $G \approx G'$) if $\exists$ *a* 1–1 correspondence *(isomorphism)* $A \leftrightarrow A'$, $B \leftrightarrow B' : AB \leftrightarrow A'B'$. If $G' = G$, the isomorphism is an *automorphism.* [(Greek) *morphe, isos, autos, homos* $\equiv$ "form", "equal", "self", "same".]

Thus, isomorphic groups possess the same *structure* but may differ in their notation and in the nature of their elements, i.e. isomorphic abstract groups are structurally identical and so may be regarded as the same group. All representations of the same abstract group are isomorphic. Isomorphism is thus a technically rich and valuable asset since it permits us to recognise that vastly different sets of objects may yet have the same hidden structure. Group theory is largely concerned with the properties of a group which are shared by isomorphic groups. *Query:* If a subgroup is isomorphic to one of its subgroups, what can you say about its order?

If the correspondence between two groups is not 1–1, we have a *homomorphism*. Accordingly, isomorphism is a special case of the more general concept of homomorphism.

EXAMPLE 94 (illustration of isomorphism).

Four isomorphic Abelian groups of order 4 are:

$G_1 = \{1, i, -1, -i\}$ under the operation of multiplication;

$G_2 = \left\{\begin{bmatrix}1 & \cdot \\ \cdot & 1\end{bmatrix}, \begin{bmatrix}\cdot & 1 \\ -1 & \cdot\end{bmatrix}, \begin{bmatrix}-1 & \cdot \\ \cdot & -1\end{bmatrix}, \begin{bmatrix}\cdot & -1 \\ 1 & \cdot\end{bmatrix}\right\}$ under the operation of matrix multiplication;

$G_3 = \{1, 2, 3, 4\}$ (mod 5) under the operation of multiplication then reduction mod 5;

$G_4 = \{0, 1, 2, 3\}$ (mod 4) under the operation of addition then reduction mod 4.

It is readily seen that these four groups all have the same multiplication table as C_4, i.e. they are concrete representations of the abstract cyclic group C_4. Interpretations of the abstract equation $CB = A$ are thus, for,

$G_1: -i \cdot -1 = i;$

$G_2: \begin{bmatrix}\cdot & -1 \\ 1 & \cdot\end{bmatrix}\begin{bmatrix}-1 & \cdot \\ \cdot & -1\end{bmatrix} = \begin{bmatrix}\cdot & 1 \\ -1 & \cdot\end{bmatrix};$

$G_3: 4 \times 3 \equiv 2 \pmod 5;$

$G_4: 3 + 2 \equiv 1 \pmod 4.$

Note. A group of order 4 which is isomorphic to K would not, of course, be isomorphic to C_4.

A famous theorem, due to Cayley, 1854, asserts: *Every finite group is isomorphic to a permutation group.*

§ 75. TYPICAL PROBLEMS IN ELEMENTARY GROUP THEORY

EXAMPLE 95.

(i) $\boxed{\text{If } BA = CA \ (A, B, C \in G), \text{ then } B = C.}$ (171)

(This is the *right cancellation law*. Likewise, $\exists$ a left cancellation law.)

Solution. Post-multiply both sides of the equation by A^{-1}.

$$\therefore BAA^{-1} = CAA^{-1}$$

$$\therefore BI = CI \qquad \because AA^{-1} = I$$

$$\therefore B = C.$$

(ii) $\boxed{(AB)^{-1} = B^{-1}A^{-1}.}$ (172)

Solution.

$AB(AB)^{-1} = I$ by definition of an inverse.

$\therefore A^{-1}AB(AB)^{-1} = A^{-1}$ pre-multiplying both sides by A^{-1}.

$\therefore B(AB)^{-1} = A^{-1}$ $\because A^{-1}A = I$.

$\therefore B^{-1}B(AB)^{-1} = B^{-1}A^{-1}$ pre-multiplying both sides by B^{-1}.

$\therefore (AB)^{-1} = B^{-1}A^{-1}$ $\because B^{-1}B = I$.

[Using the symbols T, S instead of A, B the result becomes $(TS)^{-1} = S^{-1}T^{-1}$, i.e. inverse of shirt on, tie on is tie off, shirt off!] From (ii) it follows that $(ABC)^{-1} = C^{-1}B^{-1}A^{-1}$.

(iii) If A, B and AB are all of period 2, then A and B commute.

Solution.

$ABAB = I$ $\because (AB)^2 = I$ (given).

$\therefore AABABB = AB$ pre-multiplying by A, post-multiplying by B.

$\therefore A^2BAB^2 = AB$

$\therefore BA = AB$ $\because A^2 = B^2 = I$ (given).

$\therefore$ A and B commute.

[The conditions of the problem apply to the Klein group K.]

(iv) I is unique.

Solution. Suppose $\exists$ another identity I^*.

$\therefore I^*A = A = IA$ by (170) (iii)

$\therefore I^* = I$ by Example 95(i).

Characteristic features of mathematical thinking are, *inter alia*, the search for invariance under transformations, the seeking after common structural patterns in diverse situations, and the generalisation and abstraction of theory from a mass of seemingly unrelated material. No topic we have yet studied exemplifies these qualities to the degree that group theory does.

Galois groups

Every algebraic equation, Galois showed, is connected with a group, its *Galois group*, which consists of those permutations which can be made among the roots of the equation such that any function of the roots is invariant under the permutations. Concepts like these lead to the *Galois theory of equations*.

§ 76. ABSTRACT RINGS AND FIELDS

Frequently, in problems relating to the physical world, the components of vectors are real numbers, while in electrical circuit theory complex vector components occur. Hence, mathematicians are interested in dealing with properties of general (= abstract) systems whose elements combine according to some unspecified operation(s). Particular interpretations may be given to the abstract elements and operations in a concrete situation.

Denote by $a, b, c, \ldots$ the elements of some unspecified set of objects, 0 and 1 being identity elements. Designate by $+$ and $\cdot$ two unstated operations. Axioms A_{1-5}, M_{1-5}, D_1, D_2 of (103) applied in this context then provide the structure of an *abstract field* (= abstract commutative division ring). Under the operation $+$, elements of the field form an additive Abelian group, while non-zero elements form a multiplicative Abelian group. Comments similar to those in § 44 for number fields apply, of course, in the generalised context.

Likewise, as in § 44, we have the axioms for an *abstract ring* (and an *abstract integral domain*). Interpreting elements $a, b, c, \ldots$ and operations $+, \cdot$ appropriately, we have a *matrix ring*, a *quaternion ring*, a *polynomial ring* and a *ring of linear transformations*, for instance. (Refer to § 52 and Exercises 14.59 and 14.60.)

Notice that fields and rings require two operations (conventionally, $+$ and $\cdot$)—as does Boolean algebra—whereas groups require just one operation ($+$ or $\cdot$). Accordingly, the group concept is a less restrictive notion than that of ring or field.

Herewith is a table summarising the minimum conditions for each of these basic algebraic systems.

System	Operation(s)	Laws (Axioms)
Group	$+$ or $\cdot$	A_{1-4} or M_{1-4}
Ring	$+$ and $\cdot$	A_{1-5}, D_{1-2}, M_{1-2}
Field	$+$ and $\cdot$	A_{1-5}, D_{1-2}, M_{1-5}

(173)

Evidently, a ring is an additive Abelian group which is also a multiplicative semigroup, and satisfies both right and left distribution of multiplication over addition. Results true for additive groups naturally carry over to the additive aspects of a ring.

Main abstract algebraic systems

Schematically, the main abstract algebraic structures are interrelated as follows:

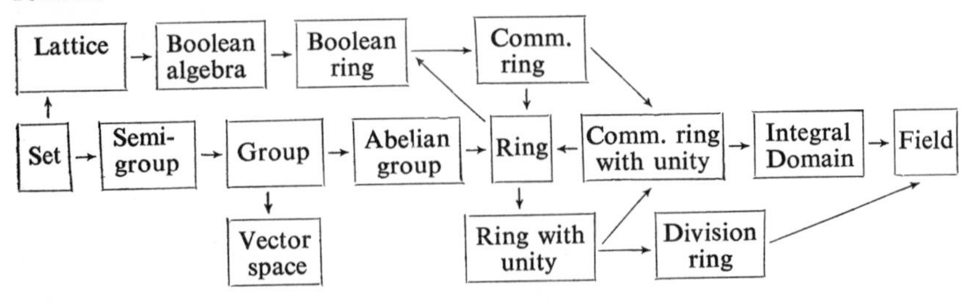

EXAMPLE 96 (abstract ring property). $a0 = 0a = 0$.

Solution. $b+0 = b$ (A_3)

$\therefore a(b+0) = ab$ (pre-multiplying by a)

$\therefore ab+a0 = ab$ (D_1)

$\therefore a0 = 0$ (A_3).

Post-multiplication by a likewise yields $0a = 0$.

EXAMPLE 97 (fundamental abstract field property). A field has no divisors of zero.

Solution. Suppose $ab = 0 \Rightarrow a \neq 0,\ b \neq 0$, i.e. suppose there are (non-zero) divisors of zero.

$$\begin{aligned} b &= 1b && \text{(by } M_3, M_5) \\ &= (a^{-1}a)b && (M_4) \\ &= a^{-1}(ab) && (M_2) \\ &= a^{-1}0 && \text{(hypothesis)} \\ &= 0 && \text{(Example 96).} \end{aligned}$$

This is contrary to hypothesis. Hence, $ab = 0 \Rightarrow a = 0$ or $b = 0$.

Modern physical theories often involve algebraic systems in which the commutative or associative laws (or both) are invalid. Examples of such non-associative algebras occur in Exercises 14.65–14.72. Present-day algebraic geometry, at its most advanced levels, draws heavily on more arcane knowledge of abstract groups, rings, fields and related structures.

Suggested topics for further study

(1) Dihedral groups.
(2) Permutation groups.
(3) Proof of Lagrange's theorem: cosets.
(4) Invariant subgroups: homomorphism, factor (difference) groups.

(5) Ideals (an ideal is a type of ring).
(6) Geometric groups of the five regular polyhedra.
(7) Galois theory of equations.
(8) Braids (E. Artin, *American Scientist*, **38**, 112–19).

References

Texts in the algebra portion of the bibliography, together with:

(a) *Introduction to the Theory of Finite Groups*, W. Ledermann (Oliver & Boyd, 1961).
(b) *Theory and Problems: Abstract Algebra*, Joong Fang (Schaum, 1963).
(c) *A Survey of Modern Algebra*, G. Birkhoff and S. MacLane (Macmillan, 1965).
(d) *Algebraic Structure and Matrices*, E. A. Maxwell (C.U.P., 1965) (Vol. 2 of his *Advanced Algebra*). Also, for historical reasons, have a look at:
(e) *Oeuvres mathematiques*, E. Galois (Gauthier-Villars, 1897).
[Postulates defining a group are discussed in a research article by J. V. Whittaker, *The American Mathematical Monthly*, **62** (9), 636–40 (1955).]

Groups and geometry

Previously, in Chapter 11, the idea of a general non-singular real linear transformation in the plane (131) was introduced. Using 2×2 matrices to represent these transformations (131.1), we find (Exercise 14.5) that they form a group, called the *full linear group*, written $L(2, \mathcal{R}^*)$, the symbolism suggesting that the transformations are linear and expressible by means of 2×2 matrices whose elements belong to $\mathcal{R}^*$. Otherwise stated, $L(2, \mathcal{R}^*)$ is isomorphic to the group of all non-singular 2×2 real matrices. Plainly, the orthogonal group $O(2, \mathcal{R}^*)$ is a subgroup of $L(2, \mathcal{R}^*)$.

A wider concept than the linear transformation is the *affine transformation*, consisting of linear transformations and translations, which constitute the *affine group* $A(2, \mathcal{R}^*)$. An important subgroup of $A(2, \mathcal{R}^*)$ is the Euclidean group $E(2, \mathcal{R}^*)$ consisting of just rotations and translations (§ 79), each of which separately forms a group (Example 90(iv), Exercise 14.25), and therefore a subgroup of $E(2, \mathcal{R}^*)$ and $A(2, \mathcal{R}^*)$. It is known that $E(2, \mathcal{R}^*)$ and $A(2, \mathcal{R}^*)$ completely characterise (metric) Euclidean geometry and affine geometry respectively. Later (Chapter 15), these geometries are seen to be generalised into projective geometry, which is characterised by the projective group $P(2, \mathcal{R}^*)$. Consequently, we have the chain of (sub)groups:

$$E(2, \mathcal{R}^*) \subset A(2, \mathcal{R}^*) \subset P(2, \mathcal{R}^*).$$

Discovery of this astounding relationship between groups and different types of geometry is one of the most far-reaching in mathematics and is due to the penetrating insight of Klein. Accepting a Chair of Mathematics at Erlangen in 1872, Klein in his inaugural public dissertation formulated the modern view of geometry known as his *Erlanger Programm* [(German) ≡ "Erlangen programme"], namely: A geometry is a set of properties of figures which remain invariant under the transformations of a certain group.

Contemporary fundamental research in geometry has moved somewhat away from Klein's synthesis and codification. Some newer geometries, indeed, lie outside the scope of Klein's *Programm*. Nevertheless, his concept describes a large part of geometrical behaviour. It represents a triumph for the human intellect and constitutes a landmark in creative mathematical thinking.

EXERCISES 14

Which of the following sets 1–16 form a group? (If a particular set does not form a group, say why.)

1. Rationals under addition. **2.** Rationals under multiplication.

3. Integers under subtraction. **4.** Complex numbers for which $|z| = 1$, under multiplication.

5. Non-singular $n \times n$ matrices having real numbers for elements, under matrix multiplication (e.g. linear transformations, cf. Example 90(iv)).

6. All $n \times n$ matrices under matrix multiplication. **7.** $\mathcal{J}_3$ under addition.

8. $\mathcal{J}_3 - 0$ under multiplication. **9.** Odd integers under addition.

10. Odd integers under multiplication.

11. Positive ($\geqslant 0$) real numbers under addition.

12. Vectors under (vector) addition. **13.** Vectors under the inner product.

14. Vectors under the outer product. **15.** Real numbers under division.

16. $\{1, 3, 4, 5, 9, 10\}$ mod 11 under multiplication.

17. Show that the inverse A^{-1} in a multiplicative group is unique.

18. What is the corresponding statement for an additive group?

19–21. State the results (i), (ii), (iii) of Example 95 for an additive group.

22. In an additive group, the identity is unique. Prove.

23. Construct a simple counter-example of a 2×2 matrix to vindicate the truth of the statement: $n \times n$ non-singular matrices with integer elements do not form a group.

24. Distinct group elements A, B imply the existence of a unique X: $AX = B$. Justify.

25. Translations $T: x' = x+h,\ y' = y+k$ in the plane form a group. Prove. (The product T_2T_1 of two translations means that we perform T_1 first.)

26. Complete in the unique way possible the following multiplication table for the commutative group of order 5:

	A	B	C	D	E
A	B	C			
B			E	A	
C				B	
D	E				
E	A		C	D	E

27. Show that the matrices $\begin{bmatrix}1 & \cdot\\ \cdot & 1\end{bmatrix}, \begin{bmatrix}1 & \cdot\\ \cdot & -1\end{bmatrix}, \begin{bmatrix}-1 & \cdot\\ \cdot & 1\end{bmatrix}, \begin{bmatrix}-1 & \cdot\\ \cdot & -1\end{bmatrix}$ under multiplication, and the residues 1, 3, 5, 7 (mod. 8) under multiplication and then reduction mod 8, form isomorphic groups.

28. Does the set of matrices $\begin{bmatrix}a & b\\ -b & a\end{bmatrix}$ with $a^2+b^2 = 1$ form a group under matrix multiplication (a, b rational)?

29. Why the restriction on a and b in Exercise 14.28?

30. Equilibrium configuration for the hydrogen and oxygen atoms of a molecule of water are given by the four matrices

$$I = \begin{bmatrix}1 & \cdot & \cdot\\ \cdot & 1 & \cdot\\ \cdot & \cdot & 1\end{bmatrix}, \quad A = \begin{bmatrix}1 & \cdot & \cdot\\ \cdot & 1 & \cdot\\ \cdot & \cdot & -1\end{bmatrix}, \quad B = \begin{bmatrix}-1 & \cdot & \cdot\\ \cdot & 1 & \cdot\\ \cdot & \cdot & 1\end{bmatrix}, \quad C = \begin{bmatrix}-1 & \cdot & \cdot\\ \cdot & 1 & \cdot\\ \cdot & \cdot & -1\end{bmatrix}.$$

Establish that they form a group.

Describe the group of reflectional symmetries of a:

31. Rhombus. **32.** Parallelogram.

33. Analyse the group of rotational symmetries of a regular n-pointed pyramid (i. e. a pyramid whose base is a regular n-gon).

34. Confirm that the matrices $\begin{bmatrix}1 & \cdot\\ \cdot & 1\end{bmatrix}, \begin{bmatrix}\varepsilon & \cdot\\ \cdot & \varepsilon^2\end{bmatrix}, \begin{bmatrix}\varepsilon^2 & \cdot\\ \cdot & \varepsilon\end{bmatrix}, \begin{bmatrix}\cdot & 1\\ 1 & \cdot\end{bmatrix}, \begin{bmatrix}\cdot & \varepsilon^2\\ \varepsilon & \cdot\end{bmatrix}, \begin{bmatrix}\cdot & \varepsilon\\ \varepsilon^2 & \cdot\end{bmatrix}$ form a group isomorphic with the cross-ratio group, ε being a complex cube root of unity.

35. *Galilean transformations* for rectilinear motion are given by the matrices $G(v) = \begin{bmatrix}1 & -v\\ 0 & 1\end{bmatrix}$, where v is the velocity of one observer relative to another. Show that they form a group *(Galilean group)*.

[Galilean transformations preserve the invariance of the laws of classical (= Newtonian) mechanics which describe a large part of Nature with considerable accuracy.]

Einstein's special theory of relativity requires the *Lorentz transformation* $x' = k(x-vt)$, $t' = k\left(\frac{-vx}{c^2}+t\right)$, where v represents the velocity of an object moving in a straight line, c is the velocity of light, and k is the Lorentz factor (Exercise 1.26).

36. Form the Lorentz matrix $L(v)$ to describe this relativistic motion and prove that $L(v)$ is non-singular.

37. Prove that $L(v)$ form a group (the *Lorentz group*).

38. Write down the reverse Lorentz transformation and (see Exercise 12.54) compute the Jacobians $J = \dfrac{\partial(x, t)}{\partial(x', t')}$, $J' = \dfrac{\partial(x', t')}{\partial(x, t)}$.

39. Obtain the rule for adding two velocities in special relativity.

40. Show that the Lorentz transformation leaves $x^2-c^2t^2$ invariant.

[Laws of relativity mechanics must be invariant under Lorentz transformations for which the proper setting is, of course, four dimensional space-time.]

41. Letting $\dfrac{v}{c^2} \to 0$ (i.e. the velocity of the moving object is very small compared with the velocity of light), verify that the Lorentz transformations lead to the expressions for relative motion in classical mechanics, i.e. the Galilean transformations.

42. Writing $L' = x_2'-x_1'$, $L = x_2-x_1$, express L in terms of L'. (This is the relativistic (Fitzgerald) contraction of length.) [*Hint:* Set $t_2 = t_1$ in conjunction with Exercise 14.36.]

43. Following Minkowski (1864–1909, Russian, German), substitute $T = ict$, $T' = ict'$ in the two-dimensional space-time Lorentz equations (Exercise 14.36). Interpret the result as a rotation.

44. Express the rule for adding velocities (Exercises 14.39) in terms of inverse hyperbolic tangents.

Matrices $I = \begin{bmatrix} 1 & \cdot \\ \cdot & 1 \end{bmatrix}$, $A = \begin{bmatrix} 1 & \cdot \\ \cdot & -1 \end{bmatrix}$, $B = \begin{bmatrix} \frac{-1}{2} & \frac{\sqrt{3}}{2} \\ \frac{\sqrt{3}}{2} & \frac{1}{2} \end{bmatrix}$, $C = \begin{bmatrix} \frac{-1}{2} & \frac{-\sqrt{3}}{2} \\ \frac{-\sqrt{3}}{2} & \frac{1}{2} \end{bmatrix}$,

$$D = \begin{bmatrix} \frac{-1}{2} & \frac{\sqrt{3}}{2} \\ \frac{-\sqrt{3}}{2} & \frac{-1}{2} \end{bmatrix}, \quad E = \begin{bmatrix} -\frac{1}{2} & \frac{-\sqrt{3}}{2} \\ \frac{\sqrt{3}}{2} & -\frac{1}{2} \end{bmatrix}$$ are given.

45. Infer that they form a group. **46.** Pick out a subgroup of order 3.

47. Interpret this group geometrically.

48. Cyclic groups of non-prime order always possess cyclic subgroups. Prove.

49. If every element of a group G is its own inverse, show that G is Abelian.

50. Elements z of the group G which commute with every element of G form a subgroup (the *centre* of G). Establish.

51. Abelian groups coincide with their centres. Prove.

Deduce theorems 52–55 from Lagrange's theorem:

52. The period of each element of a finite group of order g is a factor of g.

53. Groups of prime orders must be cyclic.

54. Any two subgroups of a group having mutually prime orders can contain only the unit element in common.

55. *(Fermat's theorem.)* If a is an integer and p a prime, then $a^p \equiv a \pmod{p}$. [*Hint:* Use the fact that the multiplicative group of $\mathcal{J}_p - 0$ has $p-1$ elements.] Try a few appropriate numerical values of a, p.

Given a multiplicative group mod p with $p = 2^k+1$ (prime), prove 56–58:

56. The period of 2 is $2k$.

57. $2k$ is a factor of $p-1$. [*Hint:* use Exercise 14.55.]

58. k is a power of 2.

59. Does the set of all polynomials in x with integer coefficients form an integral domain under ordinary addition and multiplication?

60. Linear transformations in n-dimensions form a ring. Is this true?

61. Do sets form a ring w.r.t. *symmetric difference* $(A-B) \cup (B-A)$ and intersection?

62. W.r.t. $\cup$ and $\cap$, do sets form a ring?

63. Discuss the nature of the ring (associativity, commutativity) formed by vectors in three-dimensions under vector addition and inner and outer multiplication.

64. In a ring with exactly n elements, $na = 0$ for all a. Prove.

In *Lie algebra* (Lie, 1842–99, Norwegian) equality and addition of matrices A, B have their usual meaning, but matrix multiplication is replaced by the operation $A \bigcirc B = AB - BA$ (where AB means ordinary matrix multiplication of A, B). Prove 65–69:

65. $A \bigcirc A = 0$. (0 is the zero for Lie algebra.)

66. $A \bigcirc B = -B \bigcirc A$ (i. e. Lie algebra is non-commutative).

67. $A \bigcirc (B+C) = A \bigcirc B + A \bigcirc C$ (i.e. $\bigcirc$ is distributive over addition).

68. Lie algebra is non-associative.

69. $(A \bigcirc B) \bigcirc C + (B \bigcirc C) \bigcirc A + (C \bigcirc A) \bigcirc B = 0$. (See Exercise 12.60.)

Jordan algebra (Pascual Jordan, 1902– , German), which is useful in quantum mechanics, defines the operation $*$ between two matrices A, B (with equality, addition and multiplication of matrices still valid) as $A*B = \frac{1}{2}(AB+BA)$. Prove 70–72:

70. Jordan algebra is commutative.

71. $A*(B+C) = A*B+A*C$ (i. e. $*$ is distributive over addition).

72. Jordan algebra is non-associative.

[You may wish to investigate commutativity, associativity and distributivity (and also whether identities and inverses exist) for the following operations (no solutions provided):

(i) $a \sim b = ab+a+b$ ($a, b \in \mathcal{R}^*$); (ii) $a \odot b = \frac{1}{a}+\frac{1}{b}$ ($a, b \in \mathcal{R}^*: a \neq 0, b \neq 0$);

(iii) $A \# B = (A \cup B) \cap (\bar{A} \cup \bar{B})$ (A, B sets); (iv) $a \oplus b = \max(a, b)$ ($a, b \in \mathcal{R}^*$).
Think up some other similar operations and discuss their nature.]

A *Boolean ring* R is a ring with unity in which $aa = a$ for all $a \in R$. Prove:

73. $a+a = 0$. **74.** Every Boolean ring is commutative.

75. The bilinear form $cxx'-ax+dx'-b = 0$ (a, b, c, d real; $ad-bc = 1$) may be expressed in the form $x' = \frac{ax+b}{cx+d}$ (a *linear fractional transformation* or *Möbius transformation*, very useful in projective geometry). Prove that Möbius transformations form a group. $\left[\textit{Hint:}\text{ Represent the transformation by the non-singular matrix } \begin{bmatrix} a & b \\ c & d \end{bmatrix}.\right]$

Notice that if $f(x) = \frac{ax+b}{cx-a}$, then $f\{f(x)\} = x$.

76. Wishing to set up a model for a certain theory in human communication, a psychologist used the law of combination $a_p \cdot a_q = a_{n-|p-q|}$ for elements $a_1, a_2, \ldots, a_n$. He wanted to know whether the elements have the group structure. Have they?

77. Roots of the equation $x^4-10x^2+1 = 0$ are permuted amongst themselves. What group leaves the set of roots invariant?

78. Referring to Exercise 10.63, obtain the Galois group of $x^3-3x+1 = 0$.
[The impossibility of the trisection of an angle by Euclidean methods results from the fact that the roots of this equation do not involve square roots or rational quantities.]

Levine [*The American Mathematical Monthly*, **67** (1), 61–63 (1960)] defined the *rim* $R(G)$ of a group G thus:

$$R(G) = \{a \in G : ab = ba \Rightarrow \exists c \in G: a = c^j,\ b = c^k \text{ for some integers } j, k\},$$

and the *anticentre* $AC(G)$ of G thus:

$$AC(G) = \{a_1, a_2, \ldots, a_n : a_i \in R(G)\}.$$

Prove.

79. Identity $I \in G \Rightarrow I \in R(G)$. **80.** $a \in R(G) \Rightarrow a^{-1} \in R(G)$.

81. $a \in R(G),\ b \in G \Rightarrow b^{-1}ab \in R(G)$. **82.** G cyclic $\Rightarrow R(G) = AC(G) = G$.

83. G finite and Abelian $\Rightarrow R(G) = AC(G) = G$ if and only if G is cyclic.

84. G Abelian $\Rightarrow R(G) = AC(G)$. **85.** $G \approx G^* \Rightarrow AC(G) \approx AC(G^*)$.

CHAPTER 15

THE NATURE OF GEOMETRY

> Aristippus, a Socratic philosopher, having been cast by shipwreck on the Rhodian shore, and having noticed the drawing of a geometrical design, is said to have exclaimed to his companions: Be of good hope, for I see the footprints of men.
>
> (Vitruvius)

> A line should be drawn somewhere.
>
> (Subject of a University debate)

Like the counting process, the consciousness of geometrical form is one of the most ancient intellectual activities of mankind. In Neolithic times, this primitive feeling for geometrical pattern was expressed in various symmetric ornamental designs on pottery belonging to the Pre-dynastic Period of Egyptian history and to the Mesopotamian Ur Period (about 4000–3000 B.C.). With the beginnings of settled community life, practical geometry became extremely important and was very effectively employed, as the Pyramids and other archaeological remains bear silent witness. Essentially, geometry was, for the practical-minded Egyptians, the "measurement of the earth" as its name suggests, and it was only under the cultured guidance of the Greeks as exemplified by Euclid that it became the deductive science as we know it. With the adjunction of coordinates and other algebraic apparatus to the purely synthetic theory, geometry took on its modern appearance.

Usages of geometry are many and varied. Cosmology and crystallography, for example, both require geometrical thinking which, indeed, permeates much of scientific and mathematical investigation (algebra, analysis, biology, kinematics). Modern geometry, in theory and in application, offers a vast and exciting field of endeavour.

Objects of this geometrically-oriented part of our course (Chapters 15–19) are:

(i) to attempt to present a clear picture of the nature of geometry, particularly its connection with groups;

(ii) to describe both the general and the special properties of conics; and

(iii) to indicate briefly some of the more interesting applications of conics to the physical world.

Assumptions which are made involve a knowledge of the basic ideas of Euclidean geometry plus a coordinate treatment of the straight line, circle, and parabola (elementary properties only).

Just now, the immediate goal is to extend the normal notions about the Euclidean plane to embrace the concept of geometrical elements at infinity. Such an advance will tidy up the problem of the intersection of parallel lines. Once we have done this, it will then be evident that our Cartesian coordinates are inadequate to describe analytically this new situation. Consequently, the discovery of a more powerful system of coordinates is necessary.

§ 77. THE PROBLEM OF PARALLELISM. ELEMENTS AT INFINITY

Points at infinity

Suppose we are given the two straight lines AB and CD whose equations are, respectively, $l_1x+m_1y+n_1 = 0$ and $l_2x+m_2y+n_2 = 0$. Solving these determinantally, or otherwise, we find that the point of intersection P has coordinates $\left(\dfrac{m_1n_2-m_2n_1}{l_1m_2-l_2m_1}, \dfrac{n_1l_2-n_2l_1}{l_1m_2-l_2m_1}\right)$. If $AB//CD$, the slopes of the lines are the same, i.e. $-\dfrac{l_1}{m_1} = -\dfrac{l_2}{m_2}$,

i.e.
$$l_1m_2-l_2m_1 = 0$$
$$\therefore \underset{\infty}{P} \equiv (\infty, \infty).$$

Since the "coordinates" of $\underset{\infty}{P}$ are infinite we say that $\underset{\infty}{P}$ is the *point at infinity* on both AB and CD, i.e. *parallel lines meet in a point at infinity*. The concept of point at infinity originated with Kepler and Desargues (1593–1662, French).] Consequently, we can make the vital statements:

(i) *any two lines in the plane meet in one point* (no matter whether they are parallel or not);

(ii) *on every line there is just one point at infinity*, namely the point of intersection of this line and all lines parallel to it.

Why just one? Why not two points at infinity on each line, one for each direction on the line? If two different points at infinity were allowed on the same line where, if anywhere, would this lead us logically? To the conclusion that a line parallel to a given line would meet it in two points, contrary to (i) above. It should be clearly understood, however, that this point at infinity is not a physical point having some geographical position, but a mathematical creation, a fictional point physically, which is required to bring completion (and add beauty) to our theory. When we represent it by a physical dot on a piece of paper we must be aware that this is a visual aid to our thinking.

Line at infinity

What is the locus of all the points at infinity in a plane? It must be a line, the *line at infinity* l_∞ in that plane, otherwise it violates property (ii).* Can a line be parallel to l_∞? Can an ordinary line make an angle with l_∞?

Plane at infinity

In three dimensions, the locus of all the lines at infinity, one for each plane of space, is the *plane at infinity*. Expressed otherwise, the plane at infinity is the locus of all the points at infinity, one for each line of space. All planes parallel to a given plane meet in the same l_∞.

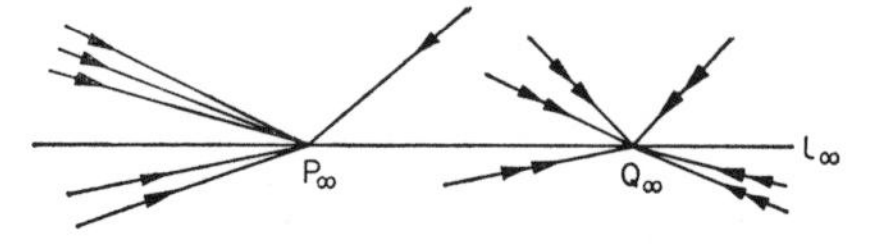

FIG. 51. Parallelism and the line at infinity

By now it has become obvious that we have extended Euclid's notions of line, plane, and space [as Euclid never used the idea of geometrical infinity] though, for convenience, we shall still refer to them as Euclidean. But can you visualise, for instance, the extended Euclidean line and plane?

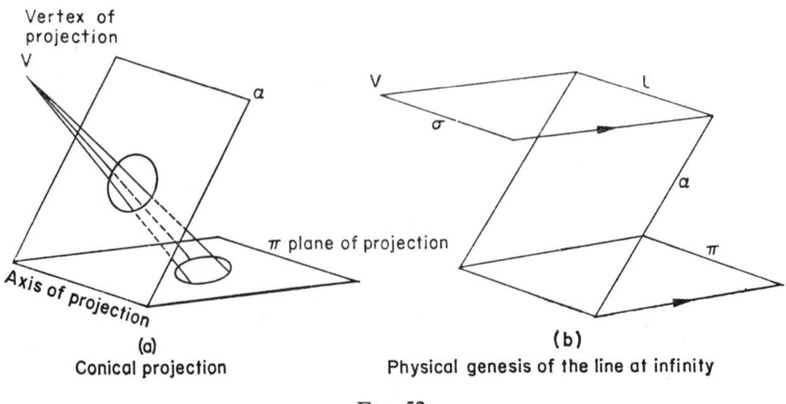

FIG. 52

* If it were curve of order $n > 1$, it would meet every line in the plane in n points (§99).

Projection and infinity

We are all familiar with the ordinary *conical* (or *central*) *projection* of Fig. 52a, which, if V is at infinity, becomes *cylindrical* (or *parallel*) *projection*. If V is such that V and l define a plane $\sigma // \pi$ (Fig. 52b), we call l the *vanishing line* of α; the projection of l from V is the line at infinity in π. Another way of expressing this is to say that l has been *projected to infinity*. Properties of figures which are invariant under conical projection form the basis of projective geometry.

§78. HOMOGENEOUS COORDINATES. CIRCULAR POINTS AT INFINITY

A. The Problem

By writing $P_\infty \equiv (\infty, \infty)$ in § 77 (and remembering that ∞ is not a number) we were merely using a convention to emphasise that the coordinates of P_∞ have increased beyond measure. Such a conventional symbolism does not allow us to distinguish the different points at infinity (one for each direction) on l_∞, for in each case the x- and y-coordinates will be infinite. Furthermore, what is the equation of l_∞?

Now consider the two circles

$$x^2+y^2 = 4, \qquad \text{(i)}$$

$$(x-1)^2+y^2 = 4, \qquad \text{(ii)}$$

which, as we see, intersect at the two points $A = \left(\frac{1}{2}, \frac{\sqrt{15}}{2}\right)$, $B = \left(\frac{1}{2}, -\frac{\sqrt{15}}{2}\right)$. But two quadratic equations (e.g. $ax^2+by^2 = 1$, $x^2+y^2 = 1$) should have four solutions, i.e. there should be four points of intersection. What has happened to the two missing solutions and where are the points that they represent?

These queries serve to underline the fact that the ordinary Cartesian system is inadequate to describe the situation fully. Search for a fresh analytical approach is therefore needed to make our partial solutions complete.

B. The solution

(a) *Homogeneous coordinates*

(i) *Trilinear and areal homogeneous coordinates.* In Fig. 53a, if a, b, c are the lengths of the sides BC, CA, AB respectively, and α, β, γ the perpendicular lengths from P to BC, CA, AB respectively, so that $a\alpha+b\beta+c\gamma = 2k$ ($k \equiv$ area of $\triangle ABC$), then $(\alpha, \beta, \gamma) \equiv$ *trilinear coordinates* of P.

For example, the incentre of ABC has trilinear coordinates (r, r, r), where r (inradius) $= 2k/p$, p being the perimeter of the triangle.

In Fig. 53b, $(p, q, r) = \left(\frac{\triangle PBC}{\triangle ABC}, \frac{\triangle PCA}{\triangle ABC}, \frac{\triangle PAB}{\triangle ABC}\right)$, i.e. $p+q+r = 1$, are the *areal coordinates* of P. For example, the centroid of a triangle has areal coordinates $\left(\frac{1}{3}, \frac{1}{3}, \frac{1}{3}\right)$.

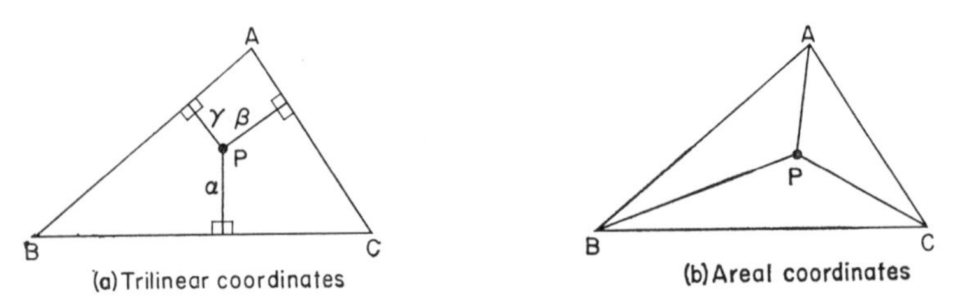

FIG. 53. Homogeneous coordinates

These illustrations reveal that the notion of three coordinates (based on length or area in the above) to represent the position of a point uniquely in a plane is not unfamiliar to us. Observe, though, that in each case a linear condition ($a\alpha+b\beta+c\gamma = 2k$, $p+q+r = 1$) is associated with the three homogeneous coordinates so that, in fact, only two of the three coordinates are independent, e.g. areal coordinates could be written $(p, q, 1-p-q)$. All this means is that, as we have stated in § 43, just two independent numbers uniquely specify a point in a plane. Trilinear and areal coordinates are examples of *homogeneous coordinates* of which the most important for our purposes are *homogeneous Cartesian coordinates.*

(ii) *Homogeneous Cartesian coordinates.* When, in Fig. 9, we specified the position of P by the coordinates (x, y) we really meant $P \equiv (x/1, y/1)$, where 1 is the chosen unit of length. Thus, we could agree to designate P by the three coordinates $(x, y, 1)$. This idea could be generalised to represent any point P by the three (real or complex) homogeneous coordinates (x, y, z) where only the ratios x/z, y/z matter, i.e.

$$(kx, ky, kz) \equiv (x, y, z) \quad (k \neq 0) \because \frac{kx}{ky} = \frac{x}{y}, \frac{ky}{kz} = \frac{y}{z}.$$

Homogeneous Cartesian coordinates (x, y, z) can always be cast in the non-homogeneous form (X, Y), where $X = x/z$, $Y = y/z$ $(z \neq 0)$ so that any equation in homogeneous Cartesian coordinates can always be put in the usual form by setting $z = 1$ and, conversely, any non-homogeneous equation can be readily made homogeneous by appropriate insertion of powers of z. Thus, the homogeneous equations of the line $lx+my+n = 0$

and of the parabola $y^2 = 4ax$ are $lx+my+nz = 0$ and $y^2 = 4azx$ respectively.

[The geometrical meaning of the corollary, § 63, is now apparent: the vanishing of the determinant is the condition for the concurrency of the three lines whose equations are given in homogeneous Cartesian coordinates.]

Clearly, since 0/0 is indeterminate, no meaning can be attached to the coordinates (0, 0, 0) so that there is no point in the plane having these coordinates.

What happens when $z = 0$?

Following Klein, consider the infinite sets of points

$$(x, y, 1),\ (x, y, 0{\cdot}1),\ (x, y, 0{\cdot}01),\ (x, y, 0{\cdot}001),\ \ldots$$

i.e. $$(x, y),\ (10x, 10y),\ (100x,\ 100y),\ (1000x,\ 1000y).\ \ldots$$

All these points lie on a straight line through the origin with slope y/x.

Eventually, when $z = 0$, we have $(x, y, 0) \equiv$ the point at infinity on the lines with slope y/x, i.e. in a certain direction. For instance, (1, 0, 0) is the point common to all lines with slope $0/1 = 0$, i.e. //x-axis, i.e. $(1, 0, 0) \equiv X_\infty$. Similarly, (0, 1, 0) is the point common to all lines with slope $1/0 = \infty$, i.e. //y-axis, i.e. $(0, 1, 0) \equiv Y_\infty$. Thus (Fig. 54),

$$\boxed{z = 0 \text{ is the equation of } l_\infty} \tag{174}$$

i.e. l_∞ is the set of points (at ∞) whose third homogeneous coordinate is zero. It has no particular physical position in the plane; for graphical purposes, it may be drawn quite arbitrarily.

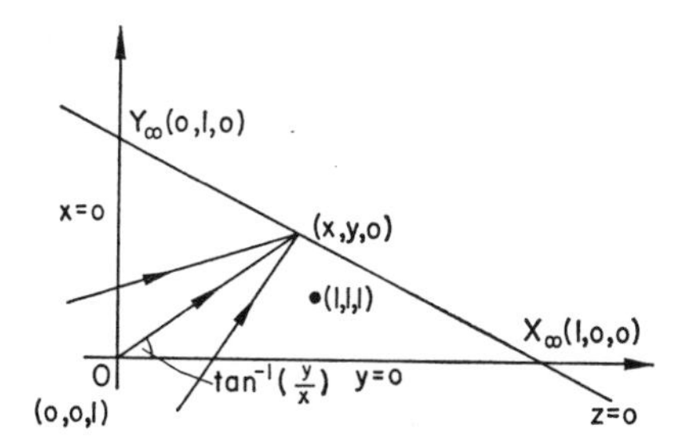

FIG. 54. Homogeneous Cartesian coordinate system

Reverting to § 77, we see that the two lines $l_1x+m_1y+n_1z = 0$, $l_2x+m_2y+n_2z = 0$, if parallel, meet at the point

$$P_\infty \equiv (m_1n_2-m_2n_1,\ n_1l_2-n_2l_1,\ 0)$$

i.e. at a point on $z = 0$.

Homogeneous Cartesian coordinates of the origin (0, 0) are (0, 0, 1).

To complete our homogeneous Cartesian coordinate system, we stress the *unit point* $(1, 1, 1) \equiv (1, 1)$ which gives the scales of measurement (units) along the x-, y-axes. Correspondingly, there exists the *unit line* $x+y+z=0$.

Notes

(i) In trilinear and areal homogeneous coordinates, the equation of l_∞ is *not* given by (174).

(ii) In homogeneous Cartesian coordinates, the equation of the line joining two fixed points (x_1, x_2, x_3). (y_1, y_2, y_3) is given determinantally by

$$\begin{vmatrix} x & y & z \\ x_1 & x_2 & x_3 \\ y_1 & y_2 & y_3 \end{vmatrix} = 0$$

i.e. more generally by $lx+my+nz = 0$, where $l = x_2y_3-x_3y_2$, etc.

(b) *The full solution to the problem of the intersecting circles*

Make (i) and (ii) of § 78(A) homogeneous, i.e. the circles have equations

$$x^2+y^2 = 4z^2 \qquad \text{(i)}'$$

$$(x-z)^2+y^2 = 4z^2 \qquad \text{(ii)}'$$

whence $z = 0, 2x$. In the latter case, $y = \pm\sqrt{15}x$ so the corresponding intersections are $A \equiv (1, \sqrt{15}, 2)$, $B \equiv (1, -\sqrt{15}, 2)$, or $\left(\frac{1}{2}, \pm\frac{\sqrt{15}}{2}\right)$ in non-homogeneous form, as before. However, in the former case the points of intersection are given by $z = 0$, $x^2+y^2 = 0$, i.e. by the points

$$\boxed{\begin{aligned} I &\equiv (1, i, 0) \\ J &\equiv (1, -i, 0) \end{aligned}}\,. \qquad (175)$$

These physically imaginary points are called the *circular points at infinity* and they lie on $z = 0$. Without doubt, they are the two most important points in the plane once the origin is fixed. Their discovery dates to about 1812 and is due to Poncelet (1788–1867, French) who wrote his classic treatise on geometry whilst a prisoner-of-war of the Russians at Saratov, after Napoleon's defeat of Krasnoi on his disastrous march on Moscow.

For obvious reasons, I and J did not appear in the partial solution. By introducing homogeneous coordinates, we have solved the problem completely.

An astounding corollary to all this is that a general circle (centre at the point (α, β) and any radius a) $(x-\alpha)^2+(y-\beta)^2 = a^2$, i.e. $(x-\alpha z)^2+(y-\beta z)^2 = a^2z^2$, cuts l_∞ always where $x^2+y^2 = 0$, i.e. always at I, J (no matter how the circle varies). Therefore, *all circles pass through the same two points I, J at infinity* [hence the name, "circular points"]. It cannot be stressed too strongly that I, J have no physical being but are mathematical creations which increase vastly our techniques and widen our horizons generally. They occupy no special physical position on l_∞, i.e. pictorially, they can be chosen quite arbitrarily on l_∞.

Query: In what four points do the two concentric circles $x^2+y^2 = 1$, $x^2+y^2 = 9$ intersect?

Equations of the tangents at I, J to the circle $x^2+y^2 = a^2z^2$ are

$$y \pm iz = \pm\frac{1}{i}(x-z) \quad \text{since} \quad \frac{dy}{dx} = -\frac{x}{y} = -\frac{1}{\pm i} \quad \text{at } I,\ J,$$

i.e. $y = \pm ix$ on simplifying.

These tangents (imaginary) meet at (0, 0, 1), i.e. at the centre (= the origin in this case). How would you represent this fact diagrammatically?

In our subsequent theory, we will generally use non-homogeneous Cartesian coordinates. However, where it suits our purpose the more sophisticated homogeneous coordinates will be used. Trying to visualise the *extended Euclidean plane*, i.e. the finite Euclidean plane with l_∞ attached, is unrewarding unless it is understood that it is a *one-sided surface* (like the *Möbius band* and some other surfaces studied in topology). Surfaces such as the sphere and the torus are two-sided.

Distinguish carefully between the notation (x, y, z) used to describe the homogeneous coordinates of a point in the plane, and the notation (x, y, z) used to give the position of a point in ordinary Cartesian coordinates in three-dimensional space. Usually, the context makes it clear which is meant.

Revert temporarily to equations (i), (ii), (iii) of § 63 and make them homogeneous.

Lines (ii), (iii) intersect in the point (A_1, B_1, C_1) where A_1, B_1, C_1 are the cofactors of a_1, b_1, c_1 in δ. Suppose $C_1 = 0$, i.e. $a_2b_3-a_3b_2 = 0$, i.e. $\frac{a_2}{b_2} = \frac{a_3}{b_3}$ (α), i.e. (ii) and (iii) are parallel and meet in the point $P_\infty \equiv (A_1, B_1, 0)$.

Next, suppose $C_2 = 0$ also, i.e. $\frac{a_1}{b_1} = \frac{a_3}{b_3}$ (β), whence $\frac{a_1}{b_1} = \frac{a_2}{b_2}$ from (α), (β) i.e. $C_3 = 0$ and so $\delta = c_1C_1+c_2C_2+c_3C_3 = 0$, i.e. the three lines are parallel with a common point at infinity, P_∞. Thus, the parallel lines $x+3y+c_1z = 0$, $2x+6y+c_2z = 0$, $4x+12y+c_3z = 0$ are concurrent at $(-3, 1, 0)$ and $C_1 = C_2 = C_3 = \delta = 0$.

[What happens if all the cofactors $A_1, \ldots, C_3$ of δ are zero? *Answer:* Effectively there is only one line (E. A. Maxwell, *Advanced Algebra*, Part 1, C.U.P., 1960, p. 260).]

Complex coordinates in geometry

With the introduction of complex coordinates our geometry is considerably extended. (Distinguish between the geometry of complex numbers, as in Chapter 10, and the use of complex coordinates in the plane.) Under these extensions, our field of activity is complex geometry, while if we restrict ourselves to real coordinates the resulting facts relate to real geometry, e.g. all the theory linked with I, J disappears. Since in mathematics there is no limit to our intellectual horizons we gladly accept complex numbers as coordinates as a technique giving us greater freedom. Many interesting results concerning complex coordinates are known, e.g. two conjugate complex points lie on every real line. Examples of this are I, J on $z = 0$ and the points $(1, \varepsilon, \varepsilon^2)$, $(1, \varepsilon^2, \varepsilon)$ on the line $x+y+z = 0$, where ε, ε^2 are complex cube roots of unity. Each complex coordinate really requires two dimensions to represent it pictorially (i.e. the Argand diagram). Strictly, then, a point like $(1, \varepsilon, \varepsilon^2)$ exists in a four-dimensional setting.

The infinite in analysis and geometry

The infinite of geometry is an actual infinite, not a limiting infinite as in the case of the symbol ∞ used in analysis (e.g. in calculus). That is to say, l_∞ is a line in exactly the same sense as ordinary lines are lines. Infinite geometrical elements, as Hardy says, are concepts "in no way dependent on the analytical doctrine of limits".

§79. EUCLIDEAN GROUP. PROJECTIVE GEOMETRY

The Euclidean group

A *Euclidean rigid motion* (= combination of a rotation and a translation) is given by the non-singular real linear transformation

$$\begin{cases} x' = x\cos\theta - y\sin\theta + h, \\ y' = x\sin\theta + y\cos\theta + k. \end{cases} \qquad (\alpha)$$

Making it homogeneous, we have

$$\begin{cases} x' = x\cos\theta - y\sin\theta + hz, \\ y' = x\sin\theta + y\cos\theta + kz, \\ z' = \qquad\qquad\qquad\qquad z, \end{cases} \qquad (\alpha')$$

with matrix representation

$$M = \begin{bmatrix} \cos\theta & -\sin\theta & h \\ \sin\theta & \cos\theta & k \\ . & . & 1 \end{bmatrix},$$

$$M^{-1} = \begin{bmatrix} \cos\theta & \sin\theta & -h\cos\theta - k\sin\theta \\ -\sin\theta & \cos\theta & -k\cos\theta + h\sin\theta \\ \cdot & \cdot & 1 \end{bmatrix}, \quad |M| = 1.$$

Matrices M will clearly form a group (non-Abelian because of the presence of a translation), the *Euclidean group* $E(2, \mathcal{R}^*)$ whose identity occurs when $\theta = h = k = 0$. The matrix of the translations occurs when $\theta = 0$. Write it out. An essential feature of $E(2, \mathcal{R}^*)$ is that it contains an orthogonal subgroup, namely, the rotations.

Examine now the behaviour of I, J in relation to the Euclidean group. Represent the homogeneous coordinates of $I(1, i, 0)$ by the column vector $X: X^T = [1, i, 0]$.

$$\begin{aligned} \therefore\quad MX &= \begin{bmatrix} \cos\theta & -\sin\theta & h \\ \sin\theta & \cos\theta & k \\ \cdot & \cdot & 1 \end{bmatrix} \begin{bmatrix} 1 \\ i \\ \cdot \end{bmatrix} \\ &= \begin{bmatrix} \cos\theta - i\sin\theta \\ i\cos\theta + \sin\theta \\ \cdot \end{bmatrix} \\ &= \begin{bmatrix} e^{-i\theta} \\ ie^{-i\theta} \\ \cdot \end{bmatrix} \qquad \text{by (110)} \\ &= e^{-i\theta} \begin{bmatrix} 1 \\ i \\ \cdot \end{bmatrix} \\ &= e^{-i\theta} X. \end{aligned}$$

But $e^{-i\theta} \neq 0$ is merely a factor of proportionality for the homogeneous coordinates, and may therefore be disregarded. That is, M leaves I (and similarly J) invariant. Since the two points I, J uniquely determine l_∞, it follows that M also leaves l_∞ invariant.

Rigid motions, as may be verified, preserve distance and angle in Euclidean geometry, and so they characterise it. Accordingly, we have the fundamental result:

> Euclidean geometry is characterised by the group of rigid motions leaving I, J invariant.

This result must be among the most striking in mathematics. Certainly, it displays a unifying use of complex numbers, matrices, determinants and groups which combine to exhibit the fundamental nature of geometry.

Only the basic theory has been developed here. Other transformations (similarity transformations) exist which account for portions of Euclidean geometry not generated by rigid motions.

Question: Besides angular and linear measure, what are some other metrical Euclidean invariants of $E(2, \mathcal{R}^*)$?

General homogeneous coordinates: the principle of duality

Homogeneous coordinates employed so far are metrical, i.e. based on measurement. Suppose now that they are abstracted from any metrical content. Then we derive the (non-metrical) *general homogeneous coordinates* (x, y, z) [$\equiv (kx, ky, kz), k \neq 0$, as before]. These are the coordinates used in projective geometry. In terms of them, the equation of a given line is $lx+my+nz = 0$, where (x, y, z) are the coordinates of the variable points on the line. Then the constant numbers (l, m, n) may be regarded as *line coordinates* of the fixed line. On the other hand, taking (x, y, z) constant and (l, m, n) variable, we may regard $lx+my+nz = 0$ as expressing the equation of the fixed point (x, y, z) through which the lines with variable line coordinates (l, m, n) pass. We have thus exhibited an instance of the *principle of duality* [see (i), (ii) below] which is fundamental in projective geometry, namely point and line are dual concepts in the plane, i.e. to every result about points and lines there is a corresponding result about lines and points. Collinearity and concurrency are thus dual concepts. (See § 68 for a similar reference to duality.) Considering a conic as a locus of points, how would you describe the dual concept?

Projective geometry

Imagine a plane like the extended Euclidean plane (i.e. containing l_∞) except that:

(a) there is no measurement or parallelism in it whatsoever; and
(b) all points are alike and all lines are alike, i.e. there are no exceptional points like I, J or lines like l_∞.

Two basic properties (foreshadowed in the extended Euclidean plane) will then be:

(i) two points determine a line uniquely; and
(ii) two lines determine a point uniquely, i.e. two lines meet in a point.

This is the starting point of *projective geometry* which may be regarded as the study of properties of figures which remain invariant under *conical projection* (Fig. 52a) from one plane to another. Clearly, conical projection distorts measurement (both angular and linear), destroys parallelism, and transforms the different conics amongst themselves (next chapter), so that projective geometry is not concerned with measurement and parallelism, but it is concerned, *inter alia*, with properties common to all conics. (Cross-ratio, § 80, is an example of a projective invariant. Name some other projective invariants.)

Algebraically, the process of conical projection can be represented by a non-singular linear transformation (= *projective transformation*) in the plane, assumed real,

$$\begin{cases} kx' = a_{11}x+a_{12}y+a_{13}z, \\ ky' = a_{21}x+a_{22}y+a_{23}z, \\ kz' = a_{31}x+a_{32}y+a_{33}z, \end{cases} \qquad (\beta)$$

i. e.

$$kX' = AX, \qquad (\beta)'$$

where $X' = \begin{bmatrix} x' \\ y' \\ z' \end{bmatrix}$, $X = \begin{bmatrix} x \\ y \\ z \end{bmatrix}$, $|A| = \begin{vmatrix} a_{11} & a_{12} & a_{13} \\ a_{21} & a_{22} & a_{23} \\ a_{31} & a_{32} & a_{33} \end{vmatrix} \neq 0$ and k is a factor of proportionality. Such transformations produce the *projective group* $P(2, \mathcal{R}^*)$. It is a subgroup of $L(3, \mathcal{R}^*)$ since matrices $\frac{1}{k}A$ $(k \neq 0)$ of the full linear group $L(3, \mathcal{R}^*)$ all yield the same projective transformation.

Problem. Construct a diagram to illustrate the interrelationships among

$$O(2, \mathcal{R}^*),\ E(2, \mathcal{R}^*),\ A(2, \mathcal{R}^*),\ P(2, \mathcal{R}^*),\ L(2, \mathcal{R}^*),\ L(3, \mathcal{R}^*).$$

Hierarchy of geometry systems

Allow the centre of projection now to be at infinity, thus producing parallel (= cylindrical) projection (§ 79). Invariants under this type of projection give rise to *affine geometry* (Latin *affinis* ≡ "related") which must accordingly be a subgeometry of projective geometry. Its associated group, the affine group $A(2, \mathcal{R}^*)$ is represented by matrices B which are particular cases of A in $(\beta)'$.

Specialising still further by placing additional restrictions on B as in $(\alpha)'$, we arrive at Euclidean geometry and its associated group, the Euclidean group. Hence Euclidean geometry is a subgeometry of affine geometry, i.e. affine geometry is an intermediate stage in the generalisation of Euclidean geometry to projective geometry.

Topology is a yet further generalisation of projective geometry. As projective geometry is known to abstract and generalise both the non-Euclidean geometries (as wall as many others), we may summarise the situation schematically thus:

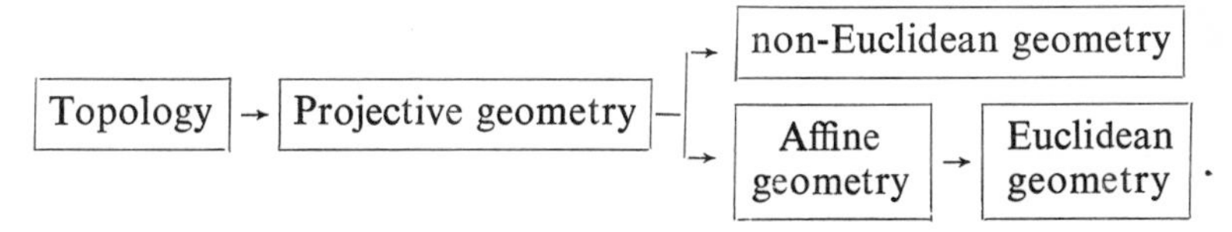

Remember that by Klein's *Erlanger Programm*, group-theoretic relationships (subgroups) correspond to this chain of geometrical relationships (subgeometries).

Unorthodox geometries

Radical developments in modern abstract algebra (e.g. non-associative and non-commutative algebras) have had a similar impact to the discovery of some unconventional geometrical systems. Besides the non-Euclidean geometries (Chapter 5) there exists, say, *non-Desarguesian geometry* (Desargues, 1593–1662, French; Moulton, 1872–1952, American), while certain special planes called *Moufang planes* (Ruth Moufang, 1905– , German) are objects of current geometrical research.

§ 80. CROSS-RATIO

In Example 61, Corollary, the idea of the cross-ratio associated with four concyclic points was introduced. This concept, but relating here to four collinear points, is now investigated in more detail. Known to Pappus (3rd cent., Greek), cross-ratio is one of the oldest geometrical invariants.

Definition. The *cross-ratio* of four collinear points A, B, C, D is written (AB, CD) and is defined thus (using directed segments, e.g. $BC = -CB$):

$$\boxed{(AB,\ CD) = \frac{AC \cdot BD}{AD \cdot BC} = \frac{AC/CB}{AD/DB} = \frac{\text{ratio in which } C \text{ divides } AB}{\text{ratio in which } D \text{ divides } AB}} \tag{176}$$

i.e. the cross-ratio of four collinear points is a number associated in a special way with those four points. [The line of collinearity is called the *base* and the set of four points is called the *range*.] From (176), e.g.,
$(1,\ 2;\ 3,\ 4) = \dfrac{(3-1)(4-2)}{(4-1)(3-2)} = \dfrac{4}{3}$
if $OA = 1$, $OB = 2$, $OC = 3$, $OD = 4$ (units) w.r.t. some origin O.

Generally, if a, b, c, d are parameters of A, B, C, D respectively, define

$$\boxed{(AB,\ CD) = (a,\ b;\ c,\ d) = (a-c)(b-d)/(a-d)(b-c)}\,. \tag{176$'$}$$

If D is at infinity, it may be proved that

$$\boxed{(AB,\ CD_\infty) = \frac{AC}{BC}}\,. \tag{177}$$

Example 98 (Interchange of points).

> There are six different cross-ratios associated with four points.

Proof. $(AB,\ CD) = \dfrac{AC \cdot BD}{AD \cdot BC}$,

$$(BA,\ DC) = \frac{BD \cdot AC}{AD \cdot BC} = (AB,\ CD),$$

$$(CD,\ AB) = \frac{CA \cdot DB}{DA \cdot CB} = \frac{-AC \cdot -BD}{-AD \cdot -BC} = \frac{AC \cdot BD}{AD \cdot BC} = (AB,\ CD),$$

$$(DC,\ BA) = \frac{DB \cdot CA}{CB \cdot DA} = (AB,\ CD).$$

$\therefore\ (AB,\ CD) = (BA,\ DC) = (CD,\ AB) = (DC,\ BA)$,

i.e. $(AB,\ CD)$ *is unaltered in value if, whenever two letters (points) of a pair are interchanged, the remaining two letters (points) are also interchanged.*

Now $\exists\ 4! = 24$ ways of arranging the four letters $A,\ B,\ C,\ D$.

$\therefore\ \exists$ 24 cross-ratios associated with $A,\ B,\ C,\ D$.

But each occurs four times.

$\therefore$ really, $\exists$ only six different cross-ratios associated with the four points.

EXAMPLE 99 (theorem of Möbius).

> If $(AB,\ CD) = \lambda$ then the other five cross-ratios derived from $A,\ B,\ C,\ D$ are $\dfrac{1}{\lambda},\ 1-\lambda,\ \dfrac{1}{1-\lambda},\ \dfrac{\lambda-1}{\lambda},\ \dfrac{\lambda}{\lambda-1}$. (178)

A B C D

(a) Range of points

A C B D

(b) Harmonic range

FIG. 55

Proof. Using Fig. 55a, we have

$$(AC,\ BD) = \frac{AB \cdot CD}{AD \cdot CB} = \frac{(AC-BC)(BD-BC)}{AD \cdot CB},$$

$$= \frac{AC \cdot BD - BC(BD - BC + AC)}{AD \cdot CB},$$

$$= \frac{BC \cdot AD - AC \cdot BD}{AD \cdot BC} \quad \text{writing } BC = -CB,$$

$$= 1 - \frac{AC \cdot BD}{AD \cdot BC},$$

$$= 1 - \lambda.$$

$\therefore (AC,\ BD) = (CA,\ DB) = (BD,\ AC) = (DB,\ CA) = 1-\lambda$

by Example (98).

Similarly for the other four cross-ratio functions.

Note. $\lambda \neq 0, 1, \infty$ for then some of the points coincide,

e.g. $$\lambda = 0 \rightarrow \frac{AC \cdot BD}{AD \cdot BC} = 0 \Rightarrow A \equiv C \text{ or } B \equiv D,$$

$$\lambda = \infty \rightarrow \ldots = \infty \Rightarrow A \equiv D \text{ or } B \equiv C,$$

$$\lambda = 1 \rightarrow AC \cdot BD = AD \cdot BC \Rightarrow A \equiv B \text{ or } C \equiv D.$$

EXAMPLE 100. Cross-ratio is invariant under projection.

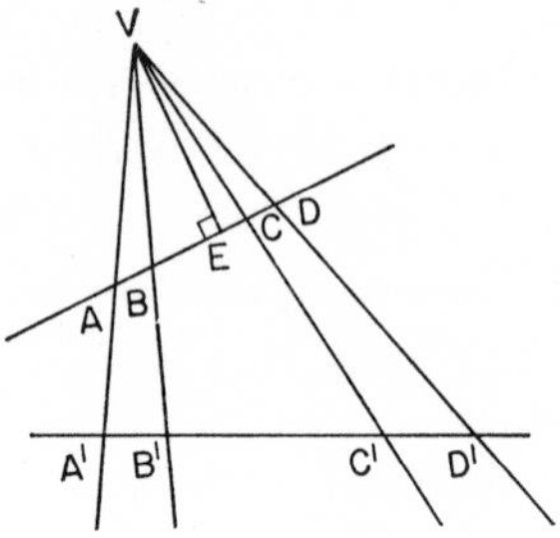

FIG. 56. Invariance of cross-ratio

Proof. $$\frac{AC}{BC} = \frac{\frac{1}{2} AC \cdot VE}{\frac{1}{2} BC \cdot VE} \quad \text{(Fig. 56)},$$

$$= \frac{\triangle VAC}{\triangle VBC},$$

$$= \frac{\frac{1}{2} VA \cdot VC \sin AVC}{\frac{1}{2} VB \cdot VC \sin BVC},$$

$$= \frac{VA \sin AVC}{VB \sin BVC}.$$

Similarly, $$\frac{AD}{BD} = \frac{VA \sin AVD}{VB \sin BVD}.$$

$$\therefore AC/BC \big/ AD/BD = \frac{VA \sin AVC}{VB \sin BVC} \cdot \frac{VB \sin BVD}{VA \sin AVD}.$$

$$= \frac{\sin AVC}{\sin BVC} \cdot \frac{\sin BVD}{\sin AVD},$$

$$= A'C'/B'C' \big/ A'D'/B'D'$$

i.e. $$(AB, CD) = (A'B', C'D').$$

A set of four concurrent lines such as VA, VB, VC, VD is called a *pencil* and there is a cross-ratio theory of pencils corresponding to that for ranges.

[How would you define the cross-ratio of a pencil?]

Harmonic cross-ratio ($\lambda = -1$)

If $(AB, CD) < 0$, then $\dfrac{AC\cdot BD}{AD\cdot BC} < 0$, i.e. $\dfrac{AC\cdot BD}{AD\cdot CB} > 0$ on writing $BC = -CB$.

$\therefore$ the range is A, C, B, D. (Note the order particularly.) See Fig. 55b.

Let $(AB, CD) = -1$. We say $\begin{cases} A, B \\ C, D \end{cases}$ are *harmonic conjugates* w.r.t. $\begin{cases} C, D \\ A, B \end{cases}$ and we call the range *harmonic*. It is fairly simple to deduce that:

(a) $\dfrac{1}{AC}+\dfrac{1}{AD} = \dfrac{2}{AB}$ ($AB \equiv$ the *harmonic mean* of AC, AD), a result known to Archytas (428–347 B. C., Greek) from his study of music;

(b) if O is the mid-point of AB, then $OA^2 = OB^2 = OC\cdot OD$ and we say that O is the *centre* of an *involution* of which A, B are *double points* and C, D a pair of *corresponding points.*

Notes

(i) $(AB, CD) = -1 = (BA, CD) = (AB, DC)$,
i.e. *the interchange of the letters of only one pair is required in the case of a harmonic range.*

(ii) When $\lambda = -1$, the six cross-ratios of Example 99 reduce to just three, viz. $-1, \frac{1}{2}, 2$.

(iii) Let D be at infinity and use (177).

$$\therefore\ (AB, CD_\infty) = -1 \Rightarrow AC = -BC, \quad \text{i.e.} \quad AC = CB.$$

$$\therefore\ C \text{ is the mid-point of } AB,$$

i.e.
$$\boxed{(AB, CD_\infty) = -1 \Leftrightarrow C \text{ is the mid-point of } AB} \tag{179}$$

i.e. if A, B are double points of an involution of which C is the centre, then the point corresponding to C in the involution is D_∞ ($= l_\infty \cap$ line ABC).

The theory of cross-ratio and involution may be extended to sets of points on a conic (and higher curves), a fact which is of great importance in projective geometry.

EXAMPLE 101. If $x_1x_2 = a^2 \neq 0$, prove that the cross-ratio $(-a, a; x_1, x_2) = -1$. If $S \equiv (x-a)^2+(y-b)^2-b^2$, $S' \equiv (x+a)^2+(y-c)^2-c^2$, where a, b, c are non-zero constants, sketch the circles $S = 0$, $S' = 0$ and one other circle of the pencil $S+kS' = 0$. Write down the quadratic equation in x whose roots determine the points of intersection of the third circle and the line $y = 0$. Hence (or otherwise) prove that a common tangent of the two circles is cut harmonically by any other circle of the pencil. [U.N.E.]

Solution. $$(-a, a; x_1, x_2) = \frac{(x_1+a)(x_2-a)}{(x_2+a)(x_1-a)}$$
$$= \frac{x_1x_2+a(x_2-x_1)-a^2}{x_1x_2+a(x_1-x_2)-a^2}$$
$$= \frac{a(x_2-x_1)}{a(x_1-x_2)} = -1. \qquad (\alpha)$$

since $x_1x_2 = a^2$ (given).

Now $S+kS' \equiv (x-a)^2+(y-b)^2-b^2+k\{(x+a)^2+(y-c)^2+c^2\} = 0$. This is cut by $y=0$ at points given by $(1+k)x^2-2a(1-k)x+(1+k)a^2=0$. If the roots of this quadratic are x_1, x_2, then by the elementary theory of equations (§ 50) we have $x_1x_2 = a^2$.

$$\therefore (-a, a; x_1, x_2) = -1 \qquad \text{by } (\alpha).$$

$\therefore$ (on $y = 0$), the points with co-ordinates x_1, x_2 harmonically separate the points with co-ordinates $-a$, a (Fig. 57).

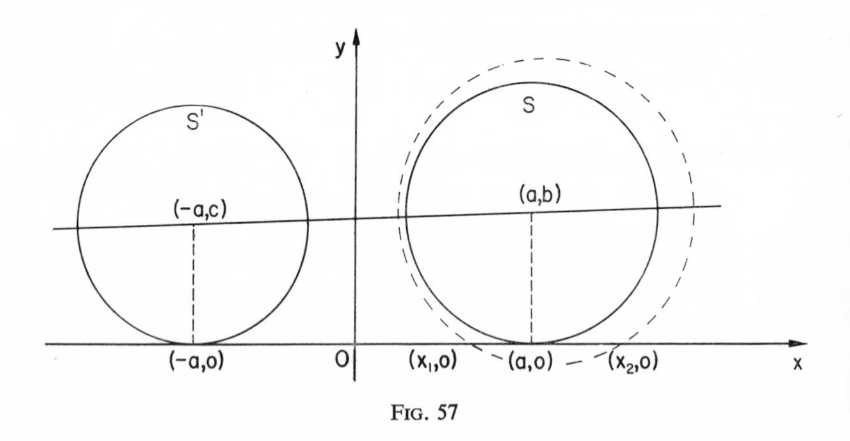

FIG. 57

Definition. A *pencil* (or system) of curves $f+kf' = 0$ is an infinite set of curves (as k varies) passing through the intersection of the curves $f = 0$, $f' = 0$, where f, f' are polynomials of the same degree. Thus, the pencil of circles $S+kS' = 0$ is the infinite set of circles passing through the four points of intersection of $S = 0$, $S' = 0$, i.e. through I, J and two other points (real, coincident, or imaginary), shown as imaginary in Fig. 57. For what values of k do we get $S = 0$, $S' = 0$?

We say that a pencil of curves (which may be lines) is a *one-parameter system* of curves (i.e. it depends on just one parameter k) or has *one degree of freedom*. A two-parameter system of curves is called a *net* (Exercise 15.25). Note the special use of the word "pencil" in Example 100.

EXAMPLE 102. The cross-ratio functions form a group.

Solution. Abbreviate the cross-ratio functions $f_i(\lambda)$ $(i = 1, \ldots, 6)$ as f_i: $f_1 = \lambda$, $f_2 = \frac{1}{1-\lambda}$, $f_3 = \frac{\lambda-1}{\lambda}$, $f_4 = \frac{1}{\lambda}$, $f_5 = 1-\lambda$, $f_6 = \frac{\lambda}{\lambda-1}$. The law of composition is the substitution of one function in another.

Then, for example,

$$f_5 f_3 = f_5\{f_3\} = 1-f_3 = 1-\frac{\lambda-1}{\lambda} = \frac{1}{\lambda} = f_4$$

and

$$f_3 f_5 = f_3\{f_5\} = \frac{f_5-1}{f_5} = \frac{1-\lambda-1}{1-\lambda} = \frac{\lambda}{\lambda-1} = f_6.$$

Therefore closure exists in this instance (and likewise in all other instances).

Also,

$$(f_5 f_3) f_4 = f_4 f_4 = f_4\left(\frac{1}{\lambda}\right) = \lambda = f_1$$

and

$$f_5(f_3 f_4) = f_5\left(\frac{f_4-1}{f_4}\right) = f_5\left(\frac{1/\lambda-1}{1/\lambda}\right) = f_5(1-\lambda) = 1-(1-\lambda) = \lambda = f_1.$$

Therefore association exists in this instance (and likewise in all other instances).

Furthermore,

$$f_2 f_3 = f_2\left(\frac{\lambda-1}{\lambda}\right) = \frac{1}{1-(\lambda-1)/\lambda} = \lambda = f_1 \quad \text{and} \quad f_1 = I \quad \text{(identity).}$$

$\therefore f_2^{-1} = f_3$ and $f_3^{-1} = f_2$ (and likewise for the other inverses).

$\therefore$ the cross-ratio functions form a non-Abelian group S of order 6.

Relabelling $f_1, f_2, f_3, f_4, f_5, f_6$ as I, A, A^2, C, D, E respectively we obtain the multiplication table for S (Example 93), i.e. the group of cross-ratio functions $\approx$ the group of rotational symmetries of the equilateral triangle.

Suggested topics for further study

(1) Pre-Greek and Greek geometry.
(2) Inversion theory (circle of inversion).
(3) Nine-point circle.
(4) One-sided surfaces, e.g. Möbius band and *Klein bottle.*
(5) Finite geometry of *GF*(2) in three dimensions (35 lines, 15 points, 15 planes).
(6) Axiomatic treatment of Euclidean geometry. [See *The Foundations of Geometry*, D. Hilbert (Open Court, 1938).]
(7) Projective geometry and the group aspect of geometry.

References

Geometry texts listed in the bibliography. The following original works should also be consulted:

(a) *Elements*, Euclid (ed. T. Heath) (Dover, 1956).
(b) *The Geometry of René Descartes*, translated from the French and Latin by D. E. Smith and Marcia Latham (Dover, 1954).
(c) *Elementary Geometry from an Advanced Standpoint*, F. Klein (Macmillan, 1932).

Additionally, look at:

(d) *A Survey of Geometry*, Vols. 1, 2, H. Eves (Allyn & Bacon, 1965).
(e) *Topics in Geometry*, Hazel Perfect (Pergamon, 1963).

EXERCISES 15

1. Solve the cross-ratio equation $(x, 4; 2, 3) = (3, 2x; 1, 4)$. ($x \neq 2$.)

2. Given $\{1, 2; 3, 4\} = \frac{4}{3}(= \lambda)$, verify Example 99 using definition (176), i.e. show, for instance, that $(1, 3; 2, 4) = 1-\lambda$.

3. Assuming $\{-2, 2; 1, x\}$ is harmonic, find x.

What happens in 4–8 if λ equals:

4. $\dfrac{1}{1-\lambda}$? **5.** $\dfrac{1}{\lambda}$? **6.** $1-\lambda$? **7.** $\dfrac{\lambda-1}{\lambda}$? **8.** $\dfrac{\lambda}{\lambda-1}$?

9. Evaluate $(0, \infty; 1, -1)$.

10. If $(AB, CD) = \sec^2\theta$, express the remaining five cross-ratios derived from A, B, C, D in terms of θ (Casey, 1820–91, Irish). By virtue of § 18 (viii) these cross-ratios are also expressible in terms of hyperbolic functions.

11. Write down the homogeneous coordinates of the point in which the line $2x+3y+1 = 0$ cuts 1_∞.

12. What is the equation of the pencil of lines through $(7, 4, 0)$?

13. If x, y are the coordinates of a pair of variable corresponding points of an involution whose double points are distant k from the origin, write down the algebraic expression for the involution in terms of x, y, k.

14. Where is the point corresponding to the centre of the involution of Exercise 15.13?

15. *Menelaus' theorem* (Menelaus, 1st cent., Greek) states that if an arbitrary line cuts the sides BC, CA, AB of a triangle in D, E, F respectively, then $\frac{BD}{DC}\cdot\frac{CE}{EA}\cdot\frac{AF}{FB} = -1.$

Which simple theorem does this become if E, F are the midpoints of CA, AB?

16. In the hyperbolic (non-Euclidean) plane, if a transversal cuts the sides of a triangle ABC so as to divide BC into segments a_1, a_2; CA into segments b_1, b_2; and AB i nto segments c_1, c_2, then it is known that $\sinh\left(\frac{a_1}{k}\right)\sinh\left(\frac{b_1}{k}\right)\sinh\left(\frac{c_1}{k}\right) = \sinh\left(\frac{a_2}{k}\right)\sinh\left(\frac{b_2}{k}\right)\sinh\left(\frac{c_2}{k}\right)$.

Demonstrate that, for small regions of the plane, this is equivalent to Menelaus' theorem (see Exercises 5.48–5.50).

17. Do the linear transformations defined by $x' = x\cos\theta + y\sin\theta$, $y' = x\sin\theta - y\cos\theta$ form a group?

18. Explain what the transformations of Exercise 15.17 mean in terms of rotations and reflections.

Lines $y = x\tan\theta$, $y = 0$ (both through the origin) cut l_∞ in points P, X. Assuming that the cross-ratio of four collinear points is the same as the cross-ratio of the parameters of these four points, and taking the parameter to be the ratio x/y of their coordinates, prove:

19. $\theta = \frac{1}{2i}\log(PX, IJ)$ (Laguerre, 1834–66, French).

20. If (PX, IJ) is harmonic, what can you say about (i) θ, (ii) OP, OX?

Project centrally to demonstrate that the points on the circumference of a semicircle are in 1–1 correspondence with:

21. Points of a straight line. **22.** Points of a line segment.

23. Homogeneous equation of a plane cubic curve is $x^3+y^3+z^3+6mxyz = 0$. Inflexions (defined in Chapter 20) of this cubic are known to be the nine points $(1, -\varepsilon^t, 0)$, $(0, 1, -\varepsilon^t)$ $(1, 0, -\varepsilon^t)$ $(t = 0, 1, 2)$ where ε is a complex cube root of unity. Verify that the Clifford matrix $U = \begin{bmatrix} \cdot & 1 & \cdot \\ \cdot & \cdot & \varepsilon^2 \\ \varepsilon & \cdot & \cdot \end{bmatrix}$ permutes these inflexions amongst themselves. [In fact it is an element of a group of order 216, the *Hessian group* (Hesse, 1811–74, German) leaving invariant the (Jacobian) configuration formed from the inflexions.]

24. The *Hessian* of a curve $f(x, y, z) = 0$ is defined to be

$H \equiv \begin{vmatrix} f_{xx} & f_{xy} & f_{xz} \\ f_{yx} & f_{yy} & f_{yz} \\ f_{zx} & f_{zy} & f_{zz} \end{vmatrix} = 0.$ Determine the Hessian of the cubic curve of Exercise 15.23.

25. The *Jacobian* of a net $\lambda f + \mu g + \nu h = 0$ of three conics $f(x, y, z) = 0$, $g(x, y, z) = 0$, $h(x, y, z) = 0$ (Chapter 16) is defined to be

$$J \equiv \begin{vmatrix} f_x & f_y & f_z \\ g_x & g_y & g_z \\ h_x & h_y & h_z \end{vmatrix} = 0.$$

Obtain the Jacobian of the net for which

$$f \equiv x^2+2nyz = 0, \quad g \equiv y^2+2nzx = 0, \quad h \equiv z^2+2nxy = 0.$$

A certain type of plane projective geometry, called *finite geometry* (Fano, 1892, Italian), has its homogeneous coordinates restricted to $GF(2)$, the Galois field of integers mod 2.

26. How many points are there in this finite geometry? List them.

27. Show that the equation of the line joining the points (1, 1, 0) and (0, 1, 1) is $x+y+z = 0$. Find another point on this line.

28. Convince yourself that there are just three points on each line and three lines through each point in this finite geometry. Draw a complete diagram showing all the points and lines of the plane.

29. A university student committee of 7 members requires 7 sub-committees with 3 committee members on each sub-committee. Analyse the arrangement of these sub-committees so that each member serves on exactly 3 sub-committees.

30. Extend Exercise 15.26 to the finite geometry whose homogeneous coordinates are restricted to $GF(3)$.

[Finite geometries are often helpful in designing statistical experiments.]

CHAPTER 16

CONICS

No one, in Greek times, supposed that conic sections had any utility: at last, in the seventeenth century, Galileo discovered that projectiles move in parabolas, and Kepler discovered that planets move in ellipses. Suddenly the work that the Greeks had done from pure love of theory became the key to warfare and astronomy.

(BERTRAND RUSSELL)

§81. CONICS AS PLANE LOCI AND AS CONIC SECTIONS

Historical

So far as we know, Hippocrates of Chios (5th cent. B.C., Greek) and Menaechmus (4th cent. B.C., Greek) first studied conics in connection with the problem of duplicating the cube. Without benefit of algebra, Hippocrates reduced the problem to that of constructing two mean proportionals between 1 and 2, i.e. of finding $x, y : \frac{1}{x} = \frac{x}{y} = \frac{y}{2}$, leading to the conics $x^2 = y$, $y^2 = 2x$ (parabola) and $xy = 2$ (rectangular hyperbola).

As sections of a cone, conics were first discussed by Apollonius of Perga (*ca.* 250 B.C., Greek) whose researches mark the most profound achievement of classical geometry.

The Greeks found that the three main conic sections could be expressed as $y^2 = px + k\frac{p}{d}x^2$, where the parabola, the ellipse, the hyperbola are distinguished by $k = 0, -1, 1$ respectively (though the Greeks expressed this equation in geometrical terms), and their names, due to Apollonius, are derived from Greek words expressing whether $y^2 >, =, < p^2$. Geometrically, p represented a side (segment) erected in a certain way, hence its Latin name, *latus rectum* (plural: *latera recta*).

Discovery of the focus-directrix property is attributed to Pappus though Archimedes reputedly used the idea of the focus in partially destroying the Roman fleet at Syracuse, Sicily. Kepler used the term "focus" to describe the optical effect whereby rays emanating from one focus of an ellipse are reflected at the curve to the other focus, a reflecting property which, in acoustics, gives rise to the phenomenon of "whispering galleries".

Conics occur naturally in a wide range of scientific and technological ways ranging from the motions of astronomical bodies to electronic orbits in the sub-atomic world. Instances will be given later in the appropriate places.

Inquiries made concerning the Sydney Opera House reveal that no simple properties of conics are used in the design of that spectacular structure.

Conics as plane loci

Definition. A *conic* is the locus of a point which moves so that its distance from a fixed point *(focus)* is in a constant ratio *(eccentricity e)* to its distance from a fixed straight line *(directrix)*, i.e. $\dfrac{SP}{PM} = e$ (Fig. 58).

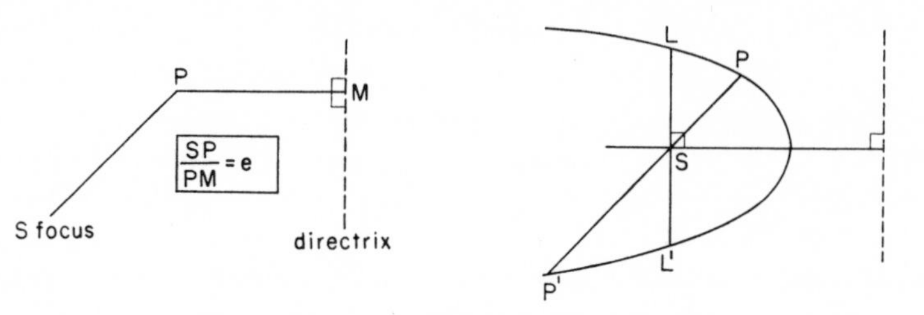

FIG. 58. Fundamental ideas about conics

Note. $e \geqslant 0$.

In Fig. 58, *PSP'*: *focal chord; SP, SP'*: *focal radii; LL'*: *latus rectum; SL = SL'*: *semi-latus rectum.*

$e > 1$ hyperbola	$e = 1$ parabola	$e < 1$ ellipse	$e = 0$ circle

. (180)

Note that the circle is a special case of the ellipse.

EXAMPLE 103 (an important result for the general conic).

> Tangents at the ends of a focal chord of a conic intersect on the corresponding directrix.

Lemma (i.e. preliminary result): The portion of the tangent intercepted between the point of contact and the directrix subtends a right angle at the corresponding focus.

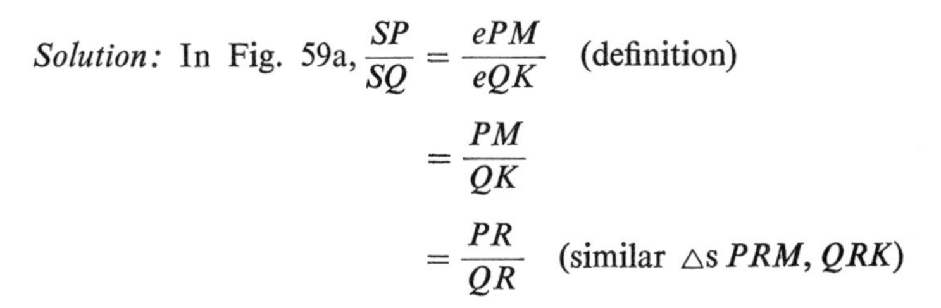

Solution: In Fig. 59a, $\dfrac{SP}{SQ} = \dfrac{ePM}{eQK}$ (definition)

$$= \frac{PM}{QK}$$

$$= \frac{PR}{QR} \quad \text{(similar } \triangle\text{s } PRM, QRK)$$

$\therefore$ SR bisects $Q\hat{S}P'$.

FIG. 59

Let $Q \to P$ (Fig. 59b) $\therefore$ $P\hat{S}R = P'\hat{S}R$

$$= \frac{\pi}{2}.$$

$\therefore$ PR subtends a right angle at the focus.

The required result follows immediately (Fig. 59c) from the Lemma.

[This proof is done by geometry only. Usually, algebraic methods are more compact. However, the special virtue of this proof is that it is valid for the general conic, i.e. for all the conics.]

Conics as conic sections

Definition. A conic (section) is the section of a cone by a plane.

In Fig. 60 the plane of section is parallel to a tangent plane of the double right circular cone.

In Fig. 61 the plane of section cuts only one sheet of the cone but is not parallel to a tangent plane.

In Fig. 62 the plane of section cuts both sheets of the cone.

From Figs. 60–62 we see how any conic may be projected into another conic from the vertex of a cone. What happens when the centre of projection is at infinity, i.e. the cone becomes a cylinder?

[A question which naturally arises now is: What surfaces (other than the cone) have interesting plane sections? One such type of surface is the *spire* (σπειρα) whose plane sections *(spiric sections)* were investigated by Perseus (2nd cent. B.C., Greek) (not the mythological slayer of the Medusa!), i.e. after Apollonius explored conic sections. The original works of Perseus are lost to us, but we know (though obscurely) of his researches through commentators. It is thought that the *torus* (Fig. 45) is a special case of the spire. A suitable plane section of the torus yields the *lemniscate of Bernoulli* (see Chapter 22), so this famous curve could be an instance of a spiric section.]

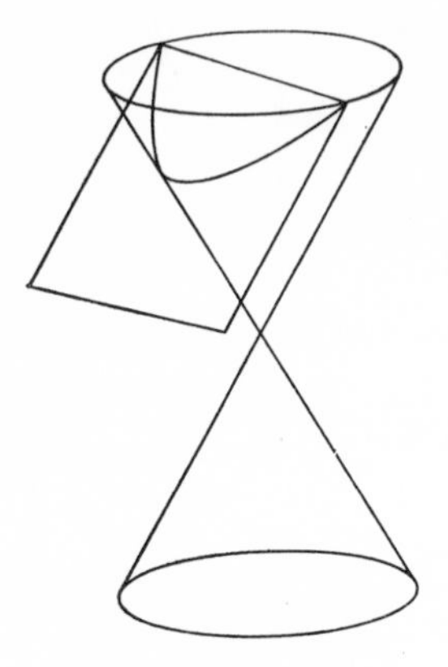

FIG. 60. Parabola as a conic section

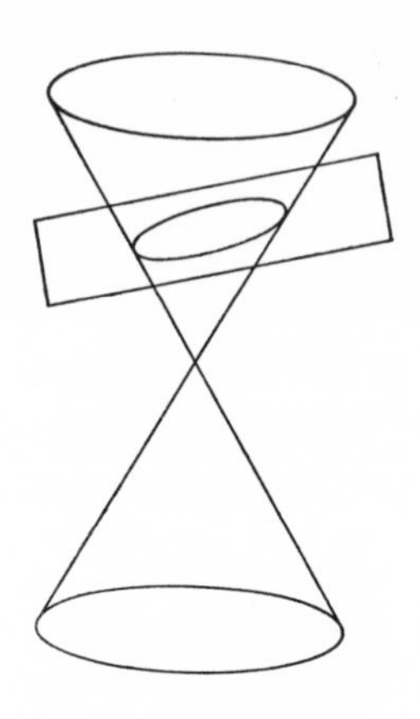

FIG. 61. Ellipse as a conic section

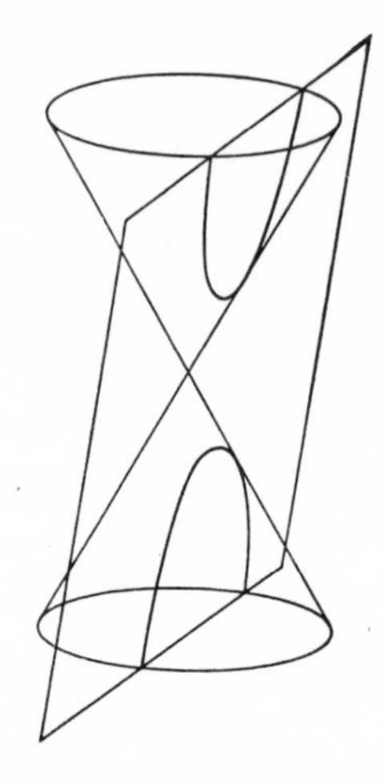

FIG. 62. Hyperbola as a conic section

It is not at all obvious that the two definitions of a conic as (i) a plane locus, and (ii) a conic section, are equivalent, so we really need to prove that this is the case. However, the proof depends on a complicated construction due 1822 to Dandelin (1794–1847, Belgian) and the reader is referred to, say, Walker [43], for the full details. Assume therefore that a conic section has the focus-directrix property. Dandelin's construction requires in the cases of the ellipse and hyperbola (Figs. 61, 62) the existence of two spheres inscribed in the cone and touching the plane of section [*Dandelin spheres*—just one in the case of the parabola (Fig. 60)]. These spheres may be shown to touch the plane of section at the foci of the conics. Attractive plastic models of Dandelin's inscribed spheres for, say, the ellipse are available on the market and add sparkle to any mathematical display.

Below is a summary of the essential features of the main conics, where α is the semi-vertical angle of the cone and β is the acute angle between the plane of section and the axis of the cone:

	Nature of plane β	Value of e	Section of cone by π
$\beta = \alpha$	Parallel to a tangent plane of the cone	1	Parabola
$\beta > \alpha$	Cuts one sheet of the cone	<1	Ellipse
$\beta < \alpha$	Cuts two sheets of the cone	>1	Hyperbola
$\beta = \frac{\pi}{2}$	Perpendicular to axis of the cone	0	Circle

It is instructive to catch something of the Greek spirit here. Apollonius' diagram for a parabola (Fig. 60a) is self-explanatory; perhaps we may add that MN is the diameter of a variable circular section of the cone.

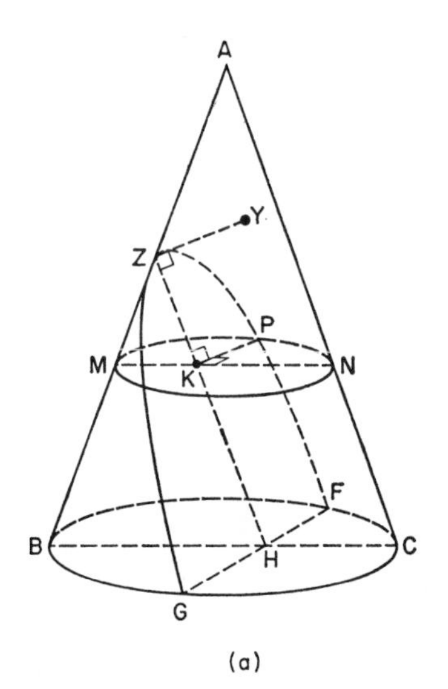

FIG. 60a. Apollonius' method of describing a parabola

Then $KP^2 = MK \cdot KN$ (basic theorem on segment of a circle)

$= \left(\frac{BH}{ZH} \cdot ZK\right) \cdot KN$ (similar triangles ZMK, ZBH)

$= \left(\frac{BH \cdot HC}{ZH}\right) \cdot ZK$ ($\because KN = HC$)

$=$ (constant)$\cdot ZK$ ($\because BH$, HC, ZH are fixed lengths determined by the given plane section).

Apollonius chose $ZY = \dfrac{BH \cdot HC}{ZH}$, and called ZY the *latus rectum* (= "side erected"); $\therefore$ he described a point P on the parabola by

$$KP^2 = ZY \cdot ZK.$$

How nearly Apollonius came to discovering (Cartesian) coordinates! His equation is exactly the standard one referred to perpendicular axes ZH, ZY as x-, y-axes with origin Z. If we recall that Archimedes had the germ of the idea of integration, it is a sobering thought to ponder on the course mathematics might have taken had Apollonius and Archimedes made the breakthroughs which eventually came nearly 2000 years later.

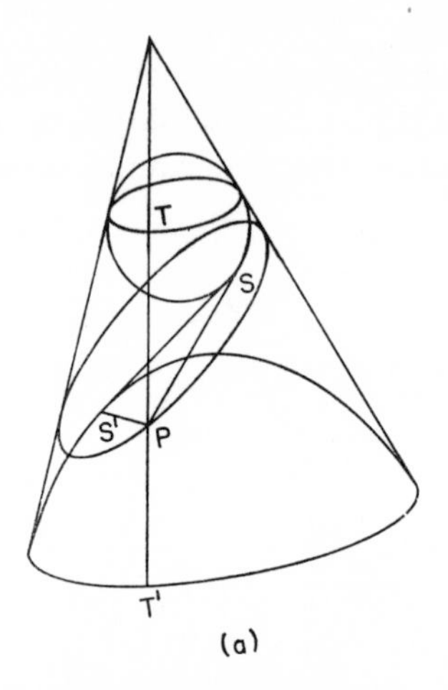

FIG. 61a. Dandelin's spheres for the ellipse

Figure 61(a) (Dandelin spheres) shows immediately that

$SP + S'P = TP + PT'$ ($\because$ PS, PT and PS', PT' are tangents from P to the two spheres),

$= \text{constant}$ ($\because$ the spheres are fixed once the plane of section is given).

This is a characteristic feature [bifocal property (220)] of the ellipse.

§ 82. GENERAL EQUATION OF A CONIC

Now $SP = ePM$ by the definition of a conic (Fig. 63).

$$\therefore \ \{(x-\alpha)^2 + (y-\beta)^2\}^{1/2} = e \cdot \pm \frac{lx + my + n}{\sqrt{l^2 + m^2}}$$

i.e. $(l^2 + m^2)\{(x-\alpha)^2 + (y-\beta)^2\} - e^2(lx + my + n)^2 = 0.$ (i)

This may be written as the general equation of the 2nd degree in x, y *($\therefore$ conics are curves of the 2nd order):*

$$f(x, y) \equiv \boxed{ax^2+by^2+2hxy+2gx+2fy+c = 0} \tag{181}$$

where a, b, c, f, g, h are functions of $\alpha, \beta, e, l, m, n$.

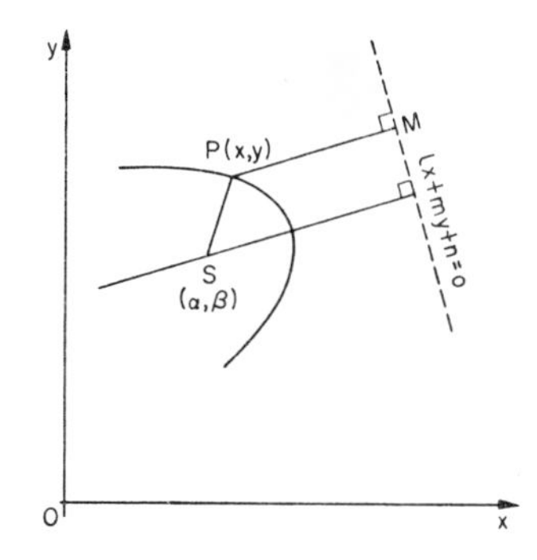

FIG. 63. The general conic

Remarks

(a) Matrix form of (181) is: $\boxed{X^T AX = 0}$ (181.1)

$$\text{where } X = \begin{bmatrix} x \\ y \\ 1 \end{bmatrix}, \quad A = \begin{bmatrix} a & h & g \\ h & b & f \\ g & f & c \end{bmatrix}. \tag{181.2}$$

(b) If $L^T = [l, m, n]$ then the matrix equation of the line $lx+my+n = 0$ is $L^T X = 0$.

Points common to a line and a conic are found by solving the linear equation (of the line) and the quadratic equation (of the conic). Consequently, *a line meets a conic in two points* which may be real, coincident, or imaginary. This fact has been assumed as early as § 81 in the definition of, for example, focal chord.

(c) Equation (181) has five independent coefficients.

$\therefore$ *a conic is uniquely determined by five points.*

Equate coefficients of x^2, y^2, xy in (i), (181)

$$\therefore \begin{cases} a = l^2+m^2-e^2l^2 & \text{(ii)} \\ b = l^2+m^2-e^2m^2 & \text{(iii)} \\ h = -e^2lm & \text{(iv)} \end{cases}$$

$$\text{whence } \frac{(a+b)^2}{ab-h^2} = \frac{(2-e^2)^2}{1-e^2} \tag{v}$$

$\therefore$ if $ab-h^2 = 0$, $e = 1$

$$\therefore \boxed{\text{condition for a parabola is } ab-h^2 = 0}. \tag{182}$$

If $a+b=0,\ e=\sqrt{2}$

$$\therefore \quad \boxed{\text{condition for a rectangular hyperbola is } a+b=0}. \qquad (183)$$

From (v), $ab-h^2 = k(1-e^2)[k>0]$

$$\therefore \quad \boxed{\begin{array}{l} \text{for an ellipse } ab-h^2>0 \\ \hline \text{for an hyperbola } ab-h^2<0 \end{array}}. \qquad \begin{array}{r}(184.1)\\(184.2)\end{array}$$

Put $e=0$ (i. e. circle) $\therefore$ (v) $\rightarrow (a-b)^2 = -4h^2$ and the left-hand side cannot be $-$ve.

$$\therefore \quad \boxed{\text{conditions for a circle are } a=b,\ h=0}. \qquad (185)$$

Conditions (185) can also be obtained by making (181) homogeneous and substituting (175) for x, y, z ($\because$ the circle passes through I, J). Then $a-b+2hi=0, a-b-2hi=0$, whence $a=b, h=0$.

§83. STANDARD EQUATIONS OF THE CONICS

Axes can be suitably chosen so that (181) is much simplified, i.e. the conics are reduced to their standard forms. Comparing coefficients in (i), (181) we have

$$\begin{cases} a = l^2+m^2-e^2l^2 \\ b = l^2+m^2-e^2m^2 \\ h = -e^2lm \end{cases} \qquad \begin{array}{l} g = -\alpha(l^2+m^2)-e^2ln \\ f = -\beta(l^2+m^2)-e^2mn \\ c = (\alpha^2+\beta^2)(l^2+m^2)-e^2n^2. \end{array}$$

Take the focus in Fig. 63 as $(\alpha, 0)$, i.e. $\beta=0$.

Take the directrix in Fig. 63 as $x=-k$, i.e. $m=0,\ k=\dfrac{n}{l}$.

Geometrically, these two algebraic operations correspond to a rotation and a translation, respectively.

$$\therefore \quad \begin{cases} a = l^2(1-e^2), \\ b = l^2 \\ h = 0 \end{cases} \qquad \begin{array}{l} g = -l^2(\alpha+e^2k) \\ f = 0 \\ c = l^2(\alpha^2-e^2k^2) \end{array}$$

$\therefore$ conic (181) is now

$$\boxed{(1-e^2)x^2+y^2-2(\alpha+e^2k)x+(\alpha^2-e^2k^2)=0}. \qquad (186)$$

Case $e=1$ $\therefore$ (186) $\Rightarrow y^2 = 2(a+k)x-(a^2-k^2)\quad (\alpha=a)$

$$= (a+k)[2x-(a-k)]$$

$$= 4ax \text{ when } k=a$$

$$\therefore \quad \boxed{\text{parabola: } y^2=4ax}. \qquad (187)$$

Case $0 \leqslant e < 1$ (i. e. $1-e^2 > 0$)

$$\therefore\ (186) \Rightarrow x^2+\frac{y^2}{1-e^2}-\frac{\alpha+e^2k}{1-e^2}\cdot 2x+\frac{\alpha^2-e^2k^2}{1-e^2} = 0$$

$$x^2+\frac{y^2}{1-e^2}-\frac{ae-e^2\cdot a/e}{1-e^2}\cdot 2x+\frac{(a^2e^2-e^2\cdot a^2/e^2)}{1-e^2} = 0, \text{ putting } \alpha = ae,\ k = -\frac{a}{e}$$

$$x^2+\frac{y^2}{1-e^2} = a^2, \quad \text{i.e. } \frac{x^2}{a^2}+\frac{y^2}{a^2(1-e^2)} = 1$$

$$\therefore \quad \boxed{\text{Ellipse: } \frac{x^2}{a^2}+\frac{y^2}{b^2} = 1} \tag{188}$$

where $\boxed{b^2 = a^2(1-e^2)}$ (189)

i.e. $\boxed{e = \sqrt{1-\frac{b^2}{a^2}}}$ (189.1)

$\boxed{\left(e = \frac{1}{\sqrt{2}}\text{: } \textit{Fagnano's ellipse}\right)}$.

If $e = 0$ (i.e. $b = a$) we get a *circle* $x^2+y^2 = a^2$ with focus $(0, 0)$ (i.e. the centre) and directrix l_∞.

Case $e > 1$ (i.e. $e^2-1 > 0$)

$$(186) \Rightarrow x^2-\frac{y^2}{e^2-1}+2\frac{(\alpha+e^2k)}{e^2-1}-\frac{(\alpha-e^2k^2)}{e^2-1} = 0$$

i. e. $$\frac{x^2}{a^2}-\frac{y^2}{a^2(e^2-1)} = 1 \quad \text{putting} \quad \alpha = ae,\ k = -\frac{a}{e}.$$

$$\therefore \quad \boxed{\text{Hyperbola: } \frac{x^2}{a^2}-\frac{y^2}{b^2} = 1} \tag{190}$$

where $b^2 = a^2(e^2-1)$ (191)

i.e. $\boxed{e = \sqrt{1+\frac{b^2}{a^2}}}$. (191.1)

If $e = \sqrt{2}$ (i.e. $b = a$) we get the *rectangular hyperbola* $x^2-y^2 = a^2$. Thus, the rectangular hyperbola bears the same relationship to the hyperbola as the circle bears to the ellipse (i.e. $b = a$).

By means of a suitable transformation (Chapter 19) the equation of a rectangular hyperbola can be cast in the form

$$\boxed{\text{Rectangular hyperbola: } xy = c}. \tag{192}$$

It is not difficult to sketch the curves as shown in Figs. 64–66. Clearly, the parabola is an open curve since $\pm y$ increases as $x \to \infty$. Also, the ellipse is a closed curve, bounded by the rectangular box whose sides have equations $x = \pm a$, $y = \pm b$. Furthermore, the hyperbola is not closed and consists of two branches. The region for which $-a < x < a$ leads to imaginary values of y. Symmetry about the x- and y-axes is fairly obvious. The statements above concerning closedness and branches need to be modified if we consider the conics in the light of their relation to l_∞.

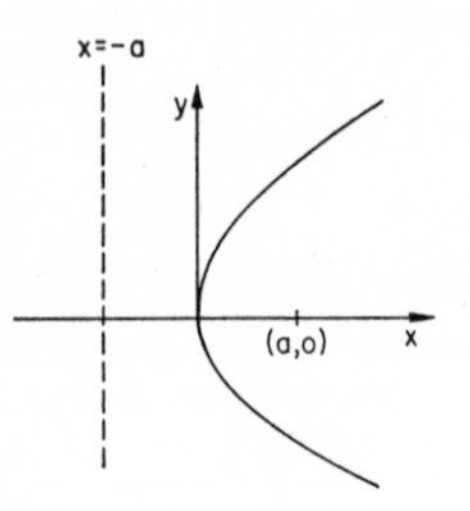

FIG. 64. The parabola $y^2 = 4ax$

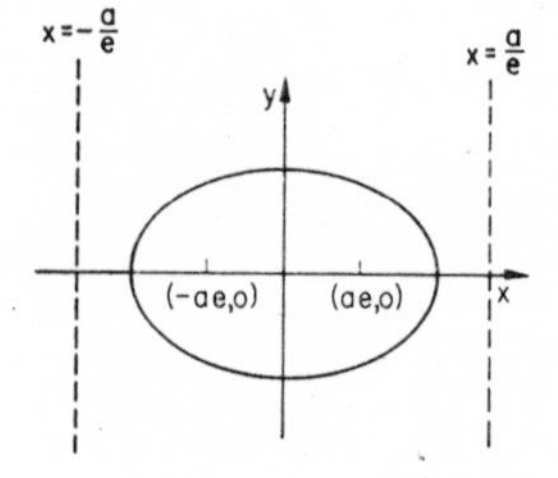

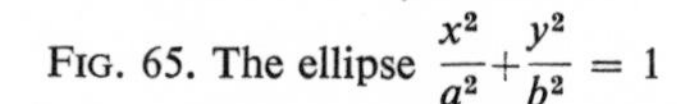

FIG. 65. The ellipse $\dfrac{x^2}{a^2}+\dfrac{y^2}{b^2} = 1$

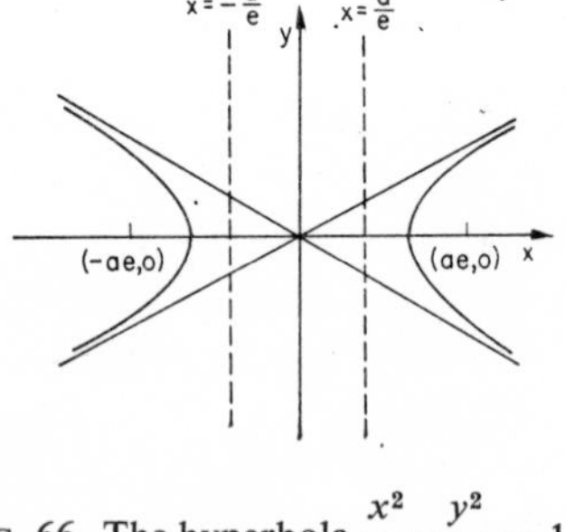

FIG. 66. The hyperbola $\dfrac{x^2}{a^2}-\dfrac{y^2}{b^2} = 1$

Note. When we say "The equation of a parabola is $y^2 = 4ax$", we really mean that we have chosen our coordinate system (axes and origin) so that the parabola has this equation. This should always be clearly understood. Similarly, of course, for the ellipse and hyperbola.

§ 84. CONICS AND THE LINE AT INFINITY

Write (181) in homogeneous form to obtain

$$f(x, y, z) \equiv \boxed{ax^2+by^2+cz^2+2fyz+2gzx+2hxy = 0}. \qquad (181a)$$

This is cut by $l_\infty (z = 0)$ in the two points given by $ax^2+2hxy+by^2 = 0$ for which $\frac{x}{y} = \frac{-h \pm \sqrt{h^2-ab}}{a}$.

Using conditions (182)–(185), we have (Fig. 67):

the parabola (for which $h^2 = ab$) cuts l_∞ in 2 coincident points;
the hyperbola (for which $h^2 > ab$) cuts l_∞ in 2 real points;
the ellipse (for which $h^2 < ab$) cuts l_∞ in 2 imaginary points.

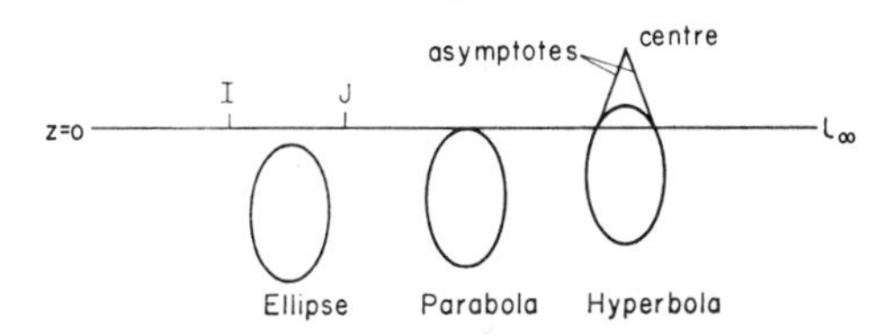

FIG. 67. Relation of conics to the line at infinity

In particular, the circle (for which $h = 0$, $b = a$) cuts l_∞ in the two imaginary points given by $x^2+y^2 = 0$, i.e. $I \equiv (1, i, 0)$ and $J \equiv (1, -i, 0)$.

Queries

(a) What are the coordinates of the point of contact of the parabola $y^2 = 4ax$ with l_∞?

(b) What are the coordinates of the intersections of the rectangular hyperbola $xy = c^2$ with l_∞?

(c) Can length be defined on l_∞?

§ 85. QUADRATIC EQUATION REPRESENTING A LINE-PAIR

Consider the two straight lines whose equations are

$$\begin{cases} lx+my+n = 0, \\ l'x+m'y+n' = 0. \end{cases}$$

$\therefore (lx+my+n)(l'x+m'y+n') = 0$ is satisfied by the coordinates of any point on either line, and by no other values. Hence, it represents the two straight lines together as a simple locus of the second degree. Conversely, if a quadratic in x and y can be factorised in the first degree, the equation obtained by equating the expression to zero represents two straight lines. E.g.:

(i) $x^2+xy-2y^2+2x-5y-3 = 0 \equiv (x-y-1)(x+2y+3) = 0$.

Therefore it represents the two straight lines $x-y-1 = 0$, $x+2y+3 = 0$.

(ii) $x^2+y^2 = r^2$ (circle) cannot be so reduced; therefore it does not represent two straight lines.

Our problem is to find the condition that the general conic (181) should break up into a pair of straight lines.

Suppose $a \neq 0$ in (181). Multiply throughout by a and complete the square with all terms involving x.

$$\therefore \quad (ax+hy+g)^2-\{(h^2-ab)y^2+2(gh-af)y+(g^2-ac)\} = 0.$$

For the second part to be perfect square,

$$(gh-af)^2 = (h^2-ab)(g^2-ac)$$

i.e. $abc+2fgh-af^2-bg^2-ch^2 = 0$ (refer to § 60, Jacobi's theorem),

$$\text{i.e.} \qquad \boxed{\Delta \equiv \begin{vmatrix} a & h & g \\ h & b & f \\ g & f & c \end{vmatrix} = 0}\,. \tag{193}$$

[Δ is the *discriminant* of the conic.]

$\therefore$ if $\Delta = 0$ the conic $\to$ 2 straight lines,

i.e. two straight lines form a *degenerate conic*. E.g.:

(i) In $x^2+xy-2y^2+2x-5y-3 = 0$,

$$a = 1,\ b = -2,\ c = -3,\ h = \tfrac{1}{2},\ g = 1,\ f = -2\tfrac{1}{2}.$$

$$\therefore \qquad \Delta = \begin{vmatrix} 1 & \frac{1}{2} & 1 \\ \frac{1}{2} & -2 & -2\frac{1}{2} \\ 1 & -2\frac{1}{2} & -3 \end{vmatrix} = 0 \quad \text{on calculation.}$$

Therefore the locus is degenerate.

(ii) In $x^2+y^2 = r^2$, $a = b = 1$, $c = -r^2$, $f = g = h = 0$.

$$\therefore \qquad \Delta = \begin{vmatrix} 1 & . & . \\ . & 1 & . \\ . & . & -r^2 \end{vmatrix} = -r^2 \neq 0.$$

Therefore the locus is not degenerate.

Next, let r vary (so that we obtain a system of a concentric circles). Let $r \to 0$.

Therefore in the limit, $\Delta \to 0$ and the circle degenerates into the line-pair given by $x^2+y^2 = 0$, i.e. by the imaginary lines $y = \pm ix$ which meet at the origin O. We sometimes say that such a circle is a *point-circle*, i.e. a circle of zero radius. [The point need not, of course, be at the origin.] Notice that I lies on $y = ix$ and J lies on $y = -ix$, i.e. I and J must lie on the circle even when it is degenerate.

§ 86. TANGENT AT A GIVEN POINT

Differentiating in (181), we obtain

$$\boxed{\frac{dy}{dx} = -\frac{(ax+hy+g)}{hx+by+f}}. \tag{194}$$

Therefore the equation of the tangent to the conic at (x_1, y_1) is

$$y-y_1 = -\frac{(ax_1+hy_1+g)}{hx_1+by_1+f}(x-x_1),$$

i.e. $\boxed{\text{tangent: } (ax_1+hy_1+g)x+(hx_1+by_1+f)y+(gx_1+fy_1+c) = 0}$ (195)

on calculation. In particular, the tangents at (x_1, y_1) are:

$$\begin{cases} \text{parabola } y^2 = 4ax & yy_1 = 2a(x+x_1) & (195.1) \\ \text{ellipse } \dfrac{x^2}{a^2}+\dfrac{y^2}{b^2} = 1 & \dfrac{xx_1}{a^2}+\dfrac{yy_1}{b^2} = 1 & (195.2) \\ \text{hyperbola } \dfrac{x^2}{a^2}-\dfrac{y^2}{b^2} = 1 & \dfrac{xx_1}{a^2}-\dfrac{yy_1}{b^2} = 1. & (195.3) \end{cases}$$

Notice that for (181a), (195) could be written in the form

$$\boxed{\left(\frac{\partial f}{\partial x}\right)_P x+\left(\frac{\partial f}{\partial y}\right)_P y+\left(\frac{\partial f}{\partial z}\right)_P z = 0} \tag{196}$$

where $f \equiv ax^2+by^2+cz^2+2fyz+2gzx+2hxy$ and $\left(\frac{\partial f}{\partial x}\right)_P$ means the value of $\frac{\partial f}{\partial x}$ at $P(x_1, y_1, z_1)$. Can you express (195) in matrix notation?

§ 87. ELEMENTARY THEORY OF POLE AND POLAR

In Fig. 68 let U divide PQ in the ratio $\lambda : 1$.

$$\therefore \qquad U \equiv \left(\frac{\lambda x+x_1}{\lambda+1}, \frac{\lambda y+y_1}{\lambda+1}\right).$$

Substitute in (181) to obtain, after simplification,

$$\boxed{\begin{aligned} &\lambda^2(ax^2+by^2+2gx+2fy+2hxy+c) \\ &+2\lambda[(ax_1+hy_1+g)x+(hx_1+by_1+f)y+(gx_1+fy_1+c)] \\ &+(ax_1^2+by_1^2+2gx_1+2fy_1+2hx_1y_1+c) = 0 \end{aligned}}. \tag{197}$$

This quadratic in λ is called *Joachimsthal's equation.* The roots λ_1, λ_2 correspond to the points U, V.

$$\text{Let } \lambda_1 = \frac{PU}{UQ}, \quad \lambda_2 = \frac{PV}{VQ}.$$

$$\therefore \frac{\lambda_1}{\lambda_2} = \frac{PU \cdot QV}{PV \cdot QU} \text{ writing } UQ = -QU,\ VQ = -QV \text{ (directed segments)}$$

$$= (PQ,\ UV).$$

Keeping P fixed, let the chord PQ vary.

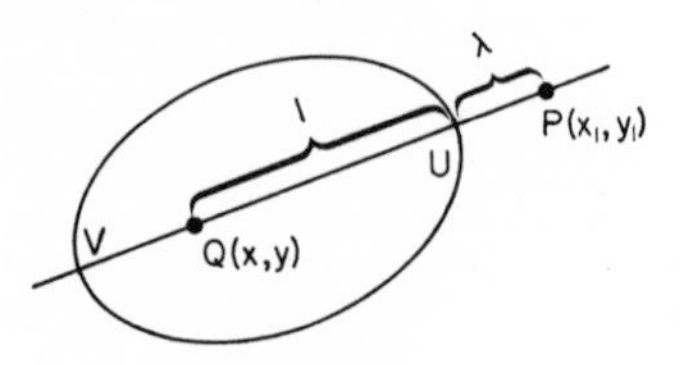

FIG. 68

Suppose we want to find the locus of Q:

$$(PQ,\ UV) = -1,$$

i.e.
$$\frac{\lambda_1}{\lambda_2} = -1,$$

i.e.
$$\lambda_1 + \lambda_2 = 0,$$

i.e. the sum of the roots of (197) is zero.

Thus, the locus of Q (the harmonic conjugate of P w.r.t. U, V) is the line with equation

$$\boxed{\text{polar: } (ax_1+hy_1+g)x+(hx_1+by_1+f)y+(gx_1+fy_1+c) = 0}. \quad (195a)$$

This line is called the *polar* of P and P is called the *pole* of the polar. Limiting positions of the variable chord are the tangents from P so that clearly the polar of P is the line p joining the points of contact of these tangents as shown in Fig. 69.

When $P(x_1, y_1)$ lies on the conic, the polar of P is the tangent at P; this is why equations (195), (195a) have the same appearance.

Equations of the polars of $P(x_1, y_1)$ for the various conics are precisely those given in (191.1)–(191.3).

An important property of polarity is the mutuality property:

> If the polar of P passes through Q,
> then the polar of Q passes through P.

To show this is so, let the polar of $P(x_1, y_1)$ pass through $Q(x_2, y_2)$ (Fig. 69b).

Thus, by (195a), $(ax_1+hy_1+g)x_2+(hx_1+by_1+f)y_2+(gx_1+fy_1+c) = 0$,

i.e. $(ax_2+hy_2+g)x_1+(hx_2+by_2+f)y_1+(gx_2+fy_2+c) = 0$,

i.e. the polar of Q passes through P; or, (geometrically):

$(PQ, UV) = -1 \Rightarrow (QP, UV) = -1$ by § 80, Note (i).

But $(PQ, UV) = -1 \Rightarrow$ polar of P passes through Q.

$\therefore$ $(QP, UV) = -1 \Rightarrow$ polar of Q passes through P.

Two points which are such that each lies on the polar of the other are called *conjugate points.*

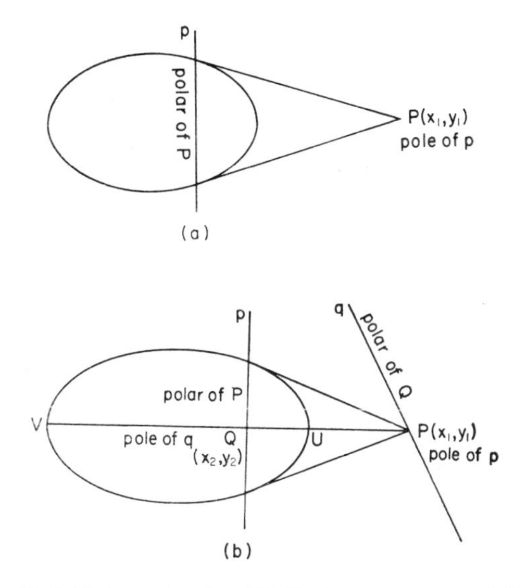

FIG. 69. (a) Pole and polar. (b) Conjugate points and lines

Corollary. If the pole of the line p lies on the line q, then the pole of the line q lies on the line p.

Lines like these are called *conjugate lines.*

EXAMPLE 104. The polar of a focus is the corresponding directrix.

Solution. Substitute (α, β) (Fig. 63) for (x_1, y_1) in (195a).

Therefore the equation of the polar of the focus $S(\alpha, \beta)$ for the general conic is

$$(a\alpha+h\beta+g)x+(h\alpha+b\beta+f)y+(g\alpha+f\beta+c) = 0,$$

i.e. $-e^2(l\alpha+m\beta+n)\ [lx+my+n] = 0$ using the values in § 84.

Now $l\alpha+m\beta+n \neq 0$, $\because$ (α, β) does not lie on the line $lx+my+n = 0$.

Therefore the polar of the focus is $lx+my+n = 0$, i.e. the directrix (Fig. 63). For example, for the ellipse (188), the polar of $(ae, 0)$ is the directrix $x = a/e$, using 195(a).

We have assumed $e \neq 0$ here. If $e = 0$, the result is still true, viz. the polar of the focus (= centre) of a circle is the corresponding directrix ($= l_\infty$) for, by (196) we see that the polar of (x_1, y_1, z_1) w.r.t. the circle $x^2+y^2-a^2z^2 = 0$ is $x_1x+y_1y-a^2z_1z = 0$, i.e. the polar of $(0, 0, 1)$ is $z = 0$.

This latter result is clearly true also for the ellipse and hyperbola. Thus, the *centre of a conic is the pole* (w.r.t. the conic) of l_∞. Asymptotes of a conic are defined to be the tangents at the points where the conic cuts l_∞ (Fig. 67). Obviously, asymptotes intersect at the centre of the conic. Only the hyperbola has real asymptotes. A rectangular hyperbola, having perpendicular axes, cuts l_∞ in two points harmoniously separating I, J. (Refer to Exercise 15.19.)

§ 88. REDUCTION OF A CENTRAL CONIC TO STANDARD FORM

Sometimes we wish to know more about the reduction of the general conic to a standard form than is given in § 83. Suppose it is desired to find the coordinates (α, β, γ) of the centre K of the conic (181a). Now, the polar of K is l_∞, i.e. by (196a),

$$x\left(\frac{\partial f}{\partial x}\right)_K+y\left(\frac{\partial f}{\partial y}\right)_K+z\left(\frac{\partial f}{\partial z}\right)_K = 0 \text{ is the same as } z = 0.$$

Thus, the coordinates of the centre are given by

$$\boxed{\left(\frac{\partial f}{\partial x}\right)_K = \left(\frac{\partial f}{\partial y}\right)_K = 0} \tag{198}$$

i.e.

$$\boxed{\begin{aligned} ax+hy+gz &= 0 \\ hx+by+fz &= 0 \end{aligned}} \tag{198.1}$$

i.e. in homogeneous coordinates

$$\boxed{K \equiv (hf-bg,\ gh-af,\ ab-h^2) = (G, F, C)} \tag{198.2}$$

or, in non-homogeneous coordinates,

$$K \equiv \left(\frac{hf-bg}{ab-h^2}, \frac{gh-af}{ab-h^2}\right) = \left(\frac{G}{C}, \frac{F}{C}\right),$$

where G, F, C are the cofactors of g, f, c in the discriminant Δ.

If $C = 0 = ab-h^2$, the "centre" is on l_∞, i.e. the conic is a parabola or a pair of parallel straight lines.

Suppose now in (181a) we make the translation (=parallel axes transformation) $x = x'+pz', y = y'+qz', z = z'$ with matrix $\begin{bmatrix} 1 & . & p \\ . & 1 & q \\ . & . & 1 \end{bmatrix}$, then

$$ax'^2+by'^2+2hx'y'+2x'z'(ap+hq+gz)+2y'z'(hp+bq+f)+cz'^2 = 0, \quad \text{(i)}$$

where $c' = ap^2+bq^2+2hpq+2gp+2fq+c = f(p, q, 1)$.

For terms in $x'z'$, $y'z'$ to vanish, we must have

$$\begin{cases} 2(ap+hq+g) = 0, \\ 2(hp+bq+f) = 0, \end{cases}$$

i.e. (198.1) satisfied by $(p, q, 1)$. Observe then that

$$c' = gp+fq+c = \frac{gG+fF+cC}{C} = \frac{\Delta}{C}.$$

Thus, the translation method and the pole and polar method for determining the centre are equivalent. With centre K, the equation of the conic is now

$$ax'^2+2hx'y'+by'^2 = k \quad \text{(ii)}$$

on making it non-homogeneous, and replacing c' by $-k$.

To remove the term in $x'\,y'$, make the transformation (128)$'$ to new coordinates X, Y. Referred to these axes, the equation of the conic is

$$a_1X^2+2h_1XY+b_1Y^2 = k, \quad \text{(iii)}$$

where
$$\begin{cases} a_1 = a\cos^2\theta+2h\cos\theta\sin\theta+b\sin^2\theta \\ b_1 = a\sin^2\theta-2h\cos\theta\sin\theta+b\cos^2\theta \\ 2h_1 = (b-a)\sin 2\theta+2h\cos 2\theta \end{cases} \quad \text{(iv)}$$

so that the term in XY disappears if the anticlockwise angle of rotation is

$$\boxed{\theta = \frac{1}{2}\tan^{-1}\left(\frac{2h}{a-b}\right)}. \quad (199)$$

Replacing $\frac{a_1}{k}, \frac{b_1}{k}$ by a, b respectively, we reach the standard form

$$aX^2+bY^2 = 1. \quad \text{(v)}$$

EXAMPLE 105 (reduction of a conic to standard form). Obtain the standard equation of the conic $f(x, y) \equiv 17x^2-12xy+8y^2-10x-20y+5 = 0$.

Solution. (a) *Analytical method.* Note that, by (184.1), the conic must be an ellipse, $\because$ $17\times 8-(-6)^2 = 100 > 0$.

Make the translation $x = x'+h$, $y = y'+k$ to get the equations for the removal of the x', y' terms: $34h-12k-10 = 0$, $-12h+16k-20 = 0$ whence $h = 1$, $k = 2$. [Alternatively (198) gives this result more readily.]

Shift the origin to (1, 2), i.e. $x = x'+1$, $y = y'+2$, and the conic is

$$17x'^2-12x'y'+8y'^2 = 20.$$

By (199), $\tan 2\theta = \dfrac{-12}{17-8} = -\dfrac{4}{3} = \dfrac{2\tan\theta}{1-\tan^2\theta}$,

i.e. $$2\tan^2\theta-3\tan\theta-2 = 0$$

$\therefore$ $$\tan\theta = 2,\ -\tfrac{1}{2}$$

whence $\sin\theta = \dfrac{2}{\sqrt{5}}$, $\cos\theta = \dfrac{1}{\sqrt{5}}$ or $\sin\theta = -\dfrac{1}{\sqrt{5}}$, $\cos\theta = \dfrac{2}{\sqrt{5}}$.

Next, make the rotational transformation $x' = \dfrac{X-2Y}{\sqrt{5}}$, $y' = \dfrac{2X+Y}{\sqrt{5}}$. Tidying up the resulting equation, we have, finally,

$$\frac{X^2}{4}+Y^2 = 1,$$

i.e. an ellipse with semiaxes 2, 1 (X-axis major) and eccentricity $\dfrac{\sqrt{3}}{2}$. (See Fig. 70.)

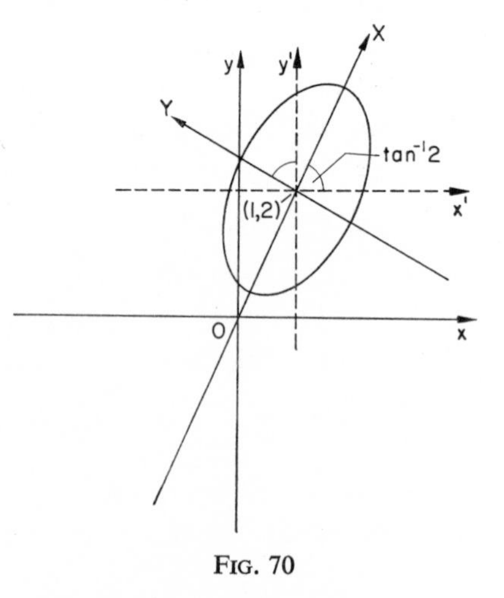

FIG. 70

Question: How is the other value of $\tan\theta$ $(= -\tfrac{1}{2})$ accounted for?

(b) *Eigenvalue (matrix) method.* Corresponding to the above analytical treatment, there is a matrix treatment. Write (ii), with $x'^T = [x', y']$, as

$$x'^T A x' = k, \tag{ii)'$$

where A is a symmetric 2×2 matrix and k is the 1×1 matrix with single element k. Make the proper orthogonal transformation (a rotation, Exercise 12.52)

$$x' = PX \quad (\text{i.e. } P^T = P^{-1},\ |P| = 1) \tag{vi}$$

where $X^I = [X, Y]$, so that (ii)′ becomes

$$X^T P^T A P X = k \tag{vii}$$

i.e.
$$X^T B X = k,$$
where
$$B = P^T A P. \tag{viii}$$

Then B is also symmetrical (Exercise 12.44).

Invariants of the transformation (vi) are:

(a) $|A| \because |B| = |P^T|\,|A|\,|P| = |P|^2\,|A| = |A|\ (\because |P| = 1)$;

(b) eigenvalues of A (Exercise 12.43) $(P^{-1} = P^T)$.

In more advanced theory, it is shown that one can find a proper orthogonal matrix $P : P^T A P = B = \text{diag.}(\lambda_1, \lambda_2)$ where λ_1, λ_2 are the eigenvalues of B (and of A also). See, for example, Reference (d), Chapter 14.

To illustrate this, revert to Example 105. Write the conic as $x'^T A x' = 1$,

where $$A = \begin{bmatrix} \frac{17}{20} & \frac{-6}{20} \\ \frac{-6}{20} & \frac{8}{20} \end{bmatrix} \qquad \therefore\ A - \lambda I = \begin{bmatrix} \frac{17}{20} - \lambda & \frac{-6}{20} \\ \frac{-6}{20} & \frac{8}{20} - \lambda \end{bmatrix}$$

$\therefore\ |A - \lambda I| = (\lambda - 1)(\lambda - \frac{1}{4}) \Rightarrow$ eigenvalues are $\lambda = \frac{1}{4}, 1$.

Write $v^T = [x, y]$. Recall that $Av = \lambda v \Rightarrow (A - \lambda I)v = O$.
Put $\lambda = \frac{1}{4}$, $\therefore\ (A - \frac{1}{4}\mathrm{I})v = O \Rightarrow 2x = y$, i.e. $v^T = [1, 2]$.
Put $\lambda = 1$, $\therefore\ (A - 1 \cdot I)v = O \Rightarrow x = -2y$, i.e. $v^T = [-2, 1]$.

Normalise these eigenvectors to obtain $\frac{1}{\sqrt{5}}\begin{bmatrix} 1 \\ 2 \end{bmatrix}, \frac{1}{\sqrt{5}}\begin{bmatrix} -2 \\ 1 \end{bmatrix}$. (The vector v becomes normalised on making it into the vector $\frac{1}{\sqrt{x^2+y^2}}\begin{bmatrix} x \\ y \end{bmatrix}$.) Form the matrix of normalised eigenvectors

$$P = \frac{1}{\sqrt{5}}\begin{bmatrix} 1 & -2 \\ 2 & 1 \end{bmatrix} \text{ with } |P| = 1,\ P^{-1} = \frac{1}{\sqrt{5}}\begin{bmatrix} 1 & 2 \\ -2 & 1 \end{bmatrix} = P^T,$$

i.e. P is proper orthogonal, a fact ensured by the normalising process. Observe that P expresses a rotation anticlockwise through $\theta = \sin^{-1}\left(\frac{2}{\sqrt{5}}\right)$, i.e. $\theta = \tan^{-1} 2$.

$$\begin{aligned} \therefore\ P^{-1}AP &= \frac{1}{100}\begin{bmatrix} 1 & 2 \\ -2 & 1 \end{bmatrix}\begin{bmatrix} 17 & -6 \\ -6 & 8 \end{bmatrix}\begin{bmatrix} 1 & -2 \\ 2 & 1 \end{bmatrix} \\ &= \frac{1}{100}\begin{bmatrix} 1 & 2 \\ -2 & 1 \end{bmatrix}\begin{bmatrix} 5 & -40 \\ 10 & 20 \end{bmatrix} \\ &= \begin{bmatrix} \frac{1}{4} & 0 \\ 0 & 1 \end{bmatrix} \end{aligned}$$

i.e. the conic $x'^T Ax' \equiv \frac{17}{20}x'^2 - \frac{12}{20}x'y' + \frac{8}{20}y'^2 = 1$ has become $X^T(P^{-1}AP)X \equiv$ $\equiv X^2/4 + Y^2 = 1$.

Notice that the *eigenvalues are the reciprocals of the squares of the lengths of the semi-axes.* Eigenvectors lie along the new axes.

Suggested topics for further study

(1) Matrix treatment of conics.
(2) Vector treatment of conics.
(3) Invariants of a pair of conics.

References

Geometry tests listed in the bibliography. Pioneer work such as the following should be consulted:

(a) *Conics*, Apollonius (ed. Heath) (Heffer, 1961).
(b) *Works*, Archimedes (ed. Heath) (Dover).

EXERCISES 16

1. For what value of k does the conic $x^2 - y^2 + 2kx + 4 = 0$ degenerate?

2. Simplify the matrix form $[x, y, z]\begin{bmatrix} 0 & a & b \\ -a & 0 & c \\ -b & -c & 0 \end{bmatrix}\begin{bmatrix} x \\ y \\ z \end{bmatrix} = 0$. Why does it not yield the equation of a conic?

3. Show that the equation $y^2 - k^2x^2 + 2cy + c^2 = 0$ represents a line pair and find the coordinates of the points in which it cuts l_∞.

4. A torch which casts a conical beam of light is held so that the uppermost portion of the beam is horizontal. Assuming complete darkness in the room, what conic contains the region of light on the floor? Why?

5. *(Mechanical generation of a parabola.)* A set-square KMQ, with a right angle at M, slides with one edge MK along a fixed line. A string of length MQ has one end fixed to Q and the other to a fixed point S. Then a pencil which keeps the string tight and presses against the edge MQ will describe a parabola. Justify this statement.

6. Lampshades with a circular base cast a shadow of a certain shape on the wall. Examine the nature of this shadow.

7. Invariants of the expression $S = ax^2 + 2hxy + by^2$ under the rotation $x' = x\cos\theta + y\sin\theta$, $y' = -x\sin\theta + y\cos\theta$ are $a+b$, $ab-h^2$, x^2+y^2. Justify.

8. Analyse the nature of the curve $x^{1/2} + y^{1/2} = a^{1/2}$.

9. A certain curve has the property that the subnormal always bears a constant ratio to the abscissa. Establish that it must be a conic.

10. Determine the lowest order differential equation satisfied by all conics with a given eccentricity. (A problem proposed by A. W. Walker, *The American Mathematical Monthly*, **61** (1), 50 (1954).

11. Assuming $0 < k < 1$ (k constant), show that the solutions of the differential equation $\frac{dy}{dx} = \frac{(k^2-1)x}{y}$ represent ellipses with centre at the origin. What is their common eccentricity?

12. Given the conic $x^2+y^2-2xy-2x+2y+1 = 0$, obtain $\frac{dy}{dx}$. What does this mean geometrically?

13. Consider the pencil of circles $S+kS' = 0$ formed from the circles $S \equiv x^2+y^2+2gx+c = 0$, $S' \equiv x^2+y^2+2g'x+c = 0$. What is the degenerate locus for $k = -1$?

14. Writing $\lambda = \frac{g+kg'}{1+k}$ $(k \neq -1)$, find the values of λ for which the circles of the pencil $S'+kS' = 0$ are degenerate (i. e. point circles).

15. If these points are L_1, L_2, verify that a circle through them has equation $x^2+y^2+2fy-c = 0$.

16. Show that this circle (Exercise 16.15) cuts $S = 0$ (or $S' = 0$) orthogonally.

17. T is the pole of the chord AB w.r.t. a conic. The tangent at any point C on the conic meets TA, TB, AB at H, K, D respectively. Prove that $(HK, CD) = -1$.

18. What is the pole of the line $lx+my+n = 0$ w.r.t. the hyperbola $\frac{x^2}{a^2}-\frac{y^2}{b^2} = 1$?

19. Alternative definitions of a circle, centre at the origin, are: (i) a circle is a conic which passes through I, J and whose centre is the pole of l_∞; (ii) a circle is the locus of a point whose distance from a fixed point is constant. Confirm the equivalence of these definitions.

20. Asymptotes to the curve $f(x, y, z) = 0$ are given by $b\left(\frac{\partial f}{\partial x}\right)^2-2h\frac{\partial f}{\partial x}\frac{\partial f}{\partial y}+a\left(\frac{\partial f}{\partial y}\right)^2 = 0$. Establish this equation.

21. Derive the equations of the asymptotes of the hyperbola $b^2x^2-a^2y^2 = a^2b^2$ and find where they cut l_∞.

22. Define a rectangular hyperbola to be a hyperbola which cuts l_∞ in two points harmonically separating I, J. Show that, for a rectangular hyperbola, $b^2 = a^2$.

23. Repeat Exercise 16.22 for the ellipse $b^2x^2+a^2y^2 = a^2b^2$.

24. Determine the equation of the conic through $X_\infty Y_\infty Z$.

25. When each side of a given triangle is the polar of the opposite vertex w.r.t. a conic, the triangle is *self-polar*. Obtain the equation of the conic having $X_\infty Y_\infty Z$ as a self-polar triangle.

26. Using Fig. 60, describe the special positions of the planes of section which produce degenerate ellipses (circles), parabolas, and hyperbolas.

27. Reduce the conic $37x^2-18xy+13y^2 = 40$ to its standard form.

28. Perform the reduction of Exercise 16.27 by the eigenvalue method.

29. Through the five points (0, 0), (0, 1), (2, 0), (1, 1), (1, −1) passes a unique conic. Changing axes suitably, reduce its equation to the standard form. Hence, determine the lengths of its major and minor axes, and its eccentricity.

30. Knowing the elliptic geometry formula $\cos A+\cos(B+C) = \sin B \sin C (\cos a-1)$ where A, B, C are angles of a triangle and a is a side, deduce that the angle sum of a triangle is greater than 180°. Assume $A \geqslant B \geqslant C$. [*Hint:* First obtain the right-hand side as a negative quantity, then argue that $A+B+C > \pi$.]

CHAPTER 17

THE PARABOLA

All animals are equal, but some animals are more equal than others.

(GEORGE ORWELL)

§ 89. BASIC PROPERTIES (REVISION SUMMARY)

In Fig. 71, $\boxed{\text{Definition: } SP = PM}$ by (180)

$\boxed{\text{Equation: } y^2 = 4ax}$ by (187)

$$\boxed{\textit{Latus rectum } L'SL = 4a} \tag{200}$$

$$\boxed{\text{Parametric form } \begin{cases} x = at^2 \\ y = 2at \end{cases}} \tag{201}$$

$$\boxed{t = \cot\theta = \frac{1}{m}}. \tag{202}$$

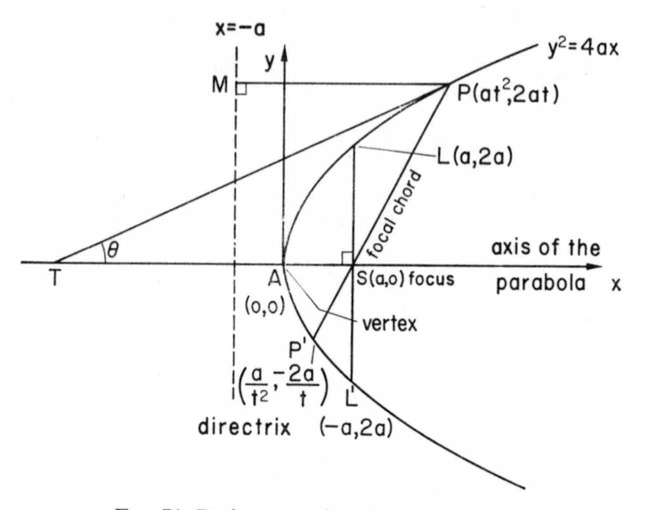

FIG. 71. Basic properties of the parabola

Special values of the parameter

$t = 0 \Rightarrow P \equiv A$; $t = \pm 1 \Rightarrow P \equiv L, L'$; $t = \pm\infty \Rightarrow P \equiv P_\infty$; i.e. the curve joins up again "at infinity".

$$\boxed{\text{Tangent: } y = \frac{x}{t} + at \left(\text{gradient } \frac{1}{t}\right)} \tag{203}$$

$$\boxed{\text{Normal: } y = -tx + 2at + at^3 \text{ (gradient } -t)} \tag{204}$$

What are the gradients of the tangent and normal for $t = 0, \pm 1, \pm\infty$?

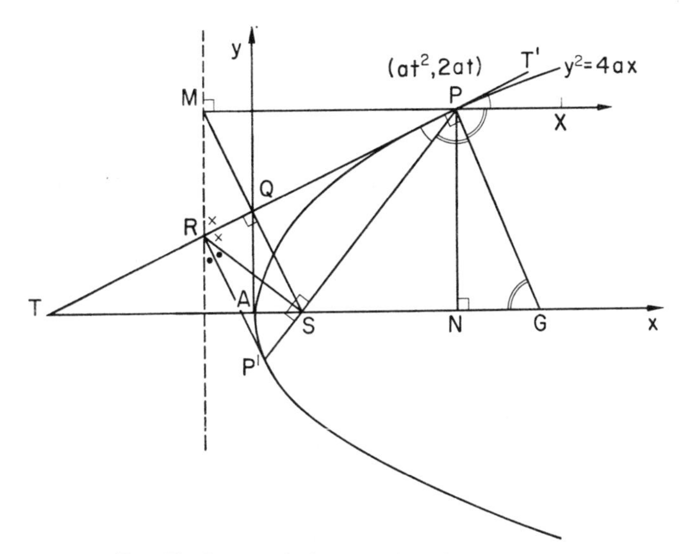

FIG. 72. Geometrical properties of the parabola

Some geometrical properties (Fig. 72)

$$\boxed{AT = AN} = at^2 \tag{205}$$

$$\boxed{SP = ST = SG = PM} = at^2 + a \tag{206}$$

$$\boxed{SPMT \text{ is a rhombus}} \tag{207}$$

$$\boxed{PT \text{ bisects } S\hat{P}M} \tag{208}$$

$$\boxed{Q \text{ is mid-point of } PT} \tag{209}$$

$$\boxed{Q \text{ lies on } SM} \tag{210}$$

$$\boxed{S\hat{Q}P = \frac{\pi}{2}} \tag{211}$$

$$\boxed{\text{Subnormal } NG = 2a} \qquad \text{(See Example 12)} \tag{212}$$

$$\boxed{\triangle\text{s } PSR,\ PMR \text{ congruent}} \tag{213}$$

$$\boxed{R\hat{S}P = R\hat{M}P = \frac{\pi}{2}}\ . \tag{214}$$

Generally speaking, it is preferable to use parametric expressions in problems dealing with conics. Indeed, an exposition of the parametric method might be said to be the guiding spirit in our approach to the parabola, ellipse, and hyperbola.

Using the fact that $P\hat{Q}S = \pi/2$, we can construct the focus of a parabola as follows: Since the equation of PQ is $y = \dfrac{x}{t}+at$, we have $Q \equiv (0, at)$. The line through Q which is perpendicular to PQ has equation $y = -xt+at$ and this cuts the x-axis at $(a, 0) \equiv S$.

§ 90. SELECTED PROBLEMS SOLVED PARAMETRICALLY

EXAMPLE 106. Tangents at the ends of a focal chord of a parabola are perpendicular and meet on the directrix. (See Example 103.)

Solution. In Fig. 73 the equation of the chord PP' is $\dfrac{y-2at'}{2a(t-t')} = \dfrac{x-at'^2}{a(t^2-t'^2)}$.

If $S(a, 0)$ lies on it we obtain $tt' = -1$ after simplification, i.e. $t' = -\dfrac{1}{t}$, i.e. the tangents are perpendicular.

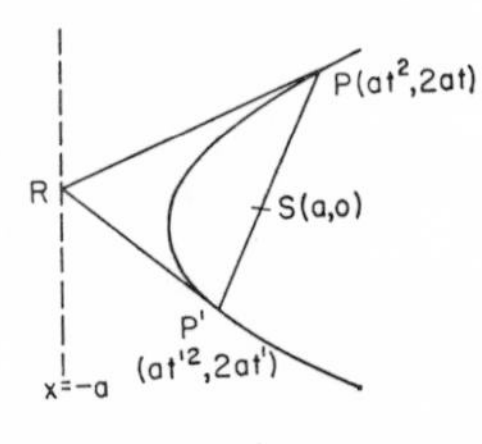

FIG. 73

Therefore equations of the tangents are $y = \dfrac{x}{t}+at,\ y = -xt-\dfrac{a}{t}$.

Solve $\therefore\ x = -a$.

Therefore the locus of the point of intersection of (perpendicular) tangents at the ends of a focal chord is the directrix.

EXAMPLE 107 (a standard type of locus problem). Determine the locus of the mid-point of RG (Fig. 74a).

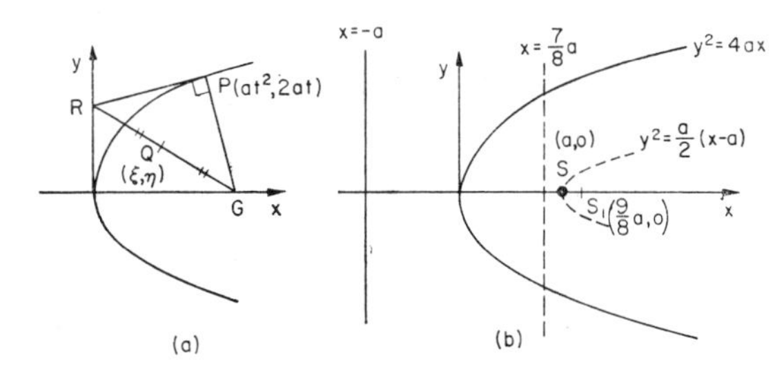

FIG. 74

Solution. Given the tangent at $P: y = \frac{x}{t}+at$ and the normal at $P: y = -tx+2at+at^3$,

$$\therefore\ G \equiv (2a+at^2, 0),\ \ R \equiv (0, at).$$

We wish to find the locus of the mid-point $Q(\xi, \eta)$ of RG.

We have $\xi = \frac{2a+at^2}{2}$, $\eta = \frac{at}{2}$ $\therefore t = \frac{2\eta}{a}$.

Eliminate $t \therefore 2\eta^2 = a(\xi-a)$.

Therefore the required locus is $y^2 = \frac{a}{2}(x-a)$ (Fig. 74b), i.e. a parabola coaxial with the original parabola, having vertex at $(a, 0)$ [= focus of original] and *latus rectum* $\frac{a}{2}\left[=\frac{1}{8}\text{ that of the original}\right]$, and having focus at $S_1\left(a+\frac{a}{8}, 0\right) = \left(\frac{9}{8}a, 0\right)$ and directrix $x = a-\frac{a}{8} = \frac{7}{8}a$.

[*Query:* What parameter, for the original curve, gives rise to the vertex of the derived parabola?]

EXAMPLE 108. Obtain the locus of the mid-points of a system of parallel chords.

Solution. Points P_1, P_2 (extremities on the parabola of a given chord of the system, Fig. 75) are given by

$$y^2 = 4a\left(\frac{y}{m}-\frac{c}{m}\right), \quad \text{where } m = \tan\alpha,$$

i.e. $y^2-\dfrac{4a}{m}y+\dfrac{4ac}{m} = 0$ (roots y_1, y_2).

$$\therefore \bar{y} = \tfrac{1}{2}(y_1+y_2) = \tfrac{1}{2}\left[-\left(\frac{-4a}{m}\right)\right] = \frac{2a}{m}$$

$$= 2a\cot\alpha$$

$$= \text{const.}$$

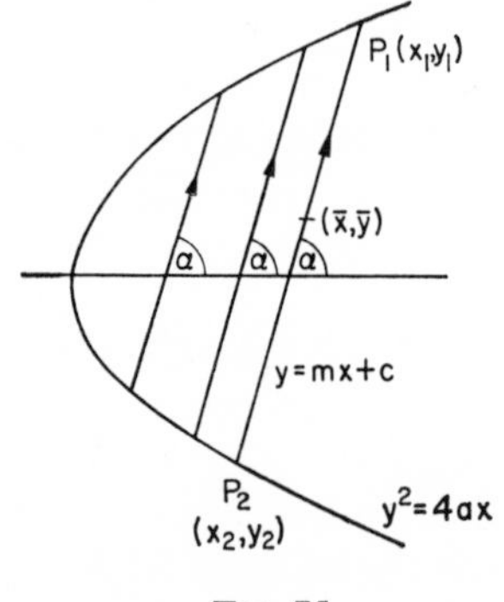

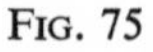
FIG. 75

Therefore *the locus of mid-points is a straight line || axis, i.e., a diameter.*

[In this example the non-parametric method has been used to add variety to our techniques. Parameters can be neatly employed if we take the special parallel chord of the system to be the focal chord so that $\bar{y} = \tfrac{1}{2}\left(2at-\dfrac{2a}{t}\right)$,

i.e. $\bar{y} = a\dfrac{(t^2-1)}{t} = 2a\cot 2\theta$ by (202),

i.e. $\bar{y} = 2a\cot\alpha$, $\therefore \alpha = 2\theta$ because $\triangle SPT$ (Fig. 72) is isosceles.]

EXAMPLE 109. The orthocentre of the triangle formed by three tangents to a parabola lies on the directrix. (*Steiner's theorem;* Steiner, 1796–1863, Swiss.)

Solution. Equations of the tangents (Fig. 76) are:

$$BC: y = \frac{x}{t'} + at', \quad CA: y = \frac{x}{t''} + at'', \quad AB: y = \frac{x}{t'''} + at'''.$$

Solve for CA, AB.

$$\therefore A \equiv (at''t''', a\,\overline{t''+t'''}).$$

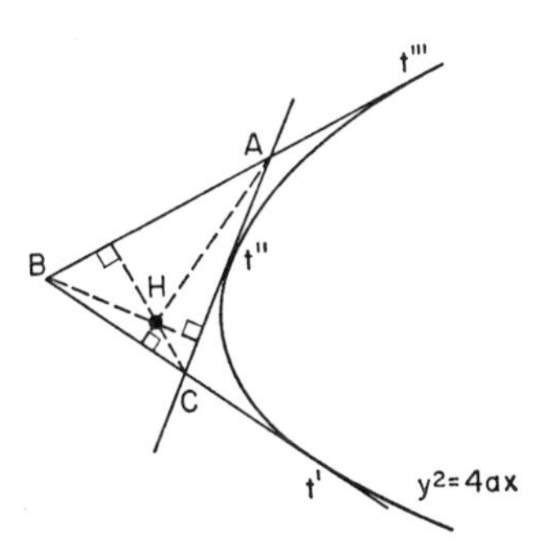

FIG. 76. Steiner's theorem

The equation of the line through this point perpendicular to BC is $y - a(t''+t''') = -t'(x - at''t''')$.

This cuts the directrix $x = -a$ in the point whose ordinate is $a(t'+t''+t'''+t't''t''')$. The symmetry of this expression shows that the other perpendiculars cut the directrix in the same point.

Therefore the orthocentre H lies on the directrix.

[It may be verified that the equation of the circumcircle of the $\triangle ABC$ is $x^2+y^2-ax(1+\sum t''+t''')-ay(\sum t'-t't''t''')+a^2\sum t''t''' = 0$. Hence, it passes through the focus $(a, 0)$.]

A parabola like that Fig. 76 is said to be *inscribed* in the $\triangle ABC$. As the parabola inscribed in $\triangle ABC$ varies, we see that (i) the locus of the focus is the circumcircle of $\triangle ABC$, and that (ii) all the directrices pass through H.

EXAMPLE 110 (link with pole and polar). Show that the polar of any point on the parabola $y^2 = 4ax$ w.r.t. the ellipse $\frac{x^2}{\alpha} + \frac{y^2}{\beta} = 1$ touches a parabola whose *latus rectum* is $\frac{\beta^2}{a\alpha}$.

Solution. By (196.1) the polar of P w.r.t. the ellipse is $x\frac{at^2}{\alpha} + y\frac{2at}{\beta} = 1$, i.e. $y = -\frac{\beta t}{2\alpha}x + \frac{\beta}{2at}$ (Fig.77).

Now the line $y = Mx+A/M$ always touches the parabola whose *latus rectum* is

$$4A = 4\frac{A}{M}M; \quad \therefore\ M = -\frac{\beta t}{2\alpha} \quad \text{and} \quad \frac{a}{M} = \frac{\beta}{2at}.$$

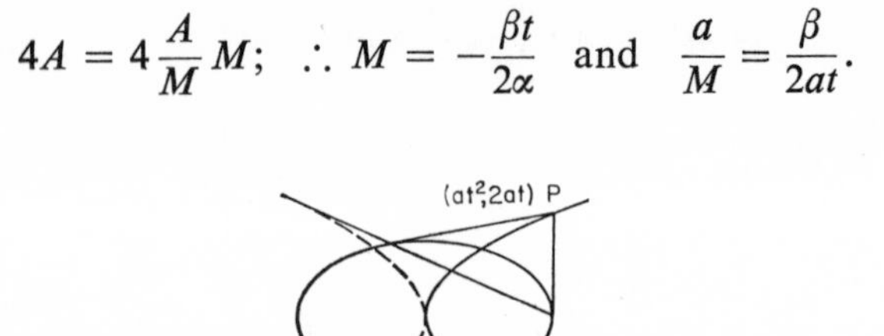

FIG. 77

Therefore the *latus rectum* of the parabola of which the polar is a tangent is

$$4\frac{\beta}{2at}\cdot -\frac{\beta t}{2\alpha} = \frac{-\beta^2}{a\alpha}, \quad \text{i.e.} \ -4A = \frac{\beta^2}{a\alpha}.$$

§ 91. NORMALS TO A PARABOLA

Let the normal at t pass through the fixed point (h, k) (Fig. 78a).

$$\therefore\ at^3+2at-ht-k = 0$$

i.e.

$$at^3+0t^2+(2a-h)t-k = 0 \tag{i}$$

(cubic in t with roots t_1, t_2, t_3).

Therefore ∃ *three normals from a point to a parabola.*

[If the point is outside the parabola then the normals are 1 real, 2 imaginary.]

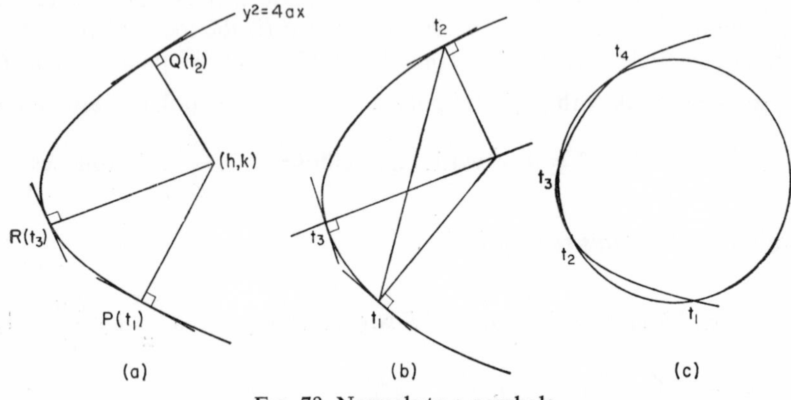

FIG. 78. Normals to a parabola

From (i), we have, by (121),

$$t_1+t_2+t_3 = 0 \tag{ii}$$

Therefore the centroid of $\triangle PQR$ has ordinate

$$\frac{y_1+y_2+y_3}{3} = \frac{2a}{3}(t_1+t_2+t_3) = 0.$$

Therefore *the centroid of the triangle formed by the feet of the normals lies on the axis of the parabola.*

Next, suppose we have a system of parallel chords. Consider one member of the system whose extremities have parameters t_1, t_2 (Fig. 78b).

$\therefore\ y_1+y_2 = \text{const.}$ (Example 108)

$\therefore\ 2a(t_1+t_2) = \text{const.}$

$\therefore\ t_1+t_2 = \text{const.}$

$\therefore\ t_3 = \text{const.}$ by (ii)

$\therefore\ y_3 = \text{const.}$

$\therefore$ the 3rd normal is a fixed line.

Therefore *normals at the extremities of a system of parallel chords intersect on a fixed straight line which is normal to the parabola.*

Suppose the parabola meets the circle $x^2+y^2+2fy+2gx+c = 0$ in points with parameters t_i $(i = 1, 2, 3, 4)$ (Fig. 78c). Solve for y.

$$\therefore\ \frac{y^4}{16a^2}+0\cdot y^3+\left(1+\frac{g}{2a}\right)y^2+2fy+c = 0 \quad \text{(quartic with roots } y_i).$$

Then by (121), we have

$$\therefore\ \sum y_i = 0,$$

i.e.

$$2a\sum t_i = 0.$$

$$\therefore\ \sum t_i = 0. \tag{iii}$$

If (ii), (iii) are simultaneously true, then $t_4 = 0$.

Therefore *the circumcircle of $\triangle PQR$ passes through the vertex of the parabola* (*Halley's theorem*, Halley, 1656–1742, English).

Scientific applications of parabolas

(i) *Reflecting properties of the parabola.* In Fig. 72, $SP = SG$ by (206).

$\therefore\ S\hat{P}G = S\hat{G}P.$

By Snell's law in physics, $S\hat{P}G = G\hat{P}X$ for light rays emanating from S (and $S\hat{P}T = X\hat{P}T'$).

$\therefore\ S\hat{G}P = G\hat{P}X$

$\therefore\ PX \,//$ axis of the parabola.

Supposing then that we have a paraboloid of revolution, i.e. a surface formed by rotating the parabola about its axis. Rays emanating from the focus S are reflected in a parallel beam.

Therefore a paraboloid of revolution forms a good searchlight if the source of light is at S. The same principle applies to theatrical spotlights, automobile headlights, and electric bar radiators (focus along the bar).

Reversely, if light comes from afar, e.g. from the Sun or a star, so that the rays are parallel, they converge at S (e.g. on a photographic plate).

Therefore a paraboloid of revolution forms a good burning glass. Indeed, it is reputed to have been used for this purpose by Archimedes in 212 B.C. when he helped destroy the Roman fleet besieging Syracuse (Sicily).

Today, paraboloidal mirrors and lenses are much used (e.g. in the French Pyrenees) for trapping the Sun's rays to develop heat to generate power for electricity and irrigation. Radio astronomy also finds the paraboloid a useful giant ear (paraboloid telescope) for catching (i.e. focusing) radio waves emitted from distant stars.

The (parabolic) section of the paraboloidal radio telescope used in ionospheric research at the University of New England has equation $y^2 = 100x$ (measurement in feet). [Mounted at the focus of this telescope, the transmitter is to obtain radar reflections from the outer layers of the Sun.]

On 13 August, 1964, the Parkes (N.S.W.) radio telescope (focal length AS = 86·1 ft, aperture = 210 ft.) got the first firm "fix" on the quasar ($\equiv$ quasi-stellar radio source), code listing 0106+01, the fast-moving celestial body on the fringe of the observable Universe, "brighter than 100 billion Suns".

(ii) *Projectile trajectories.* Neglecting air resistance, we know, as Galileo knew, that the natural path of a projectile ($\equiv$ missile, e.g., bullet, rocket) is a parabola. Sparks flung out from a Catherine wheel in a fireworks display or a jet of water are more peaceful instances of a parabolic profile.

(iii) *Other applications.* (a) Bridge construction: arches in some types of bridges are parabolic e.g. the Sydney Harbour Bridge. Also, a suspension-cable bridge is approximately parabolic if the load along the horizontal road-bed is distributed uniformly.

(b) Statistics. Sometimes in the *method of least squares* a parabola is the "best-fitting" curve for a set of experimentally observed points.

(c) Integration: *Simpson's rule* (Simpson, 1710–61, English) for approximate numerical integration is based on a set of parabolas.

Suggested topic for further study

Scientific applications of the parabola (more extensive treatment).

References

Geometry texts listed in the bibliography, together with:

(a) *Elementary Coordinate Geometry*, E. A. Maxwell (O.U.P., 1951).
(b) *Elementary Coordinate Geometry*, A. S. Ramsey (C.U.P., 1962).
(c) *Analytical Geometry*, B. Spain (Pergamon, 1963).

EXERCISES 17

(Unless otherwise stated, all questions relate to the parabola $y^2 = 4ax$.)

1. Show that the locus of the mid-point of chords which pass through the focus of a parabola is a parabola whose *latus rectum* is half that of the original parabola.

2. A tangent to $y^2 = 4ax$ meets $y^2+4bx = 0$ at A, B. What is the locus of the mid-point of AB?

3. Which points of the curve $y^2 = 2x+5$ are nearest the origin?

4. Normals at the extremities of a focal chord of the parabola $x = at^2, y = 2at$ intersect in R. Find the locus of R as the chord varies.

5. A fixed circle touches both rectangular axes. A point P moves so that its abscissa is equal to the length of the tangent from P to the circle. Obtain the locus of P.

6. The normal at the point t meets the parabola again at the point u. Obtain u as a function of t.

7. Prove that $x = 2t-1$, $y = 3t^2+2$ are parametric equations of a parabola and obtain the equation of the chord t_1t_2.

8. PQ is a variable focal chord and O the vertex of a parabola. Prove that the locus of the centroid of $\triangle POQ$ is the parabola $9y^2 = 4a(3x-2a)$.

9. Two points A, B on the parabola $x^2 = y$ have parameters a, b respectively ($b > a$). Where is the point on the parabola with parameter $a+b$? Also construct the point with parameter $b-a$.

10. The chain of a suspension bridge hangs in the form of a parabola whose axis is vertical. In the Menai Suspension Bridge (connecting North Wales with the island of Anglesey), the chain hangs symmetrically with a span of 570 ft and a dip of 43 ft. Find the *latus rectum* of the parabola and the angle of inclination to the horizon at each end of the chain.

11. Two parabolas $x^2 = 2y$, $y^2 = 4x$ intersect at O, P and the semi-*latus rectum* SL of $y^2 = 4ax$ meets OP at Q. What is the length of SQ? What are the homogeneous coordinates of the point in which SQ cuts l_∞?

12. A ray of light comes from a distant light source along the line $y = k$ and strikes the surface of the parabola $y^2 = 4ax$ at P, being then reflected through the focus to strike the surface again at Q. Along what line will it leave the parabola at Q?

13. At Jodrell Bank, the University of Manchester radio telescope has *latus rectum* 250 ft. From the deepest point (vertex) of the steel-plated reflecting surface, a mast is erected with an aerial on top coinciding with the focus. Assuming the telescope to be perfectly paraboloidal, how high should the mast and aerial together be?

14. Mid-point of the chord PQ of $y^2 = 4ax$ is M. Tangents at P, Q meet at T, and K is the mid-point of TM. Prove:

(i) TM is parallel to the axis of the parabola;
(ii) K lies on the parabola.

15. In Exercise 1.29, what is the *latus rectum* of the parabola occurring in the solution?

16. At a given point P on the parabola $y^2 = 4ax$, pairs of perpendicular lines are drawn to cut the curve in points Q_1, Q_2. The normal at P cuts $Q_1 Q_2$ at a point F which is known to be fixed for variable chords Q_1Q_2 ($F \equiv$ *Frégier point* of P). Suppose P varies. What is the locus of F?

Neglecting air resistance (i.e. ignoring forces other than gravity), we know that the position at time t of a missile fired from a gun with muzzle at the origin is given by $x = vt \cos \theta$, $y = vt \sin \theta - \frac{1}{2}gt^2$, where v is the muzzle (initial) velocity of the missile and θ is the angle of inclination to the horizontal of the initial direction of flight.

17. Prove that the trajectory ($\equiv$ path) of the missile is a parabola whose axis is // y-axis.

18. Determine the vertex, directrix, focus, and *latus rectum* of this parabola.

19. What is the horizontal range r?

20. Deduce the value of θ which gives the maximum range.

21. To what height will the missile rise?

22. Derive the total time of flight.

23. Verify that the equation of the flight path may be written as $y = \left(1 - \frac{x}{r}\right) x \tan \theta$.

24. Flight-times for two different angles of projection are t_1, t_2 for the same range r. Establish that $r = \frac{gt_1t_2}{2}$.

25. A projectile is fired with velocity v, up a plane, say, a uniformly sloping hill, inclined to the horizontal at an angle α, its initial direction of flight making an angle θ with the horizontal. Assuming that the range R of the parabolic trajectory is $2V^2 \sec^2 \alpha \cos \theta \sin (\theta - \alpha)/g$, determine the value of θ which imparts a maximum value to the range.

26. Variable points $P(p)$ and $Q(q)$ on a parabola are such that PQ always subtends a right angle at the vertex O. Prove that $pq = -4$ for all positions of P, Q and that, geometrically, this means that the variable chord PQ always passes through a fixed point on the x-axis.

27. The Mills Cross (radio telescope) near Canberra consists of two cylindrical paraboloids, each 1 mile long. The east–west cylinder has a focal length of 9·6 ft and an aperture (diameter) of 38 ft, whereas the north–south cylinder has a focal length of 16 ft and an aperture of 42 ft. (The antenna has a line of receiving dipoles along the line-focus of each of the parabolic cylinders.) Obtain the equations of the parabolic sections of each arm of the Cross, and the ratio of the *latera recta*.

28. Roof trusses are in the form of two vertical parabolas (vertices A_1, A_2 upwards, $A_1A_2 = 1$ ft) whose intersections P, Q are 20 ft apart, and A_1 is 5 ft above PQ. Vertical struts are placed at horizontal intervals of 2 ft. Let B_1B_2 be the vertical strut next to A_1A_2. First determine the equations of the parabolas and then calculate the lengths of B_1B_2 and the diagonal strut A_2B_1.

29. Degenerate conics of the pencil $\lambda P + C = 0$ passing through the four points of intersection A_i ($i = 1, \ldots, 4$) of the parabola $P \equiv y^2 - 4ax = 0$ and the circle $C \equiv (x-\alpha)^2 + (y-\beta)^2 - r^2 = 0$ are given by the cubic equation

$$\Delta\lambda^3 + \Theta\lambda^2 + \Theta'\lambda + \Delta' = 0.$$

Establish this cubic, stating the values of the coefficients $\Delta, \Theta, \Theta', \Delta'$. Explain how the degenerate conics are related to A_i.

30. What special relation does C bear to P if $\Theta = 0$ in Exercise 17.29?

CHAPTER 18

THE ELLIPSE

... the Great Bear is looking so geometrical
One would think that something or other could be proved.

(CHRISTOPHER FRY)

§92. BASIC PROPERTIES

In Fig. 79 $\boxed{\text{Definition: } SP = ePM \ (e < 1)}$ as in (180)

$$\boxed{\text{Equation: } \frac{x^2}{a^2}+\frac{y^2}{b^2} = 1}. \quad \text{as in (188)}$$

Put $x = ae$ and we find

$$\boxed{\textit{Latus rectum } LL' = \frac{2b^2}{a}} \tag{215}$$

$$\boxed{\text{Gradient at } (x_1, y_1) \text{ is } \frac{dy}{dx} = -\frac{b^2x_1}{a^2y_1}} \tag{216}$$

i.e. at L, L' gradients are $\mp e$.

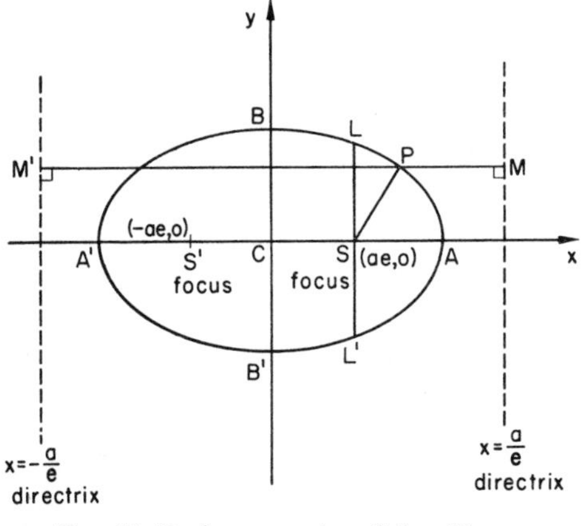

FIG. 79. Basic properties of the ellipse

We call the segments CA, CA' (each $= a$) the *semi-major axes* and CB, CB' (each $= b$) the *semi-minor axes*; AA' is the *major axis*, BB' the *minor axis*.

Regarding the circle $x^2+y^2 = a^2$ as a special case of the ellipse when $b = a$, we know that the focus is then at the centre and the directrix is the l_∞. But where is the *latus rectum*?

Problem: What is the eccentricity of an ellipse formed by a plane cutting the axis of a right circular cylinder at an angle β? (*Answer:* $e = |\cos \beta|$.) See *The American Mathematical Monthly*, **66** (8), 726 (1959), where this problem is proposed and solved. Consider the special cases $\beta = \pi/2$, $\beta \to 0$.

[More generally, for the conic section formed by a plane cutting at an angle β the axis of a right circular cone of semi-vertical angle α, $e = |\cos\beta|/\cos \alpha$. Details may be found in Walker [43].]

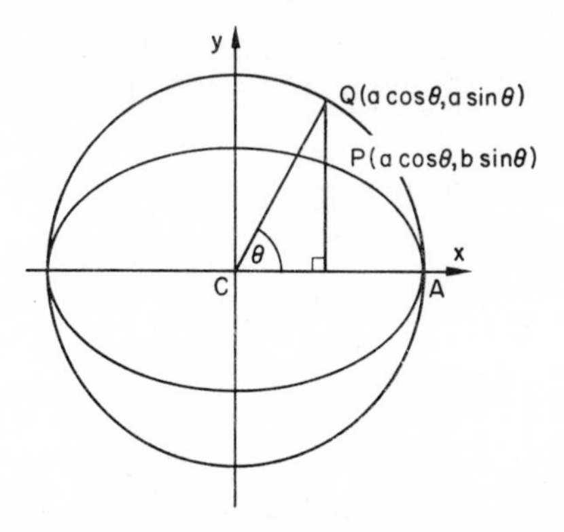

FIG. 80. Eccentric angle of a point on the ellipse

With centre C, radius CA, construct the *major auxiliary circle* $x^2+y^2 = a^2$. Complete the construction as shown in Fig. 80. Then, parametrically,

$$\boxed{P \equiv (a \cos \theta,\ b \sin \theta)} \tag{217}$$

where the parameter θ is also called the *eccentric angle* of P, e.g. at L, $\theta = \cos^{-1} e$. [Could P be given parametrically by means of the minor auxiliary circle? If so, how?] Using (216), we have that the equations of the tangent and normal at P are:

$$\boxed{\text{Tangent: } \frac{x \cos \theta}{a} + \frac{y \sin \theta}{b} = 1 \left(\text{gradient } -\frac{b}{a} \cot \theta\right)} \tag{218}$$

$$\boxed{\text{Normal: } \frac{ax}{\cos \theta} - \frac{by}{\sin \theta} = a^2e^2 \left(\text{gradient } \frac{a}{b} \tan \theta\right)}\,. \tag{219}$$

In (219), put $y = 0$ giving $x = ae^2 \cos\theta = ae \cdot e \cos\theta$, where $e < 1$, $-1 \leqslant \cos\theta \leqslant 1$.

$$\therefore\ -ae < x < ae.$$

Therefore *normals always pass between the foci.*

$$\begin{aligned} \text{Also, } SP+S'P &= e(PM+PM') \quad \text{(definition)} \\ &= eMM' \\ &= e\frac{2a}{e}, \end{aligned}$$

i.e. we obtain the *bifocal property*

$$\boxed{SP+S'P = 2a} \tag{220}$$

which is sometimes taken as the definition of an ellipse. Moreover, it enables us to construct an ellipse mechanically. [How?]

Thus, if $P \equiv B$ so that $SB = S'B = a$, the foci are constructible by drawing a circle with centre B and radius a cutting the major axis in S, S', i.e. put $y = 0$ in $x^2+(y-b)^2 = a^2$.

Putting $t = \tan\frac{\theta}{2}$, we have, in (122.1), $x = a\frac{(1-t^2)}{1+t^2}$, $y = \frac{2bt}{1+t^2}$.

$$\therefore\ \frac{x}{a} : \frac{y}{b} : 1 = 1-t^2 : 2t : 1+t^2.$$

$\therefore\ 1-\frac{x}{a} : \frac{y}{b} : 1+\frac{x}{a} = t^2 : t : 1$, i.e. $\frac{1-x/a}{y/b} = \frac{y/b}{1+x/a}$ $(= t)$, i.e. (188) in disguise.

§ 93. SELECTED PROBLEMS SOLVED PARAMETRICALLY

EXAMPLE 111 (a standard type of locus problem). Given PP' parallel to the y-axis, PQ perpendicular to OP', what is the locus of Q? (Fig. 81.)

Solution. Normal at P: $\frac{ax}{\cos\theta} - \frac{by}{\sin\theta} = a^2-b^2$.

Equation of OP' : $y = -\frac{b}{a}\tan\theta\, x$.

Solve: $\therefore\ x = \lambda a\cos\theta$, $y = -\lambda b\sin\theta$, where $\lambda = \frac{a^2-b^2}{a^2+b^2} < 1$.

Therefore the locus of Q is the ellipse $\frac{x^2}{\lambda^2 a^2}+\frac{y^2}{\lambda^2 b^2} = 1$ co-axial with the original ellipse, and having semi-axes λa, λb and

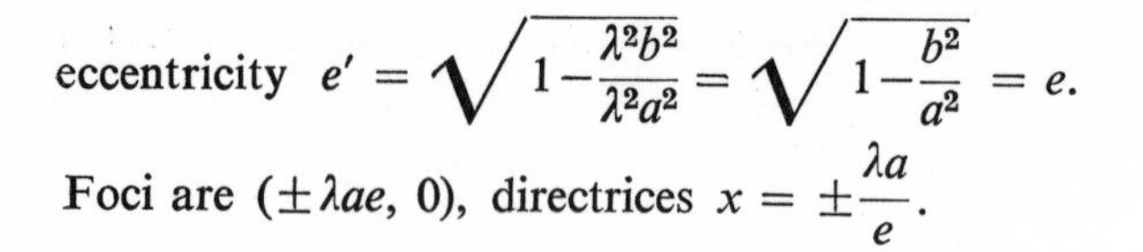

eccentricity $e' = \sqrt{1-\dfrac{\lambda^2 b^2}{\lambda^2 a^2}} = \sqrt{1-\dfrac{b^2}{a^2}} = e.$

Foci are $(\pm\lambda ae, 0)$, directrices $x = \pm\dfrac{\lambda a}{e}$.

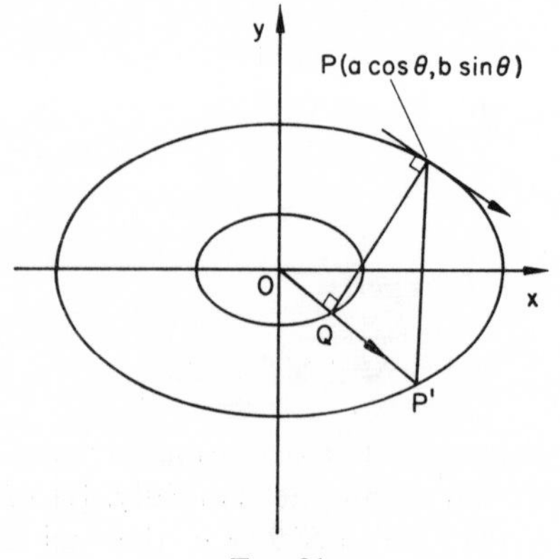

FIG. 81

EXAMPLE 112. Locus of the point of intersection of perpendicular tangents to an ellipse (the *director circle*).

Solution. By (218) the equation of the tangent at $(a \cos \theta, b \sin \theta)$ is

$$y = -\frac{b}{a} \cot \theta \cdot x + \frac{b}{\sin \theta},$$

i.e. $\quad y = mx+\sqrt{a^2m^2+b^2}$ on writing $m = -\dfrac{b}{a}\cot\theta$,

(i.e. $\exists$ two parallel tangents).

Let such a tangent pass through the point $P(\xi, \eta)$ (Fig. 82).

$$\therefore\ \eta = m\xi+\sqrt{a^2m^2+b^2}.$$

$$\therefore\ a^2m^2+b^2 = (m\xi-\eta)^2,$$

i.e. $$m^2(a^2-\xi^2)+2m\xi\eta+b^2-\eta^2 = 0.$$

This is a quadratic in m with roots m_1, m_2 which are the gradients of the two tangents from P. If these tangents are perpendicular, then $m_1m_2 = -1$,

i.e. $$\frac{b^2-\eta^2}{a^2-\xi^2} = -1,$$

i.e. $$\xi^2+\eta^2 = a^2+b^2.$$

Therefore the locus of P is the *director circle*

$$\boxed{x^2+y^2 = a^2+b^2}. \tag{221}$$

In the case of the parabola, we saw (Example 106) that the locus of the point of intersection of pairs of perpendicular tangents is the directrix. Pretty clearly, the director circle of the parabola is degenerate and consists

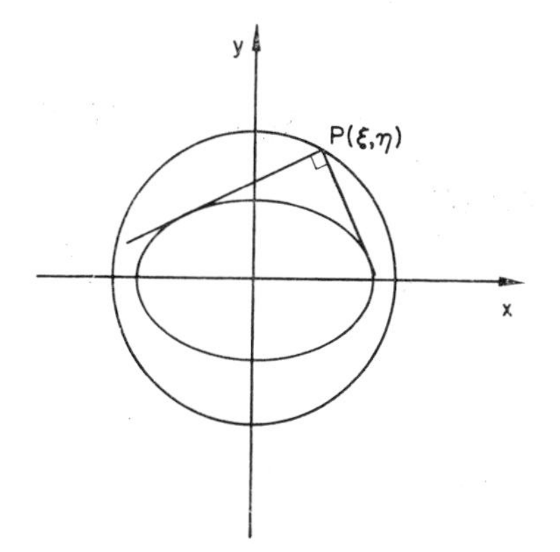

FIG. 82. Director circle

of the directrix and another line, which *must* be the l_∞—this can be seen algebraically by using homogeneous coordinates or geometrically from the fact that a circle must pass through I, J on l_∞.

Note on normals

It may be proved that, from a given point, *four normals can be drawn to an ellipse*. The working is not so elegant as that for the parabola, so we do not pursue the calculation here. But you should try to do it yourself. (Furthermore, it is a fact that the four feet of the normals are the intersections of the ellipse and a rectangular hyperbola known as the *hyperbola of Apollonius*.)

§ 94. CONJUGATE DIAMETERS

Definition. The locus of the mid-points of a system of chords parallel to a given diameter of an ellipse is another diameter; both diameters are said to be *conjugate diameters*.

Usually the relationship between the gradients of two conjugate diameters is obtained by parametric means involving a good deal of trigonometry, but a shorter method is herewith appended. Another neat treatment, which is not given here, utilises orthogonal projection. [As an exercise, you should work out the equation of a chord of an ellipse joining the points with parameters θ, θ'.]

EXAMPLE 113. If two conjugate diameters have gradients m, m', then

$$\boxed{mm' = -\frac{b^2}{a^2}}. \tag{222}$$

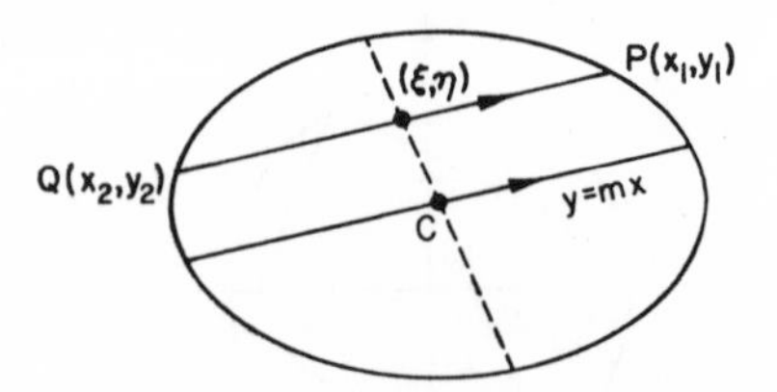

FIG. 83. Conjugate diameters

Solution. From Fig. 83, if (ξ, η) is the mid-point of the chord PQ parallel to the diameter $y = mx$, we have

$$\frac{\xi}{\eta} = \frac{x_1+x_2}{y_1+y_2} \quad \text{and} \quad m = \frac{y_1-y_2}{x_1-x_2}. \tag{i}$$

But $\dfrac{x_1^2}{a^2}+\dfrac{y_1^2}{b^2} = \dfrac{x_2^2}{a^2}+\dfrac{y_2^2}{b^2} = 1$, $\because$ P, Q lie on the ellipse.

$$\therefore\ a^2(y_1^2-y_2^2) = -b^2(x_1^2-x_2^2)$$

$$\therefore\ a^2\frac{(y_1-y_2)}{x_1-x_2} = -b^2\frac{(x_1+x_2)}{y_1+y_2},$$

i.e. $$a^2m = -b^2\frac{\xi}{\eta} \quad \text{from (i) above.}$$

Therefore the conjugate diameter has equation $b^2x+a^2my = 0$,

i.e. $$y = m'x \quad \text{where} \quad mm' = -\frac{b^2}{a^2}.$$

Comments

(i) How is this result modified in the case of the circle?

(ii) It can be shown that conjugate diameters *are* conjugate lines (see § 88, Corollary). Can you do it?

Properties of conjugate diameters

With reference to the *conjugate semi-diameters* CP, CQ in Fig. 84, the following basic properties should be obtained:

$$\boxed{\theta' = \theta \pm \frac{\pi}{2}} \tag{223}$$

$$\boxed{CP^2 + CQ^2 = a^2 + b^2} \tag{224}$$

$$\boxed{\text{Area of parallelogram } CPRQ \text{ is } ab = CP \cdot CQ \sin \psi} \tag{225}$$

$$\boxed{\psi_{\min} \Rightarrow \theta = \frac{\pi}{4}, \frac{3\pi}{4}}\,. \tag{226}$$

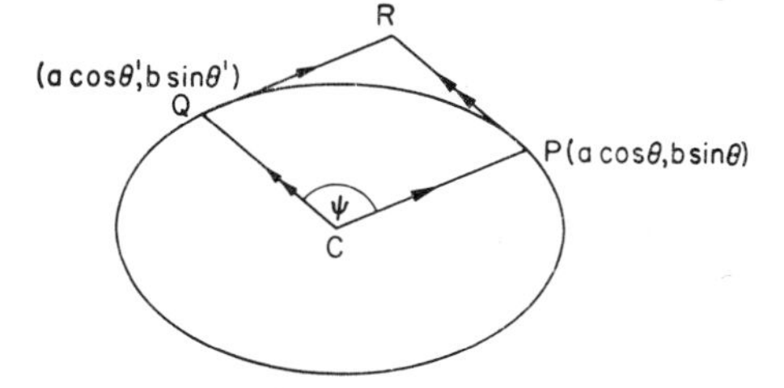

FIG. 84. Conjugate semi-diameters

The diameters which are then equal are called *equi-conjugate diameters* and their equations are $y = \pm \frac{b}{a} x$.

$$\boxed{\psi_{\max} = \frac{\pi}{2}}\,. \tag{227}$$

Natural occurrence and scientific applications of the ellipse

Orbits

(i) Planetary orbits around the Sun (as one focus), e.g. Earth's orbit is a nearly circular ellipse whose axes are in the ratio 7001 : 7000.

(ii) Cometary and meteor orbits (e.g. Halley's comet with periodicity of 76 years; and $e \doteqdot 0{\cdot}97$) if the Sun loses its gravitational attraction the elliptic cometary orbit will leave the solar system.

(iii) Moons around a planet (e.g. the moons Deimos and Phobos around Mars; our Moon); satellites and other artificial moons.

(iv) Trajectories of elementary atomic particles, i.e. electrons around atomic nucleus.

Acoustics

Sound waves emitted from one focus are reflected at the other—this is sometimes the explanation of "whispering galleries". A brass marker on the

Statuary Hall, Washington, U.S.A. (once used as the Representatives' Chamber) identifies the spot where J. Q. Adams in his early days sat and listened to his opponents plotting against him on the opposite side of the room. His ability to anticipate opposition confounded his adversaries until the mathematical secret was revealed. (See Exercise 18.17.)

Other applications

Masonry bridges are sometimes semi-elliptical. Automobile springs may be semi-elliptical. Laué spots formed on a photographic plate by radiation from an X-ray tube through crystals of rocksalt will approximate to ellipses. Elliptic gears occur in some machines. In the theory of the bending of beams occurs the ellipse of inertia. Engineers and architects use the ellipse as the projection of a circle (Fig. 52).

Suggested topics for further study

(1) Conjugate diameters.
(2) Satellite and rocket orbits. (Consult G. R. Langdale, *The Mathematical Gazette*, **47**, (360), 269–71 (1963), for a simple course on astronautics.)

References

As for Chapter 17.

EXERCISES 18

(Unless otherwise stated, all problems refer to the standard ellipse.)

1. A parabola whose axis is along the axis of x intersects the ellipse $\frac{x^2}{a^2}+\frac{y^2}{b^2} = 1$ orthogonally at the point whose eccentric angle is ϕ. Show that the *latus rectum* of the parabola is $2a \sin\phi \tan\phi$.

2. What is the eccentricity of the curve $8(x-1)^2+6(y+1)^2-1 = 0$? Also obtain the coordinates of the foci, and the equations of the directrices. Give a rough sketch of the curve.

3. Two circles have a common centre O. A variable radius cuts them in Q and Q'. Through Q and Q' are drawn lines parallel respectively to two fixed rectangular diameters. Show that the locus of their intersection is an ellipse.

4. Chords of an ellipse are drawn from one end of the major axis. Determine the locus of their mid-points.

5. In a certain ellipse, the normal to the curve at an end of the *latus rectum* passes through an end of the minor axis. What is the eccentricity of the curve?

6. Granted that the Earth moves in an ellipse with the Sun as one of its foci, which is such that the ratio of the shortest distance from the Earth to the Sun (perihelion), to the largest distance from the Earth to the Sun (aphelion), is 29:30, determine the eccentricity of the Earth's orbit.

7. What is the eccentricity of an ellipse (Fagnano's ellipse) whose foci subtend a right angle at the ends of the minor axis?

8. Eccentricities and lengths of the semi-major axes of the (elliptic) orbits of the planets Neptune and Pluto are:

	e	a
Neptune	0·0082	2793·5 × 10^6 miles
Pluto	0·25	3680 × 10^6 miles

Show that Pluto is sometimes closer than Neptune to the Sun. [Pluto will be closer than Neptune to the Sun in 1989.]

9. P is a variable point of the ellipse $\frac{x^2}{a^2}+\frac{y^2}{b^2} = 1$ and the normal at P meets the major axis in F and the minor axis in G. What is the locus of the mid-point of FG? Obtain the eccentricity of the locus and sketch it roughly.

10. Any tangent to an ellipse cuts the tangents at the vertices A and A' at points V and V'. Prove that VV' subtends a right angle at either focus.

11. Eccentricity of a standard ellipse through (1, 1) is $\frac{3}{4}$. What are the two possible equations of the ellipse?

12. Obtain the equation of a tangent at the end of a *latus rectum*, and show that it cuts the x-axis on the corresponding directrix.

13. Two points A, B are distant $2a$ apart and P is a point such that $P\hat{A}B = \theta$, $P\hat{B}A = \phi$. If $\tan\theta\tan\phi = b^2/a^2$, what is the locus of P?

14. Vectorial equation of the ellipse is $(\mathbf{r}\cdot\mathbf{k})^2-a^2(r^2+k^2)+a^4 = 0$, where $\mathbf{k}$, $-\mathbf{k}$, $\mathbf{r}$ are position vectors of the foci and an arbitrary point on the ellipse, and the major axis $= 2a$. Establish this equation.

15. A tangent to the ellipse cuts the x-, y-axes at A, B respectively. What is the locus of the mid-point of AB and where does it cut l_∞?

16. Minimise the length AB in Exercise 18.15.

17. Tangent and normal at P on the ellipse are bisectors of $S\hat{P}S'$. Establish this *reflecting property* of the ellipse.

18. A circle passes through both foci of an ellipse and touches the ellipse at two points. Determine the eccentricity of the ellipse.

19. Determine the gradients and equations of the tangents at the extremities of a *latus rectum* of the ellipse. Where do they intersect?

20. Apogee and perigee of Russia's Cosmos satellite, launched on 15 March, 1965, were 1075 miles and 165 miles respectively. What eccentricity had "Cosmos"?

[Perigee and apogee of America's 1965 Early Bird telecommunications satellite were 910 miles and 22,860 miles respectively.] (Radius of Earth $\doteqdot$ 4000 miles.)

21. Chords $B'P$ are drawn from a fixed point B' $(0, -b)$ on the ellipse to variable points P. Maximise $B'P$ and fix the position of P. (*Lampe's problem;* Lampe, 1840–1918, German.)

22. Derive the maximum distance from the centre to a normal of the ellipse.

23. Shifting the origin to $(-a, 0)$ for the ellipse and letting $e \to 1$, show that the parabola is a limiting case of the ellipse.

24. Express e in terms of θ and ϕ, the eccentricities of a focal chord. Examine the special case of the circle.

25. Eccentric angles of two points on an ellipse differ by a constant ($= 2\alpha$). What is the locus of the intersection of the tangents at these points?

26. Verify that $u = \frac{m}{h^2}\left\{1+e\cos(\phi-\omega)+\frac{3m^2e}{h^2}\phi\sin(\phi-\omega)\right\}$ is a solution of $\frac{d^2u}{d\phi^2}+u = \frac{m}{h^2}\left(1+\frac{6m^2}{h^2}e\cos(\phi-\omega)\right)$, occurring in Einstein's theory of planetary motion in his general relativity theory.

27. More compactly (in Exercise 18.26), $u = \frac{m}{h^2}\{1+e\cos(\phi-\omega-\varepsilon)\}$. Express ε in terms of ϕ. (Neglect ε^2.)

Exercises 18.26, 18.27 relate to the *advance of the perihelion of Mercury*, one of the three predictions made by Einstein to justify his theory and to remove discrepancies unexplained by Newtonian celestial mechanics. (The other two: gravitational deflection of light, in the presence of a strong field, and shift to the red end of the spectrum of a star.)

28. Reduce the ellipse $x^2+4xy\tan\phi+(4\tan^2\phi+1)y^2 = 1$ to standard form.

[Refer to the Smithsonian tables—Reference, Chapter 5—for further details of this interesting family of ellipses; in actual fact ϕ is the Gudermannian function.]

Length of a focal chord PQ of an ellipse is f and d is the length of a semi-diameter CD parallel to PQ.

29. Given $P(a\cos\theta, b\sin\theta)$, obtain the coordinates of Q.

30. Prove $f = \frac{2d^2}{a}$.

[Exercise 18.8 is taken from *Calculus and Analytic Geometry*, J. F. Randolph (Wadsworth Publishing Company, 1961, p. 47) and is here used by kind permission of the publishers.

Satellite details are obtained from the Goddard Space Flight Center, Maryland, by courtesy of the U.S. Information Service.]

CHAPTER 19

THE HYPERBOLA

How can it be that Mathematics, being after all a product of human thought independent of experience, is so admirably adapted to the objects of reality?

(EINSTEIN)

§95. BASIC PROPERTIES

Previously, we had (Fig. 85)

$$\boxed{\text{Definition: } SP = ePM(e > 1)} \tag{183}$$

$$\boxed{\text{equation: } \frac{x^2}{a^2} - \frac{y^2}{b^2} = 1}. \tag{190}$$

Now $S'P - SP = e(PM' - PM)$

$$= e\,MM'$$

$$= e \cdot \frac{2a}{e},$$

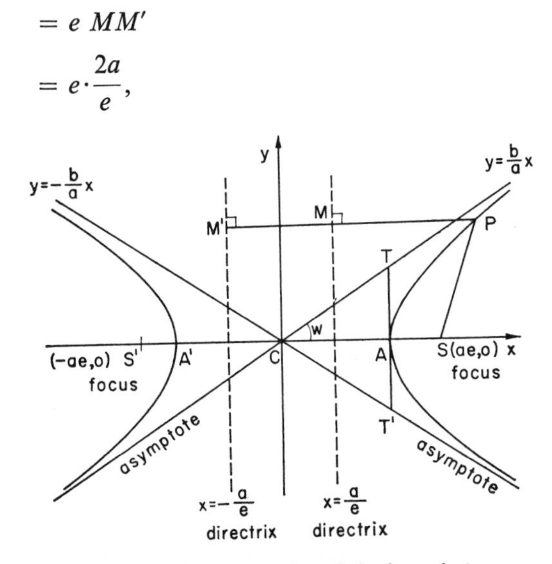

FIG. 85. Basic properties of the hyperbola

i.e. we obtain the *bifocal property*

$$\boxed{S'P - SP = 2a} \tag{228}$$

which is sometimes taken as the definition of a hyperbola. From this property, we are enabled to construct the hyperbola mechanically. We call the line SS' the *transverse axis*, the axis perpendicular to it is the *conjugate axis*.

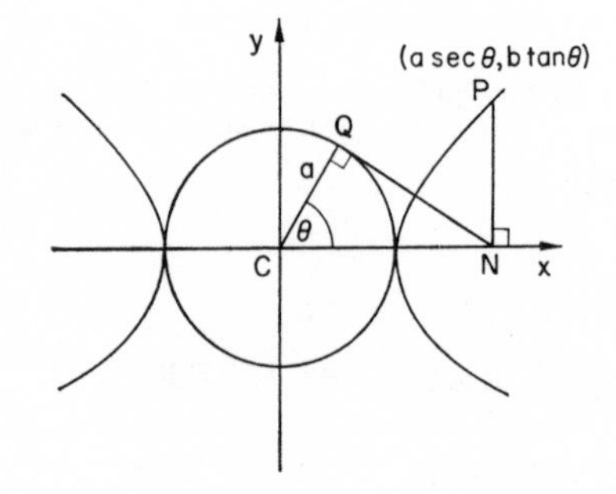

FIG. 86. Parametric coordinates of a point on the hyperbola

With centre C and radius a, construct the *auxiliary circle* as shown in Fig. 86. Parametrically, coordinates of P are

$$\boxed{\begin{aligned} x &= a \sec \theta \\ y &= b \tan \theta \end{aligned}} \tag{229}$$

where the parameter $\theta = Q\widehat{C}N$ corresponds to the eccentric angle of the ellipse.

As θ moves successively through the ranges $0 < \theta < \frac{\pi}{2}$, $\frac{\pi}{2} < \theta < \pi$, $\pi < \theta < \frac{3\pi}{2}$, $\frac{3\pi}{2} < \theta < 2\pi$, P traces the hyperbola in the first, third, second, and fourth quadrants respectively.

Equations of tangent and normal at P are

$$\boxed{\text{tangent: } \frac{x}{a} \sec \theta - \frac{y}{b} \tan \theta = 1} \tag{230}$$

$$\boxed{\text{normal: } ax \cos \theta + by \cot \theta = a^2e^2}. \tag{231}$$

As an exercise, obtain the equation of the chord joining the points with parameters θ, θ'.

Another parametric representation is ($a \cosh \phi$, $b \sin \phi$), where ϕ has a geometrical interpretation in terms of area (Exercise 23.49). But note the difficulty here due to the fact that x is always positive for real values of ϕ

(a, b positive) i.e. only the right-hand branch of the hyperbola is represented for $-\infty < \phi < \infty$. Parametric equations for the other branch are $x = -a\cosh\phi$, $y = -b\sinh\phi$.

Many basic results for the hyperbola may be derived from the corresponding ones for the ellipse by replacing b^2 by $-b^2$ (e.g., director circle: $x^2+y^2 = a^2-b^2$).

Essentially, the difference between the ellipse and the hyperbola is that the ellipse is a finite closed curve without real asymptotes, while the hyperbola is an infinite open curve with two branches and real asymptotes. Distinctive features of the hyperbola are usually concerned with the asymptotes.

Historically, it is interesting to note that the hyperbolas of Omar Khayyam (*ca.* 1045–1123, Persian) consisted of only one branch, since Omar rejected the possibility of negative numbers. For Khayyam's solution of cubic equations using conics, see A. R. Amir-Moéz, *Mathematics Magazine*, **35** (5), 269–71 (1962).

Knot a thread to a pencil at P (Fig. 85), then pass the thread around the foci S, S', keeping the thread taut; P will describe one branch of a hyperbola. Why? See Sommerville [41] p. 67.

§ 96. ASYMPTOTES

The line $y = mx+c$ and the hyperbola $y^2 = \frac{b^2}{a^2}(a^2+x^2)$ meet where

$$\left(m^2-\frac{b^2}{a^2}\right)x^2+2mcx+c^2-b^2 = 0. \tag{α}$$

If $y = mx+c$ is an asymptote (i.e. a tangent to the hyperbola at infinity), the roots of (α) are infinite. Put $x = 1/u$.

$$\therefore\ (c^2-b^2)u^2+2mcu+\left(m^2-\frac{b^2}{a^2}\right) = 0 \quad \text{has two zero roots, i.e. } u^2 = 0.$$

$$\therefore\ \frac{b^2}{a^2} = m^2 \quad \text{and} \quad mc = 0, \quad \text{i.e. } m = \pm\frac{b}{a},\ c = 0$$

$$\therefore\ \boxed{\text{asymptotes: } y = \pm\frac{b}{a}x} \tag{232}$$

which may be written $\frac{x^2}{a^2}-\frac{y^2}{b^2} = 0$. Clearly, they are the diagonals of a rectangle of sides $2a$, $2b$ centred on the origin.

Alternatively, make the equation of the hyperbola homogeneous and put $u = 0$. $\therefore\ b^2x^2-a^2y^2 = 0$ gives the coordinates of the two points in which the hyperbola cuts l_∞, i.e. the points $(x, \pm(b/a)x, 0)$. By § 78, these are the points at infinity common to the two sets of parallel lines with gradients $\pm b/a$. Since the asymptotes pass through the origin, their equations must be (232); or, use (196).

Angle of inclination w of the asymptotes to x-axis (Fig 85) is $\tan^{-1}\left(\pm\frac{b}{a}\right)$,

i.e. $\tan w = \pm\frac{b}{a} = \pm\sqrt{e^2-1}$.

$$\therefore \sec w = \sqrt{1+\frac{b^2}{a^2}} = e,$$

i.e. $$\boxed{w = \sec^{-1} e}. \tag{233}$$

Notice that the tangent at A, $x = a$, cuts the asymptotes at $T, T' \equiv (a, \pm b)$ (Fig. 85).

$$\therefore \quad CT = CT' = \sqrt{a^2+b^2} = ae.$$

This result gives a method of constructing the foci.

EXAMPLE 114. P is a point on a hyperbola (focus S) such that the tangent at P and the *latus rectum* through S meet on an asymptote. Prove that SP is parallel to the other asymptote (Fig. 87).

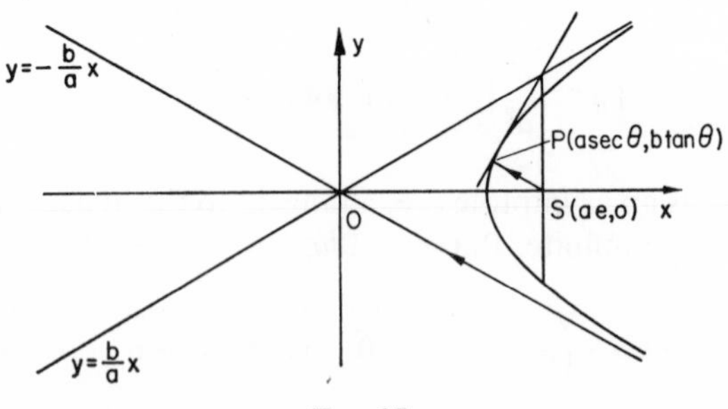

FIG. 87

Solution. Latus rectum $x = ae$ and asymptote $y = \frac{b}{a}x$ meet at (ae, be).

This lies on the tangent at P: $\frac{x}{a}\sec\theta - \frac{y}{b}\tan\theta = 1$.

$$\therefore \quad \frac{ae}{a}\sec\theta - \frac{be}{b}\tan\theta = 1,$$

$$\therefore \quad e(\sec\theta - \tan\theta) = 1,$$

$$\therefore \quad e = \tan\theta + \sec\theta,$$

i.e. $\tan\theta = -(\sec\theta - e)$,

i.e. $\dfrac{b\tan\theta}{a(\sec\theta - e)} = -\dfrac{b}{a}$,

i.e. the gradient of SP = the gradient of the asymptote $y = -\dfrac{b}{a}x$.

$\therefore$ SP is parallel to the other asymptote.

§ 97. RECTANGULAR HYPERBOLA

Let $b^2 = a^2$.

$$\therefore \boxed{e = \sqrt{2}}. \tag{234}$$

From (232) the equations of the asymptotes are thus

$$\boxed{\text{asymptotes: } y = \pm x} \tag{235}$$

which are perpendicular. (By (233), $w = \pi/4$.)

Equation of the hyperbola is now $x^2 - y^2 = a^2$.

Take these asymptotes as axes. Thus the transformation is, by (129)′ with $\phi = \pi/4$,

$$\begin{cases} X = \dfrac{x}{\sqrt{2}} + \dfrac{y}{\sqrt{2}}, \\[2ex] Y = -\dfrac{x}{\sqrt{2}} + \dfrac{y}{\sqrt{2}}, \end{cases}$$

i.e. $$\sqrt{2}X = x + y, \quad \sqrt{2}Y = -x + y.$$

Therefore the equation of the rectangular hyperbola reduces to

$$\boxed{2XY = -a^2}. \tag{236}$$

[Observe that the rectangular hyperbola bears the same relation to the hyperbola as the circle does to the ellipse since both are obtained by putting $b^2 = a^2$.]

Hyperbolas $\dfrac{x^2}{a^2} - \dfrac{y^2}{b^2} = 1$, $\dfrac{x^2}{a^2} - \dfrac{y^2}{b^2} = -1$ with the same asymptotes are *conjugate* (Fig. 88a). [Note that the relationship between a, b in (190) does not yield a horizontal or vertical hyperbola, as in the corresponding case of the ellipse. What is important is the sign ± 1 on the right-hand side.]

Parametrically, a point on the conjugate hyperbola has coordinates $(a \tan \theta, b \sec \theta)$.

Under the transformation to perpendicular asymptote axes, equations of the conjugate hyperbolas become $2XY = -a^2$ and $2XY = a^2$, i.e. in a fresh notation, $xy = -c^2$ and

$$\boxed{\text{rectangular hyperbola: } xy = c^2} \tag{237}$$

respectively (Fig. 88b).

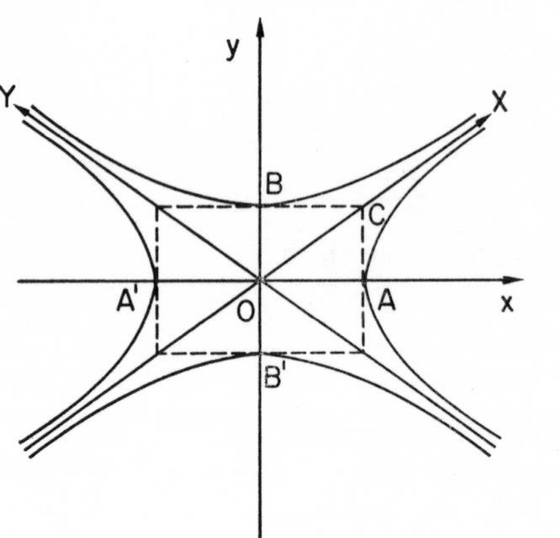

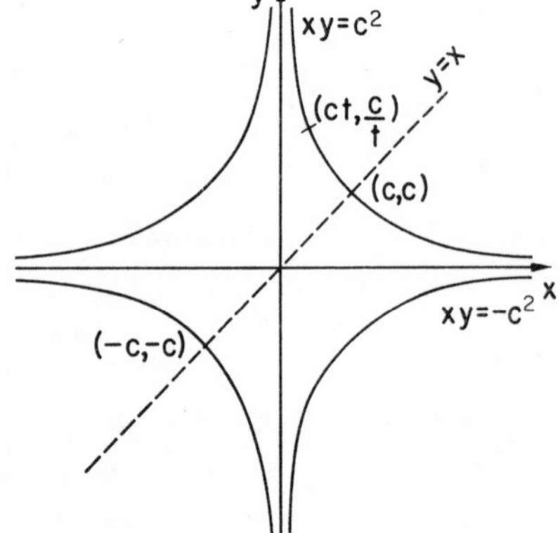

(a) Conjugate hyperbolas (b) Conjugate rectangular hyperbolas

FIG. 88

Parametrically, for (237),

$$\boxed{\begin{aligned} x &= ct \\ y &= \frac{c}{t} \end{aligned}} \tag{238}$$

where t is the parameter. (Nothing to do with the parameter t for the parabola.) Of course, the gas equation $pv = c$ (Boyle's law) relating variable pressure and volume for a gas under constant temperature, is represented by a rectangular hyperbola.

Equations of tangent and normal are, therefore,

$$\boxed{\text{tangent: } \frac{x}{t} + yt = 2c} \tag{239}$$

$$\boxed{\text{normal: } y - xt^2 = \frac{c}{t}(1 - t^4)}\,. \tag{240}$$

What is the equation of the chord joining the two points with parameters t, t'? If this chord is a normal, show that $t' = -\frac{1}{t^3}$.

Meaning of b

The tangent $x = a$ at the vertex A cuts the asymptote $y = \frac{b}{a}x$ at (a, b). Geometrically, then, $b = AC = OB$.

Just as the standard ellipse is inscribed in a rectangle of length $2a$ and breadth $2b$, so are a hyperbola and its conjugate (Fig. 88a).

EXAMPLE 115 (tangential ($\equiv$ *line*) equation). Condition for a line to touch a rectangular hyperbola.

Solution. Using (239) we see that the equation of the tangent at (x_1, y_1) is $xy_1+yx_1 = 2c^2$,

i.e. $$\frac{y_1}{2c^2}x+\frac{x_1}{2c^2}y = 1. \qquad \text{(i)}$$

Compare this with the line $lx+my+n = 0$,

i.e. $$-\frac{l}{n}x-\frac{m}{n}y = 1. \qquad \text{(ii)}$$

If $lx+my+n = 0$ is a tangent then (i) and (ii) are identical,

i.e. $$x_1 = -\frac{2c^2m}{n}, \qquad y_1 = -\frac{2c^2l}{n}.$$

But $x_1y_1 = c^2$ $\because$ (x_1, y_1) lies on the rectangular hyperbola.
Substituting, we have

$$\boxed{4c^2lm = n^2}. \qquad (241)$$

This is the required condition. It means that we can think of the rectangular hyperbola not only as a locus of points but also as an envelope of tangents, i.e. every point of the rectangular hyperbola is the point of contact of a tangent $lx+my+n = 0$ as line-coordinates l, m, n vary (§ 79). Regarding the rectangular hyperbola from this point of view, we say that (241) is its *tangential ($\equiv$ line) equation.* It defines the rectangular hyperbola just as properly as does (237). As you may have observed, it corresponds in form to the homogeneous form of the equation of the rectangular hyperbola $xy = c^2z^2$.

Verify that the tangential equations of the other conics in standard form are:

parabola:	$am^2 = ln$	(242.1)
ellipse:	$a^2l^2+b^2m^2 = n^2$	(242.2)
hyperbola:	$a^2l^2-b^2m^2 = n^2$.	(242.3)

Tangential equations are of great value in projective geometry. (What is the tangential equation of the general conic (181)?)

Scientific applications of hyperbolas

1. *Reflecting properties of the hyperbola.* For a hyperboloid of revolution, formed by rotating a hyperbola about its transverse axis, rays (of light) emanating from either focus appear, after reflection at the surface, to emanate from the other focus. (Refer to Exercise 19.14.)

2. *Radar and range-finding* (Exercise 19.13). A recent electronic aid made available to merchant ships is LORAN (long range) which can be used at distances up to 1500 miles at night regardless of fog, or snow, or rough weather. By receiving radio pulses from a chain of three transmitting stations and measuring the time difference between the receipt of the signals, the navigator fixes the ship on a lattice work of hyperbolas pre-drawn on a chart of the area. Time differences are minute (microseconds) and are measured by using a cathode ray tube to make them "visible".

3. *Orbits.* High-velocity electrons and some celestial bodies (comets, meteors) move in hyperbolic paths.

4. Certain laws of physics and chemistry, e.g. Boyle's law, are hyperbolic.

5. Cooling towers at some power stations have hyperbolic profiles.

6. Lenses are sometimes hyperbolic.

Suggested topic for further study

Scientific applications of hyperbolas (more detail).

References

As for Chapter 17.

EXERCISES 19

(Unless otherwise stated, all problems refer to the standard hyperbola.)

1. Obtain the semi-axes, eccentricity, foci, and directrices of the hyperbola $y^2-2x^2-2y-8x-9 = 0$. Sketch the curve.

2. If $x+iy = \sqrt{\phi+i\psi}$, where ϕ and ψ are real parameters, prove that $\phi =$ const. and $\psi =$ const. represent two systems of rectangular hyperbolas cutting orthogonally.

3. Asymptotes of a hyperbola meet the directrices on the auxiliary circle. Prove.

4. Prove that the product of the perpendiculars from any point P of a hyperbola to the asymptotes is constant.

5. A point P on the rectangular hyperbola $xy = 1$ is given parametrically by $\left(t, \dfrac{1}{t}\right)$. Find the equation of the tangent at P.

6. Obtain the equation of the perpendicular from the origin to this tangent.

7. If the foot of this perpendicular on the tangent at P is T, find the coordinates of T in terms of t.

8. Eliminate t to obtain the Cartesian locus of T.

9. Replace the Cartesian coordinates by polar coordinates. What *is* the locus of T?

10. Focal radius of a hyperbola parallel to an asymptote is $\frac{1}{4}$ the length of the *latus rectum*. Prove.

11. Show that the length of the tangent to the hyperbola intercepted by the asymptotes is bisected at the point of contact.

12. A tangent at P to the curve $x^m y^n = c$ cuts the x-, y-axes at X, Y respectively. Determine the ratio $PY : PX$. Write down the value of this ratio in the special cases of the rectangular hyperbola, the parabola, and the curve $pv^\gamma = c$ of adiabatic expansion.

13. Soldiers at three listening posts S_1, S_2, S_3 are endeavouring to "fix" (= pin-point) the position of an enemy gun G. The precise time at which the sound of the gun's fire reaches S_1, S_2 is recorded; likewise for S_2, S_3. Explain how the gun's position is fixed as the intersection of two hyperbolas.

14. (Reflecting property.) Tangent and normal at a point P on the hyperbola are bisectors of $S\hat{P}S'$. Prove. [Observe that the reflecting properties of the parabola, ellipse, and hyperbola are essentially the same, which is not unexpected considering the unity of conics.]

15. What is the equation of the hyperbola with foci (0, 0) and (0, 4) passing through (12, 9). [*Hint:* Use the bifocal property.]

16. In a particular instance of conformal mapping theory, two families of curves are used:

$$\frac{x^2}{[\frac{1}{2}(r+1/r)]^2}+\frac{y^2}{[\frac{1}{2}(r-1/r)]^2} = 1 \quad (r \text{ variable}),$$

$$\frac{x^2}{\cos^2\theta}-\frac{y^2}{\sin^2\theta} = 1 \qquad (\theta \text{ variable}).$$

Show that these families of ellipses and hyperbolas are orthogonal and *confocal* (i.e. have the same focus). What are the coordinates of their common foci?

17. If $x+iy = \cosh(\alpha+i\beta)$, deduce that $\dfrac{x^2}{\cosh^2\alpha}+\dfrac{y^2}{\sinh^2\alpha} = 1$, $\dfrac{x^2}{\cos^2\beta}-\dfrac{y^2}{\sin^2\beta} = 1$.

18. Normals at the four points t_i $(i = 1, \ldots, 4)$ on $xy = c^2$ are concurrent if $t_1t_2t_3t_4 = -1$ and $\sum t_1t_2 = 0$. Establish.

19. Write down the equation of the pencil of conics which pass through the four points of intersection of the hyperbola $x^2-xy+x+1 = 0$ and the circle $x^2+y^2 = 16$. Show that the pencil contains two parabolas and one rectangular hyperbola. Derive the equation of this rectangular hyperbola.

20. The tangent at P $(\tan\theta, \sec\theta)$ on the hyperbola $y^2-x^2 = 1$ cuts the x-, y-axes at X, Y respectively. Through X, Y lines are drawn parallel to the axes to intersect at Q. Prove that the locus of Q as P varies is the quartic curve $\dfrac{1}{y^2}-\dfrac{1}{x^2} = 1$. Verify that the point $\left(\dfrac{1-t^2}{2t}, \dfrac{1-t^2}{1+t^2}\right)$ lies on the quartic.

21. Deduce that four points on the quartic of Exercise 19.20 with parameters $t_i (i = 1, \ldots, 4)$ are collinear if $t_1 t_2 t_3 t_4 = -1$, $\sum t_1 t_2 = 0$. (Cf. Exercise 19.18.)

22. Confocal conics whose eccentricities are reciprocal must intersect at the extremities of the *latera recta*. Prove.

23. Define a *focal ellipse* and a *focal hyperbola* by $\dfrac{ca\,x^2}{c-a} + \dfrac{bc\,y^2}{c-b} = 1$, $\dfrac{ab\,x^2}{b-a} - \dfrac{bc\,z^2}{c-b} = 1$ in the xy-plane and xz-plane respectively. Show that the foci and vertices of the focal ellipse are the vertices and foci of the focal hyperbola.

24. Tangents at the ends of the *latera recta* of a rectangular hyperbola pass through the vertices of the conjugate hyperbola. Justify.

25. A central conic in standard form has equation $f(x, y) = 0$, and tangents parallel to $y = mx + c$ are drawn to touch it at P, Q. Establish that the equation of PQ is $\dfrac{\partial f}{\partial x} + m\dfrac{\partial f}{\partial y} = 0$.

26. From a point on the hyperbola the normal is drawn to cut the transverse and conjugate axes in P, Q respectively. What is the locus of the mid-point of PQ?

27. Polars of a point w.r.t. two conjugate hyperbolas are (i) parallel, (ii) equidistant from the centre. Prove.

28. Demonstrate that $\cosh^{-1} x + \cosh^{-1} y = m$ is a hyperbola.

29. Asymptotes in Exercise 19.28 are $y = e^m x$, $y = e^{-m} x$. Prove.

30. P is a variable point on the rectangular hyperbola $x^2 - y^2 = a^2$, T is the point of intersection of the tangent at P with the x-axis and O is the origin. Show that, as P varies, the bisector of $O\hat{P}T$ has constant direction.

CHAPTER 20

CURVES: CARTESIAN COORDINATES

There is scarcely any exercise more instructive for a student than the tracing of curves.

(SALMON, 1819–1904, Irish)

Chapters 20–22 invoke the techniques of differential calculus in dealing with geometrical properties of certain interesting and useful curves.

§98. CONCAVITY, CONVEXITY, POINT OF INFLEXION

Concavity

A curve is *concave upwards* (or *concave downwards*) at a point P if in the neighbourhood of P, it lies wholly above (or wholly below) the tangent at P (Fig. 90a).

$$\therefore \text{ for } \boxed{\begin{array}{ll} \text{concavity upwards} & \dfrac{d^2y}{dx^2} > 0 \\ \text{concavity downwards} & \dfrac{d^2y}{dx^2} < 0 \end{array}} \quad \left.\begin{array}{l} \text{i.e. gradient } \uparrow \\ \quad\;\; \text{gradient } \downarrow \end{array}\right\}. \tag{243}$$

[Concave upwards (downwards) ≡ *convex downwards (upwards)*.] What might we expect to happen in the critical case when $\dfrac{d^2y}{dx^2} = 0$?

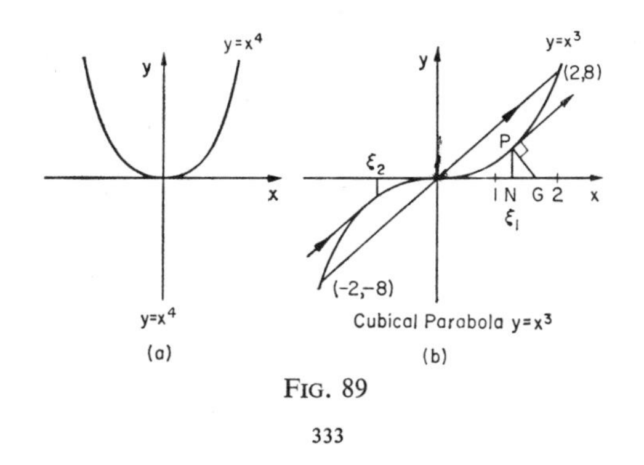

FIG. 89

Point of inflexion

For a *point of inflexion* to occur on a curve, we must have $\dfrac{d^2y}{dx^2} = 0.$ Clearly, an inflexion exists at a critical point where concavity upwards (downwards) is changing into concavity downwards (upwards), i.e. at a point $x = a$ for which $\dfrac{d^2y}{dx^2}$ changes sign as x passes through a, i.e. at a point where the curve crosses its tangent (the *inflexional tangent*) (Fig. 90b), e.g. the cubical parabola has an inflexion at the origin with $y = 0$ as the inflexional tangent (Fig. 89b). (Latin *flectere* ≡ "to bend".)

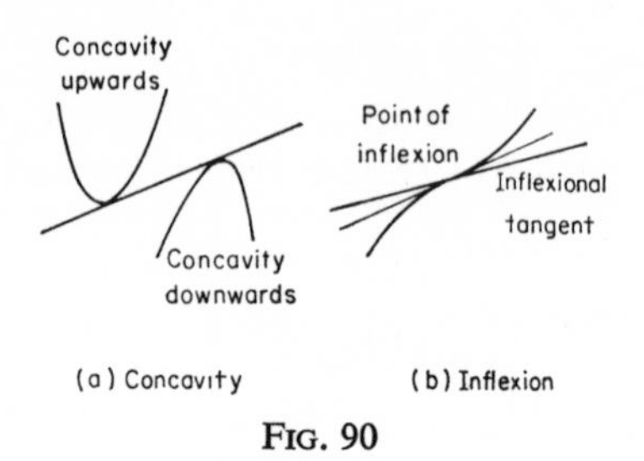

FIG. 90

At an inflexion, the rate of rotation of the tangent is momentarily zero,

i.e. $$\frac{d^2y}{dx^2} = \frac{d}{dx}\left(\frac{dy}{dx}\right) = \frac{d}{dx}(\text{gradient of tangent}) = 0.$$

Cases occur in which $\dfrac{d^2y}{dx^2} = 0$ does not yield an inflexion, e.g. $y = x^4$ (Fig. 89a) since $\dfrac{d^2y}{dx^2} = 12x^2$ ($= 0$ for $x = 0$) does not change sign as x passes through the value 0, i.e., the condition $\dfrac{d^2y}{dx^2} = 0$ is necessary for an inflexion, but not sufficient.

$$\therefore \quad \boxed{\text{inflexion: } \frac{d^2y}{dx^2} = 0, \ \frac{d^2y}{dx^2} \text{ changes sign}}. \qquad (244)$$

§99. SOME RULES FOR CURVE-SKETCHING

As we have seen in Chapter 1, a curve in Cartesian coordinates may be given either *explicitly*, i.e. in the form $y = f(x)$ [or $x = f(y)$], or *implicitly*, i.e. in the form $f(x, y) = 0$, for example the folium of Descartes $x^3+y^3 = 3axy$.

An *algebraic (plane) curve* of *order n* is one whose equation is a polynomial of degree n in x, y. Algebraic curves whose equations are of degree 1, 2, 3, 4, 5, 6, ... are called line, conic, cubic, quartic, quintic, sextic, respectively. A *transcendental curve* is one whose equation cannot be written as a polynomial expression, e.g. $y = \tan x$, $y = \log x$, $y = \sinh x$, $y = e^x$, $y = ae^{-kx^2}$ (a, k constants)—this latter is the *normal frequency curve* and it gives a theoretical distribution of a random set of results, such as intelligence quotients or examination marks (though students and staff have learned to their sorrow that in this respect practice often falls short of theory!).

Algebraic curves of order > 2, and transcendental curves, are called *higher plane curves.*

The following rules are quite sufficient to enable us to sketch (i.e. trace) the curves we usually deal with. One cannot stress too strongly that by the phrase "curve-sketching" we mean a neat, clear approximation to the shape of the curve on which the significant features are obvious. Generally, we will use ordinary Cartesian coordinates, but where desirable we can revert to homogeneous coordinates.

Incidentally, we assume a theorem due to Bézout (1730–83, French) which asserts that two curves of orders m and n intersect in mn points, e.g., cubic and conic intersect in just 6 points.

Rules

(1) *Symmetry*

(a) If no odd powers of y occur, the curve is symmetrical about the x-axis, e.g. the parabola $y^2 = 4ax$. Symbolically, $f(x, y) = f(x, -y)$ expressing *reflection in the x-axis.* [Similarly for symmetry about the y-axis.]

(b) If powers of x and y are even, the curve is symmetrical about both axes, e.g. the ellipse $\frac{x^2}{a^2}+\frac{y^2}{b^2} = 1$. Symbolically, $f(x, y) = f(-x, -y)$ expressing *reflection about O.*

(c) If, on interchanging x and y, the equation of the curve remains unchanged, there is symmetry about the line $y = x$, e.g. the rectangular hyperbola $xy = 1$. Symbolically, $f(x, y) = f(y, x)$ expressing *reflection in the line* $y = x$.

(2) *Domain of definition.* Find the range of values of real x and y. (Remember, we cannot physically draw portions of a locus with imaginary coordinates.)

(3) *Origin.* See whether the curve passes through the origin.

(4) *Intercepts.* Find where the curve cuts the axes and l_∞.

(5) *Inflexions and turning points.* Obtain any maxima, minima and inflexions.

(6) *Asymptotes.* Find the asymptotes, which may be parallel or oblique to the axes. Asymptotes are tangents to the curve at its intersections with l_∞, one asymptote for each intersection.

It is simple to prove that *any straight line cuts a curve of order n in exactly n points* (not necessarily all real). —Bézout's theorem with $m = 1$. Hence, l_∞ cuts the curve in n points. Therefore, a *curve of order n possesses exactly n asymptotes.*

(7) *Tabulation.* If necessary, tabulate some appropriate values of x and y and plot a few points. Tabulation is of especial value when the coordinates of a point are expressed parametrically.

§ 100. THE PROBLEM OF ASYMPTOTES

One of the most awkward problems connected with curve-sketching is that dealing with asymptotes. Treated rigorously, this problem requires the use of partial derivatives and some theory beyond our scope. Consequently, we will assume the rules by which asymptotes may be conveniently identified.

(a) *Asymptotes parallel to the y-axis:* Equate to zero the non-constant coefficient of the highest power of y. Similarly for asymptotes parallel to the x-axis.

(b) *Oblique asymptotes:* (i) in the equation of the curve, substitute $y = mx+c$ and arrange the equation in descending powers of x:

$$a_0x^n+a_1x^{n-1}+a_2x^{n-2}+\ldots+a_{n-1}x+a_n = 0;$$

(ii) solve simultaneously the equations $a_0 = 0$, $a_1 = 0$ to find m, c. Observe that this method for oblique axes has already been used in § 96.

EXAMPLE 116 (determination of asymptotes). Find the asymptotes of the curve $y = x+\dfrac{5}{5x+3}$ (Fig. 91).

Solution 1 (using the rules). Write the equation as $y(5x+3)-x(5x+3)-$ $-5 = 0$. Non-constant coefficient of highest power of y (namely, 1) is $5x+3 = 0$. There is no non-constant coefficient of the highest power (namely, 2) of x.

$\therefore\ \exists$ one asymptote $5x+3 = 0$ parallel to the y-axis.

Substituting $y = mx+c$ in the equation we reduce it to

$$5(m-1)x^2+(5c+3m-3)x+(3c-5) = 0$$

when, by the rules, $m-1 = 0$, $5c+3m-3 = 0$, i.e. $m = 1$, $c = 0$.

$\therefore\ \exists$ one oblique asymptote $y = x$.

[The given curve is, of course, a hyperbola (having 2 real asymptotes).]

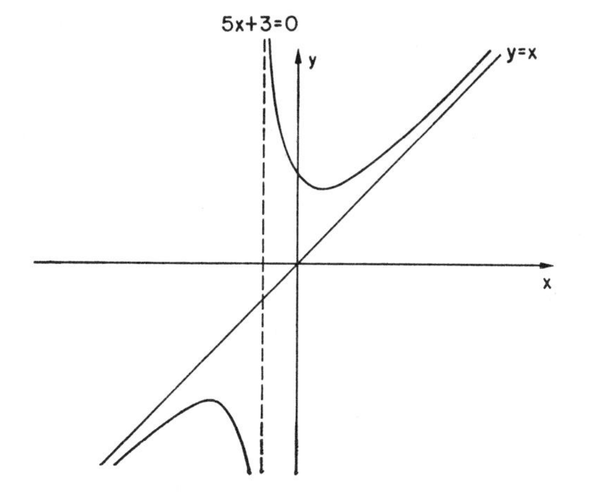

FIG. 91. Hyperbola $y = x + \dfrac{5}{5x+3}$

Solution 2 (using l_∞): Make the equation homogeneous, i.e.

$$f(x, y, z) \equiv y(5x+3z) - x(5x+3z) - 5z^2 = 0.$$

This is cut by $z = 0$ at points for which $x(y-x) = 0$, i.e. $x = 0$, $y = x$, i.e. at the points (0, 1, 0), (1, 1, 0).

Also
$$\left\{\begin{array}{llll} \dfrac{\partial f}{\partial x} = 5y - 10x - 3z & = 5 \quad \text{at } (0, 1, 0), & = -5 & \text{at } (1, 1, 0) \\ \dfrac{\partial f}{\partial y} = 5x + 3z & = 0 & \ 5 & \\ \dfrac{\partial f}{\partial z} = 3y - 3x - 10z & = 3 & \ 0. & \end{array}\right.$$

Using (195), we find that the equations of the asymptotes are $5x+3 = 0$ at (0, 1, 0) and $y = x$ at (1, 1, 0).

Solution 3 (by inspection). Observe that in $y = x + \dfrac{5}{5x+3}$ when $5x+3 \to 0$, then $y \to \infty$, so $5x+3 = 0$ must be an asymptote. [In fact a *linear expression* in the denominator of the equation of the curve always corresponds to an asymptote.]

Moreover, as $x \to \infty$, then $\dfrac{5}{5x+3} \to 0$, so $y \to \infty$ as $y - x \to 0$, i.e. $y = x$ must be the other asymptote.

[Which solution do you prefer? You may use whichever one you find more satisfying.] Since Example 116 deals with a conic, the asymptote formula of Exercise 16.20 may also be used.

§ 101. DOUBLE POINTS

Frequently in our curve-sketching, we come across a point where the curve crosses itself. Such a point is a *double point* if there are two tangents there, a *triple point* if there are three tangents there, and so on.

Assume the following conditions for a double point on a curve in homogeneous form:

$$\boxed{\frac{\partial f}{\partial x} = 0, \ \frac{\partial f}{\partial y} = 0, \ \frac{\partial f}{\partial z} = 0}. \tag{245}$$

Solve and check to see if the solution does represent a point on the curve.

The type of double point, *if it occurs at the origin*, can be determined by examining the following relationships:

$$\boxed{\left(\frac{\partial^2 f}{\partial x \partial y}\right)^2 \gtreqless \frac{\partial^2 f}{\partial x^2} \cdot \frac{\partial^2 f}{\partial y^2} \Rightarrow \begin{cases} \textit{node} \\ \textit{cusp} \\ \textit{acnode} \ (\equiv \textit{isolated point}) \end{cases}}. \tag{246}$$

At a node, cusp, or acnode the tangents are real, coincident, or imaginary respectively (Fig. 92). As its name suggests, an acnode (isolated point) is a

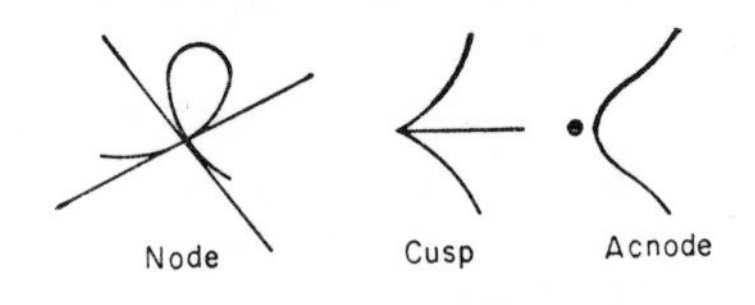

FIG. 92. Double points

point on the curve, but quite isolated from the other real points of the curve. Check, for instance, that the cubic curve $y^2 = x^2(x-1)$ has an acnode at the origin while $y^2 = x^2(1-x)$ has a node there. Often, though not so much in the elementary examples, the double point occurs at I, J or some other point at infinity. Not much emphasis is placed on this aspect of curve sketching here, but it does exhibit a nice use of partial derivatives, i.e. a link between calculus and geometry. (Latin *nodus*, *cuspis*, *acus* ≡ "knot", "point", "needle".)

§ 102. SELECTED EXAMPLES OF CURVE-SKETCHING IN CARTESIAN COORDINATES

EXAMPLE 117. Discuss and sketch the (cubic) curve $y = \dfrac{x}{(x+1)(x+2)}$ (Fig. 93—not to scale).

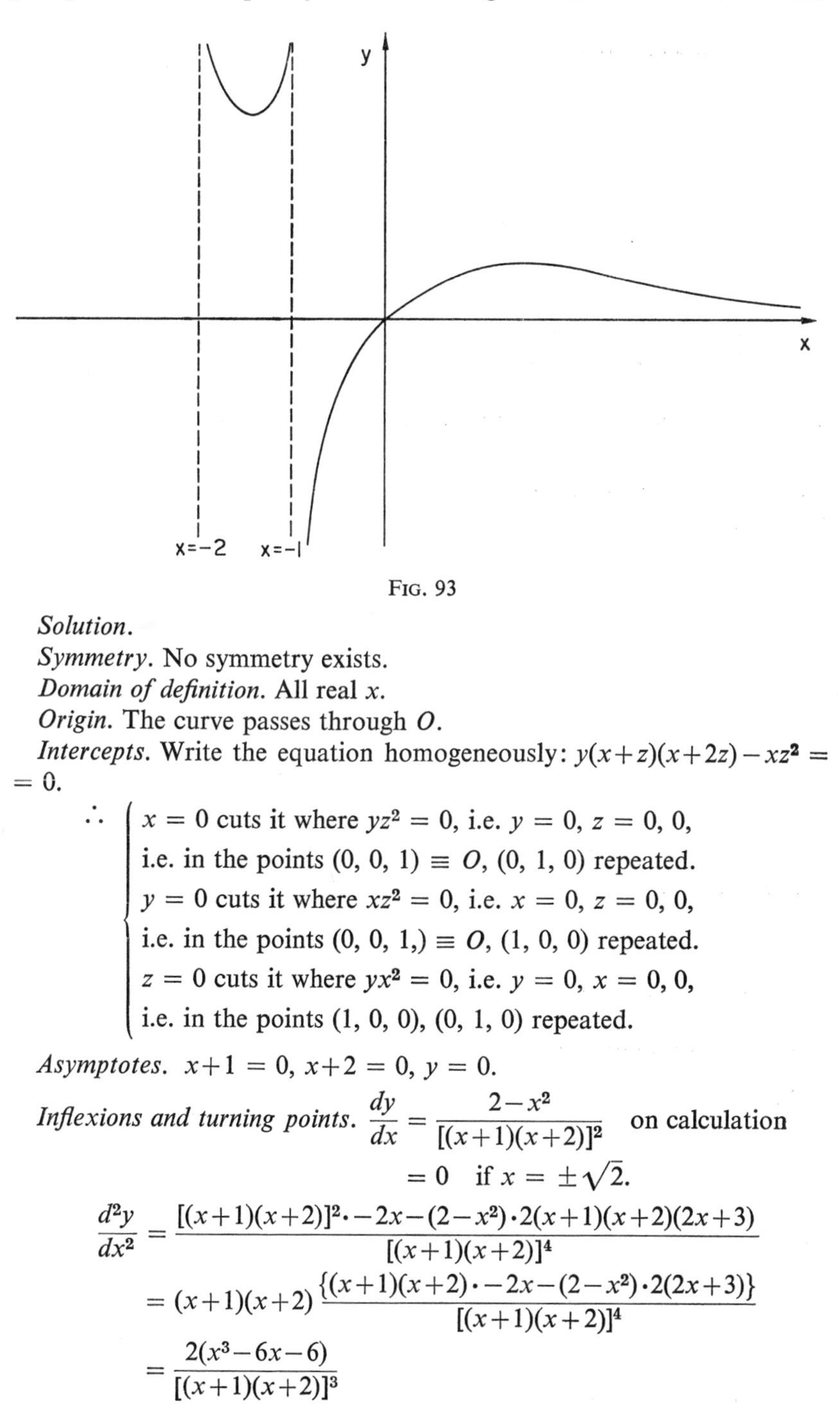

FIG. 93

Solution.

Symmetry. No symmetry exists.

Domain of definition. All real x.

Origin. The curve passes through O.

Intercepts. Write the equation homogeneously: $y(x+z)(x+2z)-xz^2 = 0$.

$\therefore$ $x = 0$ cuts it where $yz^2 = 0$, i.e. $y = 0$, $z = 0, 0$, i.e. in the points $(0, 0, 1) \equiv O$, $(0, 1, 0)$ repeated.
$y = 0$ cuts it where $xz^2 = 0$, i.e. $x = 0$, $z = 0, 0$, i.e. in the points $(0, 0, 1,) \equiv O$, $(1, 0, 0)$ repeated.
$z = 0$ cuts it where $yx^2 = 0$, i.e. $y = 0$, $x = 0, 0$, i.e. in the points $(1, 0, 0)$, $(0, 1, 0)$ repeated.

Asymptotes. $x+1 = 0$, $x+2 = 0$, $y = 0$.

Inflexions and turning points. $\dfrac{dy}{dx} = \dfrac{2-x^2}{[(x+1)(x+2)]^2}$ on calculation

$$= 0 \quad \text{if } x = \pm\sqrt{2}.$$

$$\frac{d^2y}{dx^2} = \frac{[(x+1)(x+2)]^2\cdot -2x-(2-x^2)\cdot 2(x+1)(x+2)(2x+3)}{[(x+1)(x+2)]^4}$$

$$= (x+1)(x+2)\,\frac{\{(x+1)(x+2)\cdot -2x-(2-x^2)\cdot 2(2x+3)\}}{[(x+1)(x+2)]^4}$$

$$= \frac{2(x^3-6x-6)}{[(x+1)(x+2)]^3}$$

(*note the simplification, division by* $(x+1)(x+2)$, *which must be carried out*)

$$< 0 \quad \text{if } x = \sqrt{2}$$

$$> 0 \quad \text{if } x = -\sqrt{2}$$

$$\therefore \begin{cases} \text{a maximum occurs at } (\sqrt{2}, 3+2\sqrt{2}), \\ \text{a minimum occurs at } (-\sqrt{2}, 3+2\sqrt{2}). \end{cases}$$

Inflexions are given by the roots of the cubic $x^3-6x-6 = 0$. One root is readily located ($2 < x < 3$) so that the remaining two roots are complex. Thus, there is one real inflexion occurring at a point on the curve for which $2 < x < 3$. [What happens at (0, 1, 0) and at (1, 0, 0)?]

EXAMPLE 118. Analyse and sketch the (quartic) curve $(1+x^2)y^2 = x$ (Fig. 94).

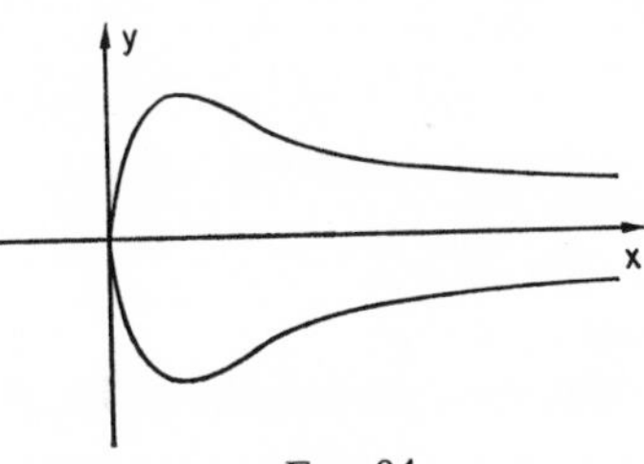

FIG. 94

Solution. Write the equation as $y = \pm\sqrt{\dfrac{x}{1+x^2}}$ so that there are two branches, a +ve branch and a −ve branch.

Symmetry. There is symmetry about the x-axis.

Domain of definition. All $x \geqslant 0$. (For $x < 0$ the curve is imaginary.)

Origin. The curve passes through the origin.

Intercepts. Homogeneously, the equation is $(z^2+x^2)y^2-xz^3 = 0$.
$\therefore x = 0$ cuts the curve where $z^2y^2 = 0$, i.e. $y = 0, 0$, $z = 0, 0$,
i.e. at the points $(0, 0, 1) \equiv O$ twice, (0, 1, 0) twice.
$y = 0$ cuts the curve where $xz^3 = 0$, i.e. $x = 0$, $z = 0, 0, 0$,
i.e. at the points (0, 0, 1), (0, 1, 0) three times.
$z = 0$ cuts the curve, where $x^2y^2 = 0$, i.e. $x = 0, 0$, $y = 0, 0$,
i.e. at the points (0, 1, 0) twice, (1, 0, 0) twice.

Asymptote. $y = 0$ repeated (once for each branch).

Inflexions and turning points. $\dfrac{dy}{dx} = \pm\dfrac{1}{2}\dfrac{(1-x^2)}{(1+x^2)^{3/2}x^{1/2}}$

$$= 0 \quad \text{if } x = \pm 1$$

$$\frac{d^2y}{dx^2} = \pm\frac{(3x^4-10x^2-1)}{4x^{3/2}(1+x^2)^{5/2}}$$

<0 if $x = 1$ for the positive branch,
>0 if $x = 1$ for the negative branch.

Therefore a maximum exists at $\left(1, \dfrac{1}{\sqrt{2}}\right)$ and a minimum at $\left(1, -\dfrac{1}{\sqrt{2}}\right)$.

Inflexions occur at points for which $3x^4-10x^2-1 = 0$, i.e. for which

$$x = \sqrt{\frac{5+\sqrt{28}}{3}}$$

i.e. at the points with coordinates approx. (1·8, ±0·6).

[What happens at (1, 0, 0) and (0, 1, 0)?]

§ 103. COMPOSITION OF CURVES

Sometimes a function is given as the sum (or difference) of two functions so that the graph of the composite function is obtained as the sum (or difference) of the two functions. Two rather interesting composite curves are drawn below. You should go through the usual formalities in discussing the features of these composite curves.

EXAMPLE 119. Sketch the curves (a) $y = \sin x - \dfrac{1}{3}\sin^3 x$, (b) $y = \dfrac{x^4-1}{x^2}$ (Fig. 95a, b).

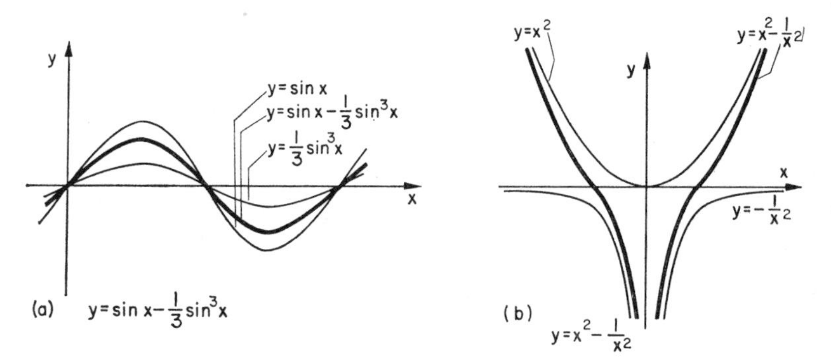

FIG. 95. Composite curves

Note the curvilinear (i.e. curve or "bent line") asymptotes $y = x^2$, $y = -\frac{1}{x^2}$, as distinct from the rectilinear (i.e. straight line) asymptotes which we ordinarily meet. (Offer a definition of a curvilinear asymptote corresponding to that for a rectilinear asymptote in § 1.)

§ 104. FAMILIES OF CURVES

One of the beautiful qualities of some general equations is that their very generality camouflages the fact that they have many seemingly unrelated special cases.

EXAMPLE 120. (i) *Family* $y = x^n$ (Fig. 96).

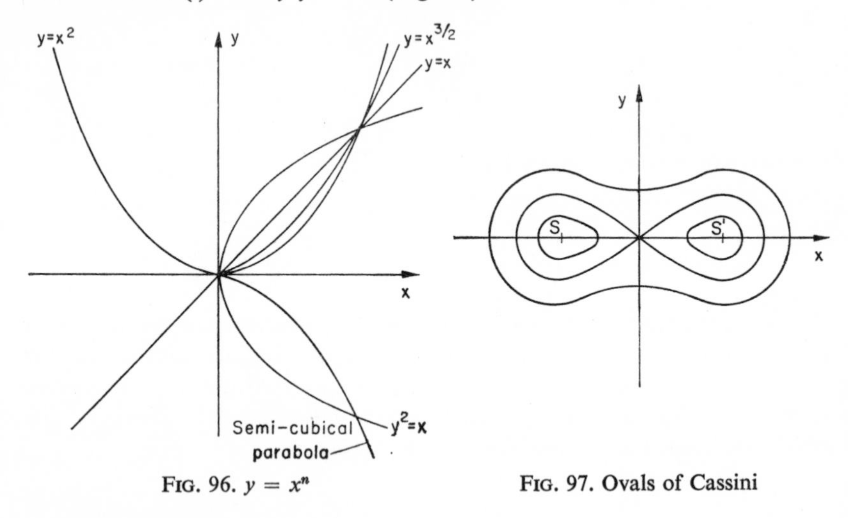

FIG. 96. $y = x^n$

FIG. 97. Ovals of Cassini

(i) *Special cases*

$n = -1$: *rectangular hyperbola*
$n = \frac{1}{2}$: *parabola*
$n = 1$: *line*
$n = \frac{3}{2}$: *semi-cubical parabola* (Neile, 1637–70, English)
$n = 2$: *parabola.*

(ii) *Family* $lr+mr' = n$ *(Cartesian ovals)*, where r, r' *(bipolar coordinates)* are the variable distances of a point P from two fixed points, and l, m, n are constants.

Special cases. $l = m \Rightarrow r+r' =$ const. (ellipse)
$l = -m \Rightarrow r-r' =$ const. (hyperbola)
$n = 0 \Rightarrow \frac{r}{r'} =$ const. (circle of Apollonius).

(iii) *Family* $rr' = b^2$ (const.) (*ovals of Cassini*, Cassini, 1625–1712, Italian) (Fig. 97), where r, r' are the variable distances of a point P from two fixed points S, S' distant $2a$ apart. Taking the mid-point of the two fixed points as origin and letting $P \equiv (x, y)$ we can obtain the Cartesian equation of the ovals as $\{(x-a)^2+y^2\}\{(x+a)^2+y^2\} = b^4$ which reduces to the polar form $r^4-2a^2r^2 \cos 2\theta = b^4-a^4$.

Case $b = a \Rightarrow r^2 = 2a^2 \cos 2\theta$ (*lemniscate of Bernoulli*, Example 131).

Bipolar loci have important physical applications, e.g in optics and magnetism. Cassinian ovals originated from a problem in astronomy.

Other families of curves which we meet are, for instance, the cycloid, strophoid and conchoid types, while in Chapter 22 are met rose-curves and spirals. (Greek *kuklos*, *strophos*, *konkhe* ≡ "circle", "twisted belt", "shell", respectively.)

Query: What shapes would you think the family of curves $x^n+y^n = 1$ $(n \neq 0)$ have? Analyse the cases n even, n odd separately. (Case $n = \frac{1}{2}$ occurs in Exercise 16.8.)

§ 105. SPECIAL HIGHER PLANE CURVES

Many of the higher plane curves sketched in Figs. 98–102 have a fascinating history, partly because of some special qualities they possess. For example, the strophoid (trisectrix of Maclaurin) and the conchoid of Nicomedes (*ca.* 200 B.C., Greek) provide techniques for trisecting a general angle. (See Exercises 20.32 and 20.33.) It is interesting to note that Nicomedes devised a machine for constructing his curve. An easy method of constructing $\sqrt[3]{2}$, i.e. of duplicating the cube, is to use the cissoid of Diocles (2nd cent. B.C., Greek) as in Exercise 20.13 (Greek *kissos* ≡ "ivy").

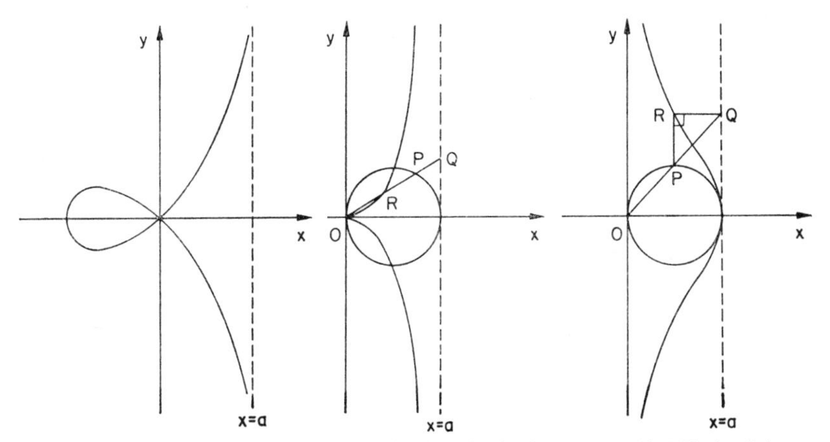

FIG. 98. Strophoid FIG. 99. Cissoid of Diocles FIG. 100. Witch of Agnes

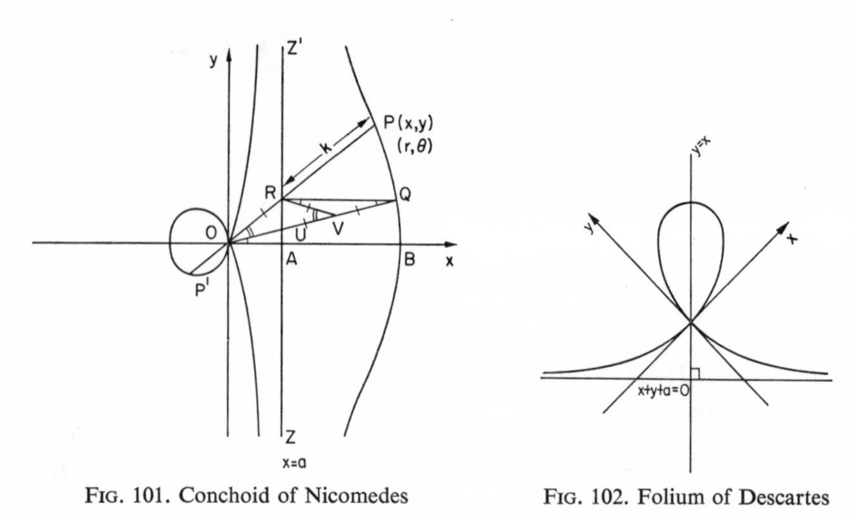

FIG. 101. Conchoid of Nicomedes

FIG. 102. Folium of Descartes

§106. PARAMETRIC CURVES

Throughout our treatment of curves, including conics, the parametric method has been emphasised. Sometimes, the Cartesian equation of a curve is too complicated for such purposes as plotting points, in which case the parametric technique is very necessary. Two such loci are the astroid (Fig. 103) and the cycloid, the latter being one of the most graceful curves in mathematics and hence useful as an arch in architecture.

EXAMPLE 121. Examine and sketch the astroid $x^{2/3}+y^{2/3} = a^{2/3}$ (a sextic curve, studied by Leibniz in 1715 (Fig. 104) (Greek *astron* ≡ "star").

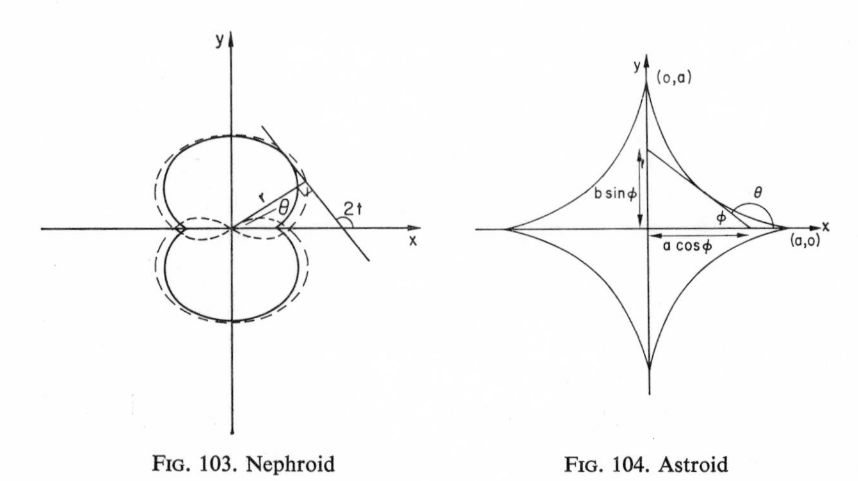

FIG. 103. Nephroid

FIG. 104. Astroid

Solution. Parametric equations: $\begin{cases} x = a\cos^3\phi = a\sin^3\psi \left(\psi = \dfrac{\pi}{2} - \phi\right) \\ y = a\sin^3\phi = a\cos^3\psi. \end{cases}$

Tabulation of values

ϕ	x/a	y/a
0	1	0
$\pi/6$	$\frac{3\sqrt{3}}{8}$	$\frac{1}{8}$
$\pi/4$	$\frac{\sqrt{2}}{4}$	$\frac{\sqrt{2}}{4}$
$\pi/3$	$\frac{1}{8}$	$\frac{3\sqrt{3}}{8}$
$\pi/2$	0	1

$$\frac{\pi}{2} < \phi < \pi \Rightarrow \cos^3\phi < 0,\ \sin^3\phi > 0$$

$$\pi < \phi < \frac{3\pi}{2} \Rightarrow \cos^3\phi < 0,\ \sin^3\phi < 0$$

$$\frac{3\pi}{2} < \phi < 2\pi \Rightarrow \cos^3\phi > 0,\ \sin^3\phi < 0$$

$$\frac{dy}{dx} = -\frac{3\cos\phi\sin^2\phi}{3\sin\phi\cos^2\phi} = -\tan\phi = \tan(\pi-\theta)$$

$$\therefore\ \phi = \pi - \theta.$$

$\therefore$ equation of the tangent at the point t is

$$y - a\sin^3\phi = -\tan\phi(x - a\cos^3\phi).$$

$\therefore$ intercepts on the axes are $x = a\cos\phi$, $y = a\sin\phi$.

Therefore the length of the tangent intercepted between the axes is a (= constant). The astroid is unique in having this property. It means, for example, that a ladder, or rod, sliding along the ground and against a wall will always be tangent to an astroid. (See also Exercise 20.39.)

Now take $a = 2$ whence $x = 2\cos^3\phi$, $y = 2\sin^3\phi$.

Rotate the curve anti-clockwise through $\pi/4$. This has the effect of reducing ϕ by $\pi/4$. Hence new coordinates X, Y on the rotated astroid are

$$\begin{cases} X = 2\cos^3\left(\phi-\frac{\pi}{4}\right) = 2\left(\frac{\cos\phi+\sin\phi}{\sqrt{2}}\right)^3 \\ \quad = \frac{1}{\sqrt{2}}(\cos^3\phi+3\cos^2\phi\sin\phi+3\cos\phi\sin^2\phi+\sin^3\phi) \\ Y = 2\sin^3\left(\phi-\frac{\pi}{4}\right) = 2(\sin\phi-\cos\phi)^3 \\ \quad = \frac{1}{\sqrt{2}}(\sin^3\phi-3\sin^2\phi\cos\phi+3\sin\phi\cos^2\phi-\cos^3\phi). \end{cases}$$

By (129),

$$\begin{cases} x = \frac{X+Y}{\sqrt{2}} = \frac{2}{\sqrt{2}\sqrt{2}}(-\sin^3\phi-3\sin\phi(1-\sin^2\phi)) = -3\sin\phi+2\sin^3\phi \\ y = \frac{-X+Y}{\sqrt{2}} = \frac{2}{\sqrt{2}\sqrt{2}}(-\cos^3\phi-3\cos\phi(1-\cos^2\phi)) \\ \quad = -3\cos\phi+2\cos^3\phi. \end{cases}$$

Replace ϕ by $\pi-\theta$ (Fig. 104).

$$\therefore \begin{cases} x = 3\sin\theta-2\sin^3\theta, \\ y = 3\cos\theta-2\cos^3\theta, \end{cases}$$

where θ is the inclination of the tangent to the positive direction of the x-axis.

Referring now to Exercise 1.18, we see that $t = \theta$ and the parametric coordinates are those of the standard astroid rotated through $\pi/4$ with cusps on the lines $y = \pm x$. (How many axes of symmetry has an astroid?)

EXAMPLE 122. Investigate and sketch the cycloid $x = a(\theta-\sin\theta)$, $y = a(1-\cos\theta)$ (Fig. 105).

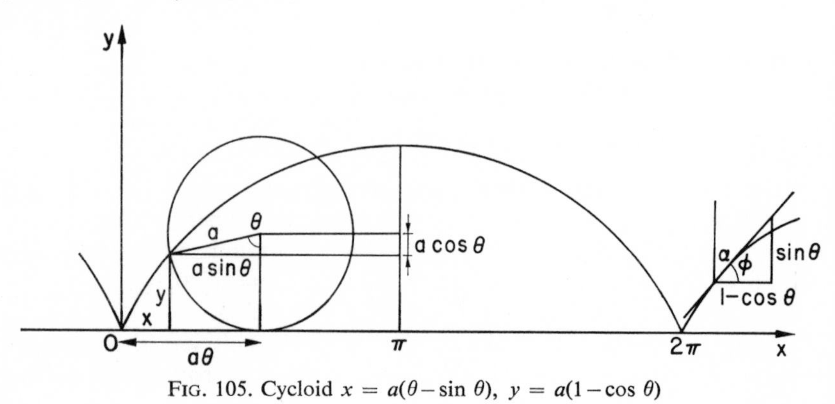

FIG. 105. Cycloid $x = a(\theta-\sin\theta)$, $y = a(1-\cos\theta)$

Solution. Clearly, $\exists$ an infinite number of "congruent" arches of the curve of which the standard arch ($0 \leqslant \theta \leqslant 2\pi$) is graphed (Fig. 105) from

θ	x/a	y/a
0	0	0
$\pi/2$	0·57	1
π	3·14	2
$3\pi/2$	5·71	1
2π	6·28	0

the tabulated values. Now (Exercise 1.20)

$$\frac{dy}{dx} = \cot\frac{\theta}{2} = \frac{\sin\theta}{1-\cos\theta}$$

$$= \infty \quad \text{at} \quad O,$$

i.e. the tangent at O is perpendicular to the x-axis, i.e. it is the y-axis. Also,

$$\frac{d^2y}{dx^2} = -\frac{1}{a(1-\cos\theta)^2} \neq 0,$$

i.e. the cycloid has no inflexions.

Evidently $(x-a\theta)^2+(y-a)^2 = a^2$, i.e. the point (x, y) on the cycloid lies on the moving circle with centre $(a\theta, a)$. This fact suggests that the cycloid is generated physically as the path traced out by a fixed point on a moving circle which rolls without slipping on a fixed straight line.

Basic properties of the cycloid (and the astroid) are developed as problems in this and later chapters. (Also see Examples 41 and 123.)

General comments on the cycloid

(i) Historically, the cycloid, associated with the name of Galileo, and several others, has had a colourful existence and there is some justification for its being called the "Helen (of Troy) of geometers".

(ii) Practical applications of the cycloid are many and varied:

(a) Its aesthetic appeal as the form of an arch interested architects like Wren;

(b) Huygens used it for his cycloidal pendulum;

(c) Romer (1644–1710, Danish) knew of the value of the cycloid and related curves in gear-wheel teeth profiles for converting non-linear motion into linear motion;

(d) Electrons often move in cycloidal orbits (Exercises 1.20, 20.44).

(iii) In 1696 John Bernoulli posed the *brachistochrone* (Greek ≡ "shortest time") problem: a particle is to travel from a point A to a lower point B along a smooth curve under no forces other than gravity; what is the nature of this curve for the quickest time of descent? (*Answer:* the inverted cycloid.) This problem opened up a new branch of mathematics, the *calculus of variations*. Typical questions in this might, for instance, be: What (closed) curve of given perimeter encloses maximum area? Along what path does a light-ray travel most quickly in a non-uniformly dense atmosphere?

Note that, in Example 125, a slight alteration to the parametric equations of the cycloid "inverts" the curve into a congruent cycloid.

Curves related to the cycloid

(1) A *trochoid* is described as the locus of a fixed point which is not on the rolling circle but is inside it or outside it (Greek (*trokhos* ≡ "wheel").

(2) *Hypocycloids and epicycloids* (Greek *epi, hupo* ≡ "upon", "under"). Suppose a circle of radius b rolls, without slipping, on a fixed circle of radius a. The locus of a point on the circle which rolls on the outside (inside) of the fixed circle is called an *epicycloid (hypocycloid)* (Figs. 106, 107). Parametrically, the points on the epicycloid are given by $x = (a+b)\cos\theta - b\cos\left(\frac{a+b}{b}\right)\theta$, $y = (a+b)\sin\theta - b\sin\left(\frac{a+b}{b}\right)\theta$ while those on the hypocycloid are obtained by replacing b by $-b$.

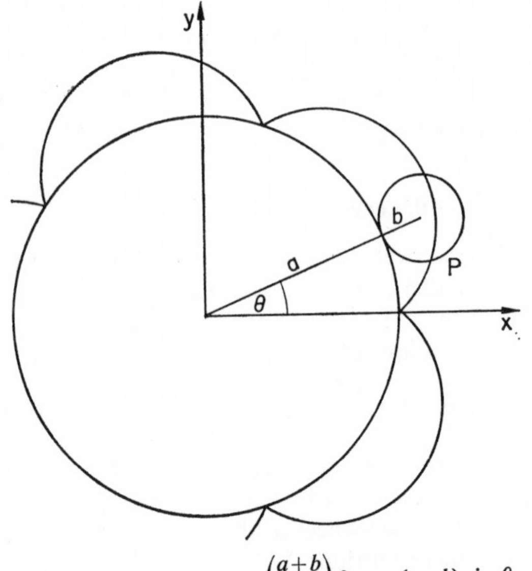

FIG. 106. Epicycloid $x=(a+b)\cos\theta-b\cos\left(\frac{a+b}{b}\right)\theta$, $y=(a+b)\sin\theta-b\sin\left(\frac{a+b}{b}\right)\theta$.

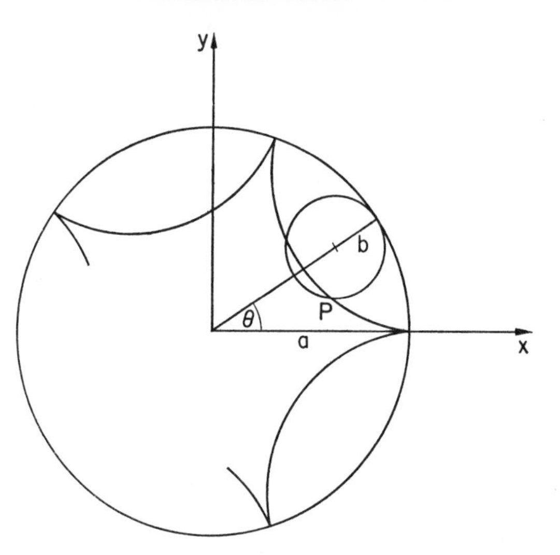

FIG. 107. Hypocycloid

Special cases

(i) $a = \infty$: cycloid.
(ii) $b = a/4$: astroid.
(iii) $b = a$: cardioid (Chapter 22).

Until the acceptance of the Copernican theory to explain the movements of celestial bodies, Ptolemaic astronomy relied on *epitrochoids* and *hypotrochoids* to explain the apparent motion relative to the Earth of the Sun, planets, and stars.

Miscellaneous examples illustrating the use of parameters

EXAMPLE 123 (area of cycloidal arch).

Solution. Using Fig. 105 we have that the area of the cycloidal arch is

$$\begin{aligned} A &= \int y\,dx \\ &= \int_0^{2\pi} a(1-\cos\theta)\cdot a(1-\cos\theta)\,d\theta, \quad \because\ dx = a(1-\cos\theta)\,d\theta \\ &= a^2 \int_0^{2\pi} \left(1-2\cos\theta+\frac{1+\cos 2\theta}{2}\right) d\theta, \quad \because\ \cos^2\theta = \frac{1+\cos 2\theta}{2} \\ &= a^2 \int_0^{2\pi} \left(\frac{3}{2}-2\cos\theta+\frac{\cos 2\theta}{2}\right) d\theta, \\ &= a^2 \left[\frac{3}{2}\theta-2\sin\theta+\frac{\sin 2\theta}{4}\right]_0^{2\pi}, \\ &= 3\pi a^2, \end{aligned}$$

i.e. the area of the cycloidal arch is three times that of the generating circle, a result first known experimentally to Galileo.

EXAMPLE 124 (pedal of a parabola w.r.t. the vertex). What is the locus of the foot of the perpendicular from the vertex of a parabola to a variable tangent to the parabola? [Such a locus is called a *pedal* curve w.r.t. A (Fig. 108).]

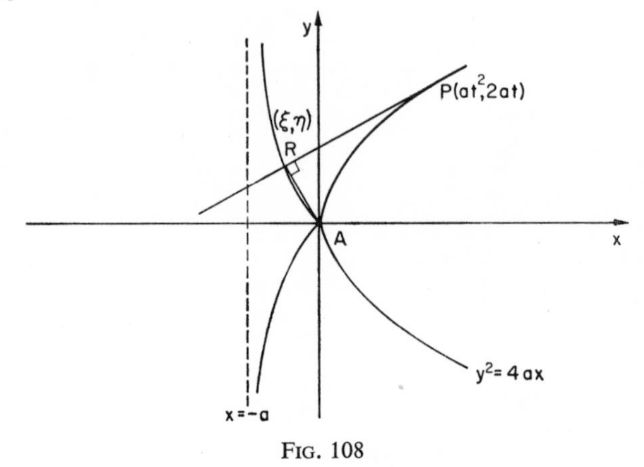

FIG. 108

Solution. Equation of the tangent at P is $y = x/t + at$
$\therefore$ equation of AR is $y = -tx$.

Solve, therefore $$\xi = -\frac{at^2}{1+t^2}, \quad \eta = \frac{at^3}{1+t^2}.$$

Eliminate t $$\therefore \xi^3 = -\frac{a^3t^6}{(1+t^2)^3}, \quad a\eta^2 = \frac{a^3t^6}{(1+t^2)^2}.$$

$$\therefore a\eta^2 = -\xi^3(1+t^2) \quad \text{and} \quad 1+t^2 = \frac{a}{a+\xi}.$$

$$\therefore \text{the locus of } R \text{ is } a\eta^2 = -\xi^3 \cdot \frac{a}{a+\xi},$$

i.e. the pedal is $y^2 = -x^3/(a+x)$ [cissoid of Diocles, see Fig. 99].

Note. A neater method is to eliminate t from the equations $y = x/t + at$,

$$y = -tx \text{ (i.e. } t = -y/x).$$

Suggested topics for further study

(1) Any of the curves discussed in this chapter, e.g. the cissoid of Diocles. (Consult J. P. McCarthy, *The Mathematical Gazette*, **25** (263), 12–16 (1941).)

(2) Women mathematicians, e.g. Hypatia (375–415, Greek); Maria Agnesi (1718–99, Italian); Sonja Kowalewski (1850–91, Russian); Emmy Nöther (1882–1935, German). (See J. L. Coolidge, *Scripta Mathematica*, **17,** 20–31 (1951), Edna Kramer, *Scripta Mathematica* **23**, 83–95 (1957); Sister Mary Thomas à Kempis, *Scripta Mathematica*, **6**, 211–17 (1939); H. Weyl, *Scripta Mathematica*, **3**, 1–20 (1935)).

References

(Differential) calculus texts listed in the bibliography, plus:

(a) *An Elementary Course of Infinitesimal Calculus*, H. Lamb (C.U.P., 1947).
(b) *A Book of Curves*, E. H. Lockwood (C.U.P., 1961).
(c) *Mathematical Models*, H. M. Cundy and A. P. Rollett (O.U.P., 1952).
(d) *The Advanced Geometry of Plane Curves and their Applications*, C. Zwikker (Dover, 1963) (complex numbers used).
(e) *Analytische Geometrie spezieller ebener Kurven*, Kuno Fladt (Akademische Verlagsgesellschaft, Frankfurt-am-Main, 1962).

EXERCISES 20

Sketch the curves 1–8 indicating any maxima, minima, inflexions, and asymptotes

1. $y = x \log x$. **2.** $y = \dfrac{\log x}{x}$. **3.** $y = 2x^2\sqrt{1-x}$.

4. $y = xe^{-x}$. (Obtain also the length of the subnormal to this curve at the inflexion.)

5. $y = \dfrac{x}{1+x^2}$ *(serpentine curve)*. **6.** $y = \dfrac{x}{(1+x)^2}$.

7. $xy+1 = x^3$ *(trident curve)*. (What is the gradient of the tangent to this curve at an inflexion?)

8.
$$y = \begin{vmatrix} a+x & b & c \\ a & b+x & c \\ a & b & c+x \end{vmatrix}$$
(a determinantal locus, i.e. a locus which can be represented as a determinant.)

9. Find the maxima and minima of the curve $y = e^{-x}\sin x$. Show that any three successive maxima are in geometric progression. Indicate the general shape of the curve.

10. Prove that the minimum point on the curve $y = \log\cosh x - x/2$ lies on the line $x+y = \log\left(\dfrac{2}{\sqrt[4]{3}}\right)$.

11. For a particle moving along a cycloidal path (Fig. 105), let α be the angle between the y-axis and the tangent at any point of the path. Prove that $\dfrac{\sin\alpha}{\sqrt{y}} = \text{constant}$. (This property is used in the brachistochrone problem.) (Refer to Example 122 and Exercises 1.20, 1.21.)

12. (Generation of the *cissoid of Diocles*.) Lines $y = mx$ are drawn to cut the circle centre $(a/2, 0)$ and radius $a/2$ at O and P, and to cut the line $x = a$ at Q. Determine the coordinates of P and Q. Hence obtain the length of PQ. Show that the locus of the point R on OQ for which $OR = PQ$ is the cissoid $y^2 = \dfrac{x^3}{a-x}$ (Fig. 99).

13. (Duplication of the cube.) With $a = 1$ in Exercise 20.12, let the line joining $A(1, 0)$ and $B(0, 2)$ cut the cissoid at C, and let OC cut the asymptote at D. Deduce that $AD = \sqrt[3]{2}$.

14. The cissoid of Diocles $y^2 = \dfrac{(a-x)^3}{x}$ is given parametrically as $\dfrac{x}{1} = \dfrac{y}{t^3} = \dfrac{a}{a+t^2}$. If the chord PQ subtends a right angle at the origin, prove that the mid-point of PQ lies on a fixed line. Can you also prove that the tangents at P and Q meet on a fixed circle?

15. A special case of *Lissajous' curves* (used in acoustics) has parametric equation $x = a \cos (nt+\varepsilon)$, $y = b \cos nt$, where ε is a constant. By eliminating the parameter t, obtain the Cartesian equation of this curve. Can you determine which sort of conic it is? Investigate the loci when, in addition, (i) $\varepsilon = 0$, (ii) $\varepsilon = \pi$.

16. Which curve has the property that its subnormal is always reciprocally proportional to its ordinate? (Leibniz)

17. Where are the double points on the curve $x^2 - y^2 = x^2y^2$? Determine the nature of the double point at the origin.

18. The semicubical parabola $ay^2 = x^3$ is given parametrically by $x : y : a = t^2 : t^3 : 1$. Find the equations of the chord (t_1), (t_2) and the tangent at (t). (See Fig. 96.)

19. Taking $a = 1$ in Exercise 20.18, let the tangent at P cut the x-axis at T and the curve at Q. Find the coordinates of Q.

With reference to the diagram of Exercise 20.19, establish 20–22 where N is the foot of the perpendicular from P to the x-axis, and OR is a chord parallel to PQ:

20. $ON = 3 \cdot OT$. **21.** $OR = 3 \cdot PQ$. **22.** $PT = 8 \cdot TQ$.

23. Parametric coordinates of the semi-cubical parabola $27ay^2 = 4x^3$ may be taken as $(3at^2, 2at^3)$. Determine the condition that three points with parameters t_1, t_2, t_3 be collinear.

24. A point on the folium of Descartes $x^3+y^3 = 3xy$ (See Fig. 102) is given parametrically by $\left(\dfrac{3t}{1+t^3}, \dfrac{3t^2}{1+t^3}\right)$. Find the values of t for which the tangent is (i) parallel to the x-axis, (ii) parallel to the y-axis.

25. What is the condition that three points with parameters t_1, t_2, t_3 on the folium of Descartes $x^3+y^3 = xy$ may be collinear?

26. How many tangents may be drawn from a fixed point on the folium to touch the folium elsewhere?

27. Determine the parametric criterion for six points on a general conic to be also on a folium.

28. (Generation of the *witch of Agnesi*.) Lines $y = mx$ are drawn to cut the circle centre $(a/2, 0)$ and radius $a/2$ at O and P, and to cut the line $x=a$ at Q. Through P, Q draw lines parallel to the y- and x-axes respectively to meet at R. Prove that the locus of R is the witch of Agnesi $y^2 = a^2 \dfrac{(a-x)}{x}$ (Fig. 100). [Agnesi's witch is sometimes called by its Italian name, *versiera*.]

29. Two curves $f(x, y) = 0$, $g(x, y) = 0$ intersect at $P(x_1, y_1)$. Find the conditions that, at P, the curves (i) touch, (ii) cut orthogonally.

30. Use Exercise 20.29 (ii) to find the condition for the circles $x^2+y^2+2gx+2fy+c = 0$, $x^2+y^2+2g'x+2f'y+c' = 0$ to cut orthogonally. Express the answer in determinantal form, if possible.

31. Do the ellipse $\dfrac{x^2}{\cos^2\alpha}+\dfrac{y^2}{\sin^2\alpha}=1$ and hyperbola $\dfrac{x^2}{\cosh^2\alpha}-\dfrac{y^2}{\sinh^2\alpha}=1$ cut orthogonally? (Also, refer to Exercises 19.16, 19.17.)

32. (Generation of the *conchoid of Nicomedes.*) Through a fixed point O, lines are drawn to cut a fixed line $Z'AZ$ (A the foot of the perpendicular from O to $Z'AZ$) in R. Points P, P' are collinear with R and $RP = RP' = k$. Given $OA = a$, show that, with OA as x-axis and a line through O perpendicular to OA as the y-axis, the loci of P and P' are branches of the conchoid (of $Z'AZ$ w.r.t. O) $x^2+y^2=\dfrac{k^2x^2}{(x-a)^2}$ (Fig. 101). What is the equation of the conchoid in polar coordinates? [According as $k >, =, < 0$, the conchoid will have a node, a cusp, an acnode, at the origin. A generalised conchoid is produced if $Z'AZ$ is replaced by a curve.]

33. (Trisection of an angle.) Through R on $Z'AZ$ (Exercise 20.32) at which $OR = \frac{1}{2}RP$, $(= \frac{1}{2}k)$ a line is drawn parallel to the x-axis to cut the conchoid at Q. Show that OQ trisects $A\hat{O}P$. [*Hint:* Join R to V, the mid-point of UQ, where $U = OQ \cap Z'AZ$ (Fig. 101).]

34. What is the pedal curve of the parabola w.r.t. the foot of the directrix?

35. Determine the pedal (trisectrix of Maclaurin) of the parabola w.r.t. $(-3a, 0)$. (Pedals of a parabola w.r.t. points on its axis form a system of strophoids of which the cissoid (Example 124) is a special case. What happens if the point is the focus?) [See Exercises 20.36, 22.4.]

36. (Trisection of an angle.) Let A, B be the points (2, 0), (3, 0) respectively, and $B\hat{A}P = 3\theta$, where P is a point on $y^2=\dfrac{x^2(3-x)}{1+x}$. ($B$ also lies on the curve.) Prove that a line AQ through A parallel to OP trisects $B\hat{A}P$.

37. Sketch $x = a(2\cos t+\cos 2t)$, $y = a(2\sin t-\sin 2t)$ (*Steiner's deltoid* $\equiv$ 3 cusped hypocycloid, resembling the Greek letter, Δ). Show that its pedal w.r.t. the origin is a three-leafed rose (§ 114). [Laué spots of a certain crystal take the form of a deltoid.]

38. Establish that the pedal of an astroid w.r.t. the origin is a four-leafed rose (§ 114).

39. A ladder slides against a wall which is at right angles to the ground. Show that any point of the ladder describes an ellipse during the sliding.

40. (Generation of the quadratrix of Hippias—refer to Example 7(e).) Given a semicircle of unit radius OA, let the line OR (starting from initial position OA) rotate with uniform velocity in an anti-clockwise sense about O, and at the same time let the line QN, perpendicular to OA (starting as a tangent at A) move uniformly towards O; let OR and QN arrive simultaneously at OT. Taking x- and y-axes along OA and OT respectively, show that the locus of P, the intersection of OR and QN, is the quadratrix $y = x\cot\left(\dfrac{\pi x}{2}\right)$.

41. [Quadrature of the circle.] In Exercise 20.40, the radius of the circle is the mean proportional between OE and the arc length of the quadrant of the circle, where E is the intersection of the y-axis and the quadratrix. Prove.

42. Draw the graph of the *staircase* $(=$ *step) function* $f(x) = [x]$ (=greatest integer $\leqslant x$).

43. Parametric equations of a certain curve are $x = f(t)/h(t)$, $y = g(t)/h(t)$. Express determinantally the equation of the chord joining the points t, u.

44. Equations of motion of a particle of mass m and charge e repelled from a negatively charged zinc sheet illuminated with ultraviolet light under a magnetic field H (where V is the electric intensity) are $m\ddot{x} = Ve-He\,\dot{y}$, $m\ddot{y} = He\,\dot{x}$. Setting $\omega = \dfrac{He}{m}$, verify that the particle moves in the cycloidal path $x = \frac{V}{\omega H}(1-\cos \omega t)$, $y = \frac{V}{\omega H}(\omega t - \sin \omega t)$.[Piaggio (Reference Chapter 5), pp. 47–48.]

45. The solution of a problem associated with Foucault's pendulum is

$$z = \frac{a}{2q}\{(q+n)e^{i(q-n)t}+(q-n)e^{-i(q+n)t}\} = x+iy \quad (q^2 = p^2+n^2).$$

Prove that it represents a hypocycloid contained between two concentric circles of radii a and an/q. [Piaggio, p. 247.]

CHAPTER 21

CURVATURE

A single curve, drawn in the manner of the curve of prices of cotton, describes all that the ear can possibly hear as the result of the most complicated musical performance... That to my mind is a wonderful proof of the potency of Mathematics.

(LORD KELVIN)

§ 107. INTRINSIC COORDINATES

Nature of the problem

We want a method of measuring the curvature (i.e. bending) of a curve at any point, e.g. the curving of steel tracks in railroad construction or the bending of a racetrack. This is best approached through the introduction of a new system of coordinates in which the two coordinates are (i) an arc-length of the curve, and (ii) an angle.

In Fig. 109a

$$s, \psi = \textit{intrinsic coordinates} \text{ of } P$$

(s independent of the axes).

A curve whose equation is $s = f(\psi)$ is then said to be given *intrinsically*, e.g. in Fig. 109b, the intrinsic equation of the circle is

$$s = a\left(\psi - \frac{\pi}{2}\right).$$

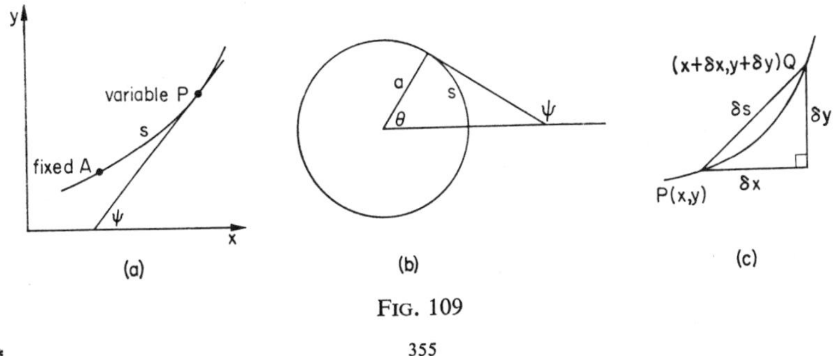

FIG. 109

From Fig. 109c we have $(\delta s)^2 \doteqdot (\delta x)^2+(\delta y)^2$,

$$\therefore \frac{\delta s}{\delta x} \doteqdot \sqrt{1+\left(\frac{\delta y}{\delta x}\right)^2},$$

i.e. in the limit

$$\boxed{\frac{ds}{dx} = \sqrt{1+\left(\frac{dy}{dx}\right)^2}} \tag{247}$$

i.e.,

$$\boxed{ds^2 = dx^2+dy^2}. \tag{247.1}$$

But $\tan\psi = \dfrac{dy}{dx}$, $\therefore$ by (247) $\dfrac{ds}{dx} = \sec\psi$.

$$\therefore \boxed{\begin{aligned} \cos\psi &= \frac{dx}{ds} \quad (248.1)\\ \sin\psi &= \frac{dy}{ds} \quad (248.2)\end{aligned}}.$$

§108. CURVATURE

Definition. Curvature at $P(x, y)$ is $\boxed{\varkappa = \dfrac{d\psi}{ds}}$, (249)

i.e. curvature measures the rate at which angle ψ varies w.r.t. the arc length. Clearly $\varkappa$ may be > 0, $= 0$, < 0. (For a straight line, $\varkappa = 0$.) Unit of measure of $\varkappa$ is radians/unit length.

Now $\tan\psi = \dfrac{dy}{dx}$, so $\sec^2\psi\dfrac{d\psi}{ds} = \dfrac{d}{ds}\left(\dfrac{dy}{dx}\right) = \dfrac{d^2y}{dx^2}\dfrac{dx}{ds}$,

$$\therefore \varkappa = \frac{\cos\psi}{\sec^2\psi}\frac{d^2y}{dx^2} = \frac{d^2y}{dx^2} \div \sqrt{(1+\tan^2\psi)^3}$$

$$\therefore \boxed{\varkappa = \frac{d^2y/dx^2}{\{1+(dy/dx)^2\}^{3/2}}}. \tag{250}$$

Therefore at an inflexion, curvature is zero. The sign of the curvature depends on the sign of $\dfrac{d^2y}{dx}$, i.e. on the concavity of the curve. Plainly, for very small $\dfrac{dy}{dx}$, $\varkappa \doteqdot \dfrac{d^2y}{dx^2}$ (a form used in the bending of bars, beams, etc.).

Comparison with (249) shows that ψ small $\Rightarrow \dfrac{dy}{dx}(= \tan\psi) \to \psi$ and $dx \doteqdot$

ds, i.e. $\dfrac{d\psi}{ds} \doteqdot \dfrac{d^2y}{dx^2}$. For a parametric curve $x = f(t)$, $y = g(t)$, $\dfrac{dy}{dx} = \dfrac{\dot{g}}{\dot{f}}$

and $$\frac{d^2y}{dx^2} = \frac{\dot{f}\ddot{g} - \ddot{f}\dot{g}}{\dot{f}^3}.$$

$$\therefore \quad \boxed{\varkappa = \frac{\dot{f}\ddot{g} - \ddot{f}\dot{g}}{(\dot{f}^2 + \dot{g}^2)^{3/2}}} \qquad (251)$$

which is unchanged by a functional transformation of parameter. (Verify.)

Newton's method (applicable at a point having $x = 0$, or $y = 0$, as tangent there)—assume:

At O (Fig. 110)

$$\boxed{\varkappa = \lim_{x \to 0} \left(\frac{2y}{x^2}\right)} \cdot \qquad (252)$$

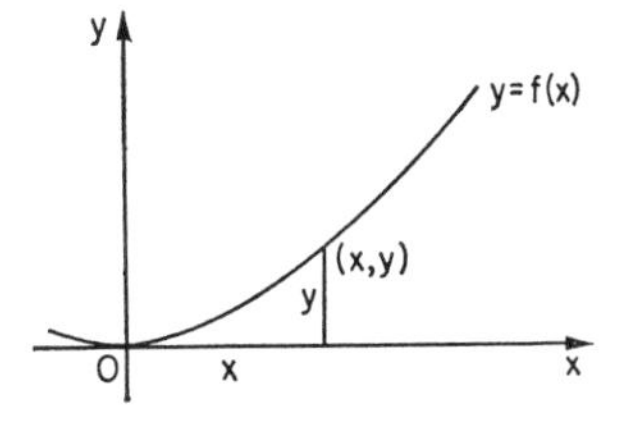

FIG. 110. Newton's method

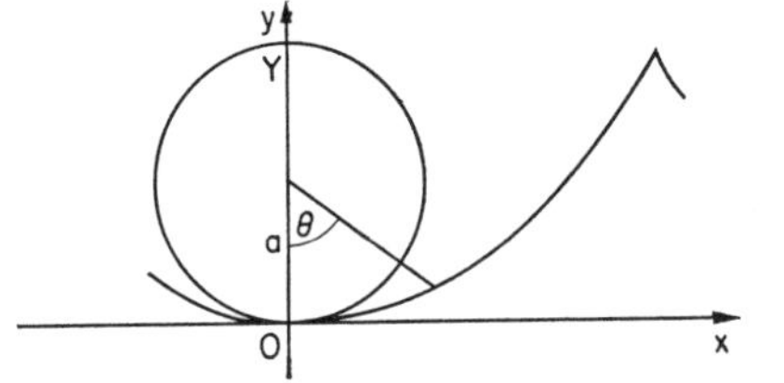

FIG. 111. Curvature of the cycloid $x = a(\theta + \sin\theta)$, $y = a(1 - \cos\theta)$

If the tangent is the y-axis then

$$\boxed{\varkappa = \lim_{y \to 0} \left(\frac{2x}{y^2}\right)} \cdot \qquad (252.1)$$

EXAMPLE 125 [curvature of the cycloid at a vertex (Fig. 111—note Fig. 105)].

Solutions. (a) Now $\dfrac{dy}{dx} = \dfrac{\sin\theta}{1 + \cos\theta} = \tan\dfrac{\theta}{2}$.

$$\therefore \frac{d^2y}{dx^2} = \frac{d}{d\theta}\left(\frac{\sin\theta}{1 + \cos\theta}\right)\frac{d\theta}{dx} = \frac{1}{a(1 + \cos\theta)^2},$$

$$\therefore \varkappa = 1\Big/\left[a(1 + \cos\theta)^2\left\{1 + \left(\frac{\sin\theta}{1 + \cos\theta}\right)^2\right\}^{3/2}\right] = \frac{1}{4a} \quad \text{at } \theta = 0.$$

(b) Newton's method: $\dfrac{2y}{x^2} = \dfrac{4\sin^2(\theta/2)}{a(\theta+\sin\theta^2)} = \dfrac{\left(\dfrac{\sin\theta/2}{\theta/2}\right)^2}{a\left(1+\dfrac{\sin\theta}{\theta}\right)^2}$,

$$\therefore\ \varkappa = \lim_{\substack{x\to 0\\ \theta\to 0}}\left(\frac{2y}{x^2}\right) = \frac{1}{4a} = \frac{1}{2OY}\quad \text{using (6).}$$

(c) Assume (see Exercise 149 (ii)): the intrinsic equation of the cycloid is $s = 4a\sin\psi$ $(\psi = \theta/2)$.

Intrinsically: $\dfrac{ds}{d\psi} = 4a\cos\psi \quad \therefore\ \varkappa = \dfrac{1}{4a\cos\psi}$

$$= \frac{1}{4a}\quad \text{at } O.$$

§ 109. RADIUS OF CURVATURE

EXAMPLE 126 (curvature of a circle of radius ϱ).

Solution: $x = \varrho\cos\theta,\ y = \varrho\sin\theta$

$$\therefore\ \frac{dx}{d\theta} = -\varrho\sin\theta,\ \frac{dy}{d\theta} = \varrho\cos\theta\ \therefore\ \frac{dy}{dx} = -\cot\theta$$

$$\therefore\ \frac{d^2y}{dx^2} = \frac{d}{d\theta}(-\cot\theta)\cdot\frac{d\theta}{dx} = -\frac{1}{\varrho\sin\theta}\quad \therefore\ \varkappa = -\frac{1}{\varrho\sin^3\theta}\cdot\frac{1}{[1+\cot^2\theta]^{3/2}}$$

$$\therefore\ \varkappa = -\frac{1}{\varrho}.$$

Ignoring the $-$ve sign (i.e. considering only the absolute value of $\varkappa$) we *define* for any curve:

$$\textit{radius of curvature}\quad \boxed{\varrho = \frac{1}{\varkappa}}\,. \tag{253}$$

Therefore if we construct, at a point on the curve, a circle having the same tangent as the curve, with radius $= \varrho$, and centre on the concave side of the curve, then the circle has the same curvature as the curve. It is called the *circle of curvature*, its centre is the *centre of curvature* and any chord of this circle is a *chord of curvature;*

$\varrho \equiv$ *radius of curvature*. (See Fig. 112.)

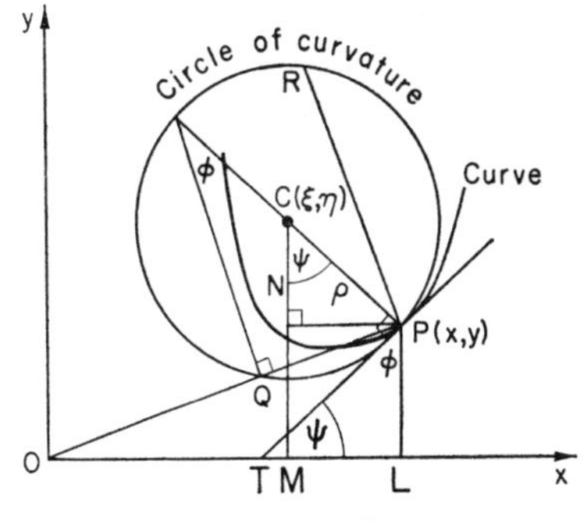

FIG. 112. Circle of curvature

[Actually, $\frac{dy}{dx}$ is the same for the curve as for the circle at P; similarly for $\frac{d^2y}{dx^2}$. Thus, it has higher degree of contact at P than any other circle has and hence it is also called the *osculating circle* (Latin *osculare* ≡ "to kiss").]

Note that $N\hat{C}P = \frac{\pi}{2} - N\hat{P}C = \frac{\pi}{2} - \left(\frac{\pi}{2} - N\hat{P}T\right) = N\hat{P}T = \psi.$

Centre of curvature (C):

$\xi = OL - ML = x - \varrho \sin \psi,$ $= x - \frac{dy}{d\psi}$	$\eta = MN + NC = y + \varrho \cos \psi$ $= y + \frac{dx}{d\psi}$

(254)

Evolute of a given curve ≡ locus of the centre of curvature.

EXAMPLE 127 (curvature of the catenary (Fig. 113)).

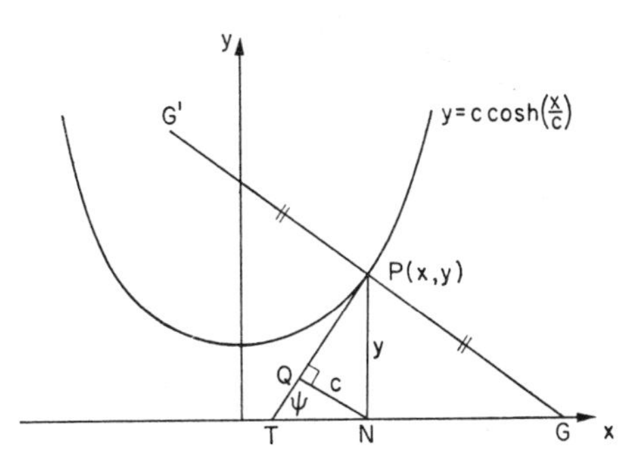

FIG. 113. Curvature of the catenary

Solution. Recalling Fig. 8, we have

$$\varrho = \frac{[1+\sinh^2 x/c]^{3/2}}{(1/c)\cosh(x/c)} \quad \text{by formulae (253) and (250)}$$

$$= c\cosh^2 x/c$$

$$= \frac{y^2}{c}$$

$$= \frac{y^2}{QN} \quad \text{by Example 14}$$

$$= PG \quad \text{from similar triangles } PQN,\ PNG$$

$$= PG' \quad \text{by construction,}$$

i.e. G' is the centre of curvature (for P).

$$\text{At } (0, 1), \quad \varrho = c.$$

[Assume: the intrinsic equation of the catenary is $s = c\tan\psi$ (proved in Example 149),

$$\therefore \varrho = \frac{ds}{d\psi} = c\sec^2\psi = c \text{ at } (0, 1).]$$

EXAMPLE 128. Normals are drawn from any point (x, y) to the parabola $y^2 = 4ax$. If $\varrho_1, \varrho_2, \varrho_3$ are the radii of curvature at the feet of the normals (Fig. 114) prove that

$$\sum_{i=1}^{3} \varrho_i^{2/3} = 4^{1/3}a^{-1/3}(2x-a).$$

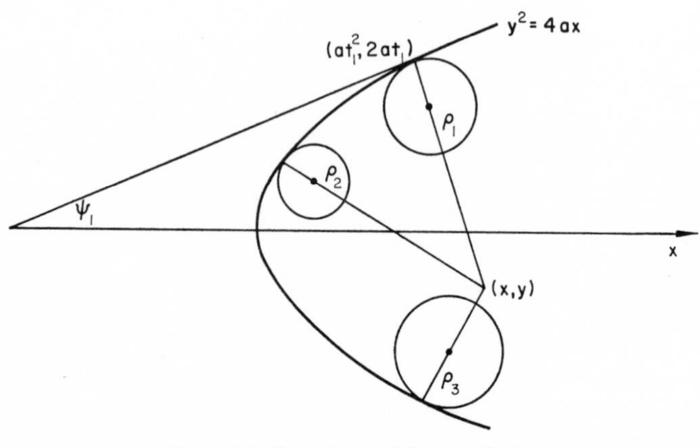

FIG. 114. Curvature of the parabola

Solution. At $(at^2, 2at)$, we have $\dfrac{dy}{dx} = \dfrac{1}{t} = \tan\psi$ by (202).

$$\therefore \quad \frac{d^2y}{dx^2} = \frac{d}{dt}\left(\frac{1}{t}\right)\frac{dt}{dx} = -\frac{1}{2at^3} = -\frac{\tan^3\psi}{2a},$$

$$\therefore \quad \varrho = -\frac{2a(1+\tan^2\psi)^{3/2}}{\tan^3\psi} \quad \text{by (250), (252)}$$

$$= -\frac{2a}{\sin^3\psi},$$

$$\therefore \quad \varrho^{2/3} = \frac{4^{1/3}a^{2/3}}{\sin^2\psi} = 4^{1/3}a^{2/3}(1+t^2),$$

$$\therefore \sum_{i=1}^{3} \varrho_i^{2/3} = 4^{1/3}a^{2/3}(3+t_1^2+t_2^2+t_3^2)$$

$$= 4^{1/3}a^{2/3}\left\{3+\left(\sum_{i=1}^{3} t_i\right)^2 - 2\sum t_1t_2\right\}$$

$$= 4^{1/3}a^{2/3}\left\{3-2\left(\frac{2a-x}{a}\right)\right\} \quad \text{using § 91(i), (ii)}$$

$$= 4^{1/3}a^{-1/3}(2x-a).$$

Note. In Fig. 114, circles of curvature are understood to cross the parabola as in Fig. 112, except at the vertex. Check the above work in the case $t = 0, 1, -1$ (A, L, L' in Fig. 71).

References

Calculus texts in the bibliography.

EXERCISES 21

1. How does the curvature of a circle of radius 4 compare with that of a circle of radius 1?

Find the radius of curvature of each of the loci 2–6:

2. $x^2/a^2+y^2/b^2 = 1$. **3.** $ay^2 = x^3$. **4.** $x^{2/3}+y^{2/3} = a^{2/3}$.

5. Tractrix. **6.** $x = \cos t + t\sin t$, $y = \sin t - t\cos t$.

7. Establish the formula $\varrho y\dfrac{d^2y}{dx^2} = n\left\{1+\left(\dfrac{dy}{dx}\right)^2\right\}$ ($n = PN$, Fig. 6).

8. Use Exercise 21.7 to find the numerical relationship between ϱ and n for the cycloid.

9. For the tractrix show that $\varrho n = c^2$ where n is the length of the normal PN intercepted between the point P and the x-axis.

10. Radius of curvature of the ellipse at P is proportional to CQ^3, where CP, CQ are conjugate semi-diameters (Fig. 84). Prove.

11. Perpendicular tangents are drawn at two points P_1, P_2 on the catenary $y = \cosh x$. Show that the sum of the curvatures at P_1, P_2 is 1.

12. Where, on $y = e^x$, is the curvature maximum? What is the radius of curvature at this point?

13. Determine the evolute of the parabola $y^2 = 4ax$.

14. Prove that the six points of intersection of the parabola and its evolute (Exercise 21.13) are two real points M, M' and two imaginary points repeated. Write down the values of ϱ, ξ, η for the parabola at M, M'.

15. From M (M') [Exercise 21.14] a tangent is drawn to the semi-cubical parabola to cut the parabola again at $Q(P)$. What are the coordinates of Q? Show that PQ subtends a right-angle at the vertex of the parabola.

16. On the semi-cubical parabola (Exercise 21.14), a point has coordinates $(2a+3at^2, 2at^3)$. If the parameter of a point on the parabola is u, what is the relationship between t and u at M?

17. Tangents to the evolute at M, M' (Exercise 21.14) are normals to the parabola. Prove, and find the parameters of these normals.

18. Exercise 21.15 is really a special case of the general result that a normal to a curve at a point P is the tangent to its evolute at a point Q, i.e. the evolute is the envelope of normals. A standard procedure (which we assume) for calculating the centre of curvature when we know the parametric equation of the normal $f(x, y, t) = 0$, t a parameter, is to find $\partial f/\partial t = 0$, then to get x, y in terms of t (giving the coordinates of ξ, η) and finally to eliminate t. Use this technique to find the evolute of the parabola.

19. Carry out the same steps for the ellipse.

20. What curve is the evolute of the tractrix (Fig. 8)?

21. Apply the parametric formula for curvature (251) to verify the value of the radius of curvature of the astroid (Exercise 21.4).

22. Form the differential equation which represents all the circles in the plane. [*Hint:* First write down the equation of the circle with centre (a, b) and radius r, then, by repeated differentiation, eliminate the constants.] (See also Exercise 8.1.)

23. How may the same differential equation be obtained using the notion of curvature?

24. Perpendicular tangents are drawn from two points on the cycloid at which the radii of curvature are ϱ_1, ϱ_2. Establish the formula $\varrho_1^2+\varrho_2^2 = \text{const}$.

25. Obtain the evolute of a cycloid.

CHAPTER 22

CURVES: POLAR COORDINATES

Mathematics, rightly viewed, possesses not only truth but supreme beauty—a beauty cold and austere, like that of sculpture, without appeal to any part of our weaker nature, without the gorgeous trappings of painting or music, yet sublimely pure, and capable of a stern perfection such as only the greatest art can show.

(BERTRAND RUSSELL)

§110. EQUATIONS OF LINE AND CIRCLE IN POLAR COORDINATES

(a) *Line*

In Fig. 115, $ON = OP\cos(\theta-\alpha)$

$$\therefore \quad \boxed{r\cos(\theta-\alpha) = p}. \tag{255}$$

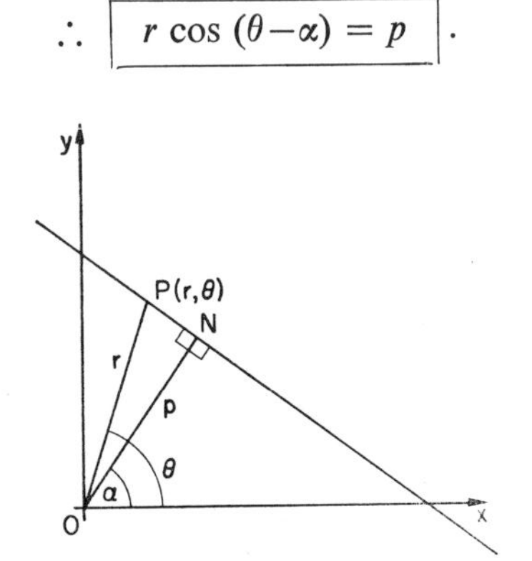

FIG. 115. Polar equation of the straight line

This becomes $x\cos\alpha+y\sin\alpha = p$ in Cartesian coordinates.

Special cases:

$$\begin{cases} \alpha = 0 \Rightarrow r\cos\theta = p, \text{ i.e. the line } x = p. \\ \alpha = 0,\ \theta \to \pi/2-\theta \Rightarrow r\sin\theta = p, \text{ i.e. the line } y = p. \\ \theta = \alpha \text{ (const.)} \Rightarrow y = x\tan\alpha \text{ (i.e., } y = mx). \end{cases}$$

(b) *Circle*

$$\left.\begin{array}{c}\text{In Fig. 116a,}\\ r = a\\ \text{i.e. } x^2+y^2 = a^2\end{array}\right\} \quad \left.\begin{array}{c}\text{In Fig. 116b,}\\ r = a\cos\theta\\ \text{i.e. } x^2+y^2-ax = 0\end{array}\right\} \quad \left.\begin{array}{c}\text{In Fig. 116c,}\\ r = a\sin\theta\\ \text{i.e., } x^2+y^2-ay = 0\end{array}\right\}. \quad (256)$$

Query: Can you express vectorially the equations of the circles in Fig. 116a–c?

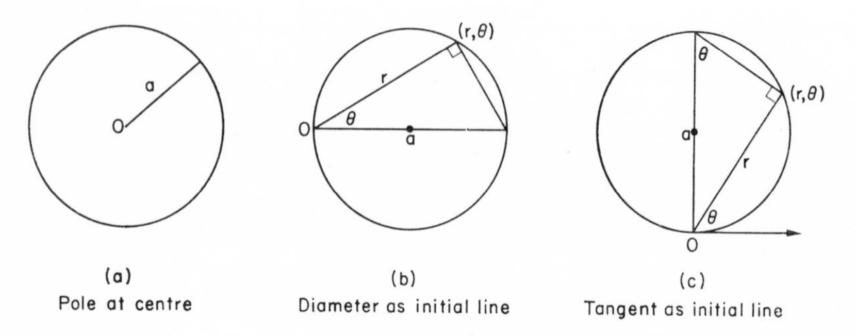

FIG. 116. Polar equations of the circle

§111. EQUATIONS OF CONICS IN POLAR COORDINATES

(a) *Centre as pole*

The ellipse $\dfrac{x^2}{a^2}+\dfrac{y^2}{b^2} = 1$ becomes $\dfrac{\cos^2\theta}{a^2}+\dfrac{\sin^2\theta}{b^2} = \dfrac{1}{r^2}$.

For the circle, $b = a$, $\therefore$ $x^2+y^2 = a^2$ becomes $r = a$.

The hyperbola $\dfrac{x^2}{a^2}-\dfrac{y^2}{b^2} = 1$ becomes $\dfrac{\cos^2\theta}{a^2}-\dfrac{\sin^2\theta}{b^2} = \dfrac{1}{r^2}$.

For the rectangular hyperbola, $b = a$ $\therefore$ $x^2-y^2 = a^2$ becomes $r^2\cos 2\theta = a^2$. Let $\theta \to \pi/2-\theta$ $\therefore$ $r^2\sin 2\theta = a^2$ for the rectangular hyperbola i.e.

$$r^2\sin\theta\cos\theta = a^2/2,$$

$$\therefore\ xy = a^2/2.$$

(b) *Focus as pole* (Fig. 117)

$$\begin{aligned} l &= eLQ \qquad \text{(definition)}\\ &= eSZ\\ &= e(SN+NZ)\\ &= eSN+ePM\\ &= er\cos\theta+r \end{aligned}$$

$$\therefore\ \boxed{\frac{l}{r} = 1+e\cos\theta}\ . \qquad (257)$$

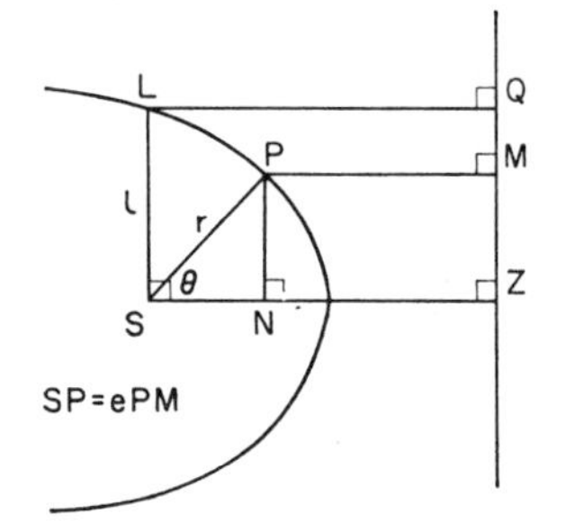

FIG. 117. Polar equation of the conic (focus as pole)

$$\therefore \begin{cases} \text{ellipse} & \dfrac{l}{r} = 1+e\cos\theta \quad (e<1) & (257.1) \\ \text{circle} & l = r \quad (e=0) & (257.2) \\ \text{hyperbola} & \dfrac{l}{r} = 1+e\cos\theta \quad (e>1) & (257.3) \\ \text{rect. hyp.} & \dfrac{l}{r} = 1+\sqrt{2}\cos\theta \quad (e=\sqrt{2}) & (257.4) \\ \text{parabola} & \dfrac{l}{r} = 1+\cos\theta \quad (e=1). & (257.5) \end{cases}$$

From (257.5), $\begin{cases} \dfrac{2a}{r} = 2\cos^2(\theta/2) \quad \therefore r\cos^2(\theta/2) = a \\ 2a = r+x \quad \therefore y^2 = 4a(a-x). \end{cases}$

Note. For any conic the sum of the reciprocals of the focal radii of any focal chord is constant.

To prove this (Fig. 118), we have $\begin{cases} \dfrac{l}{r} = 1+e\cos\theta \quad \text{and} \\ \dfrac{l}{r'} = 1+e\cos(\pi+\theta) = 1-e\cos\theta \end{cases}$

$$\therefore \frac{l}{r}+\frac{l}{r'} = 2 \quad \text{i.e.} \quad \frac{1}{SP}+\frac{1}{SP'} = \frac{2}{l} \quad \text{(see § 80)},$$

i.e. the semi-*latus rectum* is the *harmonic mean* between the focal radii of any focal chord.

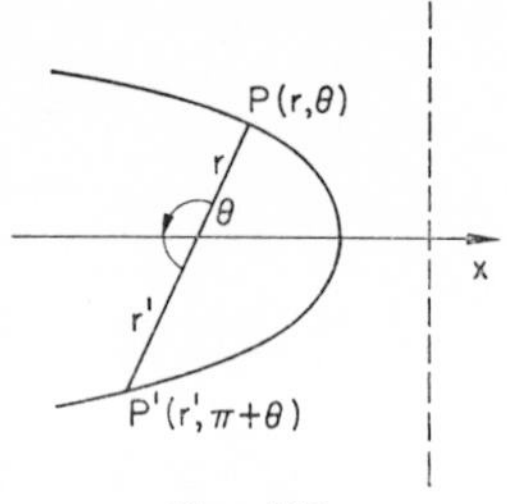

FIG. 118

§ 112. SOME RULES FOR CURVE-SKETCHING

(1) *Symmetry*

(a) If the equation is unchanged when θ is replaced by $\theta \pm \pi$, then the curve is symmetrical about O, e.g. curve $r^2 = a^2 \tan \theta$ (Fig. 119a).

(b) If the equation is unchanged when θ is replaced by $-\theta$, then the curve is symmetrical about the x-axis, e.g. cardioid $r = a(1+\cos \theta)$.

(c) If the equation is unchanged when θ is replaced by $\pi-\theta$, then the curve is symmetrical about the y-axis, e.g. cardioid $r = a(1+\sin \theta)$.

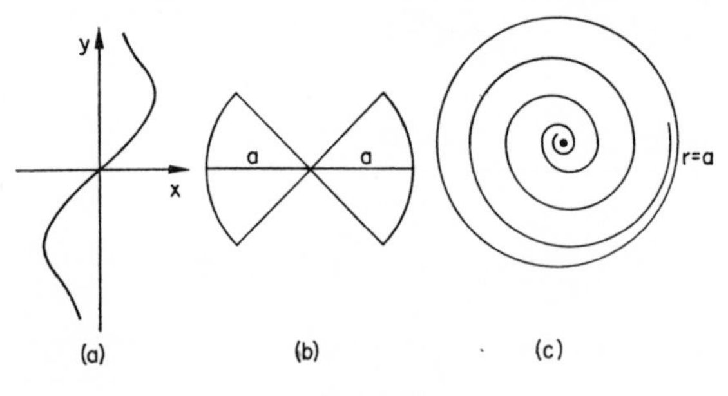

FIG. 119

(2) *Ranges of r, θ*

E.g. (i) $r = a\dfrac{\sin \theta}{\theta}$ *(cochleoid)* (Latin *cochlea* ≡ "snail"):

clearly $|r| < a$ ∴ the curve lies wholly within the circle $r = a$. [Can you sketch the cochleoid?]

(ii) $r^2 = a^2 \cos 2\theta$: $|r| \leqslant a$; ∵ r^2 cannot be < 0, 2θ must lie in $\left(-\dfrac{\pi}{2}, \dfrac{\pi}{2}\right)$ or in $\left(\dfrac{3\pi}{2}, \dfrac{5\pi}{2}\right)$, i.e. $-\dfrac{\pi}{4} \leqslant \theta \leqslant \dfrac{\pi}{4}$ or $\dfrac{3\pi}{4} \leqslant \theta \leqslant \dfrac{5\pi}{4}$,

i.e. the curve cannot pass outside the sectors shown in Fig. 119b. The curve (the lemniscate of Bernoulli) is sketched fully in Example 131.

(3) Examine whether the curve has any asymptotes either rectilinear or curvilinear,

e.g. $r = \dfrac{a\theta}{1+\theta} \to a$ as $\theta \to \infty$.

$\therefore$ the circle $r = a$ is a curvilinear asymptote to the curve $r = \dfrac{a\theta}{1+\theta}$ (Fig. 119c).

(4) Form a table of corresponding values of r and θ.

§ 113. SELECTED EXAMPLES OF CURVE-SKETCHING IN POLAR COORDINATES

EXAMPLE 129.

cardioid $r = a(1+\cos\theta)$ $[= 2a\cos^2\theta/2]$ (Fig. 120).

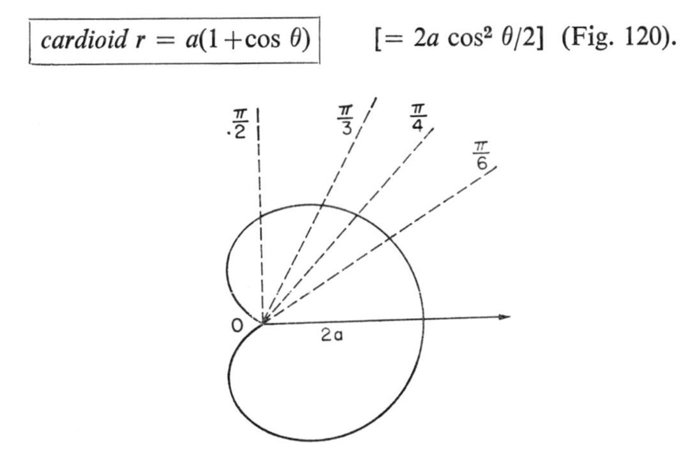

FIG. 120. Cardioid $r = a(1+\cos\theta)$

Tabulation

θ	0	$\pi/6$	$\pi/4$	$\pi/3$	$\pi/2$	$2\pi/3$	$3\pi/4$	$5\pi/6$	π
r/a	2	1·9...	1·7...	$1\frac{1}{2}$	1	$\frac{1}{2}$	0·3...	0·1...	0

Notes

(1) The cardioid (= epicycloid of one loop) is generated mechanically as the locus of a fixed point on a moving circle which rolls on a fixed circle of the same radius. (See § 106.)

(2) Allied cardioids are: $r = a(1-\cos\theta)$, $r = a(1+\sin\theta)$. Can you draw them?

(3) Chords of a cardioid through O are of constant length, for (Fig. 121) $POP' = a[1+\cos\theta+1+\cos(\pi+\theta)]$

$$= 2a.$$

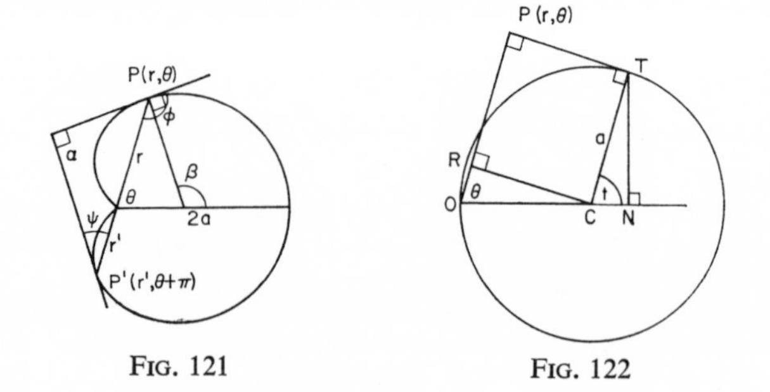

FIG. 121 FIG. 122

(4) From Fig. 122, $r = OR+RP$

$$= a\cos\theta+a$$

$$= a(1+\cos\theta)$$

∴ the pedal curve of a circle w.r.t. a point on the circumference is a cardioid.

(5) Greek *kardia* ≡ "heart".

(6) The *limaçon* (French ≡ "snail") has equation $r = a+b\cos\theta$ (*Pascal's snail*, after Etienne Pascal (1588–1651, French), father of Blaise Pascal) (Fig. 123). Clearly, the limaçon is a generalisation of the cardioid.

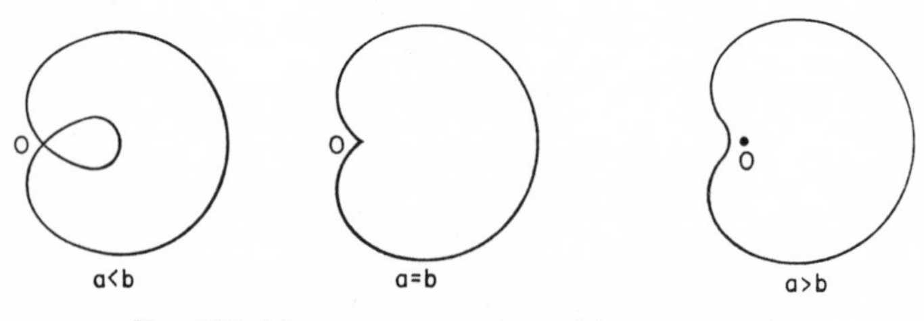

FIG. 123. Limaçons $r = a+b\cos\theta$ ($a <, =, > b$)

(7) The *trisectrix* $r = a(1+2\cos\theta)$ used in the trisection of an angle, is the special limaçon $b = 2a$. See Exercise 23.58.

Hereafter, we will not, in general, carry out the tabulation but will be content to give a diagram showing the salient features of the curve.

EXAMPLE 130. Find the maximum value of the ordinate $y = r\sin\theta$ for the curve $4r = 5+4\cos\theta$.

Solution. In Fig. 124, $y = r \sin \theta = \frac{5}{4} \sin \theta + \sin \theta \cos \theta$

$$\therefore \frac{dy}{d\theta} = \frac{5}{4} \cos \theta + 2 \cos^2 \theta - 1$$

$$= 0 \quad \text{if} \quad 8 \cos^2 \theta + 5 \cos \theta - 4 = 0$$

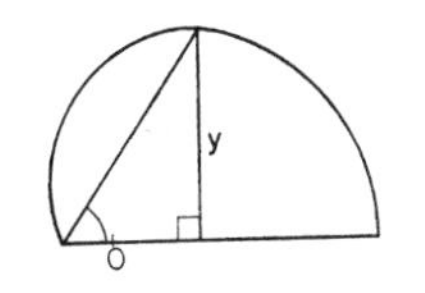

FIG. 124. Limaçon $r = 1\frac{1}{4} + \cos \theta$

$$\text{i.e. } \cos \theta = \frac{-5 \pm \sqrt{153}}{16} \doteqdot \frac{-5 \pm 12{\cdot}3693}{16} \doteqdot 0{\cdot}4606$$

$$\therefore \theta = 62°34'.$$

Clearly, $\frac{d^2y}{d\theta^2}$ is $-$ve so $\theta = 62°34'$ gives a maximum.

$\therefore y_{max} = \sin 62°34' \, (1{\cdot}25 + 0{\cdot}4606) \doteqdot 0{\cdot}8875 \times 1{\cdot}71 = 1{\cdot}4.$

EXAMPLE 131 | $r^2 = a^2 \cos 2\theta$ *(lemniscate of Bernoulli)* | (Fig. 125).

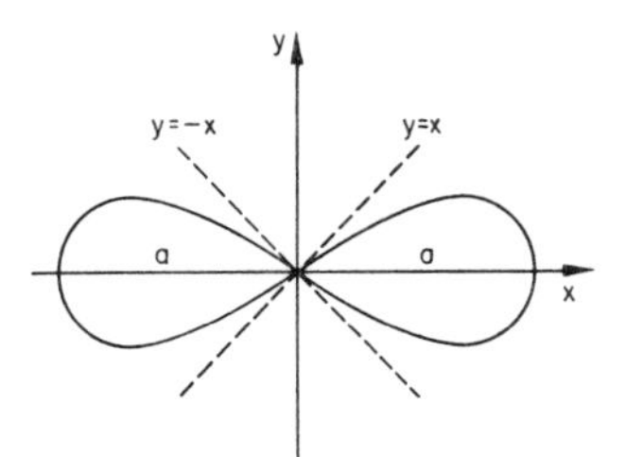

FIG. 125. Lemniscate of Bernoulli

Notes

(i) The lemniscate, which was discovered by James Bernoulli in 1694, is a special case of the ovals of Cassini. (See § 104.)
(ii) The lemniscate possesses two branches, one +ve, one −ve $\because r = \pm a\sqrt{\cos 2\theta}$.
(iii) The lemniscate occurs in crystallography.
(iv) The lemniscate is the pedal curve of the rectangular hyperbola w.r.t. the origin (Exercise 19.8).

(v) The range $\frac{3\pi}{4} \leqslant \theta \leqslant \frac{5\pi}{4}$ mentioned in § 112 (2)(ii) merely duplicates the values of the range $-\frac{\pi}{4} \leqslant \theta \leqslant \frac{\pi}{4}$.

(vi) At O, the lemniscate has a *biflecnode* (i.e. two nodes which are also inflexions) and the biflecnodal tangents are $y = \pm x$. (See Exercise 22.44.)

(vii) Parametric equations of the lemniscate are $x = a \cos \theta\sqrt{\cos 2\theta}$, $y = a \sin \theta\sqrt{\cos 2\theta}$.

(viii) $r^2 = a^2 \cos 2\theta$ is a solution of the differential equation

$$r^4 + r^2 \left(\frac{dr}{d\theta}\right)^2 = a^4.$$

(ix) Greek *lemniskos* $\equiv$ "ribbon".

Incidentally, what is the equation of the lemniscate in Cartesian coordinates? (Refer to Exercise 19.8.)

What happens if, in the equation of the lemniscate, θ is replaced by $\theta - \alpha$ ($\alpha = \pi/4$, say)? (See Exercise 22.9.)

§ 114. SPIRALS AND ROSE CURVES

EXAMPLE 132 $r = a\theta^n$ *(parabolic spirals)*.

Special cases. These spirals are called "parabolic" by analogy with the (Cartesian) parabolic curves $y = ax^n$.

$$\begin{cases} n = 1 & \textit{spiral of Archimedes} \\ n = -1 & \textit{hyperbolic spiral} \\ n = -\frac{1}{2} & \textit{lituus} \\ n = \frac{1}{2} & \textit{Fermat's spiral} \end{cases}$$

(a) Spiral of Archimedes $r = a\theta$ (Fig. 126).

Notes

(i) The dotted portion of Fig. 126 arises from $-$ve values of θ.

(ii) The spiral is the locus of a point moving with uniform velocity (starting at the pole) along the radius vector while the radius vector moves with uniform angular velocity.

(iii) The spiral may be used to illustrate the Newlands–Mendeléef law of octaves by arranging the elements along the curve in the order of their atomic weights.

(iv) Archimedes' spiral can be used as suitable outline of a cam as in a sewing-machine winder to control the regular to and fro motion associated with a regular rotation.

(v) Use in the trisection of an angle. Let $A(\alpha, \alpha)$, $B(\beta, \beta)$ be two points on the spiral $r = \theta$ (Fig. 127). With centre O and radius OA, draw an arc

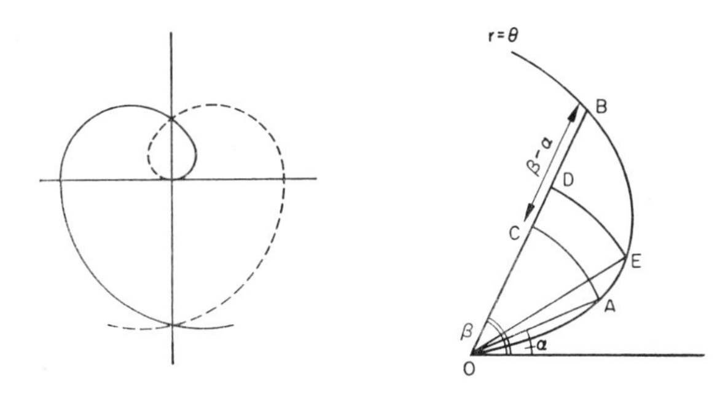

FIG. 126. Spiral of Archimedes FIG. 127. Trisection of an angle

of a circle to cut OB at C. On OB take D: $CD = \frac{1}{3}CB$. With centre O and radius OD, draw an arc of a circle to cut the spiral at E. Then we show that OE trisects $A\hat{O}B$.

$$\text{Now} \quad CD = \frac{1}{3}CB = \frac{\beta-\alpha}{3}$$

$$\begin{aligned} \therefore OE &= OD \\ &= OC+CD \\ &= \alpha+\frac{\beta-\alpha}{3} \\ &= \frac{\beta+2\alpha}{3} \end{aligned}$$

$$\therefore A\hat{O}E = \frac{\beta+2\alpha}{3}-\alpha = \frac{\beta-\alpha}{3}$$

$\therefore$ OE trisects $A\hat{O}B$.

(vi) Psychiatrists, we are told, sometimes use this spiral to detect possible brain damage leading to emotional disturbances.

Readers should consult *On Spirals*, Reference (b), Chapter 16, to savour the richness of Archimedes' original contribution.

(b) Hyperbolic spiral $r\theta = a$ $\quad \therefore r = \frac{a}{\theta}$ (Fig. 128).

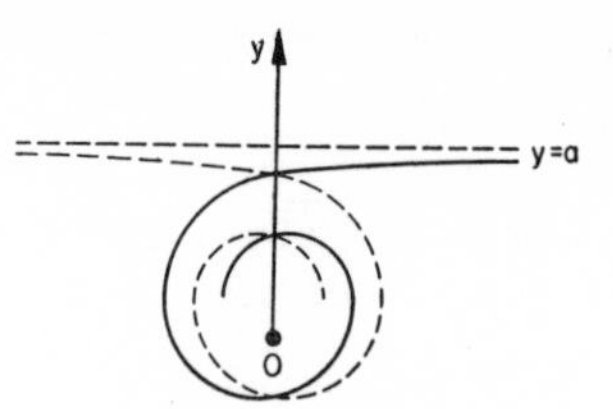

FIG. 128. Hyperbolic spiral

Notes

(i) It is called the hyperbolic (sometimes, reciprocal) spiral by analogy with the Cartesian form of the rectangular hyperbola $xy = a$.

(ii) The dotted portion of the diagram refers to $-$ve values of θ.

(iii) $y = r \sin \theta$

$$= a \frac{\sin \theta}{\theta}$$

$$\to a \text{ in the limit as } \theta \to 0$$

$$\therefore y = a \text{ is an asymptote.}$$

(c) **Lituus $r^2 \theta = a^2$** $\quad \therefore r = \pm \dfrac{a}{\sqrt{\theta}}$ (Fig. 129).

Notes

(i) Portions of Fig. 129 dotted refer to $-$ve values of r.

(ii) See Exercise 23.31 for the generation of the lituus.

(iii) For $r > 0$, the curve resembles the involute in the capital of an Ionic pillar.

(iv) Roman trumpeters played a musical instrument shaped like the lituus which emitted a high-pitched sound. Readers may also remember having seen the French messenger, Montjoy, blow a lituus in the film *Henry V*.

(v) Latin *lituus* $\equiv$ [bishop's (or shepherd's)] "crook".

(d) **Fermat's spiral $r^2 = a^2\theta$** $\quad$ i.e. $r = \pm a\sqrt{\theta}$ (Fig. 130).

(Dotted portions in Fig. 130 refer to $-$ve values of r.)

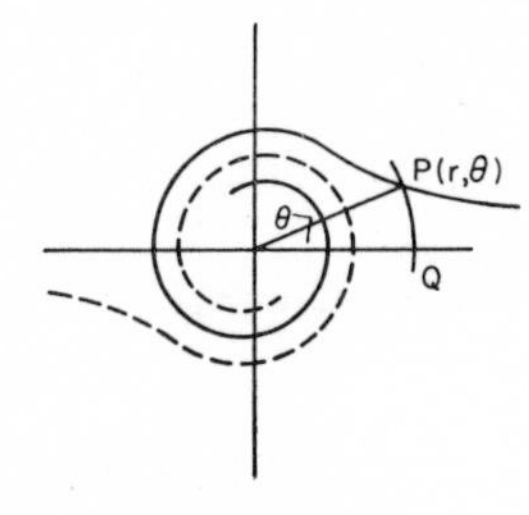

FIG. 129. Lituus

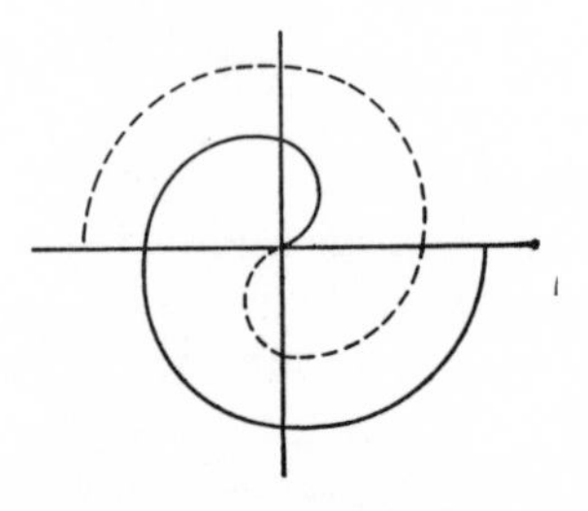

FIG. 130. Fermat's spiral

EXAMPLE 133 *rose curves* $r = a \sin n\theta$, $r = a \cos n\theta$ (Figs. 131–3).

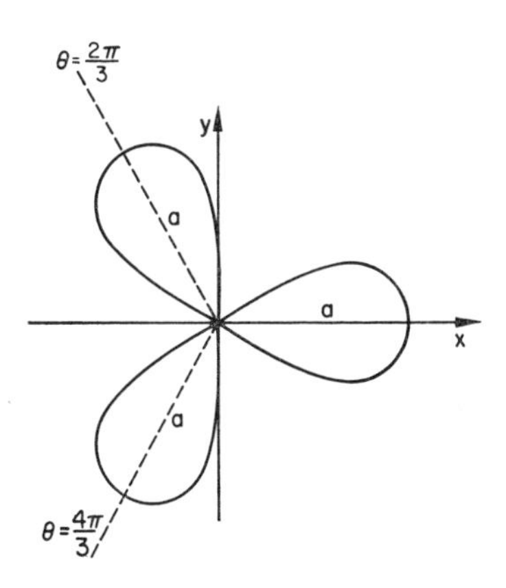

FIG. 131.
Three-leafed rose $r = a \cos 3\theta$

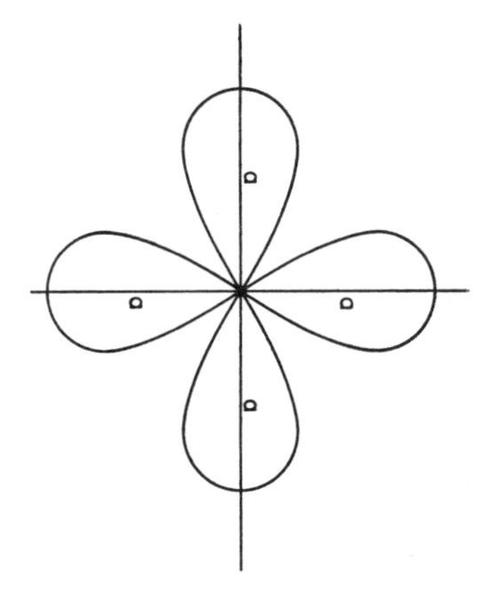

FIG. 132.
Four-leafed rose $r = a \cos 2\theta$

Tabulation

θ	3θ	r/a
0	0	1
$\pi/18$	$\pi/6$	$\sqrt{3}/2$
$\pi/12$	$\pi/4$	$\frac{1}{\sqrt{2}}$
$\pi/9$	$\pi/3$	$\frac{1}{2}$
$\pi/6$	$\pi/2$	0
$\pi/4$	$3\pi/4$	$-\frac{1}{\sqrt{2}}$
$\pi/3$	π	-1
$\pi/2$	$3\pi/2$	0

Curves $r = a \sin n\theta$ were called *rhodoneae* by Abbé Guido Grandi (in 1723 in his book, *Flores Geometrici*) because of a fancied resemblance to rose petals. They may be drawn with one continuous sweep of the pencil.

Notes

(1) $\left.\begin{array}{l} r = a \cos n\theta \\ r = a \sin n\theta \end{array}\right\{ \begin{array}{l} n \text{ odd} \Rightarrow n \text{ leaves,} \\ n \text{ even} \Rightarrow 2n \text{ leaves.} \end{array}$
Why is this so?

(2) The numbering of the leaves in Fig. 133 denotes the order in which they are generated.

(3) $r = 1 \cos n(\theta - \alpha)$ is the n-leafed rose rotated through $\alpha \left(= \frac{\pi}{2n} \text{ say}\right)$.

What happens if negative values of r are disallowed? Under these circumstances, compare $r^2 = a^2 \cos 2\theta$, $r = a \cos 2\theta$.

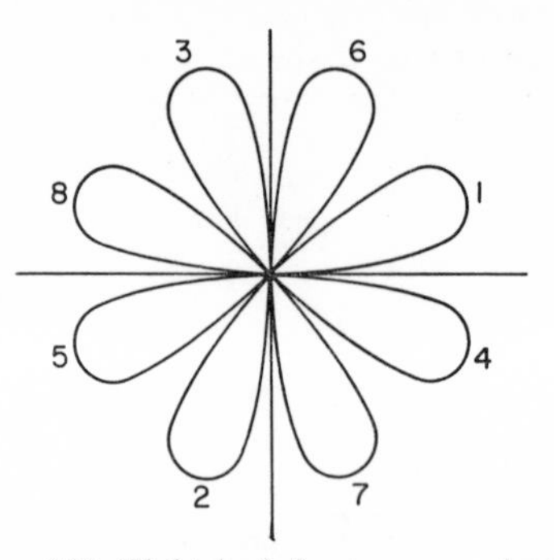

FIG. 133. Eight-leafed rose $r = a \sin 4\theta$

EXAMPLE 134 $\boxed{r^n = a^n \cos n\theta}$ (= *sinusoidal spirals*).

Special cases

$n = 2$	$r^2 = a^2 \cos 2\theta$	lemniscate of Bernoulli
$n = 1$	$r = a \cos \theta$	circle
$n = \frac{1}{2}$	$r = \frac{a}{2}(1+\cos\theta)$	cardioid
$n = -\frac{1}{2}$	$r = \frac{2a}{1+\cos\theta}$	parabola
$n = -1$	$a = r\cos\theta = x$	straight line
$n = -2$	$x^2 - y^2 = a^2$	rectangular hyperbola
$n = -\frac{1}{3}$		Tschirnhausen's cubic (Exercise 22.53).

§115. MEANING OF $r\,d\theta/dr$

$$\left.\begin{aligned} PN &= r \sin \delta\theta \\ QN &= r + \delta r - r\cos\delta\theta \end{aligned}\right\} \text{ from Fig. 134a}$$

$$= \delta r + r(1-\cos\delta\theta)$$

$$\therefore \tan P\hat{Q}O = \frac{r \sin \delta\theta}{\delta r + r(1-\cos\delta\theta)}.$$

In the limit as $Q \to P$ (Fig. 134b)

$$\boxed{\tan\phi = r\frac{d\theta}{dr}} \tag{258}$$

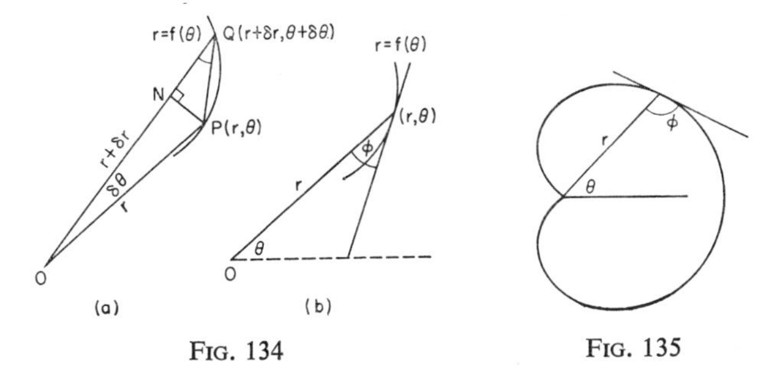

FIG. 134 FIG. 135

i.e. $r\dfrac{d\theta}{dr}$ = tan of the angle between the tangent at a given point and the radius vector at that point.

EXAMPLE 135. Find θ for the cardioid $r = a(1+\cos\theta)$ (Fig. 135).

Solution. $r = a(1+\cos\theta) = 2a\cos^2(\theta/2)$

$$\therefore \log r = \log 2a + 2\log\cos(\theta/2),$$

$$\therefore \frac{1}{r}\frac{dr}{d\theta} = -\tan(\theta/2).$$

But $\tan\phi = r\dfrac{d\theta}{dr}$.

$$\therefore \cot\phi = -\tan(\theta/2) = \frac{1}{r}\frac{dr}{d\theta}$$

$$= \cot\left(\frac{\pi}{2}+\frac{\theta}{2}\right)$$

$$\therefore \phi = \frac{\pi}{2}+\frac{\theta}{2}.$$

[Therefore $\phi = \dfrac{\pi}{2}$ when $\theta = 0$ showing the smoothness of the curve at this point.]

EXAMPLE 136. Find the angle of intersection of the cardioid $r = a(1+\sin\theta)$ and the circle $r = 3a\sin\theta$ (Fig. 136).

Solution. Solve: $\theta = \dfrac{\pi}{6}, \dfrac{5\pi}{6}$.

Circle: $\tan \phi_1 = r\dfrac{d\theta}{dr}$ cardioid: $\tan \phi_2 = \dfrac{1+\sin \theta}{\cos \theta}$

$= \tan \theta$ $= \sqrt{3}$ at P

$= \dfrac{1}{\sqrt{3}}$ at P.

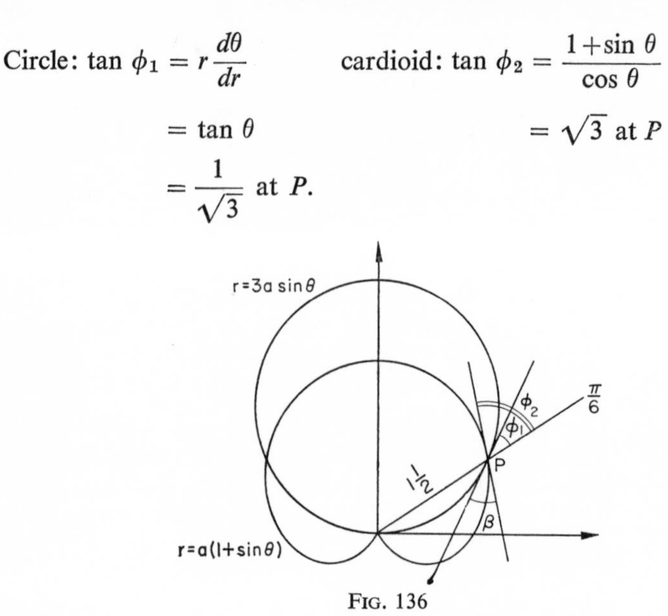

FIG. 136

Therefore angle of intersection is $\beta = \phi_2 - \phi_1$

$$= \tan^{-1}\left(\frac{\sqrt{3}-\dfrac{1}{\sqrt{3}}}{1+\sqrt{3}\cdot\dfrac{1}{\sqrt{3}}}\right)$$

$$= \tan^{-1}\left(\frac{1}{\sqrt{3}}\right)$$

$$\therefore \beta = 30°.$$

Similarly for $\theta = \dfrac{5\pi}{6}$.

At the origin, the angle of intersection is 90°.

§ 116. TANGENT IN POLAR COORDINATES

In Fig. 137, $\psi = \theta + \phi$

$$\therefore \tan \psi = \frac{\tan \theta + \tan \phi}{1 - \tan \theta \tan \phi}$$

$$\therefore \boxed{\text{gradient} = \frac{\tan \theta + r\, d\theta/dr}{1 - \tan \theta \cdot r\dfrac{d\theta}{dr}}}. \tag{259}$$

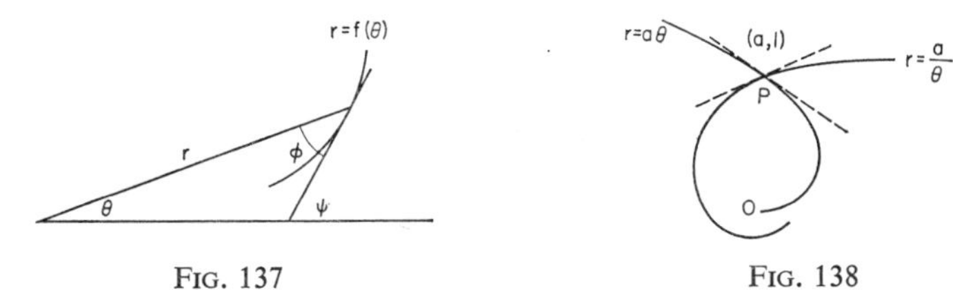

FIG. 137 FIG. 138

EXAMPLE 137. Obtain the gradients of the spiral of Archimedes $r = a\theta$ and the hyperbolic spiral $r = a/\theta$ at $(a, 1)$ (Fig. 138).

Solution. Spiral of Archimedes:

$$\tan \psi_1 = \frac{\tan \theta + \theta}{1 - \theta \tan \theta} \quad \text{by (259)}$$

$$= \frac{\tan 1 + 1}{1 - \tan 1} \quad \text{at } P.$$

Hyperbolic spiral:

$$\tan \psi_2 = \frac{\tan \theta - \theta}{1 + \theta \tan \theta}$$

$$= \frac{\tan 1 - 1}{1 + \tan 1} \quad \text{at } P$$

$$= -\frac{1}{\tan \psi_1}.$$

Therefore the spirals cut orthogonally at $(a, 1)$.

What happens at the other points of intersection of the two spirals?

§ 117. EQUIANGULAR SPIRAL

Given $r\dfrac{d\theta}{dr} = \tan\alpha$ (= const.) (Fig. 139),

$$\therefore \int \frac{dr}{r} = \cot\alpha \int d\theta$$

$$\therefore \log\frac{r}{a} = \theta\cot\alpha \quad (\log a = \text{const. of integration})$$

$$\therefore \boxed{r = ae^{\theta\cot\alpha}} \quad \textit{(equiangular spiral).}$$

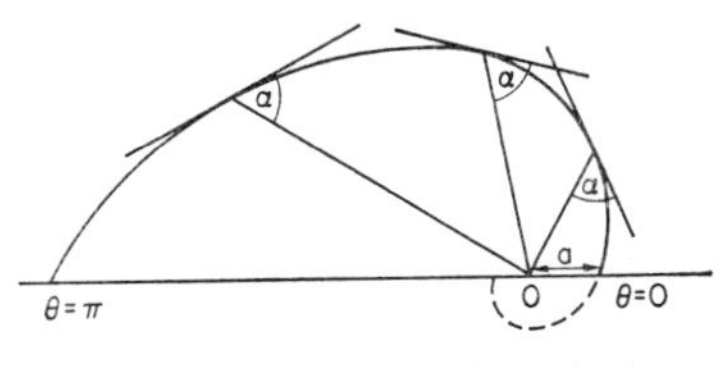

FIG. 139. Equiangular spiral

Notes

(i) In Fig. 139 the dotted locus refers to −ve values of θ.

(ii) Special case of the equiangular spiral: $\alpha = \pi/2 \Rightarrow$ circle, i.e. the equiangular spiral is a generalisation of this aspect of the circle.

(iii) The equiangular spiral is also called *Bernoulli's spiral* (after James Bernoulli), though it was first studied by Descartes in 1638. Bernoulli was so impressed with the property of the spiral by which various curves deduced from it reproduced the original spiral that he requested that an equiangular spiral be engraved on his tombstone with the Latin inscription *eadem mutata resurgo* ("though changed I shall arise again unchanged").

(iv) It is also called the *logarithmic spiral* (Bernoulli) or *proportional spiral* (Halley) (since parts of a radius cut off by successive whorls are in continued proportion) or the *geometric spiral* (Nicolas) (since radii at equal polar angles are in geometric progression).

(v) Since $\begin{cases} r_2^2 = r_1 r_3 = a^2 e^{\pi \cot \alpha} \\ r_3^2 = r_2 r_4 = \ldots, \end{cases}$

we have the right angles as shown in Fig. 140.

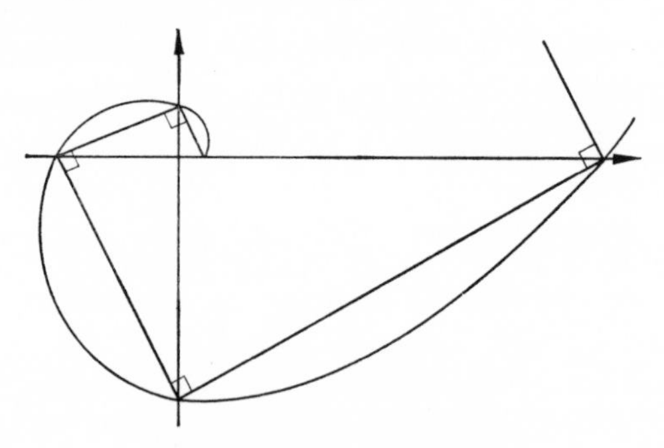

FIG. 140. Nest of rectangles

Therefore the spiral produces a *nest of rectangles*.

(vi) *Mechanical generation*. The equiangular spiral is the locus of a point moving along the radius vector with velocity increasing as its distance from its pole.

(vii) The occurrence in Nature of the equiangular spiral is widespread ranging from the convolutions of sea-shells (e.g. the "astonishing perfection", as Weyl says, of the chambered *Nautilus* for which $\alpha \doteqdot 80°$) to the forms of faraway spiral nebulae, from the growth of some plants to certain cuts of marble. Insects of a certain kind have their eyes so fixed that they are relentlessly drawn in towards a source of light. Florets of the giant sunflower *(Helianthus maximus)* and certain other flowers arrange themselves into two sets of equiangular spirals of opposite coiling, the numbers in each set for a given flower being successive Fibonacci numbers, e.g. a pyrethrum was found to have 21 right-hand coiling equiangular spirals (for which $\alpha \doteqdot 64°$) and 34 left-hand coiling spirals (for which $\alpha \doteqdot 50°$). Spiders' webs also conform fairly accurately to the equiangular spiral. For these, and similar reasons, the equiangular spiral has been called the "curve of life". Without doubt, it is one of the most fascinating loci one can meet in the realm of mathematics. Students interested in a scholarly treatment of the relation of this spiral to biological forms could consult *On Growth and Form*, by D'Arcy Thompson (C.U.P., 1961).

EXAMPLE 138 (curvature of the equiangular spiral).

Solution. Now $\psi = \theta+\alpha$ for the equiangular spiral $r = ae^{\theta \cot \alpha}$ (Fig. 141).

$$\therefore \varrho = \frac{ds}{d\psi} = \frac{ds}{d\theta} = \sqrt{r^2+\left(\frac{dr}{d\theta}\right)^2} = \frac{r}{\sin \alpha} \quad \text{using (48), (249), (253),}$$

i.e.

$$\cos\left(\frac{\pi}{2}-\alpha\right) = \frac{r}{\varrho},$$

i.e. the radius of curvature subtends a right-angle at the origin. (C is the centre of the circle of curvature, radius ϱ.)

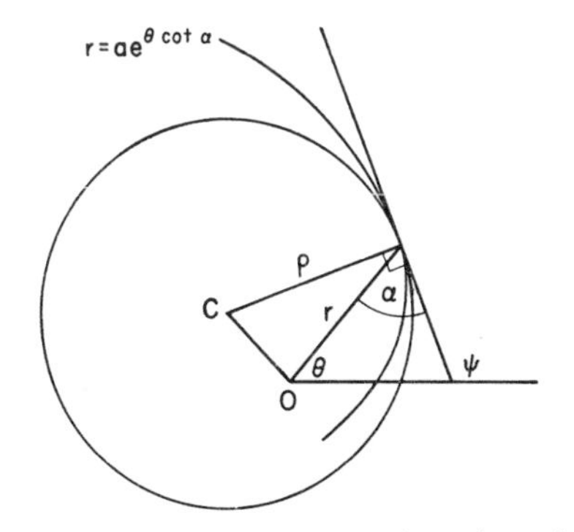

FIG. 141. Curvature of the equiangular spiral

Scientific applications of polar curves

Physical occurrences of polar curves are, for example, the cardioid in optics and in electrical circuit theory, and the three-leafed rose in crystallography. Equiangular spirals appear as the boundary of two bacteria colonies, or two crystals, which are growing at different rates. Lemniscates, occurring in electrical transmission theory, are also of practical value for designing the curve of a bend in road-construction, though a more precise curve for this purpose is the *clothoid* (= *Cornu's spiral*), which also arises in optics.

Suggested topic for further study

(1) Any polar coordinate curve which especially interests you (more detail).

References

As for Chapter 20.

EXERCISES 22

1. Convert the equation of the cardioid $r = a(1+\cos\theta)$ from polar to Cartesian coordinates.

2. Transform the equation of the lemniscate of Bernoulli $r^2 = a^2\cos 2\theta$ from polar to Cartesian coordinates. What is the order of the lemniscate?

3. Change the equation of the cissoid of Diocles $y^2 = \dfrac{x^3}{a-x}$ into polar coordinates.

4. Shift the origin of the trisectrix of Maclaurin $y^2 = \dfrac{x^2(3a-x)}{a+x}$ from the node to the foot Z of the directrix of the parabola. (Refer to Exercises 20.35, 20.36). Hence, derive the polar equation $r = a\sec\left(\dfrac{\theta}{3}\right)$ for the trisectrix.

Sketch the curves 5–9:

5. $4r = 3+4\cos\theta$. **6.** $r = a(1-\cos 2\theta) = 2a\sin^2\theta$.
7. $r = a\sin 2\theta$. **8.** $r = a\sin^2 2\theta$. **9.** $r^2 = a^2\sin 2\theta$.

[Distinguish carefully between (7) and (8) regarding the order in which the leaves are generated.]

10. Find the maximum breadth of the lemniscate of Bernoulli.

11. What is the maximum ordinate $y = r\sin\theta$ for the cardioid $r = 3(1+\cos\theta)$?

12. Given the cardioid $r = a(1-\cos\theta)$, find ϕ.

13. In the cardioid $r = a(1-\cos\theta)$, find the points at which the tangent is vertical.

14. Find the angle of intersection of the cardioid $r = a(1-\cos\theta)$ and the circle $r = 2a\cos\theta$.

15. Do the cardioids $r = a(1+\cos\theta)$, $r = b(1-\cos\theta)$ cut orthogonally?

16. By suitably changing the origin on the x-axis, show that $x = a(2\cos t-\cos 2t)$, $y = a(2\sin t-\sin 2t)$ is a cardioid.

17. Kepler's *true anomaly* in astronomy is $\theta = A\hat{S}P$ for a point $P(a\cos\phi, b\sin\phi)$ on the ellipse (Fig. 79). Prove that $\dfrac{\sin\phi}{\sin\theta} = \dfrac{\sqrt{1-e^2}}{1+e\cos\theta}$.

18. Solve $r\,d\theta - \tanh\alpha\cdot dr = 0$ (α const.). Determine α and the arbitrary constant of integration if the curve passes through (2, 0) and cuts the radius vector $\theta = 0$ at an angle $\pi/4$. [U.N.E.]

19. Verify that the point $T(a+a\cos t,\ a\sin t)$ lies on the circle $x^2+y^2 = 2ax = 0$ for all values of t. Indicate the geometrical meaning of t. A perpendicular is drawn from the origin to the tangent at T, meeting this tangent at P; by finding both the Cartesian and polar coordinates of P, obtain the locus of P as t varies (Fig. 122).

20. *Polar subtangent* of a curve is $OT = r^2\dfrac{d\theta}{dr}$, where O is the pole and T is the intersection of the tangent at $P(r, \theta)$ with the line through O perpendicular to OP. Given that when $r = \infty$, $\theta = 0$, what curve has constant polar subtangent?

21. *Polar subnormal* of a curve is $ON = \dfrac{dr}{d\theta}$ where N is the intersection of the normal at $P(r, \theta)$ with the line through O perpendicular to OP. Assuming $\theta = 0$ when $r = 0$, which curve has constant subnormal?

At the point on the cardioid $r = a(1+\cos\theta)$ for which $\theta = \tan^{-1}\left(\dfrac{5}{12}\right)$ determine the lengths of:

22. The polar subnormal. **23.** The polar subtangent.

Prove:

24. $\cos\phi = \dfrac{dr}{ds}$. **25.** $\sin\phi = r\dfrac{d\theta}{ds}$.

26. Establish the curvature formula $\varkappa = \dfrac{r^2+2(dr/d\theta)^2-r(d^2r/d\theta^2)}{\{r^2+(dr/d\theta)^2\}^{3/2}}$ for polar coordinates.

Determine the curvature of the curves 27–32:

27. $r = a\cos 3\theta$ at $\theta = \pi/6$. **28.** $r = a\sin 2\theta$ at $\theta = \pi/4$.

29. $r = a\theta$ at $\theta = 0$. **30.** $r = a/\theta$.

31. $r = ae^{\theta\cot\alpha}$. (See Example 138.) **32.** $r^2 = a^2\cos 2\theta$ at $\theta = 0$.

33. Where, on the cardioid $r = a(1+\cos\theta)$, is the curvature maximum?

34. Let the perpendicular from O to the tangent at P to the curve $f(r, \theta) = 0$ be of length p. Writing $u = \dfrac{1}{r}$, obtain the formula $\dfrac{1}{p^2} = \dfrac{1}{r^4}\left(\dfrac{ds}{d\theta}\right)^2 = u^2+\left(\dfrac{du}{d\theta}\right)^2$ (used in orbit problems). [$(r, p) \equiv$ *pedal coordinates* of P.]

35. Derive the formula $\varrho = r\dfrac{dr}{dp}$.

36. Establish the equation $r^3 = 2ap^2$ of the cardioid $r = a(1-\cos\theta)$ in pedal coordinates and find its radius of curvature in terms of r.

37. Tangents at the ends of a cuspidal chord of the cardioid are perpendicular (Fig. 121). Prove.

38. Inclination to the initial line of the normal at (r, θ) on the cardioid $r = a(1+\cos\theta)$ is $\dfrac{3\theta}{2}$ (Fig. 121). Prove.

39. For the lemniscate, what is the angle of inclination of the normal to the initial line?

40. At the point $(2a, 0)$ on the cardioid $r = a(1+\cos\theta)$ a tangent is drawn perpendicular to a tangent at (r, θ). Deduce that $\theta = \pi/3$.

41. Polar angles of two points on the cardioid from which perpendicular tangents can be drawn differ by $\pi/3$. Establish this result.

42. Determine the positions of the double points of the cardioid.

43. Verify that the double point of the cardioid at the origin is a cusp.

44. Investigate the nature of the double points of the lemniscate.

45. Radii of curvature at the extremities of the cuspidal chord of a cardioid (Exercise 23.37) ar ϱ_1, ϱ_2. Show that $\varrho_1^2+\varrho_2^2 = \dfrac{16a^2}{9}$.

Obtain the lengths of the chords of curvature at a given point:

46. Along the radius vector. **47.** Perpendicular to the radius vector.

48. Spirals $r = \theta$, $r\theta = 1$ have radii of curvature denoted by ϱ_A, ϱ_H respectively. At points where the spirals intersect, prove that $\varrho_H = 3\varrho_A$.

49. If the circle of curvature at any point P on the lemniscate cuts OP at Q, determine the ratio $OP : QP$.

50. What is the gradient of the tangent to the lituus $r^2\theta = 1$ at $(\sqrt{2}, \frac{1}{2})$?

51. From a point O on the circumference of a circle a chord OQ is drawn and P, P' are points on $OQ : QP = QP' =$ const. Show that the locus of P (and P') as Q varies is a cardioid with cusp at O. (This is the *conchoidal property* of the cardioid.)

52. Mark, in the Argand diagram, the region simultaneously satisfied by $|z-1| < R(z)$, $|1-z^{1/2}| < 1$.

53. (Trisection of an angle.) Consider the parabola of Fig. 72. Through P draw a perpendicular to SP and on this perpendicular select a point Z: $S\hat{Z}P = S\hat{P}T$. Then the locus of Z is $r = a\sec^3\left(\frac{\theta}{3}\right)$, *Tschirnhausen's cubic* [Tschirnhausen, 1651–1708, German] where S is the pole and SA the initial line, i.e. $A\hat{S}Z = \theta$. Prove.

[This cubic is also called *the trisectrix of Catalan* (Catalan 1814–94, Belgian) since in its derivation an angle is trisected.]

54. Extremities of the polar subnormals (Exercise 22.21) of the equiangular spiral $r = ae^{\theta \cot \alpha}$ lie on another equiangular spiral. Prove.

55. (Generation of the cardioid.) A circle of radius a rolls without slipping on a circle of equal radius. Deduce that the locus of a point $P(r, \theta)$ on the rolling circle is the cardioid $r = 2a(1-\cos\theta)$.

CHAPTER 23

GEOMETRICAL APPLICATIONS OF THE DEFINITE INTEGRAL

> I do not know what I may appear to the world, but to myself I seem to have been only like a boy playing on the seashore, and diverting myself in now and then finding a smoother pebble or a prettier shell than ordinary, whilst the great ocean of truth lay all undiscovered before me.
>
> (Newton)

Previous theory and problems illustrated the fact that the calculus is indeed a most powerful key for unlocking the secrets of Nature. Emphasis in the concluding portion of our exposition is in (geometrical) applications of calculus to curves rather than to applications from the physical world.

§118. AREA IN POLAR COORDINATES

We seek to ascertain the area in polar coordinates of the sector AOB of the curve $r = f(\theta)$ (Fig. 142a), of which a very small portion is the sector POQ, where P, Q are neighbouring points on the curve. Now the area of the sector POQ is approximately that of the area of the triangle OPQ (Fig. 142b).

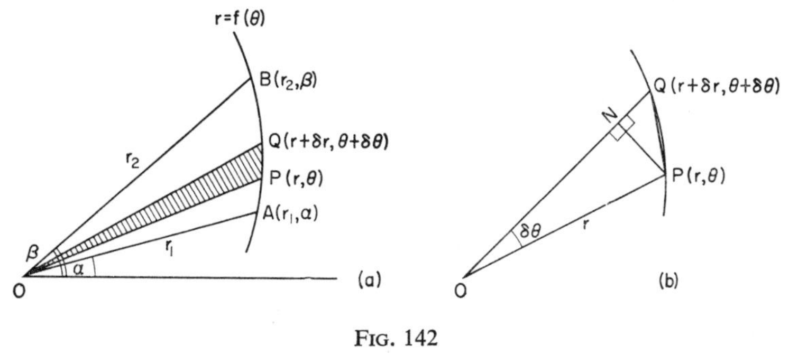

Fig. 142

$$\therefore \text{ area sector } POQ \doteqdot \tfrac{1}{2}OQ\cdot NP$$
$$= \tfrac{1}{2}(r+\delta r)r \sin \delta\theta$$
$$= \tfrac{1}{2}r^2 \sin \delta\theta + \tfrac{1}{2}r\, \delta r \sin \delta\theta$$
$$\doteqdot \tfrac{1}{2}r^2\, \delta\theta$$

since $\delta\theta$ is very small and the product of the two increments has been discarded.

Summing such small sectorial areas and proceeding to the limit, we have area of sector $AOB = \lim\limits_{\delta\theta\to 0} (\sum \tfrac{1}{2}r^2\, \delta\theta)$

i.e.
$$\boxed{A = \tfrac{1}{2}\int_\alpha^\beta r^2\, d\theta}. \tag{260}$$

[Students frequently forget the factor $\tfrac{1}{2}$ occurring in formula (260). You have been warned!]

Some fundamental area properties of a circle are (Fig. 143):

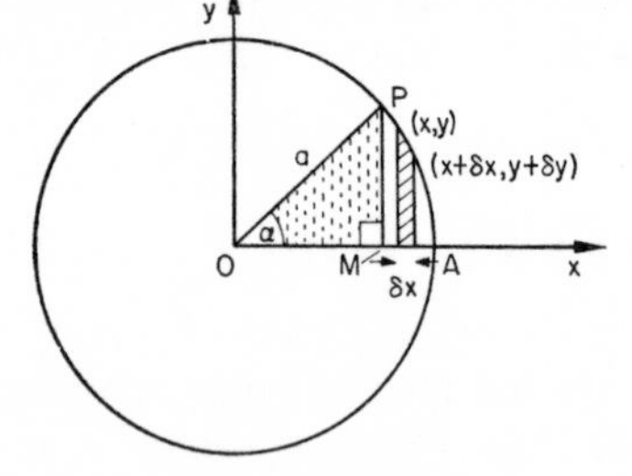

FIG. 143. Circular sector

(i) area of circular sector $AOP = \tfrac{1}{2}a^2\alpha$
(ii) area of circle $= \pi a^2$
(iii) area of semi-segment $AMP = \tfrac{1}{2}a^2\,(\alpha - \sin\alpha\cos\alpha)$.

These should be checked as exercises.

Certain logical difficulties arise in some derivations of the area formula (i) since (i) is used to obtain $\lim\limits_{x\to 0} \dfrac{\sin x}{x} = 1$ which in turn is used to obtain $\dfrac{d}{dx}\sin x = \cos x$ which, further, is used in the integration of $\int\sqrt{a^2-x^2}\,dx$. Consult, for example, A. S. Ramsey, *Elementary Calculus* (C.U.P., 1962), pp. 52–53, 136–7.

EXAMPLE 139 (Areas of conics).

Solution.

(i) Circle $r = 2a \sin \theta$ (Fig. 116c with a replaced by $2a$) has area

$$A = \tfrac{1}{2} \int_0^{\pi} 4a^2 \sin^2 \theta \, d\theta$$

$$= 2a^2 \int_0^{\pi} \frac{1-\cos 2\theta}{2} \, d\theta$$

$$= a^2 \left[\theta - \frac{\sin 2\theta}{2} \right]_0^{\pi}$$

$$= \pi a^2$$

or, use symmetry and take twice the area for $0 \leqslant \theta \leqslant \pi/2$.

(ii) From § 111, ellipse $\dfrac{\cos^2 \theta}{a^2} + \dfrac{\sin^2 \theta}{b^2} = \dfrac{1}{r^2}$ (Fig. 144a) has area

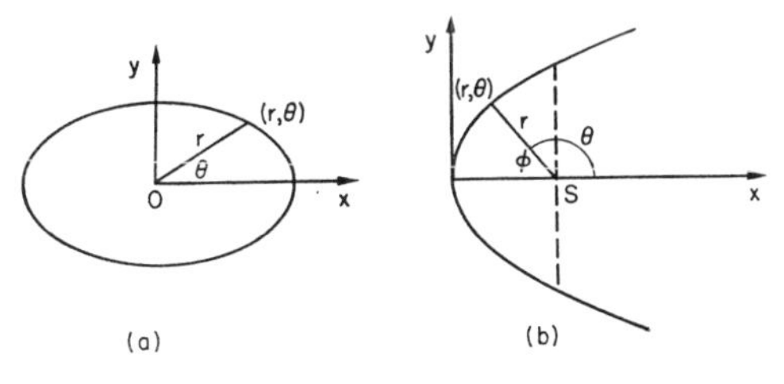

FIG. 144

$$A = 4 \times \tfrac{1}{2} \int_0^{\pi/2} \frac{a^2 b^2 \, d\theta}{b^2 \cos^2 \theta + a^2 \sin^2 \theta} \quad \text{(using symmetry)}$$

$$= 2a^2 b^2 \cdot \frac{\pi}{2ab} \quad \text{(by Example 39 (ii))}$$

$$= \pi ab$$

$$= \frac{b}{a} \times \text{area of the auxiliary circle (a result due to Archimedes).}$$

(iii) (Focus S as pole) Parabola $r = \dfrac{2a}{1+\cos \phi} = \dfrac{a}{\cos^2 \phi/2}$ (Fig. 144b) has area

$$A = 2\times\tfrac{1}{2}\int_0^{\pi/2} a^2 \sec^4\frac{\phi}{2}\,d\phi \quad \text{(using symmetry)}$$

$$= 2a^2\int_0^{\phi=\pi/2}\left(\tan^2\frac{\phi}{2}+1\right)d\tan(\phi/2)$$

$$= 2a^2\left[\frac{1}{3}\tan^3(\phi/2)+\tan(\phi/2)\right]_0^{\pi/2}$$

$$= \frac{3}{8}a^2.$$

Note. The rigorous procedure by which Archimedes obtained the area of a parabolic segment is virtually integration, though this process is disguised by his techniques, the method of exhaustion. (See *Quadrature of the Parabola*, Reference (b), Chapter 16.)

Notes

(i) Areas obtained using (260) in polar coordinates should also be obtained using § 33 for Cartesian coordinates. (For the circle and ellipse, see Example 34a.)

(ii) Using the strain matrix of Example 64 and assuming the area of a circle, we can obtain the area of an ellipse, thus (Fig. 145):

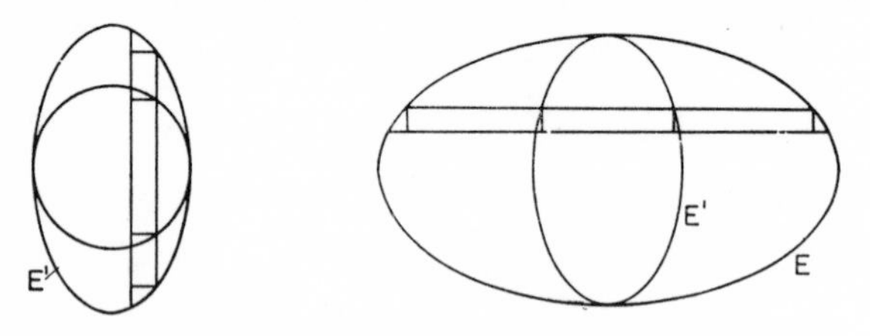

FIG. 145. Strain transformations and the ellipse

The strain transformation with matrix $\begin{bmatrix}1 & \cdot\\ \cdot & b\end{bmatrix}$ carries the unit circle $x^2+y^2 = 1$ (of area π) into the ellipse $E' : x^2+\dfrac{y^2}{b^2} = 1$ whose area is πb (because each rectangle of area of the circle is multiplied by b). The further strain transformation with matrix $\begin{bmatrix}a & \cdot\\ \cdot & 1\end{bmatrix}$ carries E' into the ellipse $E: \dfrac{x^2}{a^2}+\dfrac{y^2}{b^2} = 1$ whose area is πab (because each rectangle of area of the ellipse E' is a multiplied by a).

EXAMPLE 140 (Cardioid areas). (a) Determine the area of the cardioid $r = a(1+\cos\theta)$.

Solution. Using Fig. 120, we have, for the area of the cardioid,

$$A = 2\times\tfrac{1}{2}\int_0^{\pi} a^2(1+\cos\theta)^2\,d\theta \qquad \text{by symmetry}$$

$$= a^2\int_0^{\pi}\left(1\tfrac{1}{2}+2\cos\theta+\frac{\cos 2\theta}{2}\right)d\theta$$

$$= a^2\left[\frac{3\theta}{2}+2\sin\theta+\frac{\sin 2\theta}{4}\right]_0^{\pi}$$

$$= \frac{3\pi a^2}{2} = 6\times\text{area of the generating circle.}$$

(b) Find the area inside the circle $r = a$ and outside the cardioid $r = a(1-\cos\theta)$. [See (Fig. 146).]

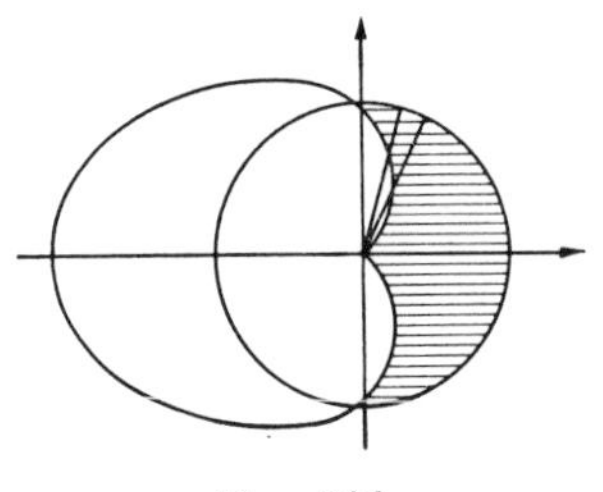

FIG. 146

Solution. The curves intersect at $\theta = \pi/2,\ -\pi/2$.

$$\therefore\ A = 2\times\tfrac{1}{2}\int_0^{\pi/2} a^2\{1-(1-\cos\theta)^2\}\,d\theta \qquad \text{by symmetry}$$

$$= a^2\int_0^{\pi/2}(2\cos\theta-\cos^2\theta)\,d\theta$$

$$= a^2\int_0^{\pi/2}\left(2\cos\theta-\frac{1+\cos 2\theta}{2}\right)d\theta$$

$$= a^2\left[2\sin\theta-\frac{\theta}{2}-\frac{\sin 2\theta}{4}\right]_0^{\pi/2}$$

$$= a^2\left(2-\frac{\pi}{4}\right).$$

EXAMPLE 141 (lemniscate of Bernoulli). What is the total area of the lemniscate of Bernoulli?

Solution. Using Fig. 125, we have, for both loops,

$$\text{Area} = 4\times\tfrac{1}{2}\int_0^{\pi/4} a^2 \cos 2\theta \, d\theta \qquad \text{by symmetry}$$

$$= 2a^2\left[\frac{\sin 2\theta}{2}\right]_0^{\pi/2}$$

$$= a^2.$$

EXAMPLE 142 (area of the loop of the folium of Descartes).

Solution. The polar equation of the folium (Fig. 102) is readily found to be $r = 3a\,\dfrac{\sin\theta\cos\theta}{\cos^3\theta+\sin^3\theta}$. Hence the area of the loop (in the first quadrant) is

$$A = \tfrac{1}{2}\int_0^{\pi/2} \frac{9a^2\sin^2\theta\cos^2\theta}{(\cos^3\theta+\sin^3\theta)^2}\,d\theta$$

$$= \frac{9a^2}{2}\int_0^{\infty}\frac{t^2\,dt}{(1+t^3)^2} \quad \text{(putting } t = \tan\theta\text{)}$$

$$= \frac{3a^2}{2}\int_0^{\infty}\frac{dw}{1+w^2} \quad \text{(putting } w = t^3\text{)}$$

$$= -\frac{3a^2}{2}\left[\frac{1}{1+b}-1\right]_0^{\infty}$$

$$= \frac{3a^2}{2}.$$

EXAMPLE 143 [area common to two ellipses (Fig. 147)].

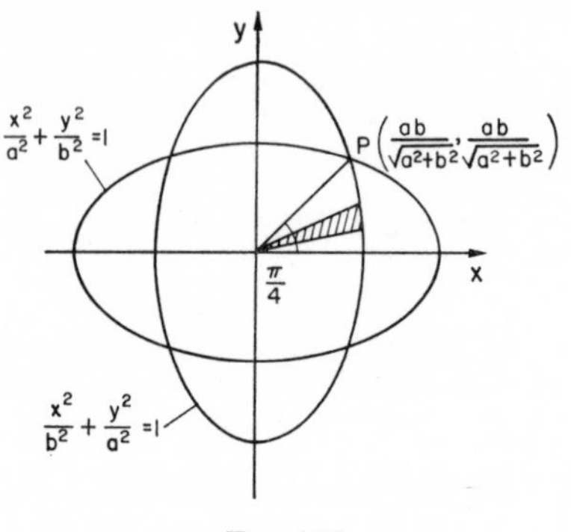

FIG. 147

Solution. Complete common area (by symmetry)

$$= 8\times\tfrac{1}{2}\int_0^{\pi/4} \frac{a^2b^2}{a^2\cos^2\theta + b^2\sin^2\theta}\,d\theta$$

$$= 4a^2b^2\left[\frac{1}{ab}\tan^{-1}\left(\frac{b}{a}\tan\theta\right)\right]_0^{\pi/4} \qquad \text{using Example 24(e)}$$

$$= 4ab\tan^{-1}\left(\frac{b}{a}\right).$$

§ 119. VOLUME OF A SOLID OF REVOLUTION

Rotating the area under the curve $y = f(x)$ bounded by A and B about the x-axis (Fig. 148), we generate a *solid of revolution* (sense of rotation irrelevant). To find the volume inside this figure, we consider the summation of thin discs such as that based on the neighbouring points P, Q: they are approximately cylindrical, of radius y and height δx.

Volume of cylindrical disc $PQQ'P' = \pi y^2\,\delta x$ from Fig. 148.

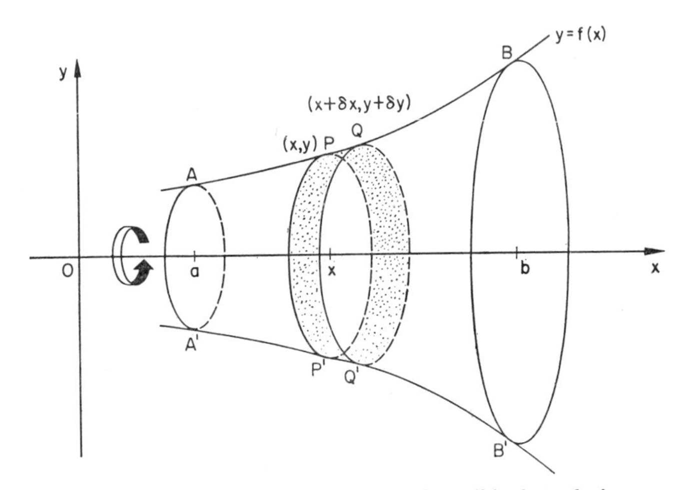

FIG. 148. Volume and surface area of a solid of revolution

Therefore volume of solid of revolution $= \lim\limits_{\delta x\to 0} \pi(\sum y^2\,\delta x)$

i.e.
$$\boxed{V = \pi\int_a^b y^2\,dx}\cdot \qquad (261)$$

Similarly, if the curve $x = f(y)$ is rotated about the y-axis,

$$V = \pi \int_c^d x^2\, dy.$$

EXAMPLE 144 (volume of a sphere).

Lemma. Volume of a spherical cap, height h, is

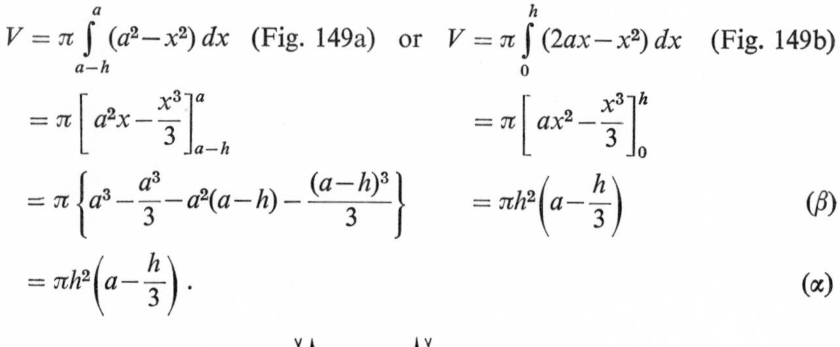

$$V = \pi \int_{a-h}^{a} (a^2-x^2)\, dx \quad \text{(Fig. 149a)} \quad \text{or} \quad V = \pi \int_0^h (2ax-x^2)\, dx \quad \text{(Fig. 149b)}$$

$$= \pi \left[a^2x - \frac{x^3}{3} \right]_{a-h}^{a} \qquad\qquad = \pi \left[ax^2 - \frac{x^3}{3} \right]_0^h$$

$$= \pi \left\{ a^3 - \frac{a^3}{3} - a^2(a-h) - \frac{(a-h)^3}{3} \right\} \qquad = \pi h^2 \left(a - \frac{h}{3} \right) \qquad (\beta)$$

$$= \pi h^2 \left(a - \frac{h}{3} \right). \qquad (\alpha)$$

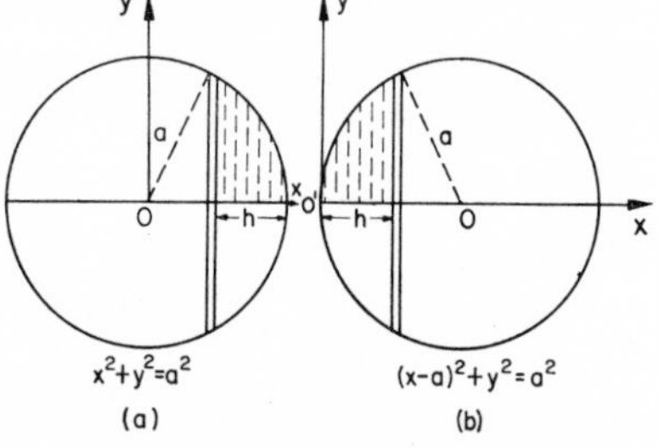

FIG. 149. Volume of a sphere

Put $h = a$ in (α) and double (for symmetry) or, put $h = 2a$ in (β).

Therefore the volume of the sphere $= \frac{4}{3}\pi a^3$

$= \frac{2}{3} \times$ volume of the circumscribed circular cylinder.

[This famous result is due to Archimedes. When Archimedes was accidentally slain by a Roman soldier after the siege of Syracuse (212 B.C.), the Roman general, Marcellus, erected a splendid monument to Archimedes on which was engraved a sphere inscribed in a cylinder.]

EXAMPLE 145. The area bounded by the y-axis and the portion of the catenary $y = c \cosh \left(\frac{x}{c}\right)$ between $x = 0$, $x = c$, is rotated about the y-axis (Fig. 150). Determine the volume of the solid revolution thus generated.

Solution. $V = \pi \int_{c}^{c\cosh 1} x^2\,dy$ (rotation about y-axis)

$$= \pi \int_0^c \frac{x^2(e^{x/c}-e^{-x/c})}{2}\,dx$$

$$= \frac{\pi}{2}\left\{\int_0^c x^2 e^{x/c}\,dx - \int_0^c x^2 e^{-x/c}\,dx\right\}$$

$$= \frac{\pi}{2}\{A-B\},$$

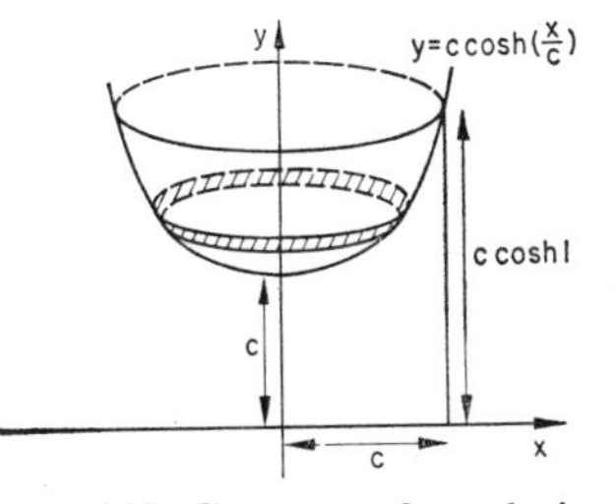

FIG. 150. Catenary of revolution

where $A = \int_0^c x^2 e^{x/c}\,dx = c\int_0^c x^2 \frac{de^{x/c}}{dx}\,dx$

$$= c\left\{\left[x^2 e^{x/c}\right]_0^c - 2\int_0^c x e^{x/c}\,dx\right\}$$

$$= c\left\{c^2 e - 2c\left(\left[x e^{x/c}\right]_0^c - \int_0^c e^{x/c}\,dx\right)\right\}$$

$$= c\left\{c^2 e - 2c\left(ce - c\left[e^{x/c}\right]_0^c\right)\right\}$$

$$= c^3(e-2).$$

Similarly, $B = c^3\left(2-\frac{5}{e}\right).$

$$\therefore\ V = \frac{\pi c^3}{2}\left(e+\frac{5}{e}-4\right).$$

§120. LENGTH OF A CURVE

By the *length* of a curve we mean the limit to which the perimeter of an inscribed polygon (open or closed) tends as the lengths of its sides are made arbitrarily small. (This process is sometimes called *rectification* (Latin *rectus* ≡ "straight"), i.e. the curve is regarded as the limiting sum of straight lines.) (Fig. 151.)

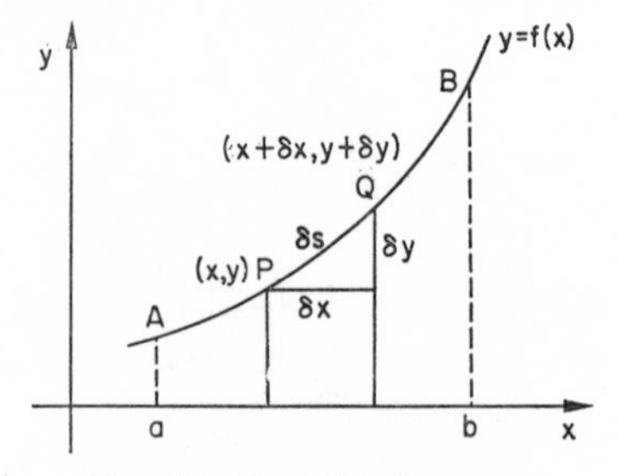

FIG. 151. Length of a curve

From (247) the arc-length AB of $y = f(x)$ is

$$\boxed{s = \int_a^b \sqrt{1+\left(\frac{dy}{dx}\right)^2}\, dx}. \tag{262}$$

If the curve is $x = f(y)$, then

$$s = \int_c^d \sqrt{1+\left(\frac{dx}{dy}\right)^2}\, dy.$$

If the curve is given parametrically (parameter t), then

$$\boxed{s = \int_{t_1}^{t_2} \sqrt{\left(\frac{dx}{dt}\right)^2+\left(\frac{dy}{dt}\right)^2}\, dt}. \tag{262.1}$$

By (48) and (247.1) if $r = f(\theta)$, then

$$\boxed{s = \int_\alpha^\beta \sqrt{r^2+\left(\frac{dr}{d\theta}\right)^2}\, d\theta}. \tag{263}$$

If $\theta = f(r)$, $\quad s = \displaystyle\int_{r_1}^{r_2} \sqrt{1+\left(r\frac{d\theta}{dr}\right)^2}\, dr.$

EXAMPLE 146 (perimeter p of a circle).

Solution (see Fig. 116). By (262) and (263), we have from the Cartesian equation $x^2+y^2 = a^2$ or from the polar equation $r = 2a \sin \theta$ the two equivalent expressions

$$4\int_0^a \sqrt{1+\left(-\frac{x}{y}\right)^2}\,dx = p \qquad = \int_0^\pi \sqrt{4a^2 \sin^2\theta+4a^2\cos^2\theta}\,d\theta$$

$$= 4a\int_0^a \frac{dx}{\sqrt{a^2-x^2}} \qquad = 2a\int_0^\pi d\theta$$

$$= 4a\left[\sin^{-1}\left(\frac{x}{a}\right)\right]_0^a \qquad = 2\pi a \qquad = 2a\left[\theta\right]_0^\pi.$$

EXAMPLE 147 [parabolic arc bounded by the *latus rectum* (Fig. 71)].

Solution. Arc length $AL = \int_0^a \sqrt{1+\left(\frac{dy}{dx}\right)^2}\,dx$

$$= 2a\int_0^1 \sqrt{1+t^2}\,dt \quad \because x = at^2,\ y = 2at$$

$$= 2aI.$$

Now $$I = \int_0^1 \sqrt{1+t^2}\,\frac{dt}{dt}\,dt$$

$$= \left[t\sqrt{1+t^2}\right]_0^1+\int_0^1 \frac{dt}{\sqrt{1+t^2}}-I$$

$$\therefore I = \tfrac{1}{2}\left[t\sqrt{1+t^2}+\log(t+\sqrt{1+t^2})\right]_0^1$$

$$\therefore AL = 2a\cdot\tfrac{1}{2}(\sqrt{2}+\log(1+\sqrt{2}))$$

$$= a(\sqrt{2}+\log(\sqrt{2}+1)) \doteqdot 2{\cdot}295a.$$

EXAMPLE 148 [perimeter of cardioid (Fig. 120)].

Solution. $$s = \int_0^{2\pi} \sqrt{a^2(1+\cos\theta)^2+a^2\sin^2\theta}\,d\theta$$

$$= 2a\int_0^\pi \sqrt{2(1+\cos\theta)}\,d\theta$$

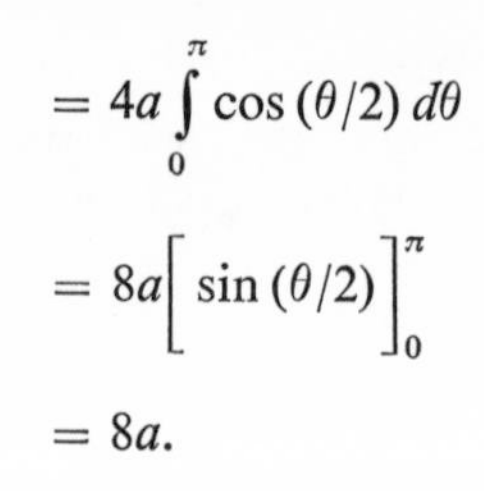

$$= 4a \int_0^{\pi} \cos(\theta/2)\, d\theta$$

$$= 8a\Big[\sin(\theta/2)\Big]_0^{\pi}$$

$$= 8a.$$

EXAMPLE 149 (intrinsic equations of the catenary and cycloid).

Solution. (i) *catenary* $y = c \cosh(x/c)$ (See Fig. 113)

$$\therefore \quad \tan\psi = dy/dx = \sinh(x/c) \text{ at } (x, y)$$

$$s = \int_0^{x} \sqrt{1+\sinh^2(x/c)}\, dx = \int_0^{x} \cosh(x/c)\, dx$$

$$= c \sinh(x/c)$$

$$\therefore s = c \tan\psi.$$

(ii) *cycloid* $\begin{cases} x = a(\theta+\sin\theta) \\ y = a(1-\cos\theta) \end{cases}$ (See Fig. 111).

$$\therefore \quad \tan\psi = \frac{\sin\theta}{1+\cos\theta} = \tan\theta/2 \;\therefore\; \theta/2 = \psi \quad \text{(Refer to Example 125).}$$

$$s = \int_0^{\theta} \sqrt{1+\left(\frac{\sin\theta}{1+\cos\theta}\right)^2}\cdot a(1+\cos\theta)\, d\theta$$

$$= 2a \int_0^{\theta} \cos(\theta/2)\, d\theta = 4a \sin(\theta/2)$$

$$\therefore s = 4a \sin\psi.$$

EXAMPLE 150 [whorl of an equiangular spiral (Fig. 141)].

Solution.

$$s = \int_0^{2\pi} \sqrt{a^2 e^{2\theta\cot\alpha} + \cot^2\alpha \cdot a^2 e^{2\theta\cot\alpha}}\, d\theta$$

$$= a \operatorname{cosec}\alpha \int_0^{2\pi} e^{\theta\cot\alpha}\, d\theta$$

$$= a \sec\alpha\, (e^{2\pi\cot\alpha} - 1) (= \text{length of one } \textit{whorl}\ (0 \leqslant \theta \leqslant 2\pi) \text{ of the spiral).}$$

EXAMPLE 151 [perimeter p of ellipse (Fig. 80)].

Solution. Parametrically, $x = a\cos\theta$, $y = b\sin\theta \Rightarrow \dfrac{dy}{dx} = -\dfrac{b\cos\theta}{a\sin\theta}$.

$$\therefore\ p = 4\int_{\pi/2}^{0} \sqrt{1+\frac{b^2\cos^2\theta}{a^2\sin^2\theta}}\cdot -a\sin\theta\, d\theta$$

$$= 4\int_{0}^{\pi/2} \sqrt{a^2\sin^2\theta+b^2\cos^2\theta}\, d\theta \qquad \text{using (66)}$$

$$= 4a\int_{0}^{\pi/2} \sqrt{1-e^2\cos^2\theta}\, d\theta \qquad \text{using (189)}$$

$$= 4aE.$$

Note. This integral E, called an *elliptic integral of the second kind*, cannot be evaluated by the elementary techniques at our command. Special function *(elliptic functions)* allow us to evaluate E. Legendre (1752–1833, French) tabulated values of E on this basis. Otherwise, an approximation to the value of E can be made using Simpson's (parabolic) rule.

Thus, the perimeter of an ellipse can only be *approximated* to by elementary means. Fagnano's ellipse $\left(e = \dfrac{1}{\sqrt{2}}\right)$, for instance, has perimeter $\doteqdot 5{\cdot}4a$ ($n = 6$ in Simpson's rule).

Ramanujan (1887–1920, Indian) in 1914 derived the approximation expression $\pi[3(a+b)-\sqrt{(a+3b)(3a+b)}]$ for the perimeter of an ellipse, leading to $2\pi a$ when $b = a$ (circle).

EXAMPLE 151 *(continued)*. [*When e is small*, we can approximate to the value of E, thus: $(1-e^2\cos^2\theta)^{1/2} = 1-e^2\dfrac{\cos^2\theta}{2}$ (neglecting higher powers of e)

$$\therefore\ p = 4a\int_{0}^{\pi/2} \left(1-e^2\frac{(1+\cos 2\theta)}{4}\right) d\theta$$

$$= 4a\left[\theta\left(1-\frac{e^2}{4}\right)-e^2\frac{\sin 2\theta}{8}\right]_0^{\pi/2}$$

$$= 2\pi a\left(1-\frac{e^2}{4}\right) \qquad (e = 0 \Rightarrow \text{circle}).$$

§ 121. SURFACE AREA OF A SOLID OF REVOLUTION

Several techniques exist for determining the surface area generated by the notation of a curve about a given line. Reverting to Fig. 148, consider the element of surface area δS generated by rotating the element of arc-length $\delta s = PQ$ of the curve $y = f(x)$ around the x-axis.

Then the area generated is approximately the surface area of a small cylinder of radius y and height δs. (Important: why δs and not δx, as in § 119?)

$\therefore \delta S = 2\pi y \, \delta s.$

Summing for the whole curve, we deduce

$$S = 2\pi \int y \, ds.$$

$\therefore$ by (262)

$$\boxed{S = 2\pi \int_a^b y \sqrt{1+\left(\frac{dy}{dx}\right)^2} \, dx}. \tag{264}$$

Rotation about the y-axis yields

$$S = 2\pi \int x \, ds = 2\pi \int_c^d x \sqrt{1+\left(\frac{dx}{dy}\right)^2} \, dy.$$

EXAMPLE 152 [surface area of a sphere (Fig. 149a)].

Solution. $S = 2{\cdot}2\pi \int_0^a \sqrt{a^2-x^2} \cdot \sqrt{1+\frac{x^2}{a^2-x^2}} \, dx$ (by symmetry)

$$= 4\pi a \int_0^a dx$$

$$= \pi a^2$$

$= 4\times$area of generating circle (Archimedes).

[Notice that the sphere is completely generated by the rotation of a semicircle, i.e. the whole circle is not required.]

EXAMPLE 153 (surface area of a prolate spheroid).

[A *prolate spheroid* is the surface generated by the revolution of an ellipse about the major axis.]

Solution. $S = 2{\cdot}2\pi \int_0^a y \sqrt{1+\frac{b^4x^2}{a^4y^2}} \, dx$

$$= \frac{4\pi}{a^2} \int_0^a \sqrt{a^4y^2 + b^4x^2}\, dx$$

$$= \frac{4\pi\, be}{a} \int_0^a \sqrt{\left(\frac{a}{e}\right)^2 - x^2}\, dx \quad \because b^2 = a^2(1-e^2)$$

$$= \frac{4\pi be}{a} \cdot \tfrac{1}{2} \left[x \sqrt{\left(\frac{a}{e}\right)^2 - x^2} + \left(\frac{a}{e}\right)^2 \sin^{-1}\left(\frac{xe}{a}\right) \right]_0^a$$

$$= \frac{2\pi be}{a} \left\{ \frac{a^2}{e} \sqrt{1-e^2} + \frac{a^2}{e^2} \sin^{-1} e \right\}$$

$$= 2\pi b \left\{ b + \frac{a}{e} \sin^{-1} e \right\}.$$

[*Oblate spheroid* (planetary ellipsoid) $\equiv$ surface generated by the revolution of an ellipse about its minor axis, e.g. the Earth and the figure of Jupiter (a technical term used in mathematical astronomy) approximate to this.]

EXAMPLE 154 [surface generated by lemniscate of Bernoulli (Fig. 125)].

Solution. $S = 2 \cdot 2\pi \int_0^{\pi/4} y \sqrt{r^2 + \left(\frac{dr}{d\theta}\right)^2}\, d\theta$ (by symmetry)

$$= 4\pi \int_0^{\pi/4} r \sin\theta \sqrt{a^2 \cos 2\theta + a^2 \frac{\sin^2 2\theta}{\cos 2\theta}}\, d\theta$$

$$= 4\pi \int_0^{\pi/4} a \sqrt{\cos 2\theta} \sin\theta \cdot \frac{a}{\sqrt{\cos 2\theta}}\, d\theta$$

$$= 4\pi a^2 \left[-\cos\theta\right]_0^{\pi/4}$$

$$= 4\pi a^2 \left(1 - \frac{1}{\sqrt{2}}\right).$$

§ 122. APPROXIMATE (NUMERICAL) INTEGRATION. CONCLUDING REMARKS

Reasons for approximate integration

(i) Occasionally, as we have seen, it is impossible to express the integral by means of elementary functions, e.g.

$$\int_0^{\pi/2} \frac{\sin x}{x} \doteqdot 1{\cdot}36.$$

(ii) Sometimes all that is known about a function is a table of values obtained from experiments.

(iii) Frequently, only approximations are required, as often happens in problems from engineering, chemistry, and physics (e.g. Wegscheider, 1902, in integrating the velocity equations for the speed of hydrolysis of sulphonic esters).

Best known of the numerical methods is Simpson's rule, which can usually be manipulated to give the result to the desired degree of accuracy.

Complicated integrals arising from practical problems are most readily evaluated numerically by means of electronic computers. Often, the computing machines base their calculations on Simpson's rule or on some other numerical rule. Consequently, the mathematical value of Simpson's rule is not greatly lessened by the advent of computers.

Retrospect

Looking back, we can see the patterns of mathematical thought revealed to us. Our introduction to calculus has demonstrated the tremendous power of the concept of an infinite limiting process and, at the same time, the limitations of the elementary techniques.

Studying geometry, we have seen the inadequacy of older ideas and the necessity for establishing a new system of coordinates, incorporating elements at infinity to give logical completion, and a sense of perfection to this ancient discipline.

Our survey has shown us something of the nature, interrelations, and practical value of abstract algebraic structures, and of some important unifying concepts and new developments in mathematics.

Although the various branches—algebra, analysis, calculus, geometry—touched on in this "outline" exist somewhat independently, the full force and beauty of mathematics is best appreciated when they are shown to act in harmony, each illuminating the others. Featuring this interdependence, this orchestral quality, has been one of the prime objects of this venture.

Cohesion and unity existing in mathematics are reflected in applications to the world of reality for which mathematics is the great coordinating power. Nature speaks to us through mathematics, revealing the mysteries and the essential character of the universe about us, exhibiting therein pattern and order amid diversity.

Suggested topics for further study

(1) Numerical integration (e.g. Simpson's rule, trapezoidal rule)—theory and accuracy.
(2) Pappus' (Guldin's) theorems on centre of gravity (Guldin, 1577–1643, Swiss).
(3) Area of closed curves not symmetrical about an axis

$$[A = \int(x\,dy - y\,dx)].$$

(4) Use of the definite integral in applied mathematics and physics, particularly in problems on centres of gravity and moments of inertia.
(5) The method of cylindrical shells for calculating volumes of solids of revolution, as in Thomas [27].

References

As for Chapter 20, together with:

(a) *Pure Mathematics: a Second Course*, J. K. Backhouse, S.P.T., Houldsworth and B. E. D. Cooper (Longmans, 1961).
(b) *Introduction to Calculus*, C. C. T. Baker (Newnes, 1964).
(c) *Differential and Integral Calculus*, Vol. 1, R. Courant (Blackie, 1948).
(d) *Advanced Level Pure Mathematics*. Part III: *Algebra and Analysis*, S. L. Green (University Tutorial Press, 1954).
(e) *A Course in Pure and Applied Mathematics*, H. J. Halstead and D. A. Harris (Macmillan, 1963).
(f) *Analytical Geometry and Calculus*, L. M. Kells (Prentice-Hall, 1963).
(g) *Ancillary Mathematics*, H. S. W. Massey and H. Kestelman (Pitman, 1959).
(h) *Higher Mathematics for Students of Chemistry and Physics*, J. W. Mellor (Dover, 1946).
(i) *An Outline of the Calculus*, C. O. Oakley (Barnes and Noble, 1944).
(j) *Calculus, Differential and Integral*, G. M. Peterson and R. F. Graesser (Littlefield, Adams, 1961).
(k) *A New Calculus*, Vols. 1, 2, A. W. Siddons, K. S. Snell, and J. B. Morgan (C.U.P., 1958).

EXERCISES 23

1. What is the total area between the x-axis and the curve $y = xe^{-x^2}$? Sketch the curve, indicating any maxima, minima and inflexions.

2. Sketch the rose curve $r = a \sin 3\theta$. Obtain the area of a loop.

3. Compute the area between the curve $4r = 5+4\cos\theta (0 \leqslant \theta \leqslant \pi)$ and the initial line $\theta = 0$.

4. Sketch the spiral of Archimedes $r = 2\pi - \theta$ in the range $0 \leqslant \theta \leqslant \pi$. Let θ be the pole and P, Q the points on this spiral for which $\theta = 0$, $\theta = \pi$ respectively. Semi-circles with OP and OQ as radii are drawn, having areas A_1, A_2 respectively. If the area of the spiral in the range stated is A, find $\dfrac{A_1 - A}{A - A_2}$.

5. Obtain the area swept out by the radius vector of the equiangular spiral $r = e^\theta$ in two complete revolutions of the spiral about the pole, starting with $\theta = 0$.

6. Calculate the volume generated by revolving about the x-axis the area under the curve $(1+x)y^2 = 1-x$ bounded by the x-axis and $x = 0$, $x = 1$.

7. Determine the volume of the astroidal solid of revolution formed by rotating $x^{2/3}+y^{2/3} = a^{2/3}$ about an axis.

8. Obtain the surface area generated by the revolution about the initial line of the cardioid $r = a(1+\cos\theta)$.

9. Calculate the area in the first quadrant between the parabolas $y^2 = 4x$, $x^2 = 4y$.

10. Rotate the area in the first quadrant between the parabolas $y^2 = 4x$, $x^2 = 4y$ about the x-axis to obtain a solid. What is its volume?

11. Encased in a metal cylinder is a hollow parabolic reflector (up to the *latus rectum*). What is the volume of metal between the cylinder and the reflector?

12. What is the area between the coordinate axes and the curve $x^{1/2}+y^{1/2} = a^{1/2}$ (Exercise 16.8)?

13. Ascertain the arc-length of a tractrix.

14. Determine the intrinsic equation of the tractrix between the point given by $\theta = \pi/2$, $\theta = \theta$. [See (35).]

15. For the catenary, prove that $y^2 = s^2+c^2$.

16. A parabolic segment of base $2a$ and height h rotates about the base. What is the volume of the resulting solid, *Cavalieri's lemon*? (Cavalieri, 1598–1647, Italian.)

With $c = 1$ in the catenary of Fig. 8, do 17–21.

17. Show that PQ = arc-length OP.

18. Prove that $\varrho = 1+s^2$.

19. Establish $s = \log\sqrt{1+\varrho^2}$ for the tractrix.

20. Radius of curvature of the tractrix equals the arc-length of the catenary. True?

21. Arc-lengths s_1, s_2 are measured from the lowest points of the catenary $y = \cosh x$ to the points P_1, P_2 of Exercise 21.11. Prove $|s_1 s_2| = 1$.

22. Let A be the area in the first quadrant under the curve $y^m = x^n$ between $b \leqslant x \leqslant a$, with B similarly defined for $b^{n/m} < y < a^{n/m}$. Determine $A : B$.

23. An arch of the sinusoidal curve $y = \sin x$ rotates about the x-axis. Obtain the surface area of the "spindle" generated.

24. (Generation of a torus, Fig. 45.) What is the surface area of the torus formed by rotating about a line a circle of radius b whose centre is distant a ($> b$) from that line? (Compare this area with the surface area of cylinder of radius b and height $2a$.) [Torus problems, and many others, are often conveniently handled by *Pappus' theorem* on centroids, but this topic is omitted here, and left for private investigation—see topic (2) of this Chapter.]

25. Find the perimeter of a cycloidal arch.

26. What is the area under a cycloidal arch?

27. Prove that the perimeter of the cardioid $r = a(1-\cos\theta)$ above the initial line is bisected by $\theta = 2\pi/3$.

28. Determine the arc-length of the semi-cubical parabola $x = t^2$, $y = t^3$ between the points $t_1, 0$. If $t_1^2 = \frac{5}{9}$, find the arc length.

29. Obtain the volume of the solid generated by rotating the witch of Agnesi (Exercise 20.28 with $a = 1$) about the x-axis. ($\frac{1}{2} \leqslant x \leqslant 1$.)

30. At a distance $2a \sin 10°$ from the base of a hemisphere of radius a, a plane is drawn parallel to the base. Show that it bisects the hemispherical volume.

31. (Generation of the lituus.) A point P moves so that the area of the circular sector whose bounding radii are OP and OQ ($= OP$) along the initial line is a constant. Prove that the locus of P is the lituus $r^2\theta = a^2$.

32. Sketch the normal frequency (error) curve $y = e^{-x^2}$ and find the area between the curve and the x-axis.

33. Obtain the area of the surface generated by rotating the astroid (Fig. 104) about the x-axis.

34. Determine the area between the strophoid $y^2 = \dfrac{x^2(a+x)}{a-x}$ and its asymptote (Fig. 98). (Refer to Exercise 8.29.)

35. Which curves have the property that the area included between two ordinates is proportional to the arc of the curve between these ordinates?

36. What is the total area of the nephroid $x = a(3\cos t - \cos 3t)$, $y = a(3\sin t - \sin 3t)$? [Same equations as in Example 2, but in slightly different form with $a = \frac{1}{4}$.]

37. Determine the pedal of the nephroid w.r.t. the origin.

38. Photographs of the Earth's surface are taken from a camera in a satellite. What surface area can be covered in a photograph at the moment when the satellite is at a height h above the Earth?

39. Calculate the surface area of the pseudosphere generated by rotating the tractrix (35) about the x-axis. Compare the form of the answer with the corresponding surface area of a sphere. [Also, consult the article, "The catenary and tractrix", by R. C. Yates, in *The American Mathematical Monthly*, **66** (6)500–5 (1959).]

40. Determine the volume of the solid generated by revolving the witch of Agnesi $y^2 = \dfrac{a^2(a-x)}{x}$ about the y-axis.

41. When the loading of a suspension bridge due to the roadway is large compared with the weight of the chains, the equation for the curve of suspension is $\dfrac{dy'}{dx} = k$, where y' means the first derivative of y w.r.t. x and k is a constant involving tension. Show that the suspension curve is a parabola. Simplify the equation further, given that the ends are at the same horizontal level and the origin is at the vertex.

42. Rotate a cycloidal arch about the x-axis. What is the volume of the solid generated?

43. Calculate the surface of revolution of the cycloidal solid of Exercise 23.42.

44. Establish the result $s^2 + \varrho^2 = 16a^2$ for the cycloid.

45. Compute the area of one leaf of the rose $r = a \cos n\theta$.

46. Calculate the area of the rose $r = \cos 3\theta$ which is outside the circle $r = a/2$.

47. Transform the Cartesian equation of the ellipse $ax^2 + 2hxy + by^2 = 0$ to polar coordinates. Hence, find the area of the ellipse.

48. Check the result (area) of Exercise 23.47 using a rotation of axes to bring the ellipse to standard form.

49. Take P ($a \cosh \phi$, $b \sinh \phi$) on the branch of the hyperbola $\dfrac{x^2}{a^2} - \dfrac{y^2}{b^2} = 1$ whose centre C is at the origin and vertex is A. Show that the area $\mathcal{A}$ of the hyperbolic sector

CAP is $\frac{1}{2} ab\,\phi$, i. e. the geometrical meaning of the parameter ϕ is $\phi = \dfrac{2\mathcal{A}}{ab}$, i.e. ϕ is proportional to the area of the sector CAP.

50. Two points in the same vertical plane support a perfectly flexible cable of uniform density. No forces other than gravity act on the cable. Taking the y-axis vertically upwards through the lowest point and the x-axis along the horizontal in the plane of the curve, we know, from mechanical considerations, that the differential equation of the cable curve is $k\dfrac{d^2y}{dx^2} = \sqrt{1+\left(\dfrac{dy}{dx}\right)^2}$ (k a constant). What is the form of the cable?

51. Gravitational attraction between a planet $P(r, \theta)$ orbiting around the Sun (at the origin) leads to the polar equation $r\dfrac{d\omega}{dt}+2\omega\dfrac{dr}{dt} = 0$, where the angular velocity $\omega = \dfrac{d\theta}{dt}$. Deduce that $r^2\omega = \text{const}$. Interpret this result in terms of Kepler's second law of motion.

52. If (ξ, η) are the coordinates of the centre of curvature, show that $\dfrac{d\xi}{d\eta} = -\cot\psi$. Use this to confirm that normals to a curve are tangents to its evolute.

53. Deduce, from Exercise 23.52, that $s = \varrho + c$, where s refers to the arc-length from a given point to (ξ, η) of the evolute of the curve for which ϱ is the curvature at (x, y).

54. Perimeter of the deltoid (Exercise 20.37) is $16a$. Derive.

55. The cissoid of Diocles $y^2 = \dfrac{x^3}{x-1}$ (variation of Fig. 99) is rotated about the x-axis. Determine the volume of the solid of revolution thus generated.

56. Do the same when the cissoid revolves about its asymptote.

57. In the vicinity of the double point of the lemniscate, $\varrho s \doteqdot \text{const}$. Justify this approximation (an important property of the lemniscate, useful in designing the bend of a road).

58. Calculate the area of the inner loop of the limaçon (the *trisectrix*) $r = 2a(1+2\cos\theta)$. Sketch the curve.

[This limaçon may be used to trisect an angle and also to construct angles of $\pi/5$, $2\pi/5$ and hence to construct a regular pentagon. It should not be confused with the trisectrix of Maclaurin $r = a\sec\theta/3)$ (Exercise 20.35) or with the trisectrix of Catalan $(r = a\sec^3(\theta/3)$ (Exercise 22.53).]

One whorl of Archimedes' spiral $r = a\theta (0 \leqslant \theta \leqslant 2\pi)$ starts at $O(0, 0)$ and ends at $X(2\pi a, 2\pi)$. Through O, $OY (= y)$ is drawn perpendicular to OX, and $O\hat{X}Y = \phi$ (XY is tangent at X). Show that:

59. The area of the whorl is one-third area of the circle on OX as radius.

60. $y = 2\pi x$ $(x = 2\pi a)$.

61. Area $\triangle OXY$ = area of circle, radius OX.

[This means that we have constructed a rectilinear figure whose area equals that of a circle.]

Given the unit circle, centre O and the point $A = (1, 0)$ and the equiangular spiral $r = e^{\theta}$ emanating from A, let the radius vector OCS cut the circle in C and the spiral in S, and let the tangents at C and S intersect in P. Then:

62. Show that $\triangle CPS$ is isosceles.

63. Deduce that the arc-length AS of the spiral is equal to SP.

64. If the locus of P is given by $r^2 = f(\theta)$ as OCS varies, what is $f(\theta)$?

65. Radii of lengths 2 and 4 bound an area with the curve $r = 2e^{3\theta}$. What is this area?

Evaluate 66–68:

66. $\int_0^{\pi a} x\, ds / \int_0^{\pi a} ds$, where $x^2+y^2 = a^2$.

67. $\int_0^a 2xy\, dx / \int_0^a 2y\, dx$, where $y^2 = 4ax$.

68. $\int_0^a \pi\, xy^2\, dx / \int_0^a \pi y^2\, dx$, where $x^2+y^2 = a^2$.

Respectively, these give the x-coordinate $(\bar{x})$ of the *centres of gravity* of (i) a thin uniform semicircular wire with y-axis as base, (ii) a homogeneous parabolic lamina $y^2 = 4ax$ bounded by the *latus rectum*, and (iii) a homogeneous (uniform) solid hemisphere with y-axis as base.

69. Derive the total length of the "sandstar" $x = a(-\frac{3}{2}\cos\theta + \cos\frac{3}{2}\theta)$, $y = a(-\frac{3}{2}\sin\theta - \sin\frac{3}{2}\theta)$.

70. Compute the volume of the solid of revolution generated by rotating the three-leafed rose $r = a\cos 3\theta$ $(0 \leqslant \theta \leqslant \pi/6)$ about the initial line.

71. Length of a complete undulation of the trochoid $x = a\theta + k\sin\theta$, $y = a - k\cos\theta$ equals the perimeter of an ellipse whose semi-axes are $a+k$, $a-k$. Demonstrate.

72. Through the centre of a metal sphere of radius a, a hole of diameter a is bored. What volume of metal remains? $\left[\textit{Answer: } \frac{\sqrt{3}}{2}\pi a^3. \right]$

73. Surface area of the oblate spheroid formed from the standard ellipse is $2\pi a^2 + \frac{\pi b^2}{e}\log\left(\frac{1+e}{1-e}\right)$. Prove.

Exhibit the truth of:

74. $\int_0^{\pi/2} \log\sin x\, dx = -\frac{\pi}{2}\log 2.$

75. $\int_0^{\pi/2} x\log\sin dx = -\frac{\pi^2}{2}\log 2.$

NEW HORIZONS

"Cheshire-Puss . . . would you tell me, please, which way I ought to go from here?"
"That depends a good deal on where you want to get to," said the Cat.

(LEWIS CARROLL)

SUITABLE topics for a more advanced study of mathematics are listed below under several broad classifications, none of which are mutually exclusive.

Analysis and calculus

Differential equations (ordinary and partial)
Analysis of a real variable
Analysis of a complex variable
Advanced calculus
Riemann integration and Lebesgue integration
Inequalities
Fourier analysis
Special functions. Elliptic-functions
Integral equations
Calculus of variations
Hilbert space
Point-set ($\equiv$ analytical) topology

Algebra and geometry

Linear algebra (vector spaces, matrices, quadrics)
Abstract algebra (groups, rings, fields, Boolean algebra)
Differential geometry of curves and surfaces
Projective geometry (analytical and synthetic)
Algebraic (and combinatorial) topology
Theory of numbers (congruences)

Applied mathematics, statistics, miscellaneous

Theory of games. Linear programming
Probability. Statistics

Newtonian mechanics
Tensors. Cartesian tensors (elasticity)
Vector differential operators
Relativity (special and general theories)
Quantum theory
Potential theory (hydrodynamics; electromagnetism)
Numerical analysis
Computer programming.

Unsolved problems

Finally, the reader's attention is directed to two famous unsolved problems in mathematics, both of which may be expressed in simple terms. They are:

(1) Fermat's theorem in number theory relating to the equation $x^n + y^n \equiv z^n$ (x, y, z, n integers); and
(2) the four-colour problem in topology.

Enduring fame awaits the men (women) whose researches can penetrate the mysteries of these problems.

> Our revels now are ended. These our actors,
> As I foretold you, were all spirits and
> Are melted into air, into thin air.
>
> (SHAKESPEARE)

SOLUTIONS TO EXERCISES

The woods are lovely, dark and deep,
But I have promises to keep,
And miles to go before I sleep.

(ROBERT FROST)

CONTENTS

EXERCISES 1

1. $f'(x) = \dfrac{(x+\sqrt{x})\cdot 1 - x\left(1+\dfrac{1}{2\sqrt{x}}\right)}{(x+\sqrt{x})^2} = \dfrac{\sqrt{x}}{2(x+\sqrt{x})^2}.$

2. $f'(x) = \dfrac{(1+\cos x)\cdot \cos x - \sin x \cdot - \sin x}{(1+\cos x)^2} = \dfrac{1+\cos x}{(1+\cos x)^2} = \dfrac{1}{1+\cos x} = \dfrac{1}{2}\sec^2\dfrac{x}{2};$

or (better), $f(x) = \dfrac{2\sin\dfrac{x}{2}\cos\dfrac{x}{2}}{2\cos^2\dfrac{x}{2}} = \tan\dfrac{x}{2}\quad \therefore\ f'(x) = \dfrac{1}{2}\sec^2\dfrac{x}{2}.$

3. $f'(x) = \dfrac{1}{2}\sec^2\dfrac{x}{2}\quad \because\ \dfrac{1-\cos x}{\sin x} = \dfrac{\sin x}{1+\cos x}$ (Exercise 1.2).

4. $f'(x) = 3\sec^2 x + 3\tan^2 x\sec^2 x = 3\sec^2 x(1+\tan^2 x) = 3\sec^4 x.$

5. $f'(x) = \cos^2(x^n)\cdot 1 + x\cdot nx^{n-1}\cdot 2\cos x^n \cdot - \sin x^n = \cos^2 x^n - nx^n \sin(2x^n).$

6. $f'(x) = 4\cdot 2\sin^3 2x\cos 2x - 4\cdot 2\cos^3 2x\sin 2x$

$= -8\sin 2x\cos 2x(\cos^2 2x - \sin^2 2x) = -4\sin 4x\cos 4x = -2\sin 8x.$

7. $E(uv) = \dfrac{x}{uv}\dfrac{d(uv)}{dx} = \dfrac{x}{uv}\left(u\dfrac{dv}{dx}+v\dfrac{du}{dx}\right) = \dfrac{x}{u}\dfrac{du}{dx}+\dfrac{x}{v}\dfrac{dv}{dx} = E(u)+E(v).$

8. $E(u^n) = \dfrac{x}{u^n}\dfrac{du^n}{dx} = \dfrac{x}{u^n}\dfrac{d(u^n)}{du}\dfrac{du}{dx} = \dfrac{x}{u^n}\cdot nu^{n-1}\dfrac{du}{dx} = n\dfrac{x}{u}\dfrac{du}{dx} = nE(u).$

9. $E\left(\dfrac{u}{v}\right) = \dfrac{x}{u/v}\dfrac{d}{dx}\left(\dfrac{u}{v}\right) = \dfrac{vx}{u}\left(\dfrac{v\,du/dx - u\,dv/dx}{v^2}\right) = \dfrac{x}{u}\dfrac{du}{dx} - \dfrac{x}{v}\dfrac{dv}{dx} = E(u)-E(v).$

10. $\dfrac{d}{dy}\left(\dfrac{x^2}{y}\right) = \dfrac{y\dfrac{d(x^2)}{dy} - x^2\cdot 1}{y^2} = \dfrac{2xy\dfrac{dx}{dy} - x^2}{y^2} = \dfrac{x}{y^2}\left(2y\dfrac{dx}{dy} - x\right)$

$\therefore\ A = 2y\dfrac{dx}{dy} - x.$

11. $a = \dfrac{dv}{dt} = \dfrac{dv}{dx}\dfrac{dx}{dt} = v\dfrac{dv}{dx} = \dfrac{d}{dv}\left(\dfrac{1}{2}v^2\right)\dfrac{dv}{dx} = \dfrac{d}{dx}\left(\dfrac{1}{2}v^2\right).$

12. $F = ma = \dfrac{d}{dx}\left(\dfrac{1}{2}mv^2\right)\dfrac{dE}{dx}$ (Exercise 1.11) $\therefore$ F is given by the gradient of the curve $E = f(x)$.

13. $v = cn\cos(nt+k)\quad \therefore\ a = -cn^2\sin(nt+k) = -n^2x.$

14. $\dfrac{da}{dx} = -n^2 = \text{constant}.$

15. $v^2 - ax = c^2n^2[\cos^2(nt+k)+\sin^2(nt+k)] = c^2n^2 = \text{constant}.$

16. $x\dfrac{da}{dt} = x\cdot - cn^3\cos(nt+k) = -c^2n^3\sin(nt+k)\cos(nt+k) = av.$

17. $\dfrac{dx}{dt} = a \sin t \sec^2 t,\ \dfrac{dy}{dt} = b \sec^2 t \quad \therefore \quad \dfrac{dy}{dx} = \dfrac{b}{a} \operatorname{cosec} t.$

18. $\dfrac{dx}{dt} = 3 \cos t - 6 \sin^2 t \cos t = 3 \cos t \cos 2t$

$\dfrac{dy}{dt} = -3 \sin t + 6 \cos^2 t \sin t = 3 \sin t \cos 2t$

$\therefore \quad \dfrac{dy}{dx} = \tan t.$ ($\therefore$ the geometrical meaning of the parameter t is that it is the angle between the tangent to the curve and the positive direction of the x-axis.)

19. $\dfrac{dx}{dt} = \dfrac{1-2t^3}{(1+t^3)^2},\ \dfrac{dy}{dt} = \dfrac{t(2-t^3)}{(1+t^3)^2} \quad \therefore \quad \dfrac{dy}{dx} = \dfrac{t(2-t^3)}{1-2t^3}.$

20. $\dfrac{dx}{d\theta} = a(1-\cos\theta),\ \dfrac{dy}{d\theta} = a \sin\theta \quad \therefore \quad \dfrac{dy}{dx} = \dfrac{\sin\theta}{1-\cos\theta} = \cot\dfrac{\theta}{2} = \tan\left(\dfrac{\pi}{2}-\dfrac{\theta}{2}\right).$

($\therefore$ the angle between the tangent to the curve and the positive direction of the x-axis is $\dfrac{\pi}{2}-\dfrac{\theta}{2}$, i. e. the complement of $\theta/2$.)

21. $x = a(\omega t - \sin \omega t), \quad y = a(1-\cos \omega t)$

$\therefore\ \dot{x} = a\omega(1-\cos\omega t), \quad \dot{y} = a\omega \sin \omega t$

$\ddot{x} = a\omega^2 \sin \omega t, \quad \ddot{y} = a\omega^2 \cos \omega t$

$\therefore\ [(\ddot{x})^2+(\ddot{y})^2]^{1/2} = a\omega^2 = \text{constant}.$

Notice the differential equations of motion $\ddot{x} = \omega\dot{y},\ \ddot{y}+\omega\dot{x}-a\omega^2 = 0.$

22. $\dfrac{2}{3} y^{-1/3} \dfrac{dy}{dx} = -\dfrac{2}{3} x^{-1/3} \quad \therefore \quad \dfrac{dy}{dx} = -\left(\dfrac{y}{x}\right)^{1/3} = \pm\left(\dfrac{3\sqrt{3}a/8}{a/8}\right)^{1/3}$

at $\left(\dfrac{a}{8},\ \pm\dfrac{3\sqrt{3}a}{8}\right)$

$\therefore$ gradients at $x = \dfrac{a}{8}$ are $\pm\sqrt{3}$.

Parametric equations may be taken as $x = a \sin^3 t,\ y = a \cos^3 t.$

23. $\dfrac{d}{dx}(y^{-2}) = -4x^3+2kx \quad \therefore \quad -\dfrac{2}{y^3}\dfrac{dy}{dx} = -4x^3+2kx$

$\therefore \quad \dfrac{dy}{dx} = 2x^3y^3 - kxy^3$, and $\dfrac{y}{x} = \dfrac{y^3}{xy^2} = \dfrac{y^3}{x}(-x^4+kx^2)$

$\therefore \quad \dfrac{dy}{dx}+\dfrac{y}{x} = 2x^3y^3 - kxy^3 - x^3y^3 + kxy^3 = x^3y^3.$

[The substitution $z = y^{-2}$ reduces it to the simpler form $\dfrac{dz}{dx} - \dfrac{2z}{x} = -2x^3.$]

24. $E = c(m_0^2c^2+p^2)^{1/2} \quad \therefore \quad v = \dfrac{dE}{dp} = cp(m_0^2c^2+p^2)^{-1/2}$

$\therefore \quad p^2c^2 = m_0^2c^2v^2+p^2v^2 \quad \therefore \quad p^2\left(1-\dfrac{v^2}{c^2}\right) = m_0^2v^2 \quad \therefore \quad p = m_0 v\left(1-\dfrac{v^2}{c^2}\right)^{-1/2}.$

25. $m^2(c^2-v^2) = m_0^2c^2 \quad \therefore \quad m^2\left(c^2-\dfrac{p^2}{m^2}\right) = m_0^2c^2 \quad \therefore \quad p = c(m^2-m_0^2)^{1/2}.$

$$\therefore \quad \frac{dp}{dm} = \frac{cm}{\sqrt{m^2-m_0^2}} = cm\cdot\frac{c}{p} = \frac{c^2}{v} \quad \therefore \quad \frac{dm}{dp} = \frac{v}{c^2}.$$

26. $\dfrac{dx'}{dt} = k\left(\dfrac{dx}{dt}-v\right),\ \dfrac{dt'}{dt} = k\left(1-\dfrac{v}{c^2}\dfrac{dx}{dt}\right)$

$$\therefore \quad \frac{dx'}{dt'} = \frac{\dfrac{dx}{dt}-v}{1-\dfrac{v}{c^2}\dfrac{dx}{dt}} = \frac{c-v}{1-\dfrac{v}{c^2}\cdot c} = c \text{ when } \frac{dx}{dt} = c.$$

[Alternatively, differentiate x', t' w.r.t. x and use $\dfrac{dx}{dt} = \left(\dfrac{dt}{dx}\right)^{-1}$.]

27. Differentiate both sides of the equation w.r.t. p.

$$\therefore \quad \left(p+\frac{a}{v^2}\right)\frac{dv}{dp}+(v-b)\left(1-\frac{2a}{v^3}\frac{dv}{dp}\right) = 0$$

$$\therefore \quad \frac{dv}{dp} = -(v-b)\left(p-\frac{a}{v^2}+\frac{2ab}{v^3}\right)^{-1}.$$

28. $\dfrac{d}{dt}v^2 = \dfrac{d}{dt}\left(\dfrac{2R^2g}{x}+c\right) \quad \therefore \quad \dfrac{dv^2}{dv}\dfrac{dv}{dt} = \dfrac{d}{dx}\left(\dfrac{2R^2g}{x}+c\right)\dfrac{dx}{dt}$

$$\therefore \quad 2v\ddot{x} = \frac{-2R^2g}{x^2}\cdot v \quad \therefore \quad \ddot{x} = \frac{-R^2g}{x^2} \quad \therefore \quad k = -R^2mg.$$

29. Substitute $v = V, x = R$ in $v^2 = \dfrac{2R^2g}{x}+c \quad \therefore \quad c = V^2-2Rg$

$$\therefore \quad v^2 = \frac{2R^2g}{x}+V^2-2Rg.$$

Let $x \to \infty$ (§ 6) $\quad \therefore \quad v^2 = V^2-2Rg > 0$ for escape.

$\therefore \quad V^2 > 2Rg \doteqdot 2\times 4000\times 5280\times 32\ (\text{ft/sec})^2$

i.e. $V \doteqdot 6\cdot 9$ miles/sec ($\doteqdot$ 25,000 m.p.h.) on calculation.

30. $u = (w')^{-1/2}\ldots$ (i), $v = w(w')^{-1/2}\ldots$ (ii) $\quad \therefore \quad w = v/u$ from (i), (ii).

$$\therefore \quad w' = \frac{uv'-vu'}{u^2} \qquad \text{(iii)}$$

Also, from (i) $w' = \dfrac{1}{u^2}$ (iv)

$\therefore$ (iii), (iv) $\Rightarrow uv'-vu' = 1$ (v)

$\therefore \quad uv''+u'v'-vu''-v'u' = 0$ differentiating (v) $\quad \therefore \quad \dfrac{v''}{v} = \dfrac{u''}{u}.$

31. (a) $y = \dfrac{x}{1+y}\ldots$ (i). $\quad \therefore \quad y^2+y-x = 0\ldots$(ii). $\quad \therefore \quad 2y\dfrac{dy}{dx}+\dfrac{dy}{dx}-1 = 0$

$\therefore \quad \dfrac{dy}{dx} = \dfrac{1}{1+2y}\ldots$ (iii) $\left[\text{or from (i), } x = y+y^2 \text{ whence } \dfrac{dx}{dy} = 1+2y = \right.$

$$\left. = \frac{1}{\dfrac{dy}{dx}}\right].$$

Repeated substitution of y from (i) in (i) or (iii) will reveal what a continued fraction really looks like.

(b) $x = 1$ in (ii) gives $y^2+y-1 = 0 \quad \therefore \; y = \dfrac{\pm\sqrt{5}-1}{2}$. Choice of the positive root in (i) leads to

$$\frac{\sqrt{5}-1}{2} = \cfrac{1}{1+\cfrac{1}{1+\cfrac{1}{1+\dots\dots}}} \quad \textit{(ad infinitum ad nauseam!)}$$

32. $P = 2\pi R$ where P, R are the circumference and radius of the Earth, respectively.

$$\therefore \; P+\delta P = 2\pi(R+\delta R) \quad \therefore \; \delta R = \frac{\delta P}{2\pi} \doteqdot 2'' \text{ when } \delta P = 12''.$$

33. $\dfrac{1}{y} = \dfrac{1}{f} - \dfrac{1}{x} \quad \therefore \quad -\dfrac{1}{y^2}\dfrac{dy}{dx} = \dfrac{1}{x^2} \quad \therefore \quad \dfrac{dy}{dx} = -\left(\dfrac{y}{x}\right)^2 \doteqdot \dfrac{\delta y}{\delta x} \quad \because \; \delta x, \delta y$ are small.

i.e. $\left|\dfrac{\delta y}{\delta x}\right| = \left(\dfrac{y}{x}\right)^2$.

34. $A = \pi r^2 \quad \therefore \; \dfrac{dA}{dt} = 2\pi r \dfrac{dr}{dt} = 2\pi \cdot 12 \cdot 3 \text{ ft}^2/\text{sec} = 72\pi \text{ ft}^2/\text{sec}.$

35. $A = kx(x^2+a^2)^{-3/2} \quad \therefore \; \dfrac{dA}{dx} = k\dfrac{(a^2-2x^2)}{(x^2+a^2)^{5/2}} = 0$ if $x = \dfrac{a}{\sqrt{2}}$. As in Example 3, this maximises A and $A_{max} = \dfrac{2k}{3\sqrt{3}a^2}$.

36. $k\,di = \sec^2 y\,dy \; \therefore \; E = \dfrac{\delta i}{i} \doteqdot \dfrac{di}{i} = \dfrac{\sec^2 y}{\tan y} \cdot dy = \dfrac{2c}{\sin 2y} \quad \because \; dy = \delta y = c$ (constant). $\left(\text{Clearly, } E \text{ is a minimum when } \sin 2y \text{ is a maximum, i.e., } y = \dfrac{\pi}{4}.\right)$

Now $\dfrac{dE}{dy} = \dfrac{-4c\cos 2y}{(\sin 2y)^2} = 0$ when $\cos 2y = 0$, i.e. $y = \dfrac{\pi}{4}$.

As y passes through the value $\dfrac{\pi}{4}$, $\dfrac{dE}{dy}$ changes from < 0 to > 0.

Hence, $y = \dfrac{\pi}{4}$ gives a minimum value $(= 2c)$ to E.

37. Let $z = x^2y^3 = (10-y)^2y^3 = 100y^3-20y^4+y^5$.

$\therefore \; \dfrac{dz}{dy} = 300y^2-80y^3+5y^4 = 0$ when $y^2-16y+60 = 0$, i.e., when $y = 6, 10 \; (y \neq 0)$.

(The latter root is inadmissible since it implies $x = 0$, contrary to data.)

$\dfrac{d^2z}{dy^2} = 600y-240y^2+20y^3 = -720 \; (< 0)$ when $y = 6$.

$\therefore \; y = 6$ gives a maximum value $(= 3{,}456)$ to z.

38. Let $v = k\left(\dfrac{\lambda}{a}+\dfrac{a}{\lambda}\right)^{1/2} = kl$ (say) for brevity, where k is a factor (constant) of proportionality.

$\therefore \; \dfrac{dv}{d\lambda} = \dfrac{k}{2l}\dfrac{(\lambda-a)(\lambda+a)}{a\lambda^2} = 0$ if $\lambda = \pm a$. ($\lambda = -a$ is physically meaningless.)

As λ increases from $< a$ to $> a$, $\dfrac{dv}{d\lambda}$ changes from < 0 to > 0.

$\therefore$ $\lambda = a$ gives a minimum value $(= \sqrt{2}k)$ to the velocity.

39. $\dfrac{ds^2}{dx} = 2\sum_{i=1}^{n}(x-x_i) = 2\left(nx-\sum_{i=1}^{n}x_i\right) = 0$ when $x = \dfrac{1}{n}\sum_{i=1}^{n}x_i$. $\quad \dfrac{d^2s^2}{dx^2} = 2n > 0$

$\therefore$ the stationary value of x gives a minimum to s^2.

40. Constant perimeter $p = 2r+2h+\pi r \;\ldots.\;$ (i)

Window area $A = 2rh+\pi\dfrac{r^2}{2} = pr-2r^2-\dfrac{\pi r^2}{2}$ substituting for $2h$ from (i).

$$\therefore \quad \frac{dA}{dr} = p-4r-\pi r = 2h-2r \text{ (using (i))} = 0 \text{ if } r = h.$$

Also,
$$\frac{d^2A}{dr^2} = -2 \;(< 0).$$

$\therefore$ $r = h$ gives a maximum value $\left[= \left(2+\dfrac{\pi}{2}\right)r^2\right]$ to A and therefore to the quantity of light admitted.

41. Intensity $I = k\left\{\dfrac{\frac{8}{27}}{x^2}+\dfrac{1}{(a-x)^2}\right\}$ where $AB = a$, and k is a proportionality factor.

$\therefore$ $\dfrac{dI}{dx} = -2k\left\{\dfrac{8}{27x^3}-\dfrac{1}{(a-x)^3}\right\} = 0$ if $27x^3 = 8(a-x)^3$ i.e. $3x = 2(a-x)$ (taking cube roots), i.e. $x = \frac{2}{5}a$.

Clearly, $\dfrac{d^2I}{dx^2} > 0$ $\therefore$ for minimum illumination, the convict should cross at a point $X: AX = \frac{2}{5}AB$.

42.
$$\frac{dE}{dp} = \frac{(p+\tan\alpha)(1-2p\tan\alpha)-(p-p^2\tan\alpha)}{(p+\tan\alpha)^2}$$
$$= \frac{-\tan\alpha}{(p+\tan\alpha)^2}(p^2+2p\tan\alpha-1) = 0 \text{ if } p^2+2p\tan\alpha-1 = 0$$

i.e. $p = \sec\alpha-\tan\alpha$ (negative root $-\sec\alpha-\tan\alpha$ is mechanically inadmissible).

[Verification that this value of p does indeed maximise E is left to the reader. Use (9.2).]

43. Let the radius and height of the cylinder be a, h respectively, and the height and slant height of the cone be k, l respectively, i.e., $l = k\sec\theta$. (Provide your own diagram.)

$\therefore$ constant volume $V = \pi a^2(\frac{1}{3}k+h) \ldots$ (i)

$\therefore$ canvas area $S = \pi a(k\sec\theta+2h)$

$$= \pi a\left(k\sec\theta+\frac{2V}{\pi a^2}-\frac{2}{3}k\right) \text{ from (i)}$$

$$= \pi a^2\left(\frac{2V}{\pi a^3}+\frac{1}{\sin\theta}-\frac{2\cos\theta}{3\sin\theta}\right) \quad \because k = a\cot\theta$$

$$= \pi a^2\left(\frac{2V}{\pi a^3}+\frac{3-2\cos\theta}{\sin\theta}\right)$$

$$\therefore \quad \frac{dS}{d\theta} = \pi a^2\left\{\frac{2-3\cos\theta}{\sin^2\theta}\right\} \text{ on calculation}$$

$$= 0 \text{ if } \cos\theta = \tfrac{2}{3}.$$

As $\cos\theta$ passes through values $> \dfrac{2}{3}$ to values $< \dfrac{2}{3}$ (i.e. θ increasing), $\dfrac{dS}{d\theta}$ changes from < 0 to > 0.

$\therefore$ $S_{\min}$ requires $\theta = \cos^{-1}(\frac{2}{3})$.

44. Let x be the number of articles over 200 produced per day, and let y be the total profit in dollars.

$\therefore$ $y = (200+x)\left(16-\dfrac{x}{50}\right)$ (a mathematical model for the economic situation)

$$= \frac{-x^2}{50}+12x+32\,000$$

$$\therefore \quad \frac{dy}{dx} = \frac{-x}{25}+12 = 0 \text{ if } x = 300.$$

As $\dfrac{d^2y}{dx^2} < 0$, $x = 300$ gives a maximum value (= \$ 5000) to y.

$\therefore$ $y_{\max}$ occurs when 500 articles per day are produced.

45. Let $C = k\left(4+\dfrac{v^3}{1000}\right)$ where k is a factor of proportionality. Suppose the distance from London to Sydney is a nautical miles.

$\therefore$ time in hours for the trip is $t = \dfrac{a}{v}$.

$\therefore$ time rate of expenditure is $E = k\dfrac{a}{v}\left(4+\dfrac{v^3}{1000}\right) = k\left(\dfrac{4a}{v}+\dfrac{av^2}{1000}\right)$.

$\therefore$ $\dfrac{dE}{dv} = k\left(\dfrac{-4a}{v^2}+\dfrac{2av}{1000}\right) = 0$ when $v^3 = 2000$.

Also, $\dfrac{d^2E}{dv^2} = k\left(\dfrac{8a}{v^3}+\dfrac{a}{500}\right) > 0$ when $v^3 = 2000$.

$\therefore$ $E_{\min}$ requires $v = \sqrt[3]{2000} = 10\sqrt[3]{2} = 12{\cdot}6$ (knots) approximately.

EXERCISES 2

1. $\sec^{-1}\tan\dfrac{\pi}{4} = \sec^{-1}1 = 0$.

2. $\cot\sin^{-1}\left(-\dfrac{1}{\sqrt{2}}\right) = \cot\left(\dfrac{-\pi}{4}\right) = -1$.

3. $\cos\operatorname{cosec}^{-1}2 = \cos\dfrac{\pi}{6} = \dfrac{\sqrt{3}}{2}$.

4. $f(x) = \cos^{-1}\sin x = \cos^{-1}\cos\left(\dfrac{\pi}{2}-x\right) = \dfrac{\pi}{2}-x \quad \therefore f'(x) = -1$.

5. $f'(x) = -\sin(\sin^{-1}x).\dfrac{1}{\sqrt{1-x^2}} = \dfrac{-x}{\sqrt{1-x^2}}$.

6. $f'(x) = \dfrac{-1}{\sqrt{1-(1-x)^2}} = \dfrac{-1}{\sqrt{2x-x^2}}$.

7. $f'(x) = \dfrac{\cos x}{2\sqrt{\sin x}} \cdot \dfrac{1}{\sqrt{1-(\sqrt{\sin x})^2}} = \dfrac{\cos x\sqrt{1+\sin x}}{2\sqrt{\sin x}\sqrt{1-\sin x}\sqrt{1+\sin x}} =$

$= \frac{1}{2}\sqrt{\operatorname{cosec} x+1}.$

8. $f'(x) = n\left[\dfrac{x^{n-1}}{1+x^{2n}}+\dfrac{(\tan^{-1}x)^{n-1}}{1+x^2}\right].$

9. $f'(x) = \dfrac{(1+x^2)\left\{\tan^{-1}x+\dfrac{x}{1+x^2}\right\}-x\tan^{-1}x\cdot 2x}{(1+x^2)^2} = \dfrac{x+(1-x^2)\tan^{-1}x}{(1+x^2)^2}.$

10. Let $\sin^{-1}x = t$ $\therefore$ $f(x) \to t+\left(\dfrac{\pi}{2}-t\right) = \dfrac{\pi}{2}$ $\therefore$ $f'(x) = 0.$

11. Write $\tan^{-1}x = t$ $\therefore$ $f(x) \to t+\left(\dfrac{\pi}{2}-t\right) = \dfrac{\pi}{2}$ $\therefore$ $f'(x) = 0.$

12. If $x = \tan t$, then $f(x) = \tan^{-1}\left(\dfrac{2x}{1-x^2}\right) = \tan^{-1}\tan 2t = 2t = 2\tan^{-1}x$

$$\therefore\ f'(x) = \frac{2}{1+x^2}.$$

13. Consider the right-angled triangle with sides $1-x^2$, $2x$ and $1+x^2$ (hypotenuse).

$\therefore$ $f(x) = \cos^{-1}\left(\dfrac{1-x^2}{1+x^2}\right) = \tan^{-1}\left(\dfrac{2x}{1-x^2}\right)$ $\therefore$ $f'(x) = \dfrac{2}{1+x^2}$ from Exercise 2.12.

14. Put $\tan^{-1}x = t$ $\therefore$ $\tan\left(t+\dfrac{\pi}{4}\right) = \dfrac{1+x}{1-x}$

$$\therefore\ f(x) = t+\frac{\pi}{4} = \tan^{-1}x+\frac{\pi}{4}\ \therefore\ f'(x) = \frac{1}{1+x^2}.$$

15. $f'(x) = \sin^{-1}3x+x\cdot\dfrac{3}{\sqrt{1-9x^2}}+\dfrac{1}{3}\cdot\dfrac{-9x}{\sqrt{1-9x^2}} = \sin^{-1}3x.$

16. $f(x) = \tan^{-1}\left(\dfrac{x}{2}\right)+\tan^{-1}\left(\dfrac{x}{2}\right) = 2\tan^{-1}\left(\dfrac{x}{2}\right)$

$\therefore$ $f'(x) = 2\cdot\dfrac{1}{2}\cdot\dfrac{1}{1+\left(\dfrac{x}{2}\right)^2} = \dfrac{4}{4+x^2}.$

17. $f'(x) = \sqrt{1-x^2}+x\cdot\dfrac{-x}{\sqrt{1-x^2}}+\dfrac{1}{\sqrt{1-x^2}} = \sqrt{1-x^2}+\dfrac{1-x^2}{\sqrt{1-x^2}} = 2\sqrt{1-x^2}.$

18. Set $\tan t = x$ (so $t = \tan^{-1}x$).

$\therefore$ $f(x) \to f(t) = \cot^{-1}\left(\dfrac{1+\sec t}{\tan t}\right) = \cot^{-1}\left(\dfrac{1+\cos t}{\sin t}\right) = \cot^{-1}\cot\left(\dfrac{t}{2}\right) = \dfrac{t}{2}.$

$\therefore$ $f'(x) = \dfrac{d}{dt}\left(\dfrac{t}{2}\right)\dfrac{dt}{dx} = \dfrac{1}{2}\,\dfrac{1}{1+x^2} = \dfrac{1}{2(1+x^2)}.$

19. $f'(x) = (\cos^{-1} x)^2 + x \cdot \dfrac{-2\cos^{-1} x}{\sqrt{1-x^2}} - 2\cos^{-1} x \cdot \dfrac{-x}{\sqrt{1-x^2}} - 2\sqrt{1-x^2} \cdot \dfrac{-1}{\sqrt{1-x^2}} - 2$ $= (\cos^{-1} x)^2$.

20. Let $\sin^{-1} x = a$, $\sin^{-1} y = b$; $\therefore$ $\sin a = x$, $\sin b = y$. But $\sin(a+b) =$ $= \sin a \cos b + \cos a \sin b = x\sqrt{1-y^2} + y\sqrt{1-x^2}$. Hence the result.

21. Write $x = \tan t$; $\therefore$ $\sec \tan^{-1} x = \sec t = \sqrt{1+x^2}$ from the right-angled triangle with sides 1, x, $\sqrt{1+x^2}$ (hypotenuse).

22. $\cos(2\tan^{-1} x) = \cos 2t = \cos^2 t - \sin^2 t = \dfrac{1-x^2}{1+x^2}$ using the notation of Exercise 2.21.

23. $\dfrac{d}{dx}\{\tan^{-1}(\sec x + \tan x)\} = \dfrac{\sec^2 x + \sec x \tan x}{1+(\sec x+\tan x)^2} = \dfrac{\sec x(\sec x+\tan x)}{2\sec x(\sec x+\tan x)} = \dfrac{1}{2}$.

The answer suggests that $\tan^{-1}(\sec x+\tan x) = \dfrac{x}{2}+c$, i.e. $\sec x+\tan x = \tan\left(\dfrac{x}{2}+c\right)$.

$$\text{Now } \sec x+\tan x = \frac{1+\sin x}{\cos x} = \frac{1+\cos\left(\frac{\pi}{2}-x\right)}{\sin\left(\frac{\pi}{2}-x\right)} = \cot\left(\frac{\frac{\pi}{2}-x}{2}\right) =$$

$$\cot\left(\frac{\pi}{4}-\frac{x}{2}\right) = \tan\left(\frac{x}{2}+\frac{\pi}{4}\right) \quad \therefore \ c = \frac{\pi}{4}.$$

24. $$\tan^{-1}\frac{1}{5}+\tan^{-1}\frac{1}{8} = \tan^{-1}\left(\frac{\frac{1}{5}+\frac{1}{8}}{1-\frac{1}{5}\cdot\frac{1}{8}}\right) = \tan^{-1}\left(\frac{13}{39}\right) = \tan^{-1}\left(\frac{1}{3}\right).$$

$$\tan^{-1}\frac{1}{10}+\tan^{-1}\frac{8}{21} = \tan^{-1}\left(\frac{\frac{1}{10}+\frac{8}{21}}{1-\frac{1}{10}\cdot\frac{8}{21}}\right) = \tan^{-1}\left(\frac{101}{202}\right) = \tan^{-1}\left(\frac{1}{2}\right).$$

$$\therefore \text{angle} = \tan^{-1}\left(\frac{1}{3}\right)+\tan^{-1}\left(\frac{1}{2}\right) = \tan^{-1}\left(\frac{\frac{1}{3}+\frac{1}{2}}{1-\frac{1}{3}\cdot\frac{1}{2}}\right) = \tan^{-1} 1 = \frac{\pi}{4}.$$

25. $$f'(x) = \frac{2\cdot -1}{\sqrt{1-\left(\frac{a-x}{a-b}\right)}} \cdot \frac{1}{2\sqrt{\frac{a-x}{a-b}}} \cdot \frac{-1}{(a-b)} = \frac{1}{\sqrt{(x-b)(a-x)}}.$$

26. $f(x) = 2\tan^{-1}\sqrt{\dfrac{x-b}{a-x}} = 2\cos^{-1}\sqrt{\dfrac{a-x}{a-b}}$ from the right-angled triangles having sides $\sqrt{a-x}$, $\sqrt{x-b}$ and $\sqrt{a-b}$ (hypotenuse).

$\therefore$ $f'(x) = 1\,\dfrac{1}{\sqrt{(x-b)(a-x)}}$ (Exercise 2.25).

27. $f'(x) = \frac{2}{\sqrt{a^2-b^2}} \cdot \frac{1}{1+\frac{a-b}{a+b}\tan^2\frac{x}{2}} \cdot \sqrt{\frac{a-b}{a+b}} \cdot \frac{1}{2}\sec^2\frac{x}{2} =$

$$= \frac{\sec^2\frac{x}{2}}{(a+b)+(a-b)\tan^2\frac{x}{2}} = \frac{1}{(a+b)\cos^2\frac{x}{2}+(a-b)\sin^2\frac{x}{2}} = \frac{1}{a+b\cos x}.$$

28. $\sqrt{\frac{1-\cos x}{1+\cos x}} = \sqrt{\frac{(1-\cos x)\ (1-\cos x)}{(1+\cos x)\ (1-\cos x)}} = \frac{1-\cos x}{\sin x} = \tan\frac{x}{2}.$

$\therefore\ f(x) = \tan^{-1}\tan\frac{x}{2} = \frac{x}{2}\ \therefore\ f'(x) = \frac{1}{2}$. (Refer to Exercise 2.23.)

29. Write $\cos t = x$; $\therefore\ y = \cos kt\ \therefore\ \frac{dy}{dx} = -k\sin kt\frac{dt}{dx} = \frac{k\sin kt}{\sin t}$.

$\therefore\ \frac{d^2y}{dx^2} = \frac{d}{dt}\left(\frac{k\sin kt}{\sin t}\right)\frac{dt}{dx} = -k\frac{(k\cos kt-\sin kt\cot t)}{1-x^2}\quad \because\ \sin t = \sqrt{1-x^2}$

$\therefore\ (1-x^2)\frac{d^2y}{dx^2}-x\frac{dy}{dx}+k^2y = -k^2\cos kt+k\sin kt\cot t-k\sin kt\cot t+k^2\cos kt = 0.$

30. Consider the right-angled triangle of Exercise 2.13.

$\therefore\ \tan^{-1}\left(\frac{2x}{1-x^2}\right) = \sin^{-1}\left(\frac{2x}{1+x^2}\right) = y$, say. $\therefore\ \frac{d\tan^{-1}\left(\frac{2x}{1-x^2}\right)}{d\sin^{-1}\left(\frac{2x}{1+x^2}\right)} = \frac{dy}{dy} = 1.$

EXERCISES 3

1. For a value $+1, \frac{1}{x} = \frac{\pi}{2}(4n+1)$; $\therefore\ x = \frac{2}{\pi(4n+1)}$.

So $\frac{1}{8\pi} \leqslant \frac{2}{\pi(4n+1)} \leqslant \frac{1}{\pi}$ i.e., $16 \geqslant 4n+1 \geqslant 2$, i.e., $15 \geqslant 4n \geqslant 1$.

$\therefore\ n = 1, 2, 3$, i.e., the curve attains the value $+1$ three times.

$$\frac{d\sin\left(\frac{1}{x}\right)}{dx} = -\frac{1}{x^2}\cos\left(\frac{1}{x}\right) = -\frac{\pi^2}{18}\text{ at } x = \frac{3}{\pi}.$$

2. By (15), $\lim_{x\to\infty}\left(\frac{x}{\sqrt{9x^2+1}}\right) = \lim_{x\to\infty}\left(\frac{1}{\sqrt{9+\frac{1}{x^2}}}\right) = \frac{1}{3}$. [Form ∞/∞]

3. $\lim_{x\to 0}\left\{\frac{\sin 7x}{3x}\right\}$ is of the form $\frac{0}{0}$.

$\therefore$ by (15), $\lim_{x\to 0}\left\{\frac{\sin 7x}{3x}\right\} = \lim_{x\to 0}\left\{\frac{7\cos 7x}{3}\right\}$

$$= \frac{7}{3}\lim_{x\to 0}(\cos 7x) = \frac{7}{3}\cdot 1 = \frac{7}{3}.$$

Alternative method

$$\lim_{x\to 0} \frac{\sin 7x}{3x} = \lim_{x\to 0}\left\{\frac{7}{3}\cdot\frac{\sin 7x}{7x}\right\}$$

$$= \frac{7}{3}\lim_{x\to 0}\left\{\frac{\sin 7x}{7x}\right\} = \frac{7}{3}\cdot 1 \left(\text{since } \lim_{y\to 0}\left(\frac{\sin y}{y}\right) = 1\right) = \frac{7}{3}.$$

4. By (15), $\lim_{x\to 0}\left(\frac{\sin ax}{\sin bx}\right) = \frac{a}{b}\lim_{x\to 0}\left(\frac{\cos ax}{\cos bx}\right) = \frac{a}{b}.$

5. $\lim_{x\to 0}\left\{\frac{(3+x)^2-9}{x}\right\} = \lim_{x\to 0}\left\{\frac{9+6x+x^2-9}{x}\right\} = \lim_{x\to 0}(6+x) = 6.$

6. $\lim_{x\to\infty}\cos x$ is indeterminate.

7. By (15), $\lim_{x\to a}\left\{\frac{x^p-a^p}{x^q-a^q}\right\} = \lim_{x\to a}\left\{\frac{px^{p-1}}{qx^{q-1}}\right\} = \lim_{x\to a}\left(\frac{px^{p-q}}{q}\right) = \frac{pa^{p-q}}{q}.$

8. Multiply appropriately to reduce the form $\infty-\infty$ to the form $\frac{\infty}{\infty}$.

$$\therefore \quad \lim_{x\to\infty}\left(\sqrt{x}\{\sqrt{x+a}-\sqrt{x}\}\right) = \lim_{x\to\infty}\left(\sqrt{x}\{\sqrt{x+a}-\sqrt{x}\}\left\{\frac{\sqrt{x+a}+\sqrt{x}}{\sqrt{x+a}+\sqrt{x}}\right\}\right)$$

$$= \lim_{x\to\infty}\left(\frac{\sqrt{x}(x+a-x)}{\sqrt{x+a}+\sqrt{x}}\right) = a\lim_{x\to\infty}\left(\frac{1}{\sqrt{1+\frac{a}{x}}+1}\right) = \frac{a}{2}.$$

9. By (15), $\lim_{x\to 2}\left(\frac{\sin \pi x}{x-2}\right) = \lim_{x\to 2}\left(\frac{\pi\cos\pi x}{1}\right) = \pi.$

Alternative method. Put $y = x-2$. $\therefore\ \lim_{x\to 2}\left(\frac{\sin\pi x}{x-2}\right) = \lim_{y\to 0}\left(\frac{\sin(2+y)\pi}{y}\right)$

$$= \lim_{y\to 0}\left(\frac{\sin\pi y}{y}\right) (\because\ \sin(y+2)\pi = \sin 2\pi\cos\pi y+\cos 2\pi\sin\pi y) = \pi\lim_{y\to 0}\left(\frac{\sin\pi y}{\pi y}\right) = \pi$$

10. By (15), $\lim_{x\to\pi}\left(\frac{\sin x}{\sqrt{x-\pi}}\right) = \lim_{x\to\pi}\left(\frac{\cos x}{\frac{1}{2\sqrt{x-\pi}}}\right) = 2\lim_{x\to\pi}(\sqrt{x-\pi}\cos x) = 0.$

11. By (15) applied twice, $\lim_{x\to 0}\left(\frac{x^3}{1-\cos x}\right) = \lim_{x\to 0}\left(\frac{3x^2}{\sin x}\right) = \lim_{x\to 0}\left(\frac{6x}{\cos x}\right) = 0.$

12. By (15), $\lim_{x\to 0}\left(\frac{x+\sin 2x}{x-\sin 2x}\right) = \lim_{x\to 0}\left(\frac{1+2\cos 2x}{1-2\cos 2x}\right) = -3.$

13. By (15), $\lim_{x\to 0}\left(\frac{\tan x-x}{x-\sin x}\right) = \lim_{x\to 0}\left(\frac{\sec^2 x-1}{1-\cos x}\right) = \lim_{x\to 0}\left(\frac{1-\cos^2 x}{\cos^2 x(1-\cos x)}\right)$

$$= \lim_{x\to 0}\left(\frac{1+\cos x}{\cos^2 x}\right) = 2.$$

14. Applying (15) three times, we have $\lim_{x\to 0}\left(\frac{\sin x - x}{x\cos x - x}\right)$

$$= \lim_{x\to 0}\left(\frac{\cos x-1}{-x\sin x+\cos x-1}\right) = \lim_{x\to 0}\left(\frac{-\sin x}{-x\cos x-2\sin x}\right)$$

$$= \lim_{x\to 0}\left(\frac{-\cos x}{x\sin x-3\cos x}\right) = \frac{1}{3}.$$

15. By (15), $\lim_{x\to 0}\left(\frac{\sin^{-1} x}{x}\right) = \lim_{x\to 0}\left(\frac{1}{\sqrt{1-x^2}}\right) = 1.$

16. By (15), $\lim_{x\to\pi/2}\left(\left\{x-\frac{\pi}{2}\right\}\tan x\right) = \lim_{x\to\pi/2}\left(\frac{x-\frac{\pi}{2}}{\cot x}\right) = \lim_{x\to\pi/2}\left(\frac{1}{-\operatorname{cosec}^2 x}\right) = -1.$

17. By (15), $\lim_{x\to\infty}\left(\frac{\frac{\pi}{2}-\tan^{-1} x}{\frac{1}{x}}\right) = \lim_{x\to\infty}\left(\frac{-\frac{1}{1+x^2}}{-\frac{1}{x^2}}\right) = \lim_{x\to\infty}\left(\frac{x^2}{1+x^2}\right)$

$$= \lim_{x\to\infty}\left(\frac{1}{\frac{1}{x^2}+1}\right) = 1.$$

18. The curve is continuous at P (and hence everywhere continuous), but it is not differentiable at P since the gradient is not unique there.

19. Use Cauchy's M.V.T., with $f(x) = \cos x$, $g(x) = \sin x$, and the result follows.

20. Consider $a < x_1 < b$, $a < x_2 < b$, $x_1 < x_2$. By the M.V.T.,

$$\frac{f(x_2)-f(x_1)}{x_2-x_1} = f'(\xi) = 0 \quad \therefore \quad f(x_2) = f(x_1).$$

(Hence, if two functions have the same derivative at all points of an interval, the functions must differ by a constant.)

21. $f'(x) > 0$ in the given interval $\Rightarrow f(x_2) > f(x_1)$, i.e., $f(x)$ is monotonically increasing (§ 11).

22. $f(0) = f(2) = 0$ and $f(x)$ is single valued in $0 \leqslant x \leqslant 2$.

However, $f'(x) = -\frac{2}{3(x-1)^{1/3}} \neq 0$ for $0 < x < 2$.

Transforming the origin to (1, 1), we have $Y^3 = -X^2$ ($Y = y-1$, $X = x-1$), i.e. $Y = -X^{2/3}$. The curve is a semi-cubical parabola (Fig. 96) with cusp upwards at (1, 1) and axis of symmetry $x = 1$.

23. $\lim_{x\to 0}\left(x^2 \sin\frac{1}{x}\right) = 0$ $\therefore$ define $f(0)$

24. $f'(0) = \lim_{\delta x\to 0}\left\{\frac{f(\delta x)-f(0)}{\delta x}\right\} = \lim_{\delta x\to 0}\left\{\frac{(\delta x)^2\sin 1/\delta x - 0}{\delta x}\right\}$

$$= \lim_{\delta x\to 0}\left\{\delta x \sin\frac{1}{\delta x}\right\} = 0.$$

25. $f'(x) = 2x \sin \frac{1}{x} - \cos \frac{1}{x}$.

$\therefore \lim_{x\to 0} f'(x)$ does not exist ($\because \lim_{x\to 0} \cos \frac{1}{x}$ does not exist).

$\therefore \lim_{x\to 0} f'(x) \neq f'(0) \;\therefore\; f'(x)$ is not continuous at $x = 0$.

26. In the M.V.T., put $b-a = h$ and the required result follows ($\xi = a+\theta(b-a)$).

27. Put $f(x) = \tan^{-1} x$ in the M.V.T. $(a \leqslant x \leqslant b) \;\therefore\; \frac{\tan^{-1} b - \tan^{-1} a}{b-a}$

$$= f'(\xi) = \frac{1}{1+\xi^2} \quad \therefore \quad \frac{b-a}{1+b^2} < \tan^{-1} b - \tan^{-1} a < \frac{b-a}{1+a^2} \quad (a < b).$$

This also follows from the fact that $\tan^{-1} b - \tan^{-1} a = \frac{b-a}{1+ab}$.

Let $a = 1$, $b = \frac{3}{2}$ and the required numerical inequalities follow.

28. Supply your own diagram. $f(x) = x^3 - 12x$ is single-valued and continuous in $0 \leqslant x \leqslant 2\sqrt{3}$ and differentiable in $0 < x < 2\sqrt{3}$, and $f(0) = f(2\sqrt{3}) = 0$. $\therefore$ the conditions of Rolle's theorem apply. $\therefore f'(x) = 3x^2 - 12 = 0$ if $x = \pm 2$. $\therefore \xi = 2$ ($\because$ the negative solution is outside the given interval).

29. Provide your own diagram. $f(x) = x^2+x+1$ is single-valued and continuous in $-1 \leqslant x \leqslant 3$ and differentiable in $-1 < x < 3$ $\because$ the conditions of the M.V.T. apply.

$\therefore f'(\xi) = 2\xi+1 = \frac{f(3)-f(-1)}{3-(-1)} = \frac{13-(1)}{4} = 3 \;\therefore\; \xi = 1.$ $\therefore$ the required point is (1, 3).

30. Draw your own graph of the parabola $y = x^2$ and parallel the diagram of Fig. 2. We must find a $\delta > 0$ such that, for a given $\varepsilon > 0$, $|x^2-9| < \varepsilon$ whenever $|x-3| < \delta$. Now if $x-3 < \delta$ then $x+3 < \delta+6$. $\therefore |x^2-9| = |(x-3)(x+3)| = |x-3||x+3| < \delta(\delta+6)$. $\therefore$ our assertion that $\lim_{x\to 3} x^2 = 9$ is true if $\delta(\delta+6) \leqslant \varepsilon$ i.e., $\delta^2+6\delta \leqslant \varepsilon$. *One* way of finding such a δ is to say that, simultaneously,

$$\delta^2 \leqslant \frac{\varepsilon}{2}, \; 6\delta \leqslant \frac{\varepsilon}{2}, \text{ i.e. } \delta \leqslant \sqrt{\frac{\varepsilon}{2}}, \; \delta \leqslant \frac{\varepsilon}{12}.$$

Choose $\delta = \min.\left(\frac{\sqrt{\varepsilon}}{2}, \frac{\varepsilon}{12}\right)$. Hence $\lim_{x\to 3} x^2 = 9$.

Clearly (i) $\delta = \frac{1}{1200}$ when $\varepsilon = 0{\cdot}01$

(ii) $\delta = \frac{1}{12\,000\,000}$ when $\varepsilon = 0{\cdot}000001$.

EXERCISES 4

1. $y = x^{\log x} \Rightarrow \log y = \log x \log x = (\log x)^2$.

2. $f(x) = e^{\log \cos x} = \cos x \;\therefore\; f'(x) = -\sin x$.

3. $f'(x) = e^{\sin^2 x}\cdot 2\sin x\cos x = \sin 2x\cdot e^{\sin^2 x}$.

4. $f'(x) = e^{x^x}\dfrac{d}{dx}(x^x) = e^{x^x}x^x(1+\log x)$.

5. $f'(x) = -e^x\sin(e^x)$.

6. $f'(x) = x^2e^{1/x}\cdot\dfrac{-1}{x^2}+e^{1/x}\cdot 2x = e^{1/x}(2x-1)$.

7. $f'(x) = e^{-x^2}\cdot -\sin 2x\cdot 2+\cos 2x\cdot e^{-x^2}\cdot -2x = -2e^{-x^2}(\sin 2x+x\cos 2x)$.

8. $f(x) = e^{-\log x} = e^{\log(1/x)} = \dfrac{1}{x}\quad\therefore\quad f'(x) = -\dfrac{1}{x^2}$.

9. $f'(x) = -3x^2e^{x^3}(1-e^{2x^3})^{-1/2}$. **10.** $f'(x) = \dfrac{1}{x\log x}$.

11. $f'(x) = \dfrac{1}{x+\sqrt{x^2-a^2}}\left(1+\dfrac{2x}{2\sqrt{x^2-a^2}}\right) = \dfrac{1}{\sqrt{x^2-a^2}}$.

12. $f'(x) = \dfrac{1}{\sqrt{x+1}+\sqrt{x-1}}\left(\dfrac{1}{2\sqrt{x+1}}+\dfrac{1}{2\sqrt{x-1}}\right) = \dfrac{1}{2\sqrt{x^2-1}}$.

13. $f'(x) = \dfrac{(\log x)^2\cdot 1-x\cdot 2\log x\cdot\dfrac{1}{x}}{(\log x)^4} = \dfrac{\log x-2}{(\log x)^3}$.

14. $f'(x) = \dfrac{1}{x(1+x^2)^{-1/2}}\cdot(1+x^2)^{-3/2} = \dfrac{1}{x(1+x^2)}$ (by Example 1(i)).

15. $f'(x) = \dfrac{2x\cdot -\sin(1+x^2)}{\cos(1+x^2)} = -2x\tan(1+x^2)$.

16. $f'(x) = \dfrac{1}{2\sqrt{x}}-\dfrac{1}{2\sqrt{x}(1+\sqrt{x})} = \dfrac{1}{2(1+\sqrt{x})}$.

17. $f'(x) = \log 10\dfrac{d}{dx}\left(\dfrac{1}{\log x}\right) = \dfrac{-\log 10}{x(\log x)^2}$.

18. $f'(x) = \dfrac{e^x}{1+e^x}$. **19.** $f'(x) = \dfrac{\sec^2(\log x)}{x}$.

20. $$f'(x) = \frac{\sec^2\left(\frac{x}{2}+\frac{\pi}{4}\right)}{2\tan\left(\frac{x}{2}+\frac{\pi}{4}\right)} = \frac{\cos\left(\frac{x}{2}+\frac{\pi}{4}\right)}{2\cos^2\left(\frac{x}{2}+\frac{\pi}{4}\right)\sin\left(\frac{x}{2}+\frac{\pi}{4}\right)}$$

$$= \frac{1}{\sin\left(x+\frac{\pi}{2}\right)} = \sec x.$$

21. Let $y = (\sin x)^{\cos x}$. Then $\log y = \cos x\cdot\log\sin x$.

$$\therefore\quad \frac{1}{y}\frac{dy}{dx} = -\sin x\log\sin x+\cos x\frac{d}{dx}\log\sin x = -\sin x\log\sin x+\cos x\cot x.$$

$$\therefore\quad \frac{dy}{dx} = (\sin x)^{\cos x}(\cos x\cot x-\sin x\log\sin x).$$

22. $f'(x) = \tan^{-1} x + \dfrac{x}{1+x^2} - \dfrac{1}{\sqrt{1+x^2}} \cdot \dfrac{2x}{2\sqrt{1+x^2}} = \tan^{-1} x.$

23. $f'(x) = x^a \cdot a^x \log a + a^x \cdot ax^{a-1} = a^x x^{a-1}(x \log a + a).$

24. $f'(x) = \dfrac{1}{1+x} + \dfrac{1}{1-x} = \dfrac{2}{1-x^2}.$ **25.** $f'(x) = e^{-x}e^{-e^{-x}} = e^{-x-e^{-x}}.$

26. $\dfrac{dN}{dt} = cke^{kt} = kN \quad \therefore \quad a = k.$

27. Let $y = (\tfrac{1}{2})^x e^x \quad \therefore \quad \log y = x \log(\tfrac{1}{2}) + \log e^x = -x \log 2 + x.$

$\therefore \quad \dfrac{1}{y}\dfrac{dy}{dx} = 1 - \log_e 2$ (which is constant) $= 1 - \dfrac{\log_{10} 2}{\log_{10} e} = 1 - \dfrac{0{\cdot}3010}{0{\cdot}4343}$

(using four-figure log tables) $= 0{\cdot}31$ (to 2 decimal places).

28. $\dfrac{dy}{dx} = ae^x - be^{-x}, \; \dfrac{d^2y}{dx^2} = ae^x + be^{-x} = y \quad \therefore \quad k = 0, \; m = -1.$

29. $x = ae^{-kt/2} \cos(qt+\varepsilon) \quad \therefore \quad \dot{x} = -ae^{-kt/2}\left\{q \sin(qt+\varepsilon) + \dfrac{k}{2}\cos(qt+\varepsilon)\right\}$ and

$$\ddot{x} = ae^{-kt/2}\left\{\left(\frac{k^2}{4} - q^2\right)\cos(qt+\varepsilon) + kq \sin(qt+\varepsilon)\right\}$$

$\therefore \quad \ddot{x} + k\dot{x} + n^2 x = ae^{-kt/2} \cos(qt+\varepsilon)\left(n^2 - q^2 - \dfrac{k^2}{4}\right) = 0$ when $n = \pm\sqrt{q^2 + \tfrac{1}{4}k^2}.$

30. By (15), $\lim\limits_{R\to 0} j = E \lim\limits_{R\to 0}\left(\dfrac{1-e^{-Rt/L}}{R}\right) = E \lim\limits_{R\to 0}\left(\dfrac{(t/L)e^{-Rt/L}}{1}\right) \div \dfrac{Et}{L}.$

31. By (15), $\lim\limits_{x\to 0}\left\{\dfrac{2^x - 3^x}{x}\right\} = \lim\limits_{x\to 0}\left\{\dfrac{2^x \log 2 - 3^x \log 3}{1}\right\} = \log 2 - \log 3 = \log\left(\dfrac{2}{3}\right).$

32. By (15), $\lim\limits_{x\to\infty}\left\{\dfrac{x^n}{e^x}\right\} = \lim\limits_{x\to\infty}\left\{\dfrac{nx^{n-1}}{e^x}\right\}$ $\left(\text{still of the form } \dfrac{\infty}{\infty}\right)$

$= \lim\limits_{x\to\infty}\left\{\dfrac{n(n-1)x^{n-2}}{e^x}\right\}$ by (15)$\left(\text{form } \dfrac{\infty}{\infty}\right) = \lim\limits_{x\to\infty}\left\{\dfrac{n!}{e^x}\right\}$ (applying (15) n times) $= 0$

33. $\lim\limits_{x\to\infty}\left(\dfrac{x+\log x}{x \log x}\right) = \lim\limits_{x\to\infty}\left(\dfrac{1}{\log x} + \dfrac{1}{x}\right) = 0$ (or, use (15)).

34. $\lim\limits_{x\to\infty}\{(1+x)^{1/x}\} = y$ is of the form ∞^0.

Now $\lim\limits_{x\to\infty}\left\{\dfrac{\log(1+x)}{x}\right\} = \log y$ is of the form $\dfrac{\infty}{\infty}$.

$\therefore$ by (15), $\log y = \lim\limits_{x\to\infty}\left(\dfrac{1}{1+x}\right) = 0 \quad \therefore \quad \lim\limits_{x\to\infty}\{(1+x)^{1/x}\} = e^0 = 1.$

35. $y = \lim\limits_{x\to 1}(x^{1/(x-1)}) \therefore \log y = \lim\limits_{x\to 1}\left(\dfrac{\log x}{x-1}\right) = \lim\limits_{x\to 1}\left(\dfrac{1}{x}\right) = 1$ by (15) $\therefore \; y = e.$

36. By (15), $\lim\limits_{x\to 2}\left\{\dfrac{x^2 \log x - 4 \log 2}{x^2 - 4}\right\} = \lim\limits_{x\to 2}\left(\dfrac{2x \log x + x}{2x}\right)$

$= \lim\limits_{x\to 2}\left(\dfrac{2 \log x + 1}{2}\right)$(dividing by x) $= \log 2 + \dfrac{1}{2} = \log 2\sqrt{e}.$

37. Take logarithms; $\therefore$ $\log p+\gamma \log v = \log c$ $\therefore$ $\dfrac{1}{p}\dfrac{dp}{dv}+\dfrac{\gamma}{v}=0$ $\therefore$ $\dfrac{dp}{dv}=\dfrac{-p\gamma}{v}$.

38. Let $y = x^{1/x}$; $\therefore$ $\log y = \dfrac{1}{x}\log x$; $\therefore$ $\dfrac{1}{y}\dfrac{dy}{dx}=\dfrac{1}{x^2}-\dfrac{\log x}{x^2}$

i.e. $\dfrac{dy}{dx} = x^{(1/x)-2}(1-\log x) = 0$ when $\log x = 1$, i.e. when $x = e$.

$$\frac{d^2y}{dx^2} = -x^{(1/x)-3}+(1-\log x)\frac{d}{dx}\{x^{(1/x)-2}\} = -e^{(1/e)-3} < 0 \text{ when } x = e.$$

Thus, $x = e$ gives a maximum value $(= e^{1/e})$.

39. Write $y = \dfrac{\log x}{x}$ $\therefore$ $\dfrac{dy}{dx} = \dfrac{x\cdot 1/x-\log x}{x^2} = \dfrac{1-\log x}{x^2} = 0$ when $\log x = 1$,

i.e., $x = e$. As x changes from $< e$ to $> e$, $(1-\log x)/x^2$ changes from +ve to −ve, and thus $x = e$ gives a maximum value $(= e^{-1})$.

40. By Exercise 4.39, $x = \pi \Rightarrow \dfrac{\log \pi}{\pi} < \dfrac{1}{e} \Rightarrow \log \pi < \dfrac{\pi}{e} \Rightarrow \pi < e^{\pi/e} \Rightarrow \pi^e < e^\pi$.

[Actually, $\pi^e \doteqdot 22{\cdot}4$, $e^\pi \doteqdot 23{\cdot}2$.]

41. By (18.1), $x^{\frac{1}{\log x}} = e^{\frac{1}{\log x}\cdot\log x} = e$.

42. $E(y) = \dfrac{x}{y}\dfrac{dy}{dx} = \dfrac{1/y\, dy}{1/x\, dx} = \dfrac{d\log y}{d\log x}$ $\therefore$ $E(y) = k \Rightarrow \log y = k\log x+\log C \Rightarrow$

$\Rightarrow y = Cx^k$.

[Ignore $\log C$ (i.e., take $\log C = 0$ $(C = 1)$ at this stage, if you wish.]

43. Let the principal be P dollars.

$\therefore$ $2P = Pe^{\frac{5}{100}} \Rightarrow \dfrac{t}{20} = \log 2 \doteqdot 0{\cdot}6932$ $\therefore$ $t \doteqdot 13{\cdot}8$ years (on calculation).

44. In $\triangle PMN$, $PN = y\sec\theta = y\sqrt{1+\tan^2\theta}$. Hence the result.

45. In $\triangle PTN$, $PT = PN/\tan\theta$. Hence the result.

46. Subnormal $y\dfrac{dy}{dx} = v\dfrac{dv}{ds} = \dfrac{ds}{dt}\dfrac{dv}{ds} = \dfrac{dv}{dt} = a$.

47. Let $v = kx^2\log(1/x)$ where k is a factor of proportionality.

$$\therefore\ \frac{dv}{dx} = kx^2\cdot x\cdot\frac{-1}{x^2}+k\log(1/x)\cdot 2x = k\{-x+2x\log(1/x)\}$$

$$= kx\{2\log(1/x)-1\} = 0 \text{ when } \log\frac{1}{x} = \frac{1}{2}, \text{ i.e., } \sqrt{e} = \frac{1}{x}, \text{ i.e., } x = \frac{1}{\sqrt{e}}.$$

Also, $\dfrac{d^2v}{dx^2} = k\left\{2x\cdot\dfrac{-1}{x}+2\log\dfrac{1}{x}-1\right\} = k\left\{2\log\dfrac{1}{x}-3\right\} = -2k$ when $x = \dfrac{1}{\sqrt{e}}$.

$\therefore$ $x = 1/\sqrt{e}$ gives a maximum value $\left(=\dfrac{k}{2e}\right)$ to v.

48. $\log(1+x) = \log(1-x)+\log e \Rightarrow \log(1+x) = \log e(1-x) \Rightarrow 1+x = e(1-x)$

$\therefore x = \dfrac{e-1}{e+1}$.

49. $x = \frac{1}{k}\left\{gt+\frac{g-ku}{k}(e^{-kt}-1)\right\}$ $\therefore$ $\dot{x} = \frac{1}{k}\left\{g-k\frac{(g-ku)}{k}e^{-kt}\right\}$,

$\ddot{x} = \frac{1}{k}\cdot k(g-ku)e^{-kt}$.

Now $g-k\dot{x} = g-\frac{k}{k}\left\{g-(g-ku)e^{-kt}\right\} = (g-ku)e^{-kt} = \ddot{x}$.

50. $f = e^{-x/2}(1+e^{-x}+e^{-2x}+\ldots) = \frac{e^{-x/2}}{1-e^{-x}} = \frac{e^{x/2}}{e^x-1}$

$\therefore$ $\log f = \frac{x}{2}-\log(e^x-1)$ $\therefore$ $\frac{d}{dx}\log f = \frac{1}{2}-\frac{e^x}{e^x-1} = \frac{-(e^x+1)}{2(e^x-1)}$.

Now $x = \frac{h\nu}{KT}$, $\therefore$ $\frac{dx}{dT} = \frac{-h\nu}{KT^2}$ $\therefore$ $\frac{d}{dT}\log f = \frac{h\nu}{KT^2}\cdot\frac{e^x+1}{2(e^x-1)}$.

$\therefore$ $E = NKT^2\frac{d}{dT}\log f = \frac{Nh\nu}{2}\frac{(e^x+1)}{(e^x-1)}$.

51. $R = \frac{m_0}{m_n} = \frac{m_0}{m_1}\cdot\frac{m_1}{m_2}\ \ldots\ \frac{m_{n-1}}{m_n} = \left(1+\frac{v}{nc}\right) = e^{v/c}$ in the limit.

52. When $v = 2c$, $R \geqslant e^2$.

53. Let $y = (\cos\sqrt{x})^{1/x}$; $\therefore$ $\log y = \frac{\log\cos\sqrt{x}}{x}$.

By (15), $\lim_{x\to 0}\left\{\frac{\log\cos\sqrt{x}}{x}\right\} = \lim_{x\to 0}\left\{\frac{-\tan\sqrt{x}}{2\sqrt{x}}\right\} = \lim_{x\to 0}\left(\frac{-\sec^2\sqrt{x}}{2\cdot 2\sqrt{x}\cdot\frac{1}{2\sqrt{x}}}\right)$

$= -\frac{1}{2}\lim_{\alpha\to 0}(\sec^2\sqrt{x}) = -\frac{1}{2}$.

$\therefore$ $y = e^{-1/2}$. (Notice also that $\lim_{x\to 0}\left(\frac{\tan\sqrt{x}}{\sqrt{x}}\right) = \lim_{x\to 0}\left\{\sec\sqrt{x}\left(\frac{\sin\sqrt{x}}{\sqrt{x}}\right)\right\}$

$= 1\cdot 1 = 1$.)

54, 55. No detailed solutions are offered, as the calculations, though a little complicated, are straightforward.

56. Apply Rolle's theorem to $f(x) = e^{-x}-\sin x$ (which satisfies the conditions of the theorem).
$\therefore$ 2 solutions of $e^{-x}-\sin x = 0$ (i.e. $e^x\sin x = 1$) $\Rightarrow$ one solution (at least) of $f'(x) = 0$, i.e. of $-e^{-x}-\cos x = 0$, i.e. $e^x\cos x = -1$.

57. Put $f(x) = \log x$ which satisfies the conditions of the M.V.T. in $a \leqslant x \leqslant b$.

$$\therefore\quad \frac{\log b-\log a}{b-a} = f'(\xi) = \frac{1}{\xi}\quad (a < \xi < b)$$

$$\therefore\ \frac{1}{b} < \frac{\log b-\log a}{b-a} < \frac{1}{a}\ \therefore\ 1-\frac{a}{b} < \log\left(\frac{b}{a}\right) < \frac{b}{a}-1\quad (a > 0,\ b > 0).$$

Put $b = 2$, $a = 1$. Then $\frac{1}{2} < \log 2 < 1$.

58. Put $f(x) = e^x$ which satisfies the conditions of the M.V.T. in $0 \leqslant x \leqslant b$.

$$\therefore \frac{e^b - e^0}{b-0} = f'(\xi) = e^\xi \qquad (0 < \xi < b)$$

$$\text{i.e. } \frac{e^b - 1}{b} = e^\xi \qquad \therefore 1 < \frac{e^b - 1}{b} < e^b.$$

$$\text{Put } b = \frac{1}{100} \ \therefore \frac{1}{100} < e^{\frac{1}{100}} - 1 < \frac{1}{100} e^{\frac{1}{100}} \ \therefore \frac{101}{100} < e^{\frac{1}{100}} < \frac{100}{99}.$$

$$\therefore (1{\cdot}01)^{100} < e < (1{\cdot}\dot{0}\dot{1})^{100}, \text{ i.e. } \left(\frac{101}{100}\right)^{100} < e < \left(\frac{100}{99}\right)^{100}.$$

59. (i) $x = 2a^{f(x)}$ Hence $f^{-1}(x) = 2a^x$.

(ii) $\cos^{-1} f(2) = \cos^{-1} \log_a 1 = \cos^{-1} 0 = \dfrac{\pi}{2}$.

60. See (30)–(33), § 14. $\phi(2x) = \{\phi(x)\}^2 + \{\psi(x)\}^2$; $\psi(2x) = 2\phi(x)\psi(x)$.

EXERCISES 5

1. $\sinh x = \dfrac{4}{3} \Rightarrow \cosh x = \dfrac{5}{3}$ and $\tanh x = \dfrac{4}{5}$

$\sinh y = \dfrac{3}{4} \Rightarrow \cosh y = \dfrac{5}{4}$ and $\tanh y = \dfrac{3}{5}$

$\therefore$ by (32) $\sinh(x+y) = \sinh x \cosh y + \cosh x \sinh y = \dfrac{4}{3}\cdot\dfrac{5}{4} + \dfrac{5}{3}\cdot\dfrac{3}{4} = \dfrac{35}{12}$.

2. Also by (30) and (32), $\tanh(x+y) = \dfrac{\tanh x + \tanh y}{1 + \tanh x \tanh y} = \dfrac{\frac{4}{5} + \frac{3}{5}}{1 + \frac{4}{5}\cdot\frac{3}{5}} = \dfrac{35}{37}$.

3. $$2 \sinh\left(\frac{A+B}{2}\right) \cosh\left(\frac{A-B}{2}\right) = \frac{2\{e^{(A+B)/2} - e^{-(A+B)/2}\}}{2} \frac{\{e^{(A-B)/2} + e^{-(A-B)/2}\}}{2}$$

$$= \tfrac{1}{2}\{e^A + e^B - e^{-B} - e^{-A}\} = \frac{e^A - e^{-A}}{2} + \frac{e^B - e^{-B}}{2} = \sinh A + \sinh B.$$

4. $$\frac{\sinh x}{\cosh x + 1} = \frac{2 \sinh(\frac{1}{2}x) \cosh(\frac{1}{2}x)}{2 \sinh^2(\frac{1}{2}x) + 1 + 1} = \frac{2 \sinh(\frac{1}{2}x) \cosh(\frac{1}{2}x)}{2 \cosh^2(\frac{1}{2}x)} = \tanh(\tfrac{1}{2}x). \quad \text{(i)}$$

$$\frac{\cosh x - 1}{\sinh x} = \frac{2 \sinh^2(\frac{1}{2}x) + 1 - 1}{2 \sinh(\frac{1}{2}x) \cosh(\frac{1}{2}x)} = \tanh(\tfrac{1}{2}x). \quad \text{(ii)}$$

$$\therefore \sqrt{\frac{\cosh x - 1}{\cosh x + 1}} = \sqrt{\frac{2 \sinh^2(\frac{1}{2}x) + 1 - 1}{2 \cosh^2(\frac{1}{2}x)}} = \tanh(\tfrac{1}{2}x). \text{ (Or, (i)} \times \text{(ii).)}$$

5. $\tanh x = \dfrac{e^{2x} - 1}{e^{2x} + 1} = \dfrac{4}{5}$ $\therefore 5e^{2x} - 5 = 4e^{2x} + 4$ $\therefore e^{2x} = 9$ $\therefore (e^x)^2 = 3^2$

$$\therefore e^x = 3 \ \therefore x = \log 3.$$

6. $a^2 = 25\cosh^2 x - 40\cosh x \sinh x + 16\sinh^2 x$

$b^2 = 25\sinh^2 x - 40\cosh x \sinh x + 16\cosh^2 x$

$$\therefore \sqrt{a^2-b^2} = \sqrt{9(\cosh^2 x - \sinh^2 x)} = \sqrt{9\cdot 1} = 3.$$

7. Subtangent $\dfrac{y}{\dfrac{dy}{dx}} = \dfrac{c\cosh \dfrac{x}{c}}{\sinh \dfrac{x}{c}} = c\coth \dfrac{x}{c}.$

8. Subnormal $y\dfrac{dy}{dx} = c\cosh\dfrac{x}{c}\sinh\dfrac{x}{c} = \dfrac{1}{2}c\sinh\dfrac{2x}{c}.$

9. From $\triangle QMP$, in Fig. 8, $QM = y\cos\phi = \dfrac{y}{\sqrt{1+\tan^2\phi}} = \dfrac{y}{\sqrt{1+\left(\dfrac{dy}{dx}\right)^2}}.$

10. In Fig. 8, $QM = \dfrac{c\cosh\dfrac{x}{c}}{\sqrt{1+\sinh^2\dfrac{x}{c}}} = \dfrac{c\cosh\dfrac{x}{c}}{\cosh\dfrac{x}{c}} = c.$

11. $f'(x) = \dfrac{1}{\tanh x}\cdot\operatorname{sech}^2 x = \dfrac{\cosh x}{\sinh x}\cdot\dfrac{1}{\cosh^2 x} = \dfrac{2}{2\sinh x\cosh x} = 2\operatorname{cosech} 2x.$

12. $f(x) = \tanh^{-1}\left(\dfrac{\tanh X + \tanh A}{1+\tanh X\tanh A)}\right)$ putting $\begin{cases} a = \tanh A \\ x = \tanh X\end{cases}$

$= \tanh^{-1}\tanh(X+A) = X+A$

$$\therefore f'(x) = \frac{d}{dx}(X+A) = \frac{d}{dx}\tanh^{-1} x + 0 = \frac{1}{1-x^2}.$$

13. $f(x) = \dfrac{e^x}{e^{-x}} = e^{2x} \therefore f'(x) = 2e^{2x} = 2(\cosh x + \sinh x)^2.$

14. $f(x) = \sinh\log(x+\sqrt{1+x^2}) = \sinh\sinh^{-1} x = x \therefore f'(x) = 1 \therefore c = 1.$

15. If $x = a\cosh nt + b\sinh nt \therefore \dot{x} = na\sinh nt + nb\cosh nt$

$\therefore \ddot{x} = n^2a\cosh nt + n^2b\sinh nt$. Thus, $\ddot{x} = n^2x$.

If $x = a\cos nt + b\sin nt \therefore \dot{x} = -na\sin nt + nb\cos nt$

$\therefore \ddot{x} = -n^2a\cos nt - n^2b\sin nt$. Thus, $\ddot{x} = -n^2x$.

16. $\dfrac{e^{a/2}-e^{-a/2}}{e^{a/2}+e^{-a/2}} = e^{-b} \Rightarrow \dfrac{e^a-1}{e^a+1} = e^{-b} \Rightarrow e^a = \dfrac{e^b+1}{e^b-1} \Rightarrow a = \log\left(\dfrac{e^b+1}{e^b-1}\right) =$

$= \log\coth\left(\dfrac{b}{2}\right)$. (Of course, $b = \log\coth a/2$.)

17. $\sinh b = \dfrac{e^b-e^{-b}}{2} = \dfrac{\coth a/2 - \tanh a/2}{2} = \dfrac{\cosh^2 a/2 - \sinh^2 a/2}{2\sinh a/2\cosh a/2} = \dfrac{1}{\sinh a}.$

18. $\sin\alpha = \dfrac{2\tan\alpha/2}{1+\tan^2\alpha/2} = \dfrac{2e^{-h/k}}{1+e^{-2h/k}} = \dfrac{2}{e^{h/k}+e^{-h/k}} = \operatorname{sech}(h/k).$

Also, $1-\sin^2\alpha = 1-\operatorname{sech}^2 h/k \therefore \cos\alpha = \tanh h/k$ (taking square roots).

19. Let $\tanh^{-1} x = y$ $\therefore$ $\tanh y = x$ $\therefore$ $\text{sech}^2 y = 1-x^2$

$$\therefore (\cosh y =)\ \cosh \tanh^{-1} x = \frac{1}{\sqrt{1-x^2}}.$$

20. $$\tanh \frac{x}{2} = \frac{\sinh x}{1+\cosh x} = \frac{\tan \phi}{1+\sec \phi} = \frac{\sin \phi}{1+\cos \phi} = \tan \frac{\phi}{2}$$

(using Exercise 5.4 and the Gudermannian relationships).

$\therefore$ the Gudermannian $\phi = 2 \tan^{-1} \tanh \dfrac{x}{2}$ ($= \tan^{-1} \sinh x$ by definition).

21. By (15), $$\lim_{x\to 1} \left(\frac{\sinh x - \sinh 1}{\cosh x - \cosh 1}\right) = \lim_{x\to 1} \left(\frac{\cosh x}{\sinh x}\right) = \coth 1.$$

22. By (15) applied twice, $$\lim_{x\to 0} \left\{\frac{\log \cosh 2x}{\log \cosh 3x}\right\} = \lim_{x\to 0} \left(\frac{2 \tanh 2x}{3 \tanh 3x}\right) =$$

$$= \frac{2}{3} \lim_{x\to 0} \left\{\frac{2}{3}\,\frac{\text{sech}^2\, 2x}{\text{sech}^2\, 3x}\right\} = \frac{4}{9}.$$

23. Let $y = \lim_{x\to\infty} (\cosh x)^{1/x}$ $\therefore$ by (15), $\log y = \lim_{x\to\infty} \left\{\dfrac{\log \cosh x}{x}\right\}$

$$= \lim_{x\to\infty} \tanh x = 1 \quad \therefore y = e.$$

24. $\sinh 2x = 2 \sinh x \cosh x$, $\cosh 2x = \cosh^2 x + \sinh^2 x$

$\therefore \sinh 3x = \sinh (2x+x) = \sinh 2x \cosh x + \cosh 2x \sinh x$

$= 2 \sinh x \cosh^2 x + \sinh x (\cosh^2 x + \sinh^2 x) = \sinh x (3 \cosh^2 x + \sinh^2 x)$

$\cosh 3x = \cosh (2x+x) = \cosh 2x \cosh x + \sinh 2x \sinh x$

$= \cosh x (\cosh^2 x + \sinh^2 x) + 2 \sinh^2 x \cosh x = \cosh x (3 \sinh^2 x + \cosh^2 x)$

$$\therefore \frac{\sinh 3x}{\sinh x} - \frac{\cosh 3x}{\cosh x} = 2 (\cosh^2 x - \sinh^2 x) = 2.$$

or $$\frac{\sinh 3x}{\sinh x} - \frac{\cosh 3x}{\cosh x} = \frac{e^{3x} - e^{-3x}}{e^x - e^{-x}} - \frac{e^{3x} + e^{-3x}}{e^x + e^{-x}} = 2 \text{ on simplifying.}$$

25. $$\frac{dx}{d\theta} = c\left\{-\frac{1}{2} \operatorname{cosec}^2 \frac{\theta}{2} \tan \frac{\theta}{2} + \sin \theta\right\} = c\left\{-\frac{1}{\sin \theta} + \sin \theta\right\} = \frac{-c \cos^2 \theta}{\sin \theta},$$

$\dfrac{dy}{d\theta} = c \cos \theta$ $\therefore$ $\dfrac{dy}{dx} = -\tan \theta = \tan (\pi - \theta)$ $\therefore$ *QM is* a tangent to the tractrix

26. Equation of tangent QM is $y - c \sin \theta = -\tan \theta\, (x - c\, \{\log \cot \theta/2 - \cos \theta\})$. At M, $y = 0$ whence $x = c \log \cot \theta/2$.

$$\therefore QM = c \sqrt{\{(\log \cot \theta/2 - \cos \theta)^2 - \log \cot \theta/2\}^2 + \{\sin \theta - 0\}^2}$$

$$= c \sqrt{\cos^2 \theta + \sin^2 \theta} = c.$$

27. From (35), $$x = c \log \cot \theta/2 - c \cos \theta = c \log \left(\frac{1+\cos \theta}{\sin \theta}\right) - c \cos \theta$$

$$= c \log \left(\frac{1+\sqrt{1-y^2/c^2}}{y/c}\right) - c\sqrt{1-\frac{y^2}{c^2}} \quad \because y = c \sin \theta$$

$$= c \log \left(\frac{c+\sqrt{c^2-y^2}}{y}\right) - \sqrt{c^2-y^2}.$$

28. $\dfrac{dx}{dy} = c\cdot\dfrac{y}{c+\sqrt{c^2-y^2}}\cdot\dfrac{\dfrac{y\cdot -y}{\sqrt{c^2-y^2}}-(c+\sqrt{c^2-y^2})}{y^2}+\dfrac{y}{\sqrt{c^2-y^2}}$

$= \dfrac{-\sqrt{c^2-y^2}}{y}$ (on simplifying) $= -\cot\theta$ using $y = c\sin\theta$.

$\therefore \dfrac{dy}{dx} = -\tan\theta$ (as in Exercise 5.25).

29. Since $\tan\phi = \sinh x = \dfrac{dy}{dx}$ when $y = \cosh x$, it follows that ϕ is the inclination of the tangent at a variable point on the catenary $y = \cosh x$ to the positive direction of the x-axis.

30. Let $y = \log x \;\therefore\; \tanh\log x = \dfrac{e^{2\log x}-1}{e^{2\log x}+1} = \dfrac{e^{\log x^2}-1}{e^{\log x^2}+1} = \dfrac{x^2-1}{x^2+1}$ using (18.1) and (28.3)

$\therefore \tanh^{-1}\left\{\dfrac{x^2-1}{x^2+1}\right\} = \log x.$

31. $v = c\tanh\dfrac{gt}{c} \;\therefore\; a = \dfrac{dv}{dt} = c\cdot\dfrac{g}{c}\operatorname{sech}^2\dfrac{gt}{c} = g\left(1-\tanh^2\dfrac{gt}{c}\right).$

$\therefore ma = mg - mg\tanh^2\dfrac{gt}{c}$, i.e. $ma = mg-kv^2$.

32. $\lim\limits_{t\to\infty} v = c\lim\limits_{t\to\infty}\tanh\dfrac{gt}{c} = c\cdot 1 = c$ using § 16(ii). (Here c has nothing to do with the speed of light.)

33. $y+\delta y = \sinh(x+\delta x) = \dfrac{e^{x+\delta x}-e^{-(x+\delta x)}}{2}$ and $y = \sinh x = \dfrac{e^x-e^{-x}}{2}$

$\therefore \delta y = \dfrac{1}{2}\{e^x(e^{\delta x}-1)-e^{-x}(e^{-\delta x}-1)\}$

$= \dfrac{1}{2}\left\{e^x\left(\delta x+\dfrac{(\delta x)^2}{2!}+\ldots\right)-e^{-x}\left((-\delta x)+\dfrac{(-\delta x)^2}{2!}+\ldots\right)\right\}$

$\therefore \dfrac{\delta y}{\delta x} = \dfrac{1}{2}\left\{e^x\left(1+\dfrac{\delta x}{2!}+\ldots\right)-e^{-x}\left(-1+\dfrac{(-\delta x)}{2!}+\ldots\right)\right\}$

$\therefore \dfrac{dy}{dx} = \lim\limits_{x\to 0}\left(\dfrac{\delta y}{\delta x}\right) = \dfrac{1}{2}(e^x+e^{-x}) = \cosh x.$

34. $x = \sinh y = \dfrac{1}{\operatorname{cosech} y} \Rightarrow \sinh^{-1}x = y = \operatorname{cosech}^{-1}\left(\dfrac{1}{x}\right).$

35. $x = \sinh y \Rightarrow \cosh y = \sqrt{1+\sinh^2 y} = \sqrt{1+x^2}$

$\therefore \sinh^{-1}x = y = \cosh^{-1}\sqrt{1+x^2}.$

$\therefore \cosh\sinh^{-1}x = \cosh\cosh^{-1}\sqrt{1+x^2} = \sqrt{1+x^2}$ (i.e. $\cosh\sinh^{-1}1 = \sqrt{2}$).

36. $x = e^y \Rightarrow \cosh^{-1}\dfrac{1}{2}\left(x+\dfrac{1}{x}\right) = \cosh^{-1}\dfrac{1}{2}(e^y+e^{-y}) = \cosh^{-1}\cosh y = y = \log x$

$\left[= \tanh^{-1}\left(\dfrac{x^2-1}{x^2+1}\right)\right.$ by Exercise 5.30$\left.\right]$.

37. From § 18, $\tan\frac{\phi}{2} = \frac{e^x-1}{e^x+1} = \frac{e^{x/2}-e^{x/2}}{e^{x/2}+e^{-x/2}} = \tanh\frac{x}{2}$

$\therefore\ \tanh^{-1}\tan\frac{\phi}{2} = \frac{x}{2} = \frac{1}{2}gd^{-1}\phi.$

38. $x = \coth y = \frac{e^{2y}+1}{e^{2y}-1}\ \therefore\ e^{2y}x-x = e^{2y}+1\ \therefore\ e^{2y}(x-1) = x+1$

$\therefore\ 2y = \log\left(\frac{x+1}{x-1}\right)\ \therefore\ y = \coth^{-1}x = \frac{1}{2}\log\left(\frac{x+1}{x-1}\right)\quad (|x| > 1).$

39. $\tan\left\{\frac{\pi}{2}(e^{\log 2}-e^{-\log 2})\right\} = \tan\left\{\frac{\pi}{2}(2-\frac{1}{2})\right\} = \tan\frac{3\pi}{4} = -1.$

40. $\cosh^{-1}\left(\frac{e^{\log 3}+e^{-\log 3}}{e^{\log 3}-e^{-\log 3}}\right) = \cosh^{-1}\left(\frac{3+1/3}{3-1/3}\right) = \cosh^{-1}\frac{5}{4}$

$$= \pm\log\left(\frac{5}{4}+\sqrt{\left(\frac{5}{4}\right)^2-1}\right) = \pm\log 2.$$

41. By Exercise 5.38, $e^{-\coth^{-1}(13/5)} = e^{-(1/2)\log(18/8)} = e^{-\log 3/2} = \frac{2}{3}.$

42. $1+2\sum_{p=1}^{n}\cos px = 1+e^x+e^{2x}+\ldots+e^{nx}+e^{-x}(1+e^{-x}+\ldots+e^{-(n-1)x})$

$$= \frac{1-e^{(n+1)x}}{1-e^x}+e^{-x}\frac{(1-e^{-nx})}{1-e^{-x}}\quad \text{(Example 44)}$$

$$= \frac{-1+e^{(n+1)x}+1-e^{-nx}}{e^x-1} = \frac{e^{1/2x}(e^{(n+1/2)x}-e^{-(n+1/2)x})}{e^{1/2x}(e^{1/2x}-e^{-1/2x})} = \frac{\sinh(n+\frac{1}{2})x}{\sinh\frac{1}{2}x}.$$

43. $\sec gd\,(x+y) = \frac{e^{x+y}+e^{-(x+y)}}{2} = \frac{e^xe^y+e^{-x}e^{-y}}{2}$

$= \sec gd\,x\cdot\sec gd\,y\ +\tan gd\,x\cdot\tan gd\,y,$

after simplification; § 18(viii) has been used.

44. $\tan gd\,(x+y) = \frac{e^{x+y}-e^{-(x+y)}}{2} = \frac{e^xe^y-e^{-x}e^{-y}}{2}$

$= \tan gd\,x\cdot\sec gd\,y+\tan gd\,y\cdot\sec gd\,x.$

45. $\sin gd(x+y) = \frac{\sin gd\,x+\sin gd\,y}{1+\sin gd\,x\cdot\sin gd\,y}$ on dividing in Exercises 5.43, 5.44.

46. $\cos gd\,(x+y) = \frac{\cos gd\,x\cdot\cos gd\,y}{1+\sin gd\,x\cdot\sin gd\,y}$ on dividing in Exercise 5.43.

47. Given

$$4e^x-4e^{-x}+3e^y-3e^{-y} = 14 \qquad \text{(i)}$$

$$4e^x+4e^{-x}-3e^y-3e^{-y} = 0, \qquad \text{(ii)}$$

$$\text{(i)+(ii)} \Rightarrow 4e^x-3e^{-y} = 7 \qquad \text{(iii)}$$

$$\text{(ii)}-\text{(i)} \Rightarrow 4e^{-x}-3e^y = -7 \qquad \text{(iv)}$$

$$\text{(iii)}\times e^y \Rightarrow 4e^{x+y}-3 = 7e^y \qquad \text{(iii)}'$$

$$\text{(iv)}\times e^x \Rightarrow 4-3e^{x+y} = -7e^x. \qquad \text{(iv)}'$$

Eliminate e^{x+y} from (iii)′ (iv)′ $\therefore\ 3e^y-4e^x = 1\ \therefore\ e^{-y} = \frac{3}{1+4e^x}.$ (v)

Substitute from (v) in, say, (iii) to obtain the quadratic in e^x:

$$2e^{2x}-3e^x-2 = 0 \text{ whence } e^x = 2, \ -\tfrac{1}{2}.$$

Discard the negative root $\because e^x > 0$ always.

$\therefore e^x = 2 \Rightarrow e^y = 3$ in, say, (iii) $\therefore$ solution is $x = \log 2$, $y = \log 3$.

48. For k large compared with a, $e^{a/k} = 1+\dfrac{a}{k}+\dfrac{1}{2}\left(\dfrac{a}{k}\right)^2$, $e^{-a/k} = 1-\dfrac{a}{k}+\dfrac{1}{2}\left(\dfrac{a}{k}\right)^2$ (approx.).

$\therefore \sinh\dfrac{a}{k} = \dfrac{a}{k}$, $\cosh\dfrac{a}{k} = 1+\dfrac{a^2}{2k^2}$.

$\therefore \sinh\dfrac{a}{k} : \sinh\dfrac{b}{k} = \dfrac{a}{k} : \dfrac{b}{k} = a : b$, etc.

$\therefore \sin\lambda : \sin\mu : \sin\nu = a : b : c$ (Sine law).

49. $1+\dfrac{c^2}{2k^2} = \left(1+\dfrac{a^2}{2k^2}\right)\left(1+\dfrac{b^2}{2k^2}\right)-\dfrac{a}{k}\cdot\dfrac{b}{k}\cos\nu$

$\therefore c^2 = a^2+b^2-2ab\cos\nu$ (Cosine law).

50. $\nu = \dfrac{\pi}{2}$ in (49) $\Rightarrow c^2 = a^2+b^2$ (Pythagoras' theorem). Notice that in this case (i.e. a right-angled triangle) $\sin\nu = 1$. $\therefore$ from Exercise 5.48 $\sin\lambda = \dfrac{a}{c}$ suggesting (perhaps) that in the general triangle $\sin\lambda = \dfrac{\sinh\dfrac{a}{k}}{\sinh\dfrac{c}{k}}$, which is in fact correct.

EXERCISES 6

1.

$$\left.\begin{aligned} x\frac{\partial u}{\partial x} &= x\left(\frac{-z}{x^2}+\frac{1}{y}\right) = -\frac{z}{x}+\frac{x}{y} \\ y\frac{\partial u}{\partial y} &= y\left(\frac{1}{z}-\frac{x}{y^2}\right) = \frac{y}{z}-\frac{x}{y} \\ z\frac{\partial u}{\partial z} &= z\left(-\frac{y}{z^2}+\frac{1}{x}\right) = -\frac{y}{z}+\frac{z}{x} \end{aligned}\right\} \qquad \therefore \sum x\frac{\partial u}{\partial x} = 0.$$

2. $\dfrac{\partial z}{\partial y} = \dfrac{xe^{yx}}{x} = e^{yx} \quad \therefore \quad \dfrac{\partial^2 z}{\partial x\partial y} = ye^{yx}$

$$\frac{\partial z}{\partial x} = \frac{x\cdot ye^{yx}-e^{yx}\cdot 1}{x^2} = \frac{e^{yx}(xy-1)}{x^2}$$

$$\therefore \quad \frac{\partial^2 z}{\partial y\partial x} = \frac{(xy-1)\,xe^{yx}+e^{yx}\cdot x}{x^2} = ye^{yx}$$

$$\therefore \quad \frac{\partial^2 z}{\partial x\partial y} = \frac{\partial^2 z}{\partial y\partial x}.$$

$\dfrac{\partial^2}{\partial x\partial y}\left(\dfrac{e^{xy}}{y}\right) = xe^{xy}$ since the roles played by x, y have been interchanged.

3. $\dfrac{\partial f}{\partial x} = -\dfrac{x}{\sqrt{1-yx^2}} \quad \therefore \dfrac{\partial^2 f}{\partial x^2} = \dfrac{-\sqrt{1-yx^2}\cdot 1 + x[-2xy/2\sqrt{1-yx^2}]}{1-yx^2}$

$$= -(1-yx^2)^{-3/2}.$$

4. $\dfrac{\partial u}{\partial x} = z\cdot\dfrac{1}{1+(x/y)^2}\cdot\dfrac{1}{y} = \dfrac{zy}{x^2+y^2} \quad \therefore \dfrac{\partial^2 u}{\partial x^2} = \dfrac{-2xyz}{(x^2+y^2)^2}$

$$\frac{\partial u}{\partial y} = z\cdot\frac{1}{1+(x/y)^2}\cdot\frac{-x}{y^2} = \frac{-zx}{x^2+y^2} \quad \therefore \frac{\partial^2 u}{\partial y^2} = \frac{2xyz}{(x^2+y^2)^2}$$

$$\frac{\partial u}{\partial z} = \tan^{-1}\left(\frac{x}{y}\right) \qquad \therefore \frac{\partial^2 u}{\partial z^2} = 0 \qquad \therefore \sum \frac{\partial^2 u}{\partial x^2} = 0.$$

5. Given $u = \sum a_{\alpha\beta}x^\alpha y^\beta$, write $u_{\alpha\beta} = a_{\alpha\beta}x^\alpha y^\beta$

$$\therefore \frac{\partial u_{\alpha\beta}}{\partial x} = \alpha a_{\alpha\beta}x^{\alpha-1}y^\beta$$

$$\therefore x\frac{\partial u_{\alpha\beta}}{\partial x} = \alpha a_{\alpha\beta}x^\alpha y^\beta. \text{ Similarly, } y\frac{\partial u_{\alpha\beta}}{\partial y} = \beta a_{\alpha\beta}x^\alpha y^\beta.$$

$$\therefore \sum x\frac{\partial u_{\alpha\beta}}{\partial x} = (\alpha+\beta)a_{\alpha\beta}x^\alpha y^\beta$$

$$= nu \quad \text{where } n = \alpha+\beta.$$

6. Given $u = x^3-3x^2y+5xy^2-y^3$

$$\therefore x\frac{\partial u}{\partial x} = 3x^3-6x^2y+5xy^2, \quad y\frac{\partial u}{\partial y} = -3x^2y+10xy^2-3y^3$$

$$\therefore \sum x\frac{\partial u}{\partial x} = 3(x^3-3x^2y+5xy^2-y^3) = 3u.$$

7. $z = x^2\tan^{-1}\left(\dfrac{y}{x}\right) - y^2\tan^{-1}\left(\dfrac{x}{y}\right).$

$$\therefore \frac{\partial z}{\partial x} = \frac{x^2}{1+y^2/x^2}\cdot\frac{-y}{x^2} + 2x\tan^{-1}\left(\frac{y}{x}\right) - \frac{y^2}{1+x^2/y^2}\cdot\frac{1}{y}$$

$$= \frac{-yx^2}{x^2+y^2} - \frac{y^3}{x^2+y^2} + 2x\tan^{-1}\left(\frac{y}{x}\right) = -y+2x\tan^{-1}\left(\frac{y}{x}\right)$$

$$\therefore \frac{\partial^2 z}{\partial y\partial x} = -1+2x\cdot\frac{1}{x}\cdot\frac{1}{1+y^2/x^2} = -1+\frac{2x^2}{x^2+y^2} = \frac{x^2-y^2}{x^2+y^2}.$$

Check, obtaining $\dfrac{\partial z}{\partial y}$ first.

8. $\dfrac{\partial V}{\partial r} = \dfrac{\partial V}{\partial x}\dfrac{\partial x}{\partial r} + \dfrac{\partial V}{\partial y}\dfrac{\partial y}{\partial r} = \cos\theta\dfrac{\partial V}{\partial x} + \sin\theta\dfrac{\partial V}{\partial y} \qquad$ (i)

$$\frac{\partial V}{\partial \theta} = \frac{\partial V}{\partial x}\frac{\partial x}{\partial \theta} + \frac{\partial V}{\partial y}\frac{\partial y}{\partial \theta} = r\left(-\sin\theta\frac{\partial V}{\partial x} + \cos\theta\frac{\partial V}{\partial y}\right). \qquad \text{(ii)}$$

$$\left.\begin{aligned} &\text{(i)}\times\cos\theta - \text{(ii)}\times\frac{\sin\theta}{r} \Rightarrow \frac{\partial V}{\partial x} = \cos\theta\frac{\partial V}{\partial r} - \frac{\sin\theta}{r}\frac{\partial V}{\partial \theta} \\ &\text{(i)}\times\sin\theta + \text{(ii)}\times\frac{\cos\theta}{r} \Rightarrow \frac{\partial V}{\partial \theta} = \sin\theta\frac{\partial V}{\partial r} + \frac{\cos\theta}{r}\frac{\partial V}{\partial \theta} \end{aligned}\right\}.$$

[Further partial differentiation and simplification lead to

$$\frac{\partial^2 V}{\partial x^2}+\frac{\partial^2 V}{\partial y^2} = \frac{\partial^2 V}{\partial r^2}+\frac{1}{r}\,\frac{\partial V}{\partial r}+\frac{1}{r^2}\,\frac{\partial^2 V}{\partial \theta^2},$$

i.e. we have transformed from Cartesian to polar coordinates.]

9. If $z = f(u)+g(v)$, where $u = x-ct$, $v = x+ct$, then

$$\begin{cases} \dfrac{\partial u}{\partial t} = -c, & \dfrac{\partial v}{\partial t} = c \\ \dfrac{\partial u}{\partial x} = 1, & \dfrac{\partial v}{\partial x} = 1. \end{cases}$$

$$\therefore \begin{cases} \dfrac{\partial z}{\partial x} = \dfrac{\partial}{\partial u}f(u)\,\dfrac{\partial u}{\partial x}+\dfrac{\partial}{\partial v}g(v)\,\dfrac{\partial v}{\partial x} = f'(u)+g'(v) \\ \dfrac{\partial^2 z}{\partial x^2} = f''(u)+g''(v) \\ \dfrac{\partial z}{\partial t} = \dfrac{\partial}{\partial u}f(u)\,\dfrac{\partial u}{\partial t}+\dfrac{\partial}{\partial v}g(v)\,\dfrac{\partial v}{\partial t} = -cf'(u)+cg'(v) \\ \dfrac{\partial^2 z}{\partial t^2} = c^2 f''(u)+c^2 g''(v) \end{cases}$$

$$\therefore \quad \frac{\partial^2 z}{\partial t^2} = c^2\,\frac{\partial^2 z}{\partial x^2}. \qquad \left[\text{Also } \frac{\partial^2 z}{\partial u \partial v} = 0.\right]$$

10. If $z = e^u \cos v$, where $u = x+y$, $v = x-y$, i.e. $z = e^{x+y}\cos(x-y)$,

then $\dfrac{\partial u}{\partial x} = 1$, $\dfrac{\partial v}{\partial x} = 1$, $\dfrac{\partial u}{\partial y} = 1$, $\dfrac{\partial v}{\partial y} = -1$.

$$\therefore \begin{cases} \dfrac{\partial z}{\partial x} = e^{x+y}\cdot -\sin(x-y)+e^{x+y}\cos(x-y) \\ \qquad = e^{x+y}\{\cos(x-y)-\sin(x-y)\} \\ \dfrac{\partial z}{\partial y} = e^{x+y}\{\cos(x-y)+\sin(x-y)\}. \end{cases}$$

11. Given $z = (x-3)^2+y^2$, where $x = 5\sin t$, $y = 4\cos t$

$$\therefore \begin{cases} \dfrac{\partial z}{\partial x} = 2(x-3) \\ \dfrac{\partial z}{\partial y} = 2y \end{cases} \qquad \therefore \begin{cases} dx = 5\cos t\,dt \\ dy = -4\sin t\,dt. \end{cases}$$

Hence,
$$\begin{aligned} \frac{dz}{dt} &= \frac{\partial z}{\partial x}\,\frac{dx}{dt}+\frac{\partial z}{\partial y}\,\frac{dy}{dt} \\ &= 2(x-3)\cdot 5\cos t-8y\sin t \\ &= 2(5\sin t-3)\cdot 5\cos t-32\sin t\cos t \\ &= 6\cos t(3\sin t-5) \\ &= 0 \text{ when } \cos t = 0 \text{ or } \sin t = \tfrac{5}{3} \text{ (impossible)} \end{aligned}$$

$$\text{i.e. } t = \frac{\pi}{2}, \frac{3\pi}{2}.$$

Further, $\dfrac{d^2z}{dt^2} = 18\cos^2 t - 6\sin t(3\sin t - 5)$

$$= 18\cos 2t + 30\sin t$$

$$\begin{cases} > 0 \text{ when } t = \pi/2, \\ < 0 \text{ when } t = 3\pi/2. \end{cases}$$

Thus, the maximum value occurs when $t = 3\pi/2$, i.e. $x = -5$, $y = 0$; so $z = 64$, i.e. $\sqrt{z} = 8$.

The minimum value occurs when $t = \pi/2$, i.e. $x = 5$, $y = 0$; so $z = 4$, i.e., $\sqrt{z} = 2$. $\therefore$ maximum and minimum focal distances SP (S a focus) are 8 and 2, and occur when P is at A' and A, respectively. (See Fig. 79.)

12. $\dfrac{\partial V}{\partial x} = e^{-ht}\dfrac{\partial W}{\partial x} \quad \therefore \dfrac{\partial^2 V}{\partial x^2} = e^{-ht}\dfrac{\partial^2 W}{\partial x^2}$

$\dfrac{\partial V}{\partial t} = -he^{-ht}W + e^{-ht}\dfrac{\partial W}{\partial t} \quad \therefore$ the given equation transforms into

$-he^{-ht}W + e^{-ht}\dfrac{\partial W}{\partial t} = e^{-ht}\dfrac{\partial^2 W}{\partial x^2} - he^{-ht}W$ i.e. $\dfrac{\partial W}{\partial t} = \dfrac{\partial^2 W}{\partial x^2}$.

13. $\dfrac{\partial W}{\partial t} = nAe^{-kx}\cos p \quad (p = nt - kx \text{ for brevity})$

$$\frac{\partial W}{\partial x} = -kAe^{-kx}\sin p - kAe^{-kx}\cos p$$

$$\therefore \quad \frac{\partial^2 W}{\partial x^2} = k^2Ae^{-kx}\sin p + k^2Ae^{-kx}\cos p + k^2Ae^{-kx}\cos p - k^2Ae^{-kx}\sin p$$

$$= 2k^2Ae^{-kx}\cos p$$

$$\therefore \quad \frac{\partial W}{\partial t} + \frac{\partial^2 W}{\partial x^2} \Rightarrow n = 2k^2.$$

14. $\dfrac{\partial V}{\partial r} = (nr^{n-1} - nr^{-n-1})\sin n\theta$

$$\therefore \quad \frac{\partial^2 V}{\partial r^2} = \{n(n-1)r^{n-2} + n(n+1)r^{-n-2}\}\sin n\theta$$

$$\frac{\partial V}{\partial \theta} = (r^n + r^{-n})\cdot n\cos n\theta$$

$$\therefore \quad \frac{\partial^2 V}{\partial \theta^2} = (r^n + r^{-n})\cdot -n^2\sin n\theta$$

$$\therefore \quad \frac{\partial^2 V}{\partial r^2} + \frac{1}{r}\frac{\partial V}{\partial r} + \frac{1}{r^2}\frac{\partial^2 V}{\partial \theta^2}$$

$$= \sin n\theta\{r^{n-2}[n(n-1) + n - n^2] + r^{-n-2}[n(n+1) - n - n^2]\} = 0.$$

15. $\dfrac{\partial u}{\partial x} = \dfrac{f'}{y}, \ \dfrac{\partial u}{\partial y} = \dfrac{-xf'}{y^2} \quad \therefore x\dfrac{\partial u}{\partial x} + y\dfrac{\partial u}{\partial y} = 0.$

16. The section is the ellipse $\dfrac{x^2}{a^2} + \dfrac{y^2}{b^2} = 1$. Its gradient at any point is $\dfrac{dy}{dx} = \dfrac{-b^2x}{a^2y}$ $\left(= \dfrac{\partial y}{\partial x}\right.$, as we are thinking of the ellipse as formed from a surface $f(x, y, z) = 0$ with z temporarily held constant.)

17. $v = \frac{RT}{p}$, $T = \frac{pv}{R}$, $p = \frac{RT}{v}$.

$$\therefore \frac{\partial v}{\partial T}\cdot\frac{\partial T}{\partial p}\cdot\frac{\partial p}{\partial v} = \frac{R}{p}\cdot\frac{v}{R}\cdot\frac{-RT}{v^2} = -1 \quad \because pv = RT.$$

[Note that $\frac{\partial v}{\partial T}\frac{\partial T}{\partial p} = -\frac{\partial v}{\partial p}$. Obtain some similar results.]

18. From $F(x, y, z) = 0$ form the total differential.

$\therefore 0 = dF = a\,dx + b\,dy + c\,dz$ say where a, b, c stand for partial derivatives whose actual nature, as we will see, is irrelevant.

$$\therefore dx = \frac{-b}{a}dy - \frac{c}{a}dz \text{ (expressing the total differential } dx).$$

$$\therefore \frac{\partial x}{\partial y} = -\frac{b}{a},\ \frac{\partial x}{\partial z} = -\frac{c}{a} \text{ (using the expression for the total differential } dx).$$

Similarly, $\frac{\partial y}{\partial z} = -\frac{c}{b}$, $\frac{\partial z}{\partial x} = -\frac{a}{c}$.

$$\therefore \frac{\partial x}{\partial y}\cdot\frac{\partial y}{\partial z}\cdot\frac{\partial z}{\partial x} = -\frac{b}{a}\cdot -\frac{c}{b}\cdot -\frac{a}{c} = -1.$$

19–25. No detailed solution offered: calculations are straightforward, but involved.

EXERCISES 7

1. $$\int \frac{dx}{\sqrt{x(1-x)}} = \int \frac{d(x-\frac{1}{2})}{\sqrt{\frac{1}{4}-(x-\frac{1}{2})^2}} = \sin^{-1}\left(\frac{x-\frac{1}{2}}{\frac{1}{2}}\right)+c = \sin^{-1}(2x-1)+c$$

Alternative method.

$$\int \frac{dx}{\sqrt{x(1-x)}} = \int \frac{2\sin\theta\cos\theta}{\sin\theta\cos\theta}d\theta$$

[where $x = \sin^2\theta$
$\therefore dx = 2\sin\theta\cos\theta\, d\theta$

$$= 2\theta + c' = 2\sin^{-1}\sqrt{x}+c'.$$

[Verify that these two answers are, indeed, equivalent.]

2. $$\int \frac{x\,dx}{(x^2+9)^{5/2}} = \frac{1}{2}\int y^{-5/2}\,dy \text{ where } y = x^2+9$$

$$\therefore dy = 2x\,dx = \frac{1}{2}\cdot\frac{-2}{3}\cdot y^{-3/2}+c = \frac{-1}{3(x^2+9)^{3/2}}+c.$$

3. $$\int \frac{dx}{\sin^2 x\cos^2 x} = \int \frac{(\cos^2 x+\sin^2 x)}{\sin^2 x\cos^2 x}dx \text{ writing } \cos^2 x+\sin^2 x \text{ for } 1$$

$$= \int \operatorname{cosec}^2 x\,dx + \int \sec^2 x\,dx = -\cot x + \tan x + c$$

or $$\int \frac{dx}{\sin^2 x\cos^2 x} = \int \frac{4dx}{(\sin^2 2x)} = 4\int \operatorname{cosec}^2 2x\,dx = -2\cot 2x + c.$$

[Verify that these two answers are really equivalent.]

4. $\int \frac{dx}{x \log x} = \int \frac{d \log x}{\log x} = \log \log x + c \quad \left[\because d \log u = \frac{du}{u}\right].$

5. $\int \frac{dx}{x(\log x)^2} = \int \frac{d \log x}{(\log x)^2} = -\frac{1}{\log x} + c.$

6. $\int \frac{(\tan^{-1} x)^3\, dx}{1+x^2} = \int (\tan^{-1} x)^3\, d \tan^{-1} x = \frac{1}{4}(\tan^{-1} x)^4 + c$

$$\left[\because d \tan^{-1} x = \frac{dx}{1+x^2}\right].$$

7. $\int \sin x \cos x\, dx = \frac{1}{2} \int \sin 2x\, dx = -\frac{1}{4} \cos 2x + K$

or $\int \sin x \cos x\, dx = \int \sin x d(\sin x) = \frac{1}{2} \sin^2 x + C \quad (\because d \sin x = \cos x\, dx).$

$$\left[\text{Note } C = K - \frac{1}{4}.\right]$$

8. $\int \frac{\sin x}{\cos^2 x}\, dx = -\int \frac{d \cos x}{\cos^2 x} = \frac{1}{\cos x} + c = \sec x + c \; [\because d \cos x = -\sin x\, dx].$

9. $\int \operatorname{cosec}^2 x\, dx = -\int \cot x + C.$

[This is almost a standard integral (§ 24) and should be recognisable.]

10. $\int \frac{dx}{(1-x)\sqrt{1-x^2}} = \int \frac{-\sin t\, dt}{(1-\cos t)\sin t}$ where $x = \cos t$

$\therefore dx = -\sin t\, dt = -\frac{1}{2} \int \frac{dt}{\sin^2\left(\frac{t}{2}\right)} = \cot \frac{t}{2} + c$ (from Exercise 7.9) $= \sqrt{\frac{1+x}{1-x}} + c.$

11. $\int \frac{\sqrt{1-x^2}}{x^4}\, dx = -\int \frac{\sin \theta \sin \theta\, d\theta}{\cos^4 \theta}$ (where $x = \cos \theta \; \therefore dx = -\sin \theta\, d\theta$)

$= -\int \frac{\sin^2 \theta}{\cos^4 \theta}\, d\theta = -\int \tan^2 \theta \sec^2 \theta\, d\theta = -\int \tan^2 \theta\, d(\tan \theta) \quad \because d \tan \theta = \sec^2 \theta\, d\theta$

$$= -\frac{1}{3} \tan^3 \theta + c = -\frac{(1-x^2)^{3/2}}{3x^3} + c.$$

12. $\int \frac{dx}{\sqrt{x-2}} = 2 \int \frac{q\, dq}{q-2}$ (where $x = q^2 \; \therefore dx = 2q\, dq$)

$= 2 \int \left(1 + \frac{2}{q-2}\right) dq = 2(q + 2 \log \{q-2\}) + c = 2\sqrt{x} + 4 \log (\sqrt{x} - 2) + c.$

13. $\int \frac{\sqrt{1+\log x}}{x}\, dx = \int \sqrt{y}\, dy$ putting $y = 1 + \log x \; \therefore dy = \frac{dx}{x}$

$$= \frac{2y^{3/2}}{3} + c = \frac{2(1+\log x)^{3/2}}{3} + c.$$

14. $\int \cos 2x \cos 4x\, dx = \frac{1}{2} \int \cos 6x\, dx + \frac{1}{2} \int \cos 2x\, dx = \frac{\sin 6x}{12} + \frac{\sin 2x}{4} + c$

or $\int \cos 2x \cos 4x\, dx = \int \cos 2x(1 - 2 \sin^2 2x)\, dx = \frac{1}{2} \sin 2x - \frac{1}{3} \sin^3 2x + c.$

[These alternative answers are equivalent—verify.]

15. $\int x \sec^2 x\, dx = \int x\, d \tan x = x \tan x - \int \tan x\, dx = x \tan x - \log \sec x + C$ integrating by parts.

16. $\displaystyle\int \frac{dx}{x^2+2x+2} = \int \frac{d(x+1)}{(x+1)^2+1} = \tan^{-1}(x+1)+C.$

17. $\displaystyle\int \frac{dx}{\sqrt{x^2+2x+2}} = \int \frac{d(x+1)}{\sqrt{(x+1)^2+1}} = \log\left(x+1+\sqrt{x^2+2x+2}\right)+C.$

18. $\displaystyle\int \frac{x\, dx}{x^2+2x+2} = \frac{1}{2}\int \frac{2x+2}{x^2+2x+2}\, dx - \int \frac{dx}{x^2+2x+2}$

$= \frac{1}{2}\log(x^2+2x+2) - \tan^{-1}(x+1)+C = \log\sqrt{x^2+2x+1} - \tan^{-1}(x+1)+C.$

19. $\displaystyle\int \frac{2x-3}{x^2-x-42}\, dx = \frac{11}{13}\int \frac{dx}{x-7} + \frac{15}{13}\int \frac{dx}{x+6}$ using partial fractions

$\displaystyle = \frac{11}{13}\log(x-7) + \frac{15}{13}\log(x+6)+C = \log\{k(x-7)^{11/13}(x+6)^{15/13}\}$ where $\log k = C.$

20. $\displaystyle I = \int \sqrt{a^2+x^2}\, dx = x\sqrt{a^2+x^2} - \int \frac{x\cdot 2x}{2\sqrt{a^2+x^2}}\, dx$ integrating by parts

$\displaystyle = x\sqrt{a^2+x^2} - \int \frac{a^2+x^2}{\sqrt{a^2+x^2}}\, dx + \int \frac{a^2\, dx}{\sqrt{a^2+x^2}}$

$\displaystyle \therefore 2I = x\sqrt{a^2+x^2} + a^2\int \frac{dx}{\sqrt{a^2+x^2}} \quad \therefore I = \frac{x}{2}\sqrt{a^2+x^2} + \frac{a^2}{2}\log\left(x+\sqrt{a^2+x^2}\right)+C.$

21. $\displaystyle\int \frac{\sin \log x}{x}\, dx = \int \sin \log x\, d(\log x) = -\cos \log x + C.$

22. $\displaystyle\int \frac{dx}{1+\cos^2 x} = \int \frac{\sec^2 x\, dx}{\sec^2 x+1} = \int \frac{d \tan x}{2+\tan^2 x} = \frac{1}{\sqrt{2}}\tan^{-1}\left(\frac{\tan x}{\sqrt{2}}\right)+C.$

23. $\displaystyle\int \frac{dx}{1+\sin x} = \int \frac{1-\sin x}{1-\sin^2 x}\, dx = \int \frac{dx}{\cos^2 x} - \int \frac{\sin x}{\cos^2 x}\, dx = \tan x - \sec x + C.$

24. $\displaystyle\int \frac{x \sin^{-1} x}{\sqrt{1-x^2}}\, dx = \int y \sin y\, dy \ \Bigg($where $y = \sin^{-1} x$, i.e. $x = \sin y$

$\displaystyle \therefore dy = \frac{dx}{\sqrt{1-x^2}}\Bigg) = -\int y\, d(\cos y) = -y\cos y + \int \cos y\, dy$

$= -y\cos y + \sin y + C = -\sqrt{1-x^2}\sin^{-1} x + x + C.$

25. $\int x^2 \cos x\, dx = \int x^2\, d(\sin x) = x^2 \sin x - 2\int x \sin x\, dx$

$= x^2 \sin x + 2\int x\, d(\cos x) = x^2\sin x + 2x\cos x - 2\int \cos x\, dx$

$= x^2\sin x + 2x\cos x - 2\sin x + C = (x^2-2)\sin x + 2x\cos x + C.$

26. $\displaystyle\int x^2 e^{3x}\, dx = \frac{1}{3}\int x^2 \frac{de^{3x}}{dx}\, dx = \frac{1}{3}x^2e^{3x} - \frac{2}{3}\int xe^{3x}\, dx$

$\displaystyle = \frac{x^2e^{3x}}{3} - \frac{2}{9}\int x\frac{de^{3x}}{dx}\, dx = \frac{x^2e^{3x}}{3} - \frac{2xe^{3x}}{9} + \frac{2}{9}\int e^{3x}\, dx$

$\displaystyle = \frac{x^2e^{3x}}{3} - \frac{2xe^{3x}}{9} + \frac{2e^{3x}}{27} + C = \frac{e^{3x}}{3}\left(x^2 - \frac{2}{3}x + \frac{2}{9}\right)+C.$

27. $\displaystyle\int \frac{dx}{(e^x-1)^2} = \int \frac{dy}{y^2(y+1)}$ putting $y = e^x - 1 \quad \therefore\ dx = \dfrac{dy}{1+y}$

$$= \int \left(\frac{1}{y^2} - \frac{1}{y} + \frac{1}{1+y}\right) dy = -\frac{1}{y} - \log y + \log(1+y) + \log C$$

$$= -\frac{1}{e^x-1} + \log\left\{\frac{ce^x}{e^x-1}\right\} \quad \text{using partial fractions.}$$

28. $\displaystyle\frac{1}{y(y-1)(2y-1)} = \frac{A}{y} + \frac{B}{y-1} + \frac{C}{2y-1} = \frac{(2A+2B+C)y^2 - (3A+B+C)y + A}{y(y-1)(2y-1)}$

Equate coefficients of y^2, y, constants

$$\therefore\ 2A+2B+C = 0, \quad 3A+B+C = 0, \quad A = 1.$$

Solving, we have $A = 1, \quad B = 1, \quad C = -4$

$$\therefore\ \frac{1}{y(y-1)(2y-1)} = \frac{1}{y} + \frac{1}{y-1} - \frac{4}{2y-1}.$$

$$\therefore\ -t = \int \frac{dy}{y(y-1)(2y-1)} = \int \frac{dy}{y} + \int \frac{dy}{y-1} - \int \frac{4dy}{2y-1}$$

$$= \log y + \log(y-1) - 2\log(2y-1) + \log K = \log\left\{\frac{Ky(y-1)}{(2y-1)^2}\right\}$$

$$\therefore\ t = \log\left\{\frac{(2y-1)^2}{Ky(y-1)}\right\}.$$

29. $\displaystyle\int x^2 \sqrt{a^2-x^2}\, dx$

$$= a^4 \int \sin^2 t \cos^2 t\, dt$$

$$= \frac{a^4}{4} \int \sin^2 2t\, dt$$

$$= \frac{a^4}{4} \int \left(\frac{1-\cos 4t}{2}\right) dt$$

$$= \frac{a^4 t}{8} - \frac{a^4}{8\cdot 4} \sin 4t + C$$

$$= \frac{a^4 t}{8} - \frac{a^4 \cdot 2 \cdot 2 \sin t \cdot \cos t \cdot \cos 2t}{8 \cdot 4} + C$$

where $x = a \sin t$

$\therefore\ dx = a \cos t\, dt$

and $\sin t = \dfrac{x}{a}$

$\therefore\ \cos t = \dfrac{\sqrt{a^2-x^2}}{a}$

$\therefore\ \cos 2t = 1 - 2\dfrac{x^2}{a^2}$

$= \dfrac{a^2-2x^2}{a^2}$

$$= \frac{a^4}{8} \sin^{-1}\left(\frac{x}{a}\right) - \frac{a^4}{8} \cdot \frac{x}{a} \cdot \frac{\sqrt{a^2-x^2}}{a} \cdot \frac{(a^2-2x^2)}{a^2} + C$$

$$= \frac{a^4}{8} \sin^{-1}\left(\frac{x}{a}\right) + \frac{x}{8}(2x^2-a^2)\sqrt{a^2-x^2} + C.$$

30. $\displaystyle\int \frac{dx}{(a-x)\sqrt{b-x}} = 2b \int \frac{\sin\theta \cos\theta\, d\theta}{(a-b\sin^2\theta)\sqrt{b}\cos\theta}$

$$= -2\sqrt{b} \int \frac{d\cos\theta}{a-b+b\cos^2\theta}$$

$$= \frac{-2}{\sqrt{b}} \int \frac{d\cos\theta}{(a/b-1)+\cos^2\theta}$$

where $x = b\sin^2\theta$

$\therefore\ dx = 2b \sin\theta \cos\theta$

and $\sin\theta = \sqrt{\dfrac{x}{b}}$

$\therefore\ \cos\theta = \sqrt{\dfrac{b-x}{b}}$

$$= \frac{-2}{\sqrt{b}} \cdot \frac{1}{\sqrt{a/b-1}} \tan^{-1}\left(\frac{\cos\theta}{\sqrt{a/b}-1}\right)+C$$

$$= \frac{-2}{\sqrt{\dfrac{b(a-b)}{b}}} \tan^{-1}\left(\frac{\sqrt{b-x}}{\sqrt{b}\sqrt{a-b}/\sqrt{b}}\right)+C$$

$$= \frac{-2}{\sqrt{a-b}} \tan^{-1}\sqrt{\frac{b-x}{a-b}}+C.$$

EXERCISES 8

1. $\int x\,dx+\int y\,dy = 0 \quad \therefore \frac{x^2}{2}+\frac{y^2}{2}-C = 0$ i.e. $x^2+y^2 = 2C.$

As C takes on different values, this equation represents a family of concentric circles.

2. $\sqrt{1-x^2}\,dy = x\,dx \quad \therefore \int dy = \int \frac{x}{\sqrt{1-x^2}}\,dx$

$$\therefore y = -\sqrt{1-x^2}+C \qquad (1)$$

i.e. $$(y-C)^2+x^2 = 1.$$

As C takes on different values, the equation (1) represents a family of *semi*-circles [since $y = C-\sqrt{1-x^2}$ (not $\pm$)] with centres $(0, C)$ and radius unity.

3. $\tan y\,dx+\tan x\,dy = 0 \ldots$ (i), or multiply throughout by $\cos x \cos y$

$\therefore \int \cot x\,dx+\int \cot y\,dy = 0$

$\therefore \log \sin x+\log \sin y = \log C$

$\therefore \log (\sin x \sin y) = \log C$

$\therefore \sin x \sin y = C$

$\therefore \sin y \cos x\,dx+\sin x \cos y\,dy = 0 \qquad$ (ii)

i.e. $d/dx\,(\sin x \cos y) = 0$

i.e. $\sin x \sin y = C.$

(Equation (ii) is an exact differential equation $\because \partial M/\partial y = \cos x \cos y = \partial N/\partial x$ but its original form (i) is not exact.)

4. As in Example 33, $u = ke^{at/b}$.

5. Let y be the quantity of bacteria present at time t

$\therefore dy/dt = ky \quad \therefore y = ce^{kt}$ (Example 33).

$t = 0 \Rightarrow c = y_0;\ t = 1 \Rightarrow 2y_0 = y_0e^k \quad \therefore e^k = 2 \quad \therefore$ solution is $y = y_0 \cdot 2^t$.

At time t_1 (noon), $y_1 = y_0 2^{t_1}$. At time t_2 (midnight), $y_2 = y_0 2^{t_1+12} = 2^{12}y_1$

$\therefore$ the population will have increased by the factor 2^{12}.

6. $$\frac{ds}{dr} = \frac{ds}{dt}\bigg/\frac{dr}{dt} = \frac{kp}{-k(1-p)} = \frac{p}{p-1} = \frac{s/(r+s)}{-r/(r+s)} = -\frac{s}{r}$$

$\therefore \frac{dr}{r} = \frac{-ds}{s} \quad \therefore \log r = -\log s+\log c \quad \therefore rs = c.$

7. $$\frac{ds}{dt} = \frac{ks}{r+s} = \frac{ks}{c/s+s} = \frac{ks^2}{s^2+c} = kp \text{ using Exercise 8.6.}$$

$\therefore s^2 = s^2p+cp \quad \therefore s^2 = cp(1-p)^{-1}.$

8. $\dfrac{dI}{E-RI} = \dfrac{dt}{L} \quad \therefore \; -\dfrac{1}{R}\log(E-RI) = \dfrac{t}{L}+C.$

Initially, $-\dfrac{1}{R}\log E = C. \quad \therefore \; -\dfrac{R}{L}t = \log\left(\dfrac{E-RI}{E}\right) = \log\left(1-\dfrac{R}{E}t\right)$

$\therefore \; I = \dfrac{E}{R}\left(1-e^{-\frac{R}{L}t}\right).$

9. $\displaystyle\int_0^1 \frac{1-x^2}{1+x^2}\,dx = \int_0^1\left(-1+\frac{2}{1+x^2}\right)dx = \Big[-x\Big]_0^1 + 2\Big[\tan^{-1}x\Big]_0^1 = -1+2\cdot\frac{\pi}{4} = \frac{\pi}{2}-1.$

10. $\displaystyle\int_1^2 \frac{dx}{x(x+1)} = \int_1^2\left(\frac{1}{x}-\frac{1}{x+1}\right)dx = \Big[\log x - \log(x+1)\Big]_1^2 = \log\left(\frac{4}{3}\right).$

11. $\displaystyle I = \int_0^\infty e^{-x}\sin x\,dx = \Big[-e^{-x}\cos x\Big]_0^\infty - \int_0^\infty e^{-x}\,d\sin x = 1 - \Big[e^{-x}\sin x\Big]_0^\infty$

$$-\int_0^\infty e^{-x}\sin x\,dx$$

$$\therefore \; 2I = 1-0 \quad \therefore \; I = \tfrac{1}{2}.$$

12. $\displaystyle\int_0^1 \sin^{-1}x\,dx = \Big[x\sin^{-1}x\Big]_0^1 - \int_0^1 \frac{x}{\sqrt{1-x^2}}\,dx = \frac{\pi}{2} + \Big[\sqrt{1-x^2}\Big]_0^1 = \frac{\pi}{2}-1.$

[Observe the need for a limiting process at $x = 1$ in the improper integral in the first step.]

13. $\displaystyle\int_0^{\log 2} \sqrt{e^x-1}\,dx = \int_1 \frac{\sqrt{y-1}}{y}\,dy$ putting $y = e^x$ i.e., $x = \log y \;\therefore\; dx = \dfrac{dy}{y}$

$\displaystyle = 2\int_0^{\pi/4} \tan^2\theta\,d\theta$ putting $y = \sec^2\theta \;\therefore\; \dfrac{dy}{d\theta} = \dfrac{2\sin\theta}{\cos^3\theta}$

$\displaystyle = 2\int_0^{\pi/4} (\sec^2\theta-1)\,d\theta = 2\Big[\tan\theta-\theta\Big]_0^{\pi/4} = 2\left(1-\frac{\pi}{4}\right) = 2-\frac{\pi}{2},$

or

make the substitution $t^2 = e^x-1$. [You should try this alternative method yourself. It is a useful exercise.]

14. $\displaystyle\int_0^1 x\log x\,dx = \frac{1}{2}\int_0^1 \log x\,\frac{dx^2}{dx}\,dx = \frac{1}{2}\Big[x^2\log x\Big]_0^1 - \frac{1}{2}\int_0^1 x^2\cdot\frac{1}{x}\,dx$

$\displaystyle = 0-\frac{1}{2}\left[\frac{x^2}{2}\right]_0^1 = -\frac{1}{4}.$

[Note: At $x = 0$, $x \log x$ is indeterminate (form $0 \cdot -\infty$), so a limiting process ($\lim_{x\to 0} x^2 \log x = 0$) is really involved. Also $x \to 0 \Rightarrow x \to 0_+$ only, in this problem.]

15. $\dfrac{1}{x^2(x+1)} = \dfrac{1}{x^2} - \dfrac{1}{x} + \dfrac{1}{x+1}$ (partial fractions)

$$\therefore \int_1^\infty \frac{1}{x^2(x+1)} = \left[-\frac{1}{x} - \log x + \log(x+1)\right]_1^\infty = \left[-\frac{1}{x} + \log\left(\frac{1+x}{x}\right)\right]_1^\infty$$

$$= 0 + \lim_{x\to\infty} \log\left(\frac{1+x}{x}\right) + 1 - \log 2 = 1 - \log 2$$

$$\because \log\left(\frac{1+x}{x}\right) = \log\left(1+\frac{1}{x}\right) \to 0 \text{ as } x \to \infty.$$

16. $$\int_0^1 (\log x)^2\, dx = \int_0^1 (\log x)^2 \frac{dx}{dx}\, dx = \Big[x(\log x)^2\Big]_1^1 - \int_0^1 x \cdot \frac{2\log x}{x}\, dx$$

$$= 0 - 2\Big[x \log x\Big]_0^1 + 2\int_0^1 x \cdot \frac{1}{x}\, dx = 2.$$

17. $$\int_0^1 \frac{dx}{e^x + e^{-x}} = \int_1^e \frac{de^x}{1+e^{2x}} = \Big[\tan^{-1}(e^x)\Big]_0^{x=1} = \tan^{-1} e - \frac{\pi}{4}.$$

18. $$\int_0^a \sqrt{\frac{x}{a-x}}\, dx = \int_0^{\pi/2} \frac{\sqrt{a}\sin t \cdot 2a \sin t \cdot \cos t\, dt}{\sqrt{a}\cos t} \quad \text{where } x = a\sin^2 t$$

$$\therefore dx = 2a \sin t \cos t\, dt$$

$$= 2a \int_0^{\pi/2} \sin^2 t\, dt = a\left[t - \frac{\sin 2t}{2}\right]_0^{\pi/2} = \frac{\pi a}{2}.$$

[Notice that the integral is improper at $x = a$; hence a limiting process is involved.]

19. $$\int \log_2 x\, dx = \int \frac{\log_e x}{\log_e 2}\, dx = \log_2 e \int \log_e x \frac{dx}{dx}\, dx$$

$$= \log_2 e(x \log_e x - x) = x(\log_2 x - \log_2 e) = x \log_2\left(\frac{x}{e}\right)$$

$$\therefore \int_1^e \log_2 x\, dx = \left[x \log_2\left(\frac{x}{e}\right)\right]_1^e = e \log_2 1 - \log_2\left(\frac{1}{e}\right) = \log_2 e.$$

20. $$\int_{\sqrt{3}}^{2\sqrt{3}} t^3(t^2-3)^{3/2}\, dt = \tfrac{1}{2}\int_0^9 (y+3)y^{3/2}\, dy \quad \text{putting } y = t^2 - 3 \quad \therefore dy = 2t\, dt$$

$$= \tfrac{1}{2}\int_0^9 (y^{5/2} + 3y^{3/2})\, dy = \tfrac{1}{2}\left[\tfrac{2}{7}y^{7/2} + 3 \cdot \tfrac{2}{5}y^{5/2}\right]_0^9$$

$$= \left[\frac{y^{7/2}}{7} + \frac{3y^{5/2}}{5}\right]_0^9 = \frac{3^7}{7} + \frac{3^6}{5} = \frac{16\,038}{35} = 458\frac{8}{35} \text{ on calculation.}$$

21. $\displaystyle\int_0^{\pi/4} \frac{\cos\sqrt{x}}{\sqrt{x}}\,dx = 2\int_0^{\pi/4} d\sin\sqrt{x} = \Big[2\sin\sqrt{x}\Big]_0^{\pi/4} = 2\sin\left\{\frac{\sqrt{\pi}}{2}\right\}.$

[An improper integral at $x = 0$, hence a limiting process is involved.]

22. $\displaystyle\int_{\pi/4}^{\pi/2} \frac{dx}{\sin x} = -\int_{\pi/4}^{0} \frac{dy}{\cos y}$ putting $x = \frac{\pi}{2} - y \;\therefore\; dx = -dy$

$$= \int_0^{\pi/4} \frac{dy}{\cos y} = \int_0^{\pi/4} \frac{dx}{\cos x} \text{ since the choice of variable is immaterial}$$

$$= \left[\log\tan\left(\frac{x}{2}+\frac{\pi}{4}\right)\right]_0^{\pi/4} = \log\tan\left(\frac{3\pi}{8}\right).$$

Now $\tan\frac{\pi}{8} = \tan\left(\frac{\pi}{4}-\frac{\pi}{8}\right) = \frac{1-\tan\pi/8}{1+\tan\pi/8}$ whence $\tan^2\left(\frac{\pi}{8}\right)+2\tan\frac{\pi}{8}-1 = 0$

$\therefore\; \tan\frac{\pi}{8} = -1\pm\sqrt{2}$ i.e. $\tan\frac{\pi}{8} = \sqrt{2}-1 \;\because\; \tan\frac{\pi}{8} > 0.$

$\therefore\; \tan\frac{3\pi}{8} = \tan\left(\frac{\pi}{4}+\frac{\pi}{8}\right) = \frac{1+\tan\pi/8}{1-\tan\pi/8} = \frac{\sqrt{2}}{2-\sqrt{2}}\cdot\frac{2+\sqrt{2}}{2+\sqrt{2}} = \sqrt{2}+1.$

$\therefore\; \displaystyle\int_0^{\pi/4} \frac{dx}{\cos x} = \log(\sqrt{2}+1).$

23. $P = K\Big[\log(x+\sqrt{x^2+a^2}) - \log(x+\sqrt{x^2+b^2})\Big]_0^\infty = K\left[\log\left\{\frac{x+\sqrt{x^2+a^2}}{x+\sqrt{x^2+b^2}}\right\}\right]_0^\infty$

$$= K\left\{\lim_{x\to\infty}\log\left(\frac{1+\sqrt{1+a^2/x^2}}{1+\sqrt{1+b^2/x^2}}\right) - \log\left(\frac{a}{b}\right)\right\} = K\left\{\log\left(\frac{2}{2}\right)+\log\left(\frac{b}{a}\right)\right\}$$

$$= \log\left(\frac{b}{a}\right)^K.$$

24. $\displaystyle\frac{dp}{dh} = -K\left(\frac{R}{R+h}\right)^2 p \quad\therefore\; \int\frac{dp}{p} = -KR^2\int\frac{dh}{(R+h)^2}$ i.e. $\log p = \dfrac{KR^2}{R+h}+\log C$

$\therefore\; p = Ce^{KR^2/(R+h)}.$

When $h = 0$, $p = p_0$ (given) $\;\therefore\; p_0 = Ce^{KR} \quad\therefore\; C = p_0e^{-KR}.$

$\therefore\; p = p_0e^{\frac{KR^2}{R+h}-KR} = p_0e^{-KR\left(1+\frac{R}{h}\right)}$ on simplification.

25. $\therefore\; \displaystyle\lim_{h\to\infty} p = p_0e^{-KR} = C.$

26. $y^2 = 2ax - x^2$ may be written $(x-a)^2+y^2 = a^2$, i.e. it is a circle with centre $(a, 0)$ and radius a. The circle and the parabola $y^2 = ax$ intersect at points $(0, 0)$, $(a, \pm a)$. Area of parabola above the x-axis from $x = 0$ to $x = a$ is

$$\int_0^a \sqrt{ax}\,dx = \sqrt{a}\cdot\frac{2}{3}\Big[x^{3/2}\Big]_0^a = \frac{2a^2}{3}.$$

Area of quadrant of circle is $\dfrac{\pi a^2}{4}$.

Thus, area between curves and above x-axis is $\left(\dfrac{\pi}{4}-\dfrac{2}{3}\right)a^2$.

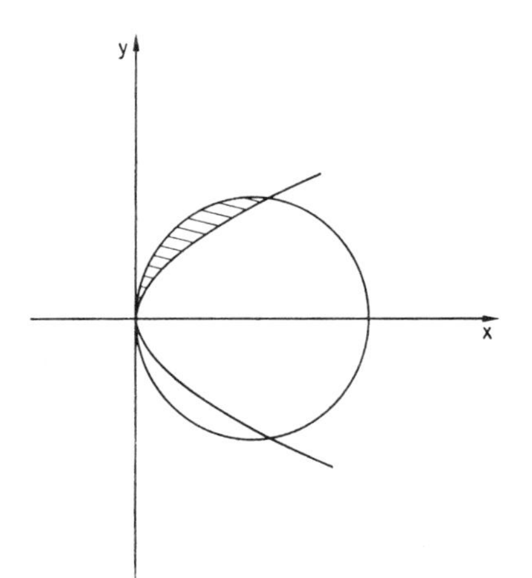

27. By symmetry, area $= 2\int_0^1 y\,dx = 2\int_0^1 \sqrt{\dfrac{x^3}{1-x}}\,dx$ (improper at $x = 1$)

$= 4\int_0^{\pi/2} \sin^4\theta\,d\theta$ putting $x = \sin^2\theta \quad \therefore\ dx = 2\sin\theta\cos\theta\,d\theta$

$= 4\cdot\dfrac{3}{4}\cdot\dfrac{1}{2}\cdot\dfrac{\pi}{2}$ (by (74)) $= \dfrac{3\pi}{4} = 3\times$area of generating circle.

28. By symmetry, $A = 2\int_0^1 \sqrt{\dfrac{1-x}{x}}\,dx$ (improper at $x = 0$)

$= 2\int_0^{\pi/2} \dfrac{\cos\theta\cdot 2\sin\theta\cos\theta\,d\theta}{\sin\theta}$ putting $x = \sin^2\theta \quad \therefore\ dx = 2\sin\theta\cos\theta\,d\theta$

$= 4\int_0^{\pi/2} \cos^2\theta\,d\theta = 4\cdot\dfrac{1}{2}\cdot\dfrac{\pi}{2}$ (by (74)) $= \pi = 4\times$area of generating circle.

29. By symmetry, area $= 2\int_{-1}^0 x\sqrt{\dfrac{1+x}{1-x}}\,dx$

$= 2\int_{\pi/2}^0 \sin\theta\sqrt{\dfrac{1-\sin\theta}{1+\sin\theta}}\cos\theta\,d\theta$ putting $x = -\sin\theta \quad \therefore\ dx = -\cos\theta\,d\theta$

$$= 2\int_{\pi/2}^{0} \sin\theta\cos\theta\sqrt{\frac{(1-\sin\theta)^2}{\cos^2\theta}}\,d\theta = 2\int_{\pi/2}^{0}(\sin\theta - \sin^2\theta)\,d\theta$$

$$= 2\Big[-\cos\theta\Big]_{\pi/2}^{0} - 2\int_{\pi/2}^{0}\frac{\cos 2\theta+1}{2}\,d\theta = -2+2\left[\frac{\sin 2\theta}{4}+\frac{\theta}{2}\right]_{\pi/2}^{0} = \frac{\pi}{2}-2.$$

[*Note:* $\pi/2-2<0$. The reason for negative area is that we have considered only the +ve branch of $y = +x\sqrt{\frac{1+x}{1-x}}$ which, for $-1 \leqslant x \leqslant 0$, is below the x-axis.]

30. Area $= \int_0^2 (e^x - e^{-x})\,dx = 2\int_0^2 \sinh x\,dx = 2\,[\cosh x]_0^2 = 2\,(\cosh 2 - 1)$

$= (e - e^{-1})^2.$

31. $\displaystyle\int_0^{2\pi} I^2\sin^2(\omega x+\varepsilon)\,dx = I^2\int_0^{2\pi}\frac{1-\cos 2(\omega x+\varepsilon)}{2}\,dx = \frac{I^2}{2}\left[x - \frac{\sin 2(\omega x+\varepsilon)}{2}\right]_0^2 = \pi I^2$

$\therefore$ r.m.s. $= \left\{\dfrac{1}{2\pi}\cdot\pi I^2\right\}^{1/2} = \dfrac{I}{\sqrt{2}}.$

32. $\displaystyle\int_1^2 x\log x\,dx = \left[\frac{x^2}{4}(2\log x - 1)\right]_1^2 = 2\log 2 - \frac{3}{4}$ (Exercise 8.14)

$\displaystyle\int_1^2 \log x\,dx = [x(\log x - 1)]_1^2 = 2\log 2 - 1$ (Example 25(b))

$\therefore$ mean value $= \left(2\log 2 - \dfrac{3}{4}\right)/(2\log 2 - 1).$

33. $f(x) = -\int_5^x 3^{x^2}\,dx \quad \therefore f'(x) = -3^{x^2}$ (by (65)) $\quad \therefore f'(2) = -3^4 = -81.$

34. $E = \dfrac{1}{2}ma^2n^2\sin^2 nt \quad \because \dfrac{dx}{dt} = v = -an\sin nt$

$\therefore E_{\text{mean}} = \dfrac{1}{\pi}\displaystyle\int_0^{\pi}\frac{1}{2}ma^2n^2\left(\frac{1-\cos 2nt}{2}\right)dt = \frac{m^2a^2n^2}{4\pi}\left[t - \frac{\sin 2nt}{2n}\right]_0^{\pi} = \frac{ma^2n^2}{4}.$

35. $\dfrac{dE}{dt} = \dfrac{ma^2n^2\sin 2nt}{2} = 0$ if $2nt = \pi \quad \therefore \dfrac{d^2E}{dt^2} = ma^2n^3\cos 2nt < 0$ for $2nt = \pi$

$\therefore 2nt = \pi$ gives a maximum value $(= \frac{1}{2}ma^2n^2)$ to E.

$\therefore E_{\text{mean}} = \frac{1}{2}E_{\text{max}}$ (Exercise 8.34).

36. Write $E = \dfrac{1}{2}ma^2n^2\left(1 - \dfrac{x^2}{a^2}\right)$

$\therefore E_{\text{mean}} = \dfrac{ma^2n^2}{2}\cdot\dfrac{1}{a-(-a)}\displaystyle\int_{-a}^{a}\left(1-\frac{x^2}{a^2}\right)dx = \frac{2}{3}\frac{ma^2n^2}{2} \quad \therefore E_{\text{mean}} = \frac{2}{3}E_{\text{max}}.$

37. $W = \dfrac{k}{2l_0}\left[(x-l_0)^2\right]_{l_0}^{1} = \dfrac{k(1-l_0)^2}{2l_0}.$

38. $F(x) = kx \quad \therefore\ F(2) = 2k = 4 \quad \therefore\ k = 2$ (lbs/inch) $\quad \therefore\ F(x) = 2x$

$\therefore\ W = \int_0^5 2x\,dx = \left[x^2\right]_0^5 = 25$ (in/lb) $= 2\frac{1}{12}$ (ft/lb). [k is called the *spring constant* of the given spring.]

39. $\int_P^p \dfrac{dp}{p+b/a} = a\int_0^t dt \quad \therefore\ \left[\log\left(p+\dfrac{b}{a}\right)\right]_P^p = a\left[t\right]_0^t = at.$

$\therefore\ p+\dfrac{b}{a} = \left(P+\dfrac{b}{a}\right)e^{at}.$

40. $\dfrac{dx}{dt} = -kx \quad \therefore\ x = ce^{-kt}$ (Example 34).

$t = 0,\ c = a$ (say) $\Rightarrow c = a \quad \therefore\ x = ae^{-kt}.$

41. Let T represent temperature and t time.

$\therefore\ \dfrac{dT}{dt} = -k(T-f(T))$ (negative rate since temperature is falling)

$= -k(T-40)$ using the given information

$\therefore\ \int_{T_0}^{T} \dfrac{dy}{T-40} = -k\int_0^t dt \quad \therefore\ \left[\log\,(T-40)\right]_{T_0}^{T} = -kt$

$\therefore\ T-40 = (T_0-40)e^{-kt}$. [Hence, given T, T_0, t we may determine k.]

42. $\int_0^\infty e^{-(p-q)x}dx = \dfrac{1}{q-p}\left[e^{-(p-q)x}\right]_0^\infty = \dfrac{1}{p-q}$ if $p > q$.

43. Let $J_1 = \int_0^\infty e^{-px}\sin\omega x\,dx$. Replace a by $-p$, b by ω in Example 25(d′)

$\therefore\ J_1 = -\left[\dfrac{e^{-px}}{p^2+\omega^2}(p\sin\omega x+\omega\cos\omega x)\right]_0^\infty = \dfrac{\omega}{p^2+\omega^2}.$

44. By Example 33(iii), (Corollary), $2178 = 1000\,e^{k/2} \quad \therefore\ \dfrac{k}{2} = \log_e 2{\cdot}178 = 1$

$\therefore\ k = 2 \quad \therefore$ law of bacterial growth is $N = 1000\,e^{2t}$.

45. By Example 33(iii) (Corollary), $1840 = 5000\,e^{-10k}$

$\therefore\ -10k = \log_e \dfrac{1840}{5000} = \log_e 0{\cdot}3680 = \log_e e^{-1} = -1$ (§ 11)

$\therefore\ k = \dfrac{1}{10}.$

$\therefore$ estimated population in 10 years' time is $5000e^{-2} = 0{\cdot}1353\times 5000$ (§ 11) $= 677$ (fractions of people disallowed!).

46. $\frac{dv}{dt} = -kv$ (k a factor of proportionality) $\therefore v = ce^{-kt}$ (Example 34)

$$t = 0, v = v_0 \text{ (say)} \Rightarrow c = v_0 \quad \therefore v = v_0 e^{-kt} = \frac{dx}{dt}$$

$$\therefore \int_0^x dx = v_0 \int_0^s e^{-kt}\, dt = \frac{v_0}{k}\Big[-e^{-kt}\Big]_0^5 \quad \therefore x = \frac{v_0}{k}(1-e^{-5t}).$$

47. Death law of the victims is $\frac{9}{10} N = Ne^{-4k}$ where N was the number present before the attack. $\therefore k = -\frac{1}{4}\log\left(\frac{9}{10}\right)$.

Number of ants after 2 hours is $300e^{2\left\{\frac{-1}{4}\log\left(\frac{9}{10}\right)\right\}} = 300e^{-\frac{1}{2}\log\left(\frac{9}{10}\right)} = 300e^{\log\sqrt{\frac{10}{9}}}$

$$= 300\frac{\sqrt{10}}{3} = 316.$$

48. $I = \int_0^\infty \frac{1}{1+x^a}\cdot\frac{1}{1+x^2}\, dx \ldots \text{(i)} = \int_\infty^0 \frac{1}{1+1/t^a}\cdot\frac{1}{1+1/t^2}\cdot -\frac{1}{t^2}\, dt$ putting $x = \frac{1}{t}$

$$= \int_0^\infty \frac{t^a}{1+t^a}\cdot\frac{1}{1+t^2}\, dt = \int_0^\infty \frac{x^a}{1+x^a}\cdot\frac{1}{1+x^2}\, dx \ldots \text{(ii) reverting to the variable } x$$

$$= \frac{1}{2}\left\{\int_0^\infty \frac{1+x^a}{1+x^a}\cdot\frac{1}{1+x^2}\, dx\right\} \quad \text{using the two forms (i), (ii) of } I$$

$$= \frac{1}{2}\int_0^\infty \frac{1}{1+x^2}\, dx = \frac{1}{2}\Big[\tan^{-1} x\Big]_0^\infty = \frac{\pi}{4}.$$

49. $$\int_0^{\pi/2} \frac{\cos x\, dx}{1-\sin^2\alpha\cos^2 x} = \int_0^1 \frac{d\sin x}{1-\sin^2\alpha\,(1-\sin^2 x)} \quad \because d\sin x = \cos x\, dx$$

$$= \int_0^1 \frac{d\sin x}{\cos^2\alpha+\sin^2\alpha\sin^2 x} = \operatorname{cosec}^2\alpha \int_0^1 \frac{d\sin x}{\cot^2\alpha+\sin^2 x}$$

$$= \operatorname{cosec}^2\alpha\cdot\frac{1}{\cot\alpha}\left[\tan^{-1}\left(\frac{\sin x}{\cot\alpha}\right)\right]_0^{x=\pi/2} = \frac{2\alpha}{\sin 2\alpha}.$$

50. $$I = \int_0^\infty \frac{dx}{(x+\sqrt{x^2+1})^n}\ (n > 1) = \int_0^{\pi/2} \frac{\sec^2\theta\, d\theta}{(\tan\theta+\sec\theta)^n}\ (x = \tan\theta)$$

$$= \left[\tan\theta\cdot\frac{1}{(\tan\theta+\sec\theta)^n}\right]_0^{\pi/2} + n\int_0^{\pi/2} \frac{\sec\theta\cdot\tan\theta\, d\theta}{(\tan\theta+\sec\theta)^n} \quad \text{(by parts)}$$

$$= 0+n\left[\sec\theta\cdot\frac{1}{(\tan\theta+\sec\theta)^n}\right]_0^{\pi/2}+n^2I \text{ (by parts)}$$

$$\therefore I = \frac{-n}{1-n^2} = \frac{n}{n^2-1} \quad (n > 1).$$

51. $$\int_0^{\pi/2}\frac{\tan x}{1+3\tan^2 x}\,dx = \int_0^{\infty}\frac{t\,dt}{(1+t^2)(1+3t^2)} \quad \left(\text{putting } t = \tan x \quad \therefore dt = \sec^2 x\,dx = (1+t^2)\,dx\right)$$

$$= \frac{1}{2}\int_0^{\infty}\left\{\frac{3t}{1+3t^2}-\frac{t}{1+t^2}\right\}dt \text{ using partial fractions}$$

$$= \frac{1}{4}\left[\log\left(\frac{1+3t^2}{1+t^2}\right)\right]_0^{\infty} = \frac{1}{4}\left\{\lim_{t\to\infty}\log\left(\frac{1/t^2+3}{1/t^2+1}\right)-\log 1\right\}$$

$$= \frac{1}{4}\log 3.$$

52. $$\int_0^{\infty} x^{2n+1}e^{-x^2}\,dx = \tfrac{1}{2}\int_0^{\infty} u^n e^{-u}\,du \text{ putting } x^2 = u \quad \therefore du = 2x\,dx$$

$$= \tfrac{1}{2}n! \text{ since the integral is the gamma function.}$$

53. $$I_1 = \int_0^{\pi}\sin\phi\cos\left(\frac{\phi}{2}\right)d\phi = 2\int_0^{\pi}\cos^2\left(\frac{\phi}{2}\right)d\phi = \int_0^{\pi}(1+\cos\phi)\,d\phi = \Big[\phi+\sin\phi\Big]_0^{\pi}$$

$$= \pi$$

$$I_{n+1}-I_n = \int_0^{\pi}[\sin(n+1)\phi-\sin n\phi]\cot\left(\frac{\phi}{2}\right)d\phi$$

$$= 2\int_0^{\pi}\cos\left(n+\frac{1}{2}\right)\phi\,\sin\frac{\phi}{2}\cdot\frac{\cos(\phi/2)}{\sin(\phi/2)}\,d\phi = 2\int_0^{\pi}\cos\left(n+\frac{1}{2}\right)\phi\cos\frac{\phi}{2}\,d\phi$$

$$= \int_0^{\pi}[\cos(n+1)\phi+\cos n\phi]\,d\phi = \left[\frac{\sin(n+1)\phi}{n+1}+\frac{\sin n\phi}{n}\right]_0^{\pi} = 0$$

$$\therefore I_{n+1} = I_n = I_{n-1} = \ldots = I_2 = I_1 = \pi.$$

54. $$\psi(\theta) = \frac{1}{2\pi}\int_0^{\pi}[\cos n(\theta+\phi)-\cos n(\theta-\phi)]\cot\left(\frac{\phi}{2}\right)d\phi$$

$$= -\frac{1}{\pi}\int_0^{\pi}\sin n\theta\sin n\phi\cdot\cot\frac{\phi}{2}\,d\phi$$

$$= -\frac{\sin n\theta}{\pi}I_n$$

$$= -\sin n\theta.$$

55. $c(t) = \int_0^t (t-u)^2 e^u \, du = \int_0^t (t^2 - 2tu + u^2) e^u \, du$

$$= t^2 \int_0^t e^u \, du - 2t \int_0^t ue^u \, du + \int_0^t u^2 e^u \, du$$

$$= t^2(e^t - 1) - 2t(te^t - e^t + 1) + (t^2 e^t - 2te^t + 2e^t - 2) \text{ integrating by parts}$$

$$= 2e^t - t^2 - 2t - 2.$$

Check using $c(t) = \int_0^t e^{t-u} u^2 \, du$ (i.e. roles played by $a(t)$, $b(t)$ interchanged).

56. $c(t) = \int_0^t \sin(t-u) \sin u \, du = \frac{1}{2} \int_0^t (\cos(t-2u) - \cos t) \, du$

$$= \tfrac{1}{2} [-\tfrac{1}{2} \sin(t-2u) - u \cos t]_0^t = \tfrac{1}{2}(\sin t - t \cos t).$$

57. $\int_0^t a(t-u) b(u) \, du = \int_t^0 a(w) \, b(t-w) \cdot -dw$ putting $t - u = w$

$$= \int_0^t b(t-w) a(w) \, dw$$

$\therefore$ convolution is commutative (clearly so in Exercise 8.56; also true in Exercise 8.55, if checked).

58. Let $y = 1 + e \cos \theta$

$$\therefore \frac{d}{d\theta}\left(\frac{e \sin \theta}{y}\right) = \frac{e \cos \theta}{y} + e \sin \theta \cdot -\frac{1}{y^2} \cdot -e \sin \theta = \frac{e \cos \theta}{y} + \frac{e^2 \sin^2 \theta}{y^2}$$

$$= \frac{y-1}{y} + \frac{e^2\{1 - ((y-1)/e)^2\}}{y^2} = \frac{e^2 - 1}{y^2} + \frac{1}{y} \qquad \text{(i)}$$

$$\therefore \int_0^\pi \frac{d\theta}{(1 + e \cos \theta)^2} = -\frac{1}{1-e^2} \int_0^\pi \frac{d}{d\theta}(e \sin \theta / y) \, d\theta + \frac{1}{1-e^2} \int_0^\pi \frac{d\theta}{1 + e \cos \theta}$$

integrating by parts using (i)

$$= -\frac{1}{1-e^2}\left[\frac{e \sin \theta}{1 + e \cos \theta}\right]_0^\pi + \frac{1}{1-e^2}\left[\frac{2}{\sqrt{1-e^2}} \tan^{-1}\left\{\sqrt{\frac{1+e}{1-e}} \tan \frac{\theta}{2}\right\}\right]_0^\pi$$

by Example 24(c)

$$= \frac{1}{1-e^2} \cdot \frac{2}{\sqrt{1-e^2}} \tan^{-1} \infty = \frac{\pi}{(1-e^2)^{3/2}}.$$

59. $PN = y \sqrt{1 + \left(\frac{dy}{dx}\right)^2} = 1 \Rightarrow \frac{dy}{dx} = \frac{\sqrt{1-y^2}}{y}$

$$\therefore \int dx = \int \frac{y}{\sqrt{1-y^2}} \, dy = -\sqrt{1-y^2} + c.$$

Taking $c = 0$ for simplicity and squaring, we have $x^2 = 1-y^2$, i.e. $x^2+y^2 = 1$. This tells us the elementary fact that $PN = PO = 1$ if O is the centre of this circle of unit radius, i.e. a circle is the only curve for which PN is constant. (Also see Exercise 8.2.)

60. $\dfrac{dE}{dm} = \dfrac{dE}{dp}\dfrac{dp}{dm} = v\cdot\dfrac{c^2}{v} = c^2 \quad \therefore\ dE = c^2\,dm \quad \therefore\ E = mc^2.$

61. $$A = k\int_0^{x=a} \frac{k\,dy}{\sqrt{(\sinh a/k \sec\alpha)^2 - y^2}} \qquad \left(y = \sinh\frac{x}{k}\right)$$

$$= k^2\left[\sin^{-1}\left(\frac{\sinh(x/k)}{\sinh(a/k)\sec\alpha}\right)\right]_0^a = k^2 \sin^{-1}\cos\alpha = k^2\left(\frac{\pi}{2}-\alpha\right).$$

62. $$\int_0^y \frac{dy}{y(N-y)} = k\int_0^t dt \quad \therefore\ kt = \int\left(\frac{1}{N-y}+\frac{1}{y}\right)dy = \log(N-y)+\log y - \log c$$

$$\therefore\ kt = \log\left(\frac{y}{c(N-y)}\right) \quad \therefore\ \frac{y}{N-y} = ce^{kt} \quad \therefore\ y = \frac{N}{1+(1/c)e^{-kt}}.$$

$$y = \frac{N}{2},\ t = T \Rightarrow c = e^{-kt} \quad \therefore\ y = N\{1+e^{-k(t-T)}\}^{-1}.$$

63. $$\int_a^{\log x} \frac{e^t}{t}\,dt = \int_{e^a}^{x} \frac{du}{\log u} = l(x) \text{ if } e^a = 2 \quad \therefore\ a = \log 2 \quad (t = \log u).$$

64. $$\int_{\log 2/e}^{x} \frac{e^t}{t+1}\,dt = e^{-1}\int_2^{e^{x+1}} \frac{du}{\log u} = e^{-1}l(e^{x+1}) \quad (\log u = t+1).$$

65. $$\frac{dy}{dx} = k\frac{dy}{dx} \quad \therefore\ \frac{dy}{y} = k\frac{dx}{x} \quad \therefore\ \log y = k\log x + \log c \quad \therefore\ y = cx^k.$$

(Refer to Exercise 1.7.)

66. $$B\left\{\int_0^x \left(\frac{dy}{dx}-k\right)dx\right\} = \omega\left[\frac{x^4}{24}-\frac{ax^3}{12}\right]_0^x \quad \text{on integrating,}$$

i.e. $B(y-kx) = \dfrac{\omega x^3}{24}(x-2a)\ldots$ (i) $\quad (x = 0 \Rightarrow y = 0)$.

Also, $x = a \Rightarrow y = 0 \quad \therefore\ Bk = \dfrac{\omega a^3}{24}\ldots$ (ii). Substitute from (ii) in (i).

$$\therefore\ By = \frac{\omega x}{24}(x^3-2ax^2+a^3) = \frac{\omega x}{24}(a-x)(a^2+ax-x^2),$$

$$\therefore\ \text{value of } y \text{ at } x = \frac{a}{2} \text{ (sag at mid-point)} = \frac{5}{384}\frac{\omega a^4}{B}.$$

67. $$\frac{d^2x}{dt^2} = \frac{d}{dx}\left(\tfrac{1}{2}v^2\right) = \frac{-gR^2}{x^2} \quad \text{(Exercise 1.11)}$$

$$\therefore\ \int \frac{d}{dx}\left(\tfrac{1}{2}v^2\right)dx = -gR^2\int\frac{dx}{x^2} \quad \therefore\ \tfrac{1}{2}v^2 = \frac{gR^2}{x}+c.$$

Now $t = 0 \Rightarrow v = v_0,\ x = R+h \quad \therefore\ \frac{1}{2}v_0^2 = \frac{gR^2}{R+h}+c \quad \therefore\ c = \frac{1}{2}v_0^2 - \frac{gR^2}{R+h}$

$$\therefore\ v^2 - v_0^2 = 2gR^2\left(\frac{1}{x}-\frac{1}{R+h}\right)$$

$x = R \Rightarrow v = V \quad \therefore\ V^2 - v_0^2 = 2gR^2\left(\frac{1}{R}-\frac{1}{R+h}\right) = 2gR \quad \because\ \frac{2gR^2}{R+h} \to 0$ for $h \to \infty$

$\therefore$ impact velocity $= \sqrt{2gR+v_0^2}$ ($= \sqrt{2gR}$ if the meteorite were replaced by an object which is let fall, i.e. has initial velocity zero).

68. $\int dW = k\int \frac{r-R}{(R+r)^3}\,dR = k\int\left\{\frac{A}{R+r}+\frac{B}{(R+r)^2}+\frac{C}{(R+r)^3}\right\}dR$

$= k\int\left\{-\frac{1}{(R+r)^2}+\frac{2r}{(R+r)^3}\right\}dR$ on computing the partial fractions

$= k\left\{\frac{1}{R+r}-\frac{r}{(R+r)^2}\right\}+c.$

$\therefore\ W = k\,\frac{R}{(R+r)^2} \qquad \because\ c = 0$ under the given conditions.

69. $F = 2\omega\int_1^{-1}(t-5)\sqrt{1-t^2}\,dt\ (y+5 = t) = 2\omega\left\{\int_1^{-1} t\sqrt{1-t^2}\,dt - 5\int_1^{-1}\sqrt{1-t^2}\,dt\right\}$

$= 2\omega\left[-\frac{1}{3}(1-t^2)^{3/2}-\frac{5}{2}\left\{t\sqrt{1-t^2}+\sin^{-1}t\right\}\right]_1^{-1}$ [Example 25(c)] $= 5\pi\omega$ (lb/unit area).

70. $I = \frac{\pi}{2}\cdot\frac{M}{(4/3)\pi a^3}\int_{-a}^{a}(a^4-2a^2x^2+x^4)\,dx = \frac{3M}{8a^3}\left[a^4x-2a^2\frac{x^3}{3}+\frac{x^5}{5}\right]_{-a}^{a}$

$= \frac{3M}{8a^3}\cdot 2a^5\left(1-\frac{2}{3}+\frac{1}{5}\right) = \frac{3Ma^2}{4}\cdot\frac{8}{15} = \frac{2}{5}Ma^2$

$\therefore\ k = \sqrt{\frac{I}{M}} = \sqrt{\frac{2}{5}}\,a.$

71. $B(m, n) = \int_0^1 x^{m-1}(1-x)^{n-1}\,dx = -\int_1^0 (1-y)^{m-1}y^{n-1}\,dy$ (putting $y = 1-x$

$= \int_0^1 y^{n-1}(1-y)^{m-1}\,dy = B(n, m).$ $\therefore\ dy = -dx$)

72. $B(m, n) = 2\int_0^{\pi/2}\sin^{2m-1}\theta\cos^{2n-1}\theta\,d\theta$ putting $x = \sin^2\theta$ (with a similar integral if we had put $x = \cos^2\theta$)

$= 2u_{2m-1,2n-1}\ldots$ (i) using the notation of Example 40 (c).

$B(m+1,\ n) = 2\int_0^{\pi/2}\sin^{2m+1}\theta\cos^{2n-1}\theta\,d\theta = 2u_{2m+1,2n-1}$ by Example 40(c)

$= 2\cdot\frac{(2m+1)-1}{(2m+1)+(2n-1)}u_{(2m+1)-2,\,2n-1}$ by (75) with roles played by m, n interchanged

$= 2\cdot\frac{m}{m+n}u_{2m-1,\,2n-1} = \frac{m}{m+n}B(m, n)$ by (i).

73. $B(\frac{1}{2}, \frac{1}{2}) = 2\int_0^{\pi/2} d\theta$ using Exercise 8.72(i) (i.e. $2m-1 = 2n-1 = 0$ when $m = n = \frac{1}{2}$)

$$= \pi \qquad (\alpha)$$

$$= \frac{\Gamma(\frac{1}{2})\Gamma(\frac{1}{2})}{\Gamma(1)} \quad \text{using the assumption}$$

$$= \{\Gamma(\tfrac{1}{2})\}^2 \qquad (\beta)$$

$\therefore\ \Gamma(\frac{1}{2}) = \int_0^\infty e^{-x}x^{-1/2}\,dx = \sqrt{\pi}$ using (α), (β) and the definition of $\Gamma\,(n+1)$.

74. $\int_0^\infty e^{-y^2}dy = \frac{1}{2}\int_0^\infty e^{-x}x^{-1/2}\,dx$ putting $y^2 = x \quad \therefore\ dy = \frac{1}{2}x^{-1/2}\,dx$

$$= \frac{\sqrt{\pi}}{2} \quad \text{by Example 8.73.}$$

75. $A = \int_0^1 \frac{t^4(1-4t+6t^2-4t^3+t^4)}{1+t^2}\,dt = \int_0^1 \left(t^6-4t^5+5t^4-4t^2+4-\frac{4}{1+t^2}\right)dt$

$$= \frac{1}{7}-\frac{2}{3}+1-\frac{4}{3}+4-4\cdot\frac{\pi}{4} \text{ (on calculation)} = \frac{22}{7}-\pi$$

$$B = \int_0^1 t^4(1-4t+6t^2-4t^3+t^4)\,dt = \frac{1}{5}-\frac{2}{3}+\frac{6}{7}-\frac{1}{2}+\frac{1}{9} = \frac{1}{630}.$$

Now $\frac{B}{2} < A < B \quad (0 \leqslant t \leqslant 1) \qquad \therefore\ \frac{1}{1260} < \frac{22}{7}-\pi < \frac{1}{630}.$

76. $\frac{dI}{dx} = -\frac{k}{100}I \quad \therefore\ x = \frac{-100}{k}\int\frac{dI}{I} = \frac{-100}{k}\log I + c$ (x measures the distance vertically downward).

$$x = 0,\ I = I_0 \Rightarrow c = \frac{100}{k}\log I_0 \quad \therefore\ x = \frac{100}{k}\log\left(\frac{I_0}{I}\right).$$

$$I = \frac{I_0}{4} \Rightarrow x = \frac{100}{k}\log 4 = \frac{200}{k}\log 2.$$

77. $\frac{d\log V}{d\log l} = 3 \quad \therefore\ \int d\log V = 3\int d\log l \quad \therefore\ V = 3\,(\log l + \log c) = \log\,(cl)^3$

$\therefore\ V = (cl)^3$, i.e. the box is a cube.

78. Solution of the S.H.M. equation is $y = A\cos nx + B\sin nx$.

$y = 0,\ x = 0 \Rightarrow 0 = A;\ y = 0,\ x = l \Rightarrow 0 = B\sin nl \quad \therefore\ nl = \pi \quad \therefore\ P = \pi^2 f/l^2.$

79. $x = c\sinh^{-1}\left(\frac{s}{c}\right) + kcs + K_1,\ y = \sqrt{c^2+s^2} + \frac{ks^2}{2} + K_2.$

Initial conditions give $K_1 = K_2 = 0$.

$\therefore$ parametric coordinates are $\left(\sinh^{-1}\left(\frac{s}{c}\right) + kcs,\ \sqrt{c^2+s^2} + \frac{ks^2}{2}\right).$

80. From Exercise 8.67, $\dfrac{d^2x}{dt^2} = \dfrac{-gR^2}{x^2}$ $\therefore\ v^2 = 2gR^2\left(\dfrac{1}{x}-\dfrac{1}{x_0}\right)$ where $x(x_0)$ are distances from Moon to surface (centre) of Earth; $v_0 = 0$.

$$\therefore\ \frac{dx}{dt} = -\sqrt{2g}\,R\sqrt{\frac{1}{x}-\frac{1}{x_0}}$$

$$\therefore\ t = -\frac{1}{\sqrt{2g}\,R}\int_{x_0}^{R}\frac{dx}{\sqrt{1/x-1/x_0}} = -\frac{1}{\sqrt{2g}\,R}\int_{x_0}^{R}\frac{\sqrt{xx_0}}{\sqrt{x-x_0}}\,dx$$

$$= -\frac{x_0^{3/2}}{\sqrt{2g}\,R}\int_{x=x_0}^{x=R}(1-\cos 2\theta)\,d\theta \quad (x = x_0\sin^2\theta)$$

$$= \frac{-x_0^{3/2}}{\sqrt{2g}\,R}\left[\sin^{-1}\sqrt{\frac{x}{x_0}}-\sqrt{\frac{x}{x_0}}\sqrt{1-\frac{x}{x_0}}\right]_{x_0}^{R}$$

$$\left(\because\ \int\cos 2\theta\,d\theta = \ = \frac{\sin 2\theta}{2} = \sin\theta\cos\theta\right)$$

$$= \frac{-x_0^{3/2}}{\sqrt{2g}\,R}\left\{\sin^{-1}\sqrt{\frac{R}{x_0}}-\sqrt{\frac{R}{x_0}\left(1-\frac{R}{x_0}\right)}-\frac{\pi}{2}\right\}$$

$$= \frac{x_0^{3/2}}{\sqrt{2g}\,R}\left\{\cos^{-1}\sqrt{\frac{R}{x_0}}-\sqrt{\frac{R}{x_0}\left(1-\frac{R}{x_0}\right)}\right\} \quad \text{by (13)}$$

$$\doteqdot \frac{x_0^{3/2}}{\sqrt{2g}\,R} \quad \because\ \frac{R}{x_0}\text{ is small.}$$

EXERCISES 9

1. $R = \dfrac{a\sqrt{n}}{\sqrt{1+b(n-1)}} = \dfrac{a}{\sqrt{1/n+b-b/n}}$ $\therefore\ \lim\limits_{n\to\infty} R = \dfrac{a}{\sqrt{b}}$.

2. $u_n = \dfrac{1}{n!}$, $u_{n+1} = \dfrac{1}{(n+1)!}$ $\therefore$ by d'Alembert's test,

$$\lim_{n\to\infty}\left(\frac{u_{n+1}}{u_n}\right) = \lim_{n\to\infty}\left(\frac{n!}{(n+1)!}\right) = \lim_{n\to\infty}\left(\frac{1/n}{1/n+1}\right) = 0 \text{ which} < 1.$$

Thus, the series is convergent ($= e-1$).

3. Let $u_n = \dfrac{1}{2n+3}$, $v_n = \dfrac{1}{n}$. Now $\lim\limits_{n\to\infty}\left(\dfrac{u_n}{v_n}\right) = \lim\limits_{n\to\infty}\left(\dfrac{n}{2n+3}\right) = \dfrac{1}{2}$ which is finite.

Thus $\sum\dfrac{1}{2n+3}$ diverges by comparison by limits with $\sum\dfrac{1}{n}$

or use Cauchy's integral test.

4. $\sum u_n = \sum \frac{1+n}{2+n^2}$. Compare this with $\sum v_n = \sum \frac{1}{n}$.

$$\lim_{n\to\infty}\left(\frac{u_n}{v_n}\right) = \lim_{n\to\infty}\left(\frac{1/n+1}{2/n^2+1}\right) = 1 \text{ (which is finite).}$$

Since $\sum \frac{1}{n}$ is a divergent series, $\sum \frac{1+n}{2+n^2}$ is divergent

or, using Cauchy's integral test, we have

$f(x) = \frac{1+x}{2+x^2}$ is a monotonically decreasing function of x as x increases, $x \geqslant 1$;

$$\int_1^\infty f(x)\,dx = \int_1^\infty \frac{1+x}{2+x^2}\,dx = \int_1^\infty \frac{dx}{2+x^2} + \frac{1}{2}\int_1^\infty \frac{dx^2}{2+x^2} = \left[\frac{1}{\sqrt{2}}\tan^{-1}\left(\frac{x}{\sqrt{2}}\right) + \frac{1}{2}\log(2+x^2)\right]_1^\infty$$

which is not finite. Thus, the series diverges.

5. Let $S = 1^{\log x} + 2^{\log x} + 3^{\log x} + 4^{\log x} + \ldots$

$$= \frac{1}{1^{-\log x}} + \frac{1}{2^{-\log x}} + \frac{1}{3^{-\log x}} + \frac{1}{4^{-\log x}} + \ldots$$

$$= \frac{1}{1^p} + \frac{1}{2^p} + \frac{1}{3^p} + \frac{1}{4^p} + \ldots$$

which is convergent if $p > 1$, and divergent if $p \leqslant 1$,

i.e. conv. if $-\log x > 1$, div. if $-\log x \leqslant 1$,

i.e. conv. if $\log x < -\log e$, div. if $\log x \geqslant -\log e$,

i.e. conv. if $x < 1/e$, div. if $x \geqslant 1/e$.

Thus, the series $\sum n^{\log x}$ is convergent if $x < 1/e$, and divergent if $x \geqslant 1/e$.

6. $\sum u_n = \sum nx^{n-1}$. Apply D'Alembert's test.

$$\therefore \quad \frac{u_{n+1}}{u_n} = \frac{(n+1)x^n}{nx^{n-1}} = x\left(1+\frac{1}{n}\right). \quad \therefore \lim_{n\to\infty}\left(\frac{u_{n+1}}{u_n}\right) = x.$$

Thus, the series is convergent if $x < 1$, divergent if $x > 1$. If $x = 1$ the test fails, but the series becomes $1+2+3+4+\ldots$ which is divergent.

7. $u_n = \frac{n^3}{e^n}$, $u_{n+1} = \frac{(n+1)^3}{e^{n+1}}$ $\therefore \lim_{n\to\infty}\left(\frac{u_{n+1}}{u_n}\right) = \lim_{n\to\infty}\left\{\frac{(1+1/n)^3}{e}\right\} = \frac{1}{e}$.

$\therefore$ the series converges by D'Alembert's test.

8. By Cauchy's test, $\int_2^\infty \frac{dx}{x(\log x)^2} = \left[-\frac{1}{\log x}\right]_2^\infty = \frac{1}{\log 2}$ $\therefore$ the series converges.

9. By Cauchy's test, $\int_2^\infty \frac{dx}{x\log x\log\log x} = \left[\log\log\log x\right]_2^\infty = \infty$

$\therefore$ the series diverges.

10. We know $\sum_{r=1}^{n} r = \frac{1}{2}n(n+1)$ [(Example 37(i)]

$$\therefore \text{ required limit } = \lim_{n\to\infty}\left\{\frac{n(n+1)}{2n^2}\right\} = \lim_{n\to\infty}\left\{\frac{1+1/n}{2}\right\} = \frac{1}{2}.$$

11. Also, $\sum_{r=1}^{n} r^2 = \frac{1}{6}n(n+1)(2n+1)$ [(Example 37(ii)]

$$\therefore \text{ required limit } = \lim_{n\to\infty}\left\{\frac{n(n+1)(2n+1)}{6n^3}\right\} = \lim_{n\to\infty}\left\{\frac{(1+1/n)(2+1/n)}{6}\right\} = \frac{1}{3}.$$

12. Let $S_n = 1+\frac{1}{2}+(\frac{1}{2})^2+(\frac{1}{2})^3+\ldots+(\frac{1}{2})^{n-1}$ and $S_\infty = \sum_{0}^{\infty}(\frac{1}{2})^n$.

By Example 44, $S_\infty - S_n = \dfrac{ax^n}{1-x} = \dfrac{(\frac{1}{2})^n}{1-\frac{1}{2}}$ (when $a = 1,\ x = \frac{1}{2}$) $= 2^{1-n}$.

Now $2^{1-n} < 10^{-10}$ (given) i.e. $(1-n)\log 2 < -10$ (logarithms to base 10)

i.e. $(1-n) < -10/\log 2$ $\therefore n > 1+\dfrac{10}{0{\cdot}301}$ $\therefore n > 34{\cdot}2$.

Thus, the least integral value n can have is 35.

13. $$\sum\frac{1}{(10+n)^2} = \frac{1}{121}+\frac{1}{144}+\frac{1}{169}+\frac{1}{196}+\frac{1}{225}+\ldots$$

Compare with $\sum\dfrac{1}{n^2}$ which is convergent $\therefore \dfrac{1}{(10+n)^2} < \dfrac{1}{n^2}$ $\therefore \sum\dfrac{1}{(10+n)^2}$ converges.

By the theory of the proof of Cauchy's integral test,

$$\int_1^\infty \frac{dx}{(10+x)^2} < S < u_1 + \int_1^\infty \frac{dx}{(10+x)^2}$$

where S = the sum of the series, u_1 = the first term of the series $= \dfrac{1}{11^2}$,

$$\text{i.e. } \left[-\frac{1}{10+x}\right]_1^\infty < S < \frac{1}{121}+\left[-\frac{1}{10+x}\right]_1^\infty$$

$$\frac{1}{11} < S < \frac{1}{121}+\frac{1}{11} \quad \text{i.e.} \quad \frac{1}{11} < S < \frac{12}{121}.$$

14. Now $f(x) = f(0)+\dfrac{xf'(0)}{1!}+\dfrac{x^2f''(0)}{2!}+\dfrac{x^3f'''(0)}{3!}+\ldots$ (Maclaurin's series)

Let $f(x) = \sinh x = \dfrac{e^x-e^{-x}}{2}$ $\therefore f(0) = 0$

$$\because \begin{cases} f'(x) = \dfrac{e^x+e^{-x}}{2} \\ f''(x) = \dfrac{e^x-e^{-x}}{2} \\ \ldots\ldots\ldots \end{cases} \quad \therefore \begin{cases} f'(0) = 1 \\ f''(0) = 0 \\ \ldots\ldots \end{cases}$$

$$\therefore \sinh x = x+\frac{x^3}{3!}+\frac{x^5}{5!}+\ldots$$

15. Let $f(x) = \cosh x = \dfrac{e^x+e^{-x}}{2}$ $\quad\therefore\ f(0) = 1$

$$\therefore\ f'(x) = \frac{e^x-e^{-x}}{2} \qquad f'(0) = 0$$

$$f''(x) = \frac{e^x+e^{-x}}{2} \qquad f''(0) = 1$$

$$\ldots\ldots\ldots\ldots\ldots \qquad \ldots\ldots\ldots$$

$$\therefore\ \cosh x = 1+\frac{x^2}{2!}+\frac{x^4}{4!}+\ldots$$

16. By (91.1), (91.2), $\tan x = \left(x-\dfrac{x^3}{3!}+\dfrac{x^5}{5!}-\ldots\right)\left(1-\left\{\dfrac{x^2}{2!}-\dfrac{x^4}{4!}+\ldots\right\}\right)^{-1}$

$$= \left(x-\frac{x^3}{3!}+\frac{x^5}{5!}-\ldots\right)\left\{1+\left(\frac{x^2}{2!}-\frac{x^4}{4!}+\ldots\right)+\left(\frac{x^2}{2!}-\frac{x^4}{4!}+\ldots\right)^2+\ldots\right\}$$

$= x+\dfrac{x^3}{3}+\dfrac{2x^5}{15}+\ldots$ on calculating. (The next term is $\dfrac{17x^7}{315}$.)

Or use Maclaurin's series for $f(x) = \tan x$.

17. $$\tan^{-1}\left(\frac{1}{70}\right)-\tan^{-1}\left(\frac{1}{99}\right) = \tan^{-1}\left(\frac{\frac{1}{70}+\frac{1}{99}}{1+\frac{1}{70}\cdot\frac{1}{99}}\right) = \tan^{-1}\left(\frac{29}{6931}\right)$$

$$= \tan^{-1}\left(\frac{1}{239}\right).$$

Use (102) and the identity follows.

18. $$\tfrac{1}{2}\int_0^{\pi}(\pi-x)\,dx = \int_0^{\pi}(\sin x+\tfrac{1}{2}\sin 2x+\tfrac{1}{3}\sin 3x+\ldots)\,dx$$

i.e. $$\frac{1}{2}\left[\pi x-\frac{x^2}{2}\right]_0^{\pi} = -\left[\cos x+\frac{1}{2^2}\cos 2x+\frac{1}{3^2}\cos 3x+\frac{1}{4^2}\cos 4x+\ldots\right]_0^{\pi}$$

i.e. $$\frac{1}{2}\cdot\frac{\pi^2}{2} = 2\left(1+0+\frac{1}{3^2}+0+\frac{1}{5^2}+\ldots\right)$$

i.e. $$\frac{\pi^2}{8} = \frac{1}{1^2}+\frac{1}{3^2}+\frac{1}{5^2}+\ldots$$

19.
$$f(x) = \sin^{-1}x \qquad \therefore f(0) = 0$$
$$f'(x) = (1-x^2)^{-1/2} \qquad \therefore f'(0) = 1$$
$$f''(x) = x(1-x^2)^{-3/2} \qquad \therefore f''(0) = 0$$
$$f'''(x) = \frac{1+2x^2}{(1-x^2)^{5/2}} \qquad \therefore f'''(0) = 1$$
$$f^{\text{iv}}(x) = \frac{x(6x^2-9)}{(1-x^2)^{7/2}} \qquad \therefore f^{\text{iv}}(0) = 0$$
$$f^{\text{v}}(x) = \frac{3(8x^4+24x^2+3)}{(1-x^2)^{9/2}} \qquad \therefore f^{\text{v}}(0) = 9$$

$$\therefore\ \sin^{-1}x = x+\frac{x^3}{3!}+\frac{9x^5}{5!}+\ldots\ldots$$

Put $x = \frac{1}{2}$

$$\therefore \frac{\pi}{6} = \frac{1}{2}+\frac{1}{48}+\frac{3}{1280}+\ldots.$$

20. $$\frac{\pi^2}{6} = \int_1^0 \frac{\log x}{1-x}\,dx = -\int_0^1 \frac{\log(1-y)}{y}\,dy \quad (y = 1-x;\text{ note behaviour at limits})$$

$$= \int_0^1 \left(1+\frac{y}{2}+\frac{y^2}{3}+\frac{y^3}{4}+\ldots\right) dy \quad \text{(by (94))} = \left[y+\frac{y^2}{2^2}+\frac{y^3}{3^2}+\frac{y^4}{4^2}+\ldots\right]_0^1$$

$$\therefore \frac{\pi^2}{6} = \frac{1}{1^2}+\frac{1}{2^2}+\frac{1}{3^2}+\frac{1}{4^2}+\ldots \text{ (due to Euler and John Bernoulli).}$$

21. $$\left(1-\frac{2}{3}\right)^{-3/2} = 1+\frac{\frac{3}{2}\cdot\left(\frac{2}{3}\right)}{1!}+\frac{\frac{3}{2}\cdot\frac{5}{2}}{2!}\left(\frac{2}{3}\right)^2+\frac{\frac{3}{2}\cdot\frac{5}{2}\cdot\frac{7}{2}}{3!}\left(\frac{2}{3}\right)^3+\ldots$$

$$= 2+\frac{\frac{3}{2}\cdot\frac{5}{2}}{2!}\left(\frac{2}{3}\right)^2+\frac{\frac{3}{2}\cdot\frac{5}{2}\cdot\frac{7}{2}}{3!}\left(\frac{2}{3}\right)^3+\frac{\frac{3}{2}\cdot\frac{5}{2}\cdot\frac{7}{2}\cdot\frac{9}{2}}{4!}\left(\frac{2}{3}\right)^4+\ldots$$

$$= 2+\frac{3\cdot5}{2!}\frac{1}{3^2}+\frac{3\cdot5\cdot7}{3!}\frac{1}{3^3}+\frac{3\cdot5\cdot7\cdot9}{4!}\frac{1}{3^4}+\ldots$$

$$= 2+\frac{5}{2!3}+\frac{5\cdot7}{3!\,3^2}+\frac{5\cdot7\cdot9}{4!\,3^3}+\ldots$$

which is the required expression, and thus is equal to $\left(\frac{1}{3}\right)^{-3/2} = 3\sqrt{3}.$

22. By Leibniz's theorem,

$$D^n(uv) = D^nu\cdot v+nD^{n-1}u\cdot Dv+\frac{n(n-1)}{2!}D^{n-2}u\cdot D^2v+\ldots+nDu\cdot D^{n-1}v+uD^nv.$$

Let $u = x$ and $v = \sin ax$.

$\therefore\ Du = 1 \qquad Dv = a\cos ax$

$D^2u = 0 \qquad D^2v = -a^2\sin ax$

$D^3u = 0 \qquad D^3v = -a^3\cos ax$

$\ldots\ldots\ldots \qquad D^4v = a^4\sin ax$

$$D_nu = 0 \qquad D^nv = \begin{cases} (-1)^{n/2}a^n\sin ax & (n\text{ even}) \\ (-1)^{\frac{n-1}{2}}a^n\cos ax & (n\text{ odd}) \end{cases}$$

i.e. $$D^nv = a^n\sin\left(ax+\frac{n\pi}{2}\right)$$

For n even

$$D^n(x\sin ax) = n\cdot1\cdot(-1)^{n/2-1}a^{n-1}\cos ax+x\cdot(-1)^{n/2}a^n\sin ax$$
$$= (-1)^{n/2-1}a^{n-1}(n\cos ax-xa\sin ax)$$

For n odd

$$D^n(x\sin ax) = n\cdot 1\cdot a^{n-1}(-1)^{(n-1)/2}\sin ax + x(-1)^{(n-1)/2}a^n\cos ax$$
$$= (-1)^{(n-1)/2}a^{n-1}(n\sin ax + xa\cos ax)$$

i.e. $D^n(x\sin ax) = xa^n \sin\left(ax+\frac{n\pi}{2}\right)+na^{n-1}\sin\left(ax+[n-1]\frac{\pi}{2}\right).$

23. By Example 44, $1+\frac{1}{m}+\left(\frac{1}{m}\right)^2+\left(\frac{1}{m}\right)^3+\ldots = 1\cdot\frac{1}{1-\frac{1}{m}} = \frac{m}{m-1} = \frac{100}{99}$ when $m = 100$.

$\therefore$ Achilles catches the tortoise at a distance $1\frac{1}{99}$ from his starting point. To every position of Achilles there is a corresponding position of the tortoise. That is, if Achilles is to overtake the tortoise at U, then the segment A_1U must contain the same number of points as the segment T_1U. For the Greeks, this was an impossible idea, and it was left to Cantor to put the theory of equivalent infinite sets on a logical basis. [See Chapter 13.]

Did Zeno really believe his argument? Some authorities consider that he merely used the paradox to discredit certain philosophic doctrines current in his day.

24. Graphically, $y = \frac{1}{x\log x}$ resembles the curve $y = \frac{1}{x}$. With a diagram like Fig. 19, commence at $n = 2$.

$$\therefore \int_2^n \frac{dx}{x\log x} = \int_{x=2}^{x=n}\frac{d\log x}{\log x} = \Big[\log\log x\Big]_2^n = \log\left[\frac{\log n}{\log 2}\right] = \log_e(\log_2 n).$$

Area of rectangles $= \frac{1}{2\log 2}+\frac{1}{3\log 3}+\ldots+\frac{1}{n\log n}$ since the width of each rectangle is 1.

Area under the curve bounded by $x = 2$, $x = n$ is $\int_2^n \frac{dx}{x\log x} = \log(\log_2 n)$.

$$\therefore S_n \equiv \frac{1}{2\log 2}+\frac{1}{3\log 3}+\frac{1}{4\log 4}+\ldots+\frac{1}{n\log n} > \log(\log_2 n).$$

Now as $n\to\infty$, $\log(\log_2 n)\to\infty$. Hence S_n increases indefinitely. Thus S_n is a divergent series.

If $n = 512$, $\log_2 n = 9$. $\therefore \log_e(\log_2 n) = \log_e 9 > 2$ as $e < 3$ $\therefore S_n > 2$.

25. $\lim_{n\to\infty}(S_{2n}-\log 2n) = \gamma$ $\quad\therefore \lim_{n\to\infty}(S_{2n}-\log n) = \gamma+\log 2.$

But $\lim_{n\to\infty}(S_n-\log n) = \gamma$.

Subtract $\quad\therefore \lim_{n\to\infty}\{S_{2n}-\log n-(S_n-\log n)\} = \gamma+\log 2-\gamma = \log 2$

i.e. $\lim_{n\to\infty}(S_{2n}-S_n) = \log 2$, i.e. $\frac{1}{n+1}+\frac{1}{n+2}+\ldots+\frac{1}{2n} = \log 2.$

Next, $\frac{1}{jn}+\frac{1}{jn+1}+\ldots+\frac{1}{kn} = S_{kn}-S_{jn} \quad (j < k).$

But $\lim_{n\to\infty} (S_{jn}-\log jn) = \gamma = \lim_{n\to\infty} (S_{jn}-\log j-\log n)$

$$\therefore \lim_{n\to\infty} \left(\frac{1}{jn}+\frac{1}{jn+1}+\ldots+\frac{1}{kn}\right) = \lim_{n\to\infty} (S_{kn}-S_{jn})$$

$$= \lim_{n\to\infty} (S_{kn}-\log n)-\lim_{n\to\infty} (S_{jn}-\log_n) = (\gamma+\log k)-(\gamma+\log j) = \log\left(\frac{k}{j}\right).$$

26. $A(=\lim_{n\to\infty} A_n) = \frac{4}{3}\Delta+\frac{4}{3}\cdot\frac{\Delta}{3^2}\left(1+\frac{4}{3\cdot 3}+\ldots\right)$

$$= \frac{4}{3}\Delta+\frac{4}{3}\cdot\frac{\Delta}{3^2}\cdot\frac{1}{1-4/9} \quad \text{using Example 44}$$

$$= \frac{8}{5}\Delta.$$

27. By (91.2), $\cos\frac{c}{k} \to 1-\frac{1}{2!}\left(\frac{c}{k}\right)^2$. $\therefore$ the formula becomes

$$1-\frac{c^2}{2k^2} \doteqdot \left(1-\frac{a^2}{2k^2}\right)\left(1-\frac{b^2}{2k^2}\right) \text{ i.e. } c^2 \doteqdot a^2+b^2.$$

28. $\alpha > \frac{\pi}{2}-p \quad \therefore \tan\left\{\frac{\alpha}{2}\right\} > \tan\left(\frac{\pi}{4}-\frac{p}{2}\right) = \frac{1-\tan(p/2)}{1+\tan(p/2)}$.

But $\tan\left\{\frac{\alpha}{2}\right\} = e^{-x/k} \quad \therefore e^{x/k} < \frac{1+\tan(p/2)}{1-\tan(p/2)}$.

$$\therefore \frac{x}{k} < \log\left(\frac{1+\tan(p/2)}{1-\tan(p/2)}\right) \quad \left(\text{assuming } \frac{p}{2} < \frac{\pi}{4}\right)$$

$$= 2\left[\tan(p/2)+\frac{1}{3}\tan^3\left(\frac{p}{2}\right)+\frac{1}{5}\tan^5\left(\frac{p}{2}\right)+\ldots\right] \quad \text{by (95).}$$

Also $\tan p = \frac{2\tan(p/2)}{1-\tan^2(p/2)} = 2\left[\tan(p/2)+\tan^3\left(\frac{p}{2}\right)+\tan^5\left(\frac{p}{2}\right)+\ldots\right]$

$$\therefore \frac{x}{k} < \tan p.$$

29. Conditionally convergent since $1-\frac{1}{2}+\frac{1}{3}-\frac{1}{4}+\ldots = \log 2$ by (93) while $1+\frac{1}{2}+\frac{1}{3}+\frac{1}{4}+\ldots$ (harmonic series) diverges.

30. Absolutely convergent since $1+\frac{1}{2!}+\frac{1}{3!}+\frac{1}{4!}+\ldots$ is convergent (Exercise 9.2).

31. Conditionally convergent since $1-\frac{1}{3}+\frac{1}{5}\ldots = \frac{\pi}{4}$ by (101) while $1+\frac{1}{3}+\frac{1}{5}+\frac{1}{7}+\ldots$ diverges by D'Alembert's test. (See Exercise 9.3.)

32. Absolutely convergent since $1+\frac{1}{2^2}+\frac{1}{3^2}+\frac{1}{4^2}+\ldots$ is convergent by (87) ($p = 2$). By Exercise 9.20 its sum is $\pi^2/6$.

33. Absolutely convergent by the comparison test since $\left|\dfrac{\sin nx}{n^2}\right| \leqslant \dfrac{1}{n^2}$ and $\sum_{n=1}^{\infty} \dfrac{1}{n^2}$ converges.

Note that $\displaystyle\int_1^{\infty} \frac{\sin(\pi/x)}{x^2}\,dx = -\frac{1}{\pi}\int_{\pi}^{0} \sin\omega\, d\omega \left(\omega = \frac{\pi}{x}\right)$

$= \dfrac{1}{\pi}\Big[\cos\omega\Big]_{\pi}^{0} = \dfrac{2}{\pi} \quad \therefore \sum \dfrac{\sin(\pi/n)}{n^2}$ converges.

[Irrespective of their known values, the series 29–33 could have been checked for convergence by (88).]

34. $x(e^x-1)^{-1} = (1+X)^{-1}$ where $X = \dfrac{x}{2!}+\dfrac{x^2}{3!}+\dfrac{x^3}{4!}+\dfrac{x^4}{5!}+\ldots$

$$= 1-X+X^2-X^3+X^4-X^5+\ldots\ldots$$

$$= 1-\frac{1}{2!}x+x^2\left(-\frac{1}{3!}+\frac{1}{(2!)^2}\right)+x^3\left(-\frac{1}{4!}+\frac{2}{2!\,3!}-\frac{1}{(2!)^3}\right)$$

$$+x^4\left(-\frac{1}{5!}+\frac{1}{(3!)^2}+\frac{2}{2!\,4!}-\frac{3}{(2!)^2 3!}+\frac{1}{(2!)^4}\right)$$

$$+x^5\left(-\frac{1}{6!}+\frac{2}{3!\,4!}+\frac{2}{2!\,5!}-\frac{3}{2!(3!)^2}-\frac{3}{(2!)^2 4!}+\frac{4}{(2!)^3 3!}-\frac{1}{(2!)^5}\right)+\ldots$$

$$= 1-\frac{1}{2!}x+\frac{x^2}{12}+0\cdot x^3-\frac{1}{720}x^4+0\cdot x^5+\ldots$$

$$\therefore B_0 = 1,\ B_1 = -\tfrac{1}{2},\ B_2 = \tfrac{1}{6},\ B_4 = -\tfrac{1}{30},\ \ldots B_3 = B_5 = \ldots = 0.$$

35. $\dfrac{u_{n+1}}{u_n} = \dfrac{(a+n)(b+n)}{(1+n)(c+n)}x \to x$ as $n \to \infty$.

$\therefore$ the series converges for $|x| < 1$, diverges for $|x| > 1$. Cases $x = \pm 1$ require the use of Gauss' test.

36. $F(1, b, b; x)$ (say). **37.** $F(-n, b, b; -x)$ (say).

38. $\dfrac{F(a, b, b; -x)-1}{-a}$, then put $a = 0$, or $xF(1, 1, 2; -x)$.

39. $F_{-1} = 0 = A+B\ldots$ (i). $F_0 = 1 = Aa+Bb\ldots$ (ii). $F_1 = 1 = Aa^2+Bb^2\ldots$ (iii).

$\therefore$ (i), (ii), (iii) $\Rightarrow B = -A,\ A = \dfrac{1}{a-b},\ a+b = 1. \quad \therefore b = 1-a\ldots$ (iv).

Now $F_{n+1} = F_n+F_{n-1}$ (recurrence relation)

$$\Rightarrow A(a^{2+n}-b^{n+2}) = A(a^{n+1}-b^{n+1})+A(a^n-b^n)$$

i.e. $A\{a^n(a^2-a-1)-b^n(b^2-b-1)\} = 0 \quad (A \neq 0)$

$\therefore (a^n-b^n)(a^2-a-1) = 0 \quad \because b^2-b-1 = a^2-a-1$ using (iv)

$\therefore a^2-a-1 = 0\,(= b^2-b-1) \quad \because b \neq a$

$\therefore a, b$ are roots of $x^2-x-1 = 0 \left(a+b = 1,\ ab = -1,\ a-b = \sqrt{5},\ A = \dfrac{1}{\sqrt{5}}\right)$.

40. If $\sinh\alpha = \frac{1}{2}$, then $\cosh\alpha = \dfrac{\sqrt{5}}{2}$ $\because \cosh^2\alpha - \sinh^2\alpha = 1$

$$\therefore\ a = \frac{1+\sqrt{5}}{2} = \sinh\alpha+\cosh\alpha = e^{\alpha},\ b = \frac{1-\sqrt{5}}{2} = \sinh\alpha-\cosh\alpha = -e^{-\alpha}$$

$$\therefore\ a^{n+1}-b^{n+1} = e^{(n+1)\alpha}-(-1)^{n+1}e^{-(n+1)\alpha} = \begin{cases} e^{(n+1)\alpha}-e^{-(n+1)\alpha}\ (n \text{ odd}) \\ = 2\sinh(n+1)\alpha \\ e^{(n+1)\alpha}+e^{-(n+1)\alpha}\ (n \text{ even}) \\ = 2\cosh(n+1)\alpha \end{cases}$$

$$\therefore\ F_n = \frac{a^{n+1}-b^{n+1}}{\sqrt{5}} = \frac{\sinh(n+1)\alpha}{\cosh\alpha}\ (n \text{ odd}), = \frac{\cosh(n+1)\alpha}{\cosh\alpha}\ (n \text{ even}).$$

41. By Exercise 9.39, $\lim\limits_{n\to\infty}\left(\dfrac{F_n}{F_{n-1}}\right) = \lim\limits_{n\to\infty}\left(\dfrac{a^{n+1}-b^{n+1}}{a^n-b^n}\right)$

$$= \lim_{n\to\infty}\left(\frac{a^{n+1}}{a^n}\right)\ \left(\because \lim_{n\to\infty} b^n = 0 \text{ because } b < 1\right) = a = e^{\alpha}.$$

42. By Exercise 9.39, $F_{n-1}F_{n+1}-F_n^2 = \frac{1}{5}\{(a^n-b^n)(a^{n+2}-b^{n+2})-(a^{n+1}-b^{n+1})^2\}$

$= \frac{1}{5}\{a^{2n+2}+b^{2n+2}-a^nb^n(a^2+b^2)-a^{2n+2}-b^{2n+2}+2a^{n+1}b^{n+1}\}$

$= \frac{1}{5}\{-3(ab)^n+2(ab)^{n+1}\}$ $\because a^2+b^2 = 3$

$= \frac{1}{5}\{3(ab)^{n+1}+2(ab)^{n+1}\} = (ab)^{n+1} = (-1)^{n+1}$ $\because ab = -1.$

43. $F_0 = F_2-F_1,\ F_1 = F_3-F_2,\ F_2 = F_4-F_3,\ F_3 = F_5-F_4,\ \ldots,\ F_{n-1} = F_{n+1}-F_n,\ F_n = F_{n+2}-F_{n+1}.$

Addition gives the result.

44.
$$\begin{aligned}(1-\overline{x+x^2})^{-1} &= 1+x+x^2+(x+x^2)^2+(x+x^2)^3+(x+x^2)^4+\ldots \\ &= 1+x+(1+1)x^2+(2+1)x^3+(1+3+1)x^4+(1+4+3)x^5 \\ &\quad +(1+5+6+1)x^6+\ldots \\ &= F_0+F_1x+F_2x^2+F_3x^3+F_4x^4+F_5x^5+\ldots = \sum_{n=0}^{\infty} F_nx^n.\end{aligned}$$

Observe that the coefficient of x^n is $\binom{n}{0}+\binom{n-1}{1}+\binom{n-2}{2}+\binom{n-3}{3}+\ldots = F_n$

(Can you establish this formula ?)

45. 1, 2; 2, 1 respectively **46.** 1, 3; 2, 1. **47.** 2, 4; 2, 1. **48.** a, $a+d$; 2, 1.

49. a, aq; $q+1$, q. **50.** 1, 1; 1, -1. **51.** 2, 1; 1, -1. **52.** 2, 3; 3, 2.

53. 1, 2; 2, -1. **54.** 2, $2\cos\theta$; $2\cos\theta$, 1. **55.** 1, $2\cos\theta$; $2\cos\theta$, 1.

56. Assume a solution $V_n = Aa^n+Bb^n$.

$\therefore\ V_0 = 2 = A+B,\ V_1 = 1 = Aa+Bb = 1$ (a, b as in Exercise 9.39)

$\therefore\ A = B = 1$ $\therefore\ V_n = a^n+b^n$.

57. $U_nV_n = \dfrac{(a^n-b^n)}{\sqrt{5}}(a^n+b^n) = \dfrac{a^{2n}-b^{2n}}{\sqrt{5}} = U_{2n}$

58. The sequence is monotonically increasing. Since $u_{n+1}^2 = 1+u_n$, we have

$$u_{n+1} = \frac{1+u_n}{u_{n+1}} < \frac{1+u_{n+1}}{u_{n+1}} < 1+\frac{1}{u_{n+1}} \quad \therefore\ 1 < u_{n+1} < 2 \text{ for all } n.$$

$$\therefore \text{ as } n \to \infty,\ u_{n+1} \to a : a = 1+\frac{1}{a} \text{ i.e. } a^2-a-1 = 0,$$

i.e. the limit of the sequence is a (the +ve root of $x^2-x-1 = 0$—see Exercise 9.39.

59. $$\left|\frac{21n+35-3(7n-1)}{7(7n-1)}\right| < \varepsilon \Rightarrow \frac{38}{7(7n-1)} < \varepsilon \Rightarrow n > \frac{1}{7}\left(\frac{38}{7\varepsilon}+1\right) = \frac{1}{7}\left(\frac{38000}{7}+1\right)$$

$$= 775\frac{32}{49}$$

$\therefore\ N \geqslant 776$ (i.e. least value of N is 776)

$\therefore$ all terms of the sequence beyond the 776th term differ from $\frac{3}{7}$ in (absolute) value by less than 0·001.

60. The verification is straightforward.

EXERCISES 10

1. $\sqrt[3]{2}\cdot\sqrt[3]{4} = \sqrt[3]{8} = 2$. Thus $\sqrt[3]{2}\cdot\sqrt[3]{4}$ is rational.

2. $\sqrt{2}$ and $\sqrt{3}$ are both irrational. Thus, $\sqrt{2}+\sqrt{3}$ is irrational.

3. $\dfrac{\sqrt{27}}{\sqrt{3}} = \dfrac{3\sqrt{3}}{\sqrt{3}} = 3$. Thus $\dfrac{\sqrt{27}}{\sqrt{3}}$ is rational.

4. $\sqrt{2}-1$ is irrational since $\sqrt{2}$ is irrational.

5. $\sqrt{625}+\sqrt{841} = 25+29 = 54$. Thus $\sqrt{625}+\sqrt{841}$ is rational.

6. Let $x = 0{\cdot}9999\ldots$ $\therefore\ 10x = 9{\cdot}9999\ldots$ $\therefore\ 9x = 9{\cdot}0$ (subtracting) $\therefore\ x = 1$. Thus $\cdot\dot{9}$ is rational.

7. $$\sin 7\tfrac{1}{2}^\circ = \sqrt{\frac{1-\cos 15^\circ}{2}} = \sqrt{\frac{1}{2}\left\{1-\sqrt{\frac{1+\cos 30^\circ}{2}}\right\}}$$

$$= \sqrt{\frac{1}{2}\left\{1-\frac{1}{2}\sqrt{2+\sqrt{3}}\right\}}$$

which is irrational.

8. $\log_{10} k = n$ (rational) if $k = 10^n$.

9. No, since there is no multiplicative unity.

10. No, since there is no additive inverse.

11–14. Yes, commutative rings with unity and without zero-divisors (i. e. integral domains).

15. Yes, a commutative ring with unity, but with zero-divisors, since $2\times2 \equiv 0 \pmod 4$ (i.e. not an integral domain).

16. No, since there is no additive inverse.

17. Yes, a commutative ring with additive inverse $(-f)(x) = -[f(x)]$ and zero $0(x) = 0$.

18, 21, 23. Ring and field. (Real numbers thus constitute a subring and a subfield of $\mathcal{C}$.)

19. Ring but not field. (Note Exercise 9.39 for multiplicative closure.)

20. Neither ring nor field, since multiplicatively not closed.

22. Ring but not field since there is no multiplicative inverse, e.g.

$$\frac{1}{3+\sqrt{2}} = \frac{3}{7} - \frac{1}{7}\sqrt{2} \quad \text{and} \quad \frac{3}{7}, \quad \frac{1}{7} \notin \mathcal{J}.$$

24. Ring but not field, since multiplication is non-commutative.

25. Euclid's proof. Suppose there are exactly n (finite) primes arranged in order: 2, 3, 5, 7, ..., p_n. Consider the number $N = 2\cdot3\cdot5\cdot7 \ldots p_n+1$. Either N is a prime or it is not a prime. If N is not a prime, then it is divisible by some number less than itself. But it is not divisible by 2, 3, 5, 7, ..., p_n. Therefore, N is a prime and so we have found a prime in addition to the n primes given. Thus, the hypothesis is false. Therefore, the number of primes is infinite. [Reference: Euclid's *Elements*, Book 9, Proposition 20. Euclid's actual wording, given in terms of line-segments, is essentially identical with our statement.]

26. $1-5i$. **27.** $26-2i$.

28. $\dfrac{5-3i}{4+2i} \times \dfrac{4-2i}{4-2i} = \dfrac{14-22i}{20} = \dfrac{7-11i}{10}$.

29. $z^{1/2} = x+iy \Rightarrow |z^{1/2}| = \sqrt{x^2+y^2}$ and $z = (x+iy)^2 = x^2-y^2+2xyi$

$$\Rightarrow |z| = \sqrt{(x^2-y^2)^2+(2xy)^2} = x^2+y^2 \quad \therefore \ |z|^{1/2} = |z^{1/2}| \,(= \sqrt{x^2+y^2}).$$

$z = -15+8i \Rightarrow |z| = 17 \Rightarrow |z|^{1/2} = \sqrt{17} = |\pm(1+4i)| = |z^{1/2}|$ where, to obtain $z^{1/2}$, we write $z^{1/2} = x+iy$ whence $z = x^2-y^2+2xyi = -15+8i$; then solve for real and imaginary parts, namely $x^2+y^2 = -15$, $2xy = 8$.

30. $$\left(\frac{1-i\sqrt{3}}{2}\right)^3 = \frac{1}{8}(1-i\sqrt{3})^3 = \frac{1}{8}(1-3\cdot i\sqrt{3}+3\cdot 3i^2-i^3\, 3\sqrt{3})$$

$$= \frac{1}{8}(-8-3i\sqrt{3}+3i\sqrt{3}) = -1.$$

$$\left[\text{Notice that } \frac{1-i\sqrt{3}}{2} \text{ is a cube root } -\varepsilon \text{ of } -1 \text{ so that } (-\varepsilon)^3 = -1.\right]$$

31. $\dfrac{1}{(1+i)^2} + \dfrac{1}{(1-i)^2} = \dfrac{1-2i-1+1+2i-1}{(1+i)^2\,(1-i)^2} = 0.$

32. $\dfrac{1+\cos\theta+i\sin\theta}{\cos\theta/2+i\sin\theta/2} = \dfrac{1+e^{i\theta}}{e^{i\theta/2}} = e^{-i\theta/2}+e^{i\theta/2} = 2\cos\dfrac{\theta}{2}.$

33. $\dfrac{2+3i}{3-2i} = \dfrac{2+3i}{3-2i}\cdot\dfrac{3+2i}{3+2i} = \dfrac{6+13i-6}{9+4} = \dfrac{13i}{13} = i \quad (\text{i.e. } 0+1\cdot i)$

$\therefore$ modulus $= 1$, argument $= \tan^{-1}\left(\dfrac{1}{0}\right) = \tan^{-1}\infty = \dfrac{\pi}{2}.$

34. $e^z = e^{x+iy} = e^x\cdot e^{iy} = e^x(\cos y+i\sin y) = e^x\cos y+i\,e^x\sin y.$

$\therefore$ modulus $= e^x$, argument $= y$.

35. $(1+i) = \sqrt{2}\left(\dfrac{1}{\sqrt{2}}+\dfrac{i}{\sqrt{2}}\right) = \sqrt{2}\left\{\cos\dfrac{\pi}{4}+i\sin\dfrac{\pi}{4}\right\} = 2^{1/2}\cdot e^{(\pi/4)i}$

$\therefore (1+i)^{1/2} = \pm\, 2^{1/4}\cdot e^{(1/8)\pi i} \quad \therefore$ modulus $= 2^{1/4}$, argument $= \frac{1}{8}\pi$.

36. $(3-3i) = 3\sqrt{2}\left(\dfrac{1}{\sqrt{2}}-\dfrac{i}{\sqrt{2}}\right) = 3\sqrt{2}\left\{\cos\dfrac{\pi}{4}-i\sin\dfrac{\pi}{4}\right\} = 3\sqrt{2}\, e^{-i\pi/4}$

$(3-3i)^{2/3} = 18^{1/3}\cdot e^{-i\pi/6} \quad \therefore$ modulus $= 18^{1/3}$, argument $= -\dfrac{\pi}{6}$.

37. $2^i = e^{i\log 2} = \cos\log 2 + i\sin\log 2$.

38. $i^{-\pi} = (e^{i\pi/2})^{-\pi} = e^{-i\pi^2/2} = \cos\dfrac{\pi^2}{2} - i\sin\dfrac{\pi^2}{2}$.

39 $(-i)^{-i} = (e^{-i\pi/2})^{-i} = e^{-\pi/2}$.

40. $1+i = \sqrt{2}\, e^{i\pi/4} \quad \therefore \log(1+i) = \log\{\sqrt{2}\, e^{i\pi/4}\} = \log\sqrt{2} + i\dfrac{\pi}{4}$

$\therefore\ i^{\log(1+i)} = (e^{i\pi/2})^{\{\log\sqrt{2}+i\pi/4\}} = e^{\frac{i\pi\log\sqrt{2}}{2}}\cdot e^{-\frac{\pi^2}{8}}$

$= e^{\frac{i\pi\log 2}{4}}\cdot e^{-\frac{\pi^2}{8}} = e^{-\pi^2/8}\left\{\cos\left(\dfrac{\pi\log 2}{4}\right)+i\sin\left(\dfrac{\pi\log 2}{4}\right)\right\}$.

41. $(1+i)^{-i} = e^{\pi/4}\left(\sqrt{2}\right)^{-1} = e^{\pi/4}\cdot e^{-i\log\sqrt{2}} = e_{\pi/4} \qquad \sqrt{2} - i\, e^{\pi/4}\sin\log\sqrt{2}$.

42. $e^{1+i} = e^1 e^i = e(\cos 1 + i\sin 1) = e\cos 1 + ie\sin 1$.

43. $i^{1/\pi} = (e^{\pi/2})^{1/\pi} = e^{i/2} = \cos\frac{1}{2} + i\sin\frac{1}{2}$.

44. $e^{1+\pi i} = e^1 e^{\pi i} = -e$.

45. $e^{3-4\pi i} = e^3 e^{-4\pi i} = e^3$.

46. $\sinh(1-i) = \frac{1}{2}[e^{1-i}-e^{-1+i}] = \frac{1}{2}[e(\cos 1 - i\sin 1) - e^{-1}(\cos 1 + i\sin 1)]$

$= \dfrac{1}{2}\left[\left(e-\dfrac{1}{e}\right)\cos 1 - i\left(e+\dfrac{1}{e}\right)\sin 1\right] = \sinh 1\cos 1 - i\cosh 1\sin 1$

$= k(\cos\alpha + i\sin\alpha)$ where $\alpha = \tan^{-1}(\tan 1\coth 1)$,

$k = (\sinh^2 1\cos^2 1 + \cosh^2 1\sin^2 1)^{1/2} = (\sin^2 1 + \sinh^2 1)^{1/2}$.

47. $1-i = \sqrt{2}\left\{\cos\dfrac{\pi}{4} - i\sin\dfrac{\pi}{4}\right\}$ *or:* $\dfrac{1-i}{1+i} = \dfrac{(1-i)(1-i)}{(1+i)(1-i)}$

$= \sqrt{2}\, e^{-i\pi/4} \qquad\qquad = \dfrac{-2i}{2}$

$1+i = \sqrt{2}\, e^{i\pi/4} \qquad\qquad = -i$

$\therefore\ \dfrac{1-i}{1+i} = e^{-i\pi/2} \qquad\qquad = e^{-i\pi/2}$

$\therefore \log\left(\dfrac{1-i}{1+i}\right) = -\dfrac{i\pi}{2} = \left(\dfrac{\pi}{2i}\right)$.

48. $C+iS = 1 + e^{2\pi i/n} + e^{4\pi i/n} + \ldots + e^{2(n-1)\pi i/n} = \dfrac{1-(e^{2\pi i/n})^n}{1-e^{2\pi i/n}}$

$= \dfrac{1-e^{2\pi i}}{1-e^{2\pi i/n}} = \dfrac{1-1}{1-e^{2\pi i/n}} = 0.$

Equate real and imaginary parts $\therefore C = 0, S = 0$.

49. $\sqrt{-1}^{\sqrt{-1}} = (-1)^{1/i} = (-1)^{-i} = (e^{\pi i})^{-i} = e^{\pi}$.

$$\therefore \log_e\left(\sqrt{-1}^{\sqrt{-1}}\right) = \pi; \qquad \log_{10}\left(\sqrt{-1}^{\sqrt{-1}}\right) = \pi \log_{10} e \doteqdot 0{\cdot}4343 \times 3{\cdot}1416 \doteqdot 1{\cdot}3644$$

$$\therefore \qquad \sqrt{-1}^{\sqrt{-1}} \doteqdot 23{\cdot}14.$$

50. Given $z_1 z_2 = z_3^2$ i.e. $\dfrac{z_1}{z_3} = \dfrac{z_3}{z_2}$ $\therefore \arg\left(\dfrac{z_1}{z_3}\right) = \arg\left(\dfrac{z_3}{z_2}\right)$

$\therefore \arg z_1 - \arg z_3 = \arg z_3 - \arg z_2$ i.e. $\theta_1 - \theta_3 = \theta_3 - \theta_2$ i.e. $\theta_3 = \frac{1}{2}(\theta_1 + \theta_2)$

i.e. OZ_3 bisects $\widehat{Z_1 O Z_2}$.

51. Let $z = x + iy$

$$\therefore \begin{cases} z+2 = x+2+iy & \text{and} \quad |z+2| = \sqrt{x^2+4x+4+y^2} \\ z-5i = x+(y-5)i & \text{and} \quad |z-5i| = \sqrt{x^2+y^2-10y+25.} \end{cases}$$

Thus, the locus is given by $x^2+4x+4+y^2 = x^2+y^2-10y+25$,

i.e. $4x+10y-21 = 0$, which is a straight line,

i.e. $(2-5i)z+(2+5i)\bar{z}-21 = 0$ by (124).

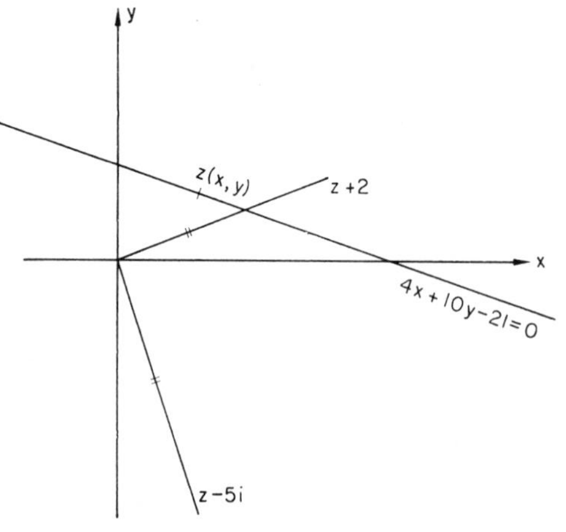

52. *Analytical solution.* Let $z = x+iy$. Then $|z| = 15 \Rightarrow \sqrt{x^2+y^2} = 15$ (1)

$\therefore |z-4| = 13 \Rightarrow \sqrt{(x-4)^2+y^2} = 13$ i.e. $\sqrt{x^2+y^2-8x+16} = 13$. (2)

Solving (1) and (2) we have $225-8x+16 = 169$ $\therefore x = 9, y = \pm 12$. Thus the required complex numbers are $9+12i$, $9-12i$.

Geometrical solution. (1) represents a circle, centre (0, 0) radius 15; (2) represents a circle, centre (4, 0) radius 13.

Clearly, these circles intersect at (9,12) and (9, −12).

53. $\dfrac{2i-3}{(1+i)^2} = x+iy = r\cos\theta+ir\sin\theta.$

$\therefore 2i-3 = (x+iy)(1+2i-1)$ i.e. $2i-3 = 2i\,x-2y.$

Equate real and imaginary parts: $\therefore x = 1,\ y = 1\frac{1}{2}$ i.e. $r\cos\theta = 1,\ r\sin\theta = 1\frac{1}{2}.$

$\therefore r = \dfrac{\sqrt{13}}{2}$ and $\cos\theta = \dfrac{2}{\sqrt{13}}$ i.e. $\theta = \cos^{-1}\left(\dfrac{2}{\sqrt{13}}\right) = 56°18'.$

54. $\dfrac{\sqrt{2}e^{-ix}}{2+i} = \dfrac{1-3i}{5}$ $\therefore 5\sqrt{2}\cos x-5\sqrt{2}\,i\sin x = 2-5i+3$

i.e. $\sqrt{2}\cos x-\sqrt{2}\,i\sin x = 1-i.$

Equate real and imaginary parts $\therefore \sqrt{2}\cos x = 1,\quad \sqrt{2}\sin x = 1\ \therefore x = \dfrac{\pi}{4}.$

55. $\sinh(a+ib) = 1+i = \dfrac{e^{a+ib}-e^{-a-ib}}{2}$

$\therefore 2+2i = e^a\cos b+i\,e^a\sin b-e^{-a}\cos b+ie^{-a}\sin b = (e^a-e^{-a})\cos b+$
$+(e^a+e^{-a})i\sin$ b.

Equate real and imaginary parts $\therefore 2 = (e^a-e^{-a})\cos b,\quad 2 = (e^a+e^{-a})\sin b$

$\therefore \tan b = \dfrac{e^a-e^{-a}}{e^a+e^{-a}} = \tanh a\ \therefore b = \tan^{-1}(\tanh a).$

56. $\sinh(x+iy) = \dfrac{e^{x+iy}-e^{-x-iy}}{2} = \dfrac{e^x(\cos y+i\sin y)-e^{-x}(\cos y-i\sin y)}{2}$

$= \left(\dfrac{e^x-e^{-x}}{2}\right)\cos y+i\left(\dfrac{e^x+e^{-x}}{2}\right)\sin y = \sinh x\cos y+i\cosh x\sin y$

$\therefore |\sinh(x+iy)| = \sqrt{\sinh^2 x\cos^2 y+\cosh^2 x\sin^2 y} = \sqrt{\cosh^2 x-\cos^2 y}$

$\therefore \arg\{\sinh(x+iy)\} = \tan^{-1}\left\{\dfrac{\cosh x\sin y}{\sinh x\cos y}\right\} = \tan^{-1}(\tan y\coth x).$

57. Roots of $x^4-hx^3-kx+1 = 0$ are a, b, c, d.

$\therefore \sum a = (a+b+c+d) = h,\quad \sum ab = 0,\quad \sum abc = k,\quad abcd = 1.$

Hence $\sum\dfrac{1}{a} = \dfrac{\sum abc}{abcd} = \dfrac{k}{1} = k,\quad \sum a^2 = (\sum a)^2-2\sum ab = h^2,$

$\sum\dfrac{1}{a^2} = \dfrac{(\sum abc)^2}{(abcd)^2} = \dfrac{(\sum abc)^2-2abcd\sum ab}{(abcd)^2} = k^2.$

58. Roots of $x^3+px^2+qx+r = 0$ are a, b, c.

$\therefore a+b+c = -p,\quad ab+bc+ac = q,\quad abc = -r.$

Now $b+c,\ c+a,\ a+b$ are the roots of equation $x^3+sx^2+tx+w = 0.$

Then $2(a+b+c) = -s$ i.e. $s = 2p$ (1)

and $(b+c)(c+a)+(b+c)(a+b)+(a+b)(a+c) = t$

i.e. $(a+b+c)^2+(ab+bc+ac) = t$ i.e. $t = p^2+q$ (2)

and $(b+c)(c+a)(a+b) = -w$ i.e. $(a+b+c)(ab+bc+ac)-abc = -w$

i.e. $w = pq-r.$ (3)

So, the required equation is $y^3+2py^2+(p^2+q)y+pq-r = 0.$

Alternative solution: Now $b+c = a+b+c-a = -p-a$,
i.e the root $b+c$ in the new equation corresponds to the root a in the original equation and we may write $y = -p-x$ i.e. $x = -p-y$.

Substitute this expression for x in the original equation

$\therefore (-p-y)^3+p(-p-y)^2+q(-p-y)+r = 0$ i.e. $y^3+2py^2+(p^2+q)y+pq-r = 0$.

59. $\log \sin (x+iy) = \alpha+i\beta \quad \therefore \sin (x+iy) = e^{\alpha+i\beta}$

$\therefore \sin x \cos iy+\cos x \sin iy = e^\alpha (\cos \beta+i \sin \beta)$

$\therefore \sin x \cosh y+i \cos x \sinh y = e^\alpha (\cos \beta+i \sin \beta)$

Equating real and imaginary parts, we have

$$e^\alpha \cos \beta = \sin x \cosh y \qquad (1)$$

$$e \ \sin \beta = \cos x \sinh y. \qquad (2)$$

Square (1) and (2) and add $\therefore e^{2\alpha} = \sin^2 x \cosh^2 y+\cos^2 x \sinh^2 y =$

$= (1-\cos^2 x) \cosh^2 y+\cos^2 x (\cosh^2 y-1) = \cosh^2 y-\cos^2 x$

$\therefore 2e^{2\alpha} = 2 \cosh^2 y-1-2 \cos^2 x+1 = \cosh 2y-\cos 2x$.

60. For each complex number given, obviously $R(z) = [I(z)]^2$, i.e. for a general complex point $z = x+iy$ on the locus, we have $y^2 = x$. Hence, the curve is a parabola, symmetrical about the axis of reals and passing through the origin (0, 0). Just five points (e.g. those given) fix a conic (and $\therefore$ the parabola) uniquely (Chapter 16). Points on it are of the form $z = y^2+iy$. Conjugates $\bar{z} = y^2-iy$ also lie on the parabola.

61. $$\int_0^1 \frac{dx}{x+i} = \Big[\log (x+i)\Big]_0^1 = \log \left(\frac{1+i}{i}\right) = \log (1-i) = \log (\sqrt{2}e^{-i\pi/4})$$

$$= \tfrac{1}{2} \log 2-\frac{\pi}{4}$$

$$\therefore A = \tfrac{1}{2} \log 2, \quad B = -\frac{\pi}{4}.$$

62. $f(\theta) = \cos \theta+i \sin \theta \Rightarrow f'(\theta) = -\sin \theta+i \cos \theta = i(\cos \theta+i \sin \theta)$

$$\therefore \frac{f'(\theta)}{f(\theta)} = i \Rightarrow \int \frac{f'(\theta)\, d\theta}{f(\theta)} = i \int d\theta \Rightarrow \log f(\theta) = i\theta+C.$$

Now $\theta = 0 \Rightarrow f(0) = 1 \quad \therefore \log 1 = C \quad \therefore C = 0 \quad \therefore \log f(\theta) = i\theta \quad \therefore f(\theta) = e^{i\theta}$.

63. $y = \cos (3 \cos^{-1} x) \Rightarrow y = \cos 3\theta = 4 \cos^3 \theta-3 \cos \theta = 4x^3-3x$ $(x = \cos \theta)$. Put $\cos 3\theta = a \quad \therefore 4x^3-3x-a = 0$ which is the algebraic form of the Greek trisection problem (§ 42). Substitute $3\theta = 120°$ and $2 \cos 40° = x$; then the cubic reduces to $x^3-3x+1 = 0$. [See Exercise 14.78.]

64. $A-B = (0, 3, 1, 0)$.

65. $BA = (1+2+0-1, 1-2+0-1, 1+0+2+1, 1+1-2-0) = (2,-2, 4, 0) \neq AB$.

66. $$\frac{A}{B} = \frac{(1, 1, 1, 1)}{(1, -2, 0, 1)} \times \frac{(1, 2, 0, -1)}{(1, 2, 0, -1)}$$

$$= \frac{(1-2-0+1,\ 2+1-1-0,\ 0+1+1+2,\ -1+1+0-2)}{1+4+1} = \frac{1}{6}(0, 2, 4, -2).$$

67. Now $q\bar{q} = a^2+b^2+c^2+d^2 = N(q)$, the *norm* of q; $\{N(q)\}^{1/2} \equiv$ *modulus* of q.

$$\therefore q^{-1} = \frac{\bar{q}}{N(q)} \Rightarrow qq^{-1} = \frac{q\bar{q}}{N(q)} = 1 \quad \therefore q^{-1} = \frac{a-bi-cj-dk}{a^2+b^2+c^2+d^2}.$$

[Other interesting results: $\overline{(q_1q_2)} = \bar{q}_2\bar{q}_1$, $N(q_1, q_2) = N(q_1)N(q_2)$ for quaternions q_1, q_2.]

68–70. $e^{i(A\pm B)} = e^{iA}e^{\pm iB}$.

$\therefore \cos(A\pm B)+i\sin(A\pm B) = (\cos A+i\sin A)(\cos B\pm i\sin B)$

$= \cos A\cos B\mp\sin A\sin B+i(\sin A\cos B\pm\cos A\sin B)$.

Equate real and imaginary parts to get 69, 68 respectively; 70 follows on dividing $\sin(A\pm B)/\cos(A\pm B)$ by $\cos A\cos B$.

71. $\cosh(1+i)a = \dfrac{e^a(\cos a+i\sin a)+e^a(\cos a-i\sin a)}{2}$

$$= \cosh a\cos a+i\sinh a\sin a = ke^{i\theta}$$

where $k\sin\theta = \sinh a\sin a$, $k\cos\theta = \cosh a\cos a$ (i).

$$\text{Now } R\{e^{iwt}\operatorname{sech} a\} = R\left\{\frac{e^{iwt}}{ke^{i\theta}}\cdot\frac{e^{-i\theta}}{e^{-i\theta}}\right\} = R\left\{\frac{e^{i(wt-\theta)}}{k}\right\}$$

$$= \frac{\cos(wt-\theta)}{k} = \frac{\cos wt\cos\theta+\sin wt\sin\theta}{k}$$

$$= \frac{\sin wt\cos\varepsilon+\cos wt\sin\varepsilon}{k},$$

$$= A\sin(wt+\varepsilon)$$

where $\cos\varepsilon = \sin\theta$, $\sin\varepsilon = \cos\theta$ i.e. $\tan\varepsilon = \cot\theta$, i.e. $\varepsilon = \tan^{-1}(\cot a\coth a)$ by (i)

and $A = \dfrac{1}{k} = (\cosh^2 a\cos^2 a+\sinh^2 a\sin^2 a)^{-1/2} = (\cos^2 a+\sinh^2 a)^{-1/2}$.

72. Keeping y constant, we have $z+\delta z = x+\delta x+iy$ $\therefore \delta z = \delta x$
$\therefore w+\delta w = u(x+\delta x, y)+iv(x+\delta x, y)$ where $u(x, y)$, $v(x, y)$ are the real and imaginary parts respectively of $f(z)$.

$$\therefore \delta w = u(x+\delta x, y)-u(x, y)+i\{v(x+\delta x, y)-v(x, y)\}$$

$$\therefore \lim_{\delta z\to 0}\left(\frac{\delta w}{\delta z}\right) = \lim_{\delta x\to 0}\left(\frac{\delta u}{\delta x}+i\frac{\delta v}{\delta x}\right) \quad \therefore f'(z) = \frac{\delta u}{\delta x}+i\frac{\delta v}{\delta x}. \tag{i}$$

Similarly, $\delta z = i\delta y$ (x kept constant) and

$$\lim_{\delta z\to 0}\left(\frac{\delta w}{\delta z}\right) = \lim_{\delta y\to 0}\left(\frac{\delta u}{i\delta y}+\frac{i\delta v}{i\delta y}\right) \quad \therefore f'(z) = -i\frac{\partial u}{\partial y}+\frac{\partial v}{\partial y}. \tag{ii}$$

$$\therefore \text{(i), (ii)} \Rightarrow \frac{\partial u}{\partial x} = \frac{\partial v}{\partial y}, \quad \frac{\partial u}{\partial y} = -\frac{\partial v}{\partial x}.$$

Differentiating w.r.t. x in the left equation, y in the second

$$\Rightarrow \frac{\partial^2 u}{\partial x^2} = \frac{\partial^2 v}{\partial x\,\partial y} = -\frac{\partial^2 u}{\partial y^2}.$$

Differentiating w.r.t. y in the left equation, x in the second

$$\Rightarrow \frac{\partial^2 v}{\partial y^2} = \frac{\partial^2 u}{\partial y\,\partial x} = -\frac{\partial^2 v}{\partial x^2}$$

$$\therefore \frac{\partial^2 u}{\partial x^2}+\frac{\partial^2 u}{\partial y^2} = 0, \quad \frac{\partial^2 v}{\partial x^2}+\frac{\partial^2 v}{\partial y^2} = 0.$$

73. $w = e^z = e^x(\cos y + i \sin y) \Rightarrow u = e^x \cos y,\ v = e^x \sin y$

$$\therefore\ \frac{\partial u}{\partial x} = e^x \cos\ y = \frac{\partial v}{\partial y},\qquad \frac{\partial u}{\partial y} = -e^x \sin y = -\frac{\partial v}{\partial x}$$

$$w = \frac{1}{z} = \frac{x-iy}{x^2+y^2} \Rightarrow u = \frac{x}{x^2+y^2},\qquad v = \frac{-y}{x^2+y^2}\qquad (|z| \neq 0)$$

$$\therefore\ \frac{\partial u}{\partial x} = \frac{y^2-x^2}{(x^2+y^2)^2} = \frac{\partial v}{\partial y},\qquad \frac{\partial v}{\partial x} = \frac{2xy}{(x^2+y^2)^2} = -\frac{\partial u}{\partial y}\ \text{on calculation.}$$

Laplace's equation is automatically satisfied in both cases.

74. Cauchy–Riemann equations give $\dfrac{\partial \psi}{\partial y} = \dfrac{\partial \phi}{\partial x} = 2x+3,\quad \dfrac{\partial \psi}{\partial x} = -\dfrac{\partial \phi}{\partial y} = 2y.$

Integrate $\therefore\ \psi = 2xy+3y+F(x),\quad \psi = 2yx+G(y).$
Since these must be equal, $F(x) = 0,\ G(y) = 3y\quad \therefore\ \psi = 2xy+3y$
$\therefore\ f(z) = x^2-y^2+3x+i(2xy+3y) = (x+iy)^2+3(x+iy) = z^2+3z.$

75. See the solution by D. Zeitlin, *The American Mathematical Monthly*, **66,** 513 (1959).

76.
$$e^{pi}\ \frac{1}{2\,pi\,D}\left(1+\frac{D}{2pi}\right)^{-1}\cdot\ 1 = e^{pix}\frac{1}{2piD}\left\{\left(1-\frac{D}{2pi}+\frac{D^2}{(2p)^2i^2}-\dots\right)\cdot 1\right\}$$

$$= e^{pix}\frac{1}{2piD}\cdot 1\quad (\because\ D\cdot 1 = D^2\cdot 1 = \dots = 0) = e^{pix}\frac{x}{2pi}$$

$$\left(\because\ \frac{1}{D}\cdot 1 = D^{-1}\cdot 1 = \int 1dx = x\quad \text{taking } c = 0\right)$$

$$= \frac{x}{2pi}(\cos px+i\sin px)\ \ \therefore\ \text{real part} = \frac{x \sin px}{2p}.$$

77. $x = i\cdot\dfrac{1}{i}\log\tan\left(\dfrac{\pi}{4}+\dfrac{i}{2}\ \dfrac{\phi}{i}\right) = iG\left(\dfrac{\phi}{i}\right) = iG(-i\phi).$

$\therefore\ ix = -G\{-iG(x)\} = G\{iG(x)\}\quad \therefore\ G(x)$ is odd.

78. $G^{-1}(ix) = iG\{x\}$ from Exercise 10.77.
Replace x by ix $\therefore\ G^{-1}(-x) = iG(ix) \Rightarrow G(ix) = -iG^{-1}(-x) = iG^{-1}(x).$

79.
$$\cos G(x) = \frac{1}{2}(e^{iG(x)}+e^{-iG(x)}) = \frac{1}{2}\left[\tan\left(\frac{\pi}{4}+\frac{ix}{2}\right)+\cot\left(\frac{\pi}{4}+\frac{ix}{2}\right)\right]$$

$$= \frac{1}{2}\left[\frac{1+\tan(ix/2)}{1-\tan(ix/2)}+\frac{1-\tan(ix/2)}{1+\tan(ix/2)}\right]$$

$$= \frac{1+\tan^2(ix/2)}{1-\tan^2(ix/2)} = \frac{1}{\cos ix}\quad \therefore\ \sec G(x) = \cos ix = \frac{e^x+e^{-x}}{2}$$

$$= \cosh x$$

80. Similarly, $\sin G(x) = \dfrac{\sin ix}{i\cos ix} = \tanh x$

$\therefore\ \tan G(x) = -i\sin ix = \frac{1}{2}(e^x-e^{-x}) = \sinh x.$

EXERCISES 11

1. AC is 2×3. **2.** DA is 3×3. **3.** AD is 2×2.

4. BC is 4×3. **5.** CB cannot be defined. **6.** DAC is 3×3.

7. $BCDA$ is 4×3. **8.** No (by Exercises 11.2, 11.3).

9. No (by Exercises 11.4, 11.5).

10. $A+B$ can be defined only if A also has 3 columns and B 3 rows.

11. $A+B = \begin{bmatrix} 3 & 3 & 1 \\ 5 & -5 & 7 \\ -2 & -1 & 8 \end{bmatrix}$ **12.** $A-B = \begin{bmatrix} -1 & 3 & 3 \\ -1 & 5 & 3 \\ 14 & 3 & 6 \end{bmatrix}$

13. $AB = \begin{bmatrix} -5 & -19 & 7 \\ -36 & -10 & 3 \\ -41 & -19 & 3 \end{bmatrix}$ **14.** $BA = \begin{bmatrix} -4 & 5 & -3 \\ 5 & 11 & -5 \\ -6 & -23 & -19 \end{bmatrix}$

15. $A = \begin{bmatrix} 2 & -5 \\ 3 & 1 \end{bmatrix} \quad \therefore A^2 = \begin{bmatrix} -11 & -15 \\ 9 & -14 \end{bmatrix}$

$$\therefore \alpha I+\beta A+\gamma A^2 = \begin{bmatrix} \alpha & 0 \\ 0 & \alpha \end{bmatrix} + \begin{bmatrix} 2\beta & -5\beta \\ 3\beta & \beta \end{bmatrix} + \begin{bmatrix} -11\gamma & -15\gamma \\ 9\gamma & -14\gamma \end{bmatrix}$$

$$= \begin{bmatrix} \alpha+2\beta-11\gamma, & -5\beta-15\gamma \\ 3\beta+9\gamma, & \alpha+\beta-14\gamma \end{bmatrix} = O \quad \text{(not zero but the zero matrix of order } 2\times2)$$

i.e. if $\alpha+2\beta-11\gamma = 0$, $5\beta+15\gamma = 0$, $\alpha+\beta-14\gamma = 0$, $3\beta+9\gamma = 0$. Solving these equations, we have $\beta = -3\gamma$, $\alpha = 17\gamma$ i.e. $\gamma = K$ (say), $\alpha = 17K$, $\beta = -3K$.

16. $A = \begin{bmatrix} 1 & 3 & 2 \\ 2 & 0 & -1 \\ 1 & 2 & 3 \end{bmatrix} \quad \therefore A^2 = \begin{bmatrix} 9 & 7 & 5 \\ 1 & 4 & 1 \\ 8 & 9 & 9 \end{bmatrix}$

$$A^3 = \begin{bmatrix} 1 & 3 & 2 \\ 2 & 0 & -1 \\ 1 & 2 & 3 \end{bmatrix} \begin{bmatrix} 9 & 7 & 5 \\ 1 & 4 & 1 \\ 8 & 9 & 9 \end{bmatrix} = \begin{bmatrix} 28 & 37 & 26 \\ 10 & 5 & 1 \\ 35 & 42 & 34 \end{bmatrix}$$

$\therefore A^3-4A^2-3A+11I =$

$$= \begin{bmatrix} 28 & 37 & 26 \\ 10 & 5 & 1 \\ 35 & 42 & 34 \end{bmatrix} - \begin{bmatrix} 36 & 28 & 20 \\ 4 & 16 & 4 \\ 32 & 36 & 36 \end{bmatrix} - \begin{bmatrix} 3 & 9 & 6 \\ 6 & 0 & -3 \\ 3 & 6 & 9 \end{bmatrix} + \begin{bmatrix} 11 & 0 & 0 \\ 0 & 11 & 0 \\ 0 & 0 & 11 \end{bmatrix} = \begin{bmatrix} 0 & 0 & 0 \\ 0 & 0 & 0 \\ 0 & 0 & 0 \end{bmatrix}$$

the zero 3×3 matrix.

17. $A^2 = \begin{bmatrix} 1 & -1 & 1 \\ 1 & -1 & 1 \\ 1 & -1 & 1 \end{bmatrix} \begin{bmatrix} 1 & -1 & 1 \\ 1 & -1 & 1 \\ 1 & -1 & 1 \end{bmatrix} = \begin{bmatrix} 1 & -1 & 1 \\ 1 & -1 & 1 \\ 1 & -1 & 1 \end{bmatrix} = A$

18. $B^2 = \begin{bmatrix} 1 & -2 & 1 \\ -1 & 2 & -1 \\ -2 & 4 & -2 \end{bmatrix} \begin{bmatrix} 1 & -2 & 1 \\ -1 & 2 & -1 \\ -2 & 4 & -2 \end{bmatrix} = \begin{bmatrix} 1 & -2 & 1 \\ -1 & 2 & -1 \\ -2 & 4 & -2 \end{bmatrix} = B$

19. $AB = \begin{bmatrix} 1 & -1 & 1 \\ 1 & -1 & 1 \\ 1 & -1 & 1 \end{bmatrix} \begin{bmatrix} 1 & -2 & 1 \\ -1 & 2 & -1 \\ -2 & 4 & -2 \end{bmatrix} = \begin{bmatrix} 0 & 0 & 0 \\ 0 & 0 & 0 \\ 0 & 0 & 0 \end{bmatrix}$

and $BA = \begin{bmatrix} 1 & -2 & 1 \\ -1 & 2 & -1 \\ -2 & 4 & -2 \end{bmatrix} \begin{bmatrix} 1 & -1 & 1 \\ 1 & -1 & 1 \\ 1 & -1 & 1 \end{bmatrix} = \begin{bmatrix} 0 & 0 & 0 \\ 0 & 0 & 0 \\ 0 & 0 & 0 \end{bmatrix} \quad \therefore AB = O = BA$

i.e. A, B are divisors of zero.

20. $\therefore (A+B)^2 = (A+B)(A+B) = A^2+AB+BA+B^2 = A+0+0+B = A+B$, using Exercise 11.19.

21. $(A+B)^3 = (A+B)(A+B)^2 = (A+B)(A+B) = A+B$ by Exercise 11.20.

22. $AB = \begin{bmatrix} 0 & 0 & 0 \\ 0 & 0 & 0 \\ 0 & 0 & 0 \end{bmatrix} \quad \therefore (AB)^T = \begin{bmatrix} 0 & 0 & 0 \\ 0 & 0 & 0 \\ 0 & 0 & 0 \end{bmatrix}$

$B^T A^T = \begin{bmatrix} 1 & -1 & -2 \\ -2 & 2 & 4 \\ 1 & -1 & -2 \end{bmatrix} \begin{bmatrix} 1 & 1 & 1 \\ -1 & -1 & -1 \\ 1 & 1 & 1 \end{bmatrix} = \begin{bmatrix} 0 & 0 & 0 \\ 0 & 0 & 0 \\ 0 & 0 & 0 \end{bmatrix} \quad \therefore (AB)^T = B^T A^T.$

[As a further, and better, verification that $(AB)^T = B^T A^T$, use the A, B of Exercises 11.11–11.14.]

23. I. **24.** U. **25.** V. **26.** O. **27.** O.

28. $\begin{bmatrix} \cdot & \cdot & 1 & \cdot \\ \cdot & \cdot & \cdot & 1 \\ \cdot & \cdot & \cdot & \cdot \\ \cdot & \cdot & \cdot & \cdot \end{bmatrix}$ **29.** $\begin{bmatrix} \cdot & \cdot & \cdot & 1 \\ \cdot & \cdot & \cdot & \cdot \\ \cdot & \cdot & \cdot & \cdot \\ \cdot & \cdot & \cdot & \cdot \end{bmatrix}$ **30.** O.

31. I. **32.** I. **33.** $\dfrac{A+B}{2} = \begin{bmatrix} 2 & -1 & 1 \\ 2\frac{1}{2} & -1\frac{1}{2} & 2\frac{1}{2} \\ -\frac{1}{2} & \frac{1}{2} & \frac{1}{2} \end{bmatrix} \Rightarrow \left(\dfrac{A+B}{2}\right)^2 = I.$

34. $A-B = \begin{bmatrix} -4 & 4 & -4 \\ 1 & -1 & 1 \\ 5 & -5 & 5 \end{bmatrix} \Rightarrow (A-B)^2 = O.$

35. $\{\frac{1}{2}(I \pm A)\}^2 = \frac{1}{4}(I \pm 2A + A^2) = \frac{1}{4}(2I \pm 2A) = \frac{1}{2}(I \pm A) \quad \because A^2 = I.$

36. $\frac{1}{2}(I+A)\cdot\frac{1}{2}(I-A) = \frac{1}{4}(I-A^2) = O \quad \because A^2 = I.$

37. $(A+B)^2 = A^2+B^2+AB+BA = A^2+B^2$ if $AB = -BA$, i.e. if A, B anti-commute. Conversely, $AB+BA = O \Rightarrow A^2+AB+BA+B^2 = A^2+B^2 \Rightarrow (A+B)^2 = A^2+B^2$.

$AB = \begin{bmatrix} -3 & 2 \\ -2 & 3 \end{bmatrix} = -BA \quad \therefore A, B$ anti-commute

$$\left.\begin{array}{l} A+B = \begin{bmatrix} 2 & 0 \\ 6 & -2 \end{bmatrix} \Rightarrow (A+B)^2 = \begin{bmatrix} 4 & 0 \\ 0 & 4 \end{bmatrix} = 4I \\ A^2+B^2 = \begin{bmatrix} -1 & 0 \\ 0 & -1 \end{bmatrix} + \begin{bmatrix} 5 & 0 \\ 0 & 5 \end{bmatrix} = \begin{bmatrix} 4 & 0 \\ 0 & 4 \end{bmatrix} = 4I \end{array}\right\}.$$

38. Let $A = \begin{bmatrix} a & b \\ c & d \end{bmatrix}$ $\therefore A^2 = \begin{bmatrix} a^2+bc & b(a+d) \\ c(a+d) & d^2+bc \end{bmatrix} = O \Rightarrow d = -a, \quad a^2+bc = 0$

$\therefore$ required matrices are $A = \begin{bmatrix} a & b \\ c & -a \end{bmatrix}$ with $a^2+bc = 0$.

39. Suppose A, B commute, i.e. $AB = BA$.

$$\therefore (A-kI)(B-kI) = AB-k(A+B)+k^2I = BA-k(B+A)+k^2I$$
$$= (B-kI)(A-kI).$$

Suppose $A-kI$, $B-kI$ commute.

$$\therefore \left.\begin{aligned} (A-kI)(B-kI) &= AB-k(A+B)+k^2I \\ (B-kI)(A-kI) &= BA-k(B+A)+k^2I \end{aligned}\right\} \Rightarrow AB = BA, \text{ i.e. } A, B \text{ commute.}$$

40. Consider the point $A\ (a, b)$ $\therefore \begin{bmatrix} \cos\theta & -\sin\theta \\ \sin\theta & \cos\theta \end{bmatrix} \begin{bmatrix} a \\ b \end{bmatrix} = \begin{bmatrix} a\cos\theta & -b\sin\theta \\ a\sin\theta & +b\cos\theta \end{bmatrix}$

i.e. the point $A \equiv (a, b)$ is transformed by the rotation through θ into the point $A' \equiv (a\cos\theta - b\sin\theta,\ a\sin\theta + b\cos\theta)$ (128).

$$\therefore OA' = \sqrt{(a\cos\theta-b\sin\theta)^2+(a\sin\theta+b\cos\theta)^2} = \sqrt{a^2+b^2} = OA.$$

41. Premultiply $AB-BA = I$ (i) by A $\therefore A^2B-ABA = A$
i.e. $A^2B-(BA+I)A = A$ from (i) $\therefore A^2B-BA^2 = 2A$ and so on.

42. $ab = \begin{bmatrix} i & \cdot \\ \cdot & -i \end{bmatrix} = -ba, \quad bc = \begin{bmatrix} \cdot & i \\ i & \cdot \end{bmatrix} = -cb, \quad ca = \begin{bmatrix} \cdot & 1 \\ -1 & \cdot \end{bmatrix} = -ac$

$\therefore$ they anti-commute.

43. $a^2 = b^2 = c^2 = I$ $\therefore$ they are involutory.

44. $a^* = a = a^{-1}, \quad b^* = b = b^{-1}, \quad c^* = c = c^{-1}$ $\therefore$ they are unitary.

45. Yes, by virtue of Exercise 11.44.

46. a_{ij}, $\bar{a}_{ij}$ have no imaginary parts $\therefore a_{ij} = a_{ji}$ $\therefore H$ is symmetric.

47. For a Hermitian matrix, $a_{ij} = \bar{a}_{ji} \Rightarrow a_{ii} = \bar{a}_{ii}$ for diagonal elements. But a number equals its conjugate only if it is real $\therefore$ diagonal elements are real.

48. $ab-ba = 2ic$ **49.** $bc-cb = 2ia$ **50.** $ca-ac = 2ib$

51. Let L, M be orthogonal $\therefore L^TL = I$ (i), $M^TM = I$ (ii)
$\therefore (LM)^T(LM) = M^TL^TLM$ (Exercise 11.22) $= M^TIM = I$ (by (i), (ii)) $\therefore LM$ is orthogonal.

52. $(L^{-1})^TL^{-1} = (L^T)^TL^{-1} = LL^{-1} = I$ $\therefore L^{-1}$ is orthogonal. [Of course, L^T is orthogonal.]

53. $L = \begin{bmatrix} a & b \\ c & d \end{bmatrix}$ orthogonal $\Rightarrow \begin{bmatrix} a & c \\ b & d \end{bmatrix} \begin{bmatrix} a & b \\ c & d \end{bmatrix} = I = \begin{bmatrix} a^2+c^2 & ab+cd \\ ab+cd & b^2+d^2 \end{bmatrix}$

$\therefore a^2+b^2 = c^2+d^2 = 1, \quad ac+bd = 0.$

Solve $\therefore d = a,\ c = -b$ or $d = -a,\ c = b$. Hence, orthogonal 2×2 matrices are $\begin{bmatrix} a & b \\ -b & a \end{bmatrix}$ or $\begin{bmatrix} a & b \\ b & -a \end{bmatrix}$. (The same result is obtained if we had taken $LL^T = I$ instead of $L^TL = I$.) Rotation matrices (128), (129), (128)′ and (129)′ are orthogonal.

54. $C = BA$ $\therefore C^TC = (BA)^T(BA) = A^TB^TBA = I$ $\because A, B$ are orthogonal $\therefore C$ is orthogonal (Exercise 11.51). It exists if X, Y each have order $2p\times p$, i.e. C, A, B all have order $2p\times 2p$.

55. Consider the quaternion

$$q = (w, x, y, z);\text{ its components are the } \textit{elements} \text{ of } R_1 \text{ of } Q$$
$$\therefore\ iq = (-x, w, -z, y);\text{ its components are the } \textit{elements} \text{ of } R_2 \text{ of } Q$$
$$jq = (-y, z, w, -x);\text{ its components are the } \textit{elements} \text{ of } R_3 \text{ of } Q$$
$$kq = (-z, -y, x, w);\text{ its components are the } \textit{elements} \text{ of } R_4 \text{ of } Q.$$

Also, elements of C_1, C_2, C_3, C_4 are, respectively, the components of $\bar{q}, i\bar{q}, j\bar{q}, k\bar{q}$ where $\bar{q}$ is the conjugate quaternion of q. (See Exercise 10.67.)

56. $Q^TQ = QQ^T = (w^2+x^2+y^2+z^2)I$

$$\therefore\ Q \text{ orthogonal} \Rightarrow q\bar{q} = w^2+x^2+y^2+z^2 = 1(= N(q)).$$

57. $$\frac{Y}{y} = k \Rightarrow \frac{d}{dx}\left(\frac{Y}{y}\right) = 0 \Rightarrow \frac{y\dfrac{dY}{dx} - Y\dfrac{dy}{dx}}{y^2} = 0 \Rightarrow y\frac{dY}{dx} - Y\frac{dy}{dx} = 0 \Rightarrow W = 0.$$

[This notion extends to more than two functions.]

58. $$W = \begin{vmatrix} a\cosh nt & b\sinh nt \\ an\sinh nt & bn\cosh nt \end{vmatrix} = abn\,(\cosh^2 nt - \sinh^2 nt) = abn \neq 0$$

$\therefore$ solutions are independent.

59. $$F(\alpha)\,F(\beta) = \begin{bmatrix} \cos\alpha & -\sin\alpha \\ \sin\alpha & \cos\alpha \end{bmatrix} \begin{bmatrix} \cos\beta & -\sin\beta \\ \sin\beta & \cos\beta \end{bmatrix}$$
$$= \begin{bmatrix} \cos\alpha\cos\beta - \sin\alpha\sin\beta & -(\cos\alpha\sin\beta + \sin\alpha\cos\beta) \\ \sin\alpha\cos\beta + \cos\alpha\sin\beta & -\sin\alpha\,\sin\beta + \cos\alpha\cos\beta \end{bmatrix}$$
$$= \begin{bmatrix} \cos(\alpha+\beta) & -\sin(\alpha+\beta) \\ \sin(\alpha+\beta) & \cos(\alpha+\beta) \end{bmatrix} = F(\alpha+\beta).$$

Put $\beta = \alpha \quad \therefore\ \{F(\alpha)\}^2 = F(2\alpha)$.

Also $$\{F(\alpha)\}^3 = \{F(\alpha)\}^2\,F(\alpha) = F(2\alpha)\,F(\alpha) = F(3\alpha)$$

and $$\{F(\alpha)\}^n = \underbrace{F(\alpha)\,F(\alpha)\,F(\alpha)\ldots F(\alpha)}_{n \text{ factors}} = \{F(\alpha)\}^2\,\underbrace{F(\alpha)\ldots F(\alpha)}_{(n-2) \text{ factors}}$$
$$= F(2\alpha)\,F(\alpha)\,\underbrace{F(\alpha)\ldots F(\alpha)}_{(n-3) \text{ factors}} = F(3\alpha)\,\underbrace{F(\alpha)\ldots F(\alpha)}_{(n-3) \text{ factors}}$$
$$= F(r\alpha)\cdot\underbrace{F(\alpha)\ldots F(\alpha)}_{(n-r) \text{ factors}} \quad \text{by continued repetition}$$
$$= F(n\alpha) \quad \text{when} \quad r = n.$$

60. If $$A = \begin{bmatrix} \sqrt{3} & -1 \\ 1 & \sqrt{3} \end{bmatrix} = K \begin{bmatrix} \cos\alpha & -\sin\alpha \\ \sin\alpha & \cos\alpha \end{bmatrix},$$ then $K\cos\alpha = \sqrt{3}$, $K\sin\alpha = 1$.

Solving, we find $K = 2,\ \alpha = \dfrac{\pi}{6}$.

$$\therefore\ A = 2\begin{bmatrix} \cos\dfrac{\pi}{6} & -\sin\dfrac{\pi}{6} \\ \sin\dfrac{\pi}{6} & \cos\dfrac{\pi}{6} \end{bmatrix} = 2F\left(\frac{\pi}{6}\right).$$

61. $A^{13} = 2^{13}\left\{F\left(\frac{\pi}{6}\right)\right\}^{13} = 2^{13}F\left(\frac{13\pi}{6}\right) = 2^{13}F\left(\frac{\pi}{6}\right)$

$$= 2^{13}\begin{bmatrix} \cos\frac{\pi}{6} & -\sin\frac{\pi}{6} \\ \sin\frac{\pi}{6} & \cos\frac{\pi}{6} \end{bmatrix} = 2^{13}\begin{bmatrix} \sqrt{3}/2 & -\frac{1}{2} \\ \frac{1}{2} & \sqrt{3}/2 \end{bmatrix} \quad \text{i.e.}\quad A^{13} = 2^{12}A$$

62. $$AB = \begin{bmatrix} a & b & c \\ b & c & a \\ c & a & b \end{bmatrix}\begin{bmatrix} b & c & a \\ c & a & b \\ a & b & c \end{bmatrix} = \begin{bmatrix} \Sigma bc & \Sigma bc & \Sigma a^2 \\ \Sigma a^2 & \Sigma bc & \Sigma bc \\ \Sigma bc & \Sigma a^2 & \Sigma bc \end{bmatrix}$$

$$BA = \begin{bmatrix} b & c & a \\ c & a & b \\ a & b & c \end{bmatrix}\begin{bmatrix} a & b & c \\ b & c & a \\ c & a & b \end{bmatrix} = \begin{bmatrix} \Sigma bc & \Sigma a^2 & \Sigma bc \\ \Sigma bc & \Sigma bc & \Sigma a^2 \\ \Sigma a^2 & \Sigma bc & \Sigma bc \end{bmatrix}$$

If matrices A, B commute, i.e. $AB = BA$, then $\Sigma bc = \Sigma a^2$.

63. $$A^2 = \begin{bmatrix} \Sigma a^2 & \Sigma bc & \Sigma bc \\ \Sigma bc & \Sigma a^2 & \Sigma bc \\ \Sigma bc & \Sigma bc & \Sigma a^2 \end{bmatrix} = \Sigma a^2\begin{bmatrix} 1 & 1 & 1 \\ 1 & 1 & 1 \\ 1 & 1 & 1 \end{bmatrix}$$

64. $$A^2 = (1+\varepsilon+\varepsilon^2)\begin{bmatrix} 1 & 1 & 1 \\ 1 & 1 & 1 \\ 1 & 1 & 1 \end{bmatrix} = O \text{ since } 1+\varepsilon+\varepsilon^2 = 0$$

65. $$AB = (1+\varepsilon+\varepsilon^2)\begin{bmatrix} 1 & 1 & 1 \\ 1 & 1 & 1 \\ 1 & 1 & 1 \end{bmatrix} = O$$

66. $A^2 = O \Rightarrow I = I-A^2 \Rightarrow I = (I-A)(I+A) \Rightarrow (I-A)^{-1} = I+A.$

67. $$A^TA = \begin{bmatrix} \Sigma a^2 & \Sigma bc & \Sigma bc \\ \Sigma bc & \Sigma a^2 & \Sigma bc \\ \Sigma bc & \Sigma bc & \Sigma a^2 \end{bmatrix} = I \text{ if } \Sigma a^2 = 1, \quad \Sigma bc = 0$$

i.e. if a, b, c are the roots of $x^3+x^2+k = 0$ ($\Sigma a = -1$, $\Sigma bc = 0$, $\Sigma a^2 = 1$).

68. $(A^TPA)^T = A^TP^T(A^T)^T = A^TP^TA = -A^TPA$ $\quad(\because P^T = -P)\quad$ $\therefore A^TPA$ is skew-symmetric.

69. $(P^2)^T = (PP)^T = P^TP^T = -P\cdot -P = P^2$ $\quad(\because P^T = -P)\quad$ $\therefore P^2$ is symmetric.

70. $(PQ-QP)^T = (PQ)^T-(QP)^T = Q^TP^T-P^TQ^T = Q\cdot -P-(-P\cdot Q) = PQ-QP$
$(\because P^T = -P, Q^T = Q)$ $\quad\therefore PQ-QP$ is symmetric.

71. $(PQ)^T = Q^TP^T = Q\cdot -P = -QP = -PQ$ $(\because P^T = -P, Q^T = Q, PQ = QP)$

$\therefore PQ$ is skew-symmetric.

72. Let $$X = \begin{bmatrix} a & b & c \\ d & e & f \\ g & h & k \end{bmatrix} \quad \therefore AX = I \Rightarrow \begin{cases} a+2d+4g = 1, & 2d+3g = 0, & 3g = 0 \\ b+2e+4h = 0, & 2e+3h = 1, & 3h = 0 \\ c+2f+4k = 0, & 2f+3k = 0, & 3k = 1. \end{cases}$$

Solve $\therefore g = h = 0,\ k = \frac{1}{3},\ f = -\frac{1}{2},\ e = \frac{1}{2},\ d = 0,\ a = 1,\ b = 1,\ c = -\frac{1}{3}.$

$$\therefore X = A^{-1} = \begin{bmatrix} 1 & -1 & -\frac{1}{3} \\ 0 & \frac{1}{2} & -\frac{1}{2} \\ 0 & 0 & \frac{1}{3} \end{bmatrix} \quad \therefore A^{-1} \text{ is an upper triangular matrix.}$$

73. $Y' = PY = PAX = PAP^{-1}X'$. This expresses the coordinates of the transformed points in terms of the new axes. W.r.t. the new axes, the matrix of the transformation is PAP^{-1}. Matrices A and PAP^{-1} are said to be *similar*. [If $P^{-1} = Q$ then $PAP^{-1} = Q^{-1}AQ$.]

74–77. Write $X = \begin{bmatrix} x \\ 3x+1 \end{bmatrix} \quad \therefore SX = \begin{bmatrix} x \\ 5x+1 \end{bmatrix}, \quad EX = \begin{bmatrix} x \\ 12x+4 \end{bmatrix},$

$$SE = \begin{bmatrix} 1 & 0 \\ 2 & 4 \end{bmatrix}, \quad SEX = \begin{bmatrix} x \\ 14x+4 \end{bmatrix}, \quad ES = \begin{bmatrix} 1 & 0 \\ 8 & 4 \end{bmatrix},$$

$$ESX = \begin{bmatrix} x \\ 20x+4 \end{bmatrix}.$$

$\therefore$ the given line is transformed into the lines:

(74.) $y = 5x+1$.

(75.) $y = 12x+4$. **(76.)** $y = 14x+4$. **(77.)** $y = 20x+4$.

[Observe $SE \neq EX$, i.e. shears and elongations do not necessarily commute.]

78. Let the non-singular transformation be $X' = AX$, i.e.

$$\begin{bmatrix} x' \\ y' \end{bmatrix} = \begin{bmatrix} a & b \\ c & d \end{bmatrix} \begin{bmatrix} x \\ y \end{bmatrix} \quad \therefore X = A^{-1}X',$$

i.e. $$\begin{bmatrix} x \\ y \end{bmatrix} = \frac{1}{ad-bc} \begin{bmatrix} d & -b \\ -c & a \end{bmatrix} \begin{bmatrix} x' \\ y' \end{bmatrix}$$

$$\therefore x = \frac{dx'-by'}{ad-bc}, \quad y = \frac{-cx'+ay'}{ad-bc}.$$

Substitution in the equation of the given line, and simplification, lead to the straight line $(dl-mc)x'+(am-bl)y'+n(ad-bc) = 0$.

Putting $a = d = -1, b = c = n = 0$, we obtain $lx'+my' = 0$, i.e., the line $lx+my = 0$ through the origin is invariant.

79–86. Routine calculations.

87. $3125P^6 = 521I+2604P$. Coefficient of P on right-hand side for $5^{n-1}P^n$ on left-hand side is $5^{n-1}-5^{n-2}+5^{n-3}-\ldots$.

88. $$\lim_{n\to\infty} P^n = \frac{I+kP}{m} \Rightarrow \frac{1}{m} = \lim_{n\to\infty} \left\{ \frac{5^{n-1}-5^{n-2}+5^{n-3}-\ldots}{5^{n-1}} \right\}$$

$$= \lim_{n\to\infty} \left\{ 1-\frac{1}{5}+\frac{1}{5^2}-\frac{1}{5^3}+\ldots \right\} = \frac{1}{1-(-\frac{1}{5})}$$

(by Example 44 with $a = 1$, $x = -\frac{1}{5}$)

$$\therefore m = 6. \text{ But } k = -1+m = 5 \quad \therefore \lim_{n\to\infty} P^n = \frac{I+5P}{6} = \frac{1}{3}\begin{bmatrix} 1 & 2 \\ 1 & 2 \end{bmatrix}.$$

89. Successive coefficients of I, P are:

ω_0	ω_1	ω_2	ω_3	ω_4	ω_5	$\omega_6 \ldots$
1	4	21	104	521	2604	13021...

$\therefore \omega_{n+2} = 4\omega_{n+1}+5\omega_n$ i.e., $a = 1, \quad b = p = 4, \quad q = -5.$

90. $\cos\alpha = \dfrac{a_1}{OA}, \quad \cos\beta = \dfrac{a_2}{OA}, \quad \cos\gamma = \dfrac{a_3}{OA}$

$$\therefore \cos^2\alpha+\cos^2\beta+\cos^2\gamma = \frac{a_1^2+a_2^2+a_3^2}{OA^2} = 1 \quad \text{by (138)}$$

$$\cos\alpha = \cos\beta = \cos\gamma = x \Rightarrow 3x^2 = 1 \Rightarrow x = \frac{1}{\sqrt{3}} \Rightarrow \alpha = \beta = \gamma = \cos^{-1}\left(\frac{1}{\sqrt{3}}\right).$$

91. Direction cosines of $\overrightarrow{AB}$ are $\dfrac{x-,\ y-,\ z- \text{ components of } \overrightarrow{AB}}{|\overrightarrow{AB}|}$

$$= \frac{4}{9\sqrt{2}}, \quad \frac{-5}{9\sqrt{2}}, \quad \frac{11}{9\sqrt{2}}.$$

92. $2\mathbf{a}-\mathbf{b} = ((2\cdot2-1,\ 2\cdot-1-1,\ 2\cdot1-(-4)) = (3, -3, 6) = \mathbf{c}$

$$\therefore \hat{\mathbf{c}} = \frac{\mathbf{c}}{|\mathbf{c}|} = \frac{1}{3\sqrt{6}}(3, -3, 6) = \left(\frac{1}{\sqrt{6}}, \frac{-1}{\sqrt{6}}, \frac{2}{\sqrt{6}}\right).$$

93. Let $\mathbf{x} = (x, y, z)$ $\therefore 3+3x = 0, -3+3y = 0, 6+3z = 0$ $\therefore \mathbf{x} = (-1, 1, -2)$.

94. $|\mathbf{a}| = \sqrt{2}, |\mathbf{b}| = \sqrt{2}$ $\therefore |\mathbf{a}|\,|\mathbf{b}| = 2, \mathbf{a}\bullet\mathbf{b} = 1+0+0 = 1$ $\therefore |\mathbf{a}\bullet\mathbf{b}| < |\mathbf{a}|\,|\mathbf{b}|$
$[|\mathbf{a}\bullet\mathbf{b}| = |\mathbf{a}|\,|\mathbf{b}|\,|\cos\theta| \leqslant |\mathbf{a}|\,|\mathbf{b}| \because |\cos\theta| \leqslant 1]$.

95. $\mathbf{a}\bullet\mathbf{b} = |\mathbf{a}|\,|\mathbf{b}|\cos\theta \Rightarrow 1 = 2\cos\theta \Rightarrow \theta = \cos^{-1}\left(\dfrac{1}{2}\right) = \dfrac{\pi}{3}.$

96. Yes, since $\mathbf{u}\bullet\mathbf{v} = 30-16-14 = 0$.

97. Call the vectors **a**, **b**, **c**, **d** respectively. Then $\mathbf{a}+\mathbf{b}+\mathbf{c}-2\mathbf{d} = \mathbf{0}$. Hence, they are linearly dependent (but any 3 of them are linearly independent).

98. Assume $\exists$ a relation of the form $a_0\cdot1+a_1x+a_2x^2+\ldots+a_nx^n = 0$ ($a_0, \ldots, a_n$ constants). Differentiate n times to obtain $a_1+2a_2x+\ldots+na_nxn^{n-1} = 0, \ldots, (n-1)!\,a_{n-1}+n!a_nx = 0, n!a_n = 0$.

$\therefore a_n = a_{n-1} = \ldots = a_1 = a_0 = 0$ $\therefore 1, x, x^2, \ldots, x^n$ are linearly independent.

99. Assume $\exists$ a relation $ae^x+be^{3x} = 0$ $\therefore x = 0 \Rightarrow a+b = 0;\ x = 1 \Rightarrow e(a+ +be^2) = 0$ $(e \neq 0)$. Hence, $a = b = 0$ $\therefore e^x, e^{3x}$ are linearly independent;

or, $W = \begin{vmatrix} e^x & e^{3x} \\ e^x & 3e^{3x} \end{vmatrix} = 2e^{4x} \neq 0$ $\therefore e^x, e^{3x}$ are linearly independent.

100. Assume $\exists$ constants $a_1, a_2, \ldots, a_n : a_1\sin x+a_2\sin 2x+\ldots+a_n\sin nx = 0$.

Multiply in succession each term of this equation by $\sin mx$ $(m = 1, \ldots, n)$ (i.e. $\exists n$ equations) and integrate. Typical integrals are

$$\int_0^\pi \sin mx \sin px\,dx = \frac{1}{2}\int_0^\pi \{\cos(m-p)x-\cos(m+p)x\}\,dx$$

$$(m \neq p, p = 1, 2, \ldots, n) = \tfrac{1}{2}\left[\frac{\sin(m-p)x}{m-p} - \frac{\sin(m+p)x}{m+p}\right]_0^\pi = 0$$

$$\int_0^\pi \sin^2 mx\,dx = \frac{1}{2}\int_0^\pi (1-\cos 2mx)\,dx = \frac{1}{2}\left[x - \frac{\sin 2mx}{2}\right]_0^\pi = \frac{\pi}{2} \quad (m = p).$$

This means that for each m we have $a_m = 0$.

$\therefore$ the given functions are linearly independent in $0 \leqslant x \leqslant \pi$.

EXERCISES 12

1. $(\beta\,\delta\,\gamma\,\varepsilon\,\alpha)$ is an odd permutation of $(\alpha\,\beta\,\gamma\,\delta\,\varepsilon)$ because there are five inversions.

2. (i) Arrange the term $a_{31}a_{42}a_{14}a_{23}$ so that the first suffixes are in natural order, i.e. $a_{14}a_{23}a_{31}a_{42}$; there are five inversions in the second suffixes. Thus the sign is negative.

(ii) In the term $a_{14}a_{21}a_{33}a_{42}$ the first suffixes are in natural order and there are four inversions in the second suffixes. Thus the sign is positive.

3. The terms which occur are a^4, a^2c^2 and their coefficients are $+1$, -2.

4. $$\begin{vmatrix} 1 & 2 & 3 & 4 \\ 5 & 6 & 7 & 8 \\ 9 & 10 & 11 & 12 \\ 13 & 14 & 15 & 16 \end{vmatrix} = \begin{vmatrix} 1 & 2 & 3 & 4 \\ 5 & 6 & 7 & 8 \\ 8 & 8 & 8 & 8 \\ 8 & 8 & 8 & 8 \end{vmatrix} \quad \begin{matrix} (R_3-R_1,\ R_4-R_2) = 0 \\ \text{since 2 rows are identical.} \end{matrix}$$

5. $$\begin{vmatrix} 1 & a & b+c \\ 1 & b & c+a \\ 1 & c & a+b \end{vmatrix} = \begin{vmatrix} 1 & a+b+c & b+c \\ 1 & b+c+a & c+a \\ 1 & c+a+b & a+b \end{vmatrix} = 0$$ (2 columns identical after taking out common factor $(a+b+c)$).

6. $$\begin{vmatrix} 1+a & 1 & 1 \\ 1 & 1+b & 1 \\ 1 & 1 & 1+c \end{vmatrix} = \begin{vmatrix} 1+a & -a & -a \\ 1 & b & 0 \\ 1 & 0 & c \end{vmatrix} = ab + c(b+ab+a) = ab+bc+ac+abc$$ (expanding along R_3)

7. $$\begin{vmatrix} 3 & 2 & 2 & 2 \\ 2 & 3 & 2 & 2 \\ 2 & 2 & 3 & 2 \\ 2 & 2 & 2 & 3 \end{vmatrix} = \begin{vmatrix} 9 & 2 & 2 & 2 \\ 9 & 3 & 2 & 2 \\ 9 & 2 & 3 & 2 \\ 9 & 2 & 2 & 3 \end{vmatrix} = 9\begin{vmatrix} 1 & 2 & 2 & 2 \\ 0 & 1 & 0 & 0 \\ 0 & 0 & 1 & 0 \\ 0 & 0 & 0 & 1 \end{vmatrix} = 9$$

8. $$\begin{vmatrix} 1+x & 2 & 3 & 4 \\ 1 & 2+x & 3 & 4 \\ 1 & 2 & 3+x & 4 \\ 1 & 2 & 3 & 4+x \end{vmatrix} = \begin{vmatrix} 10+x & 2 & 3 & 4 \\ 10+x & 2+x & 3 & 4 \\ 10+x & 2 & 3+x & 4 \\ 10+x & 2 & 3 & 4+x \end{vmatrix}$$

$$= (10+x)\begin{vmatrix} 1 & 2 & 3 & 4 \\ 0 & x & 0 & 0 \\ 0 & 0 & x & 0 \\ 0 & 0 & 0 & x \end{vmatrix} = x^3(10+x)$$

9. $$\begin{vmatrix} 4 & 1 & 3 & 2 \\ 6 & 5 & -2 & 1 \\ 3 & 0 & 2 & 5 \\ 7 & -2 & 0 & 5 \end{vmatrix} = \begin{vmatrix} 10 & 1 & 3 & 2 \\ 10 & 5 & -2 & 1 \\ 10 & 0 & 2 & 5 \\ 10 & -2 & 0 & 5 \end{vmatrix} = 10 \begin{vmatrix} 1 & 1 & 3 & 2 \\ 0 & 4 & -5 & -1 \\ 0 & -1 & -1 & 3 \\ 0 & -3 & -3 & 3 \end{vmatrix}$$

$$= 10 \begin{vmatrix} 4 & -5 & -1 \\ -1 & -1 & 3 \\ -3 & -3 & 3 \end{vmatrix} = 10 \begin{vmatrix} 4 & -9 & -1 \\ -1 & 0 & 3 \\ -3 & 0 & 3 \end{vmatrix} = 90(-3+9) = 540$$

10. $$\begin{vmatrix} 1+i & 1-i & i \\ 1-i & i & 1+i \\ i & 1+i & 1-i \end{vmatrix} = \begin{vmatrix} 2+i & 1-i & i \\ 2+i & i & 1+i \\ 2+i & 1+i & 1-i \end{vmatrix} = (2+i) \begin{vmatrix} 1 & 1-i & i \\ 0 & 2i-1 & 1 \\ 0 & 2i & 1-2i \end{vmatrix}$$

$= (2+i)\{(2i-1)(1-2i)-2i\} = (2+i)(2i+4-1+2i-2i) = (2+i)(2i+3) =$
$= 7i+4$

11. Expand along R_3 $\therefore$ value of determinant is $-\cos\theta\,(\cos\theta-2\sin\theta)$ $+1\cdot(1-\sin^2\theta) = -\cos^2\theta+2\cos\theta\sin\theta+\cos^2\theta = \sin 2\theta$.

12. $$\begin{vmatrix} 1 & 2 & 4 & 8 \\ 8 & 1 & 2 & 4 \\ x & 8 & 1 & 2 \\ y & z & 8 & 1 \end{vmatrix} = \begin{vmatrix} 1 & 0 & 0 & 0 \\ 8 & -15 & -30 & -60 \\ x & 8-2x & 1-4x & 2-8x \\ y & z-2y & 8-4y & 1-8y \end{vmatrix} \quad \begin{cases} C_2-2C_1 \\ C_3-4C_1 \\ C_4-8C_1 \end{cases}$$

$$= -15 \begin{vmatrix} 1 & 2 & 4 \\ 8-2x & 1-4x & 2-8x \\ z-2y & 8-4y & 1-8y \end{vmatrix}$$ exp. along R_1 and taking out the common factor of the new R_1

$$= -15 \begin{vmatrix} 1 & 0 & 0 \\ 8-2x & -15 & -30 \\ z-2y & 8-2z & 1-4z \end{vmatrix} \quad \begin{cases} C_2-2C_1 \\ C_3-3C_1 \end{cases}$$

$$= (-15)^2 \begin{vmatrix} 1 & 2 \\ 8-2z & 1-4z \end{vmatrix}$$ (exp. along R_1 and taking out the common factor of the new R_1) $= (-15)^3$ i.e. independent of x, y, z.

13. Exp. along R_1 and the value is $(\cos^2\theta+\sin^2\theta) \begin{vmatrix} \cosh\phi & \sinh\phi \\ \sinh\phi & \cosh\phi \end{vmatrix} = 1\cdot 1 = 1.$

(This determinant occurs, for instance, in the advanced geometry of rotations and reflections.)

14. $$\begin{vmatrix} x & -3i & 1 \\ y & 1 & i \\ 0 & 2i & -i \end{vmatrix} = \begin{vmatrix} x & 2-3i & 1 \\ y & 1+2i & i \\ 0 & 0 & -i \end{vmatrix} \quad (C_2+2C_3)$$

$= -i(x+2ix-2y+3iy) = -i(x-2y)+(2x+3y) = 11i+6$ (given).

Equate real and imaginary parts $\therefore 2y-x = 11,\ 3y+2x = 6$ $\therefore x = -3,\ y = 4.$

15. $$\begin{vmatrix} 1 & 1 & 1 \\ 1 & e^{i\theta} & 1 \\ 1 & -1 & e^{-i\theta} \end{vmatrix} = \begin{vmatrix} 1 & 1 & 1 \\ 0 & e^{i\theta}-1 & 0 \\ 1 & -1 & e^{-i\theta} \end{vmatrix} = (e^{i\theta}-1)(e^{-i\theta}-1)$$ (expanding along R_2)

$= 2-(e^{i\theta}+e^{-i\theta}) = 2-2\cos\theta = 1$ when $\theta = \dfrac{\pi}{3}$, i.e. $\cos\theta = \dfrac{1}{2}$.

16. $x = r\sin\theta\cos\phi,\ y = r\sin\theta\sin\phi,\ z = r\cos\theta$

$$\frac{\partial x}{\partial r} = \sin\theta\cos\phi, \quad \frac{\partial y}{\partial r} = \sin\theta\sin\phi, \quad \frac{\partial z}{\partial r} = \cos\theta$$

$$\frac{\partial x}{\partial \theta} = r\cos\theta\cos\phi, \quad \frac{\partial y}{\partial \theta} = r\cos\theta\sin\phi, \quad \frac{\partial z}{\partial \theta} = -r\sin\theta$$

$$\frac{\partial x}{\partial \phi} = -r\sin\theta\sin\phi, \quad \frac{\partial y}{\partial \phi} = r\sin\theta\cos\phi, \quad \frac{\partial z}{\partial \phi} = 0$$

$$\begin{vmatrix} \frac{\partial x}{\partial r} & \frac{\partial x}{\partial \theta} & \frac{\partial x}{\partial \phi} \\ \frac{\partial y}{\partial r} & \frac{\partial y}{\partial \theta} & \frac{\partial y}{\partial \phi} \\ \frac{\partial z}{\partial r} & \frac{\partial z}{\partial \theta} & \frac{\partial z}{\partial \phi} \end{vmatrix} = \begin{vmatrix} \sin\theta\cos\phi & r\cos\theta\cos\phi & -r\sin\theta\sin\phi \\ \sin\theta\sin\phi & r\cos\theta\sin\phi & r\sin\theta\cos\phi \\ \cos\theta & -r\sin\theta & 0 \end{vmatrix}$$

$$= \cos\theta(r^2\cos^2\phi\sin\theta\cos\theta + r^2\sin^2\phi\sin\theta\cos\theta)$$
$$+ r\sin\theta(r\sin^2\theta\cos^2\phi + r\sin^2\theta\sin^2\phi)$$
$$= r^2\cos^2\theta\sin\theta + r^2\sin^3\theta = r^2\sin\theta(\cos^2\theta + \sin^2\theta) = r^2\sin\theta.$$

17. $$\begin{vmatrix} 1 & x & 0 & x \\ x & 1 & x & 0 \\ 0 & x & 1 & x \\ x & 0 & x & 1 \end{vmatrix} = (2x+1)\begin{vmatrix} 1 & x & 0 & x \\ 1 & 1 & x & 0 \\ 1 & x & 1 & x \\ 1 & 0 & x & 1 \end{vmatrix}$$ $(C_1+C_2+C_3+C_4)$ and taking out $(2x+1)$ from C_1

$$= (2x+1)\begin{vmatrix} 1 & x & 0 & x \\ 0 & 1-x & x & -x \\ 0 & 0 & 1 & 0 \\ 0 & -x & x & 1-x \end{vmatrix}$$ $(R_2-R_1,\ R_3-R_1,\ R_4-R_1)$

$$= (2x+1)\begin{vmatrix} 1-x & x & -x \\ 0 & 1 & 0 \\ -x & x & 1-x \end{vmatrix}$$

$$= (2x+1)(1-2x) = 0 \text{ when } x = \tfrac{1}{2} \text{ or } -\tfrac{1}{2}.$$

18. $$\begin{vmatrix} 2x-1 & x+2 & 4 \\ x & 3 & 1 \\ x-1 & x+1 & 3 \end{vmatrix} = \begin{vmatrix} -2x-1 & x-10 & 0 \\ x & 3 & 1 \\ -2x-1 & x-8 & 0 \end{vmatrix}$$ $(R_1-4R_2,\ R_3-3R_2)$

$$= -1\{-(2x+1)(x-8)+(2x+1)(x-10)\}$$
$$= 4x+2 = 0 \text{ when } x = -\tfrac{1}{2}.$$

19. $$\begin{vmatrix} 1 & 1 & 1 \\ x & a & b \\ x^3 & a^3 & b^3 \end{vmatrix} = \begin{vmatrix} 0 & 0 & 1 \\ x-b & a-b & b \\ x^3-b^3 & a^3-b^3 & b^3 \end{vmatrix}$$

$$= (x-b)(a-b)\begin{vmatrix} 0 & 0 & 1 \\ 1 & 1 & b \\ x^2+xb+b^2 & a^2+ab+b^2 & b^3 \end{vmatrix}$$

$$= (x-b)(a-b)(a^2+ab+b^2-x^2-xb-b^2)$$
$$= (x-b)(a-b)(a-x)(a+b+x) = 0$$

when $x = a$, $x = b$, $x = -(a+b)$. (Clearly $x = a$, $x = b$ are solutions since initially each of these values makes 2 columns identical.)

20. Expand along R_1 and we have

$$x(x^2+\cos^2\theta\cos^2\phi)+\sin\theta(x\sin\theta+\cos^2\theta\cos\phi\sin\phi)$$
$$-\cos\theta\sin\phi(\sin\theta\cos\theta\cos\phi-x\cos\theta\sin\phi) = 0$$
$$\therefore\ x^3+x(\cos^2\theta\cos^2\phi+\sin^2\theta+\cos^2\theta\sin^2\phi) = 0$$
$$\therefore\ x^3+x = 0 \quad \text{i.e.} \quad x(x^2+1) = 0 \quad \text{whence} \quad x = 0,\ \pm i.$$

21. (a) Given $\begin{cases} 3x-2y = 7 \\ 3y-2z = 6 \\ -2x+3z = -1 \end{cases}$ $\therefore\ D = \begin{vmatrix} 3 & -2 & 0 \\ 0 & 3 & -2 \\ -2 & 0 & 3 \end{vmatrix}$

$$= 3\cdot 9+2\cdot -4 = 19,$$

$$H_1 = \begin{vmatrix} 7 & -2 & 0 \\ 6 & 3 & -2 \\ -1 & 0 & 3 \end{vmatrix}, \quad H_2 = \begin{vmatrix} 3 & 7 & 0 \\ 0 & 6 & -2 \\ -2 & -1 & 3 \end{vmatrix}, \quad H_3 = \begin{vmatrix} 3 & -2 & 7 \\ 0 & 3 & 6 \\ -2 & 0 & -1 \end{vmatrix}$$

$$= 7\cdot 9+2(18-2) \qquad = 3(18-2)-7\cdot -4 \qquad = 3\cdot -3-2(-12-21)$$
$$= 95 \qquad = 76 \qquad = 57$$

$$\therefore\ x = \frac{H_1}{D} = 5, \quad y = \frac{H_2}{D} = 4, \quad z = \frac{H_3}{D} = 3 \quad \text{(using Cramer's rule).}$$

(b) $\left.\begin{matrix} 3x-2y = 7 \\ 3y-2z = 6 \\ -2x+3z = -1 \end{matrix}\right\} \Rightarrow \begin{bmatrix} 3 & -2 & 0 \\ 0 & 3 & -2 \\ -2 & 0 & 3 \end{bmatrix}\begin{bmatrix} x \\ y \\ z \end{bmatrix} = \begin{bmatrix} 7 \\ 6 \\ -1 \end{bmatrix}$

$$\therefore\ \begin{bmatrix} x \\ y \\ z \end{bmatrix} = \begin{bmatrix} 3 & -2 & 0 \\ 0 & 3 & -2 \\ -2 & 0 & 3 \end{bmatrix}^{-1}\begin{bmatrix} 7 \\ 6 \\ -1 \end{bmatrix} = \frac{1}{D}\begin{bmatrix} 9 & 6 & 4 \\ 4 & 9 & 6 \\ 6 & 4 & 9 \end{bmatrix}\begin{bmatrix} 7 \\ 6 \\ -1 \end{bmatrix} = \frac{1}{19}\begin{bmatrix} 95 \\ 76 \\ 57 \end{bmatrix}$$

$$= \begin{bmatrix} 5 \\ 4 \\ 3 \end{bmatrix} \quad \therefore\ \begin{cases} x = 5 \\ y = 4 \\ z = 3. \end{cases}$$

22. (a) Given $\begin{cases} x+y+z = a \\ 2x+3y+6z = b \\ 4x+5y+5z = 2c \end{cases}$ $\therefore\ D = \begin{vmatrix} 1 & 1 & 1 \\ 2 & 3 & 6 \\ 4 & 5 & 5 \end{vmatrix} = \begin{vmatrix} 1 & 0 & 0 \\ 2 & 1 & 4 \\ 4 & 1 & 1 \end{vmatrix} = -3$

$$H_1 = \begin{vmatrix} a & 1 & 1 \\ b & 3 & 6 \\ 2c & 5 & 5 \end{vmatrix} = \begin{vmatrix} a & 1 & 0 \\ b & 3 & 3 \\ 2c & 5 & 0 \end{vmatrix} = -3(5a-2c)$$

$$H_2 = \begin{vmatrix} 1 & a & 1 \\ 2 & b & 6 \\ 4 & 2c & 5 \end{vmatrix} = \begin{vmatrix} 1 & 0 & 0 \\ 2 & b-2a & 4 \\ 4 & 2c-4a & 1 \end{vmatrix} = 14a+b-8c$$

$$H_3 = \begin{vmatrix} 1 & 1 & a \\ 2 & 3 & b \\ 4 & 5 & 2c \end{vmatrix} = \begin{vmatrix} 1 & 0 & 0 \\ 2 & 1 & b-2a \\ 4 & 1 & 2c-4a \end{vmatrix} = -2a-b+2c$$

$\therefore\ x = 5a-2c, \quad y = (-14a-b+8c)/3, \quad z = (2a+b-2c)/3.$

(b) *or:*
$$\begin{bmatrix} 1 & 1 & 1 \\ 2 & 3 & 6 \\ 2 & \frac{5}{2} & \frac{5}{2} \end{bmatrix} \begin{bmatrix} x \\ y \\ z \end{bmatrix} = \begin{bmatrix} a \\ b \\ c \end{bmatrix} \Rightarrow \begin{bmatrix} x \\ y \\ z \end{bmatrix} = \frac{1}{-3/2} \begin{bmatrix} -\frac{15}{2} & 0 & 3 \\ 7 & \frac{1}{2} & -4 \\ -1 & -\frac{1}{2} & 1 \end{bmatrix} \begin{bmatrix} a \\ b \\ c \end{bmatrix}$$

$$= \begin{bmatrix} 5a-2c \\ -\frac{14a}{3}-\frac{b}{3}+\frac{8c}{3} \\ \frac{2a}{3}+\frac{b}{3}-\frac{2c}{3} \end{bmatrix} \quad \therefore \begin{cases} x = 5a-2c \\ y = \dfrac{-14a-b+8c}{3} \\ z = \dfrac{2a+b-2c}{3}. \end{cases}$$

23. $A = \begin{bmatrix} 1 & 3 & 2 \\ 2 & 0 & 5 \\ 6 & 1 & 7 \end{bmatrix} \quad \therefore\ A^T = \begin{bmatrix} 1 & 2 & 6 \\ 3 & 0 & 1 \\ 2 & 5 & 7 \end{bmatrix}$ with $|A^T| = 47 = |A|$

on calculation.

$$\therefore\ (A^T)^{-1} = \frac{1}{47} \begin{bmatrix} -5 & 16 & 2 \\ -19 & -5 & 17 \\ 15 & -1 & -6 \end{bmatrix}, \quad A^{-1} = \frac{1}{47} \begin{bmatrix} -5 & -19 & 15 \\ 16 & -5 & -1 \\ 2 & 17 & -6 \end{bmatrix},$$

$$(A^{-1})^T = \frac{1}{47} \begin{bmatrix} -5 & 16 & 2 \\ -19 & -5 & 17 \\ 15 & -1 & -6 \end{bmatrix} \quad \therefore\ (A^T)^{-1} = (A^{-1})^T.$$

24. $A^2 = \begin{bmatrix} 19 & 5 & 31 \\ 32 & 11 & 39 \\ 50 & 25 & 66 \end{bmatrix}, \quad (A^2)^{-1} = \frac{1}{47^2} \begin{bmatrix} -249 & 445 & -146 \\ -162 & -296 & 251 \\ 250 & -225 & 49 \end{bmatrix}$

From Exercise 12.23, $(A^{-1})^2 = \frac{1}{47^2} \begin{bmatrix} -249 & 445 & -146 \\ -162 & -296 & 251 \\ 250 & -225 & 49 \end{bmatrix} \quad \therefore\ (A^2)^{-1} = (A^{-1})^2.$

25. $AB = \begin{bmatrix} 1 & 3 & 2 \\ 2 & 0 & 5 \\ 6 & 1 & 7 \end{bmatrix} \begin{bmatrix} 2 & 0 & -1 \\ 3 & -5 & 2 \\ -8 & -2 & 1 \end{bmatrix} = \begin{bmatrix} -5 & -19 & 7 \\ -36 & -10 & 3 \\ -41 & -19 & 3 \end{bmatrix}, \quad |AB| = 2068$

on calculation

$$(AB)^{-1} = \frac{1}{2068} \begin{bmatrix} 27 & -76 & 13 \\ -15 & 272 & -237 \\ 274 & 684 & -634 \end{bmatrix}, \quad |B| = 44,$$

$$B^{-1} = \frac{1}{44}\begin{bmatrix} -1 & 2 & -5 \\ -19 & -6 & -7 \\ -46 & 4 & -10 \end{bmatrix}$$

$$B^{-1}A^{-1} = \frac{1}{44\cdot 47}\begin{bmatrix} -1 & 2 & -5 \\ -19 & -6 & -7 \\ -46 & 4 & -10 \end{bmatrix}\begin{bmatrix} -5 & -19 & 15 \\ 16 & -5 & -1 \\ 2 & 17 & -6 \end{bmatrix}$$

$$= \frac{1}{2068}\begin{bmatrix} 27 & -76 & 13 \\ -15 & 272 & -237 \\ 274 & 684 & -634 \end{bmatrix} \quad \therefore (AB)^{-1} = B^{-1}A^{-1}.$$

26. $$|A-\lambda I| = \begin{vmatrix} a-\lambda & b & c \\ b & c-\lambda & a \\ c & a & b-\lambda \end{vmatrix} = (a+b+c-\lambda)\begin{vmatrix} 1 & b & c \\ 1 & c-\lambda & a \\ 1 & a & b-\lambda \end{vmatrix}$$

$$= (a+b+c-\lambda)\begin{vmatrix} 1 & b & c \\ 0 & c-b-\lambda & a-c \\ 0 & a-b & b-c-\lambda \end{vmatrix}$$

$= (a+b+c-\lambda)(\lambda^2-\Sigma a^2+\Sigma bc) = \lambda^2(\Sigma a-\lambda) = 0$ when $\lambda = 0, 0, \Sigma a.$

27. $$\begin{vmatrix} 1 & 1 & 1 \\ 1 & 2 & 3 \\ 1 & 3 & K \end{vmatrix} = 0 \Rightarrow \begin{vmatrix} 1 & 1 & 1 \\ 0 & 1 & 2 \\ 0 & 2 & K-1 \end{vmatrix} = 0 \Rightarrow K = 5$$

28. $$\begin{vmatrix} 3\lambda & 5 & -7 \\ 2 & -6\lambda & -3 \\ 5 & -1 & -10\lambda \end{vmatrix} = 0 \Rightarrow 180\lambda^3-119\lambda-61 = 0 \Rightarrow (\lambda-1)(180\lambda^2+180\lambda+61) = 0$$

$\therefore$ $\lambda = 1$ is the only real value of λ making the 3 straight lines concurrent.

29. $$M = \begin{bmatrix} 2 & 7 & 6 \\ 9 & 5 & 1 \\ 4 & 3 & 8 \end{bmatrix} (s = 15) \quad \therefore |M| = 2\cdot 37-7\cdot 68+6\cdot 7 = -360$$

$$\therefore M^{-1} = -\frac{1}{360}\begin{bmatrix} 37 & -38 & -23 \\ -68 & -8 & 52 \\ 7 & 22 & -53 \end{bmatrix}.$$ Each row, column and diagonal has sum $\frac{1}{15}\left(=\frac{1}{s}\right)$.

Thus M^{-1} is also a "magic matrix".

30. Given $AX = B$ where $A = \begin{bmatrix} 16 & -8 & 1 \\ -8 & 17 & -8 \\ 1 & -8 & 16 \end{bmatrix}$, $B = \begin{bmatrix} 4 & 10 \\ 6 & 16 \\ 4 & 10 \end{bmatrix}$

i.e. $A^{-1}AX = A^{-1}B$, $IX = A^{-1}B$, $X = A^{-1}B$.

$$\text{Now } |A| = \begin{vmatrix} 0 & 26 & -15 \\ 0 & -47 & 120 \\ 1 & -8 & 16 \end{vmatrix} \begin{pmatrix} R_1+2R_2 \\ R_2+8R_3 \end{pmatrix} = 2415$$

$$\therefore\ X = \frac{1}{2415}\begin{bmatrix} 208 & 120 & 47 \\ 120 & 255 & 120 \\ 47 & 120 & 208 \end{bmatrix}\begin{bmatrix} 4 & 10 \\ 6 & 16 \\ 4 & 10 \end{bmatrix} = \frac{1}{2415}\begin{bmatrix} 1740 & 4470 \\ 2490 & 6480 \\ 1740 & 4470 \end{bmatrix}$$

$$= \frac{1}{161}\begin{bmatrix} 116 & 298 \\ 166 & 432 \\ 116 & 298 \end{bmatrix}.$$

31. $$V^2 = \begin{bmatrix} \cdot & \cdot & 1 \\ \varepsilon & \cdot & \cdot \\ \cdot & \varepsilon^2 & \cdot \end{bmatrix}\begin{bmatrix} \cdot & \cdot & 1 \\ \varepsilon & \cdot & \cdot \\ \cdot & \varepsilon^2 & \cdot \end{bmatrix} = \begin{bmatrix} \cdot & \varepsilon^2 & \cdot \\ \cdot & \cdot & \varepsilon \\ 1 & \cdot & \cdot \end{bmatrix}$$

$$V^2W = \begin{bmatrix} \cdot & \varepsilon^2 & \cdot \\ \cdot & \cdot & \varepsilon \\ 1 & \cdot & \cdot \end{bmatrix}\begin{bmatrix} \cdot & \cdot & 1 \\ \varepsilon^2 & \cdot & \cdot \\ \cdot & \varepsilon & \cdot \end{bmatrix} = \begin{bmatrix} \varepsilon & \cdot & \cdot \\ \cdot & \varepsilon^2 & \cdot \\ \cdot & \cdot & 1 \end{bmatrix}$$

32. $$WV^2 = \begin{bmatrix} \cdot & \cdot & 1 \\ \varepsilon^2 & \cdot & \cdot \\ \cdot & \varepsilon & \cdot \end{bmatrix}\begin{bmatrix} \cdot & \varepsilon^2 & \cdot \\ \cdot & \cdot & \varepsilon \\ 1 & \cdot & \cdot \end{bmatrix} = \begin{bmatrix} 1 & \cdot & \cdot \\ \cdot & \varepsilon & \cdot \\ \cdot & \cdot & \varepsilon^2 \end{bmatrix}.$$

Observe that $V^2W = \varepsilon WV^2$, i.e. V^2 and W do not commute.

33. $$V^{-1} = \begin{bmatrix} \cdot & \varepsilon^2 & \cdot \\ \cdot & \cdot & \varepsilon \\ 1 & \cdot & \cdot \end{bmatrix} = V^2 \quad \because\ |V| = 1 \text{ and } V^3 = I.$$

34. Let $$\Delta(\theta) = \begin{vmatrix} \cos\theta & 1 & 0 \\ 1 & 2\cos\theta & 1 \\ 0 & 1 & 2\cos\theta \end{vmatrix} = \cos\theta(4\cos^2\theta-1)-2\cos\theta$$

$$= 4\cos^3\theta-3\cos\theta = \cos 3\theta$$

$$\therefore\ \int_0^{\pi/6} \Delta(\theta)\,d\theta = \tfrac{1}{3}\Big[\sin 3\theta\Big]_0^{\pi/6} = 1.$$

[If, in $\Delta(\theta)$, $\cos\theta$ in the left-hand corner is replaced by $2\cos\theta$, the value of the determinant is $\dfrac{\sin 4\theta}{\sin\theta}$.]

35. $$|A-\lambda I| = \begin{vmatrix} 1-\lambda & 0 & -1 \\ 1 & 2-\lambda & 1 \\ 2 & 2 & 3-\lambda \end{vmatrix} = 0 \Rightarrow (1-\lambda)(6-5\lambda+\lambda^2-2)-(2-4+2\lambda) = 0,$$

i.e. $(1-\lambda)(4-5\lambda+\lambda^2) = 0 \quad \therefore\ (1-\lambda)(\lambda-2)(\lambda-3) = 0 \quad \therefore\ \lambda = 1, 2, 3.$

On calculation, $|P| = -2$ and $P^{-1} = -\frac{1}{2}\begin{bmatrix} 0 & 2 & -1 \\ -2 & -2 & 0 \\ 2 & 2 & 1 \end{bmatrix}$

$$\therefore\ P^{-1}AP = -\frac{1}{2}\begin{bmatrix} 0 & 2 & -1 \\ -2 & -2 & 0 \\ 2 & 2 & 1 \end{bmatrix}\begin{bmatrix} 1 & 0 & -1 \\ 1 & 2 & 1 \\ 2 & 2 & 3 \end{bmatrix}\begin{bmatrix} 1 & 2 & 1 \\ -1 & -1 & -1 \\ 0 & -2 & -2 \end{bmatrix}$$

$$= -\frac{1}{2}\begin{bmatrix} 0 & 2 & -1 \\ -2 & -2 & 0 \\ 2 & 2 & 1 \end{bmatrix}\begin{bmatrix} 1 & 4 & 3 \\ -1 & -2 & -3 \\ 0 & -4 & -6 \end{bmatrix} = \begin{bmatrix} 1 & 0 & 0 \\ 0 & 2 & 0 \\ 0 & 0 & 3 \end{bmatrix}$$

i.e. a diagonal matrix whose elements are the eigenvalues. (This is a particular case of some important theory in more advanced mathematics relating to rotation of axes—it enables equations of central quadrics to be expressed in standard form w.r.t. the coordinate axes.)

36. $\cos\alpha = \begin{vmatrix} a & c & b \\ b & 0 & a \\ c & a & 0 \end{vmatrix} \div \begin{vmatrix} 0 & c & b \\ c & 0 & a \\ b & a & 0 \end{vmatrix} = \dfrac{b^2+c^2-a^2}{2bc}.$

37. Add $C_1+(C_2+\ \dots\ +C_n)$ and take out the common factor $a+(n-1)(-1) = a-n+1$ from C_1. Now perform R_2-R_1, R_3-R_1, $\dots$, R_n-R_1. Expand down C_1. The value of the circulant is then $(a-n+1)(a+1)^{n-1}$.

38. $|B-\lambda I| = \begin{vmatrix} -\lambda & 1 & 1 \\ 1 & -\lambda & 1 \\ 1 & 1 & -\lambda \end{vmatrix} = (2-\lambda)\begin{vmatrix} 1 & 1 & 1 \\ 1 & -\lambda & 1 \\ 1 & 1 & -\lambda \end{vmatrix}$ ($C_1+C_2+C_3$, then take out common factor $2-\lambda$ from C_1.)

$= (2-\lambda)(\lambda+1)^2$ (after R_2-R_1, R_3-R_1 and exp. down C_1) $= 2+3\lambda-\lambda^3$.

39. Now, $B^2 = \begin{bmatrix} 2 & 1 & 1 \\ 1 & 2 & 1 \\ 1 & 1 & 2 \end{bmatrix}$, $B^3 = \begin{bmatrix} 2 & 3 & 3 \\ 3 & 2 & 3 \\ 3 & 3 & 2 \end{bmatrix}$

$$\therefore\ 2I+3B-B^3 = \begin{bmatrix} 2+0-2 & 0+3-3 & 0+3-3 \\ 0+3-3 & 2-0-2 & 0+3-3 \\ 0+3-3 & 0+3-3 & 2+0-2 \end{bmatrix} = O.$$

Compare the matrix equation $2I+3B-B^3 = O$ with the characteristic equation $2+3\lambda-\lambda^3 = 0$. This is an instance of the Cayley–Hamilton theorem.

40. $B^{-1} = \frac{1}{2}\begin{bmatrix} -1 & 1 & 1 \\ 1 & -1 & 1 \\ 1 & 1 & -1 \end{bmatrix}$ on calculation. Write the equations as $BX = H$, i.e. $X = B^{-1}H$

$$\therefore\ \begin{bmatrix} x \\ y \\ z \end{bmatrix} = \frac{1}{2}\begin{bmatrix} -1 & 1 & 1 \\ 1 & -1 & 1 \\ 1 & 1 & -1 \end{bmatrix}\begin{bmatrix} 3 \\ 4 \\ 5 \end{bmatrix} = \frac{1}{2}\begin{bmatrix} 6 \\ 4 \\ 2 \end{bmatrix}\quad \therefore\ x = 3,\ y = 2,\ z = 1.$$

41. Call the vectors **a**, **b**, **c** respectively and suppose $\exists$ constants p, q, r:

$p\mathbf{a}+q\mathbf{b}+r\mathbf{c} = \mathbf{0}$ ... (i)

$\therefore\ p+2q+r = 0,\ p+2r = 0,\ p+q-r = 0$ (for corresponding components).

If these three equations are simultaneously valid, then

$$D = \begin{vmatrix} 1 & 2 & 1 \\ 1 & 0 & 2 \\ 1 & 1 & -1 \end{vmatrix} = 0. \text{ On calculation, } D = 5.$$

$\therefore \nexists\ p, q, r$ as indicated in (i) i.e. **a**, **b**, **c** are linearly independent.

42. Using the method of Exercise 12.41, we have

$$D = \begin{vmatrix} 1 & -1 & 5 \\ 4 & 7 & -13 \\ 3 & 4 & -6 \end{vmatrix} = 0 \text{ on calculation.} \quad \therefore \text{ the vectors are linearly dependent.}$$

Values of p, q, r in this case are $-2, 3, 1$ respectively, on computation. Hence, if the vectors are **a**, **b**, **c** respectively, $-2\mathbf{a}+3\mathbf{b}+\mathbf{c} = \mathbf{0}$. This means that $2C_1 = 3C_2+C_3$. (What is the corresponding dependence relation for rows?)

43. $|P^{-1}AP-\lambda I| = |P^{-1}AP-\lambda P^{-1}P| \quad (\because P^{-1}P = I) = |P^{-1}(A-\lambda I)P|$

$$= |P^{-1}|\ |A-\lambda I|\ |P| = |A-\lambda I| \quad (\because |P^{-1}|\ |P| = 1)$$

$$\therefore\ |A-\lambda I| = 0 \Rightarrow |P^{-1}AP-\lambda I| = 0$$

$\therefore$ similar matrices have the same characteristic equation and $\therefore$ the same eigenvalues.

44. $A'^T = (P^{-1}AP)^T = P^TA^TP^{-1^T} = P^TAP^{T^T} = P^{-1}AP = A'$
since A symmetric $\Rightarrow A^T = A$, P orthogonal $\Rightarrow P^TP = I \ \therefore\ A'$ is symmetric.

45. Let $|A|$ be $n \times n$ and $|A^{-1}| \neq 0 \ \therefore\ |A-\lambda I| = 0 \Rightarrow \dfrac{|A^{-1}|}{\lambda^n}|A-\lambda I| = 0$

$$\Rightarrow \left|\frac{I}{\lambda}-A^{-1}\right| = 0$$

i.e. $\dfrac{1}{\lambda}$ is an eigenvalue of A^{-1}. (Or $AX = \lambda X \Rightarrow A^{-1}AX = \lambda A^{-1}X \Rightarrow A^{-1}X =$
$= \lambda^{-1}X$.)

[Check by taking $n = 2$ and writing each step out fully.]

46. $\begin{vmatrix} a-\lambda & a^{-1} \\ a^{-1} & a-\lambda \end{vmatrix} = 0 \Rightarrow \lambda^2-2\lambda a+a^2-a^{-2} = 0$ whence $\lambda = a\pm a^{-1} \quad (a = e^{\theta})$

$\therefore$ eigenvalues are $2\cosh\theta$, $2\sinh\theta$.

47. $\begin{vmatrix} a-\lambda & c(1+a) \\ b & a-\lambda \end{vmatrix} = 0 \Rightarrow \lambda^2-2\lambda a+1 = 0 \Rightarrow \lambda = a\pm\sqrt{a^2-1} = \cosh x\pm\sinh x$

$\therefore$ eigenvalues are $e^{\pm x}$.

48. $$\begin{vmatrix} 1 & 1 & 1 & 1 \\ 1 & 2 & 3 & 4 \\ 1 & 3 & 6 & 10 \\ 1 & 4 & 10 & 20 \end{vmatrix} = \begin{vmatrix} 1 & 0 & 0 & 0 \\ 1 & 1 & 2 & 3 \\ 1 & 2 & 5 & 9 \\ 1 & 3 & 9 & 19 \end{vmatrix} = \begin{vmatrix} 1 & 0 & 0 \\ 2 & 1 & 3 \\ 3 & 3 & 10 \end{vmatrix} = 1$$

49. 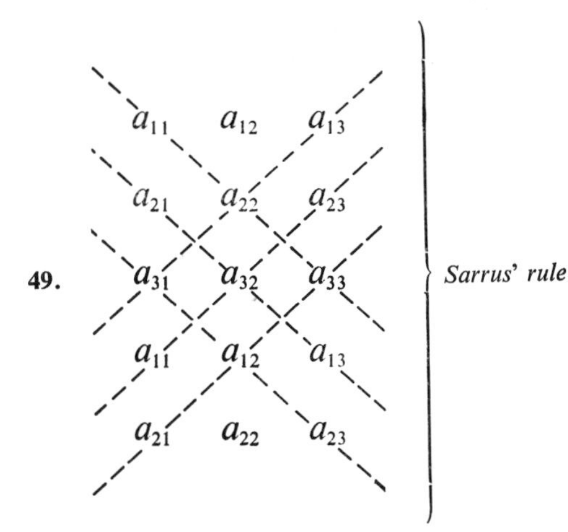

Sarrus' rule applies to a 3×3 determinant because the number of diagonals $= 3+3\ (=6) = 3! =$ the number of terms in the expansion of the determinant. This does not occur for a 4×4 determinant consisting of $4! = 24$ terms in the expansion. However, expanding along R_1 (say), we can associate with each of the 4 elements the corresponding 3×3 cofactor for which Sarrus' rule applies ($4\times6 = 24$).

50. Now $[\mathbf{a}, \mathbf{b}, \mathbf{c}] = \begin{vmatrix} a_1 & a_2 & a_3 \\ b_1 & b_2 & b_3 \\ c_1 & c_2 & c_3 \end{vmatrix} = \triangle$ and $\mathbf{b}\times\mathbf{c} = \begin{vmatrix} \mathbf{i} & \mathbf{j} & \mathbf{k} \\ b_1 & b_2 & b_3 \\ c_1 & c_2 & c_3 \end{vmatrix}$

$= A_1\mathbf{i}+A_2\mathbf{j}+A_3\mathbf{k}$, etc.

$$\therefore (\mathbf{a}\times\mathbf{b})\cdot\{(\mathbf{b}\times\mathbf{c})\times(\mathbf{c}\times\mathbf{a})\} = (\mathbf{a}\times\mathbf{b})\cdot\{[\mathbf{b}, \mathbf{c}, \mathbf{a}]\mathbf{c} - [\mathbf{c}, \mathbf{c}, \mathbf{a}]\mathbf{b}\} = \{(\mathbf{a}\times\mathbf{b})\cdot\mathbf{c}\}\,[\mathbf{b}, \mathbf{c}, \mathbf{a}]$$
$$= [\mathbf{a}, \mathbf{b}, \mathbf{c}]^2.$$

51. Determinantally, the result is $\begin{vmatrix} A_1 & A_2 & A_3 \\ B_1 & B_2 & B_3 \\ C_1 & C_2 & C_3 \end{vmatrix} = \triangle^2$ i.e. $\triangle^* = \triangle^2$.

52. L orthogonal $\Rightarrow L^TL = I \Rightarrow |L^TL| = 1 \Rightarrow |L^T|\,|L| = 1 \Rightarrow |L|^2 = 1 \Rightarrow L = \pm1$ (Remember: $|L^T| = |L|$.)

53. Multiply the skew-symmetric determinant D (of odd order) throughout by -1

$$\therefore -D = D^T = D \quad \therefore D = 0.$$

54. $$\frac{\partial(x, y)}{\partial(r, s)} = \begin{vmatrix} x_r & x_s \\ y_r & y_s \end{vmatrix} = \begin{vmatrix} x_uu_r+x_vv_r & x_uu_s+x_vv_s \\ y_uu_r+y_vv_r & y_uu_s+y_vv_s \end{vmatrix} \quad \text{by (45)}$$
$$= \begin{vmatrix} x_u & x_v \\ y_u & y_v \end{vmatrix}\begin{vmatrix} u_r & u_s \\ v_r & v_s \end{vmatrix} = \frac{\partial(x, y)}{\partial(u, v)}\,\frac{\partial(u, v)}{\partial(r, s)} \quad \text{by (134).}$$

55. Put $r = x$, $s = y$ and the result follows.

Now $x = f(u, v)$, $y = g(u, v)$ define a transformation (assumed non-singular) of points (x, y) from one plane to points (u, v) of another plane. The reverse transformation is given by $u = \phi(x, y)$, $v = \psi(x, y)$. Hence, the result shows that the Jacobians of these transformations are reciprocals of each other.

56. Direct determinantal multiplication with repeated use of (30)–(33) yields the result.

57. Expand along R_1 $\therefore \Delta_n = 2\Delta_{n-1}-\Delta'$. Expand Δ' down C_1 $\therefore \Delta' = \Delta_{n-2}$

$\therefore \Delta_n = 2\Delta_{n-1}-\Delta_{n-2}$

$$\begin{aligned}\Delta_n &= 2(2\Delta_{n-2}-\Delta_{n-3})-\Delta_{n-2} = 3\Delta_{n-2}-2\Delta_{n-3} \text{ (applying the recurrence to } \Delta_{n-1})\\ &= 3(2\Delta_{n-3}-\Delta_{n-4})-2\Delta_{n-3}=4\Delta_{n-3}-3\Delta_{n-4} \text{ (applying the recurrence to } \Delta_{n-2})\\ &= 5\,\Delta_{n-4}-4\,\Delta_{n-5} \qquad \text{(applying the recurrence to } \Delta_{n-3})\\ &= n\,\Delta_{n-(n-1)}-(n-1)\,\Delta_0 = n\,\Delta_1-(n-1)\cdot 1 = n\cdot 2-(n-1) = n+1.\end{aligned}$$

Notice that $\Delta_0 = 1, \Delta_1 = 2, \Delta_2 = 3, \Delta_3 = 4, \ldots, \Delta_n = n+1$, i.e. the determinants are alternative forms of the first $n+1$ integers, i.e. the determinantal sequence is precisely $\omega_n\,(1, 2; 2, 1)$ of Exercise 9.45.

58. Let $\mathbf{a} = (1, 1, -1)$, $\mathbf{b} = (1, -1, 1)$, $\mathbf{c} = (x, y, z)$.

$$\left.\begin{aligned}\therefore\ \mathbf{a} \perp \mathbf{c} \Rightarrow \mathbf{a}\cdot\mathbf{c} = 0 \Rightarrow x+y-z = 0\\ \mathbf{b} \perp \mathbf{c} \Rightarrow \mathbf{b}\cdot\mathbf{c} = 0 \Rightarrow x-y+z = 0\end{aligned}\right\} \Rightarrow x = 0, \quad y = z.$$

But the vector required is unit, i.e. $\dfrac{\mathbf{c}}{|\mathbf{c}|}$ $\quad\therefore\ y^2+z^2 = 1 \quad \therefore\ y = z = \dfrac{1}{\sqrt{2}} \quad \therefore$ two possible unit vectors are $\pm\dfrac{(0, 1, 1)}{\sqrt{2}}$.

59. $\mathbf{a}\times\mathbf{b} = (-2, -2)$ on calculation $\therefore\ |\mathbf{a}\times\mathbf{b}| = 2\sqrt{2}$

$\therefore$ the unit vector $\perp$ **a**, **b** is $\dfrac{(0, -1, -1)}{\sqrt{2}}$, or its negative.

60. By (150), the x-component of the expression

$$\begin{aligned}&= \{a_2(b_1c_2-b_2c_1)-a_3(b_3c_1-b_1c_3)\}+\{b_2(c_1a_2-c_2a_1)-b_3(c_3a_1-c_1a_3)\}\\ &\quad+\{c_2(a_1b_2-a_2b_1)-c_3(a_3b_1-a_1b_3)\}\\ &= 0.\end{aligned}$$

Similarly for y- and z-components. Thus, the sum is **0**.

61. $$B = \begin{bmatrix} \cdot & \cdot & \cdot & i\\ \cdot & \cdot & -i & \cdot\\ \cdot & -i & \cdot & \cdot\\ i & \cdot & \cdot & \cdot\end{bmatrix}, \quad \overline{B} = \begin{bmatrix} \cdot & \cdot & \cdot & -i\\ \cdot & \cdot & i & \cdot\\ \cdot & i & \cdot & \cdot\\ -i & \cdot & \cdot & \cdot\end{bmatrix}$$

62. On calculation, $B^2 = -I$. **63.** $\overline{B}^T B = I$.

64. $$|B-\lambda I| = \begin{vmatrix} -\lambda & \cdot & \cdot & i\\ \cdot & -\lambda & -i & \cdot\\ \cdot & -i & -\lambda & \cdot\\ -i & \cdot & \cdot & -\lambda\end{vmatrix} = 0 \Rightarrow (\lambda^2+1)^2 = 0 \text{ on evaluation.}$$

$\therefore$ eigenvalues are $\lambda = \pm i, \pm i$ (i.e. repeated roots).
Clearly, the eigenvalues of unitary B lie on the complex unit circle $|z| = 1$ at the points where it cuts the axis of imaginaries.

65. $(\hat{\mathbf{l}}\times\hat{\mathbf{m}})\cdot(\hat{\mathbf{l}}\times\hat{\mathbf{n}}) = \begin{vmatrix}\hat{\mathbf{l}}\cdot\hat{\mathbf{l}} & \hat{\mathbf{l}}\cdot\hat{\mathbf{m}}\\ \hat{\mathbf{l}}\cdot\hat{\mathbf{n}} & \hat{\mathbf{m}}\cdot\hat{\mathbf{n}}\end{vmatrix}$

$(\sin c\hat{\mathbf{w}})\cdot(\sin b\hat{\mathbf{v}}) = (1)\,(\cos a)-(\cos b)\,(\cos c)$ where $\hat{\mathbf{w}}\perp\hat{\mathbf{l}}, \hat{\mathbf{m}}, \hat{\mathbf{v}}\perp\hat{\mathbf{l}}, \hat{\mathbf{n}}$

$\therefore\ \sin b\sin c\ \hat{\mathbf{v}}\cdot\hat{\mathbf{w}} = \cos a-\cos b\cos c \quad \therefore\ \cos a = \cos b\cos c+\sin b\sin c\cos A.$

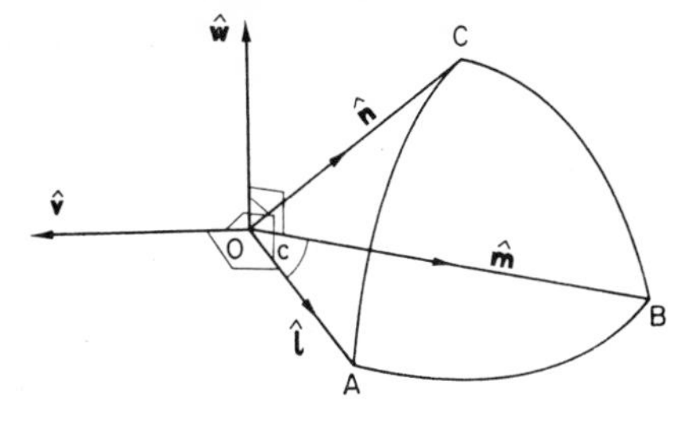

66. $(\hat{\mathbf{l}}\times\hat{\mathbf{m}})\times(\hat{\mathbf{l}}\times\hat{\mathbf{n}}) = [\hat{\mathbf{l}}, \hat{\mathbf{m}}, \hat{\mathbf{n}}]\hat{\mathbf{l}} - [\hat{\mathbf{l}}, \hat{\mathbf{m}}, \hat{\mathbf{l}}]\hat{\mathbf{n}} = [\hat{\mathbf{l}}, \hat{\mathbf{m}}, \hat{\mathbf{n}}]\hat{\mathbf{l}} \quad \because [\hat{\mathbf{l}}, \hat{\mathbf{m}}, \hat{\mathbf{l}}] = 0$

$\therefore (\sin\ c\hat{\mathbf{w}})\times(\sin\ b\ \hat{\mathbf{v}}) = [\hat{\mathbf{l}}, \hat{\mathbf{m}}, \hat{\mathbf{n}}]\hat{\mathbf{l}}$

$\therefore \sin b\ \sin c\ \sin A\ \hat{\mathbf{l}} = [\hat{\mathbf{l}}, \hat{\mathbf{m}}, \hat{\mathbf{n}}]\hat{\mathbf{l}}$

$\therefore \sin b\ \sin c\ \sin A = [\hat{\mathbf{l}}, \hat{\mathbf{m}}, \hat{\mathbf{n}}] = [\hat{\mathbf{m}}, \hat{\mathbf{n}}, \hat{\mathbf{l}}] = \sin c\ \sin a \sin B$ (cyclical permutation of symbols)

$$= [\hat{\mathbf{n}}, \hat{\mathbf{l}}, \hat{\mathbf{m}}] = \sin a \sin b \sin C$$

$$\therefore \frac{\sin A}{\sin a} = \frac{\sin B}{\sin b} = \frac{\sin C}{\sin c}.$$

67. $\operatorname{div} \mathbf{r} = \dfrac{\partial}{\partial x} x + \dfrac{\partial}{\partial y} y + \dfrac{\partial}{\partial z} z = 1+1+1 = 3.$

68. $\operatorname{grad} \mathbf{r}^2 = \sum \dfrac{\partial}{\partial x}(x^2+y^2+x^2)\mathbf{i} = \sum 2x\mathbf{i} = 2\sum x\mathbf{i} = 2\mathbf{r}.$

69. $\operatorname{Curl} \operatorname{grad} U = \begin{vmatrix} \mathbf{i} & \mathbf{j} & \mathbf{k} \\ \dfrac{\partial}{\partial x} & \dfrac{\partial}{\partial y} & \dfrac{\partial}{\partial z} \\ \dfrac{\partial U}{\partial x} & \dfrac{\partial U}{\partial y} & \dfrac{\partial U}{\partial z} \end{vmatrix} = \mathbf{0}.$

70. $\operatorname{Curl} \mathbf{F} = \mathbf{V}$ where $u = \dfrac{\partial h}{\partial y} - \dfrac{\partial g}{\partial z},\quad v = \dfrac{\partial f}{\partial z} - \dfrac{\partial h}{\partial x},\quad w = \dfrac{\partial g}{\partial x} - \dfrac{\partial f}{\partial y}$

on calculation from the determinant for curl **F**.

$$\therefore \operatorname{div}(\operatorname{curl} \mathbf{F}) = \frac{\partial}{\partial x}\left(\frac{\partial h}{\partial y} - \frac{\partial g}{\partial z}\right) + \frac{\partial}{\partial y}\left(\frac{\partial f}{\partial z} - \frac{\partial h}{\partial x}\right) + \frac{\partial}{\partial z}\left(\frac{\partial g}{\partial x} - \frac{\partial f}{\partial y}\right)$$

$$= \frac{\partial^2 h}{\partial x\,\partial y} - \frac{\partial^2 g}{\partial x\,\partial z} + \frac{\partial^2 f}{\partial y\,\partial z} - \frac{\partial^2 h}{\partial y\,\partial x} + \frac{\partial^2 g}{\partial z\,\partial x} - \frac{\partial^2 f}{\partial z\,\partial y} = 0 \text{ by (44).}$$

[We then refer to **F** as a *solenoidal* vector.]

EXERCISES 13

1. $\{1\}, \{3\}, \{5\}, \{7\}, \{1, 3\}, \{1, 5\}, \{1, 7\}, \{3, 5\}, \{3, 7\}, \{5, 7\}, \{1, 3, 5\}, \{1, 3, 7\}, \{1, 5, 7\}, \{3, 5, 7\}$ are proper subsets; O, S are improper subsets.

2. No, since it contains the 8 points $(\pm 1, \pm 2)$, $(\pm 2, \pm 1)$.

3. K contains 21 elements: (0, 0), (± 1, 0), (± 2, 0), (0, ± 1, (0, ± 2), (± 1, ± 1), (± 2, ± 1), (± 1, ± 2). Elements of P are: 11, 13, 17, 19, 23, 29, 31, 37, 41, 43, 47, 53, 59, 61, 67, 71, 73, 79, 83, 89, 97, i.e. 21 elements. Thus, statement (b), $|K| = |P|$, is correct.

4. $A \times B$ = (1, 3), (1, 4), (2, 3), (2, 4), (3, 3), (3, 4).

5. $B \times A$ = (3, 1), (3, 2), (3, 3), (4, 1), (4, 2), (4, 3) $\neq A \times B$.

6. No, $\because$ it is not symmetric, i.e. $A \subset B \nRightarrow B \subset A$ in general.

7. $m = 3^{n-1} (m \in \mathcal{M}, n \in \mathcal{N})$.

8. The set $S = \{a, b, c, d\}$ can be mapped onto itself in $4! = 24$ ways. Some rearrangements of the orderings of S (i.e. mappings) are $S \to (a, b, c, d)$, $S \to (b, a, d, c)$, $S \to (a, b, d, c)$, $S \to (b, a, c, d)$, $S \to (d, c, b, a)$.

9. 13. **10.** $\frac{5}{4}$.

11, 12. *(Diagrams only)*

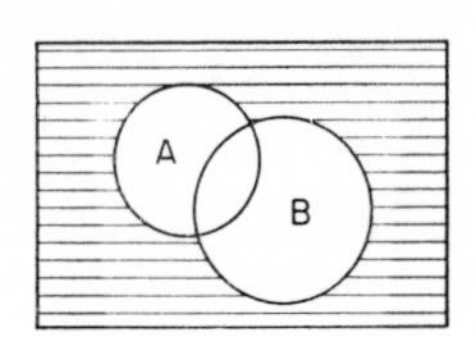

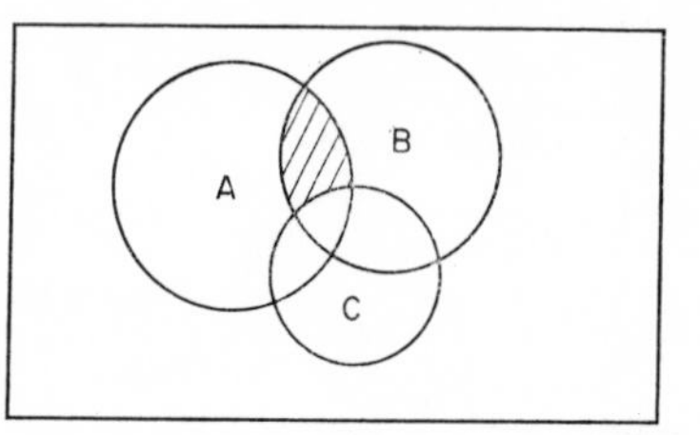

13. $(A \cap B) \cup (A \cap \bar{B}) = A \cap (B \cup \bar{B})$ (distributive law) $= A \cap I = A$.

14. Let C, F, T be the sets representing students playing cricket, football and tennis respectively.

$$\therefore n(C+F+T) = n(C)+n(F)+n(T)-n(CF)-n(FT)-n(CT)+n(CFT)$$
$$= 28+30+42-8-10-5+3 = 80$$

$\therefore$ the number playing no sport is $100-80 = 20$.

15. Students playing *only* tennis number $n(T)-n(FT)-n(CT)+n(CFT) = 42-10-$ $-5+3 = 30$.

16. The number of students playing football if and only if they play tennis is $n(FT)+n(CFT) = 5+3 = 8$.

17. *(Diagrams only)*

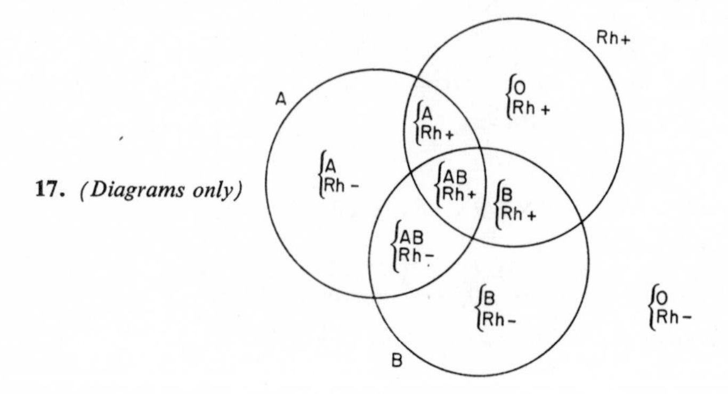

18. Since $n^C = C$ (n finite), $\aleph_0 C = C$, $CC = C$, we may interpret $\dfrac{C}{C}$ as n, $\aleph_0$ or C, so the question is ambiguous, i.e. $\dfrac{C}{C}$ is indeterminate.

19. $a0 = 0+a0$ (by B_2) $= a\bar{a}+a0$ (B_4) $= a(\bar{a}+0)$ (B_1, B_3) $= a\bar{a}$ (B_2) $= 0$ (B_4).

20. Multiply $\therefore (a+x)(a+\bar{x}) = (b+x)(b+\bar{x})$

$\therefore aa+a(x+\bar{x})+x\bar{x} = bb+b(x+\bar{x})+x\bar{x}$

$\therefore a+a1+0 = b+b1+0 \quad \therefore a+a = b+b$

$\therefore a = b$ (Example 80).

21. $a+b = b \Rightarrow \bar{b}(a+b) = \bar{b}b \Rightarrow a\bar{b}+b\bar{b} = b\bar{b}$ $\Rightarrow a\bar{b}+0 = 0 \Rightarrow a\bar{b} = 0$.

22. $a \subset b$, $b \subset c \Rightarrow a+b = b$, $b+c = c$ $\quad \therefore a+c = a+(b+c)$ (given) $= (a+b)+c$ associative law) $= b+c$ (given) $= c$ (given) $\therefore a \subset c$.

23. Let O^* be a second additive identity, i.e., suppose O is not unique. $O^* = O+O^*$ (by B_2 with $A = O^*$) $= O^*+O$ (B_1) $= O$ (B_2 with $A = O$) $\therefore O^* = O$. Similarly, I^* $(= II^* = I^*I) = I$.

24. The expression $= (\bar{\bar{A}}+\bar{B})(\bar{A}+\bar{C})\,BC$ (by De Morgan's law)

$= (A\bar{A}+A\bar{C}+\bar{B}\bar{A}+\bar{B}\bar{C})\,BC$ (distributive law and $\bar{\bar{A}} = A$)

$= OBC+A\bar{C}BC+\bar{B}\bar{A}BC+\bar{B}\bar{C}BC$ (dist. law and $A\bar{A} = O$)

$= O+O+O+O$ (comm. law with $B\bar{B} = C\bar{C} = O$ and $OX = O$)

$= O$.

25. Expression $= \{\overline{(\bar{A}+\bar{B})(A+B)}\}$ (distributive law)

$= \{\overline{\overline{AB}(A+B)}\}$ (De Morgan)

$= AB+(\overline{A+B})$ (De Morgan, double complementation)

$= AB+\bar{A}\bar{B}$ (De Morgan).

26. $(a+b)(b+c)(c+a) = (a+b)(bc+ba+c+ca)$ $\quad (\because cc = c)$

$= abc+aba+ac+aca+bbc+bba+bc+bca$

$= (abc+bca)+(aba+bba)+(ac+aca)+(bbc+bc)$

$= abc+ab+ac+bc$ (Example 80)

$= (ab+abc)+bc+ca$

$= ab+bc+ca$ (Example 82).

It is its own dual, i.e. it is a self-dual result.

27. Roles of O and I are played by 1 and 18 respectively. Complements of 2 and 9 are 9 and 2 respectively. However, 3 has no complement. Neither has 6. Thus, the set is not a Boolean algebra. [You should set out the full 6×6 tables for the L.C.M. and H.C.F.]

28. The expression $= x\bar{x}+xy+y(y+z)+y$ (by B_3) $= 0+xy+y(y+z)+y$ (B_4) $= xy+y(y+z)+y$ (B_2) $= xy+y+y$ (Example 82) $= xy+y$ (Example 80) $= y$ (Example 82).

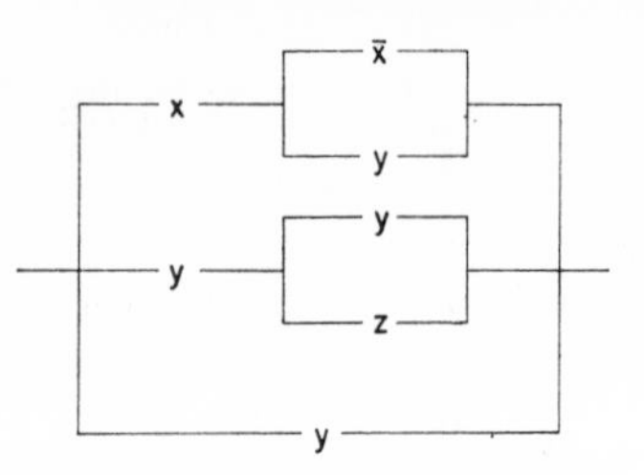

29. No, since $0 \cap (0 \cup 1) = 0 \cap 1 = 0$ while $(0 \cap 0) \cup (0 \cap 1) = 1 \cup 0 = 1$ (and $0 \neq 1$), i.e. the system is non-distributive since B_3 is invalid.

30. Routine diagrams. (See *Applied Boolean Algebra*, F. Hohn (Macmillan, 1961), pp. 9–12.)

EXERCISES 14

1. Yes (Abelian).

2. No, since the rational number 0 has no inverse under multiplication. ($\frac{1}{0} = \infty$ which is not a number.)

3. No, since association does not hold, for if a, b, c are three integers ($c \neq 0$) we have $(a-b)-c \neq a-(b-c)$.

4. Yes (Abelian); the representative points all lie on the unit circle.

5. Yes (non-Abelian).

6. No, since $n \times n$ matrices may be singular and hence not all inverses will exist.

7. Yes (finite, Abelian).

8. Yes (finite, Abelian); 1 is self-inverse, 2 is self-inverse.

9. No, since closure does not take place; also, there is no identity.

10. No, since inverses do not exist.

11. No, since there are no inverses.

12. Yes (infinite, Abelian).

13. No, since closure and associative laws are violated.

14. No, since the associative law is broken.

15. No, since the associative law is invalid.

16. No, since closure is lacking, e.g. $3 \times 10 \equiv 8 \bmod 11$.

17. Assume the existence of a second inverse $(A^*)^{-1}$.

$\therefore (A^*)^{-1} A = I = A^{-1} A \Rightarrow A^{*-1} = A^{-1}$ by the right cancellation law (171).

18. In an additive group, the inverse $-A$ is unique.

19. $B+A = C+A \Rightarrow B = C$.

20. $-(A+B) = -B-A$.

21. A, B, $A+B$ all of period 2 (i.e. $A+A = O$, $B+B = O$, $(A+B)+(A+B) = O$) $\Rightarrow$ A, B commute.

22. Identity $O^* \Rightarrow O^*+A = A = O+A \Rightarrow O^* = O$ by the right cancellation law for addition (Exercise 14.19).

23. $\begin{bmatrix} 1 & 2 \\ 3 & 4 \end{bmatrix}$ has inverse $\begin{bmatrix} -2 & 1 \\ \frac{3}{2} & -\frac{1}{2} \end{bmatrix}$ whose elements are not all integers.

24. $X = A^{-1}B \Rightarrow AX = AA^{-1}B = IB = B$. Suppose $\exists X' : AX' = B = AX$

$\therefore X' = X$ by the left cancellation law $\therefore X$ is unique.

25. Let $T_1 : x' = x+h_1,\ y' = y+h_2,\ T_2 : x' = x+k_1,\ y' = y+k_2$.

$\therefore T_2T_1 : \quad x' = x+h_1+h_2 = x+h_3,\ y' = y+k_1+k_2 = y+k_3$ i.e. a translation T_3 $(= T_1T_2$ also).

$\therefore$ closure is valid. Similarly, association for the product of 3 translations is valid. Inverse $T^{-1} : x' = x-h,\ y' = y-k$. Identity: $x' = x,\ y' = y$.

$\therefore$ translations form an infinite Abelian group.

26.

	A	B	C	D	E
A	B	C	D	E	A
B	C	D	E	A	B
C	D	E	A	B	C
D	E	A	B	C	D
E	A	B	C	D	E

This is the multiplication table for the (commutative) cyclic group of order 5. [There is only one group of order 5.]

[If you did not realise the cyclic nature of the rows (or columns), one method for obtaining the elements of the table is as follows: complete row 5, then column 4, then row 4 (using the fact that the group is commutative), then row 1, column 2, row 2, row 3.]

27. Suppose we establish the following correspondence:

Matrix:	$\begin{bmatrix} 1 & \cdot \\ \cdot & 1 \end{bmatrix}$,	$\begin{bmatrix} 1 & \cdot \\ \cdot & -1 \end{bmatrix}$,	$\begin{bmatrix} -1 & \cdot \\ \cdot & 1 \end{bmatrix}$,	$\begin{bmatrix} -1 & \cdot \\ \cdot & -1 \end{bmatrix}$	
Residue:	1	3	5	7	(mod 8)
Abstract Symbol:	I	A	B	C	

Isomorphism is evident since, for instance,

$$\begin{bmatrix} 1 & \cdot \\ \cdot & -1 \end{bmatrix}\begin{bmatrix} -1 & \cdot \\ \cdot & 1 \end{bmatrix} = \begin{bmatrix} -1 & \cdot \\ \cdot & -1 \end{bmatrix} \text{ corresponds to}$$

$$3 \times 5 \equiv 7 \pmod 8$$

i.e. $\quad AB = C.$

It is not hard to verify that the set of matrices and the set of residues have the group properties (closure, association, identity, inverse) and that their abstract multiplication table is that of the Klein group K. $\therefore$ the matrices and the residues form isomorphic Abelian groups (both $\approx K$).

28, 29. Yes, all group properties hold. The condition $a^2+b^2 = 1$ is necessary to ensure that the product of the matrix and its inverse is the unit matrix. The matrix is orthogonal—see Exercise 11.53.

Notice that $\begin{bmatrix} a & b \\ -b & a \end{bmatrix}\begin{bmatrix} c & d \\ -d & c \end{bmatrix} = \begin{bmatrix} ac-bd & ad+bc \\ -(ad+bc) & ac-bd \end{bmatrix}$ and

$(ac-bd)^2+(ad+bc)^2 = (a^2+b^2)(c^2+d^2) = 1.$

30. (Non-Abelian) Klein group K since matrices I, A, B, C correspond to the abstract elements I, A, B, C in Example 92.

31. K.

32. Just I (identity, i.e. a group with one element).

33. C_n (cyclic group of order n).

34. Identify the matrices with the elements I, A, B, C, D, E respectively of the cross-ratio group. Then $A^3 = C^2 = I$ with $(AC)^2 = E^2 = I$ and it is easy to see that the two groups are isomorphic.

35. Yes (Abelian). Closure exists since $G(v_1)G(v_2) = \begin{bmatrix} 1 & -(v_1+v_2) \\ 0 & 1 \end{bmatrix}$

$$= \begin{bmatrix} 1 & -v_3 \\ 0 & 1 \end{bmatrix} = G(v_3)\ [= G(v_1+v_2)].$$

Association is valid. Identity, inverse are $G(0)$, $G(-v)$.

36. $$L(v) = k \begin{bmatrix} 1 & -v \\ -\dfrac{v}{c^2} & 1 \end{bmatrix}, \quad \{L(v)\}^{-1} = k \begin{bmatrix} 1 & v \\ \dfrac{v}{c^2} & 1 \end{bmatrix} = L(-v)$$

$\therefore$ $L(v)$ is non-singular. Also, $L(v)$ is orthogonal since $|L(v)| = k^2\left(1-\dfrac{v^2}{c^2}\right)$ $= 1$. (Why k^2?)

37. Closure exists since $L(v_1)\ L(v_2) = L(v_3)$ where $v_3 = \dfrac{v_1+v_2}{1+(v_1v_2)/c^2}$ after much simplification. Association also exists. Identity is $L(0)$. Thus, $L(v)$ form a group (Abelian).

38. From $\{L(v)\}^{-1}$, in Exercise 14.36, $x = k(x'+vt')$, $t = k\left(\dfrac{v}{c^2}x'+t'\right)$.

$$\therefore J = k^2 \begin{vmatrix} 1 & v \\ \dfrac{v}{c^2} & 1 \end{vmatrix} = 1, \quad J' = k^2 \begin{vmatrix} 1 & -v \\ -\dfrac{v}{c^2} & 1 \end{vmatrix} = 1.$$

[Vectorial equations of the forward and reverse Lorentz transformations in four-dimensional space-time are given in *Elementary Vector Analysis*, C. E. Weatherburn, p. 60. (See our reference, § 55.) For (x, ict) space-time, these equations reduce to ours.]

39. v_3 in Exercise 14.37.

40. $$x'^2-c^2t'^2 = k^2\left\{\left(1-\frac{v^2}{c^2}\right)x^2+2tx(-v+v)+(v^2-c^2)t^2\right\} = x^2-c^2t^2.$$

41. Obvious.

42. Now $x_1' = k(x_1-vt_1)$, $x_2' = k(x_2-vt_2)$ $\therefore$ $t_2 = t_1 \Rightarrow L = k^{-1}L'$, i.e. the length of a rigid body in its direction of motion with uniform velocity is reduced by the factor k^{-1}. (What might happen if $v \to c$?)

43. $x' = x\cos\theta+T\sin\theta$, $T' = -x\sin\theta+T\cos\theta$ where $\cos\theta = k\ (> 1)$, $\sin\theta = \dfrac{ikv}{c}$, i.e. $\theta = \tan^{-1}\left(\dfrac{iv}{c}\right) = \tanh^{-1}\left(\dfrac{v}{c}\right)$. By (128), these are the coordinates of a fixed point when the axes are rotated anti-clockwise through an imaginary angle θ, i.e. the Lorentz transformations may be regarded as rotations of the coordinate axes.

44. Put $\tan\theta = \dfrac{iv}{c}$ in Exercise 14.39 and use $\tan i\theta = i\tanh\theta$. Then addition of velocities $\Rightarrow \tanh^{-1}\left(\dfrac{v_3}{c}\right) = \tanh^{-1}\left(\dfrac{v_1}{c}\right)+\tanh^{-1}\left(\dfrac{v_2}{c}\right)$.

45. The group is isomorphic with S since $A^2 = B^2 = C^2 = D^3 = I$, $D^2 = E$.

46. $\{I, D, E\}$.

47. The group represents the rotations and reflections of the equilateral triangle OPQ (where OX is along the x-axis, X being the mid-point of PQ):

D represents a cyclical anti-clockwise rotation through $\dfrac{2\pi}{3}$;

E represents a cyclical anti-clockwise rotation through $\dfrac{4\pi}{3}$;

A represents an axial rotation about the altitude OX;

$B = AD = D^2A$; $C = AD^2 = DA$.

48. Let the order of C_n generated by A be $n = pq$.

$\therefore\ A^n = I = A^{pq} = (A^p)^q = (A^q)^p$,

i. e. $A^p(A^q)$ generates a cyclic group of order $q(p)$.

49. Given $x = x^{-1}$, $y = y^{-1}$ for x, y (and $\therefore xy$) $\in G$, i.e., $x^2 = y^2 = I \therefore (xy)^2 = = I \Rightarrow xy\,xy = I \Rightarrow x^2y\,xy^2 = xIy$ (on pre-multiplying by x, post-multiplying by y) $\therefore yx = xy \therefore G$ is Abelian.

50. Let $Z = \{z : za = az$ for all $a\in G\}$. Let $y, z\in Z$, $a\in G$. $\therefore a^{-1}yz\,a = a^{-1}y\cdot aa^{-1}\cdot za$ (inserting $aa^{-1} = I$) $= (a^{-1}ya)(a^{-1}za) = yz$, i.e. $yza = ayz$, $\therefore yz\in Z$, i.e. closure is valid. Likewise for association.
Identity is $I : a^{-1}Ia = I$.
Inverses exist $\because z^{-1} = (a^{-1}za)^{-1} = a^{-1}z^{-1}(a^{-1})^{-1} = a^{-1}z^{-1}a \therefore Z$ is a subgroup.

51. G Abelian $\Rightarrow az = za$ for all $a, z\in G \therefore G$ Abelian $\Rightarrow G = Z$.

52. Each element, say a of period r, i.e. $a^r = I$, generates a cyclic subgroup.
$\therefore r$ divides g (Lagrange's theorem) $\therefore g = rk$ (k an integer) $\therefore a^g = a^{rk} = (a^r)^k = I^k = I$.

53. Let G have order p (prime). If $a(\neq I)\in G : a^r = I$, then r divides p, i.e. $r = p \because p$ is prime. Thus, G consists of powers of a, i.e. it is cyclic.

54. Let H_1, H_2 be subgroups of G with mutually prime orders h_1, h_2. Suppose $a \in H_1, H_2 \therefore$ by Exercise 14.52, $a^{h_1} = a^{h_2} = I$ i.e. h_1 divides h_2 (or vice versa). But h_1, h_2 are mutually prime, i.e. have no common factor other than 1. Thus, a can only be I.

55. $\mathcal{J}_p - 0 \equiv \{1, 2, 3, \ldots, p-1\}$, i.e. 1 is the multiplicative identity. If $a \not\equiv 0 \pmod p$, then clearly $a^{p-1} \equiv 1 \pmod p$ (by Exercise 14.52), i.e. $a^p \equiv a \pmod p$.
If $a \equiv 0 \pmod p$, the result is trivially true.

56. $2^{2k} = (2^k)^2 = (p-1)^2 = p(p-2)+1 \equiv 1 \pmod p \because p$ divides $p(p-2) \therefore$ period of 2 is $2k \pmod p$.

57. Fermat's theorem $(a = 2) \Rightarrow 2^{p-1} \equiv 1 \pmod p$. But $2^{2k} \equiv 1 \pmod p \therefore 2k$ divides $p-1$.

58. By Exercise 14.57, $2k$ divides 2^k, i.e. k divides 2^{k-1}, i.e. k is a power of 2.

59. Yes. Identities are 0 ($= 0x^0$) and 1 ($= 1x^0$). This means that the ring structure exists *(polynomial ring)*.

60. Yes, since the representative matrices form a ring. [Note that the sum of two linear transformations has not been defined, and we would really need to do this; however it is outside the scope of our course.]

61. Yes. The ring properties may be verified.

62. No, since $\nexists$ a set corresponding to the inverse of the set A. Of course, $A \cup \bar{A} = I$ (universal set), $A \cap \bar{A} = O$ (null set), but we want an element K like $\bar{A}$: $K \cup \bar{K} = O$.

63. By Exercise 14.12, vectors form a group under addition. Multiplicatively, vectors are closed $\because$ $\mathbf{a}\times\mathbf{b}(=-\mathbf{b}\times\mathbf{a})$ is a vector, but $\mathbf{a}\times(\mathbf{b}\times\mathbf{c}) \neq (\mathbf{a}\times\mathbf{b})\times\mathbf{c}$ (157.1). Thus, under vector addition and multiplication, vectors form a partial ring which is non-associative (and non-commutative).

64. This is the additive aspect of the result $a^n = I$ for a multiplicative group of order n. Let a have period k $\therefore$ $ka = 0 = \frac{n}{h}a = 0$

$\left[\because k = \frac{n}{h} \text{ (Lagrange's theorem)}\right]$ $\therefore$ $na = 0$. (See Exercise 14.52.)

65. $A\circ A = AA - AA = 0$.

66. $A\circ B = AB - BA = -(BA - AB) = -B\circ A$.

67. $A\circ(B+C) = A(B+C)-(B+C)A = AB+AC-BA-CA = (AB-BA) + (AC-CA) = A\circ B + A\circ C$.

68. $(A\circ B)\circ C = (AB-BA)C - C(AB-BA) = ABC - BAC - CAB + CBA$.

$A\circ(B\circ C) = A(BC-CB)-(BC-CB)A = ABC-ACB-BCA+CBA$.

$\therefore (A\circ B)\circ C \neq A\circ(B\circ C)$.

69. $(A\circ B)\circ C + (B\circ C)\circ A + (C\circ A)\circ B = ABC-BAC-CAB+CBA + BCA-CBA-ABC+ACB+CAB-ACB-BCA+BAC = 0$.

70. $A*B = \frac{1}{2}(AB+BA) = \frac{1}{2}(BA+AB) = B*A$.

71. $A*(B+C) = \frac{1}{2}[A(B+C)+(B+C)A] = \frac{1}{2}[AB+AC+BA+CA]$
$= \frac{1}{2}[(AB+BA)+(AC+CA)] = A*B + A*C$.

72. $A*(B*C) = \frac{1}{4}[A(BC+CB)+(BC+CB)A] = \frac{1}{4}(ABC+ACB+BCA+CBA)$

$(A*B)*C = \frac{1}{4}[(AB+BA)C+C(AB+BA)] = \frac{1}{4}(ABC+BAC+CAB+CBA)$

$\therefore A*(B*C) \neq (A*B)*C$.

73. $(a+a)+(a+a) = aa+aa+aa+aa$ given
$= (a+a)(a+a)$ on multiplication
$= a+a \ldots$ (i) given

$\therefore a+a = (a+a)+0$
$= (a+a)+\{(a+a)+\overline{(a+a)}\}$
$= (a+a)+(a+a)+\overline{(a+a)}$
$= (a+a)+\overline{(a+a)}$ by (i)
$= 0$.

74. $a = a+0 = a+(a+\bar{a}) = (a+a)+\bar{a} = 0+\bar{a}\ldots$(ii) using Exercise 14.73.

$$a+b = (a+b)(a+b) = aa+ab+ba+bb = a+ab+ba+b$$

$$\therefore\ 0 = (a+b)+(\overline{a+b}) = (a+b)+(\overline{a+b})+ab+ba = ab+ba$$

$$\therefore\ ab = \overline{ba}.$$

But $\overline{ba} = ba$ by (ii) $\therefore\ ab = ba$,
i.e. the Boolean ring is commutative.

75. The product of two Möbius transformations, represented by matrices A_1, A_2, is represented by the product matrix A_1A_2, and is $\therefore$ a Möbius transformation. The associative law clearly holds.
$\exists$ a unit Möbius transformation represented by the unit matrix I = diag. (1, 1).
$\exists$ an inverse Möbius transformation, represented by $A^{-1} = \begin{bmatrix} d & -b \\ -c & a \end{bmatrix}$
$\therefore$ the Möbius transformations form a group (non-Abelian $\because\ A_1A_2 \neq A_2A_1$ generally).

76. No, since $(a_p \cdot a_q)\cdot a_r = a_{n-|p-q|}\cdot a_r = a_{n-|n-|p-q|-r|}$
while $a_p\cdot(a_q\cdot a_r) = a_p\cdot a_{n-|q-r|} = a_{n-|n-|q-r|-p|}$
and $|n-|p-q|-r| \neq |n-|q-r|-p|$ in general, i.e. the associative law is invalid. In particular, $a_3\cdot(a_5\cdot a_2) = a_6$ while $(a_3\cdot a_5)\cdot a_2 = a_4$.
[Construct a multiplication table for, say, $n = 8$.]

77. Put $y = x^2$ $\therefore$ the equation is $y^2-10y+1 = 0$ with roots $y = 5\pm 2\sqrt{6}$.
$\therefore\ x = \pm(\sqrt{2}\pm\sqrt{3})$
$\therefore$ roots are $a = \sqrt{2}+\sqrt{3},\ b = \sqrt{2}-\sqrt{3},\ c = -\sqrt{2}+\sqrt{3},\ d = -\sqrt{2}-\sqrt{3}$.
If $\sqrt{2}(-\sqrt{2})$ is replaced by $-\sqrt{2}(\sqrt{2})$, then $f(a, b, c, d) \to f(c, d, a, b)$ by the operation $(ac)(bd)$.
If $\sqrt{3}(-\sqrt{3})$ is replaced by $-\sqrt{3}(\sqrt{3})$, we have the operation $(ab)(cd)$.
If $\sqrt{2}(-\sqrt{2})$, $\sqrt{3}(-\sqrt{3})$ are replaced by $-\sqrt{2}(\sqrt{2})$, $-\sqrt{3}(\sqrt{3})$, we have the operation $(ad)(bc)$.
These operations are those of the Klein group, i.e. the Galois group of the equation is K.

78. $x = 2\cos\theta \Rightarrow 4\cos^3\theta - 3\cos\theta = -\frac{1}{2} = \cos 3\theta$ (122) $\therefore\ 3\theta = 120°,\ 240°,\ 480°$. $\therefore\ \theta = 40°,\ 80°,\ 160°$. $\therefore$ roots are $a = 2\cos 40° = 2\cos 320°$, $b = 2\cos 80°$, $c = 2\cos 160°$.
$\therefore\ \exists$ cyclic symmetry amongst a, b, c by the operation of doubling the angle. Consider the permutation $P \equiv (abc)$ i.e. a cyclic interchange of the letters $\therefore\ Pf(a, b, c) = f(b, c, a)$, $P^2f(abc) = f(c, a, b)$.
$\therefore$ the Galois group for $x^3-3x+1 = 0$ is $C_3\{I, P, P^2\}$.

79–85. Consult the reference, also Johnson [*The American Mathematical Monthly*, **68** (5) 469–72 (1961)] where it is also proved that $AC(AC(G)) = AC(G)$.

EXERCISES 15

1. $(x, 4; 2, 3) = \dfrac{(x-2)(4-3)}{(4-2)(x-3)} = \dfrac{x-2}{2(x-3)}$;

$$(3, 2x; 1, 4) = \frac{(3-1)(2x-4)}{(3-4)(2x-1)} = \frac{4(x-2)}{(1-2x)}$$

$$\therefore\ \frac{x-2}{2(x-3)} = \frac{4(x-2)}{(1-2x)}\quad \therefore\ x \neq 2 \Rightarrow\quad 1-2x = 8x-24,\quad \text{i.e.}\quad x = 2\tfrac{1}{2}.$$

2. $\{1, 3; 2, 4\} = \dfrac{(1-2)(3-4)}{(1-4)(3-2)} = -\dfrac{1}{3} = 1-\lambda$. Similarly for the others.

3. $\{-2, 2; 1, x\} = -1 \Rightarrow \dfrac{(-2-1)(2-x)}{(-2-x)(2-1)} = -1 \Rightarrow x = 4.$

4. $\lambda^2-\lambda+1 = 0$ i.e. $\lambda = -\varepsilon$ or $-\varepsilon^2$ (ε a complex cube root of unity). This is called the *equianharmonic case* (which cannot occur if the points are all real).

5. $\lambda^2 = 1 \Rightarrow \lambda = \pm 1$. The cross-ratio is harmonic ($\because \lambda = 1$ is excluded).

6. $\lambda = \frac{1}{2} \Rightarrow$ the harmonic case.

7. $\lambda^2-\lambda+1 = 0$, the equianharmonic case.

8. $\lambda = 2, 0$ giving the harmonic case $\because \lambda = 0$ is excluded.

9. $(0, x; 1, -1) = \dfrac{(0-1)(x+1)}{(0+1)(x-1)} = \dfrac{-(x+1)}{x-1} = \dfrac{-(1+1/x)}{(1-1/x)}.$

$$\therefore\ (0, \infty; 1, -1) = \lim_{x\to\infty} (0, x; 1, -1) = \lim_{x\to\infty}\left\{\frac{-1-1/x}{1-1/x}\right\} = -1.$$

10. Given $(AB, CD) = \sec^2\phi = \lambda$ (say), then $(AC, BD) = 1-\lambda$ (by Example 99) $= 1-\sec^2\phi = -\tan^2\phi$.
Other cross ratios are by (178) $\cos^2\phi$, $-\cot^2\phi$, $\sin^2\phi$, $\operatorname{cosec}^2\phi$.

11. $2x+3y+z = 0$ cuts $z = 0$ where $2x+3y = 0$, i.e. where $\dfrac{x}{y} = \dfrac{-3}{2}$.

$\therefore$ the point has coordinates $(-3, 2, 0)$, i.e. $(3, -2, 0)$.

12. $y = \frac{4}{7}x+c$, i.e. $4x-7y+cz = 0$ in homogeneous coordinates (c constant).

13. $xy = k^2$.

14. The point at infinity on the line $\because y = \dfrac{k^2}{0}$ if $x = 0$.

15. $CE = EA,\quad AF = FB \Rightarrow \dfrac{BD}{DC} = -1$ i.e. $BD = CD$ ($\because CD = -DC$).

This can only happen if D is at infinity, i. e. $FE//BC$.
Thus, Menelaus' theorem becomes: The line joining the midpoints of two sides of a triangle is parallel to the third. [What is Ceva's theorem? (Ceva 1647–1734, Italian).]

16. In Exercise 5.48, $\sinh\left(\dfrac{a}{k}\right) = \dfrac{a}{k}$ for very large k.

$\therefore$ the equation becomes $\dfrac{a_1}{a_2}\cdot\dfrac{b_1}{b_2}\cdot\dfrac{c_1}{c_2} = 1$

which is analogous to Menelaus' theorem. Why the + sign on the right?

17. The matrix of the transformation is $M(\theta) = \begin{bmatrix}\cos\theta & \sin\theta\\ \sin\theta & -\cos\theta\end{bmatrix}$ with $|M(\theta)| = -1$,

i.e. $M(\theta)$ is an improper orthogonal matrix, and $\{M(\theta)\}^{-1} = M(\theta)$. But notice that

$$M(\theta)M(\phi) = \begin{bmatrix}\cos\theta\cos\phi+\sin\theta\sin\phi & \cos\theta\sin\phi-\sin\theta\cos\phi\\ \sin\theta\cos\phi-\cos\theta\sin\phi & \cos\theta\cos\phi+\sin\theta\sin\phi\end{bmatrix}$$

$$= \begin{bmatrix}\cos(\theta-\phi) & -\sin(\theta-\phi)\\ \sin(\theta-\phi) & \cos(\theta-\phi)\end{bmatrix}$$

which is *not* a matrix of the same form (i.e. the minus sign is in the wrong place). $\therefore$ closure is lacking $\therefore$ the transformations do not form a group.

18. Notice that $M(\theta) = \begin{bmatrix} 1 & \cdot \\ \cdot & -1 \end{bmatrix} R(\theta)$, the former being the matrix of a reflection in the x-axis and $R(\theta)$ the rotation matrix of Example 90(iv).

19. Coordinates at ∞ are $P(x, x\tan\theta, 0)$, $X(1, 0, 0)$.

$\therefore$ parameters $\dfrac{y}{x}$ for P, X, I, J are (respectively) $\tan\theta, 0, i, -i$.

$$\therefore (PX, IJ) = (\tan\theta, 0;\ i, -i) = \frac{(\tan\theta - i)\cdot i}{(\tan\theta + i)\cdot -i} = \frac{-(\sin\theta - i\cos\theta)}{\sin\theta + i\cos\theta}$$

$$= \frac{i(\cos\theta + i\sin\theta)}{i(\cos\theta - i\sin\theta)} = \frac{e^{i\theta}}{e^{-i\theta}} = e^{2i\theta} \qquad \therefore \theta = \frac{1}{2i}\log(PX, IJ).$$

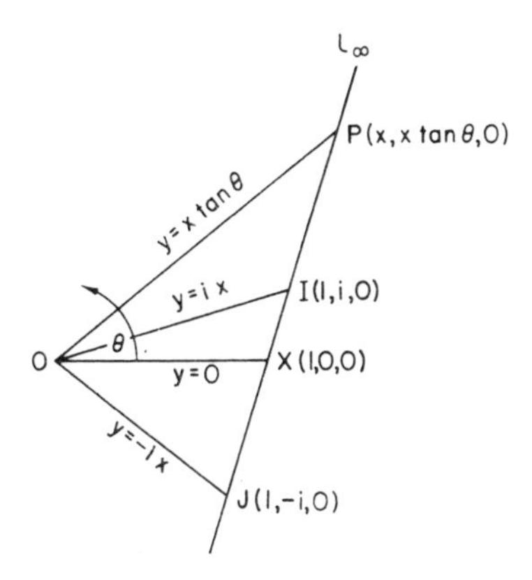

20. $(PX, IJ) = -1 \Rightarrow \theta = \dfrac{1}{2i}\log(-1) = \dfrac{1}{2i}\log e^{\pi i}$ (in the simplest exponential form)

$= \dfrac{\pi i}{2i} = \pi/2$, i.e. (i) $\theta = \pi/2$, (ii) OP is perpendicular to OX.

21. Choose the centre of projection to be the midpoint U of the diameter AB of the (inverted) semicircle, and the straight line to be the (horizontal) tangent to the semi-circle. $\therefore P, Q$ are in 1–1 correspondence.

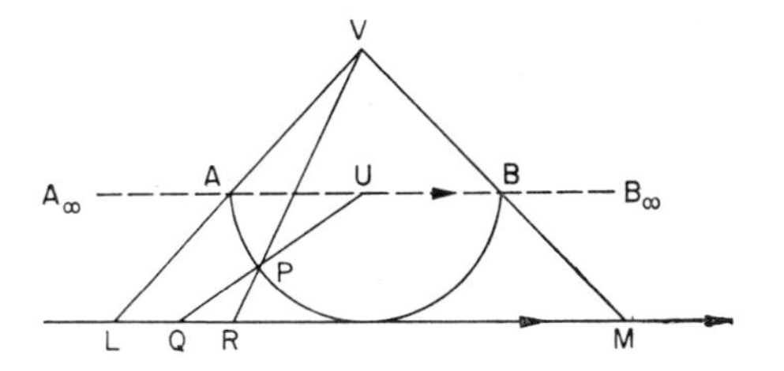

22. Take the centre of projection to be the point of intersection V of the lines joining the end-points of the (horizontal) line-segment LM to the corresponding extremities of the (inverted) semicircle.

$\therefore$ P, R are in 1–1 correspondence.

23. $$\begin{bmatrix} . & 1 & . \\ . & . & \varepsilon^2 \\ \varepsilon & . & . \end{bmatrix}\begin{bmatrix} 1 \\ -\varepsilon^t \\ 0 \end{bmatrix} = \begin{bmatrix} -\varepsilon^t \\ 0 \\ \varepsilon \end{bmatrix} = -\varepsilon^t \begin{bmatrix} 1 \\ 0 \\ -\varepsilon^{1+2t} \end{bmatrix} = \begin{bmatrix} 1 \\ 0 \\ -\varepsilon^{1+2t} \end{bmatrix}$$

$\because$ we are dealing with homogeneous coordinates and can $\therefore$ ignore the scalar factor $-\varepsilon^t$.

Similarly, $$U\begin{bmatrix} 0 \\ 1 \\ -\varepsilon^t \end{bmatrix} = \begin{bmatrix} 1 \\ -\varepsilon^{t+2} \\ 0 \end{bmatrix}, \quad U\begin{bmatrix} 1 \\ 0 \\ -\varepsilon^t \end{bmatrix} = \begin{bmatrix} 0 \\ -\varepsilon^{t+2} \\ \varepsilon \end{bmatrix} = \begin{bmatrix} 0 \\ 1 \\ -\varepsilon^{2t+2} \end{bmatrix}.$$

$\therefore$ U permutes the inflexions of the cubic among themselves. Note that $U = \varepsilon V^2$ (Exercises 12.31–12.33).

24. $$H \equiv 6^3 \begin{vmatrix} x & mz & my \\ mz & y & mx \\ my & mx & z \end{vmatrix} = 0 \Rightarrow x^3+y^3+z^3-\left(\frac{1+2m^3}{m^2}\right) xyz = 0,$$

ie. the Hessian of a cubic is a similar cubic.

25. $$J = 8\lambda\mu\nu \begin{vmatrix} x & nz & ny \\ nz & y & nx \\ ny & nx & z \end{vmatrix} = 0 \equiv H,$$ i.e. the Jacobian of a net of conics is the Hessian of the cubic.

26. Just 7 points are possible: $X(1, 0, 0)$, $Y(0, 1, 0)$, $Z(0, 0, 1)$, $A(0, 1, 1)$, $B(1, 0, 1)$, $C(1, 1, 0)$, $I(1, 1, 1) \equiv$ unit point.

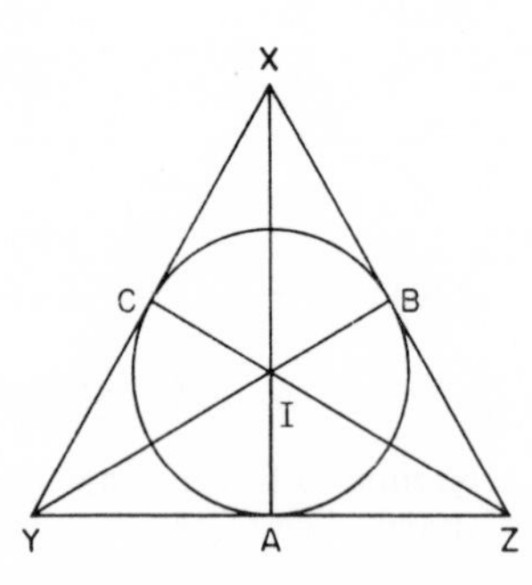

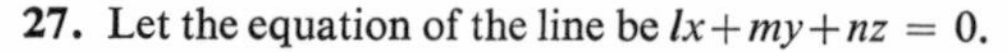

27. Let the equation of the line be $lx+my+nz = 0$.

$$\left.\begin{array}{l} (1, 1, 0) \text{ on this line} \Rightarrow 1+m = 0 \\ (0, 1, 1) \text{ on this line} \Rightarrow m+n = 0 \end{array}\right\} \Rightarrow 1 = -m = n.$$

$\therefore$ the equation of the line is $x-y+z = 0$, i.e. $x+y+z = 0$ (the unit line)

$\because$ $-1 \equiv 1 \pmod 2$. A third point on this line is $(1, 0, 1)$.

28. By duality, $\exists$ just 7 lines in the plane. The incidence of 3 points on each line and 3 lines through each point may be schematically shown in the diagram. The line ABC (whose equation was found in Exercise 15.27) must be thought of diagrammatically as a curve (a circle, say) for aesthetic purposes. [What are the equations of the other 6 lines? Their line coordinates correspond to the point coordinates of Exercise 15.26, excepting I, to which ABC corresponds.]

29. The finite geometry diagram of Exercise 15.28 gives the answer if we think of a committee man as being represented by a point and a subcommittee by a line.

30. There are 13 points and 13 lines in the plane with 4 points on each line and 4 lines through each point, e.g. points (0, 1, 2), (1, 0, 2), (1, 2, 0), (1, 1, 1) lie on the unit line $x+y+z = 0$. (Remaining details are left for the reader to wrestle with.)

EXERCISES 16

1. The conic degenerates if $\begin{vmatrix} 1 & 0 & k \\ 0 & -1 & 0 \\ k & 0 & 4 \end{vmatrix} = 0$, i.e. $k^2 = 4$ i.e. $k = \pm 2$.

Degenerate locus is $(x\pm 2)^2 - y^2 = 0$, i.e. $x+2\pm y = 0$ (2 lines)

or $x-2\pm y = 0$ (2 lines).

2. $$[x, y, z]\begin{bmatrix} 0 & a & b \\ -a & 0 & c \\ -b & -c & 0 \end{bmatrix}\begin{bmatrix} x \\ y \\ z \end{bmatrix} = [x, y, z]\begin{bmatrix} ay+bz \\ -ax+cz \\ -bx-cy \end{bmatrix} = [0],$$

i.e. the equation merely tells us $0 = 0$. The left-hand side does not yield the equation of a conic since the 3×3 matrix is skew-symmetric, not symmetric.

3. The discriminant of the conic is $\begin{vmatrix} -k^2 & 0 & 0 \\ 0 & 1 & c \\ 0 & c & c^2 \end{vmatrix} = 0$ on calculation.

$\therefore$ the conic degenerates into a line-pair.

Now $y^2 - k^2x^2 + 2cy + c^2 = 0 \Rightarrow (y+c)^2 - k^2x^2 = 0$, i.e. $(y+cz)^2 - k^2x^2 = 0$ in homogeneous form. This cuts $z = 0$ where $y^2 = k^2x^2$, i.e. $y = \pm kx$.
$\therefore$ the coordinates of the points where the lines $y+c\mp kx = 0$ cuts l_∞ are $(1, \pm k, 0)$.

4. The conic formed is a parabola, since the plane of section is parallel to the tangent plane of the cone. In Fig. 60, imagine the torch at the vertex and its light the cone —the floor is then the plane of section.

5. When the set square is in the position KMQ, the pencil P (at the point Q) is equi-

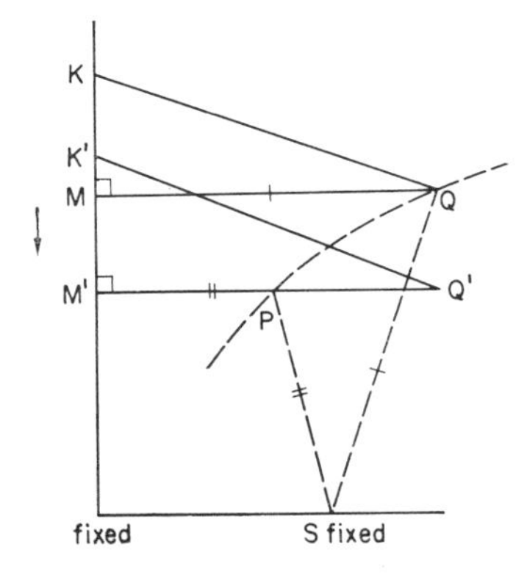

distant from the fixed line KM, and the fixed point S. When the set square is moved to the position $K'M'Q'$ the string is in the position SPQ' and clearly $SP = PM'$, i.e. the pencil is again equidistant from the fixed line KM and the fixed point S. Thus P will describe portion of a parabola.

6. Branch of a hyperbola. (See Fig. 62.)

7. $S' = a(x'\cos\theta - y'\sin\theta)^2 + b(x'\sin\theta + y'\cos\theta)^2 + 2h(x'\cos\theta - y'\sin\theta)\times$
$(x'\sin\theta + y'\cos\theta) = a'x'^2 + b'y'^2 + 2h'x'y'$ using (128)′,

$$\text{where}\begin{cases} a' = a\cos^2\theta + b\sin^2\theta + 2h\sin\theta\cos\theta \\ b' = a\sin^2\theta + b\cos^2\theta - 2h\sin\theta\cos\theta \\ h' = \tfrac{1}{2}(b-a)\sin 2\theta + h\cos 2\theta. \end{cases}$$

$\therefore a' + b' = a + b,\ a'b' - h^2 = ab - h^2$ (on lengthy calculation).

Clearly, $x^2 + y^2 = x'^2 + y'^2$ (see Exercise 11.40).

$\therefore$ some invariants of the rotation are $a + b$, $ab - h^2$, $x^2 + y^2$.

8. Square. $\therefore x + y - a = -2x^{1/2}y^{1/2}$.

Square again $\therefore x^2 + y^2 - 2xy + a^2z^2 - 2azx - 2ayz = 0$ making it homogeneous.

This conic (a parabola $\because h^2 = ab$ i. e. $(-1)^2 = 1\times 1$) cuts l_∞ where $x^2 + y^2 - 2xy = 0$, i.e. $(y - x)^2 = 0$, i.e. in the point $(1, 1, 0)$ repeated.

$\therefore$ the curve is an arc of a parabola with axis $y = x$. (Note that x, y cannot be negative.) It cuts $x = 0$ (y-axis) where $y^2 - 2ayz + a^2z^2 = 0$ i.e. $(y - az)^2 = 0$, i.e. in the coincident points $(0, a, 1)$. Similarly, it touches the line $y = 0$ (x-axis) at the point $(a, 0, 1)$. Thus, the parabola is symmetrical about its axis $y = x$ and touches the x- and y-axes at the points $(a, 0)$, $(0, a)$. Hence, its graph is easily constructed.

9. Subnormal $y\dfrac{dy}{dx} = kx$, i.e. $\displaystyle\int y\,dy = k\int x\,dx$,

i.e. $\dfrac{y^2}{2} = \dfrac{kx^2}{2} + c$, i.e. $kx^2 - y^2 + 2c = 0$ (a conic).

10. (Solution due to O. E. Stanaitis.) The equation of the general conic with given e is $SP^2 = e^2PM^2$ i.e. $(x-k)^2 + y^2 = e^2x^2 \ldots$ (i).

Differentiate w.r.t. x to eliminate p $\therefore 2(x-k) + 2y\dfrac{dy}{dx} = 2e^2x$.

Substitute in (i) to obtain $\left(e^2x - y\dfrac{dy}{dx}\right)^2 = e^2x^2 - y^2$.

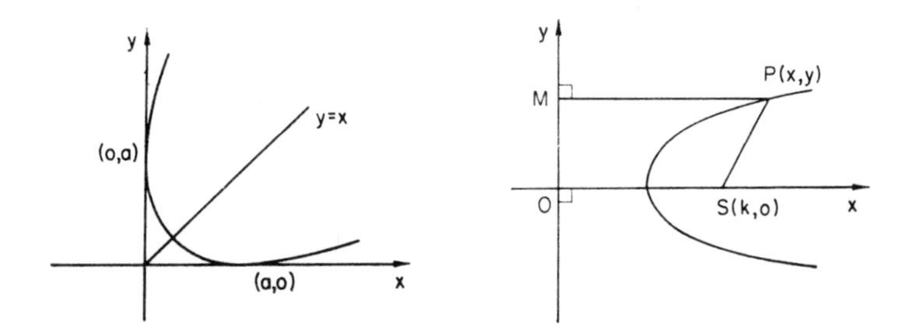

11. $\int y\,dy+(1-k^2)\int x\,dx = 0 \;\therefore\; \dfrac{y^2}{2}+(1-k^2)\dfrac{x^2}{2} = c \;\therefore\; \dfrac{x^2}{2c/(1-k^2)}+\dfrac{y^2}{2c} = 1$, i.e.

ellipses centre origin, major semi-axis $\sqrt{\dfrac{2c}{1-k^2}}$, minor semi-axis $\sqrt{2c}$.

Common eccentricity of these ellipses $= \sqrt{1-\dfrac{2c}{2c/(1-k^2)}} = \sqrt{1-(1-k^2)} = k$.

12. The discriminant $\begin{vmatrix} 1 & -1 & -1 \\ -1 & 1 & 1 \\ -1 & 1 & 1 \end{vmatrix} = 0$, showing that the conic degenerates into a line-pair.

$$2x+2y\frac{dy}{dx}-2x\frac{dy}{dx}-2y-2+2\frac{dy}{dx} = 0 \Rightarrow \frac{dy}{dx} = \frac{1+y-x}{1+y-x} = 1.$$

This means that both tangents to the conic have gradient 1, i.e. the conic degenerates into a repeated line, namely $(x-y-1)^2 = 0$.

13. Given $S \equiv x^2+y^2+2gx+c = 0$, $S' = x^2+y^2+2g'x+c = 0$, the family of circles $S+kS' = 0$ is given by

$$(1+k)(x^2+y^2)+2(g+kg')x+(1+k)c = 0,$$

i.e. $(1+k)(x^2+y^2)+2(g+kg')xz+(1+k)cz^2 = 0$ making the equation homogeneous.

When $k = -1$ this becomes $(g-g')xz = 0$ i.e. $xz = 0$ for $g \neq g'$. Thus, the degenerate locus consists of the two straight lines $x = 0$ (y-axis) and $z = 0$ (l_∞).

14. Putting $\lambda = \dfrac{k+kg'}{1+k}$ $(k \neq -1)$ we have $x^2+y^2+2\lambda x+c = 0$. This will represent point circles when

radius $= 0$ or discriminant $\begin{vmatrix} 1 & . & \lambda \\ . & 1 & . \\ \lambda & . & c \end{vmatrix} = 0$

i.e. $\sqrt{\lambda^2-c} = 0$

i.e. when $\lambda = \pm\sqrt{c}$

i.e. $c-\lambda^2 = 0$.

15. L_1, L_2 are the points $(-\lambda, 0)$, i.e. $(\mp\sqrt{c}, 0)$.

Clearly $x = \mp\sqrt{c}$, $y = 0$ satisfy the equation $x^2+y^2+2fy-c = 0$.

Thus a circle through L_1, L_2 has the equation $x^2+y^2+2fy-c = 0 \ldots (1)$

16. Now $S \equiv x^2+y^2+2gx+c = 0 \ldots (2)$

For (1), Exercise 16.15, $\dfrac{dy}{dx} = \dfrac{-x}{y+f} = m_1$; for (2), $\dfrac{dy}{dx} = -\dfrac{(x+g)}{y} = m_2$.

Points of intersection of circles are given by solving (1), (2):

i.e. $x^2+y^2+fy+gx = 0$.

$\therefore x(x+g) = -y(y+f) \quad \therefore \dfrac{-x}{y+f} = \dfrac{y}{x+g}$ i.e. $m_1 = -\dfrac{1}{m_2}$.

Thus, the circles represented by (1), (2) cut orthogonally.

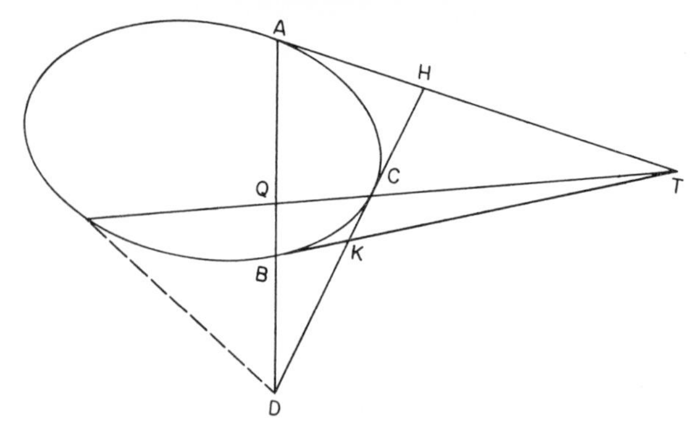

17. Polar of T passes through D. $\therefore$ polar of D passes through T. But polar of C passes through D (since C is on the curve). $\therefore$ polar of D passes through C, i.e. polar of D is CT.

$$\therefore (AB, QD) = -1, \text{ i.e. } T(AB, QD) = -1 \text{ i.e. } (HK, CD) = -1.$$

18. Let the pole have coordinates (x_1, y_1). Then its polar w.r.t. $\frac{x^2}{a^2}-\frac{y^2}{b^2} = 1$ has equation $\frac{xx_1}{a^2}-\frac{yy_1}{b^2} = 1$.

Comparing this with $lx+my = -n$, we obtain

$$\frac{x_1}{a^2} : l = \frac{-y_1}{b^2} : m = -1 : n, \text{ i.e. } x_1 = -\frac{a^2 l}{n}, \; y_1 = \frac{b^2 m}{n}.$$

Thus the pole has coordinates $\left(\frac{-a^2 l}{n}, \frac{b^2 m}{n}\right)$.

19. Consider the conic $S \equiv ax^2+by^2+2hxy+2fyz+2gzx+cz^2 = 0$.

$$I(1, i, 0) \quad \in S \Rightarrow a-b+2hi = 0.$$

$$J(1, -i, 0) \in S \Rightarrow a-b-2hi = 0.$$

$\therefore a = b, h = 0$ (always true of any circle). [Add and subtract, or equate real and imaginary parts.]

$$\therefore S \to ax^2+ay^2+2fyz+2gzx+cz^2 = 0.$$

Now, by (195a), the polar of the centre $(0, 0, 1)$ is $gx+fy+cz = 0$.
But (given) $z = 0$ is the equation of this polar.

$$\therefore f = g = 0 \quad \therefore S \to x^2+y^2 = -\frac{c}{a}z^2 \text{ i.e. } x^2+y^2 = r^2$$

(making it non-homogeneous and putting $-\frac{c}{a} = r^2$ for convenience).

This is precisely the expression for the fixed distance of a variable point (x, y) from a given centre $(0, 0)$.

20. Consider $f \equiv ax^2+by^2+cz^2+2fyz+2gzx+2hxy = 0$. This cuts l_∞ where $ax^2+by^2+2hxy \equiv b(y-\lambda x)(y-\mu x) = 0$, i.e. in the points $(1, \lambda, 0)$, $(1, \mu, 0)$. Equation of the tangent at $(1, \lambda, 0)$ is $\frac{\partial f}{\partial x}+\lambda\frac{\partial f}{\partial y} = 0$.

$$\therefore \text{ the pair of asymptotes is given by } \left(\frac{\partial f}{\partial x}+\lambda\frac{\partial f}{\partial y}\right)\left(\frac{\partial f}{\partial x}+\mu\frac{\partial f}{\partial y}\right) = 0,$$

$$\text{i.e. } \left(\frac{\partial f}{\partial x}\right)^2+(\lambda+\mu)\frac{\partial f}{\partial x}\frac{\partial f}{\partial y}+\lambda\mu\left(\frac{\partial f}{\partial y}\right)^2 = 0,$$

i.e. $b\left(\frac{\partial f}{\partial x}\right)^2 - 2h\frac{\partial f}{\partial x}\frac{\partial f}{\partial y} + a\left(\frac{\partial f}{\partial y}\right)^2 = 0 \quad \because \lambda+\mu = \frac{-2h}{b}, \ \lambda\mu = \frac{a}{b}.$

21. For the hyperbola $f \equiv b^2x^2 - a^2y^2 - a^2b^2z^2 = 0$ we have

$$\text{“}a\text{”} = b^2, \quad \text{“}b\text{”} = -a^2, \quad \text{“}h\text{”} = 0, \quad \frac{\partial f}{\partial x} = 2b^2x, \quad \frac{\partial f}{\partial y} = -2a^2y$$

$\therefore$ the asymptote-pair has equations $a^2y^2 - b^2x^2 = 0$ on simplifying i.e. $y = \pm\frac{b}{a}x$. These asymptotes cut l_∞ in the points $\left(1, \pm\frac{b}{a}, 0\right)$, i.e. 2 real points.

22. Parameters of these two points (Exercise 16.21) are $\frac{b}{a}$, $\frac{-b}{a}$.
Parameters for I, J are $i, -i$. [Note: all four points have coordinates of the form $(1, p, 0)$, where p is the parameter.]

$$\therefore \left(\frac{b}{a}, \frac{-b}{a}; i, -i\right) = -1 = \frac{(b/a - i)(-b/a + i)}{(b/a + i)(-b/a - i)} = \frac{(b/a - i)^2}{(b/a + i)^2}$$

$$\text{whence} \quad \frac{b^2}{a^2} - 2\frac{b}{a}i - 1 = -\left(\frac{b^2}{a^2} + \frac{2b}{a}i - 1\right), \quad \text{i.e.} \quad b^2 = a^2 \quad \text{i.e.} \quad \frac{b}{a} = \pm 1,$$

i.e. the equation of the rectangular hyperbola is $x^2 - y^2 = a^2$ and the perpendicular asymptotes are $y = \pm x$.

23. Asymptote pair: $a^2y^2 + b^2x^2 = 0$, i.e. $y = \pm i\frac{b}{a}x$,

i.e. the ellipse has two imaginary asymptotes cutting l_∞ in the imaginary points $\left(1, \pm i\frac{b}{a}, 0\right)$.

For the circle centre O, $b^2 = a^2$ and the equations of the imaginary asymptotes of the circle are $y = \pm ix$ (i.e. the tangents OI, OJ), cutting l_∞ in $(1, \pm i, 0)$ (i.e. I, J, of course).

24. Consider the conic $S \equiv ax^2 + by^2 + cz^2 + 2fyz + 2gzx + 2hxy = 0$.

$$\left.\begin{array}{l} X_\infty\ (1, 0, 0) \in S \Rightarrow a = 0 \\ Y_\infty\ (0, 1, 0) \in S \Rightarrow b = 0 \\ Z\ \ (0, 0, 1) \in S \Rightarrow c = 0 \end{array}\right\} \Rightarrow S \equiv fyz + gzx + hxy = 0,$$

i.e. $gx + fy + hxy = 0$ in non-homogeneous form.

25. Take $S \equiv ax^2 + by^2 + cz^2 + 2fyz + 2gzx + 2hxy = 0$.

$$\left.\begin{array}{ll} \text{Polar of } Z(0,0,1) \text{ is (195a)}: & gx + fy + cz = 0, \\ \text{in this case (given)}: & z = 0 \end{array}\right\} \Rightarrow f = g = 0.$$

Similarly, for polars of X_∞, Y_∞ we have $g = h = 0$, $f = h = 0$.

$$\therefore S \to ax^2 + by^2 + cz^2 = 0.$$

By making the transformation $x = \sqrt{a}X$, $y = \sqrt{b}Y$, $z = \sqrt{c}Z$, we find

$$S \to X^2 + Y^2 + Z^2 = 0.$$

26. Degenerate hyperbola: any plane through the vertex of the double cone and cutting both branches, i.e. 2 real lines.

Degenerate parabola: any plane tangent to the (double) cone along a (generating) st. line (the plane must pass through the vertex).

Degenerate ellipse (circle): any plane through the vertex of the cone cutting the cone elsewhere. In the case of the circle, the plane through the vertex is parallel to the base of the cone.

27. From theory, $\tan 2\theta = \dfrac{-18}{37-13} = -\dfrac{3}{4} = \dfrac{2\tan\theta}{1-\tan^2\theta}\left[\theta = \dfrac{1}{2}\tan^{-1}\left(\dfrac{-3}{4}\right)\right]$

i.e. $3\tan^2\theta - 8\tan\theta - 3 = 0$, i.e. $(3\tan\theta+1)(\tan\theta-3) = 0$,

i.e. $\tan\theta = 3, \dfrac{-1}{3}$.

Make the substitution $x = \dfrac{X-3Y}{\sqrt{10}}$, $y = \dfrac{3X+Y}{\sqrt{10}}$ (i.e. $\tan\theta = 3$

$\therefore$ $\sin\theta = 3/\sqrt{10}$, $\cos\theta = 1/\sqrt{10}$) and the conic reduces to $\dfrac{X^2}{4}+Y^2 = 1$

(ellipse, centre origin, x-axis semi-major axis $= 2$, y-axis semi-minor axis $= 1$).

Make the substitution $x = \dfrac{3X+Y}{\sqrt{10}}$, $y = \dfrac{-X+3Y}{\sqrt{10}}$ $\left(\text{i.e. } \tan\theta = \dfrac{-1}{3}\right)$

$\therefore$ $\sin\theta = \dfrac{-1}{\sqrt{10}}$, $\cos\theta = 3/\sqrt{10}$ and the conic reduces to

$X^2 + \dfrac{Y^2}{4} = 1$ (same ellipse, but with axes changed).

[The angle between the axes of this conic and the axes of the conic in the Bookwork Example is $\tan^{-1}\left(\dfrac{3-2}{1+3\cdot 2}\right) = \tan^{-1}\left(\dfrac{1}{7}\right)$, or $\tan^{-1}\left(\dfrac{\dfrac{-1}{3}+\dfrac{1}{2}}{1+\dfrac{1}{3}\cdot\dfrac{1}{2}}\right) = \tan^{-1}\left(\dfrac{1}{7}\right)$.]

28. Let $A = \begin{bmatrix} \dfrac{37}{40} & \dfrac{-9}{40} \\ \dfrac{-9}{40} & \dfrac{13}{40} \end{bmatrix}$ whence the eigenvalues are $\frac{1}{4}$, 1 on calculation.

Normalised eigenvectors corresponding to $\dfrac{1}{4}$, 1 are respectively $\dfrac{1}{\sqrt{10}}\begin{bmatrix} 1 \\ 3 \end{bmatrix}$, $\dfrac{1}{\sqrt{10}}\begin{bmatrix} -3 \\ 1 \end{bmatrix}$.

Form the matrix $P = \dfrac{1}{\sqrt{10}}\begin{bmatrix} 1 & -3 \\ 3 & 1 \end{bmatrix}$ with $|P| = 1$, $P^{-1} = \dfrac{1}{\sqrt{10}}\begin{bmatrix} 1 & 3 \\ -3 & 1 \end{bmatrix} = P^T$.

$\therefore$ $P^{-1}AP = \begin{bmatrix} \frac{1}{4} & \cdot \\ \cdot & 1 \end{bmatrix}$ on calculation

$\therefore$ the reduced equation of the conic is $\dfrac{x^2}{4}+y^2 = 1$.

29. Let the conic be $S \equiv ax^2+by^2+2hxy+2gx+2fy+c = 0$

$$\left.\begin{aligned}(0, 0) \in S &\Rightarrow c = 0\\ (0, 1) \in S &\Rightarrow b+2f = 0\\ (2, 0) \in S &\Rightarrow 4a+4g = 0\\ (1, 1) \in S &\Rightarrow a+b+2h+2g+2f+c = 0\\ (1, -1) \in S &\Rightarrow a+b-2h+2g-2f+c = 0\end{aligned}\right\} \Rightarrow c = 0,\ a = b = -g = -2f = 2h$$

$\therefore S \rightarrow x^2+y^2+xy-2x-y = 0.$

Coordinates of the centre are given by $\begin{cases}\dfrac{\partial S}{\partial x} = 2x+y-2 = 0\\ \dfrac{\partial S}{\partial y} = x+2y-1 = 0\end{cases}$ i.e. the centre is (1, 0).

The translation $x = X+1,\ y = Y \Rightarrow S\colon X^2+XY+Y^2 = 1$ on calculation.

$$\text{Tan } 2\theta = \frac{1}{0} = \infty \Rightarrow 2\theta = \frac{\pi}{2} \Rightarrow \theta = \frac{\pi}{4}.$$

$$\text{Rotation}\quad X = \frac{\xi-\eta}{\sqrt{2}},\qquad Y = \frac{\xi+\eta}{\sqrt{2}} \Rightarrow S\colon \frac{3\xi^2}{2}+\frac{\eta^2}{2} = 1,$$

i.e. with a change of notation, $\dfrac{x^2}{\frac{2}{3}}+\dfrac{y^2}{2} = 1$ which is an ellipse, centre at the new origin, y axis major axis (semi-axis length $= \sqrt{2}$), x axis minor axis (semi-axis length $= \sqrt{\frac{2}{3}}$).

$$\therefore \text{eccentricity} = \sqrt{1-\frac{\frac{2}{3}}{2}} = \sqrt{\frac{2}{3}}.$$

30. $\cos A+\cos(B+C) = -\sin B \sin C \sin^2\dfrac{a}{2} = -$ve quantity

i.e. $\cos\left(\dfrac{A+B+C}{2}\right)\cos\left(\dfrac{B+C-A}{2}\right) < 0$

i.e. factors on the left-hand side must have opposite signs.
Now $-\pi < B+C-A < \pi$ ($\because A \geqslant B \geqslant C$ and each angle in a triangle is $< \pi$)

$$\therefore \cos\left(\frac{B+C-A}{2}\right) > 0 \quad \therefore \cos\left(\frac{A+B+C}{2}\right) < 0, \quad \text{i.e. } A+B+C > \pi.$$

EXERCISES 17

1. Let $P \equiv (at_1^2, 2at_1)$, $Q \equiv (at_2^2, 2at_2)$. The equation of the chord PQ is given by

$$2x-(t_1+t_2)y+2at_1t_2 = 0.$$

But since this passes through the focus, we have $t_1t_2 = -1$. The coordinates of $M(\xi, \eta)$, the mid-point of PQ, are given by $\xi = \dfrac{a}{2}(t_1^2+t_2^2)$, $\eta = a(t_1+t_2)$. Eliminate t: $\dfrac{\eta^2}{a^2} = \dfrac{2\xi}{a}-2$, i.e. $y^2 = 2a(x-a)$.

This is a parabola whose *latus rectum* (2a) is half that of the original parabola

2. Equation of the tangent at $(at^2, 2at)$ is $y = \frac{x}{t}+at$. Solve for this tangent and the parabola $y^2+4bx = 0$.

We find $\xi = \frac{x_1+x_2}{2} = -(a+2b)t^2$, $\eta = \frac{y_1+y_2}{2} = -2bt$.

Eliminate t: $\xi = \frac{-(a+2b)}{4b^2}\eta^2$ $\therefore$ the locus of C is $y^2+\frac{4b^2}{a+2b}x = 0$, which is a parabola lying to the left of the y-axis, vertex at $(0,0)$ and coaxal with the given parabolas.

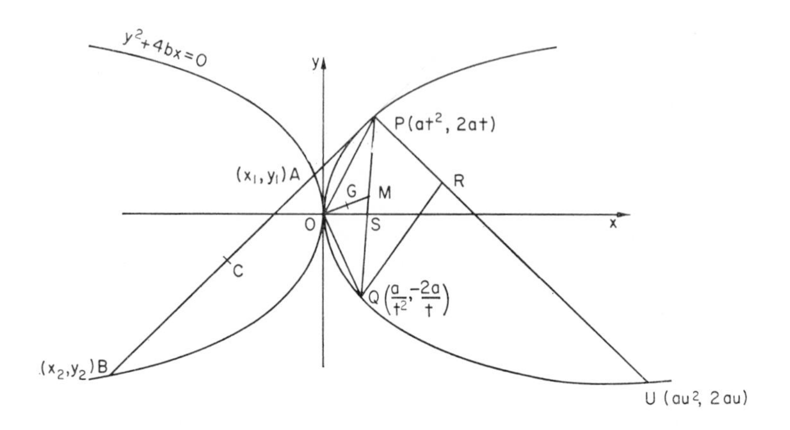

3. Let $P(x, y)$ be the point on the parabola nearest the origin. The square of this distance is $s^2 = x^2+y^2 = x^2+2x+5$ ($\because$ P lies on the parabola).

$\therefore$ $\frac{ds^2}{dx} = 2x+2 = 0$ if $x = -1$, $\frac{d^2s^2}{dx^2} = 2(>0)$ $\therefore$ $x = -1$ gives a minimum value $(= 4)$ to s^2, i.e. $s = 2$. Required points are $(-1, \pm\sqrt{3})$.

4. Equation of the normal at P is $y = -tx+2at+at^3$.

Equation of the normal at Q is $y = \frac{x}{t}-\frac{2a}{t}-\frac{a}{t^3}$.

Solving these 2 equations, we find the coordinates of R are

$$\xi = a\left(t^2+\frac{1}{t^2}+1\right) = a\left(t-\frac{1}{t}\right)^2+3a, \quad \eta = a\left(t-\frac{1}{t}\right).$$

Eliminate t: $\eta^2 = a(\xi-3a)$ $\therefore$ the required locus is the parabola $y^2 = a(x-3a)$, which is coaxal with the original; vertex is $(3a, 0)$; *latus rectum* is a, i.e. $\frac{1}{4}$ *latus rectum* of the original; focus $\left(\frac{13a}{4}, 0\right)$; directrix $x = \frac{11a}{4}$.

5. Let P be the point (x_1, y_1). Then $PT^2 = OM^2$ i.e. $AP^2-AT^2 = OM^2$ i.e. $(x_1-a)^2+(y_1-a)^2-a^2 = x_1^2$ i.e. $(y_1-a)^2 = 2ax_1$.

Move the origin to $(0, a)$. The required locus is the parabola $y^2 = 2ax$.

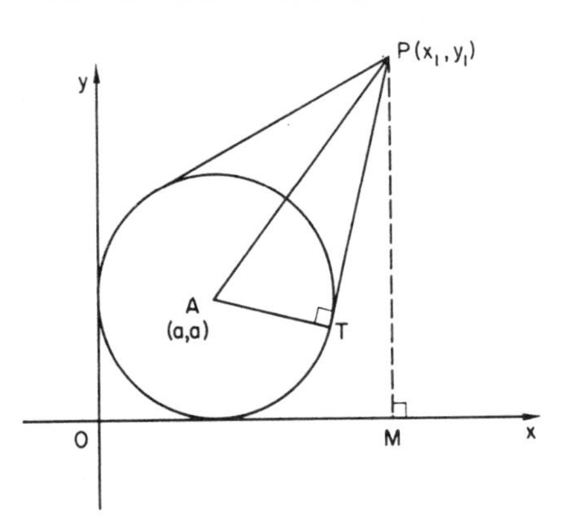

6. Equation of the normal at T is $y = -tx+2at+at^3$.
This passes through $(au^2, 2au)$.

$$\therefore\ 2au = -atu^2+2at+at^3 \quad \text{i.e. } tu^2+2u-t(2+t^2) = 0$$

$$\text{so } u = \frac{-2\pm\sqrt{4+4t^2(2+t^2)}}{2t} = -\frac{1}{t}\pm\frac{1+t^2}{t} = t \text{ or } -\frac{(2+t^2)}{t}.$$

7. Given $x = 2t-1$, $y = 3t^2+2$, eliminate t: $\dfrac{y-2}{3} = \dfrac{(x+1)^2}{4}$;

i.e. $(x+1)^2 = \frac{4}{3}(y-2)$ which is a parabola with axis $x = -1$, vertex at $(-1, 2)$ (i.e. $t = 0$), *latus rectum* $\frac{4}{3}$, focus at $(-1, \frac{7}{3})$, and directrix $y = 2-\frac{1}{3}$, i.e. $y = \frac{5}{3}$.

Now $T_1 \equiv (2t_1-1, 3t_1^2+2)$, $T_2 \equiv (2t_2-1, 3t_2^2+2)$.

$$\therefore \text{ equation of chord } T_1T_2 \text{ is } \frac{y-3t_2^2-2}{3t_1^2+2-3t_2^2-2} = \frac{x-2t_2+1}{2t_1-1-2t_2+1},$$

i.e. $3(t_1+t_2)x-2y+3(t_1+t_2)-6t_1t_2 = 4$ on simplifying.

8. Coordinates of M, mid-point of PQ, are $\left(\frac{a}{2}\left(t^2+\frac{1}{t^2}\right), a\left(t-\frac{1}{t}\right)\right)$ by Exercise 17.1. Since $G(\xi, \eta)$ is the centroid of the triangle OP_1P_2 it divides OM in the ratio 2 : 1.

$$\therefore\ \xi = \frac{2a}{3\cdot 2}\left(t^2+\frac{1}{t^2}\right),\quad \eta = \frac{2a}{3}\left(t-\frac{1}{t}\right).$$

Eliminate t: $9\eta^2 = 4a^2\left(t^2+\dfrac{1}{t^2}\right)-8a^2$ i.e. $9\eta^2 = \dfrac{4a^2\cdot 3\xi}{a}-8a^2$,

i.e. $9y^2 = 4a(3x-2a)$ which is a parabola.

9. Let P be the point on the parabola with parameter $a+b$, i.e. $P \equiv (a+b, [a+b]^2)$

Now, gradient of OP is $\dfrac{(a+b)^2}{a+b} = a+b$. Also, gradient of AB is $\dfrac{b^2-a^2}{b-a} = a+b$. Thus, P is the point on the parabola such that OP is parallel to AB. Let A' be the point $(-a, a^2)$. Draw OC parallel to $A'B$ to cut the parabola in $C(c, c^2)$.

Now, gradient of OC = gradient of $A'B = \dfrac{b^2-a^2}{b+a} = b-a$.

$\therefore$ equation of OC is $y = (b-a)x$. This line passes through (c, c^2) so $c^2 = (b-a)c$ i.e. $c = b-a$.
Thus, C is the required point with parameter $(b-a)$.

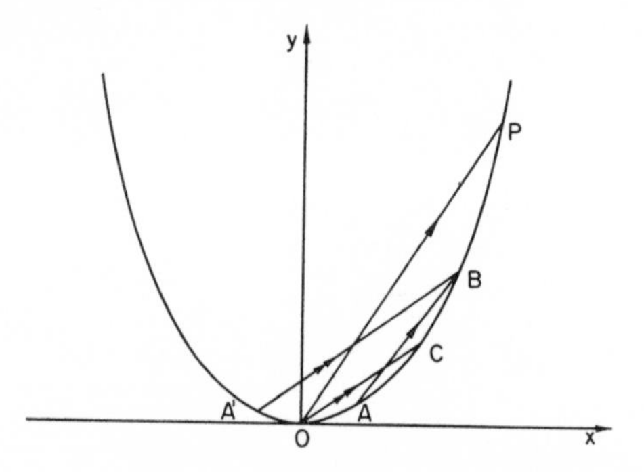

10. Equation of parabolic chain is $x^2 = 4ay$ $\therefore$ *latus rectum* $= 4a = \dfrac{x^2}{y} = \dfrac{285^2}{43}$ $\doteqdot 1889$ ft. Also, $\dfrac{dy}{dx} = \dfrac{2x}{4a} \doteqdot \dfrac{570}{1889} \doteqdot 0{\cdot}3018$ at B $\therefore$ inclination at B is $16°48'$.

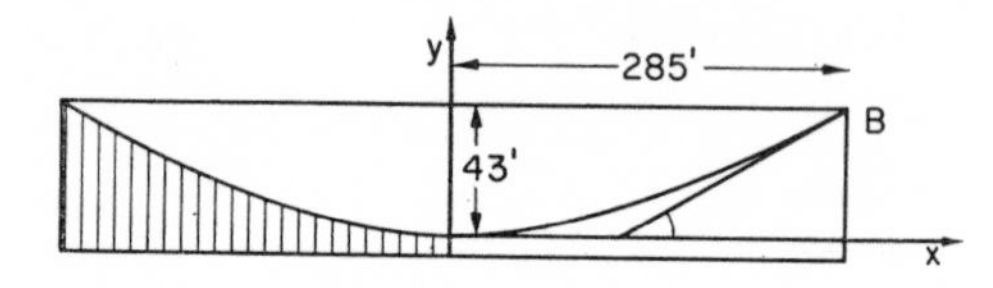

11. Solve $\therefore P \equiv \left(\sqrt[3]{16}, \sqrt[3]{32}\right)$ $\therefore$ equation of OP is $y = \sqrt[3]{2}\,x$. Equation of SL is $x = 1$. $\therefore Q \equiv \left(1, \sqrt[3]{2}\right)$, $SQ = \sqrt[3]{2}$. $\therefore$ we have found a method for constructing $2^{1/3}$, i.e. for solving the Greek problem of duplicating the cube. Clearly, $x = z$ cuts l_∞ at $(0, 1, 0)$, i.e. at Y_∞ ($SL//y$-axis).

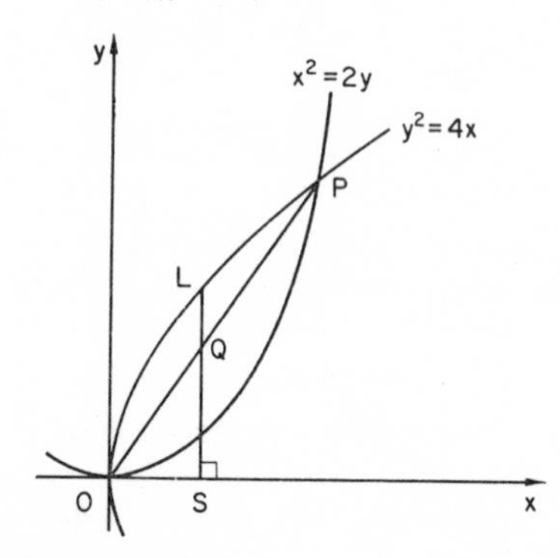

12. Equation of QR is, by Exercise 17.1, $y = \dfrac{-2a}{t} = \dfrac{-2a}{k/2a}$ $(\because k = 2at) =$

$$= \frac{-4a^2}{k}.$$

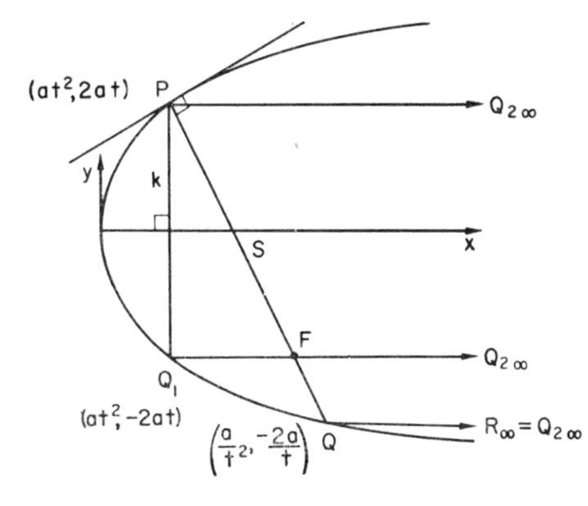

13. Equation of the parabola is $x^2 = 250y$ $\therefore OS = \frac{250}{4} = 62\frac{1}{2}$ ft. $\therefore$ combined height of aerial and mast is $62\frac{1}{2}$ ft ($O \equiv$ vertex, $S \equiv$ focus).

14. Let P, Q have parameters p, q. Equations of PT, QT are $y = \dfrac{x}{p}+ap$, $y = \dfrac{x}{q}+aq$.

Solve: $T \equiv (apq,\ a(p+q))$. But $M \equiv \left(\dfrac{a}{2}(p^2+q^2),\ a(p+q)\right)$ $\therefore$ M, T have same ordinate $\therefore$ $TM//$ x-axis . . . (i).

Coordinates of K are $x = \dfrac{a(p^2+q^2)+2apq}{4} = \dfrac{a^2}{4}(p+q)^2$, $y = a(p+q)$, which satisfy $y = 4ax$. $\therefore$ K lies on the parabola . . . (ii).

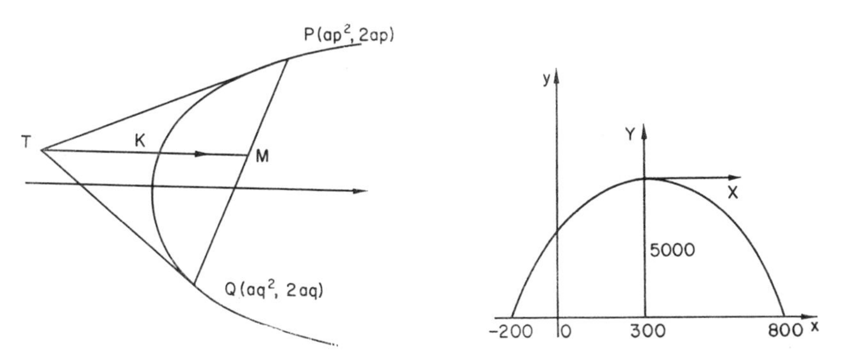

15. Equation of parabola: $50y = 25\,000-(x-300)^2$, i.e. $X^2 = -50\,Y$ transforming axes to $X = x-300$, $Y = 500-y$. $\therefore$ *latus-rectum* is 50.

16. One pair of $\perp$ chords is PQ_1, PQ_2 ($PQ_2//Q_1Q_2$). Then $F \equiv Q_1Q_2 \cap$ (normal at P). Normal at P has equation $y = -xt+at^3+2at$. For F, $-2at = -xt+at^3+2at$

$\therefore F \equiv \{a(t^2+4), -2at\} \equiv (\xi, \eta)$. Eliminate t $\therefore$ $\dfrac{\xi}{a} = \dfrac{\eta^2}{4a^2}+4$, i.e. $\xi-4a = \dfrac{\eta^2}{4a}$

$\therefore$ the locus of the Frégier points is $y^2 = 4a(x-4a)$ (another parabola, coaxal with the original).

17. Eliminate $t\left(=\dfrac{x}{v\cos\theta}\right)$ to obtain $y = vt\sin\theta-\dfrac{gx^2\sec^2\theta}{2v^2}$,

i.e. $\left(x-\dfrac{v^2}{2g}\sin 2\theta\right)^2 = \dfrac{-2v^2}{g}\cos^2\theta\left(y-\dfrac{v^2}{2g}\sin^2\theta\right)$

i.e. $X^2 = -4aY$ where $X = x-\dfrac{v^2}{2g}\sin 2\theta,\quad Y = y-\dfrac{v^2}{2g}\sin^2\theta,\quad a = \dfrac{v^2\cos^2\theta}{2g}$

(a parabola with axis // y-axis).

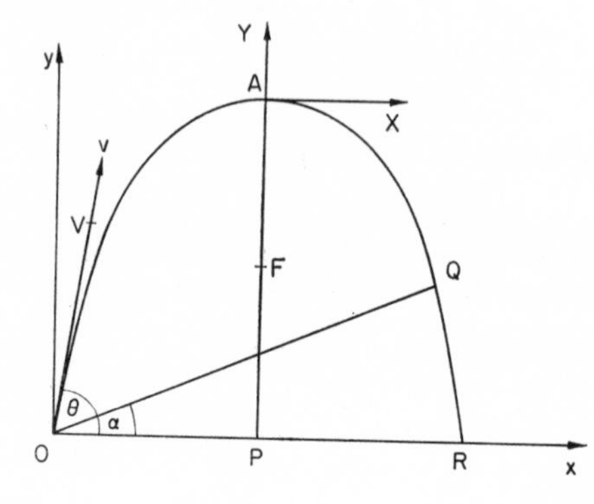

18. Vertex $\equiv\left(\dfrac{v^2}{2g}\sin 2\theta, \dfrac{v^2\sin^2\theta}{2g}\right)$. Focus F: $AF = \dfrac{v^2\cos^2\theta}{2g}$ $(=a)$,

i.e. $y = \dfrac{v^2}{2g}(\sin^2\theta-\cos^2\theta)$. Directrix: $Y = \dfrac{v^2\cos^2\theta}{2g}$ i.e. $y = \dfrac{v^2}{2g}$.

Latus rectum: $\dfrac{2v^2\cos^2\theta}{g}$ $(= 4a)$.

19. Horizontal range $OR = r = 2\cdot\dfrac{v^2\sin 2\theta}{2g} = \dfrac{v^2\sin 2\theta}{g}$.

20. $\dfrac{dr}{d\theta} = \dfrac{2v^2\cos 2\theta}{g} = 0$ if $\theta = \dfrac{\pi}{4}$ $\therefore$ $\dfrac{d^2r}{d\theta^2} = \dfrac{-4v^2\sin 2\theta}{g} < 0$ when $\theta = \dfrac{\pi}{4}$.

$\therefore$ maximum range $\left(=\dfrac{v^2}{g}\right)$ occurs when $\theta = \dfrac{\pi}{4}$. (In this case, the vertex of the parabola is at $\left(\dfrac{v^2}{2g}, \dfrac{v^2}{4g}\right)$.) [Result due to Tartaglia (1500–57), Italian.]

21. Maximum height $AP = \dfrac{v^2}{2g}\sin^2\theta$ occurring when $Y = 0$.

22. At A, vertical velocity is zero, i.e. $\dfrac{dy}{dt} = \dfrac{d}{dt}\left(vt\sin\theta-\dfrac{1}{2}gt^2\right) = v\sin\theta-gt = 0$

i.e. $t = \dfrac{v\sin\theta}{g}$ $\therefore$ total time of flight is twice this, i.e. $\dfrac{2v\sin\theta}{g}$.

23. Equation of path is $y = v\sin\theta\dfrac{x}{v\cos\theta}-\dfrac{x^2}{2v^2\cos^2\theta}\cdot\dfrac{v^2\sin 2\theta}{r}$ (using Exercises 17.17, 17.19) $= x\tan\theta\left(1-\dfrac{x}{r}\right)$.

24. $t_1 = \dfrac{2v \sin \theta}{g}$, $t_2 = \dfrac{2v \sin \phi}{g}$ (Exercise 17.22) $\Rightarrow t_1 t_2 = \dfrac{4v^2 \sin \theta \sin \phi}{g^2}$

$= \dfrac{2v^2 \sin 2\theta}{g} = \dfrac{2r}{g}$ $\because r = \dfrac{v^2 \sin 2\theta}{g} = \dfrac{v^2 \sin 2\phi}{g}$ (Exercise 17.19)

$\Rightarrow \sin \theta \cos \theta = \sin \phi \cos \phi \Rightarrow \sin \phi = \cos \theta$ ($\because \phi \neq \theta$). Hence the result.

25. $R = k \cos \theta \sin (\theta - \alpha)$ [$k = 2V^2 \sec^2 \alpha / g$ = const.]

$\therefore \dfrac{dR}{d\theta} = k[\cos (\theta-\alpha) \cos \theta - \sin \theta \sin (\theta-\alpha)] = k \cos (2\theta - \alpha) = 0$ if $2\theta - \alpha = \dfrac{\pi}{2}$,

i.e. $\theta = \dfrac{1}{2}\left(\dfrac{\pi}{2}+\alpha\right)$.

$\dfrac{d^2R}{d\theta^2} = -k \sin (2\theta - \alpha) < 0$ when $2\theta - \alpha = \dfrac{\pi}{2}$.

$\therefore \theta = \dfrac{1}{2}\left(\dfrac{\pi}{2}+\alpha\right)$ gives a maximum to R whence $Q\hat{O}V = \theta - \alpha = \dfrac{\pi}{4} + \dfrac{\alpha}{2} - \alpha =$ $\dfrac{\pi}{4} - \dfrac{\alpha}{2} = \dfrac{1}{2}\left(\dfrac{\pi}{2}-\alpha\right)$, i.e. $R_{\max}$ occurs when the angle of projection bisects the angle between the vertical and inclined plane. Clearly, $\alpha = 0 \Rightarrow R = r, \theta = \dfrac{\pi}{4}$ as in Exercises 17.19, 17.20. [Note: $\cos \theta \sin (\theta - \alpha) = \frac{1}{2}(\sin (2\theta - \alpha) - \sin \alpha)$]

26. Gradients of OP, OQ are $\dfrac{2}{p}, \dfrac{2}{q}$ $\therefore \dfrac{2}{p} \cdot \dfrac{2}{q} = -1$ $\therefore pq = -4 \ldots (\alpha)$

Chord PQ: $\dfrac{y - 2aq}{2a(p-q)} = \dfrac{x - aq^2}{a(p-q)(p+q)}$, i.e. $(p+q)y = 2x + 2apq$ i.e. $(p+q)y = 2x - 8a$ by (α) $\therefore y = 0 \Rightarrow x = 4a$ i.e. chords PQ always pass through a fixed point $(4a, 0)$.

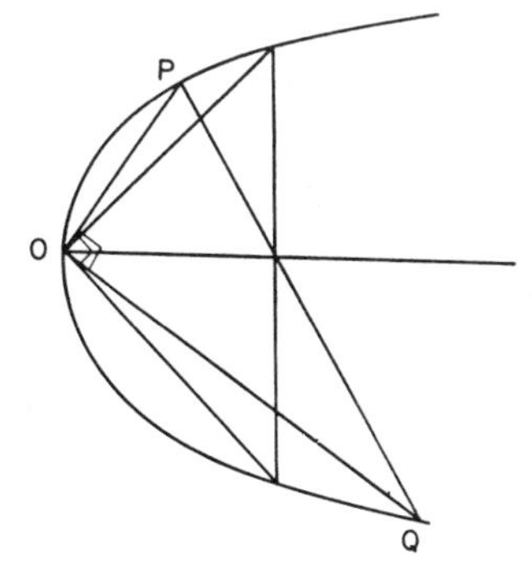

27. East–west: $y^2 = 4(9{\cdot}6)x = 38{\cdot}4\ x$; north–south: $y^2 = 64\ x$.

Ratio of *latera recta* (East–west: north–south) $= \dfrac{9{\cdot}6}{16} = \dfrac{3}{5}$.

28. Equation of outer parabola is $y^2 = 4ax$ where $10^2 = 4a \cdot 5$, i.e. $y^2 = 20x$. Equation of inner parabola is $y^2 = 4a(x-1)$, where $10^2 = 4a \cdot 4$, i.e. $y^2 = 25(x-1)$. Elementary calculations give $B_1 = (2, \frac{1}{5})$, $B_2 = (2, 2{\cdot}16)$ whence $B_1B_2 = 2{\cdot}16 - 0{\cdot}2 = 1{\cdot}96$ (ft.).

By Pythagoras' theorem, $A_2B_1 = \sqrt{(2-0)^2 + (\frac{1}{5} - 2)^2} = \frac{1}{5}\sqrt{181} \doteqdot 2{\cdot}69$ (ft.).

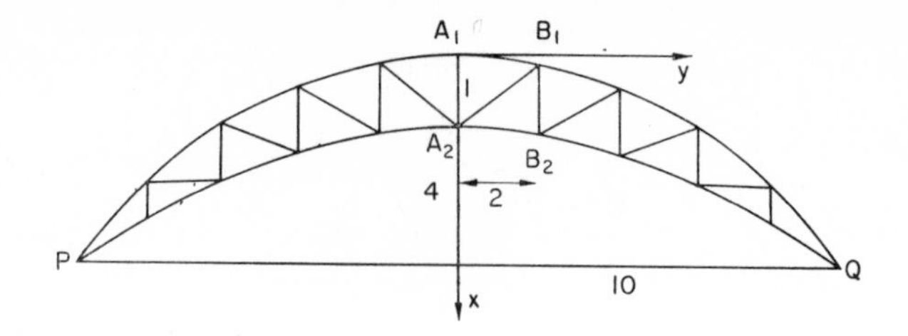

29. In matrix form, $\lambda P+C \equiv x^T(\lambda P+C)x = 0$ where $P = \begin{bmatrix} \cdot & \cdot & -2a \\ \cdot & 1 & \cdot \\ -2a & \cdot & \cdot \end{bmatrix}$

$$C = \begin{bmatrix} 1 & \cdot & -\alpha \\ \cdot & 1 & -\beta \\ -\alpha & -\beta & (\alpha^2+\beta^2-r^2) \end{bmatrix}.$$

$$|\lambda P+C| = 0, \quad \text{i.e.} \quad \begin{vmatrix} 1 & 0 & -2a\lambda-\alpha \\ 0 & \lambda+1 & -\beta \\ -2a\lambda-\alpha & -\beta & \alpha^2+\beta^2-r^2 \end{vmatrix} = 0$$

i.e. $\Delta\lambda^3+\Theta\lambda^2+\Theta'\lambda+\Delta' = 0$, where $\Delta = -4a^2$, $\Delta' = -r^2$,

$$\Theta = -4a(a+\alpha), \ \Theta' = \beta^2-4a\alpha-r^2.$$

The three degenerate conics of the system corresponding to the three roots o cubic in λ are the three line-pairs A_1A_2, A_3A_4; A_1A_3, A_2A_4; A_1A_4, A_2A_3.

30. $\Theta = 0 \Rightarrow \alpha = -a$, i.e. the centre of the circle lies on the directrix of the para bola.

EXERCISES 18

1. Gradients of the tangents to the parabola and ellipse at P are $\dfrac{2k}{b \sin\phi}$ and $\dfrac{-b}{a \tan\phi}$ respectively.

Since parabola and ellipse cut orthogonally, $\dfrac{2k}{b\sin\phi} = \dfrac{a\tan\phi}{b}$, i.e. $k = \dfrac{a\sin\phi\tan\phi}{2}$

$\therefore$ *latus rectum* $= 4k = 2a\sin\phi\tan\phi$.

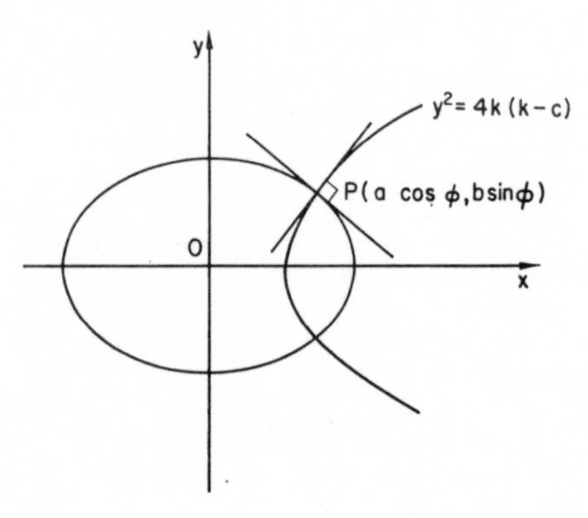

2. The equation of the ellipse $8(x-1)^2+6(y+1)^2-1 = 0$ can be written

$$\frac{(x-1)^2}{\frac{1}{8}}+\frac{(y+1)^2}{\frac{1}{6}} = 1, \text{ i.e. } \frac{X^2}{A^2}+\frac{Y^2}{B^2} = 1. \text{ (Diagram (a) below.)}$$

Since $\frac{1}{6} > \frac{1}{8}$, the Y-axis will be along the major axis.

$$\therefore\ e^2 = 1-\frac{1/8}{1/6} = 1-\frac{3}{4} = \frac{1}{4}, \text{ i.e. } e = \frac{1}{2}.$$

Coordinates of the foci w.r.t. the X-, Y-axes are $\left(0, \pm\frac{1}{2\sqrt{6}}\right)$.

Coordinates of the foci w.r.t. the x-, y-axes are $\left(1, -1\pm\frac{1}{2\sqrt{6}}\right)$.

Directrices: $Y = \pm\frac{B}{e} = \pm\frac{2}{\sqrt{6}}$ i.e. $y = -1\pm\frac{2}{\sqrt{6}}$.

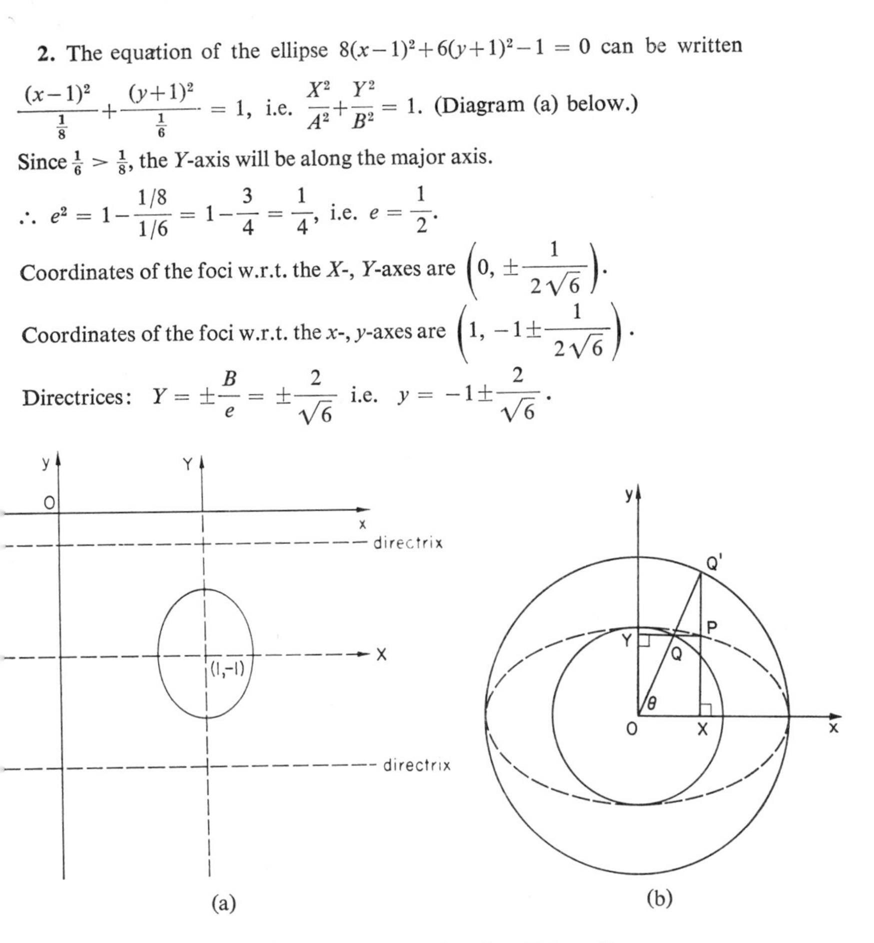

(a) (b)

3. Equations of circles are $x^2+y^2 = a^2$, $x^2+y^2 = b^2$ $(a > b)$.
Thus, $Q' \equiv (a\cos\theta, a\sin\theta)$, $Q \equiv (b\cos\theta, b\sin\theta)$, say.
Lines $Q'X$ and QY are drawn parallel to Oy and Ox respectively to intersect at P.
Clearly coordinates of P are $(a\cos\theta, b\sin\theta)$.

But these are the coordinates of a point lying on the curve $\frac{x^2}{a^2}+\frac{y^2}{b^2} = 1$.

Thus the locus of P is an ellipse. (Diagram (b) above.)

4. Let the chord join $A\ (a, 0)$ and $P\ (a\cos\phi, b\sin\phi)$.

$\therefore$ coordinates of Z, mid-point of PA, are $\xi = \frac{a}{2}(1+\cos\phi)$, $\eta = \frac{b\sin\phi}{2}$,

i.e. $\frac{2\xi-a}{a} = \cos\phi$, $\frac{2\eta}{b} = \sin\phi$.

$\therefore$ the locus is $\frac{(2\xi-a)^2}{a^2}+\frac{4\eta^2}{b^2} = 1$, i.e. $\frac{(x-a/2)^2}{a^2/4}+\frac{y^2}{b^2/4} = 1$.

Thus, the locus is an ellipse with centre $\left(\frac{a}{2}, 0\right)$ and semiaxes $\frac{a}{2}, \frac{b}{2}$.

5. Normal at $\left(-ae, \dfrac{b^2}{a}\right)$ is given by $\dfrac{x+ae}{-ae/a^2} = \dfrac{y-b^2/a}{b^2/ab^2}$, i.e. $x+ae = -ey+\dfrac{b^2e}{a}$.

This passes through $(0, -b)$ $\therefore ae = be+\dfrac{b^2e}{a}$ $\therefore a^2-ab-b^2 = 0.$

$\therefore a = \dfrac{b}{2}(\pm\sqrt{5}+1)$, i.e. $a = \dfrac{b}{2}(\sqrt{5}+1)$ since a is +ve.

$$e^2 = 1-\frac{b^2 \cdot 4}{b^2(5+2\sqrt{5}+1)} = \frac{\sqrt{5}-1}{2} \quad \therefore e = \sqrt{\frac{1}{2}(\sqrt{5}-1)}.$$

6. From the diagram, $\dfrac{ae}{a} = \dfrac{\frac{1}{2}k}{29\frac{1}{2}k} = \dfrac{1}{59}$ (k a factor of proportionality) i.e. $e = \dfrac{1}{59}$.
As this eccentricity is small the elliptic orbit is nearly circular.

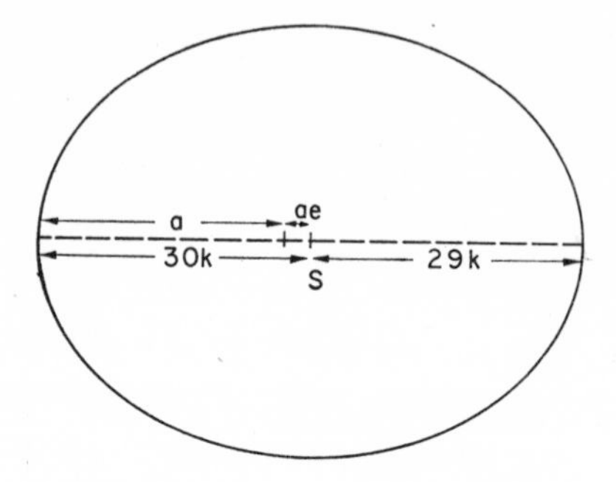

7. Equation of $S'P$: $\dfrac{y}{b} = \dfrac{x-ae}{-ae}$ $\therefore$ gradient of $S'P$ is $b/-ae$ $[P \equiv (0, b)]$. Equation of SP: $\dfrac{y}{b} = \dfrac{x+ae}{ae}$ $\therefore$ gradient of SP is b/ae. Since $S'P$ and SP are $\perp$, $b/-ae = -ae/b$,

i.e. $b^2 = a^2e^2$, $a^2(1-e^2) = a^2e^2$, $e = \dfrac{1}{\sqrt{2}}$.

Alternative method: $\triangle$'s OSP, $OS'P$ are congruent $\therefore O\hat{P}S = O\hat{P}S' = \dfrac{\pi}{4}$.

$\therefore \triangle OSP$ is isosceles $\therefore OS = OP$ $\therefore ae = b = a\sqrt{1-e^2}$ (189) $\therefore e = \dfrac{1}{\sqrt{2}}$.

8. By Exercise 6.11, the closest distance of the orbit from the Sun (focus) occurs along the major axis. Now $SA = a(1-e)$.

$$\therefore \begin{cases} (SA)_{\text{Pluto}} = 3{,}680\times10^6\times0{\cdot}75 = 2{,}760\times10^6 \text{ miles} \\ (SA)_{\text{Neptune}} = 2{,}793{\cdot}5\times10^6\times0{\cdot}9918 \doteqdot 2{,}770\times10^6 \text{ miles} \end{cases}$$

$\therefore (SA)_{\text{Pluto}} < (SA)_{\text{Neptune}}$, i.e. Pluto is sometimes closer than Neptune to the Sun.

9. Equation of normal at $P(a\cos\theta, b\sin\theta)$ is $\dfrac{ax}{\cos\theta} - \dfrac{by}{\sin\theta} = a^2e^2$. When $y = 0$,

$x = ae^2\cos\theta = \xi$. When $x = 0$, $y = -\dfrac{a^2e^2\sin\theta}{b} = \eta$.

Thus $F \equiv (ae^2\cos\theta, 0)$, $G \equiv \left(0, -\dfrac{a^2e^2\sin\theta}{b}\right)$.

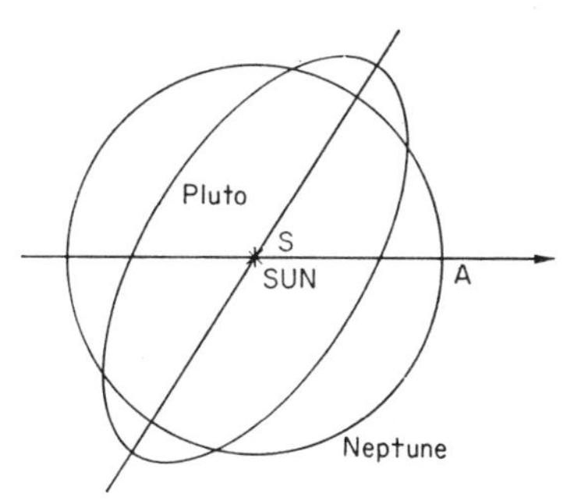

Eliminate θ: $\dfrac{\xi^2}{\left(\dfrac{ae^2}{2}\right)^2}+\dfrac{\eta^2}{\left(\dfrac{a^2e^2}{2b}\right)^2} = 1$. This is an ellipse (coaxal with the original) of the form

$\dfrac{x^2}{A^2}+\dfrac{y^2}{B^2} = 1$ where $A = \dfrac{ae^2}{2}$, $B = \dfrac{a^2e^2}{2b}$. Now $\dfrac{B}{A} = \dfrac{a^2e^2}{2b}\cdot\dfrac{2}{ae^2} = \dfrac{a}{b} > 1$. Thus, the y-axis is along the major axis for the new ellipse. Its eccentricity is $\sqrt{1-\left(\dfrac{A}{B}\right)^2} = \sqrt{1-\left(\dfrac{b}{a}\right)^2} = e$, i.e. its eccentricity is the same as that of the original ellipse. [It may be shown that P, G, S, S' are concyclic, the proof depending on Exercise 18.16.]

10. Tangent at $P(a\cos\theta, b\sin\theta)$ has equation $\dfrac{x\cos\theta}{a}+\dfrac{y\sin\theta}{b} = 1$. Tangent intersects $x = a$, and $x = -a$ at $\left(a, \dfrac{b(1-\cos\theta)}{\sin\theta}\right)$ and $\left(-a, \dfrac{b(1+\cos\theta)}{\sin\theta}\right)$. Gradient of VS is $\dfrac{b(1-\cos\theta)}{a(1-e)\sin\theta}$; gradient of $V'S$ is $\dfrac{b(1+\cos\theta)}{-a(1+e)\sin\theta}$. VS and $V'S$ will be perpendicular if $\dfrac{b(1-\cos\theta)}{a(1-e)\sin\theta} = \dfrac{a(1+e)\sin\theta}{b(1+\cos\theta)}$, i.e. if $b^2(1-\cos^2\theta) = a^2(1-e^2)\sin^2\theta$ i.e. if $b^2 = a^2(1-e^2)$ which is so. Thus VV' subtends a right angle at the focus.

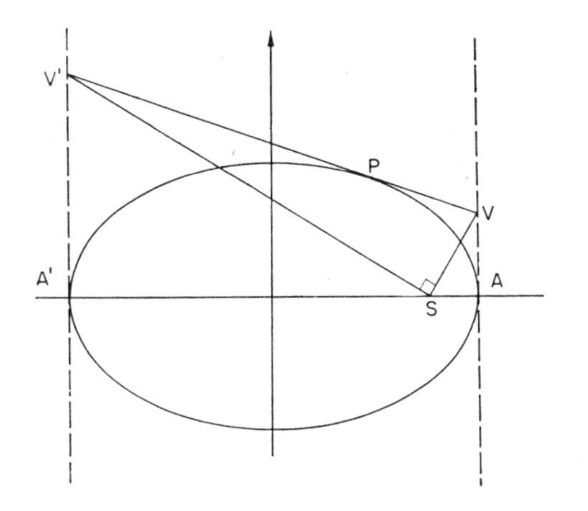

11. Ellipse $\frac{x^2}{a^2}+\frac{y^2}{b^2} = 1 : e = \frac{3}{4} \Rightarrow \frac{1}{a^2} = \frac{7}{16b^2}$; (1, 1) on ellipse $\Rightarrow \frac{1}{a^2}+\frac{1}{b^2} = 1$.

Solve $\therefore\ b^2 = \frac{23}{16},\ a^2 = \frac{23}{7}$ $\therefore$ the ellipse has equation $7x^2+16y^2 = 23$. An identical ellipse with y-axis as major axis has equation $16x^2+7y^2 = 23$.

12. Tangent at $\left(ae, \frac{b^2}{a}\right)$ has equation $\frac{ex}{a}+\frac{b^2y}{a^3} = 1$; $y = 0 \Rightarrow x = \frac{a}{e}$ (i.e. a point on the corresponding directrix).

13. Take AB as x-axis, mid-point of AB as origin O, and a line through $O \perp AB$ as y-axis. Let $P \equiv (x, y)$. Since $\tan\theta$, $-\tan\phi$ are the gradients of AP, BP, $\frac{y}{x+a} \cdot \frac{-y}{x-a} = \frac{b^2}{a^2}$, i.e. locus of P is the ellipse $\frac{x^2}{a^2}+\frac{y^2}{b^2} = 1$. [Exceptional points are $(\pm a, 0)$.]

14. $\overrightarrow{SP} = \mathbf{r}-\mathbf{k}$, $\overrightarrow{S'P} = \mathbf{r}+\mathbf{k}$, $SP+S'P = 2a \Rightarrow |\mathbf{r}-\mathbf{k}|+|\mathbf{r}+\mathbf{k}| = 2a$.
Square $\therefore\ (\mathbf{r}-\mathbf{k})\bullet(\mathbf{r}-\mathbf{k})+(\mathbf{r}+\mathbf{k})\bullet(\mathbf{r}+\mathbf{k})+2\,|\mathbf{r}-\mathbf{k}|\ |\mathbf{r}+\mathbf{k}| = 4a^2$,
i.e. $r^2+k^2-2\mathbf{r}\bullet\mathbf{k}+r^2+k^2+2\mathbf{r}\bullet\mathbf{k}+2\,|\mathbf{r}-\mathbf{k}|\ |\mathbf{r}+\mathbf{k}| = 4a^2$ writing $r = |\mathbf{r}|$, $k = |\mathbf{k}|$,
i.e. $|\mathbf{r}-\mathbf{k}|^2\,|\mathbf{r}+\mathbf{k}|^2 = (2a^2-r^2-k^2)^2$,
i.e. $(r^2+k^2-2\mathbf{r}\bullet\mathbf{k})\,(r^2+k^2+2\mathbf{r}\bullet\mathbf{k}) = (2a^2-(r^2+k^2))^2$
$\therefore\ (r^2+k^2)^2-4(\mathbf{r}\bullet\mathbf{k})^2 = 4a^4-4a^2(r^2+k^2)+(r^2+k^2)^2$,
i.e. $(\mathbf{r}\bullet\mathbf{k})^2-a^2(r^2+k^2)+a^4 = 0$ (vector equation of ellipse).

15. Coordinates of the points where the tangent $\frac{x\cos\theta}{a}+\frac{y\sin\theta}{b} = 1$ cuts the axes are $A \equiv (a\sec\theta, 0)$, $B \equiv (0, b\operatorname{cosec}\theta)$ $\therefore$ coordinates of the mid-point $M(\xi, \eta)$ are $\xi = \frac{a\sec\theta}{2}$, $\eta = \frac{b\operatorname{cosec}\theta}{2}$ $\therefore\ \cos\theta = \frac{a}{2\xi}$, $\sin\theta = \frac{b}{2\eta}$. Eliminate θ $\therefore\ \frac{a^2}{4\xi^2}+\frac{b^2}{4\eta^2} = 1$ $\therefore$ the locus of M is $\frac{a^2}{x^2}+\frac{b^2}{y^2} = 1$ i.e. $b^2x^2+a^2y^2 = x^2y^2$. Making this homogeneous, we have the equation: $x^2y^2 = (b^2x^2+a^2y^2)z^2$. This quartic cuts l_∞ where $x^2y^2 = 0$, i.e. $x = 0, 0$; $y = 0, 0$, i.e. it cuts l_∞ twice at X_∞ and twice at Y_∞.

16. $AB^2 = l^2 = a^2\sec^2\theta+b^2\operatorname{cosec}^2\theta$ $\therefore\ \frac{dl^2}{d\theta} = \frac{2(a^2\sin^4\theta-b^2\cos^4\theta)}{\cos^3\theta\sin^3\theta}$ (on calculation) $= 0$ if $a\sin^2\theta = b\cos^2\theta$, i.e. $\tan\theta = \sqrt{\frac{b}{a}}\left(\therefore\ \sin\theta = \sqrt{\frac{b}{a+b}}, \cos\theta = \sqrt{\frac{a}{a+b}}\right)$. As θ passes through this critical value, $\frac{dl^2}{d\theta}$ goes from < 0 to > 0 $\therefore\ \theta = \tan^{-1}\sqrt{\frac{b}{a}}$ gives a minimum value $= (a+b)^2$ to l^2, i.e. $l_{\min} = a+b$.

17. Let the normal at $P(a\cos\theta, b\sin\theta)$ cut the x-axis at G. $\therefore\ G \equiv (ae^2\cos\theta, 0)$ $\therefore\ SG = ae(1-e\cos\theta)$, $SP = \sqrt{a^2(e-\cos\theta)^2+b^2\sin^2\theta} = a(1-e\cos\theta) = a-ex$. (Use (189).)
$\therefore\ SG = eSP$. Similarly, $S'G = ae(1+e\cos\theta) = e(a+ex) = eS'P$.
$\therefore\ \frac{SP}{S'P} = \frac{SG}{S'G}$ $(= e)$. This means that PG (PT) is the internal (external) bisector of $S\hat{P}S'$.

18. Radius of the circle must be b $\therefore b = ae$ $\therefore b^2 = a^2e^2 = a^2(1-e^2)$ (189)

$\therefore e = \dfrac{1}{\sqrt{2}}$ (i.e. Fagnano's ellipse, Exercise 18.7).

19. $\dfrac{dy}{dx} = \dfrac{-b^2x}{a^2y} = -e(e)$ at $L(L')$.

Equation of tangent at $L(L')$ is $y \mp \dfrac{b^2}{a} = \mp e(x-ae)$, i.e. $y = \mp(ex-a)$.

Solve: $\therefore x = \dfrac{a}{e}$, $\therefore$ these tangents meet at the intersection of the corresponding directrix and the x-axis. This must be so as they are tangents at the ends of a focal chord (Example 103); symmetry suggests they also meet on the x-axis. Likewise for the other *latus rectum*. [The four tangents thus constructed form a rhombus of area $2a^2/e$—check.]

20. Let S, S' be foci of the orbit of Cosmos, C the mid-point of SS'. Take the focus S' at the centre of the Earth $\therefore S'P = 4000+165 = 4165$ miles, $S'A = 4000+1075 = 5075$ miles. Major axis $AP = AS'+S'P = 9240$ miles $\therefore a = 4620$ miles. $\therefore SS' = S'A-S'P = 5075-4165 = 910$ miles ($SA = S'P$). $\therefore CS = 455$ miles. By Pythagoras' theorem, $CB^2 = BS^2-CS^2 = (4620)^2-(455)^2 = 21{,}127{,}375$ ($SB+S'B = 2a$) $\therefore CB \doteqdot 4600$ ($= b$) miles.

$$\therefore e = \sqrt{1-\frac{21{,}127{,}375}{21{,}344{,}400}}\ ((189)) \doteqdot \sqrt{1-0{\cdot}9898} = \sqrt{0{\cdot}0102} \doteqdot \frac{1}{10}.$$

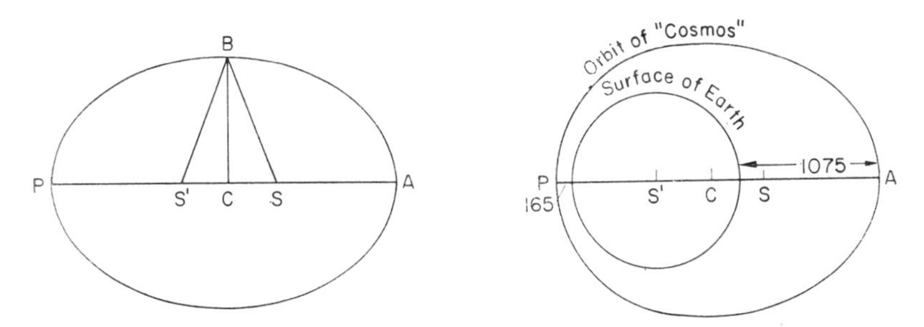

21. $B'P^2 = j = x^2+(y+b)^2 = y^2\left(1-\dfrac{a^2}{b^2}\right)+2by+a^2+b^2$.

$\therefore \dfrac{1}{2}\dfrac{dj}{dy} = y\left(1-\dfrac{a^2}{b^2}\right)+b = 0$ if $y = \dfrac{b^3}{a^2-b^2}$, giving $x = \dfrac{\pm a^2\sqrt{a^2-2b^2}}{a^2-b^2}$.

$\dfrac{1}{2}\dfrac{d^2j}{dy^2} = 1-\dfrac{a^2}{b^2} < 0$ $(a > b)$. $\therefore$ positions $\left(\dfrac{\pm a^2\sqrt{a^2-2b^2}}{a^2-b^2}, \dfrac{b^3}{a^2-b^2}\right)$ give a maximum value $\left(= \dfrac{a}{e}\right)$ to j. It is easier not to use parametric coordinates in this problem. Putting $b \sin\theta = \dfrac{b^3}{a^2-b^2}$, we see that the angular position of P is given by $\sin^{-1}\left(\dfrac{b^2}{a^2-b^2}\right)$ which may be verified by the parametric approach. Notice that if $a^2 = 2b^2$, i.e. Fagnano's ellipse, then P is at B, i.e. the maximum chord is the minor axis.

22. Perpendicular distance from O to the normal $ax\cos\theta - by\operatorname{cosec}\theta = a^2-b^2$ is $p = \dfrac{a^2-b^2}{\sqrt{a^2\sec^2\theta+y^2\operatorname{cosec}^2\theta}} = \dfrac{a^2-b^2}{q^2}$ $\therefore p_{\max} \Rightarrow q^2_{\min}$. Now $\dfrac{dq^2}{d\theta} = 0 \Rightarrow \dfrac{a^2\sin\theta}{\cos^3\theta} =$

$= \dfrac{b^2 \cos\theta}{\sin^3\theta}$ (on calculation) $\Rightarrow a\tan\theta = b\cot\theta$. Check that this does give a minimum.

$\therefore\ q^2_{\min} = (a+b)^2 \quad \therefore\ p_{\max} = \dfrac{a^2-b^2}{a+b} = a-b.$

23. Equation of ellipse w.r.t. origin $A'(-a, 0)$, i.e. $X = x+a$, $Y = y$, is $\dfrac{(X-a)^2}{a^2} + \dfrac{Y^2}{b^2} = 1$, i.e. (by (189)), $Y^2 = 2aX(1-e^2) - X^2(1-e^2) = 2aX(1-e)(1+e) - X^2(1-e)(1+e) = 2cX(1+e) - \dfrac{cX^2}{a}(1+e) = 4cX$, where $a(1-e) = c = A'S'$ is fixed, i.e. focus S' is fixed ($\therefore\ e \to 1 \Rightarrow a \to \infty$). Similarly, the parabola is a limiting case of the hyperbola.

24. Chord joining θ, ϕ: $\dfrac{y-b\sin\theta}{b(\sin\phi-\sin\theta)} = \dfrac{x-a\cos\theta}{a(\cos\phi-\cos\theta)}$. For a focal chord through $(ae, 0)$, $\dfrac{-b\sin\theta}{b(\sin\theta-\sin\phi)} = \dfrac{a(e-\cos\theta)}{a(\cos\theta-\cos\phi)} \quad \therefore\ e = \dfrac{\sin(\theta-\phi)}{\sin\theta-\sin\phi}$ (on calculation) $= \dfrac{2\sin((\theta-\phi)/2)\cos((\theta-\phi)/2)}{2\sin((\theta-\phi)/2)\cos((\theta+\phi)/2)} = \dfrac{\cos((\theta-\phi)/2)}{\cos((\theta+\phi)/2)}$ (Exercise 10.68) [For a circle, $\theta = \pi+\phi$ and $\cos\dfrac{\theta-\phi}{2} = 0$, i.e. $e = 0$].

25. Tangents at the points whose eccentric angles are $\theta-\alpha$, $\theta+\alpha$ (differing by 2α) are $\dfrac{x(\cos\theta\cos\alpha \pm \sin\theta\sin\alpha)}{a} + \dfrac{y(\sin\theta\cos\alpha \mp \cos\theta\sin\alpha)}{b} = 1$. Solve $\therefore$ point of intersection $\equiv (a\sec\alpha\cos\theta, b\sec\alpha\sin\theta)$. Eliminate θ. $\therefore$ the locus is the ellipse $\dfrac{x^2}{a^2\sec^2\alpha} + \dfrac{y^2}{b^2\sec^2\alpha} = 1.$

26. Routine calculation.

27.
$$\cos(\phi-\omega-\varepsilon) = \cos(\phi-\omega)\cos\varepsilon + \sin(\phi-\omega)\sin\varepsilon$$
$$= \cos(\phi-\omega) + \frac{3m^2}{h^2}\phi\sin(\phi-\omega).$$

ε small $\Rightarrow \cos\varepsilon = 1$, $\sin\varepsilon \doteqdot \varepsilon \quad \therefore\ \varepsilon \doteqdot \dfrac{3m^2}{h^2}\phi.$

28. As in Exercise 16.28, $|A-\lambda I| = \begin{vmatrix} 1-\lambda & 2\tan\phi \\ 2\tan\phi & 4\tan^2\phi+1-\lambda \end{vmatrix} = 0 \Rightarrow$ $\lambda^2 - 2\lambda(2\tan^2\phi+1)+1 = 0 \Rightarrow \lambda = (\tan\phi \pm \sec\phi)^2$. The reduced form is $\dfrac{x^2}{(\tan\phi+\sec\phi)^2} + \dfrac{y^2}{(\sec\phi-\tan\phi)^2} = 1$ from which $e = 2\sqrt{\sin\phi}/(1+\sin\phi)$ [(189.1)].

Angle of rotation (anticlockwise) is $\theta = \dfrac{1}{2}\tan^{-1}.\left\{\dfrac{4\tan\phi}{1-(4\tan^2\phi+1)}\right\}$ [(199)]

$= -\dfrac{1}{2}\tan^{-1}\cot\phi = -\dfrac{1}{2}\tan^{-1}\tan\left(\dfrac{\pi}{2}-\phi\right) = -\dfrac{1}{2}\left(\dfrac{\pi}{2}-\phi\right)$, i.e. major axis bisects $\dfrac{\pi}{2}-\phi$ (rotation is clockwise). $\phi = gd\,u \Rightarrow$ semi-axes $= e^u$, e^{-u}, eccentricity $= (1-e^{-4u})^{1/2}$.

29. Substitute $y = \dfrac{b \sin \theta}{a(\cos \theta - e)}(x - ae)$ (equation of focal chord) in equation of ellipse $\therefore\ x^2(1-2e\cos\theta+e^2)-2ae\sin^2\theta\cdot x - a^2(e^2\cos^2\theta-2e\cos\theta+\cos^2\theta) = 0.$

Roots are (on calculation) $x = \dfrac{ae\sin^2\theta \pm a[(1+e^2)\cos\theta - e\cos^2\theta - e]}{1-2e\cos\theta+e^2}$

$$= a\cos\theta,\ \frac{a\{2e-(1+e^2)\cos\theta\}}{1-2e\cos\theta+e^2}\quad \therefore\ y = b\sin\theta,\ \frac{-b(1-e^2)\sin\theta}{1-2e\cos\theta+e^2}.$$

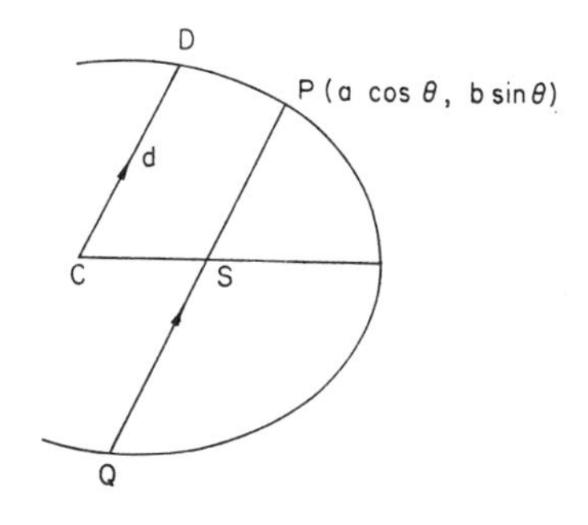

30. Focal chord length $PQ = \dfrac{2a}{1-2e\cos\theta+e^2}\times$

$$\sqrt{[e(1+\cos^2\theta)-(1+e^2)\cos\theta]^2+(1-e^2)\sin^2\theta(1-e\cos\theta)^2}$$

$$= \frac{2a(1-2e\cos\theta+e^2\cos^2\theta)}{1-2e\cos\theta+e^2} = \frac{2}{a}\,\frac{[a^2(\cos\theta-e)^2+b^2\sin^2\theta]}{1-2e\cos\theta+e^2} \qquad (\alpha)$$

Now $y = \dfrac{b\sin\theta}{a(\cos\theta-e)}x$ (CD) cuts the ellipse at $\left(\pm\dfrac{a(\cos\theta-e)}{\sqrt{1-2e\cos\theta+e^2}},\ \pm\dfrac{b\sin\theta}{\sqrt{1-2e\cos\theta+e^2}}\right)$

$$\therefore\ CD^2 = d^2 = \frac{a^2(\cos\theta-e)^2+b^2\sin^2\theta}{1-2e\cos\theta+e^2}\quad \ldots (\beta)\quad \therefore\ (\alpha),\ (\beta) \Rightarrow PQ = \frac{2d^2}{a}.$$

EXERCISES 19

1. The equation $y^2-2x^2-2y-8x-9 = 0$ may be written $\dfrac{(y-1)^2}{2}-\dfrac{(x+2)^2}{1} = 1$, i.e. a hyperbola, centre $O'(-2, 1)$. Semi axes are $1, \sqrt{2}$. Transverse axis is parallel to Oy. Distance from centre to foci $= \sqrt{3}$. Foci are $(-2, 1\pm\sqrt{3})$. By (191.1), $e = \sqrt{\tfrac{3}{2}}$.

Directrices are $y = 1 \pm \dfrac{2}{\sqrt{3}}$. Asymptotes are $y-1 = \pm\dfrac{1}{2}(x+2)$.

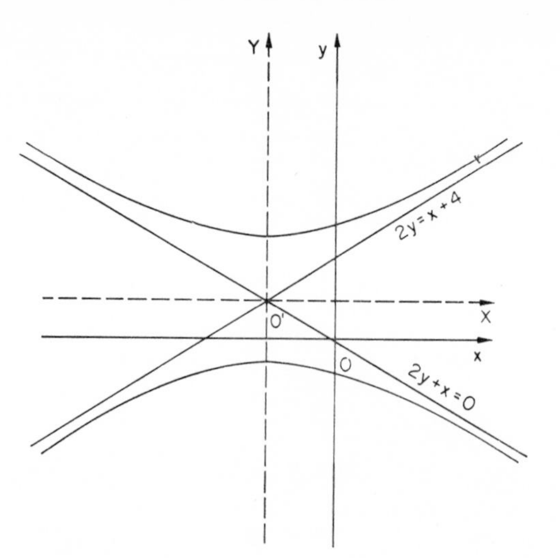

2. Given $x+iy = \sqrt{\phi+i\psi}$ $\therefore$ $x^2-y^2+2ixy = \phi+i\psi$ on squaring both sides. Equate real and imaginary parts $\therefore$ $x^2-y^2 = \phi$, $2xy = \psi$.

Clearly ϕ = const., ψ = const. represent two systems of rectangular hyperbolas. Consider two hyperbolas of the above systems, e.g. $xy = c^2$, $\dfrac{x^2}{a^2}-\dfrac{y^2}{a^2} = 1$ and let a point of intersection be $P(ct, c/t)$. Gradient of tangent to $xy = c^2$ at (ct, c/t) is $-1/t^2$. Gradient of tangent to $\dfrac{x^2}{a^2}-\dfrac{y^2}{a^2} = 1$ at $(ct, c/t)$ is t^2.

$\therefore$ the tangents are $\perp$; $\therefore$ the two systems of hyperbolas cut orthogonally.

3. Asymptotes and directrices intersect the auxiliary circle $x^2+y^2 = a^2$, where $y = \pm\dfrac{b}{a}\cdot\pm\dfrac{a}{e} = \pm\dfrac{b}{e}$, i.e. at the points $\left(\dfrac{a}{e}, \dfrac{b}{e}\right)$, $\left(-\dfrac{a}{e}, \dfrac{b}{e}\right)$, $\left(-\dfrac{a}{e}, -\dfrac{b}{e}\right)$, $\left(\dfrac{a}{e}, -\dfrac{b}{e}\right)$. For each of these points $x^2+y^2 = \dfrac{a^2}{e^2}+\dfrac{b^2}{e^2} = a^2$ by (191.1). Thus, the asymptotes of a hyperbola meet the directrices on the auxiliary circle.

4. Now $PR = \dfrac{-y_0+(b/a)x_0}{\sqrt{1+(b^2/a^2)}}$, $PQ = \dfrac{y_0+(b/a)x_0}{\sqrt{1+(b^2/a^2)}}$ ($\perp$ distance from given point $P(x_0, y_0)$ to given line)

$\therefore$ $PR\cdot PQ = \dfrac{(b^2x_0^2)/a^2-y_0^2}{1+b^2/a^2} = \dfrac{b^2x_0^2-a^2y_0^2}{a^2+b^2} = \dfrac{a^2b^2}{a^2+b^2}$ (since P lies on the curve) = const.

5. At P, $x = t$, $y = \dfrac{1}{t}$. $\therefore$ $dy/dx = -1/t^2$.

Equation of the tangent PT at P is $y-\dfrac{1}{t} = -\dfrac{1}{t^2}(x-t)$, i.e. $y = -\dfrac{x}{t^2}+\dfrac{2}{t}$.

6. Gradient of OT is t^2. Equation of OT is $\therefore$ $y = t^2x$.

7. Solving in Exercises 19.5, 19.6 we find coordinates of T are $x = \dfrac{2t}{t^4+1}$, $y = \dfrac{2t^3}{t^4+1}$.

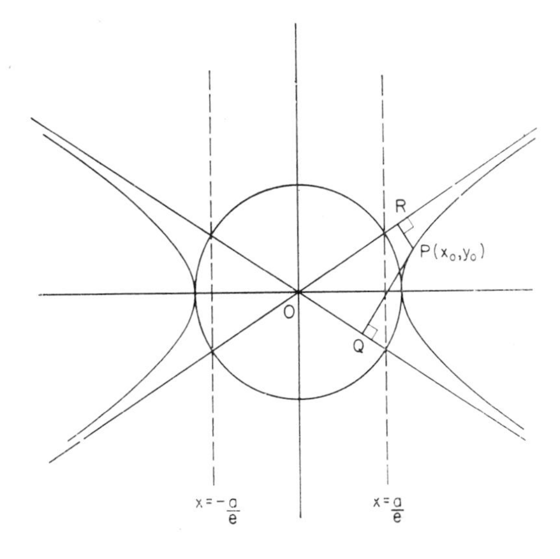

8. Eliminate t in Exercise 19.7 to obtain $(x^2+y^2)^2 = 4xy$.

9. In Exercise 19.8 put $x = r\cos\theta$, $y = r\sin\theta$. The required locus is then $r^2 = 2\sin 2\theta$ (lemniscate of Bernoulli—see Example 131).

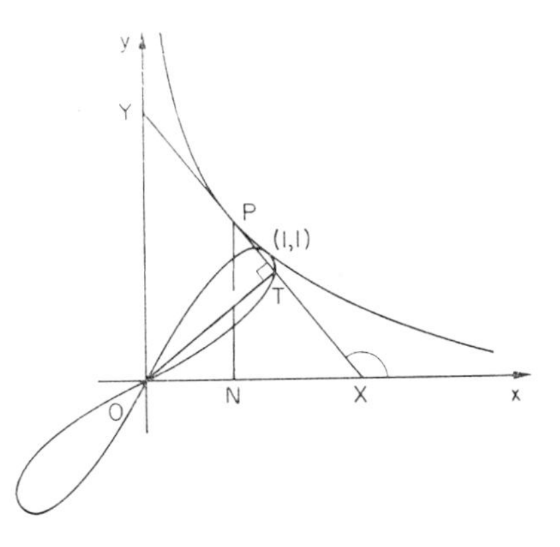

10. Equation of focal radius SP is $y = \dfrac{b}{a}(x-ae)$.

Solve this equation and the equation of the hyperbola $\therefore P \equiv \left(a\dfrac{1+e^2}{2e},\ b\dfrac{1-e^2}{2e}\right)$

$$\therefore\ SP = \sqrt{\left[a\left(1-\frac{1+e^2}{2e}\right)\right]^2+\left[b\cdot\frac{e^2-1}{2e}\right]^2} = \frac{e^2-1}{2e}\sqrt{a^2+b^2} =$$

$$= \frac{b^2}{2a}\ ((189)) = \frac{1}{4}\cdot\frac{2b^2}{a} = \frac{1}{4}\ \textit{latus rectum}.$$

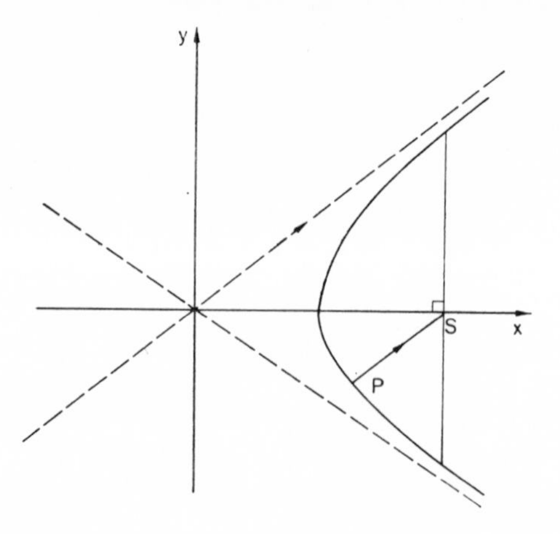

11. Tangent $\frac{x}{a}\sec\theta-\frac{y}{b}\tan\theta = 1$ at $P\,(a\sec\theta, b\tan\theta)$ cuts asymptotes $y = \frac{b}{a}x$, $y = -\frac{b}{a}x$ at $Q \equiv \left(\frac{a}{\sec\theta-\tan\theta}, \frac{b}{\sec\theta-\tan\theta}\right)$,

$$R \equiv \left(\frac{a}{\sec\theta+\tan\theta}, \frac{-b}{\sec\theta+\tan\theta}\right)$$

respectively. $\therefore$ mid-point of $QR \equiv (a\sec\theta,\ b\tan\theta)$ (using the mid-point formula) $\equiv$ $\equiv P$. [The result is, of course, also valid for the rectangular hyperbola.]

12. $\frac{dy}{dx} = -\frac{my}{nx}$, $NX = y\Big/\frac{dy}{dx} = -\frac{n}{m}x \quad \therefore \frac{PY}{PX} = \frac{ON}{NX} = \frac{x}{(n/m)x} = \frac{m}{n}$.

For $xy = c$, $x^{-1}y^2 = c$, $pv^\gamma = c$, this ratio is $1:1$ (Exercise 19.11), $-1:2$, $\gamma:1$ respectively.

13. Let $S_1G = d_1$, $S_2G = d_2$, v = speed of sound (constant). $\therefore d_1 = t_1v$, $d_2 = t_2v$ where t_1, t_2 are the (recorded) times of gunfire, i.e. t_1-t_2 is known. $\therefore (t_1-t_2)v = d_1-d_2$ = const. $\therefore$ G lies on a branch of a hyperbola with foci S_1, S_2 (the branch depending on which listening post hears it first). Similarly for the hyperbola with foci S_2, S_3. The intersection of the hyperbolas gives the position of the gun.

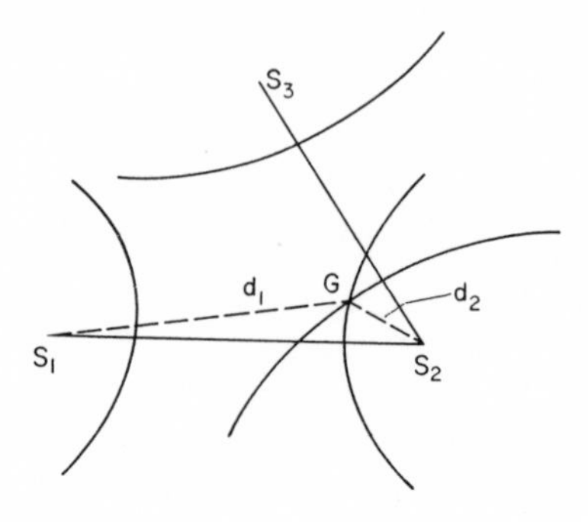

14. Proof similar to that for Exercise 18.17.

15. Let S' (0, 0), S (0, 4), P (12, 9) $\therefore$ $S'P = 15$, $SP = 13$ $\therefore S'P - SP = 2 = 2a$ (bifocal property with conventional use of a) $\therefore a = 1$. Also $SS' = 4 = 2ae$ $\therefore e = 2$ whence $b = \sqrt{3}$ $\therefore$ equation of hyperbola is $\dfrac{y^2}{3} - x^2 = 1$.

16. For the ellipse, $a = \dfrac{r+1/r}{2}$, $b = \dfrac{r-1/r}{2}$ $\therefore$ $e^2 = 1 - \dfrac{b^2}{a^2}$ [(189)] $= \dfrac{4r^2}{(r^2+1)^2}$

$$\therefore\ e = \frac{2r}{r^2+1} = \frac{2}{r+1/r} = \frac{1}{a} \Rightarrow ae = 1.$$

For the hyperbola, $A = \cos\theta$, $B = \sin\theta$, $\therefore E = 1 + \dfrac{B^2}{A^2}$ (191.1) $= 1 + \tan^2\theta =$

$$= \sec^2\theta \ \therefore E = \frac{1}{\cos\theta} = \frac{1}{A} \Rightarrow AE = 1.$$

$\therefore$ foci $(\pm ae, 0)$, $(\pm AE, 0)$ are the same, namely, $(\pm 1, 0)$.

Coordinates of common point of intersection P are

$$x_1 = \frac{r^2+1}{2r}\cos\theta,\ y_1 = \frac{r^2-1}{2r}\sin\theta.$$

For the ellipse, $\dfrac{dy}{dx} = -\dfrac{b^2}{a^2}\dfrac{x}{y} = -\dfrac{r^2+1}{r^2-1}\cot\theta$ at P.

For the hyperbola, $\dfrac{dy}{dx} = \dfrac{B}{A}\dfrac{y}{x} = \dfrac{r^2-1}{r^2+1}\tan\theta$ at P.

$$\therefore \text{ product of the gradients} = -\frac{r^2+1}{r^2-1}\cot\theta \cdot \frac{r^2-1}{r^2+1}\tan\theta = -1.$$

$\therefore$ the curves are orthogonal.

17. This is really Exercise 19.16 in disguise.

$$x + iy = \frac{e^{\alpha+i\beta} + e^{-\alpha-i\beta}}{2} = \frac{e^{\alpha}+e^{-\alpha}}{2}\cos\beta + i\frac{e^{\alpha}-e^{-\alpha}}{2}\sin\beta$$

$$= \cosh\alpha\cos\beta + i\sinh\alpha\sin\beta.$$

Equate real and imaginary parts $\therefore x = \cosh\alpha\cos\beta$, $y = \sinh\alpha\sin\beta$.

In Exercise 19.16, put $r = e^{\alpha}$, $\theta = \beta$ and we have the following in the new notation:

(i) ellipse $\dfrac{x^2}{\cosh^2\alpha} + \dfrac{y^2}{\sinh^2\alpha} = 1$, hyperbola $\dfrac{x^2}{\cos^2\beta} - \dfrac{y^2}{\sin^2\beta} = 1$;

(ii) the ellipse and hyperbola are orthogonal; (iii) the point of intersection $\equiv$ ($\cosh\alpha\cos\beta$, $\sinh\alpha\sin\beta$). [Note the special case $\beta = \alpha$.]

18. Normal at t is (240) $ct^4 - xt^3 + yt - c = 0$. Let this pass through a fixed point $H \equiv (h, k)$ $\therefore ct^4 - ht^3 + kt - c = 0$ . . .(α). This quartic has four roots. $\therefore$ from H, four normals can be drawn, i.e. four normals with parameters t_1, t_2, t_3, t_4 are concurrent if (α) is true. Special features of (α) are (121) $t_1t_2t_3t_4 = -\dfrac{c}{c} = -1$, $\sum t_1t_2 = \dfrac{0}{c} = 0$.

19. Pencil of conics: $x^2 - xy + x + 1 + k(x^2+y^2-16) = 0$, i.e. $(1+k)x^2 + ky^2 - xy + x + (1-16k) = 0$. For a parabola (182), $(1+k)k - \frac{1}{4} = 0$, i.e. $4k^2 + 4k - 1 = 0$, i.e. $\exists$ two parabolas, one for each value of k of the quadratic. For a rectangular hyperbola (183), $(1+k)+k = 0$, i.e. $k = -\frac{1}{2}$ $\therefore$ $\exists$ just one rectangular hyperbola. Its equation is $\frac{1}{2}x^2-\frac{1}{2}y^2-xy+x+9 = 0$, i.e. $x^2-y^2-2xy+2x+18 = 0$.

20. Tangent $y \sec\theta - x\tan\theta = 1$ cuts the axes at $X \equiv (-\cot\theta, 0)$, $Y \equiv (0, \cos\theta)$ $\therefore$ $Q \equiv (-\cot\theta, \cos\theta) = (\xi, \eta)$ $\therefore$ $\dfrac{1}{\eta^2}-\dfrac{1}{\xi^2} = 1$ $\therefore$ the locus of Q is the quartic $\dfrac{1}{y^2}-\dfrac{1}{x^2} = 1$. The point $\left(\dfrac{1-t^2}{2t}, \dfrac{1-t^2}{1+t^2}\right)$ is readily seen to lie on the quartic.

21. Points of intersection of the line $lx+my+n = 0$ and the quartic are (Exercise 19.20) given by the roots of $l\left(\dfrac{1-t^2}{2t}\right)+m\left(\dfrac{1-t^2}{1+t^2}\right)+n = 0$,

i.e. $-lt^4+(-2m+2n)t^3+(2n+2m)t+l = 0$ $\therefore$ $t_1t_2t_3t_4 = \dfrac{l}{-l} = -1, \sum t_1t_2 = \dfrac{0}{-l} = 0$.

22. Ellipse $\dfrac{x^2}{a^2}+\dfrac{y^2}{b^2} = 1$ $(b^2 = a^2(1-e^2), e < 1)$; hyperbola $\dfrac{x^2}{A^2}-\dfrac{y^2}{B^2} = 1$ $\left(B^2 = A^2\left(\dfrac{1}{e^2}-1\right), \dfrac{1}{e} > 1\right)$. Since they are confocal, $ae = \dfrac{A}{e}$ $\therefore A = ae^2$.

Eliminate x^2 between the two equations $\therefore$ $y^2\left(\dfrac{a^2}{b^2}+\dfrac{A^2}{B^2}\right) = a^2-A^2 \Rightarrow$

$$\Rightarrow y^2\left(\frac{1}{1-e^2}+\frac{1}{1/e^2-1}\right) = a^2(1-e^4) \Rightarrow y^2\left(\frac{1+e^2}{1-e^2}\right) = a^2(1-e^4) \Rightarrow y^2 = a^2(1-e^2)^2$$

$= a^2 \cdot \dfrac{b^4}{a^4} = \dfrac{b^4}{a^2} \Rightarrow y = \pm\dfrac{b^2}{a}$ i.e. the extremities of the *latus rectum* through $x = ae$. Similarly for the *latus rectum* through $(-ae, 0)$.

23. Vertices of the ellipse (on the x-axis) are $\left(\pm\sqrt{\dfrac{c-a}{ca}}, 0, 0\right)$.

Foci are $\left(\pm\sqrt{\dfrac{c-a}{ca}-\dfrac{c-b}{bc}}, 0, 0\right) = \left(\pm\sqrt{\dfrac{b-a}{ab}}, 0, 0\right)$.

Vertices of the hyperbola (on the x-axis) are $\left(\pm\sqrt{\dfrac{b-a}{ab}}, 0, 0\right)$.

Foci are $\left(\pm\sqrt{\dfrac{b-a}{ab}+\dfrac{c-b}{bc}}, 0, 0\right) = \left(\pm\sqrt{\dfrac{c-a}{ca}}, 0, 0\right)$.

24. Tangent at $L\left(ae, \dfrac{b^2}{a}\right)$ is $\dfrac{xe}{a}-\dfrac{y}{a} = 1$ $\therefore x = 0 \Rightarrow y = -a$. $\left[y = 0 \Rightarrow x = \dfrac{a}{e}.\right]$

25. Differentiate $\therefore$ $\dfrac{\partial f}{\partial x}+\dfrac{\partial f}{\partial y}\dfrac{dy}{dx} = 0$, $\dfrac{dy}{dx} = m$ (for P, Q) $\therefore$ $\dfrac{\partial f}{\partial x}+m\dfrac{\partial f}{\partial y} = 0$. This is linear in x, y and $\therefore$ represents a line (through O). Check, using (188), (222).

26. Normal at $(a\sec\theta, b\tan\theta)$ is $ax\cos\theta+by\cot\theta = a^2e^2$.

$y = 0 \Rightarrow P \equiv \left(\dfrac{a^2e^2}{a}\sec\theta, 0\right)$; $x = 0 \Rightarrow Q \equiv \left(0, \dfrac{a^2e^2}{b}\tan\theta\right)$

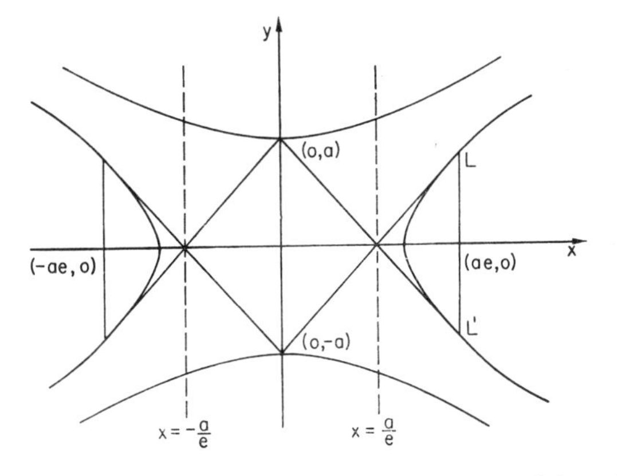

$\therefore$ coordinates of mid-point R of PQ are $x = \dfrac{a^2e^2 \sec\theta}{2a}$, $y = \dfrac{a^2e^2 \tan\theta}{2b}$

$\therefore$ the locus of R is $\dfrac{x^2}{\left(\dfrac{a^2e^2}{2a}\right)^2} - \dfrac{y^2}{\left(\dfrac{a^2e^2}{2b}\right)^2} = 1$, a hyperbola with semi-axes

$\dfrac{a^2e^2}{2a}$, $\dfrac{a^2e^2}{2b}$ and eccentricity $= \sqrt{1+\left(\dfrac{a^2e^2}{2a}\cdot\dfrac{2b}{a^2e^2}\right)} = \sqrt{1+\dfrac{b}{a}} = \dfrac{e}{\sqrt{e^2-1}}$ (191.1)

27. Polar of (x', y') w.r.t. $\begin{cases} \dfrac{x^2}{a^2}-\dfrac{y^2}{b^2} = 1 \text{ is } \dfrac{xx'}{a^2}-\dfrac{yy'}{b^2} = 1 \left(\text{gradient } \dfrac{b^2x'}{a^2y'} = m\right) \\ \dfrac{x^2}{a^2}-\dfrac{y^2}{b^2} = -1 \text{ is } \dfrac{xx'}{a^2}-\dfrac{yy'}{b^2} = -1 \text{ (gradient} = m \text{ also)} \end{cases}$

(i)

$$|OR| = \frac{a^2b^2}{\sqrt{b^4x'^2+a^4y'^2}} = OQ. \qquad \text{(ii)}$$

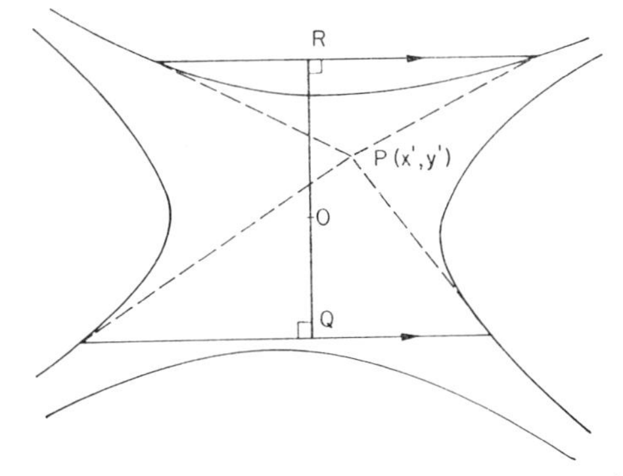

28. $\cosh^{-1} x = k$, $\cosh^{-1} y = l \Rightarrow \cosh(k+l) = \cosh m = \cosh k \cosh l + \sinh k \cdot \sinh l$,

i.e. $xy+\sqrt{x^2-1}\sqrt{y^2-1} = \cosh m$, i.e. $(x^2-1)(y^2-1) = (\cosh m - xy)^2$,

i.e. $x^2+y^2-2xy\cosh m+\sinh^2 m = 0$ (hyperbola, by (184.2)).

29. $y = ax+c$ cuts the hyperbola where $x^2(1+a^2-2a\cosh m)+2cx(a-\cosh m)+$ $+\sinh^2 m = 0$.

Asymptotes occur when points of intersection are at infinity, i.e. roots are infinite, i.e. replacing x by $\dfrac{1}{t}$, when roots are zero. Conditions are $1+a^2-2a\cosh m = 0$, $c(a-\cosh m) = 0$ whence $c = 0$, $a = e^m, e^{-m}$.

$\therefore$ asymptotes are $y = e^m x$, $y = e^{-m}x$. (Notice that $a-\cosh m = 0 \Rightarrow a^2-2a\cosh m+\cosh^2 m = 0 \Rightarrow \cosh^2 m = 1$ (by comparison with similar equation) $\Rightarrow m = 0$ which is impossible.)

30. Gradient of the tangent at $P(a\sec\theta,\ a\tan\theta)$ is $\operatorname{cosec}\theta = \tan\psi$. (i)

Gradient of OP is $\tan\theta/\sec\theta = \sin\theta = \tan\phi$. (ii)

$$\operatorname{Tan} O\hat{P}T\ (= \tan 2K) = \tan(\psi-\phi) = \frac{\tan\psi-\tan\phi}{1+\tan\psi\tan\phi} = \frac{\cos^2\theta}{2\sin\theta} \quad \text{by (i), (ii) (iii)}$$

$$\text{Now } \tan 2K = \frac{2\tan K}{1-\tan^2 K} \quad \therefore 2\tan K = \frac{\cos^2\theta}{2\sin\theta}(1-\tan^2 K) \quad \text{(by (iii))}$$

$$\therefore \cos^2\theta\tan^2 K+4\sin\theta\tan K-\cos^2\theta = 1 \quad \therefore \tan K = \left(\frac{1-\sin\theta}{\cos\theta}\right)^2,\ -\left(\frac{1+\sin\theta}{\cos\theta}\right)^2.$$

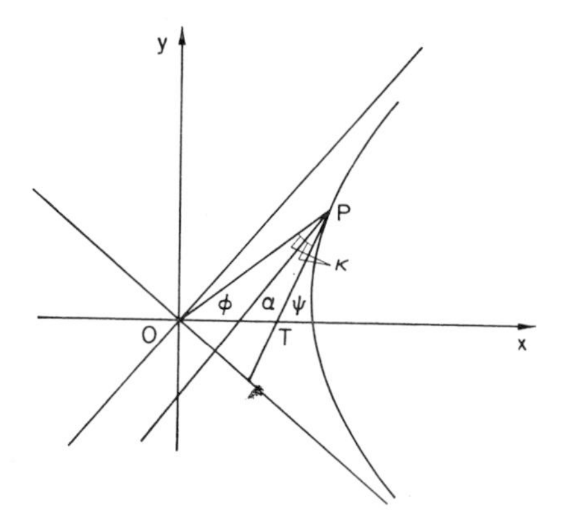

$$\operatorname{Tan}\alpha = \tan(\psi-K) = \frac{\tan\psi-\tan K}{1+\tan\psi\tan K} = 1$$ (after lengthy calculation) using the +ve root.

For the −ve root, $\tan\alpha' = -1$ upon calculation $\therefore \alpha = \dfrac{\pi}{4}$, $\alpha' = \dfrac{3\pi}{4}$.

$\therefore \alpha = \dfrac{\pi}{4}$ corresponds to the internal bisector, $\alpha' = \dfrac{3\pi}{4}$ to the external bisector.

$\therefore$ internal bisector of $O\hat{P}T$ makes a constant angle $\left(= \dfrac{\pi}{4}\right)$ with the x-axis.

EXERCISES 20

1. $\dfrac{dy}{dx} = x \cdot \dfrac{1}{x} + \log x = 1 + \log x = 0$ when $\log x = -1$, i.e. when $x = 1/e$.

$\therefore \dfrac{d^2y}{dx^2} = \dfrac{1}{x}$ which is positive when $x = 1/e$.

$\therefore x = 1/e$ gives a minimum value which occurs at $(1/e, -1/e) \doteqdot (0{\cdot}36, 0{\cdot}36)$.

Now $\dfrac{d^2y}{dx^2} \neq 0$ $\therefore$ there are no inflexions. (Diagram, below left.)

When $x = 0$, $y = 0$; $x = 2$, $y \doteqdot 1{\cdot}38$; $x = 1$, $y = 0$; $x = 3$, $y \doteqdot 3{\cdot}3$.

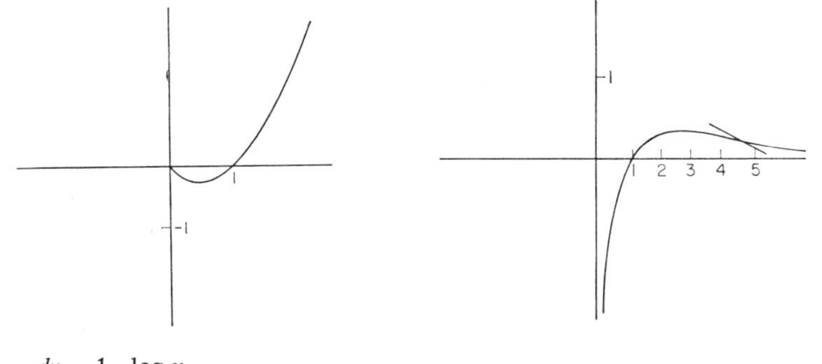

2. $\dfrac{dy}{dx} = \dfrac{1 - \log x}{x^2} = 0$ when $\log x = 1$, i.e. $x = e$.

$\therefore \dfrac{d^2y}{dx^2} = \dfrac{2 \log x - 3}{x^3}$ which is $-$ve when $x = e$.

Thus, a maximum occurs at $(e, 1/e)$. An inflexion occurs at $(e^{3/2}, \frac{3}{2}e^{3/2})$. When $x = 1$, $y = 0$; as $x \to \infty$, $y \to 0$; as $x \to 0$, $y \to -\infty$ (using (15)). There are no values for y when $x < 0$. Both $x = 0$ and $y = 0$ are asymptotes. (Diagram, above right.)

3. $\dfrac{dy}{dx} = 2x^2 \cdot \dfrac{-1}{2\sqrt{1-x}} + 4x\sqrt{1-x} = \dfrac{x(4-5x)}{\sqrt{1-x}} = 0$ when $x = 0$ or $x = \dfrac{4}{5}$.

$$\therefore \frac{d^2y}{dx^2} = \frac{\sqrt{1-x}\,(4-10x) + (4x-5x^2)/2\sqrt{1-x}}{1-x}$$

$= \dfrac{15x^2 - 24x + 8}{2(1-x)^{3/2}}$ which is $+$ve when $x = 0$ and $-$ve when $x = \dfrac{4}{5}$.

Minimum and maximum values occur at, respectively, $(0, 0)$ and $(4/5, 32\sqrt{5}/125)$, i.e. $(0{\cdot}8, 0{\cdot}57)$ (approx.).

$\dfrac{d^2y}{dx^2} = 0$ when $15x^2 - 24x + 8 = 0$, i.e. $x = \dfrac{24 \pm 4\sqrt{6}}{30} \doteqdot 1{\cdot}127$ or $0{\cdot}473$.

($x = 1{\cdot}127$ can be ignored since this makes y imaginary.) The inflexion occurs at $x \doteqdot 0{\cdot}473$. The curve cuts the x-axis at $x = 1$. (See graph on p. 526, above left.)

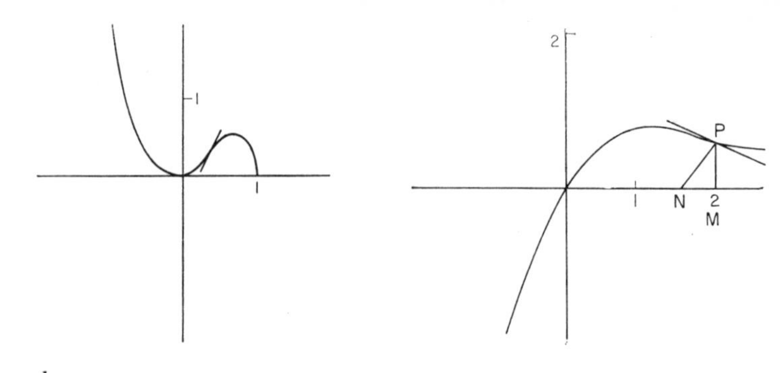

4. $\dfrac{dy}{dx} = -xe^{-x}+e^{-x}\cdot 1 = e^{-x}(1-x) = 0$ when $x = 1$.

$\therefore \dfrac{d^2y}{dx^2} = e^{-x}\cdot -1-e^{-x}(1-x) = e^{-x}(x-2)$ which is negative when $x = 1$. Thus, the maximum value is at $(1, 1/e)$, and the point of inflexion is at $(2, 2/e^2)$. The line $y = 0$ is an asymptote to the curve. (Diagram, above right.)

Subnormal $MN = y\dfrac{dy}{dx} = x(1-x)e^{-2x} = |-2e^{-4}|$ (at the inflexion) $\doteqdot \cdot 037$.

5. $\dfrac{dy}{dx} = \dfrac{(1+x^2)-x\cdot 2x}{(1+x^2)^2} = \dfrac{1-x^2}{(1+x^2)^2} = 0$ when $x = 1$, and $x = -1$.

$\therefore \dfrac{d^2y}{dx^2} = \dfrac{2x(x^2-3)}{(x^2+1)^3}$ (on calculation) which is $-$ve when $x = 1$, and $+$ve when $x = -1$. Thus, maximum and minimum values are at $(1, \frac{1}{2})$ and $(-1, -\frac{1}{2})$, respectively. Inflexions are at $(0, 0)$, $\left(\sqrt{3}, \dfrac{\sqrt{3}}{4}\right)$ and $\left(-\sqrt{3}, \dfrac{-\sqrt{3}}{4}\right)$.

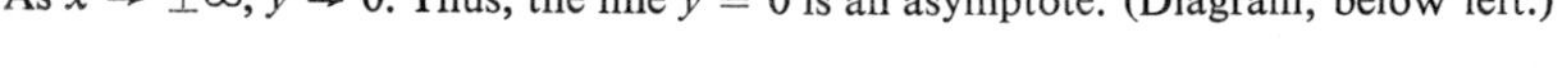

As $x \to \pm\infty$, $y \to 0$. Thus, the line $y = 0$ is an asymptote. (Diagram, below left.)

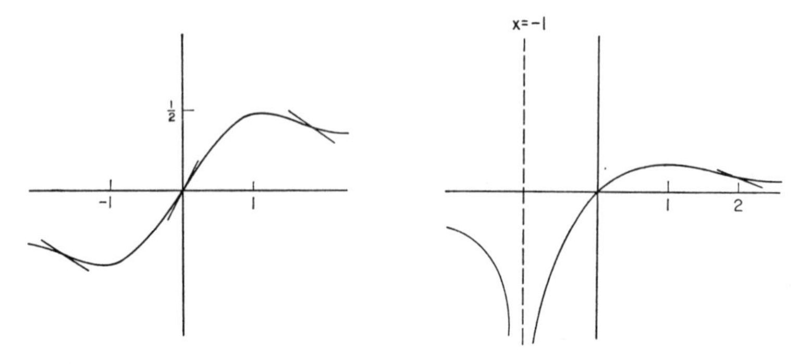

6. $\dfrac{dy}{dx} = \dfrac{(x+1)^2-x\cdot 2(x+1)}{(x+1)^4} = \dfrac{1-x}{(x+1)^3} = 0$ when $x = 1$.

$\therefore \dfrac{d^2y}{dx^2} = \dfrac{-(x+1)^3-(1-x)\cdot 3(x+1)^2}{(x+1)^6} = \dfrac{2(x-2)}{(x+1)^4}$ which is negative when $x = 1$. $\therefore x = 1$ gives a maximum value to y. $\therefore$ maximum turning point is $(1, \frac{1}{4})$. An inflexion occurs when $\frac{d^2y}{dx^2} = 0$, i.e. at $\left(2, \frac{2}{9}\right)$. Clearly, $x = -1$ is an asymptote. Since $x \to \pm\infty \Rightarrow y = 0$, then $y = 0$ is also an asymptote. (Diagram, p. 526, bottom right.)

7. $y = \frac{x^3-1}{x} \Rightarrow \frac{dy}{dx} = \frac{2x^3+1}{x^2} = 0$ when $x^3 = -\frac{1}{2}$, i.e. when $x = -\frac{1}{\sqrt[3]{2}}$

$\therefore \frac{d^2y}{dx^2} = \frac{2(x^3-1)}{x^3}$ which is +ve when $x = -\frac{1}{\sqrt[3]{2}}$.

Thus, a minimum value occurs at $(-0{\cdot}79, 1{\cdot}9)$ (approx.), and an inflexion at $(1, 0)$. Gradient of the curve at this point is $\frac{dy}{dx} = 3$ (when $x = 1$). Asymptotes to the curve are: the line $x = 0$, the parabola $y = x^2$, and the hyperbola $y = \frac{-1}{x}$. (Note the curvilinear asymptotes: Diagram, below left.)

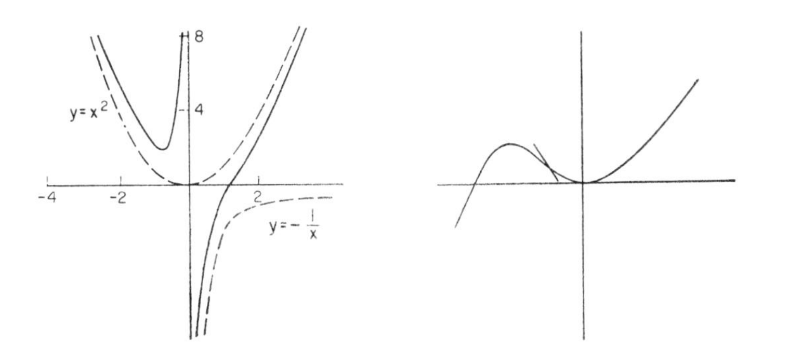

8. $\begin{vmatrix} a+x & b & c \\ a & b+x & c \\ a & b & c+x \end{vmatrix} = (a+b+c+x)\begin{vmatrix} 1 & b & c \\ 1 & b+x & c \\ 1 & b & c+x \end{vmatrix}$ $\left\{ \begin{array}{l} C_1+(C_2+C_3) \text{ and} \\ \text{taking out} \\ (a+b+c+x) \end{array} \right.$

$= (a+b+c+x)\begin{vmatrix} 1 & b & c \\ 0 & x & 0 \\ 0 & 0 & x \end{vmatrix}$ (R_2-R_1, R_3-R_1) $\therefore y = (a+b+c+x)x^2$.

$\therefore \frac{dy}{dx} = 2ax+2bx+2cx+3x^2 = \{2(a+b+c)+3x\}x = (K+3x)x$ [where $K = 2(a+b+c)$, assumed +ve] $= 0$ when $x = 0$ or $x = -\frac{K}{3}$.

$\therefore \frac{d^2y}{dx^2} = K+6x$ which is +ve when $x = 0$, −ve when $x = -\frac{K}{3}$, $= 0$ when $x = -\frac{K}{6}$.

$\therefore$ a maximum occurs at $\left(-\frac{K}{3}, \frac{K^3}{54}\right)$, a minimum at $(0, 0)$, an inflexion at $\left(-\frac{K}{6}, \frac{K^3}{108}\right)$. (The diagram, above right, has $K = 3$.)

9. $\dfrac{dy}{dx} = e^{-x}(\cos x - \sin x) = 0$ if $x = \begin{cases} \dfrac{\pi}{4}, \dfrac{5\pi}{4}, \dfrac{9\pi}{4}, \dfrac{13\pi}{4}, \dfrac{17\pi}{4}, \ldots \\ \dfrac{-3\pi}{4}, \dfrac{-7\pi}{4}, \dfrac{-11\pi}{4}, \dfrac{-15\pi}{4}, \ldots \end{cases}$

$\therefore \dfrac{d^2y}{dx^2} = e^{-x}(-\cos x - \sin x) - e^{-x}(\cos x - \sin x) = -2e^{-x}\cos x$

which is $+$ve when $x = \dfrac{5\pi}{4} \dfrac{13\pi}{4}, \ldots, \dfrac{-3\pi}{4}, \dfrac{-11\pi}{4}, \ldots,$

$-$ve when $x = \dfrac{\pi}{4}, \dfrac{9\pi}{4}, \dfrac{17\pi}{4}, \ldots, \dfrac{-7\pi}{4}, \dfrac{-15\pi}{4}, \ldots$

Three successive maxima occur at $x = \dfrac{(4n-3)\pi}{4}, \dfrac{(4n+5)\pi}{4}, \dfrac{(4n+13)\pi}{4}$.

The corresponding values of y are $\dfrac{e^{-(4n-3)\pi/4}}{\sqrt{2}}, \dfrac{e^{-(4n+5)\pi/4}}{\sqrt{2}}, \dfrac{e^{-(4n+13)\pi/4}}{\sqrt{2}}$.

Clearly these are in G.P., the common ratio being $e^{-2\pi}$.

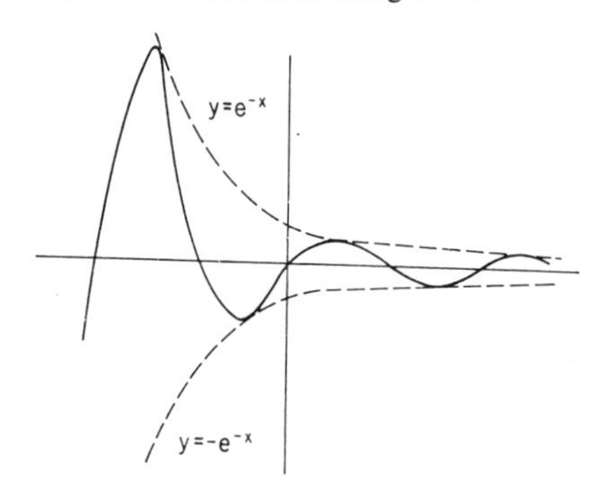

10. $\dfrac{dy}{dx} = \dfrac{\sinh x}{\cosh x} - \dfrac{1}{2} = 0$ when $\tanh x = \dfrac{1}{2}$, i.e. $\dfrac{e^x - e^{-x}}{e^x + e^{-x}} = \dfrac{1}{2}$, $e^{2x} = 3$, $x = \log\sqrt{3}$.

$\therefore \dfrac{d^2y}{dx^2} = \operatorname{sech}^2 x$ which is $+$ve when $x = \log\sqrt{3}$.

Thus, $x = \log\sqrt{3}$ gives a minimum value.

When $x = \log\sqrt{3}$ $\left(\text{i.e.}\quad \tanh x = \dfrac{1}{2} \text{ and } \cosh x = 2\sqrt{3}\right)$,

$$y = \log\left(\frac{2}{\sqrt{3}}\right) - \log\left(\sqrt[4]{3}\right) = \log\left(\frac{2}{3^{3/4}}\right)$$

$$\therefore x+y = \log\left(\frac{2}{3^{3/4}}\cdot 3^{1/2}\right) = \log\left(\frac{2}{3^{1/4}}\right).$$

Thus, the minimum point of the curve $y = \log\cosh x - \dfrac{x}{2}$ lies on the line $x+y = \log\left(\dfrac{2}{3^{1/4}}\right)$.

11. $\dfrac{dy}{dx} = \dfrac{\sin\theta}{1-\cos\theta} = \tan\phi$ with $\alpha = \dfrac{\pi}{2} - \phi$ (Fig. 105).

$$\therefore \frac{\sin\alpha}{\sqrt{y}} = \frac{\sin(\pi/2-\phi)}{\sqrt{y}} = \frac{\cos\phi}{\sqrt{y}} = \frac{1-\cos\theta}{\sqrt{\sin^2\theta+(1-\cos\theta)^2}} \cdot \frac{1}{\sqrt{a(1-\cos\theta)}}$$

$$= \frac{1}{\sqrt{2a}} = \text{const.}$$

12. Solve $\left(x - \dfrac{a}{2}\right)^2 + y^2 = \dfrac{a^2}{4}$, $y = mx$.

Then $P \equiv \left(\dfrac{a}{1+m^2}, \dfrac{am}{1+m^2}\right)$, $Q \equiv (a, am)$, $PQ = \dfrac{am^2}{(1+m^2)^{1/2}}$.

Locus of $R\ (x, y)$ is $x^2+y^2 = \dfrac{a^2m^4}{1+m^2} = \dfrac{a^2y^4/x^4}{1+(y^2/x^2)}$, i.e. $y^2 = \dfrac{x^3}{a-x}$.

13. Line $AB: y = 2(1-x)$ cuts the cissoid where $4(1-x)^3 = x^3$, i.e. $2^{2/3}(1-x) = x$

$$\therefore C \equiv \left(\frac{2^{2/3}}{1+2^{2/3}}, \frac{2}{1+2^{2/3}}\right) \Rightarrow OC: y = 2^{1/3}x \Rightarrow AD = 2^{1/3}.$$

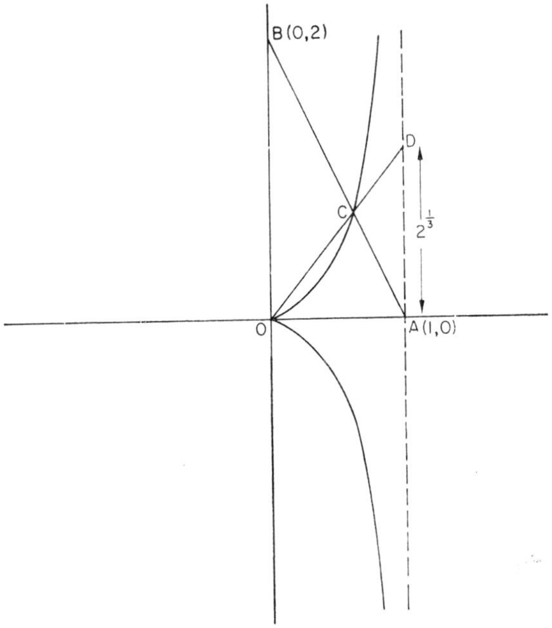

14. This cissoid is the mirror-image of Fig. 99, with the y-axis as asymptote. If P and Q have parameters t, u respectively, their coordinates are:

$$P\left(\frac{a}{1+t^2}, \frac{at^3}{1+t^2}\right),\ Q\left(\frac{a}{1+u^2}, \frac{au^3}{1+u^2}\right).$$

Let the mid-point of PQ be $R(\xi, \eta)$. Gradients of OP, OQ are t^3, u^3. Since OP is perpendicular to OQ, $u^3 = -1/t^3$, i.e. $u = -1/t$.

$$\therefore\ \xi = \frac{a}{2}\left(\frac{1}{1+t^2}+\frac{1}{1+(1/t^2)}\right) = \frac{a}{2}, \text{ and } \eta = \frac{a}{2}\left(\frac{t^3}{1+t^2}-\frac{1}{t^3(1+(1/t^2))}\right) = \frac{a}{2}\frac{(t^2-1)}{t}.$$

Thus, R lies on the line $x = \dfrac{a}{2}$.

Now $\dfrac{dy}{dt} = \dfrac{at^2(3+t^2)}{(1+t^2)^2}$, $\dfrac{dx}{dt} = \dfrac{-2at}{(1+t^2)^2}$ $\therefore \dfrac{dy}{dx} = -\dfrac{1}{2}t(3+t^2)$.

Equation of the tangent at P becomes: $y = \dfrac{-t(3+t^2)x}{2}+\dfrac{3at}{2}$.

Equation of the tangent at Q becomes: $y = \dfrac{(3t^2+1)x}{2t^3}-\dfrac{3a}{2t}$.

Solving these equations we obtain $x = \dfrac{3at^2}{(1+t^2)^2}$, $y = \dfrac{3at(1-t^2)}{2(1+t^2)^2}$.

Eliminate t and we obtain as the locus of the intersection of the tangents $x^2+y^2-\frac{3}{4}ax = 0$ i.e. $(x-\frac{3}{8}a)^2+y^2 = (\frac{3}{8}a)^2$ which is a circle with centre $(\frac{3}{8}a, 0)$ and radius $\frac{3}{8}a$.

15. $x = a\cos(nt+\varepsilon) = a\cos nt\cos\varepsilon - a\sin nt\sin\varepsilon = a\cos\varepsilon\cdot\dfrac{y}{b}-\dfrac{a}{b}\sqrt{b^2-y^2}\cdot\sin\varepsilon$ (eliminating t from $y = b\cos nt$) $\therefore (bx-ya\cos\varepsilon) = a\sqrt{b^2-y^2}\sin\varepsilon$. Square both sides and simplify. $\therefore b^2x^2-2ab\,xy\cos\varepsilon+a^2y^2-a^2b^2\sin^2\varepsilon = 0$. Now $b^2a^2-a^2b^2\cos^2\varepsilon = a^2b^2\sin^2\varepsilon$ which is positive. Thus, by (184.1), the conic is an *ellipse*.

(i) When $\varepsilon = 0$ the equation becomes $a^2y^2-2abxy+b^2x^2 = 0$,

i.e. $(ay-bx)^2 = 0$. Thus, the locus is the repeated straight line $y = \dfrac{b}{a}x$.

(ii) When $\varepsilon = \pi$ the equation becomes $a^2y^2+2abxy+b^2x^2 = 0$,

i.e. $(ay+bx)^2 = 0$. Thus, the locus is the repeated straight line $y = -\dfrac{b}{a}x$.

16. Subnormal $y\dfrac{dy}{dx} = \dfrac{k}{y} \Rightarrow y^2dy = kdx \Rightarrow y^3 = 3kx+c$, i.e. a cubical parabola (Fig. 89(b)) $\left(\text{e.g., } NG = \dfrac{1}{PN}\right)$.

17. Write $f(x, y, z) = (x^2-y^2)z^2-x^2y^2$ and use (245), (246).

Solve $\dfrac{\partial f}{\partial x} = 2x(z^2-y^2) = 0$, $\dfrac{\partial f}{\partial y} = -2y(x^2+z^2) = 0$, $\dfrac{\partial f}{\partial z} = 2z\,(x^2-y^2) = 0$.

Double points occur at (1, 0, 0), (0, 1, 0), (0, 0, 1).

At (0, 0, 1), $\dfrac{\partial^2 f}{\partial x^2}(= 2(z^2-y^2)) = 2$, $\dfrac{\partial^2 f}{\partial y^2}(= -2(x^2+z^2)) = -2$,

$$\frac{\partial^2 f}{\partial x\,\partial y}(= -4xy) = 0$$

$\therefore \left(\dfrac{\partial^2 f}{\partial x\,\partial y}\right)^2 > \dfrac{\partial^2 f}{\partial x^2}\cdot\dfrac{\partial^2 f}{\partial y^2}$ $\therefore \exists$ a node at the origin.

18. $x : y : a = t^2 : t^3 : 1$ $\therefore P_1 \equiv (at_1^2, at_1^3)$, $P_2 \equiv (at_2^2, at_2^3)$.

Equation of P_1P_2 is $\dfrac{x-at_1^2}{a(t_2^2-t_1^2)} = \dfrac{y-at_1^3}{a(t_2^3-t_1^3)}$

i.e. $y = \dfrac{t_2^3-t_1^3}{t_2^2-t_1^2}x - \dfrac{a(t_2^3-t_1^3)}{t_2^2-t_1^2}t_1^2+at_1^3 = \dfrac{t_2^2+t_2t_1+t_1^2}{t_2+t_1}x - \dfrac{at_2^2t_1^2}{t_2+t_1}$

on simplifying.

As $t_2 \to t_1$, the chord P_1P_2 becomes the tangent at P_1. Thus, the equation of the tangent is $y = \dfrac{3t_1^2}{2t_1}x - \dfrac{at_1^4}{2t_1} = \dfrac{3}{2}t_1x - \dfrac{1}{2}t_1^3a$.

$\therefore$ equation of the tangent at (t) is $3tx-2y-at^3 = 0$.

19. Solve for the tangent $y = \dfrac{3tx}{2}\dfrac{-t^3}{2}$ and the semi-cubical parabola.

$$\therefore\ x^3-\frac{9}{4}t^2x^2+\frac{3}{2}t^4x-\frac{t^6}{4} = 0 \Rightarrow (x-t^2)^2\left(x-\frac{t^2}{4}\right) = 0 \Rightarrow x = t^2,\ t^2,\ \frac{t^2}{4}.$$

Repeated roots refer to P. Hence, $Q \equiv \left(\dfrac{t^2}{4}, \dfrac{-t^3}{8}\right)$.

20. $y = 0$ in equation of tangent $\Rightarrow x = OT = \dfrac{t^2}{3}$ $\quad\therefore ON = t^2 = 3\cdot OT$.

21. Line $OR: y = \dfrac{3}{2}tx$ cuts the curve where $x = 0, 0, \dfrac{9t^2}{4}$, i.e. at the origin (twice, therefore it is a double point) and at $R \equiv \left(\dfrac{9t^2}{4}, \dfrac{27t^3}{8}\right)$.

$$\therefore\ OR = \frac{9t^2}{4}\sqrt{1+\frac{9}{4}t^2},\quad PQ = \frac{3t^2}{4}\sqrt{1+\frac{9t^2}{4}} \Rightarrow OR = 3\cdot PQ.$$

22. $PT = t^2\sqrt{\dfrac{4}{9}+t^2}$, $TQ = \dfrac{t^2}{8}\sqrt{\dfrac{4}{9}+t^2} \Rightarrow PT = 8.\ TQ.$

23. Line $lx+my+n = 0$ cuts the curve at $t_1,\ t_2,\ t_3: 2amt^3+3\ lat^2+n = 0$.

By (121), $t_1t_2+t_2t_3+t_3t_1 = 0$. $\left[\text{Replace } t \text{ by } \dfrac{1}{u} \text{ then this condition is } u_1+u_2+u_3 = 0.\right]$

24. $\dfrac{dy}{dt} = \dfrac{(1+t^3)6t-3t^2\cdot 3t^2}{(1+t^3)^2} = \dfrac{3t(2-t^3)}{(1+t^3)^2}$, $\dfrac{dx}{dt} = \dfrac{3(1-2t^3)}{(1+t^3)^2}$.

$\therefore\ \dfrac{dy}{dx} = \dfrac{t(2-t^3)}{(1-2t^3)}$ (Exercise 1.19) $= 0$, if $t = 0$ or $\sqrt[3]{2}$, $= \infty$ if $t = \sqrt[3]{\tfrac{1}{2}}$, or ∞.

$\therefore$ the tangent is parallel to (i) the x-axis at $t = \sqrt[3]{2}$, i.e. at the point $(2^{1/3}, 4^{1/3})$, (ii) the y-axis at $t = \sqrt[3]{\tfrac{1}{2}}$, i.e. at $(4^{1/3}, 2^{1/3})$.

25. Line $lx+my+n = 0$ cuts the folium at $t_1,\ t_2,\ t_3: nt^3+mt^2+lt+n = 0$. By (121) $t_1t_2t_3 = -1$. (Note the slight change of parametric representation necessary in this question.)

26. Let t_3 be a fixed point on the folium $\therefore\ t_1t_2 = -\dfrac{1}{t_3} =$ const. (by Exercise 20.25). Put $t_2 = t_1 \therefore\ t_1^2 =$ const. $\Rightarrow \exists$ 2 values of $t_1 \Rightarrow$ 2 tangents can be drawn from a given point T_3 on the folium to touch the folium at $T_1\ (= T_2)$ and $T_1'(= T_2')$.

27. By Bézout's theorem, the conic $ax^2+by^2+2hxy+2fy+2gx+c = 0$ cuts the folium of Exercise 20.25 in 6 points t_i $(i = 1, \ldots, 6)$ given by

$$a\left(\frac{t}{1+t^3}\right)^2+b\left(\frac{t^2}{1+t^3}\right)^2+2h\frac{t^3}{(1+t^3)^2}+2f\frac{t^2}{1+t^3}+2g\frac{t}{1+t^3}+c = 0,$$

$\therefore\ ct^6+2ft^5+(b+2g)t^4+2(c+h)t^3+(a+2f)t^2+2gt+c = 0.$

By (121) $t_1+t_2+t_3+t_4+t_5+t_6 = 1.$

[It is possible for all six points of intersection to coincide, in which case we speak of a *sextactic conic* having *sextactic contact*.]

28. Solve $y = mx, \left(x-\frac{a}{2}\right)^2+y^2 = \frac{a^2}{4}$; $y = mx,\ x = a\ \therefore\ R \equiv \left(\frac{a}{1+m^2},\ am\right) =$ $= (x, y) \Rightarrow x = \frac{a}{1+(y/a)^2} \Rightarrow y^2 = \frac{a^2(a-x)}{x}$. (Note the parametric coordinates of R.)

29. Tangents at P: $(y-y_1)\frac{\partial f}{\partial y}+(x-x_1)\frac{\partial f}{\partial x} = 0,\ (y-y_1)\frac{\partial g}{\partial y}+(x-x_1)\frac{\partial g}{\partial x} = 0$ (by (46)). Gradients are $\frac{-\partial f}{\partial x}\Big/\frac{\partial f}{\partial y},\ \frac{-\partial g}{\partial x}\Big/\frac{\partial g}{\partial y}$. Hence, the acute angle between the tangents is

$$\tan^{-1}\left\{\frac{-\partial g}{\partial x}\Big/\frac{\partial g}{\partial y}+\frac{\partial f}{\partial x}\Big/\frac{\partial f}{\partial y}\right\}\Big/\left\{1+\frac{\partial f/\partial x}{\partial f/\partial y}\cdot\frac{\partial g/\partial x}{\partial g/\partial y}\right\}$$

$$= \tan^{-1}\left(\frac{\partial f/\partial x\cdot\partial g/\partial y-\partial g/\partial x\cdot\partial f/\partial y}{\partial f/\partial x\cdot\partial g/\partial x+\partial f/\partial y\cdot\partial g/\partial y}\right).$$

Curves touch if $\frac{\partial f}{\partial x}\frac{\partial g}{\partial y} = \frac{\partial g}{\partial x}\frac{\partial f}{\partial y}$. (i)

Curves cut orthogonally if $\frac{\partial f}{\partial x}\frac{\partial g}{\partial x}+\frac{\partial f}{\partial y}\frac{\partial g}{\partial y} = 0.$ (ii)

30. Condition is $2\{(x+g)(x+g')+(y+f)(y+f')\} = 0$, i.e. $ff'+gg'-\frac{1}{2}(c+c') = 0$

$$= \begin{vmatrix} 1 & 0 & g \\ 0 & 1 & f' \\ g' & f' & \frac{c+c'}{2} \end{vmatrix}.$$

31. Ellipse and hyperbola intersect at $(\pm\cos\alpha\cosh\alpha,\ \pm\sin\alpha\sinh\alpha)$. (I)

By Exercise 20.29 (ii), condition for orthogonality is $4\left(\frac{x^2}{\cos^2\alpha\cosh^2\alpha}-\frac{y^2}{\sin^2\alpha\sinh^2\alpha}\right)$ $= 0$, which is true by (I), i.e. ellipse and hyperbola cut orthogonally.

32. $OP^2 = x^2+y^2 = (k+OR)^2 = \left[k\left(1+\frac{a}{x-a}\right)\right]^2 = \left(\frac{kx}{x-a}\right)^2 \quad \because\ \frac{OR}{k} = \frac{a}{x-a}$

$\therefore$ the equation of the conchoid is $x^2+y^2 = \frac{k^2x^2}{(x-a)^2}$.

Now $OR = a\sec\theta \Rightarrow$ the polar equation is $r = a\sec\theta+k$. (Actually, the equation appears as $r = a\sec\theta\pm k$, but the $-$ sign may be omitted since points on the inner branch are given by $\frac{\pi}{2} < \theta < \frac{3\pi}{2}$.)

33. Since $RP = UQ = k$ and RVQ is isosceles, $OR = UV = VQ = RV$ $\therefore$ OVR is isosceles.

$$\therefore\ V\hat{O}R = O\hat{V}R = 2\times V\hat{Q}R = 2\times A\hat{O}Q \text{ (corresponding angles } \because RQ//OA)$$

$$\therefore\ B\hat{O}Q = \tfrac{1}{3}\, B\hat{O}P.$$

34. Eliminate t from equations of tangent $y = \dfrac{x}{t}+at$ and perpendicular to it from

$$(-a, 0): y = -t(x+a), \text{ i.e. } t = -\frac{y}{x+a}.$$

$\therefore$ locus of intersection (= pedal) is $y^2 = -x\dfrac{(a+x)^2}{2a+x}$ (a strophoid, first discussed by Torricelli—it resembles Fig. 98, but "points" in the opposite direction).

35. Eliminate t from $y = \dfrac{x}{t}+at$ and $y = -t(x+3a)$. The pedal is $y^2 = -\dfrac{x(x+3a)^2}{x+4a}$ (*trisectrix of Maclaurin*, a type of strophoid).

36. In the trisectrix of Maclaurin (Exercise 20.35) put $x = 1$ and change the origin to $(-3a, 0)$, i.e. the node. Line $OP: y = mx$ cuts the strophoid where $m^2x^2(1+x)-x^2(3-x) = 0$, i.e. $x = 0,\ 0,\ \dfrac{3-m^2}{1+m^2}$.

$$\therefore\ P \equiv \left(\frac{3-m^2}{1+m^2}, \frac{m(3-m^2)}{1+m^2}\right) \Rightarrow \text{equation of } AP \text{ is } y = \frac{m(3-m^2)}{1-3m^2}(x-2)$$

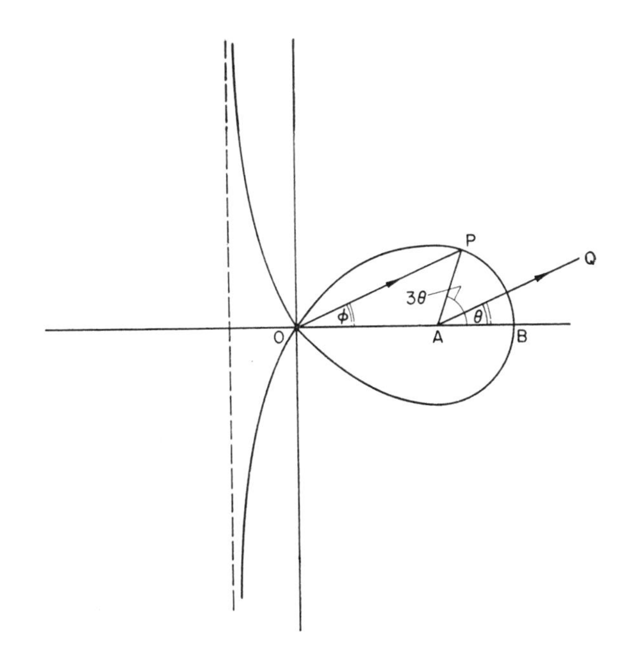

$\therefore$ gradient of AP ($= \tan 3\theta$) is $\dfrac{m(3-m^2)}{1-3m^2} = \tan 3\phi$ since $\tan 3\phi = \tan(2\phi+\phi)$

$$= \frac{\tan 2\phi+\tan\phi}{1-\tan\phi\tan 2\phi} = \frac{\dfrac{2\tan\phi}{1-\tan^2\phi}+\tan\phi}{1-\tan\phi\cdot\dfrac{2\tan\phi}{1-\tan^2\phi}} = \frac{3\tan\phi-\tan^3\phi}{1-3\tan^3\phi} = \frac{m(3-m^2)}{1-3m^2}$$

$(m = \tan\phi)$

$\therefore 3\phi = 3\theta \quad \therefore \phi = \dfrac{1}{3}\cdot 3\theta, \quad \therefore AQ$ trisects $B\hat{A}P$.

37. $\dfrac{dy}{dx} = \dfrac{2(\cos t-\cos 2t)}{-2(\sin t+\sin 2t)} = \dfrac{2\sin(3t/2)\sin(t/2)}{-2\sin(3t/2)\cos(t/2)} = -\tan\dfrac{t}{2}.$

$\therefore$ equation of the tangent is $y-a(2\sin t-\sin 2t) = -\tan\dfrac{t}{2}[x-a(2\cos t+\cos 2t)]$,

equation of the perpendicular from O to this tangent is $y = x\cot\dfrac{t}{2}$.

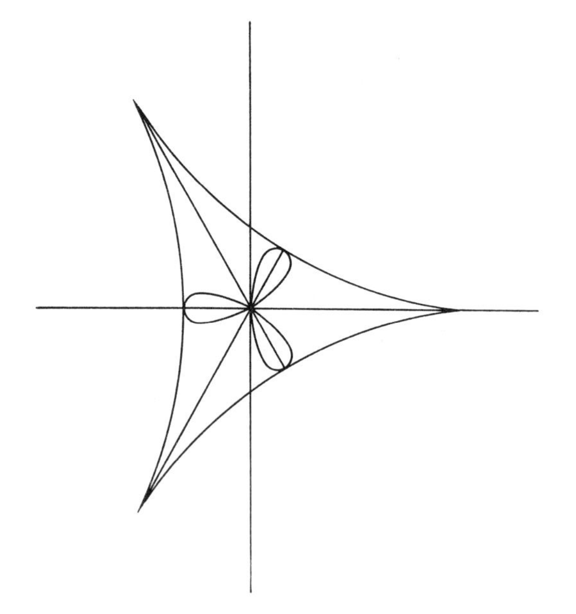

Solve: $\dfrac{x}{a} = \cos^2\dfrac{t}{2}-\cos^2 t$ on simplification. $\left(\dfrac{t}{2} = \dfrac{\pi}{2}-\theta\right)$

$$= \left[\cos\left(\frac{\pi}{2}-\theta\right)+\cos(\pi-2\theta)\right]\left[\cos\left(\frac{\pi}{2}-\theta\right)-\cos(\pi-2\theta)\right]$$

$$= 2\cos\left(\frac{3\pi}{4}-\frac{3\theta}{2}\right)\cos\left(\frac{\pi}{4}+\frac{\theta}{2}\right)\cdot 2\sin\left(\frac{3\pi}{4}-\frac{3\theta}{2}\right)\sin\left(\frac{\pi}{4}+\frac{\theta}{2}\right)$$

$$= \sin\left(\frac{3\pi}{2}-3\theta\right)\sin\left(\frac{\pi}{2}+\theta\right) = \sin 3\theta\cos\theta \text{ whence } \frac{y}{a} = \sin 3\theta\sin\theta.$$

$\therefore$ the locus of intersection is $x^2+y^2 = a^2 \sin^2 3\theta$, i.e. pedal is $r = a \sin 3\theta$ (three-leafed rose).

38. From the equations of the tangent (Example 121) and perpendicular OP to this tangent from O ($y = x \cot \phi$), $x = a \sin^2 \phi \cos \phi$, $y = a \cos^2 \phi \sin \phi$ with $\phi = \dfrac{\pi}{2} - \theta$.

$\therefore$ locus of intersection $P(r, \theta)$ is $(x^2+y^2)^3 = a^2x^2y^2$,

i.e. pedal is $r^6 = a^2r^2 \cos^2 \theta \cdot r^2 \sin^2 \theta$, i.e. $r^2 = \dfrac{a^2 \sin^2 2\theta}{4}$

i.e. $r = \dfrac{a}{2} \sin 2\theta$ (four-leafed rose).

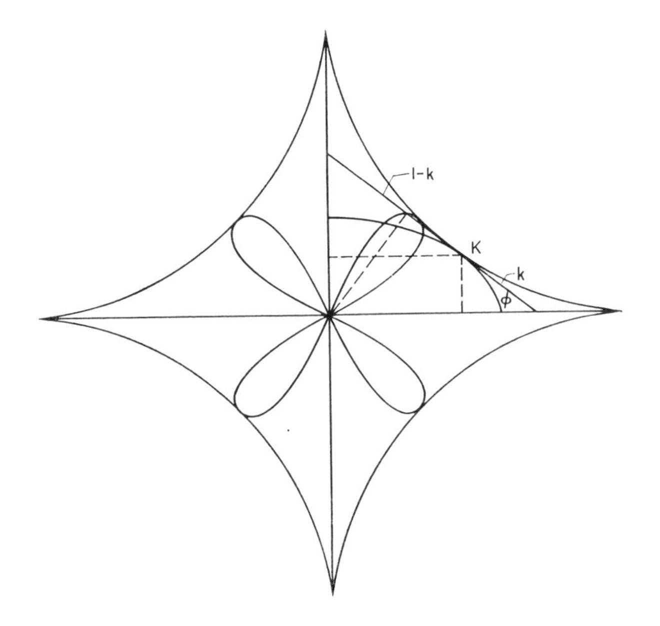

39. By Example 121, $\dfrac{x}{\cos \phi} + \dfrac{y}{\sin \phi} = 1$ is a tangent to the astroid $x^{2/3}+y^{2/3} = 1$.

Its gradient is $-\tan \phi$. From the diagram, point of tangency $K \equiv [(1-k) \cos \phi, k \sin \phi]$, i.e. $x = (1-k) \cos \phi$, $y = k \sin \phi$, (I), for the line and the astroid. But $x = \cos^3 \phi$, $y = \sin^3 \phi$ are the parametric coordinates of K, whence $1-k = \cos^2 \phi$, $k = \sin^2 \phi$ (II).

Now K, given by (I), lies on the ellipse $\dfrac{x^2}{(1-k)^2} + \dfrac{y^2}{k^2} = 1$ whose gradient at K, is, by (218), $\dfrac{-k}{1-k} \cot \phi = -\tan \phi$ by (II), i.e. the line $\dfrac{x}{\cos \phi} + \dfrac{y}{\sin \phi} = 1$ is a common tangent of the astroid and the ellipse. Such an ellipse, enveloped by the astroid, exists for every point on the astroid. (In particular, a circle radius $\frac{1}{2}$ occurs for the mid-point of the ladder.)

40. From the mechanical generation of the curve, $\frac{\theta}{x}$ (at P) $= \frac{\pi/2}{1}$ (at A) i.e. $\theta = \frac{\pi}{2}x$, $\therefore y = x \cot\left(\frac{\pi x}{2}\right)$ in $\triangle ONP$.

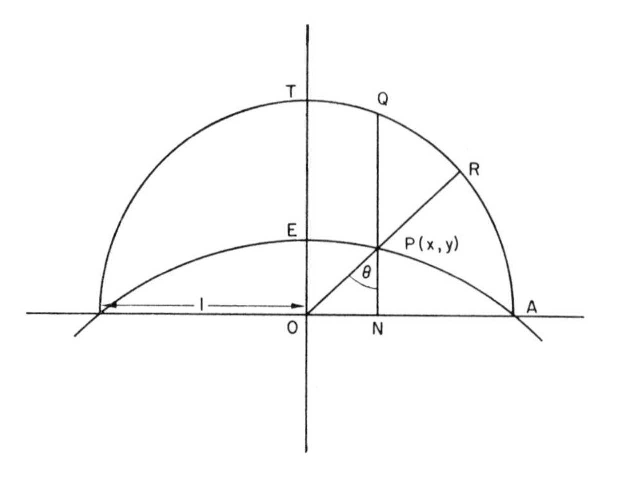

41. Now $\lim_{x\to 0} y = \frac{2}{\pi}$ by Example 7(e), i.e. $OE = \frac{\pi}{2}$ i.e. $\frac{OE}{1} = \frac{1}{\pi/2}$.

42. Note the jumps at the integers. ($0 \leqslant x < 1 \Rightarrow [x] = 0$, $0 \leqslant x < 2 \Rightarrow [x] = 1$, etc.; e.g., $x = \sqrt{2} \Rightarrow [x] = 1$, $x = 1{\cdot}\dot{9} \Rightarrow [x] = 2$—refer to Exercise 10.6.]

43. Chord: $\left(y - \frac{g(u)}{h(u)}\right) \Big/ \left(\frac{g(t)}{h(t)} - \frac{g(u)}{h(u)}\right) = \left(x - \frac{f(u)}{h(u)}\right) \Big/ \left(\frac{f(t)}{h(t)} - \frac{f(u)}{h(u)}\right)$, i.e.

$$\begin{vmatrix} x & f(t) & f(u) \\ y & g(t) & g(u) \\ 1 & h(t) & h(u) \end{vmatrix} = 0 \text{ on calculation.}$$

44. Routine computation.

45. Equate real and imaginary parts of z.

$$\therefore x = \frac{a}{2q}\{(q+n)\cos(q-n)t + (q-n)\cos(q+n)t\},$$

$$y = \frac{a}{2q}\{(q+n)\sin(q-n) + (q-n)\sin(q+n)t\}.$$

Let the radii be A, B ($A < B$). By (§ 106), parametric equations of a hypocycloid lead to $A - B = \frac{(q+n)a}{2q}$, $\frac{A-B}{-B} = \frac{q+n}{q-n}$, $-B = \frac{(q-n)a}{2q}$ whence radius of inner circle is $A = a$.

Radius of outer circle is $A - 2B = a - 2\,\frac{(q-n)a}{2q} = \frac{an}{q}$.

EXERCISES 21

1. Now $\varkappa = 1/\varrho$ where $\varkappa$ is the curvature and ϱ is the radius of curvature. Thus, for a circle of radius 1, $\varkappa = 1$. For a circle of radius 4, $\varkappa = \frac{1}{4}$. Thus, the curvature of circle radius 4 is $\frac{1}{4}$ that of a circle of radius 1.

2. By (216), $\dfrac{dy}{dx} = -\dfrac{b^2x}{a^2y}$ $\therefore$ $\dfrac{d^2y}{dx^2} = \dfrac{-a^2b^2y+a^2b^2\times dy/dx}{a^4y^2} = -\dfrac{b^4}{a^2y^3}$.

$$\text{Now } \varkappa = \frac{d^2y/dx^2}{\{1+(dy/dx)^2\}^{3/2}} = \frac{-b^4/a^2y^3}{\{1+(b^4x^2)/(a^4y^2)\}^{3/2}} = \frac{-a^4b^4}{\{a^4y^2+b^4x^2\}^{3/2}}$$

$$\therefore \varrho = \frac{1}{\varkappa} = \frac{-\{a^4y^2+b^4x^2\}^{3/2}}{a^4b^4} = l\left(=\frac{b^2}{a}\right) \text{ at } A, A', = \frac{a^2}{b} \text{ at } B, B',$$

$= l(1+e^2)^{3/2}$ at $L, L' = \dfrac{(PG)^3}{l^2}$ at any point P (G is the intersection of the normal PG and the x-axis).

3. $y = \dfrac{x^{3/2}}{\sqrt{a}} \Rightarrow \dfrac{dy}{dx} = \dfrac{1}{\sqrt{a}}\cdot\dfrac{3}{2}x^{1/2} = \dfrac{3\sqrt{x}}{2\sqrt{a}}$, $\dfrac{d^2y}{dx^2} = \dfrac{3}{2\sqrt{a}}\cdot\dfrac{1}{2}x^{-1/2} = \dfrac{3}{4\sqrt{ax}}$.

$$\therefore \varkappa = \frac{3}{4\sqrt{ax}\{1+9x/4a\}^{3/2}} = \frac{6a}{\sqrt{x}\{4a+9x\}^{3/2}} \quad \therefore \varrho = \frac{\sqrt{x}\{4a+9x\}^{3/2}}{6a}.$$

4. By Exercise 1.22, $\dfrac{dy}{dx} = -\left(\dfrac{y}{x}\right)^{1/3}$ $\therefore$ $\dfrac{d^2y}{dx^2} = \dfrac{-x^{1/3}.\frac{1}{3}y^{-2/3}(dy/dx)+y^{1/3}.\frac{1}{3}x^{-2/3}}{x^{2/3}}$

$$= \frac{a^{2/3}}{3x^{4/3}y^{1/3}} \quad \therefore \varkappa = \frac{a^{2/3}}{3x^{4/3}y^{1/3}\{1+(y/x)^{2/3}\}^{3/2}} = \frac{(axy)^{-1/3}}{3} \quad \therefore \varrho = 3(axy)^{1/3}.$$

5. By Exercise 5.25, $\dfrac{dy}{dx} = -\tan\theta$, $\dfrac{d^2y}{dx^2} = -\sec^2\theta\dfrac{d\theta}{dx} = \dfrac{\sin\theta\sec^4\theta}{c}$.

$$\therefore \varkappa = \frac{\sin\theta\sec^4\theta}{c(1+\tan^2\theta)^{3/2}} = \frac{\tan\theta}{c} \quad \therefore \varrho = c\cot\theta.$$

6. $\dfrac{dx}{dt} = t\cos t$, $\dfrac{dy}{dt} = t\sin t$ $\therefore$ $\dfrac{dy}{dx} = \tan t$ $\therefore$ $\dfrac{d^2y}{dx^2} = \sec^2 t\cdot\dfrac{1}{t\cos t} = \dfrac{\sec^3 t}{t}$

$$\therefore \varkappa = \frac{\sec^3 t}{t(1+\tan^2 t)^{3/2}} = \frac{1}{t}, \text{ i.e. } \varrho = t.$$

7. $\varrho = \dfrac{[1+(dy/dx)^2]^{3/2}}{d^2y/dx^2}$ and $n = y\left\{1+\left(\dfrac{dy}{dx}\right)^2\right\}^{1/2}$ by Exercise 4.44.

$$\therefore \varrho y\frac{d^2y}{dx^2} = n\left\{1+\left(\frac{dy}{dx}\right)^2\right\}.$$

8. By Exercise 1.20, $\dfrac{dy}{dx} = \dfrac{\sin\theta}{1-\cos\theta}$, $\dfrac{d^2y}{dx^2} = -\dfrac{1}{1-\cos\theta}\cdot\dfrac{1}{a(1-\cos\theta)}$

$$= -\frac{1}{a(1-\cos\theta)^2}.$$

By Exercise 21.7, $\varrho\cdot a(1-\cos\theta)\cdot\dfrac{1}{a(1-\cos\theta)^2} = n\left\{1+\dfrac{\sin^2\theta}{(1-\cos\theta)^2}\right\}$ ignoring $-$ve sign.

$$\therefore \varrho\cdot\frac{1}{1-\cos\theta} = n\cdot\frac{2}{1-\cos\theta} \Rightarrow \varrho = 2n.$$

9. Equation of normal at $P: y-c\sin\theta = \cot\theta\left(x-c\left(\log\cot\frac{\theta}{2}-\cos\theta\right)\right)$.

$$\therefore y = 0 \Rightarrow x = c\left(\log\cot\frac{\theta}{2}-\cos\theta\right)-c\sin^2\theta\sec\theta = ON.$$

$$\therefore PN = n = c\sqrt{(\sin^2\theta\sec\theta)^2+\sin^2\theta} = c\tan\theta = c^2\varkappa = \frac{c^2}{\varrho} \quad \text{(Exercise 21.5)}$$

$$\therefore \quad \varrho n = c^2.$$

Or, using Exercise 21.7, we have $\varrho c\sin\theta\cdot\frac{\sin\theta\sec^4\theta}{c} = n\sec^2\theta \;\therefore\; \varrho\tan^2\theta = n$.

But, from Exercise 21.5, $\tan\theta = \frac{c}{\varrho} \;\therefore\; \varrho n = c^2 \left(\therefore\; \varrho = \frac{1}{n} \text{ for } c = 1\right)$.

10. By Exercise 21.2, $\varrho = \frac{-(a^4y^2+b^4x^2)^{3/2}}{a^4b^4} = \frac{-(a^4b^2\sin^2\theta+b^4a^2\cos^2\theta)^{3/2}}{a^4b^4}$ at P

$$= \frac{-(a^2\sin^2\theta+b^2\cos^2\theta)^{3/2}}{ab} = hCQ^3 \text{ by (223) } (hab = -1).$$

11. Let x_1, x_2 be the abscissas of P_1, P_2 and let the tangents at P_1, P_2 make angles of ϕ_1, ϕ_2 with the +ve x-axis $\left(\phi_2 = \frac{\pi}{2}+\phi_1\right)$.

$$\therefore \tan\phi_1\tan\phi_2 = -1 \text{ and } \tan\phi_1 = \sinh x_1 \;\text{[by (38)]}$$

$$\therefore \sinh x_1\sinh x_2 = -1 \;\therefore\; \sinh x_2 = -\frac{1}{\sinh x_1} \qquad (\alpha)$$

$$\therefore \varkappa_1+\varkappa_2 = \frac{1}{\varrho_1}+\frac{1}{\varrho_2} = \frac{1}{\cosh^2 x_1}+\frac{1}{\cosh^2 x_2}$$

$$= \frac{1}{1+\sinh^2 x_1}+\frac{1}{1+(1/\sinh^2 x_1)} = 1 \text{ by Example 127, (29.1) and } (\alpha).$$

12. $y = e^x, \frac{dy}{dx} = e^x, \frac{d^2y}{dx^2} = e^x \;\therefore\; \varkappa = \frac{e^x}{(1+e^{2x})^{3/2}}$

$$\therefore \frac{d\varkappa}{dx} = \frac{e^x(1-2e^{2x})}{(1+e^{2x})^{5/2}} \text{ (on calculation)} = 0 \text{ when } e^{2x} = \tfrac{1}{2} \text{ i.e. } x = -\log\sqrt{2}.$$

When $e^{2x} < \frac{1}{2}, \frac{d\varkappa}{dx} > 0$; when $e^{2x} > \frac{1}{2}, \frac{d\varkappa}{dx} < 0$.

$$\therefore \varkappa_{\max} \text{ occurs at } P \equiv \left(-\log\sqrt{2}, \frac{1}{\sqrt{2}}\right).$$

Radius of curvature at P is $\varrho = (1+\frac{1}{2})^{3/2} \div \left(\frac{1}{\sqrt{2}}\right) = \frac{3\sqrt{3}}{2}$.

13. By Example 128, $\varrho = \frac{-2a}{\sin^3\theta} \;\therefore\; \xi = x-\varrho\sin\theta = 3x+2a$,

$$\eta = y+\varrho\cos\theta = \frac{-y^3}{4a^2}.$$

Eliminate x, y $\therefore$ evolute is $\eta^2 = \frac{4}{27}(\xi-2a)^3/a$.

$\therefore$ equation of the evolute is $27ay^2 = 4(x-2a)^3$ (semi-cubical parabola).

14. Solve $y^2 = 4ax$ and $27ay^2 = 4(x-2a)^3$ to obtain $x^3-6ax^2-15a^2x-8a^3 = 0$ whence $(x-8a)(x+a)^2 = 0$. Thus $M \equiv (8a, 4\sqrt{2}a)$, $M' \equiv (8a, -4\sqrt{2})$ and the imaginary points are $(-a, \pm 2ai)$ repeated ($\exists$ 6 points, by Bézout's theorem).

$$\text{At } M, M', \frac{dy}{dx} = \frac{2a}{\pm 4\sqrt{2}a} = \pm\frac{\sqrt{2}}{4} = \tan\theta \Rightarrow \cos\theta = \frac{2\sqrt{2}}{3},\ \sin\theta = \pm\frac{1}{3}.$$

$$\therefore |\varrho| = 54a \text{ and } \xi = 8a\pm 54a\left(\pm\frac{1}{3}\right) = 26a,$$

$$\eta = \pm 4\sqrt{2}a \pm 54a\left(\frac{2\sqrt{2}}{3}\right) = \mp 32\sqrt{2}a.$$

15. Tangent at $M: y = \sqrt{2}x-4\sqrt{2}\,a$ cuts x-axis at $(4a, 0)$ and the parabola at points given by $(\sqrt{2}x-4\sqrt{2}a)^2 = 4ax$, i.e. $x = 8a,\ 2a$ $\therefore Q \equiv (2a, -2\sqrt{2}a)$. Gradient of AP is $\frac{4\sqrt{2}a}{8a} = \frac{\sqrt{2}}{2}$; gradient of AQ is $\frac{-2\sqrt{2}a}{2a} = -\sqrt{2}$. Product of these gradients s -1 $\therefore$ $AP \perp AQ$ $(PQ = 6a\sqrt{3})$.

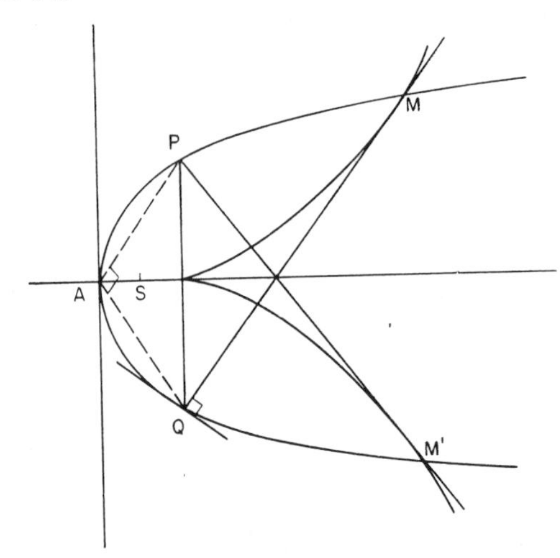

16. $au^2 = 2a+3at^2 = 8a$, $2au^2 = 2at^3 = 4\sqrt{2}a$ for x, y values respectively.

$\therefore u^2 = 2\sqrt{2},\ t^2 = \sqrt{2},\ u = t^3.$

17. Gradient of evolute is given by $54\ ay\frac{dy}{dx} = 12(x-2a)^2$ $\therefore \frac{dy}{dx} = \pm\sqrt{2}$ at M, M'. $\therefore$ tangent to evolute at $M: y-4\sqrt{2}a = \sqrt{2}(x-8a)$, i.e. $y = \sqrt{2}x-4\sqrt{2}a$. This is precisely the normal to the parabola at the point $(2a, -2\sqrt{2}a)$ with parameter $\sqrt{2}$. Similarly for M'.

18. Normal at t to $y^2 = 4ax$ is $f(x, y, t) \equiv y-t(x-2a)+at^3 = 0$

$$\therefore \frac{\partial f}{\partial t} = -(x-2a)+3at^2 = 0 \therefore x-2a = 3at^2.$$

Substitute in the equation of the normal to get $y = 2at^3$.

$$\therefore \xi = 2a+3at^2 = 2a+3x,\ \eta = 2at^3 = \frac{-y^3}{4a^2}.$$ Proceed as in Exercise 21.13.

It may be shown, using § 91 (i), (ii), that of the 3 normals p, q, r which can be drawn to a parabola from a point P, they are (a) p, q, r real and distinct, or (b) $p = q, r$ both real, or (c) $p = q = r$ real, or (d) p real, q, r imaginary, according as P lies (a) to the right of the evolute, or (b) on the evolute, or (c) at the cusp $(2a, 0)$ of the evolute, or (d) to the left of the evolute.

19. Normal at θ to ellipse: $$f(x, y, \theta) \equiv \frac{ax}{\cos\theta} - \frac{by}{\sin\theta} - (a^2-b^2) = 0 \qquad (\alpha)$$

$$\therefore \frac{\partial f}{\partial \theta} = \frac{ax\sin\theta}{\cos^2\theta} + \frac{by\cos\theta}{\sin^2\theta} = 0 \ \therefore \frac{ax}{\cos^3\theta} = \frac{-by}{\sin^3\theta} = \lambda \text{ (say)}.$$

Substitution in (α) gives $\lambda = a^2-b^2 \ \therefore \xi = \dfrac{a^2-b^2}{a}\cos^3\theta,\ \eta = \dfrac{-(a^2-b^2)}{b}\sin^3\theta.$

Eliminate θ $\therefore$ evolute is $(ax)^{2/3}+(by)^{2/3} = (a^2-b^2)^{2/3}$ (an astroidal (Lamé) curve—Lamé, 1795–1870, French).

20. From Fig. 8, Example 14, $PQ \perp MQ$ for all P, i.e. normals to the tractrix are tangents to the catenary (i.e. the catenary is the envelope of normals to the tractrix). $\therefore$ the evolute of the tractrix is the catenary.

21. $$\begin{cases} x = a\cos^3 t \Rightarrow \dot{x} = -3a\cos^2\theta\sin\theta \Rightarrow \ddot{x} = 3a(2\cos\theta\sin^2\theta - \cos^3\theta) \\ y = a\sin^3 t \Rightarrow \dot{y} = 3a\sin^2\theta\cos\theta \Rightarrow \ddot{y} = 3a(2\sin\theta\cos^2\theta - \sin^3\theta) \end{cases}$$

$$\therefore \varrho = \frac{(9a^2\cos^2\theta\sin^2\theta)^{3/2}}{-9a^2\cos\theta\sin\theta(2\sin\theta\cos^3\theta - \sin^3\theta\cos\theta + 2\cos\theta\sin^3\theta - \sin\theta\cos^3\theta)}$$

$$= \frac{27a^3\cos^3\theta\sin^3\theta}{-9a^2\cos^2\theta\sin^2\theta} = -3a\cos\theta\sin\theta = -3(axy)^{1/3}.$$

22. Equation of a general circle is $(x-a)^2+(y-b)^2 = r^2$.

Differentiate $\therefore$ $(x-a)+(y-b)\dfrac{dy}{dx} = 0.$

Differentiatc again. $\therefore$ $$1+(y-b)\frac{d^2y}{dx^2}+\left(\frac{dy}{dx}\right)^2 = 0. \qquad \text{(i)}$$

Differentiate once more. $\therefore$ $$(y-b)\frac{d^3y}{dx^3}+3\frac{dy}{dx}\frac{d^2y}{dx^2} = 0. \qquad \text{(ii)}$$

Eliminate $y-b$ from (i), (ii) $\therefore$ $$\left\{1+\left(\frac{dy}{dx}\right)^2\right\}\frac{d^3y}{dx^3} - 3\frac{dy}{dx}\left(\frac{d^2y}{dx^2}\right)^2 = 0,$$

which is the required differential equation.

23. $\dfrac{d^2y/dx^2}{\{1+(dy/dx)^2\}^{3/2}} = \varrho = \dfrac{1}{r} =$ const. Differentiate, simplify and ignore the unwanted factor. The differential equation of Exercise 21.22 remains.

24. From Example 125, $\varrho_1 = 4a\cos\theta/2$, $\varrho_2 = 4a\cos\dfrac{\phi}{2} = -4a\sin\dfrac{\theta}{2}$

$$\because \tan\frac{\theta}{2}\tan\frac{\phi}{2} = -1 \left(\text{i.e. } \frac{\theta}{2} = \frac{\pi}{2}+\frac{\phi}{2}\right) \therefore \varrho_1^2+\varrho_2^2 = 16a^2 \ (= \text{const.})$$

25. Equations of cycloid: $x = a(\theta - \sin\theta)$, $y = a(1-\cos\theta)$.

$$\therefore \frac{dy}{dx} = \frac{\sin\theta}{1-\cos\theta}, \frac{d^2y}{dx^2} = -\frac{1}{a(1-\cos\theta)^2} \text{ as in Example 125 (different } \theta).$$

By (254), coordinates of centre of curvature at (x_1, y_1) for which $\theta = \phi$ (say), are

$$\xi = a(\phi - \sin\phi) - \frac{\dfrac{\sin\phi}{1-\cos\phi}}{\left\{1+\left(\dfrac{\sin\phi}{1-\cos\phi}\right)^2\right\}^{1/2}} \cdot \frac{\left\{1+\left(\dfrac{\sin\phi}{1-\cos\phi}\right)^2\right\}^{3/2}}{-1/a(1-\cos\phi)^2} = a(\phi+\sin\phi)$$

$$\eta = a(1-\cos\phi) + \left(1\Big/\left\{1+\left(\frac{\sin\phi}{1-\cos\phi}\right)^2\right\}^{1/2}\right) \cdot \frac{\left\{1+\left(\dfrac{\sin\phi}{1-\cos\phi}\right)^2\right\}^{1/2}}{-1/a(1-\cos\phi)^2} = -a(1-\cos\phi)$$

These are the equations of an equal cycloid (parameter ϕ).

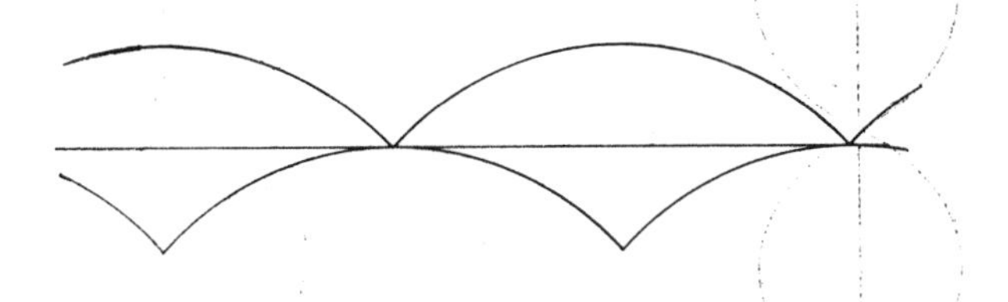

EXERCISES 22

1. $r = a(1+\cos\theta) \Rightarrow \dfrac{\sqrt{x^2+y^2}}{a} = 1 + \dfrac{x}{\sqrt{x^2+y^2}}$ by (42), i.e. $\dfrac{x^2+y^2}{a} = \sqrt{x^2+y^2} + x$,

i.e. $x^2+y^2-ax = a\sqrt{x^2+y^2}$. Square and simplify.

$\therefore$ $x^4 - 2ax^3 - 2x^2y^2 - 2axy^2 + y^4 - a^2y^2 = 0$ (a quartic curve).

2. $r^2 = a^2\cos 2\theta \Rightarrow x^2+y^2 = a^2(2\cos^2\theta - 1)$ (by (42)) $= a^2\left\{\dfrac{2x^2}{x^2+y^2} - 1\right\}$

$= \dfrac{a^2(x^2-y^2)}{x^2+y^2}$, i.e. $(x^2+y^2)^2 - a^2(x^2-y^2) = 0$ (a quartic curve).

3. $y^2 = \dfrac{x^3}{a-x} \Rightarrow r^2\sin^2\theta = \dfrac{r^3\cos^3\theta}{a - r\cos\theta}$, i.e. $(a-r\cos\theta)(1-\cos^2\theta) = r\cos^3\theta$,

$a - a\cos^2\theta - r\cos\theta = 0$, $r\cos\theta = a\sin^2\theta$, $r = a(\sec\theta - \cos\theta)$.

4. Substitute $x - 2a = X$ $\therefore$ equation of the trisectrix becomes $y^2 = \dfrac{(X+2a)^2(a-X)}{X+3a}$.

In polar coordinates, $r^2(1-\cos^2\theta)(r\cos\theta+3a) = (r\cos\theta+2a)^2(a-r\cos\theta)$,
i.e. $r^3\cos\theta + 3ar^2 = 4a^3$ (simplifying)

i.e. $\cos\theta = 4\left(\dfrac{a}{r}\right)^3 - 3\left(\dfrac{a}{r}\right) \Rightarrow \dfrac{a}{r} = \cos\left(\dfrac{\theta}{3}\right)$ [(122)], i.e. $r = a\sec\left(\dfrac{\theta}{3}\right)$.

5.

θ	0	$\frac{\pi}{3}$	$\frac{\pi}{2}$	$\frac{2\pi}{3}$	π	$\frac{4\pi}{3}$	$\frac{3\pi}{2}$	$\frac{5\pi}{3}$	2π
r	$1\frac{3}{4}$	$1\frac{1}{4}$	$\frac{3}{4}$	$\frac{1}{4}$	$-\frac{1}{4}$	$\frac{1}{4}$	$\frac{3}{4}$	$1\frac{1}{4}$	$1\frac{3}{4}$

$r = \frac{3}{4}+\cos\theta$ (limaçon). For a diagram, see Fig. 123 ($a = \frac{3}{4}$, $b = 1$).

6, 7, 8, 9. Construct your own tabulation, proceeding through multiples of $\frac{\pi}{12}$ (say). Observe, in Exercise 22.9, that r is imaginary for $\frac{\pi}{2} < \theta < \pi$, $\frac{3\pi}{2} < \theta < 2\pi$.

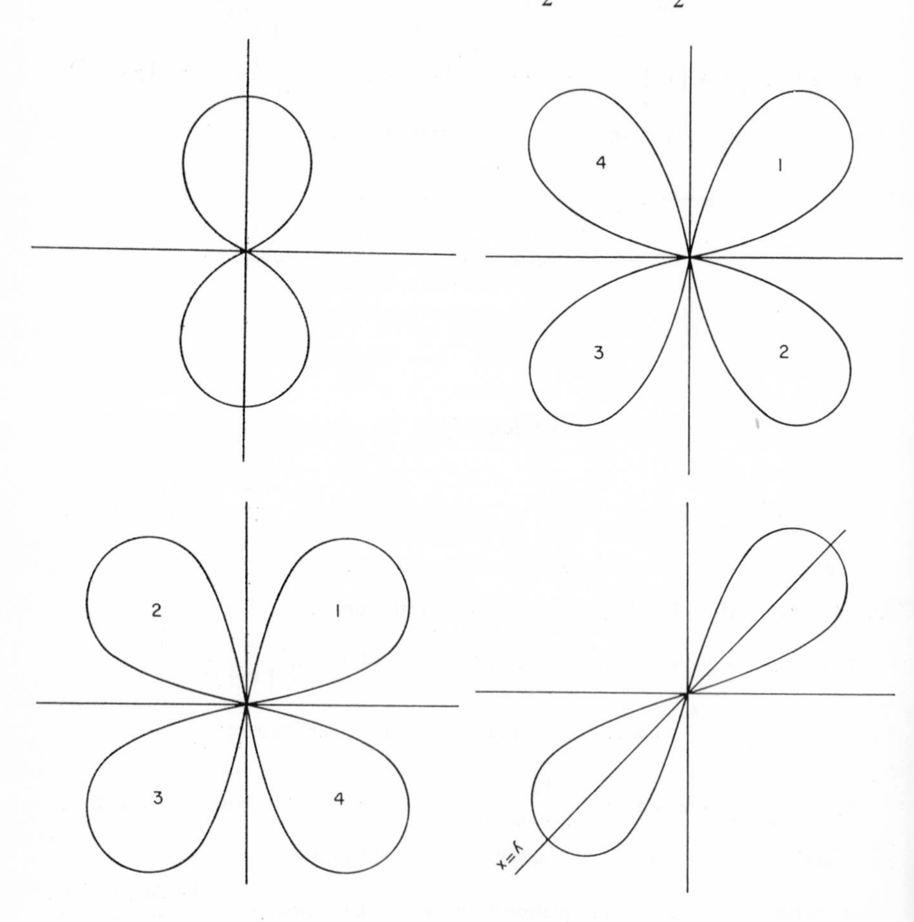

10. $r = \pm a\sqrt{\cos 2\theta} \Rightarrow y = r\sin\theta = \pm a\sin\theta\sqrt{\cos 2\theta}.$

$$\therefore \frac{dy}{d\theta} = \pm\frac{a\cos\theta}{\sqrt{\cos 2\theta}}\{1-4\sin^2\theta\} \text{ (on calculation)} = 0 \text{ if } \sin\theta = \pm\tfrac{1}{2} \text{ or}$$

$\cos\theta = 0$,

i.e. if $\theta = \pi/6, 5\pi/6, \pi/2$. But $\theta = \pi/2$ gives an imaginary value to r. Clearly, from the diagram the maximum ordinate occurs when $\theta = \dfrac{\pi}{6}, \dfrac{5\pi}{6}$. (Check.)

$$\therefore \text{ maximum breadth} = 2\cdot a\cdot\frac{1}{2}\cdot\frac{1}{\sqrt{2}} = \frac{a}{\sqrt{2}}.$$

11. $y = r\sin\theta = 3(1+\cos\theta)\sin\theta$

$$\therefore \frac{dy}{d\theta} = (3+3\cos\theta)\cos\theta - 3\sin\theta\cdot\sin\theta = 3(2\cos^2\theta+\cos\theta-1) = 0 \text{ if } \cos\theta = -1, \tfrac{1}{2}.$$

i.e. if $\theta = \pi, \dfrac{\pi}{3}$

$$\therefore \frac{d^2y}{dx^2} = -3\sin\theta(1+4\cos\theta) \text{ which is } -\text{ve when } \theta = \frac{\pi}{3}.$$

$$\therefore \theta = \frac{\pi}{3} \text{ gives a maximum value } \left(=\frac{9\sqrt{3}}{4}\right) \text{ to } y.$$

12. $r = a(1-\cos\theta) = 2a\sin^2\left(\dfrac{\theta}{2}\right) \Rightarrow \log r = \log 2a + 2\log\sin\dfrac{\theta}{2}$.

$$\therefore \frac{1}{r}\cdot\frac{dr}{d\theta} = \frac{2\cos(\theta/2)}{2\sin(\theta/2)} = \cot\frac{\theta}{2}. \text{ But } \tan\phi = r\frac{d\theta}{dr}. \therefore \cot\phi = \cot\frac{\theta}{2}$$

$$\therefore \phi = \frac{\theta}{2}.$$

13. Let the tangent at (r, θ) make an angle ψ with the +ve orientation of the initial line. $\therefore \psi = \theta+\phi$. Now $\phi = \theta/2$ (Exercise 22.12) $\therefore \psi = 3\theta/2$. Clearly the tangent will be vertical when $\psi = \pi/2, -\pi/2$ or $3\pi/2$, i.e. $\dfrac{3\theta}{2} = \dfrac{\pi}{2}, -\dfrac{\pi}{2}$, or $\dfrac{3\pi}{2}$, i.e. $\theta = \dfrac{\pi}{3}$, $-\dfrac{\pi}{3}$ or π.

14. Solve for points of intersection, i.e. $a - a\cos\theta = 2a\cos\theta$.

$\therefore \theta = \cos^{-1}(\frac{1}{3})$ [two angles, one in first and one in fourth quadrant].

For the circle: $\tan\phi_2 = r\dfrac{d\theta}{dr} = \dfrac{2a\cos\theta}{-2a\sin\theta} = -\cot\theta = \mp\dfrac{1}{2\sqrt{2}}$.

For the cardioid: $\tan\phi_1 = r\dfrac{d\theta}{dr} = \dfrac{a(1-\cos\theta)}{a\sin\theta} = \pm\dfrac{1}{\sqrt{2}}$ (i.e. $\phi_1 = 35°16'$).

$$\therefore \tan(\phi_2-\phi_1) = \frac{\tan\phi_2-\tan\phi_1}{1+\tan\phi_2\tan\phi_1} = \pm\left[\frac{1/(2\sqrt{2})+1/\sqrt{2}}{1-(1/2\sqrt{2})(1/\sqrt{2})}\right] = \pm\sqrt{2}.$$

$\therefore$ angle of intersection $\phi_2-\phi_1 = \tan^{-1}(\pm\sqrt{2}) = 54°44'$ or $125°16'$.

15. For intersection, $a+a\cos\theta = b-b\cos\theta$, i.e. $\cos\theta = \dfrac{b-a}{a+b}$, whence $r = \dfrac{2ab}{a+b}$

i.e. if $b = a$, they intersect in the y-axis at $\left(a, \dfrac{\pi}{2}\right)$.

$$\text{Tan}\,\phi_1 = r\frac{d\theta}{dr} = \frac{a(1+\cos\theta)}{-a\sin\theta} = \frac{1+(b-a)/(a+b)}{-\sqrt{1-[(b-a)/(a+b)]^2}} = -\sqrt{\frac{b}{a}}.$$

Similarly $\tan\phi_2 = \dfrac{b(1-\cos\theta)}{b\sin\theta} = \sqrt{\dfrac{a}{b}}$, where $\phi_2-\phi_1 = \theta$.

$$\therefore\ \tan\theta = \frac{\sqrt{\frac{a}{b}}+\sqrt{\frac{b}{a}}}{1-\sqrt{\frac{a}{b}}\sqrt{\frac{b}{a}}} = \infty,\ \therefore \text{ the cardioids cut orthogonally.}$$

16. Change the origin to $(a, 0)$. $\therefore\ x = a(2\cos t-\cos 2t-1),\ y = a(2\sin t-\sin 2t)$

$$\therefore\ \frac{x^2+y^2}{a^2} = 4\cos^2 t+\cos^2 2t-4\cos t\cos 2t+1-4\cos t+2\cos 2t+4\sin^2 t+ +\sin^2 2t-4\sin t\sin 2t$$

$= 4+1-4\cos t+1-4\cos t+2(2\cos^2 t-1)$ $\because\ \cos t\cos 2t+\sin t\sin 2t = \cos(2t-t) = \cos t$

$= 4-8\cos t+4\cos^2 t$, i.e. $\dfrac{r^2}{a^2} = 4(1-\cos t)^2$ $\therefore\ r = 2a(1-\cos\theta)$.

17. $\sin\phi = \dfrac{PN}{b}$ $(\because PN = b\sin\phi) = \dfrac{r\sin\theta}{a\sqrt{1-e^2}}$ by (189).

Now, the polar equation of the ellipse is $r(1+e\cos\theta) = l = a(1-e^2)$ [(257.1)]

$$\therefore\ \frac{\sin\phi}{\sin\theta} = \frac{a(1-e^2)}{a\sqrt{1-e^2}(1+e\cos\theta)} = \frac{\sqrt{1-e^2}}{1+e\cos\theta}.$$

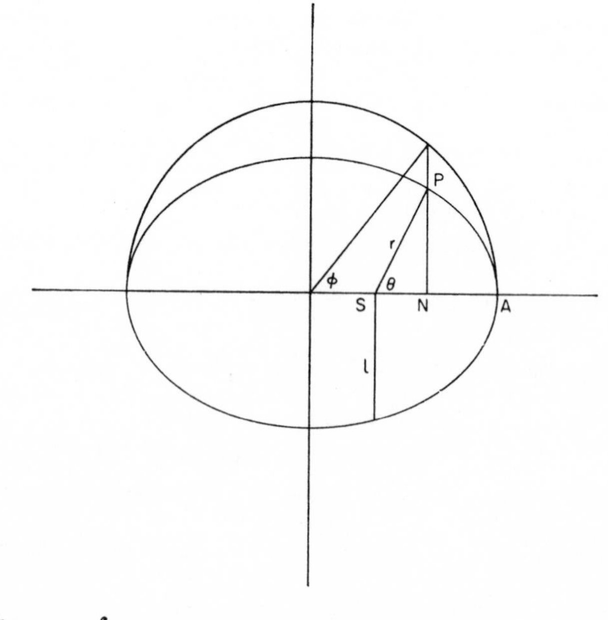

18. $\displaystyle\int\frac{dr}{r} = \cot\alpha\int d\theta \Rightarrow \log r = \theta\cot\alpha-\log k \Rightarrow r = ke^{\theta\cot\alpha}$.

(2, 0) lying on it $\Rightarrow 2 = k$, i.e. the curve is $r = 2e^{\theta\cot\alpha}$.

Now $r\dfrac{d\theta}{dr} = 2e^{\theta \cot \alpha}.\dfrac{1}{2 \cot \alpha e^{\theta \cot \alpha}} = \tan \alpha = \tan \dfrac{\pi}{4}$ by (258) and data.

$\therefore \alpha = \dfrac{\pi}{4}$ $\quad\therefore \cot \alpha = 1$ $\quad\therefore$ the curve is $r = 2e^{\theta}$ (equiangular spiral).

19. Coordinates of T on the circle are $(t+a \cos t, a \sin t)$ where $t = N\hat{C}T = N\hat{O}P = \theta$.

Tangent at $T: y-a \sin t = -\cot t(x-a\overline{1+\cos t})$ $\qquad(\alpha)$

$OP: y = x \tan t$ $\qquad(\beta)$

$\therefore$ (α), (β) $\Rightarrow$ $P \equiv [a(1+\cos t) \cos t,\ a(1+\cos t) \sin t] = (r, \theta)$ where $r = a(1+\cos t)$ with $t = \theta$, $\therefore$ the locus is the cardioid $r = a(1+\cos \theta)$. (See Fig. 122.)

20. $r^2 \dfrac{d\theta}{dr} = k \Rightarrow \displaystyle\int \frac{dr}{r^2} = \frac{1}{k}\int d\theta \Rightarrow \frac{1}{r} = -\frac{\theta}{k}+C$. Using the given conditions, we have $C = 0$

$\therefore$ the curve is $r = -\dfrac{k}{\theta}$, i.e. $r = \dfrac{a}{\theta}$ (hyperbolic spiral) $(a = -k)$.

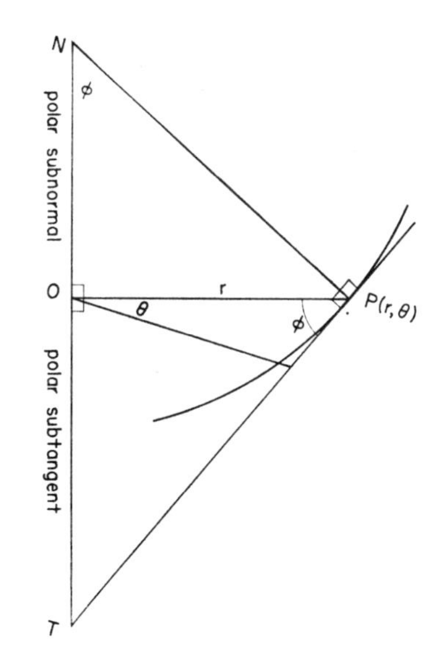

21. $\dfrac{dr}{d\theta} = k \Rightarrow r = k\theta+C$. Under the given conditions, $C = 0$.

$\therefore$ the curve is $r = k\theta$ (spiral of Archimedes).

22. Polar subnormal $ON = -a \sin \theta = \dfrac{-5}{13}a$. (Ignore the $-$ve sign.)

23. Polar subtangent $OT = \dfrac{a^2(1+\cos \theta)^2}{-a \sin \theta} = -a\dfrac{(1+12/13)^2}{5/13} = \dfrac{-125}{13}a$. (Ignore the $-$ve sign.)

24. $\tan^2\phi = r^2\left(\frac{d\theta}{dr}\right)^2$ by (258) $\therefore \sec^2\phi = 1+r^2\left(\frac{d\theta}{dr}\right)^2 = \frac{dr^2+r^2(d\theta)^2}{dr^2}$

$$= \frac{ds^2}{dr^2} \text{ by (48)}$$

$\therefore \sec\phi = \frac{ds}{dr}$ $\therefore \cos\phi = \frac{dr}{ds}$.

25. $\sin\phi = \tan\phi\cos\phi = r\frac{d\theta}{dr}\cdot\frac{dr}{ds} = r\frac{d\theta}{ds}$.

26. $\frac{1}{\varrho} = \frac{d\psi}{ds}$ and $\psi = \theta+\phi$ $\therefore \frac{1}{\varrho} = \frac{d\theta}{ds}+\frac{d\phi}{ds} = \frac{d\theta}{ds}\left(1+\frac{d\phi}{d\theta}\right)$ (i)

Now $\frac{1}{r}\frac{dr}{d\theta} = \cot\phi$ $\therefore -\operatorname{cosec}^2\phi\frac{d\phi}{d\theta} = -\frac{1}{r^2}\left(\frac{dr}{d\theta}\right)^2+\frac{1}{r}\frac{d^2r}{d\theta^2}$

$\therefore \frac{d\phi}{d\theta} = \left\{\left(\frac{dr}{d\theta}\right)^2 - r\frac{d^2r}{d\theta^2}\right\}\Big/\left(\frac{ds}{d\theta}\right)^2 \ldots$ (ii) $\because \left(\frac{ds}{d\theta}\right)^2 = r^2\operatorname{cosec}^2\theta$ (Exercise 22.25)

$$= r^2(1+\cot^2\theta) = r^2+\left(\frac{dr}{d\theta}\right)^2$$

$\therefore$ (i), (ii) $\Rightarrow \varkappa = \frac{1}{\varrho}\left\{\left(\frac{ds}{d\theta}\right)^2+\left(\frac{dr}{d\theta}\right)^2 - r\frac{d^2r}{d\theta^2}\right\}\Big/\left(\frac{ds}{d\theta}\right)^3$

$\therefore \varkappa = \left\{r^2+2\left(\frac{dr}{d\theta}\right)^2 - r\frac{d^2r}{d\theta^2}\right\}\Big/\left\{r^2+\left(\frac{dr}{d\theta}\right)^2\right\}^{3/2}$.

27. $\frac{dr}{d\theta} = -3a\sin 3\theta$, $\frac{d^2r}{d\theta^2} = -9a\cos 3\theta$.

$\therefore \varkappa = \frac{a^2(10\cos^2 3\theta+18\sin^2 3\theta)}{a^3(9\sin^2 3\theta+\cos^2 3\theta)^{3/2}} = \frac{18}{27a} = \frac{2}{3a}$ at $\theta = \frac{\pi}{6}$ $\left(= \frac{10}{a} \text{ at } \theta = 0\right)$.

28. $\frac{dr}{d\theta} = 2a\cos 2\theta$, $\frac{d^2r}{d\theta^2} = -4a\sin 2\theta$.

$\therefore \varkappa = \frac{a^2\sin^2 2\theta+2\cdot 4a^2\cos^2 2\theta+4a^2\sin^2 2\theta}{\{a^2\sin^2 2\theta+4a^2\cos^2 2\theta\}^{3/2}}$

$= \frac{8\cos^2 2\theta+5\sin^2 2\theta}{a(\sin^2 2\theta+4\cos^2 2\theta)^{3/2}} = \frac{5}{a}$ at $\theta = \frac{\pi}{4}$.

29. $\frac{dr}{d\theta} = a$, $\frac{d^2r}{d\theta^2} = 0$ $\therefore \varkappa = \frac{a^2(\theta^2+2)}{a^3(1+\theta^2)^{3/2}} = \frac{2}{a}$ at $\theta = 0$.

30. $\frac{dr}{d\theta} = -\frac{a}{\theta^2}$, $\frac{d^2r}{d\theta^2} = \frac{2a}{\theta^3}$. $\therefore \varkappa = \frac{a^2(1/\theta^2+2/\theta^4-2/\theta^4)}{a^3[1/\theta^4+1/\theta^2]^{3/2}} = \frac{\theta^4}{a(1+\theta^2)^{3/2}}$.

31. $\frac{dr}{d\theta} = r\cot\alpha$, $\frac{d^2r}{d\theta^2} = r\cot^2\alpha$ $\therefore \varkappa = \frac{r^2(1+2\cot^2\alpha-\cot^2\alpha)}{r^3[\cot^2\alpha+1]^{3/2}} = \frac{\operatorname{cosec}^2\alpha}{r\operatorname{cosec}^3\alpha}$

$$= \frac{\sin\alpha}{r}\left(\text{i.e. } \varrho = \frac{r}{\sin\alpha}\right).$$

32. $r = a\sqrt{\cos 2\theta} \quad \therefore \ \dfrac{dr}{d\theta} = -a\dfrac{\sin 2\theta}{\sqrt{\cos 2\theta}}$

$$\therefore \ \frac{d^2r}{d\theta^2} = -a\frac{\left\{\sqrt{\cos 2\theta}\cdot 2\cos 2\theta + \sin 2\theta\cdot\dfrac{\sin 2\theta}{\sqrt{\cos 2\theta}}\right\}}{\cos 2\theta} = -a\frac{(1+\cos^2 2\theta)}{\cos^{3/2} 2\theta}$$

$$\therefore \ \varkappa = a^2\frac{\left\{\cos 2\theta + 2\dfrac{\sin^2 2\theta}{\cos 2\theta} + \dfrac{1+\cos^2 2\theta}{\cos 2\theta}\right\}}{a^3\left\{\dfrac{\sin^2 2\theta}{\cos 2\theta} + \cos 2\theta\right\}^{3/2}} = \frac{3}{a}\sqrt{\cos 2\theta} = \frac{3r}{a^2} = \frac{3}{a} \text{ at } \theta = 0.$$

33. $\dfrac{dr}{d\theta} = -a\sin\theta, \ \dfrac{d^2r}{d\theta^2} = -a\cos\theta$

$$\therefore \ \varkappa = \frac{a^2\{1+2\cos\theta+\cos^2\theta+2\sin^2\theta+\cos\theta+\cos^2\theta\}}{a^3\{\sin^2\theta+1+2\cos\theta+\cos^2\theta\}^{3/2}} = \frac{6\cos^2\theta/2}{a\cdot 8\cos^3\theta/2}$$

$$= \frac{3}{4a\cos\theta/2}\left(= \frac{3}{4a\cdot\dfrac{3}{\sqrt{10}}} = \frac{\sqrt{10}}{4a} \text{ at } \theta = \tan^{-1}(\tfrac{3}{4}), \text{ say, where } r = \frac{9}{5}a\right)$$

$$\frac{d\varkappa}{d\theta} = -\frac{3}{4a}\cdot\frac{-1}{2}\frac{\sin\theta/2}{\cos^2\theta/2} = \frac{3\sin\theta/2}{8a\cos^2(\theta/2)} = 0 \text{ if } \theta = 0, 2\pi.$$

$$\frac{d^2\varkappa}{d\theta^2} = \frac{3}{8a}\left\{\frac{\cos^2\theta/2\cos\theta/2\cdot\frac{1}{2} - \sin\theta/2\cdot -2\cos\theta/2\sin\theta/2\cdot\frac{1}{2}}{\cos^4\theta/2}\right\}$$

$$= \frac{3\cos\theta/2\,(\cos^2\theta/2+2\sin^2\theta/2)}{16a\cos^4\theta/2}$$

$$= \frac{3(\cos^2\theta/2+2\sin^2\theta/2)}{16a\cos^3\theta/2} < 0 \text{ for } \theta = 2\pi,$$

i.e. $\theta = 2\pi$ gives maximum curvature.

34. $p = r\sin\phi = r^2\dfrac{d\theta}{ds}$ using Exercise 22.25.

$$\therefore \ \frac{1}{p^2} = u^4\left(\frac{ds}{d\theta}\right)^2 = u^4\left\{\frac{1}{u^2}+\left(\frac{dr}{d\theta}\right)^2\right\} \ \because \ \left(\frac{ds}{d\theta}\right)^2 = r^2+\left(\frac{dr}{d\theta}\right)^2 \ ((48), (247.1))$$

$$= u^2+u^4\left(\frac{d(1/u)}{d\theta}\right)^2 = u^2+u^4\frac{1}{u^4}\left(\frac{du}{d\theta}\right)^2 = u^2+\left(\frac{du}{d\theta}\right)^2$$

$$\therefore \ \frac{1}{p^2} = \frac{1}{r^4}\left(\frac{ds}{d\theta}\right)^2 = u^2+\left(\frac{du}{d\theta}\right)^2.$$

35. $p = r\sin\phi \Rightarrow \frac{dp}{dr} = \sin\phi + r\cos\phi\,\frac{d\phi}{dr}$

$$= r\left(\frac{d\theta}{ds}+\frac{dr}{ds}\frac{d\phi}{dr}\right) = r\left(\frac{d\theta}{ds}+\frac{d\phi}{ds}\right) = r\frac{d\psi}{ds} = \frac{r}{\varrho}.$$

36. $r = a(1-\cos\theta) \Rightarrow r\frac{d\theta}{dr} = \tan\phi = \frac{a(1-\cos\theta)}{a\sin\theta} = \tan\frac{\theta}{2} \quad \therefore \phi = \frac{\theta}{2}.$

$\therefore p = r\sin\left(\frac{\theta}{2}\right), \quad r = 2a\sin^2\frac{\theta}{2} \Rightarrow r^3 = 2ap^2 \left(\text{i.e. } p = \frac{r^{3/2}}{(2a)^{1/2}}\right)$

$\therefore \varrho = \frac{r}{dp/dr} = \frac{(2a)^{1/2}}{\frac{3}{2}r^{1/2}}\cdot(2a)^{1/3}p^{2/3} = \frac{2}{3}\sqrt{2ar}.$

37. $\tan\phi = r\frac{d\theta}{dr} = -\frac{1+\cos\theta}{\sin\theta}, \quad \tan\psi = -\frac{[1+\cos(\pi-\theta)]}{\sin(\pi+\theta)} = \frac{1-\cos\theta}{\sin\theta}$

Now $\alpha = \phi-\psi \Rightarrow \tan\alpha = \frac{\tan\phi-\tan\psi}{1+\tan\phi\tan\psi} = \frac{-\frac{1+\cos\theta}{\sin\theta}-\frac{1-\cos\theta}{\sin\theta}}{1-\frac{1-\cos^2\theta}{\sin^2\theta}} = \frac{\frac{-2}{\sin\theta}}{0} = \infty,$

$\therefore \alpha = \frac{\pi}{2} \quad \therefore PT \perp QT.$

38. $\tan\phi = r\frac{d\theta}{dr} = \frac{a(1+\cos\theta)}{-a\sin\theta} = -\cot\left(\frac{\theta}{2}\right) = \tan\left(\frac{\pi}{2}+\frac{\theta}{2}\right)$

$\therefore \beta = \theta+\frac{\theta}{2} = \frac{3\theta}{2}$ (Fig. 121).

39. $\tan\phi = r\frac{d\theta}{dr} = a\sqrt{\cos 2\theta}\cdot\frac{-\sqrt{\cos 2\theta}}{a\sin 2\theta} = -\cot 2\theta = \tan\left(\frac{\pi}{2}+2\theta\right).$

$\therefore$ inclination $\beta = \theta+2\theta = 3\theta$ (β, θ, ϕ as in Fig. 121).

40. $\tan\phi = \tan(\pi-\theta) = -\tan\theta = -\frac{1+\cos\theta}{\sin\theta}, \quad \therefore \frac{\sin\theta}{\cos\theta} = \frac{1+\cos\theta}{\sin\theta}$

$\therefore 2\cos^2\theta+\cos\theta-1 = 0, \quad \therefore \cos\theta = -1, \tfrac{1}{2}, \quad$ i.e. $\theta = \frac{\pi}{3}$ (other root inadmissible).

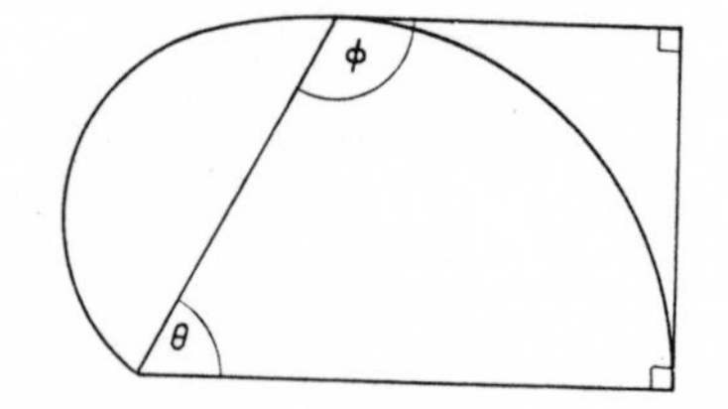

41. $\tan\phi = -\dfrac{1+\cos\theta}{\sin\theta}$, $\tan\psi = -\dfrac{1+\cos(\theta+\alpha)}{\sin(\theta+\alpha)}$, $\alpha = \left(\dfrac{\pi}{2}-\psi\right)+\phi$

(i.e. $\alpha+\psi+\dfrac{\pi}{2}+\pi+\pi-\phi = 2\pi$).

$$\therefore\quad \tan\alpha = \frac{\cot\psi+\tan\phi}{1-\cot\psi\tan\phi} = \frac{-(1+\cos\theta+\cos\alpha+\cos(\theta+\alpha))}{\sin\theta-\sin\alpha-\sin(\theta+\alpha)}.$$

Clear fractions and simplify to get $\cos(2\alpha+\theta)+\cos(\theta-\alpha)+\cos 2\alpha+\cos\alpha = 0$,

i.e. $2\cos\dfrac{2\theta+\alpha}{2}\cos\dfrac{3\alpha}{2}+2\cos\dfrac{3\alpha}{2}\cos\dfrac{\alpha}{2} = 0$, $2\cos\dfrac{3\alpha}{2}\left(\cos\dfrac{2\theta+\alpha}{2}+\cos\dfrac{\alpha}{2}\right) = 0$

$4\cos\dfrac{3\alpha}{2}\cdot\cos\dfrac{\theta}{2}\cos\dfrac{\theta-\alpha}{2} = 0$, $\quad\therefore\ \cos\dfrac{\theta}{2} = 0$ or $\cos\dfrac{\theta-\alpha}{2} = 0$ or $\cos\dfrac{3\alpha}{2} = 0$.

$\therefore\quad \dfrac{\theta}{2} = \dfrac{\pi}{2}$ or $\dfrac{\theta-\alpha}{2} = \dfrac{\pi}{2}$ or $\dfrac{3\alpha}{2} = \dfrac{\pi}{2}$ whence $\alpha = \dfrac{\pi}{3}$ as an admissible solution.

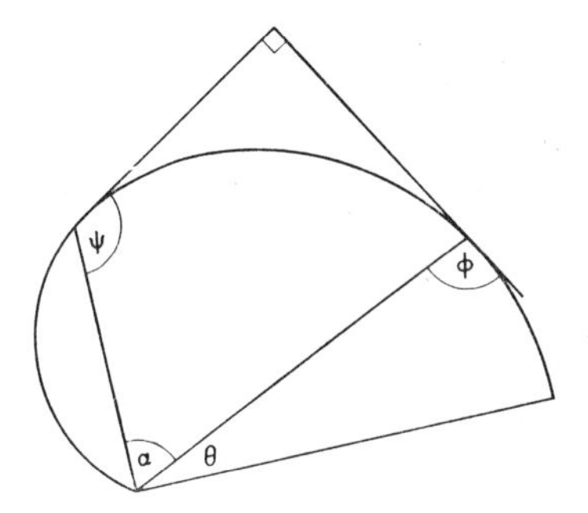

42. By Exercise 22.1, the homogeneous Cartesian equation of the cardioid is

$$f(x,y,z) \equiv (x^2+y^2-axz)^2-a^2(x^2+y^2)z^2 = 0$$

$$\left.\begin{aligned} &\frac{\partial f}{\partial x} = 2(2x-az)(x^2+y^2-axz)-2a^2xz^2 = 0\\ \therefore\ &\frac{\partial f}{\partial y} = 4y(x^2+y^2-axz)-2a^2yz^2 = 0\\ &\frac{\partial f}{\partial z} = -2ax(x^2+y^2-axz)-2a^2z(x^2+y^2) = 0 \end{aligned}\right\} \Rightarrow \text{double points at } O, I, J.$$

43. At (0, 0, 1), $\dfrac{\partial^2 f}{\partial x^2} = 4(3x^2+y^2-3axz) = 0$, $\dfrac{\partial^2 f}{\partial y^2} = 4(3y^2+x^2-axz)-2a^2z^2 = -2a$,

$$\frac{\partial^2 f}{\partial x\,\partial y} = 4y(2x-az) = 0,\ \therefore\ \left(\frac{\partial^2 f}{\partial x\,\partial y}\right)^2 = \frac{\partial^2 f}{\partial x^2}\cdot\frac{\partial^2 f}{\partial y^2} = 0,\quad \therefore\ \exists \text{ a cusp at } O.$$

44. $f(x,y,z) \equiv (x^2+y^2)^2-(x^2-y^2)z^2 = 0$,

$$\therefore \left.\begin{aligned} \frac{\partial f}{\partial x} &= 2x(2x^2+2y^2-z^2) = 0 \\ \frac{\partial f}{\partial y} &= 2y(2x^2+2y^2+z^2) = 0 \\ \frac{\partial f}{\partial z} &= -2z(x^2-y^2) \quad = 0 \end{aligned}\right\} \Rightarrow \text{double points are at } O, I, J.$$

At O, $\dfrac{\partial^2 f}{\partial x^2} = 12x^2+4y^2-2z^2 = -2$, $\dfrac{\partial^2 f}{\partial y^2} = 4x^2+12y^2+2z^2 = 2$, $\dfrac{\partial^2 f}{\partial x\,\partial y} = 8xy = 0$,

$$\therefore \quad \left(\frac{\partial^2 f}{\partial x\,\partial y}\right)^2 > \frac{\partial^2 f}{\partial x^2}\cdot\frac{\partial^2 f}{\partial y^2} \text{ at } O, \quad \therefore \ \exists \text{ a node at } O.$$

The formula for determining the nature of the double point applies only for $O\,(= Z)$ or X or Y, so we cannot employ it for I, J. In effect, we should have to make a transformation which carried I, J into say Y, X.

45. By Exercise 22.33 at $P(r, \theta)$, $\quad \varrho_1 = \dfrac{4a\cos\theta/2}{3}$

$$\therefore \text{ at } P'(r', \pi+\theta),\ \varrho_2 = \frac{4a\cos(\theta/2+\pi/2)}{3} = \frac{-4a\sin\theta/2}{3}.$$

$$\therefore \ \varrho_1^2+\varrho_2^2 = \frac{16a^2}{9} \quad \text{(Fig. 121).}$$

46. Fig. 112 $\Rightarrow PQ = 2\varrho\sin\phi$.

47. $PR = 2\varrho\cos\phi$.

48. By Exercises 22.29, 22.30, $\dfrac{\varrho_A}{\varrho_H} = \dfrac{a(1+\theta^2)^{3/2}}{2+\theta^2}\cdot\dfrac{\theta^4}{a(1+\theta^2)^{3/2}} = \dfrac{1}{3}$ for common points $r = \theta = \dfrac{1}{\theta}$, i.e. $\theta^2 = 1$.

$$\therefore \ \varrho_H = 3\varrho_A \quad \text{(Fig. 138).}$$

49. By Exercise 22.32, $\varrho = \dfrac{a}{3\sqrt{\cos 2\theta}} = \dfrac{a^2}{3r}$.

$$\therefore \ \frac{OP}{QP} = \frac{r\cdot 3r}{2a^2\sin\phi} = \frac{3\cos 2\theta}{2\sin\phi} = \frac{3}{2}$$

$$\because \ \sin\phi = \frac{1}{\sqrt{1+\cot^2\phi}} = \frac{1}{\sqrt{1+(1/r^2)(dr/d\theta)^2}} = \cos 2\theta.$$

50. $\operatorname{Tan}\phi = r\dfrac{d\theta}{dr} = \dfrac{1}{\sqrt{\theta}}\cdot -2\theta^{3/2} = -2\theta = -1$ at $\theta = \dfrac{1}{2}$ $\therefore \phi = \dfrac{3\pi}{4}$ $\therefore \psi = \dfrac{3\pi}{4}+\dfrac{1}{2}$.

51. $OQ = \dfrac{QN}{\sin\theta} = \dfrac{(a/2)\sin 2\theta}{\sin\theta} = a\cos\theta$ $\therefore r = OQ+QP = a(1+\cos\theta)$.

Similarly for P' for which $\theta \to \pi+\theta$. ($r = QP'-OQ = a(1-\cos\overline{\pi+\theta}) = a(1+\cos\theta)$.) The form of equation implies that $\exists$ a cusp at O.

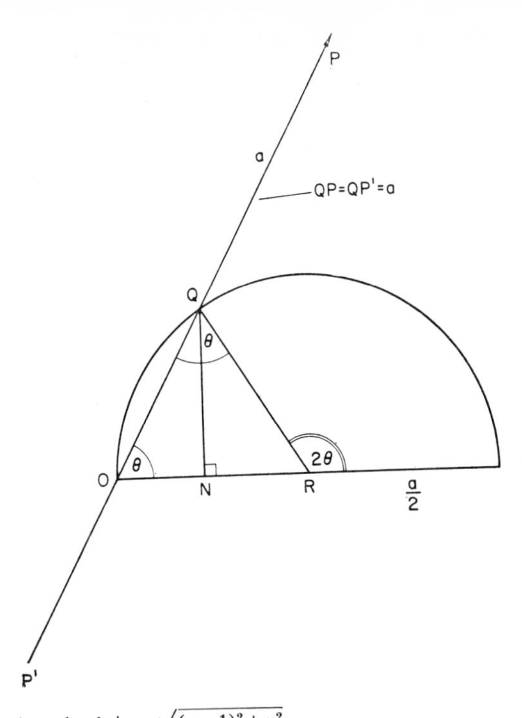

52. $|z-1| = |x-1+iy| = \sqrt{(x-1)^2+y^2}$.
$\therefore$ required locus is $\sqrt{(x-1)^2+y^2} = x \Rightarrow y^2 = 2x-1$ (parabola, vertex $(\frac{1}{2}, 0)$, axis $\equiv$ x-axis). Write $z = re^{i\theta}$ $\therefore$ $z^{1/2} = r^{1/2}\left(\cos\frac{\theta}{2}+i\sin\frac{\theta}{2}\right)$

$$\therefore\ |1-z^{1/2}| = \left|\left(1-r^{1/2}\cos\frac{\theta}{2}\right)-ir^{1/2}\sin\frac{\theta}{2}\right| = \sqrt{1-2r^{1/2}\cos\frac{\theta}{2}+r}$$

$\therefore$ required locus is $1-2r^{1/2}\cos\frac{\theta}{2}+r = 1 \Rightarrow r = 2(1+\cos\theta)$ (cardioid). The required region is hatched in the diagram.

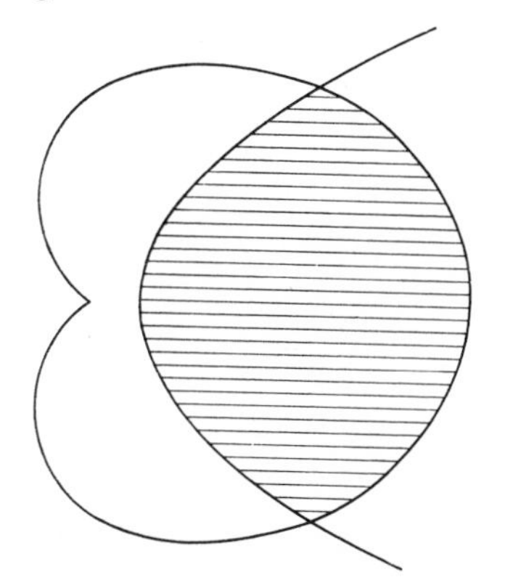

53. Note that $S\hat{Z}P = S\hat{P}T = S\hat{T}P$, i.e. PS trisects $T\hat{S}Z$.

Now $SZ = r = SP \sec \theta/3\ (\triangle SZP) = RS \sec^2 \frac{\theta}{3}\ (\triangle SPR)$

$$= SA \sec^3 \frac{\theta}{3}\ (\triangle ASR) \quad \text{i.e.} \quad r = a \sec^3 \left(\frac{\theta}{3}\right).$$

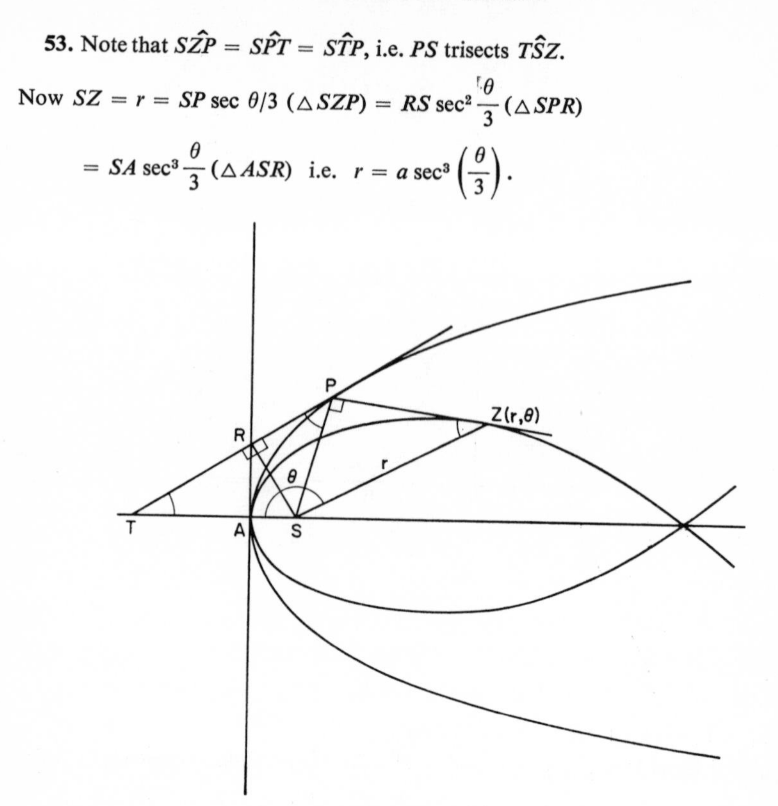

54. Polar subnormal $ON = R = \frac{dr}{d\theta} = a \cot \alpha e^{\theta \cot \alpha}$.

But $\phi = \theta + \frac{\pi}{2}$, $\quad \therefore\ R = a \cot \alpha e^{(\phi - \pi/2) \cot \alpha}$.

Generally, for the curve $r = f(\theta)$, the locus is $R = f'(\theta) = f'\left(\phi - \frac{\pi}{2}\right)$.

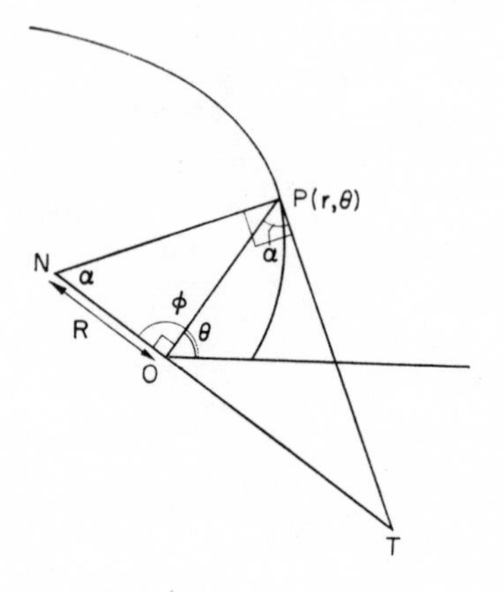

55. $OP//C_1C_2 \Rightarrow r = C_1C_2-(C_1R+SC_2) = 2a-2a\cos\theta = 2a(1-\cos\theta).$

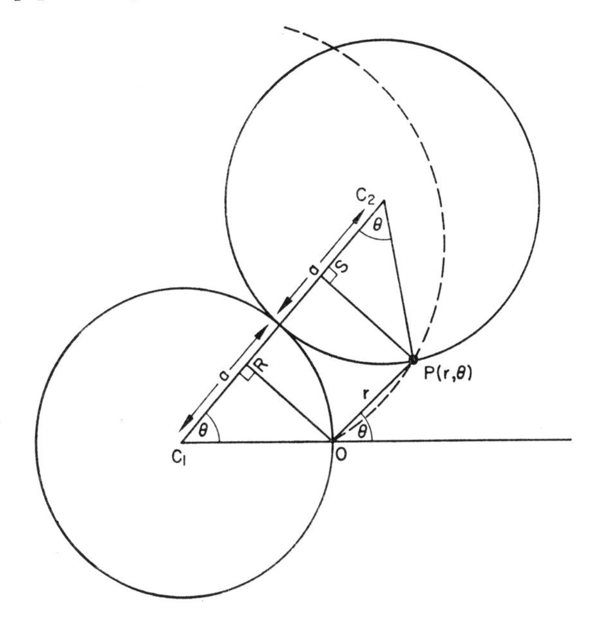

EXERCISES 23

1. By symmetry, total area $= 2\int_0^\infty xe^{-x^2}\,dx = 2\cdot-\frac{1}{2}\int_0^\infty de^{-x^2} = \left[-e^{-x^2}\right]_0^\infty = 1.$

If $y = xe^{-x^2}$, then $\dfrac{dy}{dx} = (1-2x^2)e^{-x^2} = 0$ when $x = \pm\dfrac{1}{\sqrt{2}}$.

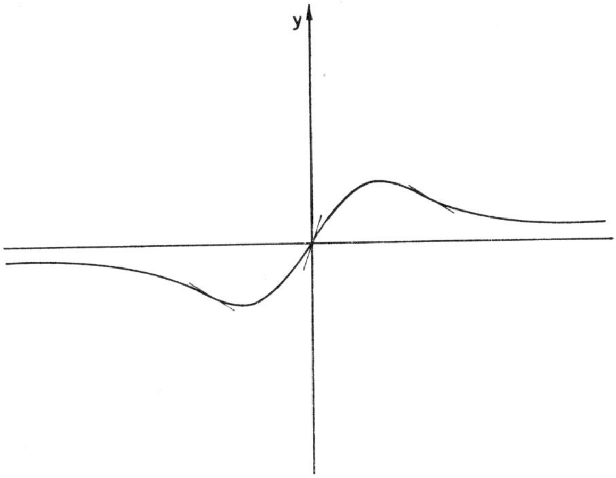

y

$\therefore \quad \dfrac{d^2y}{dx^2} = 2xe^{-x^2}(2x^2-3)$ which is $-$ve when $x = +1/\sqrt{2}$ (maximum), $+$ve when $x = -1/\sqrt{2}$ (minimum). Points of inflexion occur at $x = 0, \pm\sqrt{\tfrac{3}{2}}$.

2. Area of loop in first quadrant $= \displaystyle\int_0^{\pi/3} \frac{1}{2} r^2\, d\theta = \frac{1}{2} a^2 \int_0^{\pi/3} \sin^2 3\theta\, d\theta = \frac{1}{2}\frac{a^2}{3}\int_0^{\pi} \sin^2 u\, du$

$$\left(\text{where} \begin{cases} u = 3\theta \\ du = 3\,d\theta \end{cases}\right) = \frac{a^2}{6}\left[\frac{1}{2}u - \frac{1}{4}\sin 2u\right]_0^{\pi} = \frac{\pi a^2}{12}.$$

3. Required area (Fig. 124) $= \displaystyle\int_0^{\pi} \frac{1}{2} r^2\, d\theta = \int_0^{\pi} \left(\frac{33}{32} + \frac{5}{4}\cos\theta + \frac{\cos 2\theta}{4}\right) d\theta$

$$= \left[\frac{33}{32}\theta + \frac{5}{4}\sin\theta + \frac{\sin 2\theta}{8}\right]_0^{\pi} = \frac{33\pi}{32}.$$

4. Circular area $A_1 = \dfrac{\pi \cdot 4\pi^2}{2} = 2\pi^3$. Circular area $A_2 = \dfrac{\pi \cdot \pi^2}{2} = \dfrac{\pi^3}{2}$.

Spiral area $= A = \displaystyle\frac{1}{2}\int_0^{\pi} r^2\, d\theta = \frac{1}{2}\int_0^{\pi} (4\pi^2 - 4\pi\theta + \theta^2)\, d\theta = \frac{1}{2}\left[4\pi^2\theta - \frac{4\pi\theta^2}{2} + \frac{\theta^3}{3}\right]_0^{\pi} = \frac{7\pi^3}{6}$

$$\therefore \quad \frac{A_1 - A}{A - A_2} = \frac{5\pi^3/6}{4\pi^3/6} = \frac{5}{4}.$$

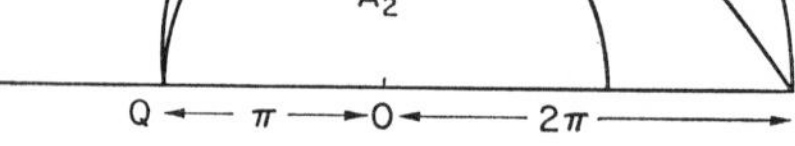

5. Stippled area in the diagram is area swept out by radius vector in one revolution (i.e. 0 to 2π).

$$\therefore \text{ area swept out in two revolutions } = \frac{1}{2}\int_{2\pi}^{4\pi} e^{2\theta}\, d\theta = \frac{1}{4}\left[e^{2\theta}\right]_{2\pi}^{4\pi} = \frac{1}{4}\, e^{4\pi}(e^{4\pi}-1).$$

[The whole point of the question is to understand correctly the limits of this integration.]

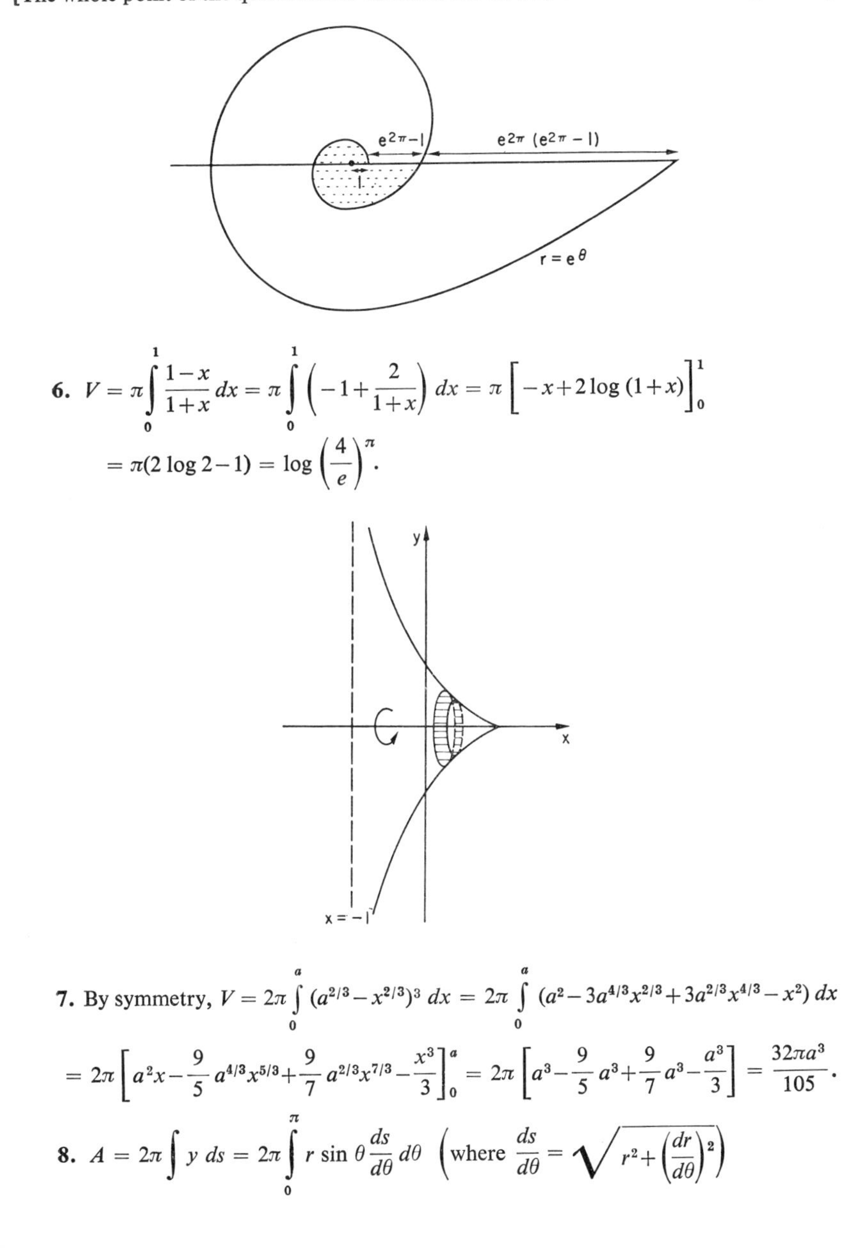

6. $V = \pi \int_0^1 \frac{1-x}{1+x}\, dx = \pi \int_0^1 \left(-1+\frac{2}{1+x}\right) dx = \pi\left[-x+2\log(1+x)\right]_0^1$

$$= \pi(2\log 2 - 1) = \log\left(\frac{4}{e}\right)^{\pi}.$$

7. By symmetry, $V = 2\pi \int_0^a (a^{2/3}-x^{2/3})^3\, dx = 2\pi \int_0^a (a^2 - 3a^{4/3}x^{2/3} + 3a^{2/3}x^{4/3} - x^2)\, dx$

$$= 2\pi\left[a^2x - \frac{9}{5}a^{4/3}x^{5/3} + \frac{9}{7}a^{2/3}x^{7/3} - \frac{x^3}{3}\right]_0^a = 2\pi\left[a^3 - \frac{9}{5}a^3 + \frac{9}{7}a^3 - \frac{a^3}{3}\right] = \frac{32\pi a^3}{105}.$$

8. $A = 2\pi \int y\, ds = 2\pi \int_0^{\pi} r\sin\theta \frac{ds}{d\theta}\, d\theta \quad \left(\text{where } \frac{ds}{d\theta} = \sqrt{r^2+\left(\frac{dr}{d\theta}\right)^2}\right)$

$$= 2\pi \int_0^{\pi} a(1+\cos\theta)\sin\theta\sqrt{a^2(1+\cos\theta)^2+a^2\sin^2\theta}\,d\theta$$

$$= 2\pi a^2 \int_0^{\pi} (1+\cos\theta)\sin\theta\sqrt{2+2\cos\theta}\,d\theta$$

$$= 2\pi a^2 \int_0^{\pi} (1+\cos\theta)\sin\theta\cdot 2\cos\frac{\theta}{2}\,d\theta = 16\,\pi a^2 \int_0^{\pi} \cos^4\left(\frac{\theta}{2}\right)\sin\left(\frac{\theta}{2}\right)d\theta$$

$$= 16\pi a^2 \int_0^{\pi} -2\cos^4\left(\frac{\theta}{2}\right)d\cos\left(\frac{\theta}{2}\right) = 32\pi a^2\left[\frac{-\cos^5(\theta/2)}{5}\right]_0^{\pi} = \frac{32\pi a^2}{5}.$$

9. $A = \int_0^4 \left\{\sqrt{4x}-\frac{x^2}{4}\right\}dx = \left[2\cdot\frac{2x^{3/2}}{3}-\frac{x^3}{12}\right]_0^4 = 5\frac{1}{3}.$

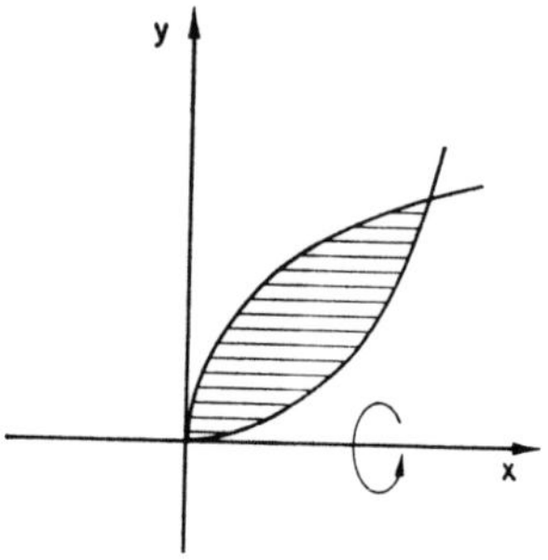

10. $V = \pi\int_0^4 \left(4x-\frac{x^4}{16}\right)dx = \pi\left[2x^2-\frac{x^5}{80}\right]_0^4 = 19\frac{1}{5}\pi.$

11. $V = \pi\int_0^a (4a^2-4ax)dx = \pi\,[4a^2x-2ax^2]_0^a = 2\pi a^3.$

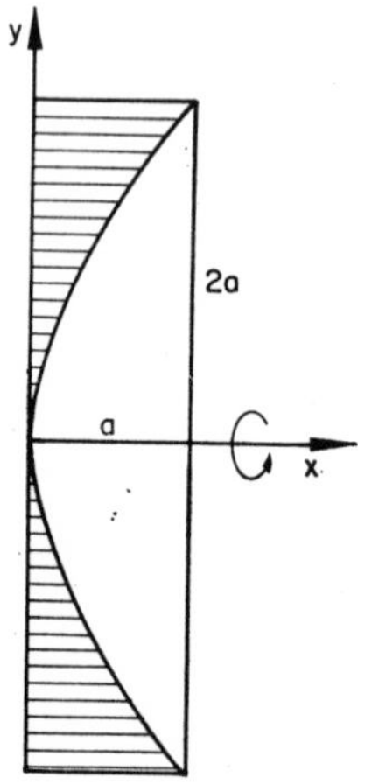

12. $A = \int_0^a (a+x-2\sqrt{ax})\,dx = \left[ax+\frac{x^2}{2}-\frac{4}{3}a^{1/2}x^{3/2}\right]_0^a = \frac{a^2}{6}$. [Note the parametric representation $x = a\sin^4\theta$, $y = a\cos^4\theta$.]

13. $s = c\int_{\pi/2}^{\theta} \sqrt{\frac{\cos^4\theta}{\sin^2\theta}+\cos^2\theta}\,d\theta = c\int_{\pi/2}^{\theta} \cot\theta\,d\theta = -[c\log\sin\theta]_{\pi/2}^{\theta} = -c\log\sin\theta$

$= c\log\frac{c}{y}$ i.e. $y = \frac{e^{-s/c}}{c}$.

14. $s = c\log\frac{c}{y}$, $y = c\sin\psi \Rightarrow s = c\log\operatorname{cosec}\psi$ (intrinsic equation)

$$\Rightarrow \frac{ds}{d\psi} = -c\cot\psi = \varrho.$$

15. $s = c\sinh\frac{x}{c}$ [Example 149(i)], $\therefore s^2+c^2 = y^2$.

16. Equation of parabola is $y = h\left(1-\frac{x^2}{a^2}\right)$.

$$\therefore V = \pi h^2\int_0^a \left(1-\frac{2x^2}{a^2}+\frac{x^4}{a^4}\right)dx = \frac{16}{15}\pi h^2 a.$$

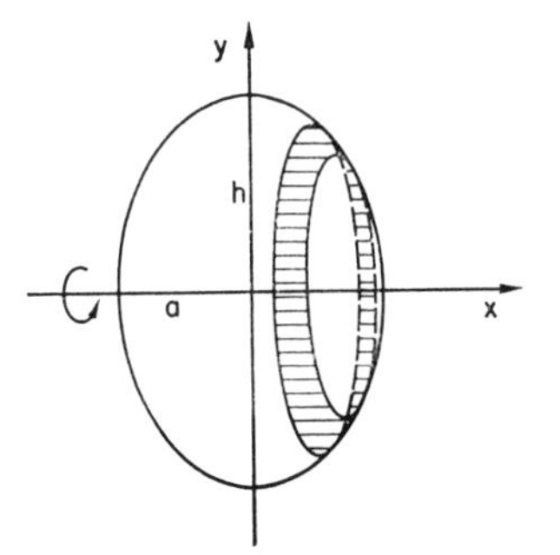

17. In $\triangle QMP$, $PQ = QM\tan\phi = 1\cdot\sinh x = s$ [Exercise 5.26, (38), Example 149(i)].

18. $\varrho = y^2 = 1+s^2$ (Exercise 23.15, Example 127).

19. $s = \log\operatorname{cosec}\theta = \log\sqrt{1+\cot^2\theta} = \log\sqrt{1+\varrho^2}$ (Exercise 21.5, Example 14).

20. $\varrho = \cot\theta = \tan\phi = \sinh x = s$ [Exercise 21.5, Example 14(iii), (38), Example 149(i)].

21. $\tan\phi_1 = \sinh x_1 = s_1 \Rightarrow s_1 s_2 = \sinh x_1\sinh x_2 = \tan\phi_1\tan\phi_2 = -1 \Rightarrow |s_1 s_2| = 1.$

22. $$\left.\begin{aligned} A &= \int_b^a x^{n/m}\,dx = \frac{m}{m+n}\left(a^{(n+m)/m} - b^{(n+m)/m}\right) \\ B &= \int_{b^n}^{a^n} y^{m/n}\,dy = \frac{n}{m+n}\left(a^{((m+n)/n)(n/m)} - b^{((m+n)/n)(n/m)}\right) \end{aligned}\right\} \Rightarrow A : B = m : n.$$

23. $$S = 2\pi\int_0^\pi \sin x\sqrt{1+\cos^2 x}\,dx = 4\pi\int_0^{\pi/2} \sin x\sqrt{1+\cos^2 x}\,dx \text{ (symmetry)}$$

$$= -4\pi\int_1^0 \sqrt{1+\cos^2 x}\,d\cos x = 4\pi\int_0^1 \sqrt{1+t^2}\,dt \ (t = \cos x)$$

$$= 2\pi(\sqrt{2}+\log(1+\sqrt{2})) \text{ (Example 147).}$$

24. $x = b\sin\theta,\ y = a-b\cos\theta \Rightarrow \dfrac{ds}{d\theta} = \sqrt{(b\sin\theta)^2+(b\cos\theta)^2} = b.$

$$\therefore S = 2\pi\int_0^{2\pi} y\,ds = 2\pi\int_0^{2\pi}(a-b\cos\theta)b\,d\theta = 2\pi b[a\theta - b\sin\theta]_0^{2\pi} = 4\pi^2 ab$$

$= \pi\times$surface area of the given cylinder.

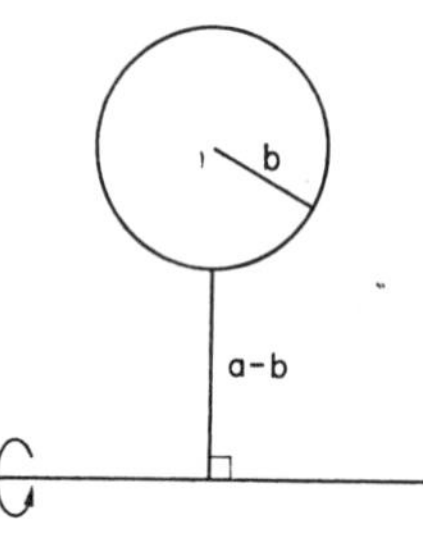

25. For the cycloid $x = a(\theta-\sin\theta)$, $y = a(1-\cos\theta)$ (Fig. 105),

$$s = \int_0^{2\pi}\sqrt{[a(1-\cos\theta)]^2+[a\sin\theta]^2}\,d\theta = 2a\int_0^\pi \sqrt{2(1-\cos\theta)}\,d\theta \text{ (symmetry)}$$

$$= 4a\int_0^\pi \sin\left(\frac{\theta}{2}\right)d\theta = -8a[\cos\theta/2]_0^\pi = 8a.$$

26. $A = a^2 \int_0^{2\pi} (1-\cos\theta)\cdot(1-\cos\theta)\, d\theta \left(= \int_0^{2\pi a} y\, dx\right)$

$$= a^2 \int_0^{2\pi} \left(1-2\cos\theta+\frac{1+\cos 2\theta}{2}\right) d\theta$$

$$= a^2 \left[\frac{3\theta}{2}-2\sin\theta+\frac{\sin 2\theta}{4}\right]_0^{2\pi} = 3\pi a^2.$$

27. Arc $s_1 = a \int_0^{2\pi/3} \sqrt{(1-\cos\theta)^2+\sin^2\theta}\, d\theta = 4a\left[-\cos\frac{\theta}{2}\right]_0^{2\pi/3} = 2a;$

$$\text{arc } s_2 = a \int_{2\pi/3}^{\pi} \sqrt{(1-\cos\theta)^2+\sin^2\theta}\, d\theta = 4a\,[-\cos\theta/2]_{2\pi/3}^{\pi} = 2a = \text{arc } s_1.$$

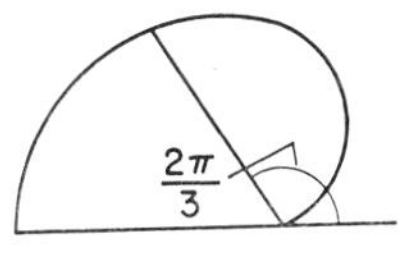

28. $S = \int_0^{t_1} \sqrt{1+\frac{9t^2}{4}}\cdot 2t\, dt \left(\because \frac{dx}{dt} = 2t, \frac{dy}{dt} = 3t^2, \frac{dy}{dx} = \frac{3t}{2}\right)$

$$= \int_0^{t_1} t\sqrt{4+9t^2}\, dt = \frac{1}{27}[(4+9t^2)^{3/2}]_0^{t_1} = \frac{1}{27}\{(4+9t_1^2)^{3/2}-8\} = \frac{19}{27} \text{ if } t_1^2 = \frac{5}{9}.$$

29. $V = \pi \int_{1/2}^{1} \frac{1-x}{x}\, dx = \pi[\log x - x]_{1/2}^{1} = \pi\left\{\log 1 - 1 - \log\left(\frac{1}{2}\right)+\frac{1}{2}\right\}$

$$= \pi\left(\log 2-\frac{1}{2}\right).$$

30. Volume between base and plane $= \pi \int_0^{2a\sin\pi/18} (a^2-x^2)\, dx = \pi\left[a^2x-\frac{x^3}{3}\right]_0^{2a\sin\pi/18}$

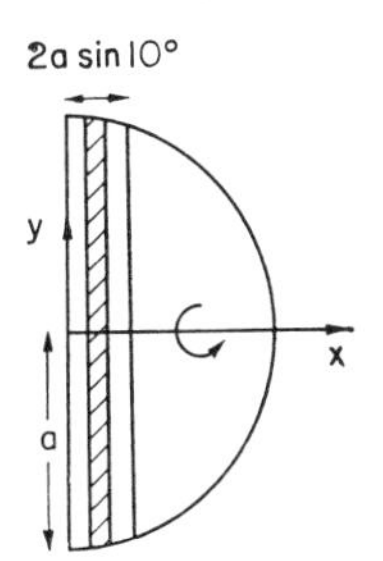

$= \pi a^3 \left(2 \sin \pi/18 - \frac{8}{3} \sin^3 \frac{\pi}{18}\right) = \pi a^3 \left\{2 \sin \pi/18 - \frac{2}{3} (3 \sin \pi/18 - \sin \pi/6)\right\}$ ((122)

$= \frac{\pi a^3}{3} = \frac{1}{2} \times$ volume of hemisphere.

31. Area of circular sector $= \frac{r^2\theta}{2} = k$ (§ 118, Lemma) $\therefore\ r^2\theta = 2k = a^2$ (say) (See Fig. 129).

32. $\frac{dy}{dx} = -2xe^{-x^2} = 0$ at $x = 0$, $\frac{d^2y}{dx^2} = -2e^{-x^2}(1-2x^2) < 0$ if $x = 0$,

$= 0$ if $x = \pm\sqrt{2}$

$\therefore\ \exists$ a maximum value $(= 1)$ at $x = 0$. Inflexions occur at $(\pm\sqrt{2}, e^{-2})$.

$$A = 2\int_0^\infty e^{-x^2}\,dx = 2\cdot\frac{\sqrt{\pi}}{2} = \sqrt{\pi} \quad \text{(Exercise 8.74).}$$

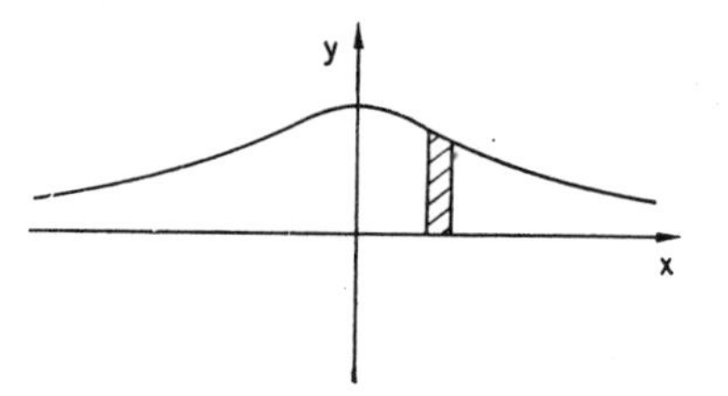

33. By symmetry, $S = 2\cdot 2\pi \int_{\pi/2}^{0} a \sin^3\phi\cdot\sqrt{1+(-\tan\phi)^2}\cdot -3a\cos^2\phi \sin\phi\, d\phi$

$= -12a^2 \int_{\pi/2}^{0} \sin^4\phi \cos^2\phi\cdot\sec\phi\, d\phi = 12a^2 \int_0^{\pi/2} \sin^4\phi \cos\phi\, d\phi$

$= \frac{12\pi a^2}{5}\left[\sin^5\theta\right]_0^{\pi/2}$ $\quad (\because \cos\phi\, d\phi = d\sin\phi) = \frac{12\pi a^2}{5}$.

34. $A = 2\int_0^a \sqrt{\frac{x^2(a+x)}{a-x}}\,dx$ (symmetry)

$= 2\int_{\pi/2}^{0} a\cos\theta\sqrt{\frac{1+\cos\theta}{1-\cos\theta}}$

$\cdot -a\sin\theta\, d\theta\ (x = a\cos\theta)$

$= 2a^2\int_0^{\pi/2} \cos\theta\sin\theta\cdot\left(\frac{1+\cos\theta}{\sin\theta}\right)d\theta$ (rationalising the square root)

$= 2a^2\int_0^{\pi/2}\left(\cos\theta+\frac{\cos 2\theta+1}{2}\right)d\theta = 2a^2\left[\sin\theta+\frac{\theta}{2}+\frac{\sin 2\theta}{4}\right]_0^{\pi/2} = 2a^2\left(1+\frac{\pi}{4}\right)$.

35. Given $A = ks$ $\therefore \int_a^x y\,dx = k\int_a^x \sqrt{1+\left(\frac{dy}{dx}\right)^2}\,dx.$

Differentiate using (65) $\therefore y = k\sqrt{1+\left(\frac{dy}{dx}\right)^2}$ $\therefore \left(\frac{dy}{dx}\right)^2 = \frac{y^2}{k^2}-1.$

Integrate $\int \frac{dy}{\sqrt{y^2/k^2-1}} = \int dx$ $\therefore \int \frac{dy}{\sqrt{y^2-k^2}} = \frac{x}{k}$ (taking $c = 0$ for simplicity)

i.e. $\cosh^{-1}\left(\frac{y}{k}\right) = \frac{x}{k}$ $\therefore$ curves are catenaries $y = k\cosh\left(\frac{x}{k}\right)$.

36. $A = 4\int_{\pi/2}^{0} 3a^2(3\sin t-\sin 3t)(-\sin t+\sin 3t)\,dt$

$= 12a^2\int_{\pi/2}^{0}(-3\sin^2 t\ +4\sin t\sin 3t-\sin^2 3t)\,dt$

$= 12a^2\int_{\pi/2}^{0}\left(\frac{3}{2}(\cos 2t-1)+2(\cos 2t-\cos 4t)+\frac{1}{2}(\cos 6t-1)\right)dt$

$= 12a^2\int_{\pi/2}^{0}\left(-2+\frac{7}{2}\cos 2t-2\cos 4t+\frac{\cos 6t}{2}\right)dt$

$= 12a^2\left[-2t+\frac{7}{4}\sin 2t-\frac{1}{2}\sin 4t+\frac{\sin 6t}{12}\right]_{\pi/2}^{0} = 12\pi a^2.$

37. Equation of the tangent to the nephroid is $y-(3\sin t-\sin 3t) = \tan 2t(x-(3\cos t-\cos 3t))$.

Solve for tangent and line $OP: y = -\frac{x}{\tan 2t}$

$\therefore P \equiv (4\sin t\sin 2t,\ -4\sin t\cos 2t)$

$\therefore$ pedal is $x^2+y^2 = 16\sin^2 t$, i.e. $r = 4\sin t$ i.e. $r = 4\sin\left(\frac{\pi}{4}+\frac{\theta}{2}\right)$

("pair of ears")

Note the geometrical meaning of $t: 2t = \pi/2+\theta$. (See Fig. 103.)

38. From similar $\triangle$'s, $\frac{a+h}{k} = \frac{k}{R-a}$ $\therefore a(R-h) = k^2+a^2-Rh = R^2-(R-a)^2+a^2 - Rh = 2Ra-Rh$

$\therefore a = Rh/(R+h)$. Surface area $= 2\pi R\int_{R-a}^{R} dx = 2\pi Ra = 2\pi R^2h/(R+h).$

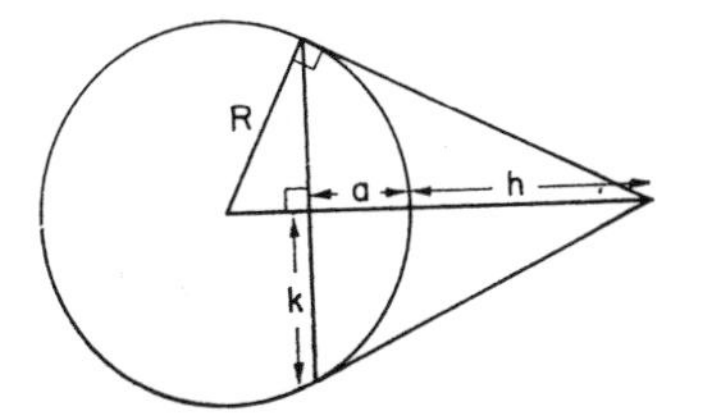

39. $$S = 2\cdot 2\pi \int_{x=0}^{x=\infty} c \sin\theta \sqrt{1+\tan^2\theta}\cdot -\frac{c\cos^2\theta}{\sin\theta}\, d\theta \quad \text{(Exercise 5.25)}$$

$$= -4\pi c^2 \int_{\pi/2}^{0} \cos\theta\, d\theta \left(x = \infty \Rightarrow \theta = 0,\ x = 0 \Rightarrow \theta = \frac{\pi}{2}\right) = -4\pi c^2 \Big[\sin\theta\Big]_{\pi/2}^{0}$$

$= 4\pi c^2 =$ surface area of sphere of radius c. (Hence the name "pseudosphere".)

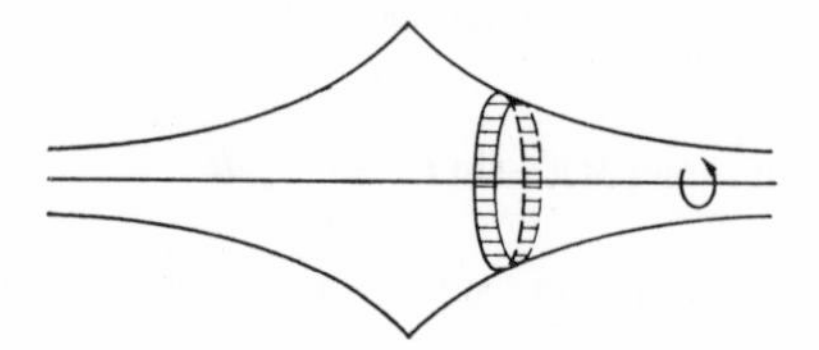

40. $$V = \pi \int_{-\infty}^{\infty} x^2\, dy = 2\pi \int_{0}^{\infty} \frac{a^6}{(y^2+a^2)^2}\, dy \quad \left(\because\ x = \frac{a^3}{y^2+a^2} \text{ for the witch}\right)$$

$$= 2\pi a^3 \int_{0}^{\pi/2} \cos^2\theta\, d\theta\ (y = a\tan\theta) = 2\pi a^3\cdot\frac{\pi}{4}\ ((74)) = \frac{\pi^2 a^3}{2}.$$

41. $$\frac{dy'}{dx} = k \Rightarrow y' = kx+c \Rightarrow y = \frac{kx^2}{2}+cx+d.$$

Initial conditions $\Rightarrow$ (i) $d = 0$ (origin at vertex), (ii) $c = 0$ (since ends at same level $\Rightarrow x = 0$ gives two equal but opposite values of y).

$\therefore$ curve of suspension is the parabola $y = ax^2 \left(a = \frac{k}{2}\right)$.

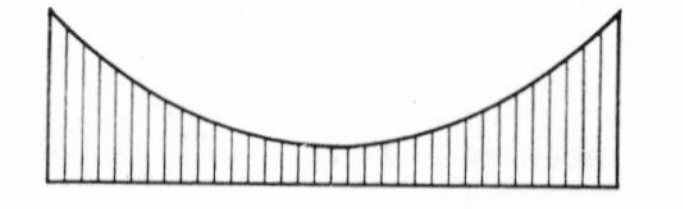

42. $$V = \pi \int_{0}^{2\pi} a^2(1-\cos\theta)^2\cdot a(1-\cos\theta)\, d\theta = 2\pi a^3 \int_{0}^{\pi} \left(2\sin^2\frac{\theta}{2}\right)^3 d\theta \quad \text{(symmetry)}$$

$$= 16\pi a^3 \int_{0}^{\pi} \sin^6\frac{\theta}{2}\, d\theta = 32\pi a^3 \int_{0}^{\pi/2} \sin^6\phi\, d\phi \left(\phi = \frac{\theta}{2}\right) \quad ((73))$$

$$= 32\pi a^3\cdot\frac{5}{6}\cdot\frac{3}{4}\cdot\frac{1}{2}\cdot\frac{\pi}{2} \quad ((74)) = 5\pi^2 a^3.$$

43. $$\frac{ds}{d\theta} = \sqrt{a^2(1-\cos\theta)^2+a^2\sin^2\theta} = 2a\sin\theta/2.$$

$$\therefore\ S = 2\pi \int_{0}^{2\pi} a(1-\cos\theta)\cdot 2a\sin\theta/2\, d\theta = 8\pi a^2 \int_{0}^{2\pi} \sin^3\theta/2\, d\theta =$$

$$= 16\pi a^2 \int_0^{\pi} \sin^3 \phi \, d\phi \quad (\phi = \theta/2)$$

$$= 32\pi a^2 \int_0^{\pi/2} \sin^3 \phi \, d\phi = 32\,\pi a^2 \cdot \frac{2}{3} = \frac{64\pi a^2}{3} \quad ((73),\ (74)).$$

44. For the cycloid $x = a(\theta + \sin\theta)$, $y = a(1 - \cos\theta)$, $s = 4a \sin\theta/2$ (Example 149(ii))

$\varrho = a(2\cos^2\theta/2)^2\,\{1 + \tan^2\theta/2\}^{3/2} = 4a\cos\theta/2$ (Example 125(a))

$\therefore\ s^2 + \varrho^2 = 16a^2$ (const.).

45. $$A = \frac{1}{2}a^2 \int_{-\pi/2n}^{\pi/2n} \cos^2 n\theta \, d\theta = \frac{a^2}{2}\int_{-\pi/2n}^{\pi/2n} \left\{\frac{\cos 2n\theta + 1}{2}\right\} d\theta = \frac{a^2}{4}\left[\frac{\sin 2n\theta}{2n} + \theta\right]_{-\pi/2n}^{\pi/2n} = \frac{\pi a^2}{4n}.$$

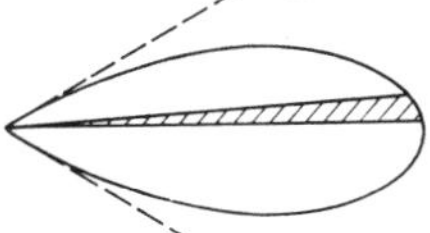

46. $$A = 3 \cdot \frac{a^2}{2} \int_{-\pi/9}^{\pi/9} (\cos^2 3\theta - 1)\, d\theta$$ ($\because$ rose and circle intersect where $\cos 3\theta = \frac{1}{2}$,

i.e. $3\theta = \pi/3$ (say) i.e. $\theta = \pi/9$)

$$= \frac{3a^2}{2}\int_{-\pi/9}^{\pi/9} \left(\frac{1+\cos 6\theta}{2} - 1\right) d\theta = \frac{3a^2}{4}\int_{-\pi/9}^{\pi/9} (\cos 6\theta - 1)\, d\theta = \frac{3a^2}{4}\left[\frac{\sin 6\theta}{6} - \theta\right]_{-\pi/9}^{\pi/9}$$

$$= \frac{3a^2}{4}\left(\sqrt{3} - \frac{2\pi}{9}\right).$$

47. Polar equation is $r^2 = \dfrac{1}{a\cos^2\theta + 2h\cos\theta\sin\theta + b\sin^2\theta}$

$$\therefore\ A = 4 \cdot \frac{1}{2}\int_0^{\pi/2} \frac{d\theta}{a\cos^2\theta + 2h\cos\theta\sin\theta + b\sin^2\theta} \quad \text{(symmetry)}$$

$$= \frac{2}{b}\int_{\theta=0}^{\theta=\pi/2} \frac{d[\tan\theta + (h/b)]}{[(ab-h)^2/b^2] + (\tan\theta + h/b)^2}$$

$$= \frac{2}{b}\cdot\frac{b}{\sqrt{ab-h^2}}\tan^{-1}\left[\frac{b(\tan\theta + h/b)}{\sqrt{ab-h^2}}\right]_0^{\pi/2} = \frac{2}{\sqrt{ab-h^2}}\tan^{-1}\infty = \frac{\pi}{\sqrt{ab-h^2}}.$$

48. Rotate axes through θ: $\tan 2\theta = \dfrac{2h}{a-b}$, $\quad\therefore\ \cos 2\theta = \dfrac{a-b}{\sqrt{(a-b)^2 + 4h^2}}$,

$$\sin 2\theta = \frac{2h}{\sqrt{(a-b)^2 + 4h^2}}$$

$\therefore$ transformed equation of ellipse is $a'x^2+b'y^2 = 1$, where

$a' = \frac{1}{2}(a+b)+\frac{1}{2}(a-b)\cos 2\theta+h\sin 2\theta$, $b' = \frac{1}{2}(a+b)-\frac{1}{2}(a-b)\cos 2\theta-h\sin 2\theta$.

$\therefore$ area of ellipse $= \pi\,[\{\frac{1}{2}(a+b)\}^2-\{\frac{1}{2}(a-b)\cos 2\theta+h\sin 2\theta\}^2]^{-1}$

(Example 139(b))

$$= \pi\left[\frac{h^2(a+b)^2+\frac{1}{4}(a^2-b^2)^2-\frac{1}{4}(a-b)^4-4h^4-2h^2(a-b)^2}{4h^2+(a-b)^2}\right]^{-1}$$

$$= \pi\left[\frac{\{4h^2+(a-b)^2\}\{ab-h^2\}}{4h^2+(a-b)^2}\right]^{-1} = \frac{\pi}{ab-h^2}.$$

49. $\left.\begin{array}{l} x = a\cosh\phi = r\cos\theta \text{ (i)} \\ y = b\sinh\phi = r\sin\theta \text{ (ii)} \end{array}\right\} \Rightarrow a\tan\theta = b\tanh\phi.$

$\therefore$ $a\sec^2\theta\, d\theta = b\,\text{sech}^2\phi\, d\phi$ on differentiating.

But $a^2\sec^2\theta = r\,\text{sech}^2\phi$ from (i) $\therefore$ $r^2\, d\theta = ab\, d\phi$

$\therefore$ area of hyperbolic sector $\mathcal{A} = \frac{1}{2}\int_0^\theta r^2\, d\theta = \frac{1}{2}ab\int_0^\phi d\phi = \frac{1}{2}ab\,\phi$

or area $\mathcal{A}$ = area $\triangle CPN$ − area ANP (N = foot of perpendicular from P to x-axis)

$$= \frac{ab\cosh\phi\sinh\phi}{2} - \int_1^x y\, dx = \frac{ab\cosh\phi\sinh\phi}{2} - ab\int_0^\phi \sinh^2\phi\, d\phi$$

$$= \frac{ab\sinh 2\phi}{4} - ab\int_0^\phi \frac{\cosh 2\phi - 1}{2}\, d\phi$$

$$= \frac{ab\sinh 2\phi}{4} - ab\left[\frac{\sinh 2\phi}{4} - \frac{\phi}{2}\right]_0^\phi = \frac{ab\phi}{2}.$$

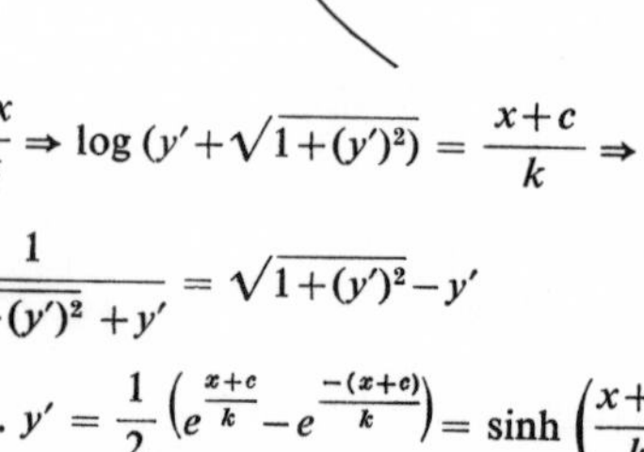

50. $\int\frac{dy'}{\sqrt{1+(y')^2}} = \int\frac{dx}{k} \Rightarrow \log(y'+\sqrt{1+(y')^2}) = \frac{x+c}{k} \Rightarrow e^{\frac{x+c}{k}} = y'+\sqrt{1+(y')^2}$ (i)

$\therefore$ $e^{\frac{-(x+c)}{k}} = \dfrac{1}{\sqrt{1+(y')^2}+y'} = \sqrt{1+(y')^2}-y'$ (ii)

Subtract (i)–(ii) $\therefore$ $y' = \dfrac{1}{2}\left(e^{\frac{x+c}{k}}-e^{\frac{-(x+c)}{k}}\right) = \sinh\left(\dfrac{x+c}{k}\right)$.

Integrate $\therefore$ $y+d = k\cosh\left(\dfrac{x+c}{k}\right)$.

Change origin to $(-c, -d)$, i.e. $c = 0$, $d = 0$ $\therefore$ equation is $y = k \cosh\left(\dfrac{x}{k}\right)$ (catenary) [$y' = 0$ when $x = 0$; $y = k$ when $x = 0$].

51. Cancelling dt, we have $\dfrac{d\omega}{\omega} = \dfrac{-2dr}{r}$ $\therefore \log\omega = -2\log r + c$ $\therefore r^2\omega = e^c = k$.

i.e. $r^2\dfrac{d\theta}{dt} = k$ and $dA = \dfrac{1}{2}r^2\,d\theta$ ((260)) $\therefore \dfrac{dA}{dt} = 2k$,

i.e. the radius vector r, for the planet, sweeps out area at a constant rate—this is Kepler's second law of planetary motion.

52. $\xi = x - \varrho\sin\psi$ $\qquad \eta = y + \varrho\cos\psi$

$$\therefore \frac{d\xi}{dx} = 1 - \varrho\cos\psi\frac{d\psi}{dx} - \sin\psi\frac{d\varrho}{dx} \qquad \therefore \frac{d\eta}{dx} = \frac{dy}{dx} - \varrho\sin\psi\frac{d\psi}{dx} + \cos\psi\frac{d\varrho}{dx}$$

$$= 1 - \frac{ds}{d\psi}\frac{dx}{ds}\frac{d\psi}{dx} - \sin\psi\frac{d\varrho}{dx} \qquad = \frac{dy}{dx} - \frac{ds}{d\psi}\frac{dy}{ds}\frac{d\psi}{dx} + \cos\psi\frac{d\varrho}{dx}$$

$$= -\sin\psi\frac{d\varrho}{dx} \ldots \text{(i)} \qquad = \cos\psi\frac{d\varrho}{dx} \ldots \text{(ii)}$$

[(using (248.1), (248.2), (249), (253), (254)]. $\therefore \dfrac{d\xi}{d\eta} = \left(\dfrac{d\xi}{dx}\right) \Big/ \left(\dfrac{d\eta}{dx}\right) = -\cot\psi$

= gradient of evolute = gradient of original curve, also.

53. Square and add in (i), (ii) of Exercise 23.52 $\therefore \left(\dfrac{d\xi}{dx}\right)^2 + \left(\dfrac{d\eta}{dx}\right)^2 = \left(\dfrac{d\varrho}{dx}\right)^2$.

Now $s = \displaystyle\int \sqrt{\left(\frac{d\xi}{dx}\right)^2 + \left(\frac{d\eta}{dx}\right)^2}\,dx$ ((262.1)) (x is a parameter for the evolute)

$= \int d\varrho$ $\therefore s = \varrho + c$.

54. Total length (by symmetry)

$$= 3\cdot 2a \int_0^{2\pi/3} \sqrt{\left\{\begin{matrix}(\cos^2 t + \cos^2 2t - 2\cos t\cos 2t) + \\ (\sin^2 t + \sin^2 2t + 2\sin t\sin 2t)\end{matrix}\right\}}\,dt$$

$$= 6a\int_0^{2\pi/3} \sqrt{2(1-\cos 3t)}\,dt = 12a\int_0^{2\pi/3} \sin\tfrac{3}{2}t\,dt = -8a\left[\cos\tfrac{3}{2}t\right]_0^{2\pi/3} = 16a.$$

55. $V = \pi\displaystyle\int_0^1 \frac{x^3}{1-x}\,dx = -\pi\int_0^1\left(1 + x + x^2 - \frac{1}{1-x}\right)dx = -\pi\left[x + \frac{x^2}{2} + \frac{x^3}{3} + \log(1-x)\right]_0^1$

$= -\pi\{\frac{11}{6} - \infty\} = \infty$. The integral is improper w.r.t. the upper limit.

56. Write $1 - x = -X$, $y = Y$ $\therefore$ equation of cissoid is $Y^2 = \dfrac{(1+X)^3}{-X}$ w.r.t. origin at (1, 0).

$$\therefore V = 2\pi\int_0^\infty X^2\,dY = 2\pi\int_0^{-1} X^2\frac{(1+X)^{1/2}(2X-1)}{X^{3/2}}\,dX$$

$$= 2\pi \int_0^{-1} X^{1/2}(1+X)^{1/2}(2X-1)\, dX$$

$$= 2\pi \int_0^{1} (1-x)^{1/2}x^{1/2}(3-2x)\, dx \quad (dx = -dX)$$

$$= 2\pi \int_0^{\pi/2} \sin\theta\cos\theta\,(3-2\sin^2\theta)2\sin\theta\cos\theta\, d\theta \quad (x = \sin^2\theta)$$

$$= 4\pi\left\{3\int_0^{\pi/2}\sin^2\theta\cos^2\theta\, d\theta - 2\int_0^{\pi/2}\sin^4\theta\cos^2\theta\, d\theta\right\}$$

$$= 4\pi\left\{3\cdot\frac{1}{4}\cdot\frac{1}{2}\cdot\frac{\pi}{2} - 2\cdot\frac{3\cdot 1}{6\cdot 4\cdot 2}\cdot\frac{\pi}{2}\right\} = \frac{\pi^2}{2}.$$

57. $r^2 = a^2\cos 2\theta,\ \dfrac{dr}{d\theta} = \dfrac{-a\sin 2\theta}{\sqrt{\cos 2\theta}},\ \dfrac{d^2r}{d\theta^2} = \dfrac{-a(1+\cos^2 2\theta)}{(\cos 2\theta)^{3/2}}$

$$\therefore\ \varkappa = \left\{a^2\cos 2\theta + 2a^2\frac{\sin^2 2\theta}{\cos 2\theta} + a^2\frac{(1+\cos^2 2\theta)}{\cos 2\theta}\right\}\bigg/\left(a^2\cos 2\theta + \frac{a^2\sin^2 2\theta}{\cos 2\theta}\right)^{3/2}$$

(Exercise 22.24)

$$= \frac{3\sqrt{\cos 2\theta}}{a}.$$

$$\therefore\ \varrho = \frac{a\sqrt{\sec 2\theta}}{3} = \frac{a}{3}(1+\tan^2 2\theta)^{1/4} \doteqdot \frac{a}{3}\tan^{1/2} 2\theta \text{ near the origin (node),}$$

where $\theta = \dfrac{\pi}{4}$, and $\tan 2\theta \to \infty$, which is large compared with 1.

$$s = \int_0^\theta \sqrt{r^2 + \left(\frac{dr}{d\theta}\right)^2}\, d\theta = \int_0^\theta a\sqrt{\sec 2\theta}\, d\theta = a\int_0^\theta (1+\tan^2 2\theta)^{1/4}\, d\theta$$

$$= \frac{a}{2}\int_{\theta=0}^{\theta=\theta} (1+w^2)^{1/4}\frac{dw}{1+w^2} \quad (w = \tan 2\theta\ \therefore\ dw = 2\sec^2 2\theta\, d\theta).$$

$$= \frac{a}{2}\int_{\theta=0}^{\theta=\theta} (1+w^2)^{-3/4}\, dw$$

$$\doteqdot \frac{a}{2}\int_{\theta=0}^{\theta=\theta} w^{-3/2}\, dw \doteqdot a\tan^{-1/2} 2\theta\ \therefore\ \varrho s \doteqdot \frac{a^2}{3}(=\text{const.}),$$

[The precise relation ϱs = constant holds for a certain spiral called the *clothoid* (= *Cornu's spiral*).]

58. Area of inner loop $= 2\cdot\dfrac{a^2}{2}\displaystyle\int_{2\pi/3}^{\pi} (4+16\cos\theta+16\cos^2\theta)\, d\theta$ (symmetry)

$$= 2a^2 \int_{2\pi/3}^{\pi} (6+8\cos\theta+4\cos 2\theta)\,d\theta = 2a^2 \Big[6\theta+8\sin\theta+2\sin 2\theta\Big]_{2\pi/3}^{\pi}$$

$$= 2a^2\left(2\pi-6\frac{\sqrt{3}}{2}\right) = 4a^2\left(\pi-\frac{3\sqrt{3}}{2}\right).$$ (See Fig. 123.)

59. $A = \frac{1}{2}\int_0^{2\pi} a^2\theta^2\,d\theta = \frac{4}{3}\pi^3 a^2 = \frac{1}{3}\cdot\pi(2\pi a)^2 = \frac{1}{3}$ (area of circle, radius OX).

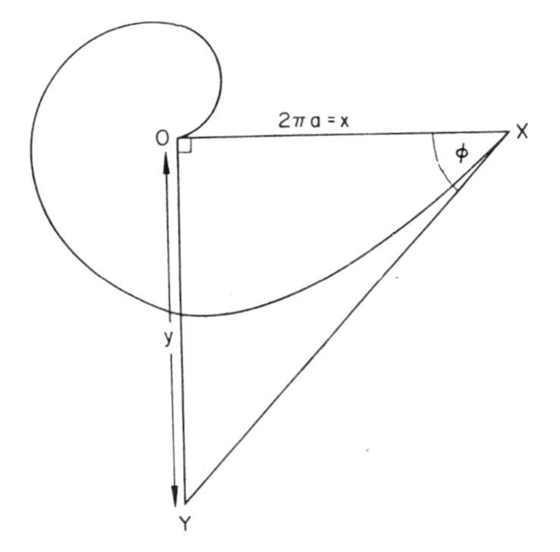

60. $\tan\phi\left(=\frac{y}{x}\right) = r\frac{d\theta}{dr} = \theta = 2\pi$ at X $\therefore$ $y = 2\pi x$ = circumference of circle, radius OX.

61. Area $\triangle OXY = \frac{1}{2}xy = 4\pi^3a^2 = \pi x^2$ = area of circle, radius OX.

62. Equation of spiral $r = e^{\theta}$ is of the form $r = e^{\theta\cot\alpha}$, where $\cot\alpha = 1$, i.e. $\alpha = 45°\left(= O\widehat{S}P\right)$ $\therefore$ the triangle CPS is a right-angled isosceles triangle.

63. Arc length of the spiral from (1, 0) to S is $\int_1^{OS}\sqrt{1+r^2\left(\frac{d\theta}{dr}\right)^2}\,dr$

$$= \int_1^{OS}\sqrt{2}\,dr = \sqrt{2}\,(OS-1) = \sqrt{2}CS = SP$$

($\because$ SPC is an isosceles right-angled triangle).

64. Now $OP^2 = OC^2+CP^2 = OC^2+CS^2 = 1+(e^{\theta}-1)^2$ i.e. the locus of P is another logarithmic spiral, its polar equation being $r^2 = 1-(e^{\theta}-1)^2$ $\therefore$ $f(\theta) = 2-2e^{\theta}+e^{2\theta}$.

[Notice that θ is not the vectorial angle of P. Where, on the diagram, is the locus $r^2 = 2-2e^{\theta}+e^{2\theta}$ where (r, θ) are the polar coordinates of a variable point on the locus?]

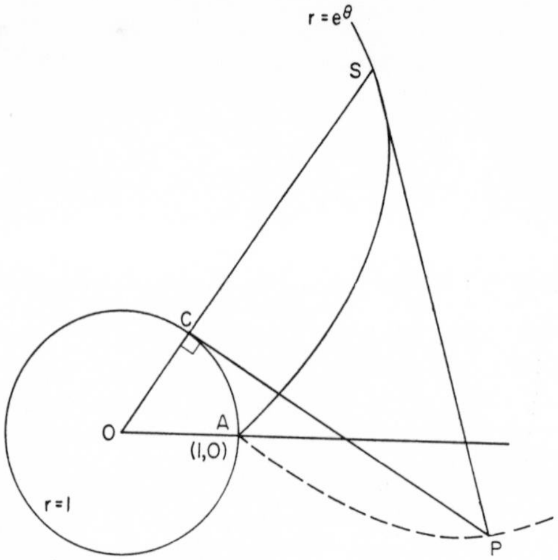

65. $A = \frac{4}{2} \int_0^{(1/3)\log 2} e^{6\theta}\, d\theta$ $(2 = 2e^{3\theta} \Rightarrow \theta = 0,\ 4 = 2e^{3\theta} \Rightarrow e^{3\theta} = 2$, i.e. $\theta = \frac{1}{3}\log 2)$

$$= \frac{2}{6}\left[e^{6\theta}\right]_0^{(1/3)\log 2} = \frac{1}{3}\{4-1\} = 1.$$

66. $$\bar{x} = \int_0^a \frac{x\sqrt{1+x^2/(a^2-x^2)}\, dx}{\pi a} = \frac{a\int_0^a x/\sqrt{a^2-x^2}\, dx}{\pi a} = \frac{a\left[-\sqrt{a^2-x^2}\right]_0^a}{\pi a} = \frac{a^2}{\pi a} = \frac{a}{\pi}.$$

67. $$\bar{x} = \frac{2\sqrt{a}\int_0^a x^{3/2}\, dx}{2\sqrt{a}\int_0^a x^{1/2}\, dx} = \frac{\frac{2}{5}a^{5/2}}{\frac{2}{3}a^{3/2}} = \frac{3}{5}a.$$

68. $$\bar{x} = \frac{\int_0^a x(a^2-x^2)\,dx}{\frac{2}{3}\pi a^3} = \frac{3}{2a^3}\left[\frac{a^2x^2}{2} - \frac{x^4}{4}\right]_0^a = \frac{3a}{2}\cdot\frac{1}{4} = \frac{3}{8}a.$$

69. Total length $= 5\cdot\frac{3}{2}a \int_{-2\pi/5}^{2\pi/5}$

$$\sqrt{\left\{\left(\cos^2\theta + \cos^2\left(\frac{3}{2}\theta\right) + 2\cos\theta\cos\left(\frac{3}{2}\theta\right)\right)\left(+ (\sin^2\theta + \sin^2\left(\frac{3\theta}{2}\right) - 2\sin\theta\sin\left(\frac{3\theta}{2}\right)\right)\right\}}\, d\theta$$

$$= \frac{15a}{2}\int_{-2\pi/5}^{2\pi/5}\sqrt{2\left(1+\cos\left(\frac{5}{2}\theta\right)\right)}\, d\theta = 15a\int_{-2\pi/5}^{2\pi/5}\cos\left(\frac{5}{4}\theta\right) d\theta = 12a\left[\sin\left(\frac{5\theta}{4}\right)\right]_{-2\pi/5}^{2\pi/5}$$

$$= 24a.$$

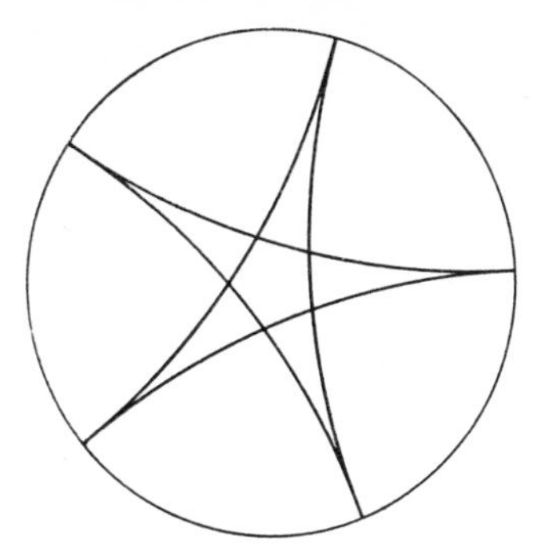

70. $V = \pi \int_{\pi/6}^{0} r^2 \sin^2 \theta \, d(r \cos \theta) = -\pi a^3 \int_{\pi/6}^{0} \sin^2 \theta \cos^2 3\theta (\sin \theta \cos 3\theta + 3 \cos \theta \sin 3\theta) \, d\theta$

Integrand $= \sin^3 \theta \cos \theta (4 \cos^3 \theta - 3 \cos \theta)^3 + 3 \sin^2 \theta \cos \theta (4 \cos^3 \theta - 3 \cos \theta)^2 (3 \sin \theta - 4 \sin^3 \theta)$ (122)

$= \sin^3 \theta \cos \theta \, [(1-\sin^2 \theta)(1-4 \sin^2 \theta)^3 + (9-12 \sin^2 \theta)\{16(1-\sin^2 \theta)^3 - 24(1-\sin^2 \theta)^2 + 9(1-\sin^2 \theta)\}]$

$= \sin^3 \theta \cos \theta (256 \sin^8 \theta - 544 \sin^6 \theta + 384 \sin^4 \theta - 106 \sin^2 \theta + 10)$

$$\therefore V = -\pi a^3 \int_{\theta=\pi/6}^{\theta=0} (256 \sin^{11} \theta - 544 \sin^9 \theta + 384 \sin^7 \theta - 106 \sin^5 \theta + 10 \sin^3 \theta) \, d \sin \theta$$

$$= \frac{\pi a^3}{2^6} \left(\frac{1}{3} - \frac{17}{5} + 12 - \frac{53}{3} + 10 \right) (\because \sin \pi/6 = \tfrac{1}{2}) = \frac{19 \pi a^3}{960}.$$

71. Length of undulation $= \int_0^{2\pi} \sqrt{1 + \left(\frac{k \sin \theta}{a + k \cos \theta} \right)^2} \, (a + k \cos \theta) \, d\theta$

$$= 2 \int_0^{\pi} \sqrt{a^2 + k^2 + 2ak \cos \theta} \, d\theta \quad \text{(symmetry)}$$

$$= 4 \int_0^{\pi/2} \sqrt{\{(a+k)^2 \cos^2 2\phi + (a-k)^2 \sin^2 2\phi\}} \, d\phi$$

$(\theta = 2\phi)$ = perimeter of ellipse $x = (a+k) \sin 2\phi$, $y = (a-k) \cos 2\phi$ (Example 151).

72. See Thomas [27], pp. 163–6.

73. Routine calculation.

74, 75. See Siegel [25], pp. 275–6.

Here is my journey's end . . .

(SHAKESPEARE)

Tomorrow to fresh woods, and pastures new.

(MILTON)

INDEX